Instructor's Guide to accompany Circuit Analysis: Theory and Practice, 3e and Circuit Analysis with Devices: Theory and Practice

Allan H. Robbins
Wilhelm C. Miller

Red River College

THOMSON
DELMAR LEARNING

Australia Canada Mexico Singapore Spain United Kingdom United States

Instructor's Guide to accompany Circuit Analysis: Theory and Practice, 3rd Edition

by Allan H. Robbins and Wilhelm C. Miller

Vice President, Technology and Trades SBU:
Alar Elken

Editorial Director:
Sandy Clark

Acquisitions Editor:
David Garza

Senior Development Editor:
Michelle Ruelos Cannistraci

Marketing Director:
Cynthia Eichelman

Channel Manager:
Fair Huntoon

Marketing Coordinator:
Casey Bruno

Production Director:
Mary Ellen Black

Production Manager:
Larry Main

Production Coordinator:
Dawn Jacobson

Senior Project Editor:
Christopher Chien

Art/Design Coordinator:
Francis Hogan

Senior Editorial Assistant:
Dawn Daugherty

Printed in the United States of America
1 2 3 4 5 XX 05 04 03

For more information contact Delmar Learning
Executive Woods
5 Maxwell Drive, PO Box 8007,
Clifton Park, NY 12065-8007
Or find us on the World Wide Web at
www.delmarlearning.com

Library of Congress Cataloging-in-Publication Data:
Card Number:

ISBN: 1-4018-1238-4

NOTICE TO THE READER

Publisher does not warrant or guarantee any of the products described herein or perform any independent analysis in connection with any of the product information contained herein. Publisher does not assume, and expressly disclaims, any obligation to obtain and include information other than that provided to it by the manufacturer.

The reader is expressly warned to consider and adopt all safety precautions that might be indicated by the activities herein and to avoid all potential hazards. By following the instructions contained herein, the reader willingly assumes all risks in connection with such instructions.

The publisher makes no representation or warranties of any kind, including but not limited to, the warranties of fitness for particular purpose or merchantability, nor are any such representations implied with respect to the material set forth herein, and the publisher takes no responsibility with respect to such material. The publisher shall not be liable for any special, consequential, or exemplary damages resulting, in whole or part, from the readers' use of, or reliance upon, this material.

Contents

Answers to Selected Even-Numbered Questions

Answers to Selected Even-Numbered Questions, Chapters 24–31
CIRCUIT ANALYSIS WITH DEVICES: THEORY AND PRACTICE

Lab Manual Answers

Answers to Selected Odd-Numbered Questions

Chapter 1

Introduction

1.3 Converting Units

1\. a. $27\ \cancel{\text{min}} \times (60\ \text{s}/\cancel{\text{min}}) = 1620\ \text{s}$

b. $0.8\ \cancel{\text{h}} \times (3600\ \text{s}/\cancel{\text{h}}) = 2880\ \text{s}$

c. $\left(2\cancel{\text{h}} \times \dfrac{3600\ \text{s}}{\cancel{\text{h}}}\right) + \left(3\ \cancel{\text{min}} \times \dfrac{60\ \text{s}}{\cancel{\text{min}}}\right) + 47\ \text{s} = 7427\ \text{s}$

d. $35\ \cancel{\text{hp}} \times (746\ \text{W}/\cancel{\text{hp}}) = 26\,110\ \text{W}$

e. $1827\ \cancel{\text{W}} \times \dfrac{1\ \text{hp}}{746\ \cancel{\text{W}}} = 2.45\ \text{hp}$

f. $23\ \cancel{\text{rev}}. \times 360^\circ/\cancel{\text{rev}} = 8280^\circ$

3\. a. $1.2\ \text{m} \times 70\ \cancel{\text{cm}} \times \dfrac{1\ \text{m}}{100\ \cancel{\text{cm}}} = 0.84\ \text{m}^2$

b. $\dfrac{1}{2}\left(25\ \cancel{\text{cm}} \times \dfrac{1\ \text{m}}{100\ \cancel{\text{cm}}}\right)(0.5\ \text{m}) = 0.0625\ \text{m}^2$

c. $\left(10\ \cancel{\text{cm}} \times \dfrac{1\ \text{m}}{100\ \cancel{\text{cm}}}\right)\left(25\ \cancel{\text{cm}} \times \dfrac{1\ \text{m}}{100\ \cancel{\text{cm}}}\right)$
$\left(80\ \cancel{\text{cm}} \times \dfrac{1\ \text{m}}{100\ \cancel{\text{cm}}}\right) = 0.02\ \text{m}^3$

d. $\dfrac{4\pi}{3}\left(10\ \cancel{\text{in}} \times \dfrac{2.54\ \cancel{\text{cm}}}{\cancel{\text{in}}} \times \dfrac{1\ \text{m}}{100\ \cancel{\text{cm}}}\right)^3 = 0.0686\ \text{m}^3$

5\. $\dfrac{15\ \text{parts}}{12\ \cancel{\text{s}}} \times \dfrac{3600\ \cancel{\text{s}}}{\text{h}} = 4500\ \text{parts/h}$

7\. $\dfrac{27\ \cancel{\text{mi}}}{\cancel{\text{gal}}} \times \dfrac{1.609\ \text{km}}{\cancel{\text{mi}}} \times \dfrac{1\ \cancel{\text{gal}}}{3.785\ \text{liters}} = 11.5\ \text{km/liter}$

9\. $\dfrac{18\cancel{^\circ}}{0.02\ \cancel{\text{s}}} \times \dfrac{1\ \text{rev}}{360\cancel{^\circ}} \times \dfrac{60\ \cancel{\text{s}}}{1\ \text{min}} = 150\ \text{rpm}$

11\. $\dfrac{60\ \text{mi}}{\cancel{\text{h}}} \times 500\ \cancel{\text{s}} \times \dfrac{1\ \cancel{\text{h}}}{3600\ \cancel{\text{s}}} = 8.33\ \text{mi}$

13\. $\dfrac{2000\ \cancel{\text{yd}}}{\cancel{\text{h}}} \times \dfrac{0.914\ \text{m}}{\cancel{\text{yd}}} \times \dfrac{1\ \cancel{\text{h}}}{3600\ \text{s}} = 0.508\ \text{m/s}$

15\. $\dfrac{3\ \text{km}}{\text{h}} \times \dfrac{8}{60}\ \text{h} + \dfrac{5\ \text{km}}{\text{h}} \times 1.25\ \text{h} + \dfrac{4\ \text{km}}{\text{h}} \times \dfrac{12}{60}\ \text{h} = 7.45\ \text{km}$

17\. $\dfrac{2\ \text{km}}{\text{h}} \times \dfrac{15}{60}\ \text{h} + \dfrac{5\ \text{km}}{\text{h}} + \dfrac{18\ \text{h}}{60}\ \text{h} + \dfrac{2.5\ \text{km}}{\text{h}} \times t_3 = 2.85\text{km}$

Thus, $t_3 = 0.34\text{h} = 20.4$ minutes.

19\. Machine 1: $\dfrac{\$0.43}{\text{min}} \times \dfrac{60\ \text{min}}{\text{h}} = \$25.80/\text{h}$

Machine 2: $\dfrac{\$200}{8\ \text{h}} = \$25.00/\text{h}$ (This one is cheaper to operate. Buy it.)

1.4 Power of Ten Notation

21\. a. 8.675×10^3

b. 8.72×10^{-3}

c. 1.24×10^3

d. 3.72×10^{-1}

e. 3.48×10^2

f. 2.15×10^{-7}

g. 1.47×10^1

23\. a. $\dfrac{1.25 \times 10^2}{1 \times 10^3} = 1.25 \times 10^{-1}$

b. $\dfrac{8 \times 10^4}{1 \times 10^{-3}} = 8 \times 10^7$

c. $\dfrac{3 \times 10^4}{1.5 \times 10^6} = 2 \times 10^4 \times 10^{-6} = 2 \times 10^{-2}$

d. $\dfrac{(16)(21.8) \times 10^{-7} \times 10^6}{(14.2)(12) \times 10^{-5}} = 2.05 \times 10^4$

25\. a. $(4 \times 10^3)(5 \times 10^{-2})^2 = (4 \times 10^3)(25 \times 10^{-4})$
$= 100 \times 10^{-1} = 10$

b. $(4 \times 10^3)(-5 \times 10^{-2})^2 = (4 \times 10^3)(25 \times 10^{-4}) = 10$

c. $\dfrac{(6 \times 10)^2}{(10 \times 10^{-1})} = \dfrac{36 \times 10^2}{1} = 3.6 \times 10^3$

d. $\dfrac{(50)^{-2}(2.5 \times 10^6)(6 \times 10^3)}{(1 \times 10^3)(2 \times 10^{-1})^2} = \dfrac{(2.5)(6) \times 10^6 \times 10^3}{(5 \times 10)^2(1 \times 10^3)(4 \times 10^{-2})}$

$= \dfrac{15 \times 10^9}{25 \times 10^2 \times 10^3 \times 4 \times 10^{-2}} = \dfrac{15 \times 10^9}{100 \times 10^3}$

$= 0.15 \times 10^6 = 15 \times 10^4$

e. $\dfrac{(-0.027)^{1/3}(-0.2)^2}{(24)^\circ \times 10^{-3}} = \dfrac{(-0.3)(-2 \times 10^{-1})^2}{1 \times 10^{-3}}$

$= \dfrac{(-0.3)(4 \times 10^{-2})}{1 \times 10^{-3}} = -12$

27. i. $(8.42 \times 10^{2})(1.4 \times 10^{-3}) = 11.79 \times 10^{-1} = 1.179$

ii. $\dfrac{3.52 \times 10^{-2}}{7.91 \times 10^{-3}} = 0.445 \times 10^{1} = 4.45$

Direct computation for these examples is less work.

29. 6.24×10^{18}

31. $\dfrac{6.24 \times 10^{18}\text{ electrons}}{1\text{ s}} \times 10.03 \times 10^{3}\text{ s}$

$= 62.6 \times 10^{21}$ electrons

33. $t = \dfrac{3.47 \times 10^{5}\text{ km}}{299\,792.458\text{ km/s}} = 1.16\text{ s}$

35. $\dfrac{3.73 \times 10^{4}\text{ m}^3}{1\text{ s}} \times \dfrac{3600\text{ s}}{1\text{ h}} \times \dfrac{1\text{ liter}}{1 \times 10^{-3}\text{ m}^3}$

$= 13.4 \times 10^{10}$ liters/h

1.5 Prefixes

37. a. kilo, k

b. mega, M

c. giga, G

d. micro, μ

e. milli, m

f. pico, p

39. a. 1.5 ms

b. 27 μs

c. 350 ns

41. a. 150×10^{3} V; 0.15×10^{6} V

b. 0.33×10^{-3} W; 33×10^{-5} W

43. a. 330 V + 150 V + 200 V = 680 V

b. 60 W + 100 W + 2.7 W = 162.7 W

45. 1500 W = 1.5×10^{3} W = 1.5 kW

47. $I_3 = I_1 + I_2 + I_4 = 12\text{ A} + 150\text{ A} + 25\text{ A} = 187\text{ A}$

49. Radio signal: $t = \dfrac{5000\text{ km}}{299\,792.458\text{ km/s}} = 16.68\text{ ms}$

Telephone signal: $t = \dfrac{5000 \times 10^{3}\text{ m}}{150\text{ m/}\mu\text{s}} = 33.33\text{ ms}$

$\therefore$ Radio signal arrives first by 16.65 ms.

1.6 Circuit Diagrams

51.

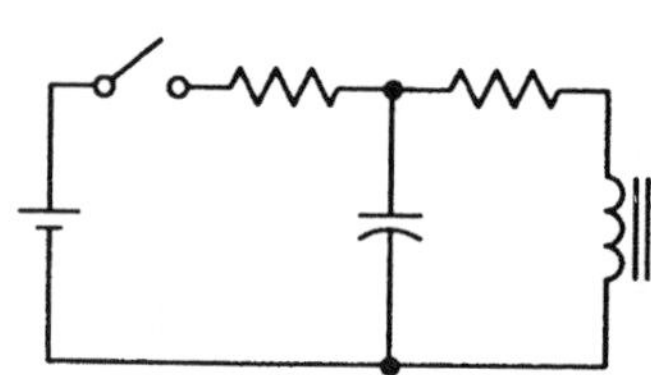

Chapter

2

Voltage and Current

2.1 Atomic Theory

1. There are of the order of 10^{23} free electrons per cm^3 at room temperature in copper.

   a. $1\ m^3 = (100\ cm)^3 = 10^6\ cm^3$. Thus, the number of electrons is

   $$N = \frac{10^{23}\ \text{electrons}}{\cancel{cm^3}} \times 10^6\ \cancel{cm^3} = 10^{29}\ \text{electrons}$$

   b. Volume =

   $$\frac{\pi d^2}{4} \times l = \frac{\pi}{4}(0.163\ cm)^2(500\ cm) = 10.4\ cm^3$$

   $$N = \frac{10^{23}\ \text{electrons}}{\cancel{cm^3}} \times 10.4\ \cancel{cm^3}$$

   $$= 10.4 \times 10^{23}\ \text{electrons}$$

3. Original: $F_1 = k\dfrac{Q_1 Q_2}{r_1^2}$

   New: $F_2 = \dfrac{k(2Q_1)(3Q_2)}{\left(\dfrac{r_1}{2}\right)^2} = \dfrac{(2)(3)}{\left(\dfrac{1}{2}\right)^2}\left[k\dfrac{Q_1 Q_2}{r_1^2}\right] = 24\ F_1$

   ∴ Force increases by a factor of 24

5. a. It has a lot of free electrons. This results from having few (e.g. one) electrons in its valence shell

   b. Inexpensive and easily formed into wires.

   c. Has a full valence shell. Therefore no free electrons.

   d. The electrical force is so great that electrons are torn from their parent atoms. This movement of electrons constitutes a current. We see the effect as a lightning discharge.

2.2 The Unit of Electrical Charge: The Coulomb

7. It has an excess or deficiency of electrons.

9. $$180\ N = \frac{9 \times 10^9 (4 \times 10^{-6}) Q_2}{(2 \times 10^{-2})^2} \quad \therefore Q_2 = 2\mu C$$

   (Attraction)

11. $$0.02\ N = \frac{9 \times 10^9 Q_1 (5\ Q_1)}{(0.5)^2}$$

    $$0.02 = 180 \times 10^9\ Q_1^2$$

    $\therefore Q_1 = 0.333\ \mu C$ and $Q_2 = 1.67\ \mu C$, both (+) or both (–).

13. $19 \times 10^{13}\ \cancel{\text{electron}} \times 1.6 \times 10^{-19}$ coulomb/$\cancel{\text{electron}}$
    $= 30.4\ \mu C$

15. $Q_1 = -(14.6 \times 10^{13} \times 1.60 \times 10^{-19}) = -23.4\ \mu C$

    $Q_2 = 1.3\ \mu C$

    $Q_{final} = Q_{initial} + Q_1 + Q_2$

    $5.6\ \mu C = Q_{initial} - 23.4\ \mu C + 1.3\ \mu C$

    $\therefore Q_{initial} = 27.7\ \mu C$ (positive)

2.3 Voltage

17. $V = \dfrac{W}{Q} = \dfrac{360\ J}{15\ C} = 24\ V$

19. $V = \dfrac{W}{Q} = \dfrac{1200\ J}{0.5\ C} = 2400\ V$

21. $W = QV = (0.5 \times 10^{-6}\ C)(8.5 \times 10^3\ V) = 4.25\ mJ$

23. $Q = \dfrac{W}{V} = \dfrac{57\ J}{12\ V} = 4.75\ C$

2.4 Current

25. $I = \dfrac{Q}{t} = \dfrac{250\ \mu C}{5\ ms} = 50\ mA$

27. $Q = It = (16.7\ mA)(20\ ms) = 334\ \mu C$

29. $Q = (93.6 \times 10^{12})(1.6 \times 10^{-19}) = 15\ \mu C$

    $I = \dfrac{Q}{t} = \dfrac{15 \times 10^{-6}\ C}{5 \times 10^{-3}\ s} = 3\ mA$

31. At $t = 0$, $q_0 = 20$ C. At $t = 1$ s, $q_1 = 100$ C

$$I = \frac{\Delta q}{\Delta t} = \frac{100\text{ C} - 20\text{ C}}{1\text{ s}} = \frac{80\text{ C}}{1\text{ s}} = 80\text{ C/s} = 80\text{ A}$$

33.

$$Q = \frac{47 \times 10^{19}\text{ electrons}}{6.24 \times 10^{18}\text{ electrons/C}} = 75.3\text{ C}$$

$$V = \frac{W}{Q} = \frac{1353.6\text{ J}}{75.3} = 18.0\text{ V}$$

$$I = \frac{Q}{t} = \frac{75.3\text{ C}}{78\text{ s}} = 0.966\text{ A}$$

2.5 Practical DC Sources

35. a. $E_T = 1.47 + 1.61 + 1.58 = 4.66$ V

b. $E_T = 1.47 + 1.61 - 1.58 = 1.50$ V

37. $$\text{Life} = \frac{\text{capacity}}{\text{drain}} = \frac{1400\text{ mAh}}{28\text{ mA}} = 50\text{ h}$$

39. From Fig 2-15, capacity at 5°C is 90% of its value MAX at 25°C. Therefore, capacity = 0.9 Max = 81 Ah. Thus, Max = 81/0.9 = 90 Ah. At –15°C, capacity = 0.65 Max = 0.65 (90) = 58.5 Ah. Thus, life ≈ 58.5 Ah/5 A = 11.7 h

41. At 5 mA, the capacity of the battery is (5 mA)(520 h) = 2600mAh. At 25 mA, its capacity is (25 mA)(115 h) = 2875 mAh. In the absence of any better information, plot these points as below and assume a straight line between them. Solving for capacity at 10 mA yields 2600 + ¼ (2875 – 2600) = 2669 mAh. This yields a life expectancy of about 2669 mAh/10 mA = 267 h.

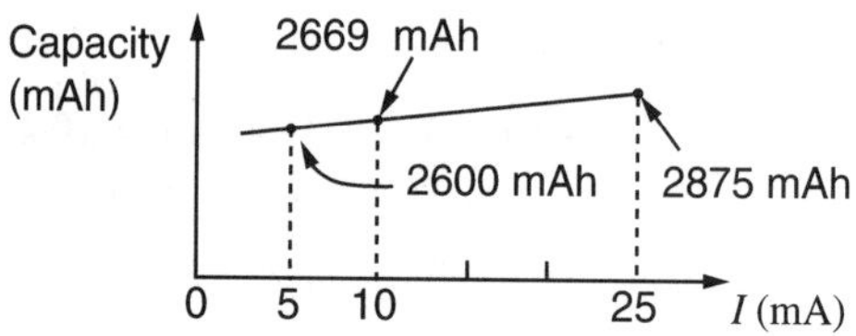

2.6 Measuring Voltage and Current

43. both

45. The voltmeter and ammeter are interchanged.

2.7 Switches, Fuses, and Circuit Breakers

47. When a fuse "blows," it becomes an open circuit with source voltage across it. The voltage rating tells you how much voltage you can use the fuse with so that it does not arc over when it blows.

Chapter

3

Resistance

3.1 Resistance of Conductors

1. a. $$R = \frac{(2.825 \times 10^{-18}\ \Omega \cdot \text{m})(100\ \text{m})}{\pi(0.5 \times 10^{-3}\ \text{m})^2} = 3.60\ \Omega$$

b. $$R = \frac{2.825 \times 10^{-8}\ \Omega \cdot \text{m})(100\ \text{m})}{\pi(1.0 \times 10^{-3}\ \text{m})^2} = 0.900\ \Omega$$

c. $$R = \frac{(2.825 \times 10^{-8}\ \Omega \cdot \text{m})(100\ \text{m})}{\pi(0.005 \times 10^{-3}\ \text{m})^2} = 36.0\ \text{k}\Omega$$

d. $$R = \frac{(2.825 \times 10^{-8}\ \Omega \cdot \text{m})(100\ \text{m})}{\pi(0.05 \times 10^{-2}\ \text{m})^2} = 36.0\ \text{m}\Omega$$

3. $$L = 250\ \text{ft} = 250\ \text{ft}\left(\frac{0.3048\ \text{m}}{1\ \text{ft}}\right) = 76.2\ \text{m}$$

$$A = \frac{\rho L}{R} = \frac{(1.723 \times 10^{-8}\ \Omega \cdot \text{m})(76.2\ \text{m})}{0.02\ \Omega}$$

$$= 6.56 \times 10^{-5}\ \text{m}^2$$

$$\text{w} = 0.25\ \text{inch} = 0.25\ \text{inch}\left(\frac{2.54 \times 10^{-2}\ \text{m}}{1\ \text{inch}}\right)$$

$$= 0.00635\ \text{m}$$

$$h = \frac{A}{\text{w}} = \frac{6.56 \times 10^{-5}\ \text{m}^2}{0.00635\ \text{m}} = 0.0103\ \text{m} = 0.407\ \text{inch}$$

5. $$R = \frac{\rho L}{A} \qquad L = \frac{RA}{\rho}$$

$$= \frac{(10.3\ \Omega)(\pi)(0.40 \times 10^{-3}\ \text{m})^2}{1.723 \times 10^{-8}\ \Omega \cdot \text{m}}$$

$$L = 300\ \text{m}$$

$$L = 986\ \text{ft}$$

7. $$R = \frac{\rho L}{A} \qquad \rho = \frac{RA}{L}$$

$$= \frac{(3.0\ \Omega)(\pi)(0.25 \times 10^{-3}\ \text{m})^2}{6.00 \times 10^{-2}\ \text{m}}$$

$$= 982 \times 10^{-8}\ \Omega \cdot \text{m}$$

Resistivity is less than ρ for carbon.

9. $$R = \frac{\rho L}{A} \qquad \rho = \frac{R \cdot A}{L}$$

$$= \frac{(32\ \Omega)(\pi)(0.75 \times 10^{-3}\ \text{m})^2}{2500\ \text{m}}$$

$$= 2.26 \times 10^{-8}\ \Omega \cdot \text{m}$$

This alloy is not as good a conductor as copper.

3.2 Electrical Wire Tables

11. $$\text{AWG 22}: R = (300\ \text{ft})\left(\frac{16.2\ \Omega}{1000\text{ft}}\right) = 4.86\ \Omega$$

$$\text{AWG 19}: R = (300\ \text{ft})\left(\frac{8.05\ \Omega}{1000\ \text{ft}}\right) = 2.42\ \Omega$$

Diameter of AWG 19 is 1.42 times the diameter of AWG 22.

The resistance of AWG 19 is $\frac{1}{2}$ the resistance of AWG 22.

13. From Table 3-2, AWG 22 can handle about 2 A of current. Since AWG 19 is 3 sizes larger, it should handle about 4 A of current.

Since AWG 30 is ten sizes smaller than AWG 20 (which can handle 3 A), AWG 30 can handle about 0.30 A.

15. $$R = \left(\frac{415\ \Omega}{1000\ \text{ft}}\right)L = 550\ \Omega$$

$$L = (550\ \Omega)\left(\frac{1000\ \text{ft}}{415\ \Omega}\right) \approx 1330\ \text{ft} \approx 405\ \text{m}$$

3.3 Resistance of Wires—Circular Mils

17. a. $D = 0.016\ \text{in} = 16\ \text{mil}$

$A = 16^2 = 256\ \text{CM}$

b. $$D = 2.0\ \text{mm} = 2.0\ \text{mm}\left(\frac{1\ \text{in}}{25.4\ \text{mm}}\right) = 0.0787\ \text{in}$$

$$= 78.4\ \text{mil}$$

$A = 78.4^2 = 6200\ \text{CM}$

c. $A = (0.25\text{in})(6.0\text{in})$

$= (250\text{mil})(6000\text{mil})A$

$= 1.50 \times 10^6\text{sq mil}$

$A = 1.91 \times 10^6\text{CM}$

$= 1910\ \text{MCM}$

19. a. $R = \frac{\rho M}{A} = \frac{\left(1036 \frac{\text{CM} \cdot \Omega}{\text{ft}}\right)(400 \text{ ft})}{256 \text{ CM}} = 16.2\ \Omega$

b. $R = \frac{\left(1036 \frac{\text{CM} \cdot \Omega}{\text{ft}}\right)(400 \text{ ft})}{6200 \text{ CM}} = 0.668\ \Omega$

c. $R = \frac{\left(1036 \frac{\text{CM} \cdot \Omega}{\text{ft}}\right)(400 \text{ ft})}{1.91 \times 10^6 \text{ CM}} = 2.17 \times 10^{-3}\ \Omega$

21. a. $R = \frac{\rho L}{A}$

$A = \frac{\left(10.36 \frac{\text{CM} \cdot \Omega}{\text{ft}}\right)(200 \text{ ft})}{0.5\ \Omega} = 4144 \text{ CM}$

$A = 4144 \text{ CM}\left(\frac{\pi \text{ sq mil}}{4 \text{ CM}}\right) = 3255 \text{ sq mil}$

b. $D = \sqrt{A} = 64.4 \text{ mil} = 0.0644 \text{ in}$

23. $D = 0.040 \text{ in} = 40 \text{ mil}$

a. $A = D^2 = 1600 \text{ CM}$

$A = 1600 \text{ CM}\left(\frac{\pi \text{ sq mil}}{4 \text{ CM}}\right) = 1260 \text{ sq mil}$

b. $R = \frac{\rho L}{A}\ L = \frac{R \cdot A}{\rho} = \frac{(12.5\ \Omega)(1600 \text{ CM})}{\left(10.37 \frac{\text{CM} \cdot \pi}{\text{ft}}\right)} = 1930 \text{ ft}$

25. *At T = –30°C:*

$R = \frac{-30° - (-236°)}{20° - (236°)}(50\ \Omega) = 40.2\ \Omega$

At T = 0°C:

$R = \frac{0° - (-236°)}{20° - (-236°)}(50\ \Omega) = 46.1\ \Omega$

At T = 200° C:

$R = \frac{200° - (-236°)}{20° - (-236°)}(50\ \Omega) = 85.2\ \Omega$

27. a. Positive temperature coefficient since as temperature increases, resistance also increases.

b. $R_2 = R_1[1 + \alpha_1(T_2 - T_1)]$

$\alpha_1 = \frac{\left(\frac{R_2}{R_1} - 1\right)}{T_2 - T_1} = \frac{\left(\frac{25\ \Omega}{20\ \Omega} - 1\right)}{85°\text{C} - 20°\text{C}} = 0.00385(°\text{C})^{-1}$

c. Temperature intercept:

$\frac{20° - \text{T}}{20\ \Omega} = \frac{85° - 20°}{25\ \Omega - 20\ \Omega}$

$\text{T} = -\frac{20\ \Omega(85° - 20°)}{25\ \Omega - 20\ \Omega} + 20° = -240°\text{C}$

At T = 0°C:

$R = \frac{100° - (-240°)}{20° - (-240°)}(20\ \Omega) = 18.5\ \Omega$

At T = 100°C:

$R = \frac{100° - (-240°)}{20° - (-240°)}(20\ \Omega) = 26.2\ \Omega$

29. $R = \frac{260° - (-2270°)}{20° - (-2270°)}(15.2\ \Omega) = 16.8\ \Omega$

31. $\text{m} = \frac{70\ \Omega}{140°\ \text{C}} = 0.5\ \Omega/°\text{C}$

$\text{R} = (0.5\ \Omega/°\text{C})\text{T} + 130\ \Omega$

$\text{T} = \frac{-130\ \Omega}{0.5\ \Omega/°\text{C}} = -260°\text{C}$

3.5 Types of Resistors

33.

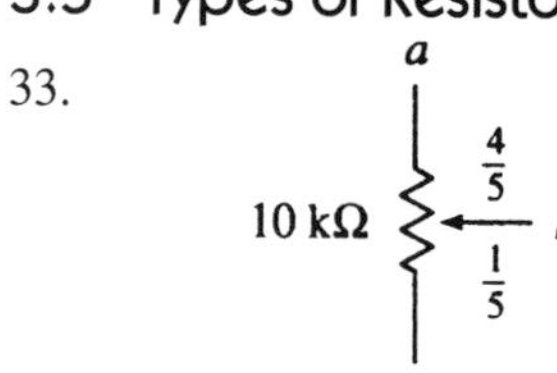

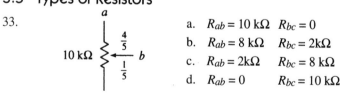

a. $R_{ab} = 10\ \text{k}\Omega$ $R_{bc} = 0$
b. $R_{ab} = 8\ \text{k}\Omega$ $R_{bc} = 2\text{k}\Omega$
c. $R_{ab} = 2\text{k}\Omega$ $R_{bc} = 8\ \text{k}\Omega$
d. $R_{ab} = 0$ $R_{bc} = 10\ \text{k}\Omega$

3.6 Color Coding of Resistors

35. a. $15 \times 10^4 \pm 10\% = 150\ \text{k}\Omega \pm 10\% = 150\ \text{k}\Omega \pm 15\ \text{k}\Omega$

b. $28 \times 0.1 \pm 5\% = 2.8\ \Omega \pm 5\%$
$= 2.8\ \Omega \pm 0.14\ \Omega$
(with a reliability of 0.001%)

c. $47 \times 10^6 \pm 5\% = 47\ \text{M}\Omega \pm 5\% = 47\ \text{M}\Omega \pm 2.4\ \text{M}\Omega$

d. $39 \times 10^0 \pm 5\% = 39\ \Omega \pm 5\%$
$= 39\ \Omega \pm 2\Omega$
(with a reliability of 0.1%)

3.7 Measuring Resistance—The Ohmmeter

37. Connect the ohmmeter between the two terminals of the light bulb. If the resistance is measured to be low (about 0 Ω), the bulb is functional. If the ohmmeter indicates an open circuit, the light bulb is burned out.

39. AWG 24 has a resistance of 25.7 Ω/1000 ft (Table 3-2)

Measure the resistance between the two ends of the wire. Calculate the approximate length (in feet) from:

$$L = \frac{R}{0.0257} \quad (L\text{–in feet})$$

3.8 Thermistors

41. a. At $T = 20°\text{C}$, $R \cong 380\ \Omega$

b. At $T = 40°\text{C}$, $R \cong 150\ \Omega$

c. The thermistor has a negative temperature coefficient since resistance decreases as temperature is increased.

3.11 Conductance

43. a. $$G = \frac{1}{R} = \frac{1}{0.25\ \Omega} = 4.0\text{ S}$$

b. $$G = \frac{1}{500\ \Omega} = 2.0\text{ mS}$$

c. $$G = \frac{1}{250\text{ k}\Omega} = 4.0\ \mu\text{S}$$

d. $$G = \frac{1}{12.5\text{ M}\Omega} = 0.08\ \mu\text{S}$$

45. $$R = (1000\text{ m})\left(\frac{1\text{ ft}}{0.3048\text{ m}}\right)\left(\frac{104\ \Omega}{1000\text{ ft}}\right) = 341\ \Omega$$

$$G = \frac{1}{341\ \Omega} = 2.93\text{ mS}$$

Chapter

4

Ohm's Law, Power and Energy

4.1 Ohm's Law

1. a. $I = \frac{E}{R} = \frac{40\text{ V}}{20\ \Omega} = 2\text{ A}$

   b. $\frac{35\text{ mV}}{5\text{ m}\Omega} = 7.0\text{ A}$

   c. $\frac{200\text{ V}}{40\text{ k}\Omega} = 5\text{ mA}$

   d. $\frac{10\text{ V}}{2.5\text{ M}\Omega} = 4\mu\text{A}$

   e. $\frac{7.5\text{ V}}{2.5 \times 10^3\ \Omega} = 3\text{ mA}$

   f. $\frac{12 \times 10^3\text{ V}}{2 \times 10^6\ \Omega} = 6\text{ mA}$

3. a. $V = IR = (1 \times 10^{-3}\text{ A})(40 \times 10^3\ \Omega) = 40\text{ V}$

   b. $(10 \times 10^{-6}\text{ A})(30 \times 10^3\ \Omega) = 0.3\text{ V}$

   c. $(10 \times 10^{-3}\text{ A})(4 \times 10^4\ \Omega) = 400\text{ V}$

   d. $(12\text{ A})(3 \times 10^{-2}\ \Omega) = 0.36\text{ V}$

5. $R = \frac{E}{I} = \frac{120\text{ V}}{1.25\text{ A}} = 96\ \Omega$

7. $V = IR = (50 \times 10^{-3}\text{ A})(560\ \Omega) = 28\text{ V}$

9. $I = GE = (0.2\text{ S})(30\text{ V}) = 6\text{ A}$

11. $R = \frac{V}{I} = \frac{33\text{ V}}{15\text{ mA}} = 2.2\text{ k}\Omega$

    ∴ Color code is Red, Red, Red

13. From its color code, $R = 22\ \Omega$. Fuse blows at 1 A. This corresponds to $V = IR = (1\text{ A})(22\ \Omega) = 22\text{ V}$

15. $\ell = (800\text{ t})(3\text{ inches/t}) = 2400\text{ in} = 200\text{ ft}$.

    From the wire table (Chapter 3), resistance is 104 Ω/1000 ft. Thus, $R = (0.2)(104\ \Omega) = 20.8\ \Omega$ at 20°C.

    a. At 20° C, $I = \frac{48\text{ V}}{20.8\ \Omega} = 2.31\text{ A}$

    b. At 40°C, (using the method of Ch 3), $R = \left(\frac{274.5}{254.5}\right)(20.8\Omega) = 22.43\ \Omega$

    Thus, $I = \frac{48\text{ V}}{22.43\ \Omega} = 2.14\text{ A}$

17. $R = \rho\frac{\ell}{A} = \frac{(2.825 \times 10^{-8})(100\text{ m})}{\frac{\pi}{4}(0.5 \times 10^{-3}\text{ m})^2} = 14.39\ \Omega$

    $E = IR = (200 \times 10^{-3}\text{ A})(14.39\ \Omega) = 2.88\text{ V}$

19. This is a linear graph. Therefore, choose any *V-I* point, for example, 80 V and 20 A. Thus,

    $R = \frac{V}{I} = \frac{80\text{ V}}{20\text{ A}} = 4\ \Omega$

21. $I_{old} = \frac{100\text{ V}}{R}$ $\quad I_{new} = 2\,I_{old} = 2\left(\frac{100\text{ V}}{R}\right)$

    Also: $I_{new} = \frac{E_{new}}{2R}$

    $\therefore \frac{2(100\text{ V})}{R} = \frac{E_{new}}{2R}$

    Cancel R. ∴ $E_{new} = 400\text{ V}$

23. $A = \frac{\pi d^2}{4} = \frac{\pi}{4}(0.1 \times 10^{-3})^2 = 0.7854 \times 10^{-8}\text{ m}^2$

    $\rho = 99.72 \times 10^{-8}\quad \Omega - \text{m}$

    $R = \frac{\rho\ell}{A} = \frac{(99.72 \times 10^{-8})(25)}{0.7854 \times 10^{-8}} = 3174\ \Omega$

    $I = \frac{12\text{ V}}{3174\ \Omega} = 3.78\text{ mA}$

4.2 Voltage Polarity and Current Direction

25. (a) + 45 V −

    (b) 4 A

    (c) − 90 V +

    (d) 7 A

4.3 Power

27. $P = \frac{W}{t} = \frac{723\text{ J}}{227\text{ s}} = 3.19\text{ J/s} = 3.19\text{ W}$

29. $P = EI = (12\text{ V})(3\text{ A}) = 36\text{ W}$

31. $P = I^2R$

$I^2 = \frac{P}{R} = \frac{1200\text{ W}}{6\ \Omega} = 200$

$\therefore I = \sqrt{200} = 14.1\text{ A}$

33. $P = \frac{V^2}{R}\ \therefore V^2 = PR$

$V^2 = (752\text{ W})(3\ \Omega) = 2256$

$V = 47.5\text{ V}$

35. $R = 10\,000\ \Omega$

$I = \sqrt{\frac{P}{R}} = \sqrt{\frac{0.25\text{ W}}{10\,000\ \Omega}} = 5\text{ mA}$

$V = \frac{P}{I} = \frac{0.25\text{ W}}{0.005\text{ A}} = 50\ V$

37. $I = \frac{P}{V} = \frac{445\text{ W}}{12\text{ V}} = 37.9\text{ A}$

39. $P = (3.56\text{ hp})(746\text{ W/hp}) = 2656\text{ W}$

41. $V = \sqrt{PR} = \sqrt{(2\text{ W})(270\ \Omega} = 23.2\text{ V}$

$I = \sqrt{\frac{P}{R}} = \sqrt{\frac{2\text{ W}}{270\ \Omega}} = 86.1\text{ mA}$

43. $V_{min} = 95\text{ V};\ Vmax = 105\text{ V}$

$\therefore P_{min} = \frac{(95\text{ V})^2}{25\ \Omega} = 361\text{ W}$

$P_{max} = \frac{(105\text{ V})^2}{25\ \Omega} = 441\text{ W}$

4.4 Power Direction Convention

45. a. $P = (12\text{ V})(4\text{ A}) = 48\text{ W} \rightarrow$

b. $P = (15\text{ V})(2\text{ A}) = 30\text{ W} \leftarrow$

c. $P = (8\text{V})(16\text{ A}) = 128\text{ W} \leftarrow$

d. $P = (30\text{ V})(8\text{ A}) = 240\text{ W} \rightarrow$

4.5 Energy

47. a. $W = Pt = (40\text{ W})\ (9\ \text{h} \times 3600\text{ s/h})$

$= 1.296 \times 10^6\text{ W–s} = 1.296 \times 10^6\text{ J}$

b. $W = (40\text{ W})(9\text{ h}) = 360\text{ Wh}$

c. Cost = (0.360 kWh)($0.08/kWh) = 2.88 cents

49. $W = (900)\left(\frac{5}{60}\right) + (120)(8)(1.7) +$

$(1100)\left(\frac{36}{60}\right) + \frac{(120)^2}{288}\left(\frac{24}{60}\right) = 2.387\text{ kWh}$

Cost = (2.387)($0.11) = $0.26

51. Per day: $W = (200\text{ W} \times 24\text{h}) + (4000\text{ W})(24\text{ h}) + (3600\text{ W})(12\text{ h}) = 144\text{ kWh}$

Per year: $W_T = 365 \times 144\text{ kWh} = 52\,560\text{ kWh}$

Cost at $0.10/kW = $5256

53. It takes 12 (1.75 min) = 21 minutes to toast the loaf.

$W = (1100\text{ W})\left(\frac{21}{60}\right) = 385\text{ Wh} = 0.385\text{ kWh}$

Cost = (0.385)($0.13) = $0.05 = 5 cents

4.6 Efficiency

55. $P_{in} = \frac{P_{out}}{\eta} = \frac{50\text{ kW}}{0.97} = 51.5\text{ kW}$

57. $P_{out} = P_{in} - P_{loss} = 1100\text{ W} - 190\text{ W} = 910\text{ W}$

$\eta = \frac{P_{out}}{P_{in}} \times 100\% = \frac{910\text{ W}}{1100\text{ W}} \times 100\% = 82.7\%$

59. $P_{in} = (120\text{ V})(15\text{ A}) = 1800\text{ W}$

$P_{out} = (0.89)(1800\text{ W}) = 1602\text{ W}$

$P_{out} = 1602\text{ W}/(746\text{ W/hp}) = 2.15\text{ hp}$

61. $\eta_T = \eta_1 \times \eta_2 = (0.95)(0.80) = 0.76$

$P_{in} = (48\text{ V})(180\text{ A}) = 8640\text{ W}$

$P_{out} = \eta_T P_{in} = (0.76)(8640\text{ W}) = 6566\text{ W}$

$\therefore P_{out} = \frac{6566\text{ W}}{746\text{ W/hp}} = 8.8\text{ hp}$

63. 1600 W → [η_1] → P_m → [0.75] → 1100 W

$P_m = \frac{1100\text{ W}}{0.75} = 1467\text{ W} = \frac{1467}{746} = 1.97\text{ hp}$

65. $W_{out} = Pt = (35\text{ kW})(24\text{ h}) = 840\text{ kWh}$

$W_{in} = \frac{W_{out}}{\eta} = \frac{840\text{ kWh}}{0.55} = 1527\text{ kWh}$

Cost = (1527 kWh)($0.09/kWh) = $137.45

4.7 Nonlinear and Dynamic Resistances

67. a. From the graph, $I = 2.5$ A $\therefore R_{dc} = \dfrac{25\text{ V}}{2.5\text{ A}} = 10\ \Omega$

b. From the graph, $I = 4.5$ A $\therefore R_{dc} = \dfrac{60\text{ V}}{4.5\text{ A}} = 13.3\ \Omega$

c. Because, for this resistor, R varies with current.

4.8 Computer-Aided Circuit Analysis

69. Use the following circuit. Set the source voltage and resistance as shown. Click the power ON/OFF switch and read the ammeter.

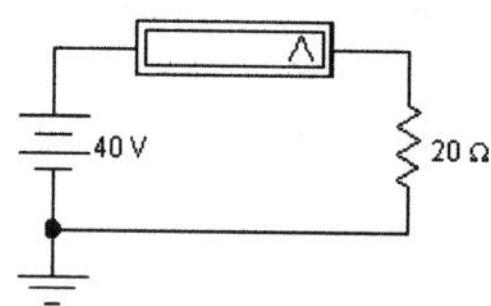

71. Click the power ON/OFF switch to the ON position, then operate switches A and B.

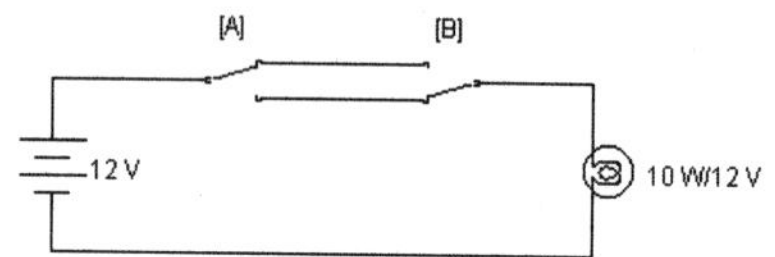

73. Following the procedure outlined in the text, build the circuit on the screen. Double-click the default voltage value beside the V1 source symbol and change it to 12.9 V, then click OK. Similarly, set V2 to 11.6 V. Double-click the 1k default resistance value and set it to 0.12 ohms. Click the New Simulation Profile icon, enter a name, click Create, select Bias Point Analysis and click OK. Click the Run icon and when simulation is complete, close the inactive window that appears. Click the Bias Point Current Display icon to read the current—see below.

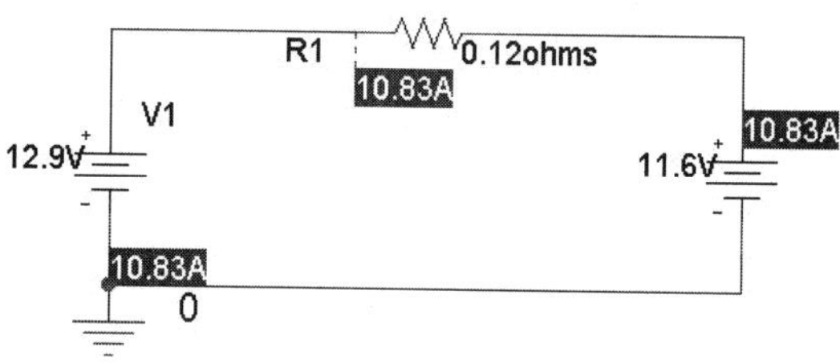

Alternatively, you can insert an IPRINT meter and use the method illustrated by Figure 4-30 of the text book.

75. See below.

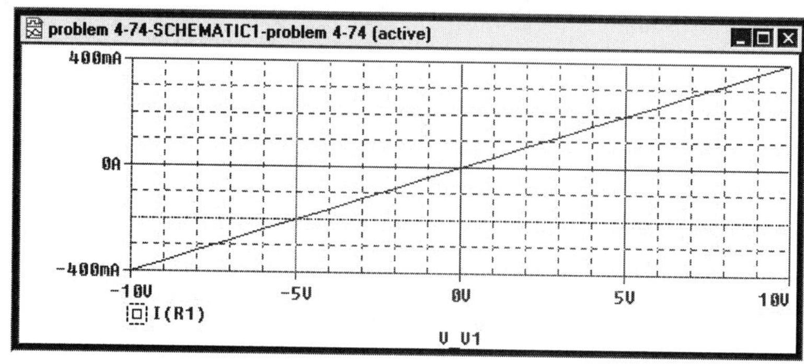

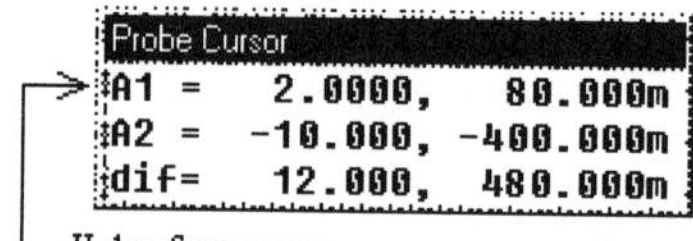

NOTE: PSpice graphic screens are printed in reversed image (i.e, in negative format) throughout this manual for improved readability.

Chapter

5

Series Circuits

5.2 Kirchhoff's Voltage Law

1. a. V = +(3A)(10 Ω) = +30 V
   b. V = −(6A)(15 Ω) = −90 V
3. a. V = +(3A)(15 Ω) = +45 V
   b. V = +(−4 A)(15 Ω) = −60 V
   c. V = +(6A)(15 Ω) = +90 V
   d. V = +(−7A)(15 Ω) = −105 V
5. a. $V_1 = 33\text{ V} - 16\text{ V} - 10\text{ V} = 7\text{ V}$
   b. $V_2 = \dfrac{12\text{ W}}{3\text{ A}} = 4\text{ V}$
   $V_1 = 6\text{ V} - 9\text{ V} + 3\text{ V} + 4\text{ V} = 4\text{ V}$
7. $V_3 = \dfrac{36\text{ W}}{3\text{ A}} = 12\text{ V}$
   $V_4 = 24\text{ V} - 10\text{ V} - 12\text{ V} = 2\text{ V}$

5.3 Resistors in Series

9. a. $R_T = 3\text{ k}\Omega + 2\text{ k}\Omega + 5\text{ k}\Omega = 10\text{ k}\Omega$
   b. $R_T = 360\text{ k}\Omega + 580\text{ k}\Omega + 2000\text{ k}\Omega$
   $= 2940\text{ k}\Omega$
   $= 2.94\text{ M}\Omega$
   c. $R = 3900\ \Omega$
   $R_T = 6(3900\ \Omega) = 23\,400\ \Omega = 23.4\text{ k}\Omega$
11. a. $R_T = 200\ \Omega + 400\ \Omega + 1000\ \Omega + 50\ \Omega = 1650\ \Omega$
   $I = \dfrac{10\text{ V}}{1.65\text{ k}\Omega} = 6.06\text{ mA}$
   b. $R_T = 1.2\text{ k}\Omega + 3.3\text{ k}\Omega + 5.6\text{ k}\Omega + 0.82\text{ k}\Omega + 2.2\text{ k}\Omega + 0.33\text{ k}\Omega + 4.7\text{ k}\Omega = 18.15\text{ k}\Omega$
   $I = \dfrac{300\text{ V}}{18.15\text{ k}\Omega} = 16.5\text{ mA}$
13. a. $I = \sqrt{\dfrac{P}{R}} = \sqrt{\dfrac{100\text{ mW}}{1\text{ k}\Omega}} = 10\text{ mA}$
   b. $R_T = \dfrac{130\text{ V}}{10\text{ mA}} = 13\text{ k}\Omega$
   c. $R = 13\text{ k}\Omega - (3\text{ k}\Omega + 4\text{ k}\Omega + 1\text{ k}\Omega) = 5\text{ k}\Omega$
   d. $V_{3\text{k}\Omega} = (3\text{ k}\Omega)(10\text{ mA}) = 30\text{ V}$
   $V_{4\text{k}\Omega} = 40\text{ V}$
   $V_{1\text{k}\Omega} = 10\text{ V}$
   $V_R = 50\text{ V}$
   e. $P_T = (130\text{ V})(10\text{ mA}) = 1300\text{ mW}$
   $P_{3\text{k}\Omega} = (10\text{ mA})2(3\text{ k}\Omega) = 300\text{ mW}$
   $P_{4\text{k}\Omega} = 400\text{ mW}$
   $P_R = 500\text{ mW}$
   $P_T = 300\text{ mW} + 400\text{ mW} + 100\text{ mW} + 500\text{ mW}$
   $= 1300\text{ mW}$ (as required.)
15. a. $I = \dfrac{4\text{ V}}{100\ \Omega} = 0.04\text{ A} = 40\text{ mA}$
   b. $V_{R_1} = (300\text{ W})(0.04\text{ A}) = 12\text{ V}$
   $V_{R_3} = (250\text{ W})(0.04\text{ A}) = 10\text{ V}$
   c. $V = 12\text{ V} + 4\text{ V} + 10\text{ V} = 26\text{ V}$
17. a. $V_{R_2} + V_{R_3} = 16\text{ V} - 7.5\text{ V} = 8.5\text{ V}$
   $V_{R_2} = \dfrac{4.7\text{ k}\Omega}{4.7\text{ k}\Omega + 3.6\text{ k}\Omega}(8.5\text{ V}) = 4.81\text{ V}$
   $V_{R_3} = \dfrac{3.6\text{ k}\Omega}{4.7\text{ K}\Omega + 3.6\text{ k}\Omega}(8.5\text{ V}) = 3.69\text{ V}$
   b. $I = \dfrac{8.5\text{ V}}{(4.7\text{ k}\Omega + 3.6\text{ k}\Omega)} = 1.02\text{ mA}$
   c. $R_1 + \dfrac{7.5\text{ V}}{1.02\text{ mA}} + 7.32\text{ k}\Omega$
19. a. $R_T = 120\ \Omega + 39\ \Omega + 78\ \Omega + 220\ \Omega = 457\ \Omega$
   b. $I = \dfrac{36\text{ V}}{457\ \Omega} = 0.0788\text{ A} = 78.8\text{ mA}$
   c. $V_1 = (120\ \Omega)(0.0788\text{ A}) = 9.45\text{ V}$
   $V_2 = 3.07\text{ V}$
   $V_3 = 6.14\text{ V}$
   $V_4 = 17.33\text{ V}$
   d. $V_T = 9.45\text{ V} + 3.07\text{ V} + 6.14\text{ V} + 17.33\text{ V}$
   $= 35.99\text{ V} \cong E$
   e. $P_1 = (0.0788\text{ A})^2(120\ \Omega) = 0.745\text{ W}$
   $P_2 = 0.242\text{ W}$
   $P_3 = 0.484\text{ W}$
   $P_4 = 1.365\text{ W}$
   f. $R_1 : 1\text{ W}$
   $R_2 : \dfrac{1}{4}\text{ W}$
   $R_3 : \dfrac{1}{2}\text{ W}$
   $R_4 : 2\text{ W}$

g. $P_T = (36\text{ V})(0.0788\text{ A})$
$= 2.836\text{ W}$
$= 0.745\text{ W} + 0.242\text{ W} + 0.484\text{ W} + 1.365\text{ W}$

5.5 Interchanging Series Components

21.

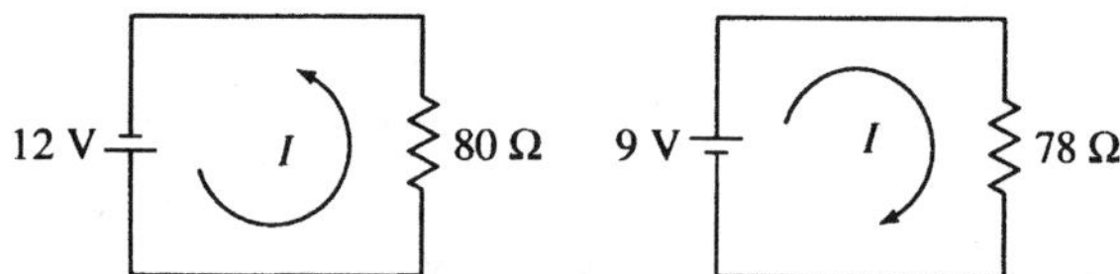

Circuit 1: $I = \frac{12\text{ V}}{80\ \Omega} = 0.15\text{ A}$

Circuit 2: $I = \frac{9\text{ V}}{78\text{ k}\Omega} = 0.115\text{ mA}$

5.6 Voltage Divider Rule

23. Circuit 1:

$R_T = 24\ \Omega$

$V_{6\Omega} = \left(\frac{6\ \Omega}{24\ \Omega}\right)24\ \Omega = 6\text{ V}$

$V_{3\Omega} = 3\text{ V}$

$V_{5\Omega} = 5\text{ V}$

$V_{8\Omega} = 8\text{ V}$

$V_{2\Omega} = 2\text{ V}$

$V_T = 6\text{ V} + 3\text{ V} + 5\text{ V} + 8\text{ V} + 2\text{ V} = 24\text{ V} = \text{E}$

Circuit 2:

$R_T = 4.3\text{ k}\Omega + 2.7\text{ k}\Omega + 7.8\text{ k}\Omega + 9.1\text{ k}\Omega = 23.9\text{ k}\Omega$

$V_{4.3\text{k}\Omega} = \left(\frac{4.3\ \Omega}{23.9\text{ k}\Omega}\right)(120\text{ V}) = 21.6\text{ V}$

$V_{2.7\text{k}\Omega} = 13.6\text{ V}$

$V_{7.8\text{k}\Omega} = 39.2\text{ V}$

$V_{9.1\text{k}\Omega} = 45.7\text{ V}$

$V_T = 21.6\text{ V} + 13.6\text{ V} + 39.2\text{ V} + 45.7\text{ V} = 120.1\text{ V}$

$\cong (170\text{ V} - 50\text{ V})$

$= E_T$

25. a. circuit (a)

$R_T = \frac{24\text{ V}}{20\text{ mA}} = 1.2\text{ k}\Omega = R_1 + R_2 + R_3$

$R_1 + 3.5R_1 + 2(3.5\ R_1) = 1.2\text{ k}\Omega$

$R_1 + 0.104\text{ k}\Omega$

$R_2 = 0.365\text{ k}\Omega$

$R_3 = 0.730\text{ k}\Omega$

b. $V_1 = \left(\frac{0.104\text{ k}\Omega}{1.2\text{ k}\Omega}\right)24\text{ V} = 2.09\text{ V}$

$V_2 = 7.30\text{ V}$

$V_3 = 14.61\text{ V}$

c. $P_1 = (20\text{ mA})2(0.104\text{ k}\Omega) = 41.7\text{ mW}$

$P_2 = 146.1\text{ m}\Omega$

$P_3 = 292.2\text{ m}\Omega$

circuit (b)

a. $V_2 = \frac{R_2}{R_1 + R_2 + R_3}(50\text{ V}) = \frac{R_2}{8\ R_2}(50\text{ V}) = 6.25\text{ V}$

$R_2 = \frac{V_2^2}{P_2} = \frac{(6.25\text{ V})^2}{0.160\text{ W}} = 244\ \Omega$

$R_1 = 4(244\ \Omega) = 977\ \Omega$

$R_3 = 3(244\ \Omega) = 732\ \Omega$

b. $V_2 = 6.25\text{ V}$

$V_1 = 25.0\text{ V}$

$V_3 = 8.75\text{ V}$

c. $P_1 = \frac{(25.0\text{ V})^2}{977\ \Omega} = 640\text{ mW}$

$P_3 = 480\text{ mW}$

$P_2 = 160\text{ mW}$ (given)

27. a. $R_T = 24(25\ \Omega) = 600\ \Omega$

$I = \frac{120\text{ V}}{600\ \Omega} = 0.2\text{ A}$

b. $V = \left(\frac{25\ \Omega}{600\ \Omega}\right)120\text{ V} = 5.0\text{ V}$

c. $P = \frac{(5\text{ V})^2}{25\ \Omega} = 1\text{ W}$

d. $R_T = 22(25\ \Omega) = 550\ \Omega$

$I = \frac{120\text{ V}}{550\ \Omega} = 0.218\text{ A}$

$V = \left(\frac{25\ \Omega}{550\ \Omega}\right)120\text{ V} = 5.45\text{ V}$

$P = \frac{(5.45\text{ V})^2}{25\ \Omega} = 1.19\text{ W}$

e. Since each of the remaining bulbs now dissipates 20% more power, the life expectancy will decrease.

5.8 Voltage Subscripts

29. circuit (a)

$V_{ab} = V_1 + V_2 = 2.09\text{ V} + 7.30\text{ V} = 9.39\text{ V}$

$V_{bc} = V_3 = 14.61\text{ V}$

circuit (b)

$V_{ab} = 25.0\text{ V}$

$V_{bc} = 6.25\text{ V}$

31. circuit (a)

$$I = \frac{54\text{ V}}{3\text{ k}\Omega + 9\text{ k}\Omega + 6\text{ k}\Omega} = 3\text{ mA}$$

$V_{3\text{k}\Omega} = (3\text{ mA})(3\text{ k}\Omega) = 9\text{ V}$

$V_{9\text{k}\Omega} = 27\text{ V}$

$V_{6\text{k}\Omega} = 18\text{ V}$

$V_a = +(3\text{ mA})(9\text{ k}\Omega + 6\text{ k}\Omega) = 45\text{ V}$

circuit (b)

$E_T = 6\text{ V} + 3\text{ V} = 9\text{ V}$

$$V_{330\Omega} = \left(\frac{330\ \Omega}{330\ \Omega + 670\ \Omega}\right)9\text{ V} = 2.97\text{ V}$$

$V_{670\Omega} = 6.03\text{ V}$

$V_a = 6.03 - 3\text{ V} = 3.03\text{ V}$

5.9 Internal Resistance of Voltage Sources

33.

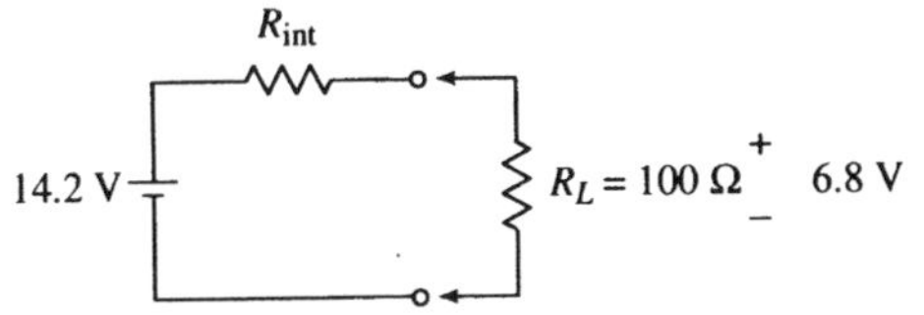

a. $VR = 14.2\text{ V} - 6.8\text{ V} = 7.4\text{ V}$

$$I = \frac{6.8\text{ V}}{100\ \Omega} = 0.068\text{ A}$$

$$R_{\text{int}} = \frac{7.4\text{ V}}{0.068\text{ A}} = 109\ \Omega$$

b. $$V_L = \left(\frac{200\ \Omega}{(109\ \Omega + 200\ \Omega)}\right)14.2\text{ V} = 9.20\text{ V}$$

5.10 Ammeter Loading Effects

35. circuit (a)

$$I_{\text{actual}} = \frac{15\text{ V}}{(10\text{ k}\Omega + 12\text{ k}\Omega + 18\text{ k}\Omega)} = 0.375\text{ mA}$$

$$I_{\text{measured}} = \frac{15\text{ V}}{(10\text{ k}\Omega + 12\text{ k}\Omega + 18\text{ k}\Omega + 0.050\text{ k}\Omega)} = 0.374532\text{ mA}$$

$$\text{loading error} = \left(\frac{0.375\text{ mA} - 0.374532\text{ mA}}{0.375\text{ mA}}\right) \times 100\% = 0.125\%$$

circuit (b)

$$I_{\text{actual}} = \frac{0.15\text{ V}}{(100\ \Omega + 120\ \Omega + 180\ \Omega)} = 0.375\text{ mA}$$

$$I_{\text{measured}} = \frac{0.15\text{ V}}{(100\ \Omega + 120\ \Omega + 180\ \Omega + 50\ \Omega)} = 0.333\text{ mA}$$

$$\text{loading error} = \frac{(0.375\text{ mA} - 0.333\text{ mA})}{0.375\text{ mA}} \times 100\% = 11.1\%$$

5.11 Circuit Analysis Using Computers

37.

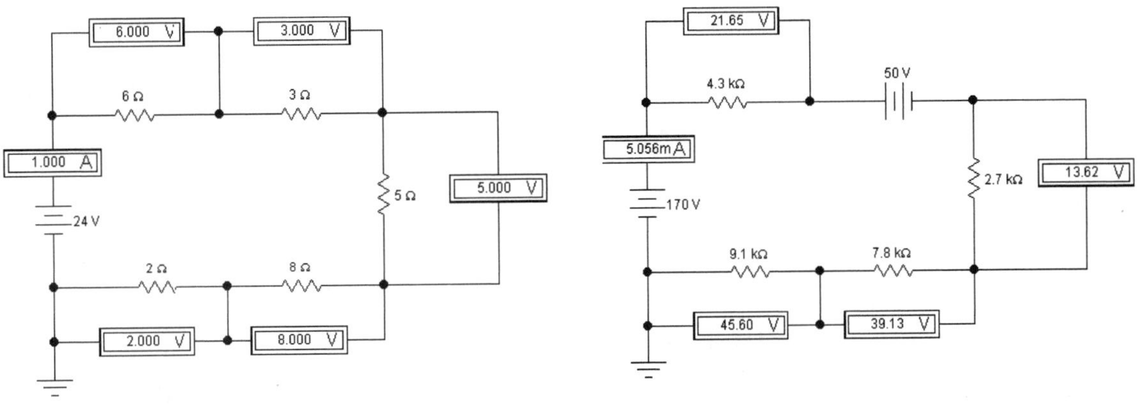

39.

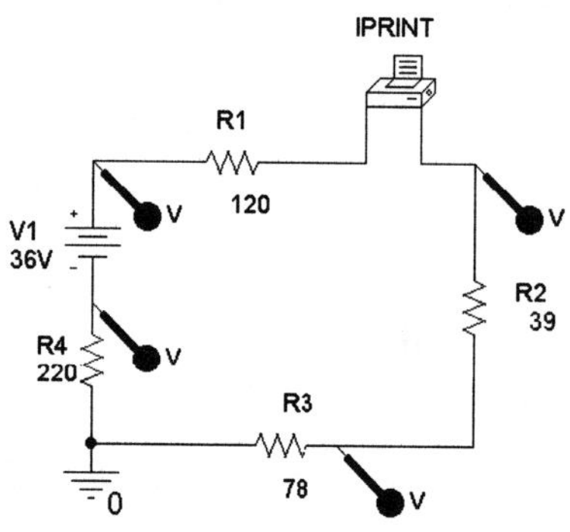

Chapter

6

Parallel Circuits

6.1 Parallel Circuits

1. a. A and B are in series
   D and E are in series
   C and F are in parallel
   b. B, C, and D are in parallel
   c. A and B are in parallel
   D and F are in parallel
   C and E are in series
   d. A, B, C, and D are in parallel

3.

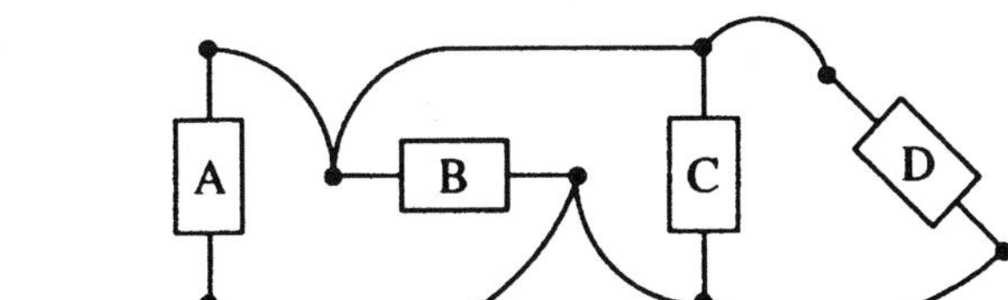

6.2 Kirchhoff's Current Law

5. a. $I_1 = 5\text{ A} - 2\text{ A} = 3\text{ A}$ (downward)
   $I_2 = 4\text{ A} - 3\text{ A} = 1\text{ A}$ (left)
   b. $I_1 = 6\text{ A} + 1\text{ A} = 7\text{ A}$ (right)
   $I_2 = 7\text{ A} - 2\text{ A} - 3\text{ A} = 2\text{ A}$ (upward)
   $I_3 = 4\text{ A} + 3\text{ A} = 7\text{ A}$ (downward)
   c. $I_1 = 15\text{ mA} - 5\text{ mA} - 6\text{ mA} = 4\text{ mA}$ (right)
   $I_2 = 5\text{ mA} + 4\text{ mA} + 6\text{ mA} + 7\text{ mA} - 2\text{ mA} = 20\text{ mA}$ (right)

7. a. $I_1 = \dfrac{50\text{ V}}{40\ \Omega} = 1.25\text{ A}$

   $I_2 = \dfrac{5\text{ V}}{60\ \Omega} = 0.0833\text{ A}$

   $I_3 = 1.25\text{ A} - 0.0833\text{ A} = 1.167\text{ A}$

   $I_4 = 0.0833 + 1.167\text{ A} = 1.25\text{ A}$

   b. $R_3 = \dfrac{5\text{ V}}{1.167\text{ A}} = 4.29\ \Omega$

9. a. $I_1 = 500\text{ mA} - 200\text{ mA} - 100\text{ mA} = 200\text{ mA}$
   $I_2 = 500\text{ mA}$
   $I_3 = 200\text{ mA} - 50\text{ mA} = 150\text{ mA}$
   $I_4 = 200\text{ mA}$
   b. $V = (25\ \Omega)(100\text{ mA}) = 2500\text{ mV} = 2.5\text{ V}$
   c. $R_1 = \dfrac{2.5\text{ V}}{200\text{ mA}} = 12.5\ \Omega$

   $R_3 = \dfrac{2.5\text{ V}}{150\text{ mA}} = 15.7\ \Omega$

   $R_4 = \dfrac{2.5\text{ V}}{50\text{ mA}} = 50\ \Omega$

6.3 Resistors in Parallel

11. a. $R_T = \dfrac{(4\ \Omega)(6\ \Omega)}{4\ \Omega + 6\ \Omega} = 2.4\ \Omega$

    b. $R_T = \dfrac{1}{\dfrac{1}{480\ \Omega} + \dfrac{1}{240\text{ k}\Omega} + \dfrac{1}{40\text{ k}\Omega}} = 32\text{ k}\Omega$

    c. $R_T = \dfrac{1}{\dfrac{1}{8.2\text{ k}\Omega} + \dfrac{1}{10\text{ k}\Omega} + \dfrac{1}{39\text{ k}\Omega}} = 4.04\text{ k}\Omega$

13. a. $\dfrac{1}{R} = \dfrac{1}{400\text{ k}\Omega} - \dfrac{1}{500\text{ k}\Omega} = 0.5\ \mu\text{S}$

    $R = 2.0\text{ M}\Omega$

    b. $\dfrac{1}{R} = \dfrac{1}{30\Omega} - \left(\dfrac{1}{50\Omega} + \dfrac{1}{90\Omega}\right) = 2.22\text{ mS}$

    $R = 450\ \Omega$

15. a. $\dfrac{1}{R_T} = \dfrac{1}{R_1} + \dfrac{1}{4R_1} + \dfrac{1}{\dfrac{R_1}{5}} = \dfrac{6.25}{R_1} = \dfrac{1}{200}\ \Omega$

    $R_1 = 1250\ \Omega$

    $R_2 = 5000\ \Omega$

    $R_3 = 250\ \Omega$

b. $I_{R_1} = \dfrac{2\text{ A}}{5} = 0.40\text{ A}$

$I_{R_2} = \dfrac{2\text{ A}}{(5)(4)} = 0.10\text{ A}$

c. $I = 0.40\text{ A} + 0.10\text{ A} + 2.0\text{ A} = 2.5\text{ A}$

17. a. $V_{R_1} = V_{R_2} = (2\text{ mA})(450\ \Omega) = 900\text{ mV}$

b. $I_2 = \dfrac{900\text{ mV}}{200\ \Omega} = 4.5\text{ mA}$

19. a. $R_T = \dfrac{1}{\dfrac{1}{600\ \Omega} + \dfrac{1}{800\ \Omega} + \dfrac{1}{800\ \Omega}} = 240\ \Omega$

b. $R_T = \dfrac{1}{\dfrac{1}{27\text{ k}\Omega} + \dfrac{1}{33\text{ k}\Omega} + \dfrac{1}{56\text{ k}\Omega} + \dfrac{1}{47\text{ k}\Omega}} = 9.392\text{ k}\Omega$

c. $R_{T_1} = 6\text{k}\Omega \| 3\text{ k}\Omega = 2\text{ k}\Omega$

$R_{T_2} = 9\text{ k }\Omega \| 9\text{ k}\Omega \| 9\text{ k}\Omega = 3\text{ k}\Omega$

$R_T = \dfrac{(2\text{ k}\Omega)(3\text{ k}\Omega)}{2\text{ k}\Omega + 3\text{ k}\Omega} = 1.2\text{ k}\Omega$

21. $I_T = \dfrac{32\text{ V}}{16\text{ k}\Omega} = 2.0\text{ mA}$

$I_1 + 3I_1 + 1.5(3I_1) = 2.0\text{ mA}$

$I_1 = 0.2353\text{ mA}$

$I_2 = 0.7059\text{ mA}$

$I_3 = 1.0589\text{ mA}$

$R_1 = \dfrac{32\text{ V}}{0.2353\text{ mA}} = 136\text{ k}\Omega$

$R_2 = \dfrac{32\text{ V}}{0.7059\text{ mA}} = 45.3\text{ k}\Omega$

$R_3 = \dfrac{32\text{ V}}{1.0589\text{ mA}} = 30.2\text{ k}\Omega$

23. a. $R_T = 12.5\text{ k}\Omega$

b. $R_T = 0\ \Omega$ (short circuit)

c. $R_T = 75\ \Omega$

25. $R_T \cong 30\ \Omega \| 30\ \Omega = 15\ \Omega$

6.4 Voltage Sources in Parallel

27. $I = \dfrac{20\text{ V}}{100\ \Omega} = 0.2\text{ A}$

$I_1 = \dfrac{0.2\text{ A}}{2} = 0.1\text{ A} = I_2$

6.5 Current Divider Rule

29. a. $I_1 = \left(\dfrac{2\ \Omega}{2\ \Omega + 8\ \Omega}\right)(10\text{ A}) = 2\text{ A}$

$I_2 = \left(\dfrac{8\ \Omega}{2\ \Omega + 8\ \Omega}\right)(10\text{ A}) = 8\text{ A}$

b. $I_1 = \left(\dfrac{1\text{ k}\Omega}{1\text{ k}\Omega + 3\text{ k}\Omega}\right)(16\text{ mA}) = 4\text{ mA}$

$I_2 = \left(\dfrac{3\text{ k}\Omega}{1\text{ k}\Omega + 3\text{ k}\Omega}\right)(16\text{ mA}) = 12\text{ mA}$

31. a. $R_T = \dfrac{1}{\dfrac{1}{4.7\text{ k}\Omega} + \dfrac{1}{3.3\text{ k}\Omega} + \dfrac{1}{1.0\text{ k}\Omega} + \dfrac{1}{2.2\text{ k}\Omega}}$

$= 0.508\text{ k}\Omega$

$I_1 = \left(\dfrac{0.508\text{ k}\Omega}{4.7\text{ k}\Omega}\right)60\text{ mA} = 6.48\text{ mA}$

$I_2 = \left(\dfrac{0.508\text{ k}\Omega}{3.3\text{ k}\Omega}\right)60\text{ mA} = 9.23\text{ mA}$

$I_3 = 30.45\text{ mA}$

$I_4 = 13.84\text{ mA}$

b. $R'_T = \dfrac{1}{\dfrac{1}{200\ \Omega} + \dfrac{1}{400\ \Omega} + \dfrac{1}{600\ \Omega}} = 109.1\ \Omega$

$I_4 = \left(\dfrac{109.1\ \Omega}{109.1\ \Omega + 300\ \Omega}\right)150\text{ mA} = 40\text{ mA}$

$I_5 = \left(\dfrac{300\ \Omega}{109.1\ \Omega + 300\ \Omega}\right)150\text{ mA} = 110\text{ mA}$

$I_1 = \left(\dfrac{109.1\ \Omega}{200\ \Omega}\right)110\text{ mA} = 60\text{ mA}$

$I_2 = \left(\dfrac{109.1\ \Omega}{400\ \Omega}\right)110\text{ mA} = 30\text{ mA}$

$I_3 = \left(\dfrac{109.1\ \Omega}{600\ \Omega}\right)110\text{ mA} = 20\text{ mA}$

33. $\left(\dfrac{R_1}{R_1 + R}\right)90\text{ mA} = 60\text{ mA}$

$\left(\dfrac{24\ \Omega}{24\ \Omega + R}\right)90\text{ mA} = 60\text{ mA}$

$24\ \Omega + R = \dfrac{(24\ \Omega)(90\text{ mA})}{60\text{ mA}}$

$R = 36\ \Omega - 24\ \Omega = 12\ \Omega$

35. a. $R_T = 24\ \Omega \| 48\ \Omega \| 16\ \Omega = 8\ \Omega$

b. $I = \dfrac{12\text{ V}}{8\ \Omega} = 1.50\text{ A}$

c. $I_1 = \left(\dfrac{8\ \Omega}{24\ \Omega}\right)1.50\text{ A} = 0.50\text{ A}$

$I_2 = \dfrac{I_1}{2} = 0.25\text{ A}$

$I_3 = \left(\dfrac{8\ \Omega}{16\ \Omega}\right)1.50\text{ A} = 0.75\text{ A}$

d. $\sum I_{in} = 1.50\text{ A}$

$\sum I_{out} = 0.50\text{ A} + 0.25\text{ A} + 0.75\text{ A} = 1.50\text{ A}$

$\sum I_{in} = \sum I_{out}$

6.6 Analysis of Parallel Circuits

37. a. $R_T = 60\Omega \| 100\ \Omega \| 75\ \Omega = 25\ \Omega$

b. $I = \dfrac{240\text{ V}}{25\ \Omega} = 9.60\text{ A}$

$I_1 = \dfrac{240\text{ V}}{60\ \Omega} = 4.0\text{ A}$

$I_2 = \dfrac{240\text{ V}}{100\ \Omega} = 2.40\text{ A}$

$I_3 = \dfrac{240\text{ V}}{75\ \Omega} = 3.20\text{ A}$

$I_4 = 2.40\text{A} + 3.20\text{ A} = 5.60\text{ A}$

c. $\sum I_{in} = 9.60\text{ A}$

$\sum I_{out} = 4.0\text{ A} + 2.40\text{ A} + 3.20\text{ A} + 5.60\text{ A} = 9.60\text{ A}$

$\sum I_{in} = \sum I_{out}$

d. $P_1 = (4.0\text{ A})^2(60\ \Omega) = 960\text{ W}$

$P_2 = (2.40\text{ A})^2(100\ \Omega) = 576\text{ W}$

$P_3 = (3.20\text{ A})^2(75\ \Omega) = 768\text{W}$

$P_T = (240\text{ V})(9.60\text{ A}) = 2304\text{ W}$

$P_T = P_1 + P_2 + P_3$

39. a. $I_1 = \dfrac{20\text{ V}}{20\ \Omega} = 1.00\text{ A}$

$I_2 = 2.0\text{ A}$

$I_3 = 5.0\text{ A}$

$I_4 = 4.0\text{ A}$

b. $I = 1.0\text{ A} + 2.0\text{ A} + 5.0\text{ A} + 4.0\text{ A} = 12.0\text{ A}$

c. $P_1 = 20\text{ W}$

$P_2 = 40\text{ W}$

$P_3 = 100\text{ W}$

$P_4 = 80\text{ W}$

41. a. $R_3 = \dfrac{48\text{ V}}{12\text{ mA}} = 4\text{ k}\Omega$

$R_4 = \dfrac{48\text{ V}}{(50\text{ mA} - 30\text{ mA} - 12\text{ mA})} = 6\text{ k}\Omega$

$R_1 = \dfrac{V^2}{P} = \dfrac{(48\text{ V})^2}{1.152\text{ W}} = 2\text{ k}\Omega$

$R_T = \dfrac{48\text{ V}}{50\text{ mA}} = 0.96\text{ k}\Omega$

$R_2 = \dfrac{1}{\dfrac{1}{0.96\text{ k}\Omega} - \dfrac{1}{4\text{ k}\Omega} - \dfrac{1}{6\text{ k}\Omega} - \dfrac{1}{2\text{ k}\Omega}} = 8\text{ k}\Omega$

b. $I_{R_1} = \dfrac{1.152\text{ W}}{48\text{ V}} = 24\text{ mA}$

$I_{R_2} = 30\text{ mA} - 24\text{ mA} = 6\text{ mA}$

$I_{R_4} = 50\text{ mA} - 30\text{ mA} - 12\text{ mA} = 8\text{ mA}$

c. $I_1 = 12\text{ mA} + 8\text{ mA} = 20\text{ mA}$

$I_2 = 20\text{ mA} + 24\text{ mA} + 6\text{ mA} = 50\text{ mA}$

d. $P_2 = (6\text{ mA})(48\text{ V}) = 288\text{ mW}$

$P_3 = (12\text{ mA})(48\text{ V}) = 576\text{ mW}$

$P_4 = (8\text{ mA})(48\text{ V}) = 384\text{ mW}$

43. $I_1 = \dfrac{1000\text{ W}}{120\text{ V}} = 8.33\text{ A}$

$I_2 = \dfrac{120\text{ V}}{24\ \Omega} = 5.00\text{ A}$

$I_3 = \dfrac{120\text{V}}{48\ \Omega} = 2.50\text{ A}$

$I_4 = 7.50\text{ A}$

$I_T = 15.83\text{ A}$

The rated current of the fuse will be exceeded; the fuse will "blow" open.

6.7 Voltmeter Loading Effects

45. a. $V_{meas} = \left(\dfrac{\text{M}\Omega}{1\text{ M}\Omega + 0.5\text{ M}\Omega}\right)30\text{ V} = 20\text{ V}$

b. $V_{ab} = 30\text{ V}$

$\text{loading effect} = \dfrac{30\text{ V} - 20\text{ V}}{30\text{ V}} \times 100\% = 33.3\%$

47. $1.2\text{ V} = \left(\dfrac{50\text{ k}\Omega}{50\text{ k}\Omega + 1000\text{ k}\Omega}\right)E$

$E = 25.2\text{ V}$

6.8 Computer Analysis

49. 

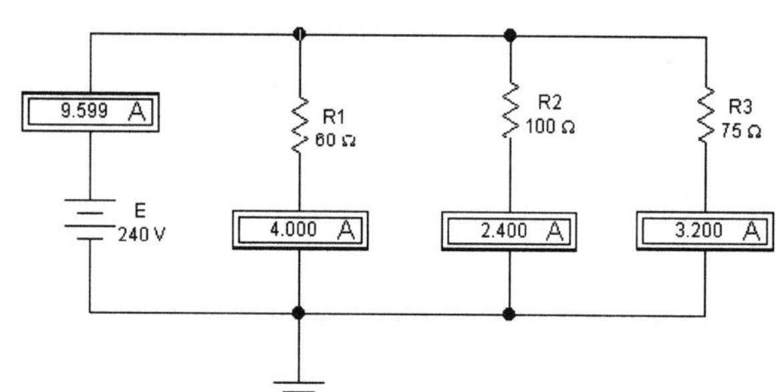

53.

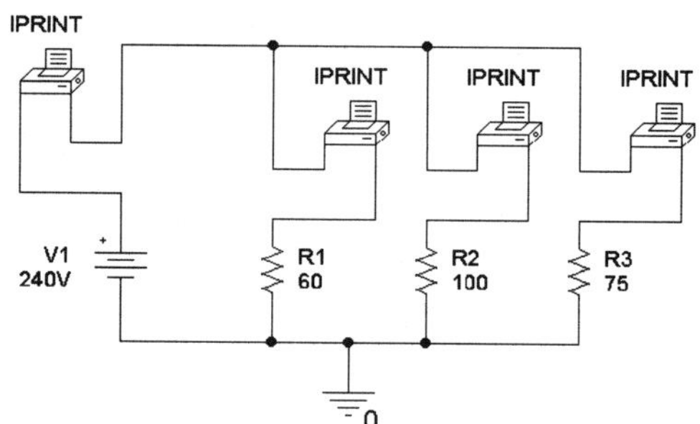

51. 

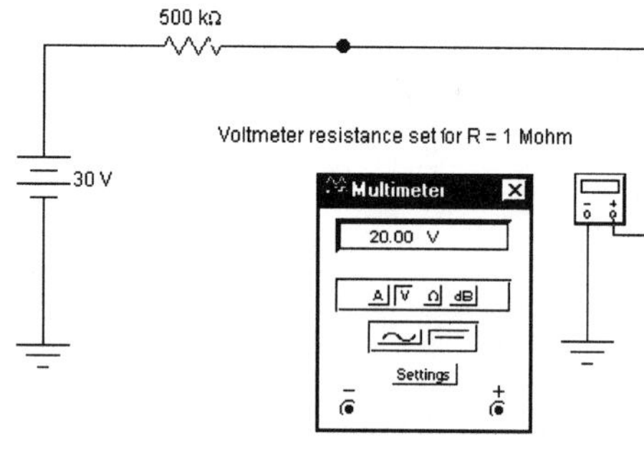

Chapter

7

Series-Parallel Circuits

7.1 The Series-Parallel Network

1. a. $R_T = R_1 + R_5 + [(R_2 + R_3)||R_4]$

   b. $R_T = (R_1||R_2) + (R_3||R_4)$

3. a. $R_{T_1} = R_1 + [(R_3 + R_4)||R_2] + R_5$

   $R_{T_2} = R_5$

   b. $R_{T_1} = R_1 + (R_2||R_3||R_5)$

   $R_{T_1} = R_5||R_3||R_2$

   (R_4 is shorted)

5. a.

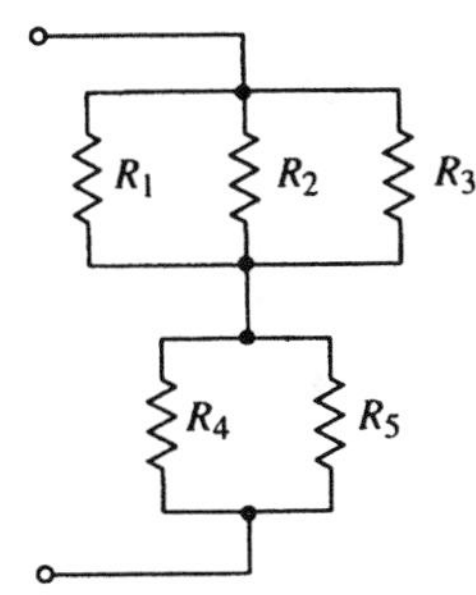

(one possible solution)

b.

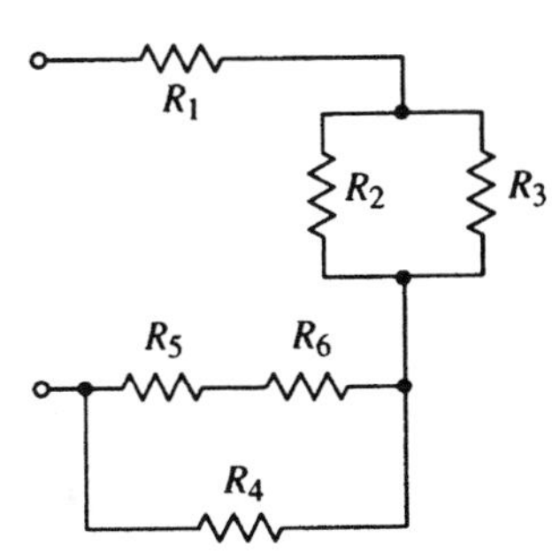

(one possible solution)

7.2 Analysis of Series-Parallel Circuits

7. a. $R_T = 300\ \Omega + [4\ \text{k}\Omega||(200\ \Omega + 300\ \Omega + 500\ \Omega)] + 400\ \Omega = 1500\ \Omega$

   b. $R_T = 5.1\ \text{k}\Omega||[1.2\ \text{k}\Omega + \{4.7\ \text{k}\Omega||(3.3\ \text{k}\Omega + 5.6\ \Omega)\}] = 2.33\ \text{k}\Omega$

9. $R_{ab} = 80\ \Omega + 40\ \Omega + [60\ \Omega||60\ \Omega||(10\ \Omega + 20\ \Omega + 30\ \Omega] = 140\ \Omega$

   $R_{cd} = 10\ \Omega||[20\ \Omega + 30\ \Omega + (60\ \Omega||60\ \Omega)] = 8.89\ \Omega$

11. a. $R_T = 100\ \Omega + [(560\ \Omega + 150\ \Omega)||(180\ \Omega + 220\ \Omega||(390\ \Omega + 910\ \Omega)]$

   $= 100\ \Omega + 710\ \Omega||400\ \Omega||1300\ \Omega$

   $= 313.78\ \Omega \cong 314\ \Omega$

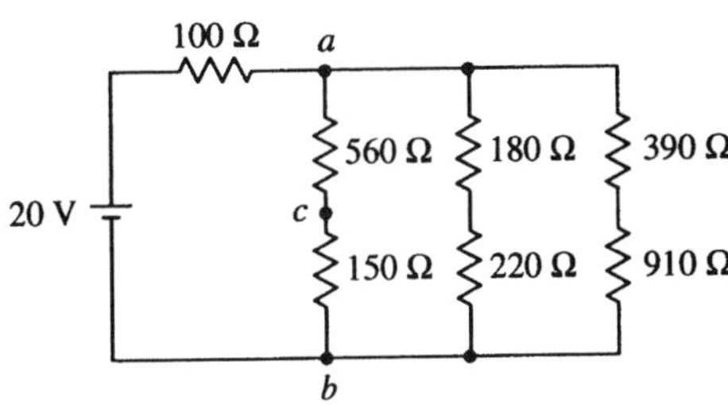

   b. $I_T = \dfrac{20\ \text{V}}{314\ \Omega} = 63.7\ \text{mA}$

   $I_1 = \left(\dfrac{213.78\ \Omega}{560\ \Omega + 150\ \Omega}\right)63.7\ \text{mA} = 19.2\ \text{mA}$

   $I_2 = 63.7\ \text{mA} - 19.2\ \text{mA} = 44.5\ \text{mA}$

   $I_3 = \left(\dfrac{213.78\ \Omega}{180\ \Omega + 220\ \Omega}\right)63.7\ \text{mA} = 34.1\ \text{mA}$

   $I_4 = \left(\dfrac{213.78\ \Omega}{390\ \Omega + 910\ \Omega}\right)63.7\ \text{mA} = 10.4\ \text{mA}$

   c. $V_{ab} = +(34.1\ \text{mA})(180\ \Omega + 220\ \Omega) = 13.6\ \text{V}$

   $V_{bc} = -(19.2\ \text{mA})(150\ \Omega) = -2.88\ \text{V}$

13. a. $R_T = 1\text{ k}\Omega + 2\text{ k}\Omega + 5\text{ k}\Omega \| [1\text{ k}\Omega + \{6\text{ k}\Omega \| (3\text{ k}\Omega + 6\text{ k}\Omega)\}] = 5.396\text{ k}\Omega$

$$I_1 = \frac{28\text{ V}}{5.396\text{ k}\Omega} = 5.\overline{189}\text{ mA}$$

$$I_2 = \left(\frac{5\text{ k}\Omega}{5\text{ k}\Omega + 4.6\text{ k}\Omega}\right)5.\overline{189}\text{ mA} = 2.\overline{702}\text{ mA}$$

$$I_3 = \left(\frac{6\text{ k}\Omega}{6\text{ k}\Omega + 3\text{ k}\Omega + 6\text{ k}\Omega}\right)2.\overline{702}\text{ mA} = 1.\overline{081}\text{ mA}$$

$I_4 = 5.\overline{189}\text{ mA} - 2.\overline{702}\text{ mA} = 2.\overline{486}\text{ mA}$

$I_5 = 2.\overline{702}\text{ mA} - 1.\overline{081}\text{ mA} = 1.\overline{621}\text{ mA}$

$I_6 = 2.\overline{702}\text{ mA}$

b. $V_{ab} = +(5\text{ k}\Omega)(2.\overline{486}\text{ mA}) = 12.\overline{432}\text{ V}$

$Vcd = +(6\text{ k}\Omega)(1.\overline{621}\text{ mA}) = 9.\overline{729}\text{ V}$

c. $P_T = (28\text{ V})(5.\overline{189}\text{ mA}) = 145.3\text{ mW}$

$P_1 = 26.9\text{ mW}$ $P_5 = 15.8\text{ mW}$

$P_2 = 7.3\text{ mW}$ $P_6 = 7.0\text{ mW}$

$P_3 = 3.5\text{ mW}$ $P_7 = 53.9\text{ mW}$

$P_4 = 30.9\text{ mW}$

$$P_T = \sum_{n=1}^{7} P_n = 145.3\text{ mW}$$

15. circuit (a)

a.

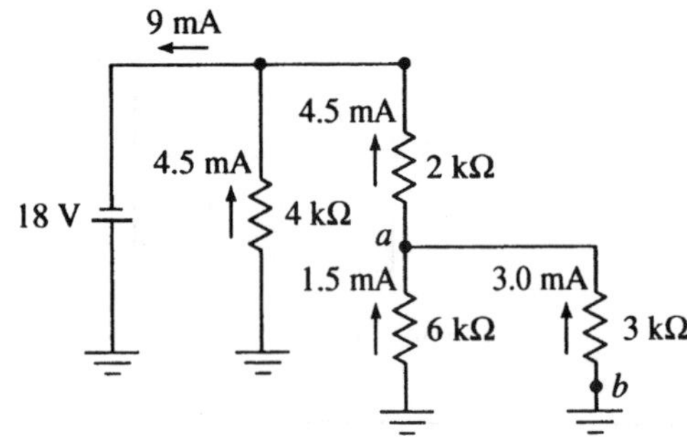

$R_T = 4\text{ k}\Omega \| (2\text{ k}\Omega + 6\text{ k}\Omega \| 3\text{ k}\Omega = 2\text{ k}\Omega$

$$I_T = \frac{18\text{ V}}{2\text{ k}\Omega} = 9.0\text{ mA}$$

$$I_2 = \frac{18\text{ V}}{4\text{ k}\Omega} = 4.5\text{ mA}$$

$$I_1 = \frac{18\text{ V}}{2\text{ k}\Omega + (6\text{ k}\Omega \| 3\text{ k}\Omega)} = 4.5\text{ mA}$$

$$I_3 = \left(\frac{3\text{ k}\Omega}{6\text{ k}\Omega + 3\text{ k}\Omega}\right)4.5\text{ mA} = 1.5\text{ mA}$$

b. $V_{ab} = -(1.5\text{ mA})(6\text{ k}\Omega) = -9.0\text{ V}$

c. $$P_T = \frac{(18\text{ V})^2}{2\text{ k}\Omega} = 162\text{ mW}$$

$P_{6\text{k}\Omega} = (1.5\text{ mA})2(6\text{ k}\Omega) = 13.5\text{ mW}$

$P_{3\text{k}\Omega} = (3.0\text{ mA})2(3\text{ k}\Omega) = 27.0\text{ mW}$

$P_{2\text{k}\Omega} = (4.5\text{ mA})2(2\text{ k}\Omega) = 40.5\text{ mW}$

$P_{4\text{k}\Omega} = (4.5\text{ mA})2(4\text{ k}\Omega) = 81.0\text{ mW}$

$$P_T = \sum_{n=1}^{4} P_n = 162\text{ mW}$$

15. circuit (b)

a. $R_T = 10\ \Omega + 16 \| [5\ \Omega \| (8\ \Omega + 4\ \Omega)] = 15.76\ \Omega$

$$I_T = I_1 = \frac{12\text{V} - 3\text{ V}}{15.76\ \Omega} = 0.571\text{ A}$$

$$I_2 = \left(\frac{16\ \Omega}{16\ \Omega + 9\ \Omega}\right)0.571\text{ A} = 0.365\text{ A}$$

$$I_3 = \left(\frac{6\ \Omega}{6\ \Omega + 12\ \Omega}\right)0.365\text{ A} = 0.122\text{ A}$$

$I_4 = 0.471\text{ A} - 0.122\text{ A} = 0.449\text{ A}$

b. $V_{ab} = -(0.365\text{ A})(5\ \Omega) = -1.827\text{ V}$

c. $P_T = (9\text{ V})(0.571\text{ A}) = 5.14\text{ W}$

$P_{10\Omega} = (0.571\text{ A})^2\,(10\ \Omega) = 3.26\text{ W}$

$P_{16\Omega} = (0.206\text{ A})^2(16\ \Omega) = 0.68\text{ W}$

$P_{5\Omega} = (0.365\text{ A})^2(5\ \Omega) = 0.67\text{ W}$

$P_{6\Omega} = (0.244\text{ A})^2(6\ \Omega) = 0.36\text{ W}$

$P_{8\Omega} = (0.122\text{ A})^2(8\ \Omega) = 0.12\text{ W}$

$P_{4\Omega} = (0.122\text{ A})^2(4\ \Omega) = 0.06\text{ W}$

$$P_T = \sum_{n=1}^{6} P_n = 5.15\text{ W}$$

7.3 Applications of Series—Parallel Circuits

17. Zener is on:

$V_1 = 14.0\text{ V}$

$$I_1 = \frac{24\text{ V} - 10\text{ V}}{150\ \Omega} = 93.3\text{ mA}$$

$V_2 = 2.06\text{ V}$

$V_3 = 7.94\text{ V}$

$$I_2 = I_3 = \frac{10\text{ V}}{39\ \Omega + 150\ \Omega} = 52.9\text{ mA}$$

$I_Z = 93.3\text{ mA} - 52.9\text{ mA} = 40.4\text{ mA}$

$P_T = (24\text{ V})(93.3\text{ mA}) = 2240\text{ mW}$

$P_Z = 404.2\text{ mW}$

$P_1 = 1306.7\text{ mW}$

$P_2 = 109.2\text{ mW}$

$P_3 = 419.9\text{mW}$

19. R_{min}:

$$V_L = \left(\frac{R}{R + 80\ \Omega}\right) 20\text{ V} = 5.6\text{ V}$$

$(20\text{ V})R = (5.6\text{ V})R + 448\text{ V} \cdot \Omega$

$$R_{min} \frac{448\text{ V} \cdot \Omega}{14.4\text{ V}} = 31.\text{T}\ \Omega$$

R_{max}:

$$I_1 = \frac{20\text{ V} - 5.6\text{ V}}{80\ \Omega} = 180\text{ mA}$$

$$I_{Z(max)} = \frac{1\text{ W}}{5.6\text{ V}} = 178.57\text{ mA}$$

$I_{L(min)} = 1.43\text{ mA}$

$$R_{max} = \frac{5.6\text{ V}}{1.43\text{ mA}} = 3.92\text{ k}\Omega$$

$R = 31.1\ \Omega \rightarrow 3900\ \Omega$

21. Using KVL: $(750\ \Omega)I_E + 0.6\text{ V} + (7.5\text{ k}\Omega)I_B - 2\text{ V} = 0$

But $I_E \cong 100\ I_B$

$(750\ \Omega)(100 I_B) + (7.5\text{ k}\Omega)I_B = 1.4\text{ V}$

$$I_B = \frac{1.4\text{ V}}{82.5\text{ k}\Omega} = 17.0\ \mu\text{A}$$

$I_E \cong 1.70\text{ mA} \cong I_C$

$V_B = (7.5\text{ k}\Omega)(17.0\ \mu\text{A}) - 2.0\text{ V} = -1.87\text{ V}$

$V_{CE} = -16\text{ V} + (3.9\text{ k}\Omega)(1.7\text{ mA}) + (0.75\text{ k}\Omega)(1.7\text{ mA}) = -8.10\text{ V}$

23. a. $I_D = 3.6\text{ mA}$

$V_S = -(-2.0\text{ V}) = 2.0\text{ V}$

b. $$R_S = \frac{2.0\text{ V}}{3.6\text{ mA}} = 0.556\text{ k}\Omega = 556\ \Omega$$

c. $V_{DS} = 15\text{ V} - (3.6\text{ mA})(1.5\text{ k}\Omega + 0.556\text{ k}\Omega) = +7.6\text{ V}$

25. $$V_B = \left(\frac{4\text{ k}\Omega}{4\ \Omega + 32\text{ k}\Omega}\right)(18\text{ V}) = 2.00\text{ V}$$

$V_E = 2.00 - 0.7\text{ V} = 1.30\text{ V}$

$$I_E = \frac{1.30\text{ V}}{0.4\text{ k}\Omega} = 3.25\text{ mA} \cong \text{I}_\text{C}$$

$V_{CE} = 18\text{ V} - 3.25\text{ mA}\ (2.40\text{ k}\Omega + 0.40\ \text{ k}\Omega) = 8.90\text{ V}$

7.4 Potentiometers

27. a. For $R_2 = 0\ \Omega$: $V_{bc} = V_L = 0\text{ V}$

For $R_2 = 10\text{ k}\Omega$:

$$V_{bc} = V_L = \left(\frac{10\text{ k}\Omega \| 10\text{ k}\Omega}{20\text{ k}\Omega + 10\text{ k} \| 10\text{ k}\Omega}\right) 36\text{ V} = 7.2\text{ V}$$

$V_L = 0 \rightarrow 7.2\text{ V}$

b. $$V_L = \frac{(2.5\text{ k}\Omega \| 10\text{ k}\Omega)}{(2.5\text{ k}\Omega \| 10\text{ k}\Omega) + 20\text{ k}\Omega + (10\text{ k}\Omega - 2.5\text{ k}\Omega)} \times 36\text{ V} = 2.44\text{ V}$$

If R_L is removed:

$$V_{ab} = \frac{7.5\text{ k}\Omega}{20\text{ k}\Omega + 10\text{ k}\Omega} = 9.0\text{ V}$$

29. $R_T = (200\ \Omega \| 50\ \Omega) + (800\ \Omega \| 100\ \Omega) = 40\ \Omega + 88.\overline{8}\ \Omega = 128.\overline{8}\ \Omega$

$$V_{bc} = \frac{50\ \Omega \| 200\ \Omega}{128.\overline{8}\ \Omega} \times 24\text{ V} = 7.45\text{ V}$$

$V_{ab} = 24\text{ V} - 7.448\text{ V} = 16.6\text{ V}$

31. a. $V_{out(min)} = 0\text{ V}$

$$V_{out(max)} = \left(\frac{(10\text{ k}\Omega\|10\text{ k}\Omega)}{(10\text{ k}\Omega\|10\text{ k}\Omega) + (R_{10}\text{ k}\Omega) + 10\text{ k}\Omega}\right)120\text{ V} = 40\text{ V}$$

b. $$V_{out} = \frac{R_2\|10\text{ k}\Omega}{(R_2\|10\text{ k}\Omega) + (R_1 10\text{ k}\Omega) + 10\text{ k}\Omega} \times 120\text{ V}$$

But $R_1 = 10\text{ k}\Omega - R_2$

$$20\text{ V} = \frac{\dfrac{(R_2)(10\text{ k}\Omega)}{R_2 + 10\text{ k}\Omega} \times 120\text{ V}}{\dfrac{(R_2)(10\text{ k}\Omega)}{R_2 + 10\text{ k}\Omega} + \dfrac{10\text{ k}\Omega - R_2)(10\text{ k}\Omega)}{10\text{ k}\Omega\, R_2 + 10\text{ k}\Omega} + 10\text{ k}\Omega}$$

$R_2 = 3.82\text{ k}\Omega$

33. $R_L = 0\ \Omega$: $V_{out} = 0\text{V}$

$R_L = 250\ \Omega$:

$$V_{out} = \frac{(250\ \Omega\|100\ \Omega)(20\text{ V})}{(250\ \Omega\|100\ \Omega) + 100\ \Omega} = 8.33\text{ V}$$

$R_L = 500\ \Omega$:

$$V_{out} = \frac{(500\ \Omega\|100\ \Omega)(20\text{ V})}{(500\ \Omega\|100\ \Omega) + 100\ \Omega} = 9.09\text{ V}$$

7.5 Loading Effects of Instruments

35. a. $$5.0\text{ V} = \frac{750\text{ k}\Omega\|200\text{ k}\Omega}{750\text{ k}\Omega\|200\text{ k}\Omega + 200\text{ k}\Omega} \times E = 0.4412E$$

$E = 11.\bar{3}\text{ V}$

b. Unloaded voltage:

$$V_{NL} = \frac{750\text{ k}\Omega}{750\text{ k}\Omega + 200\text{ k}\Omega} \times 11.\bar{3}\text{ V} = 8.95\text{ V}$$

c. $$\text{Loading effect} = \frac{8.95\text{ V} - 5.00\text{ V}}{8.95\text{ V}} \times 100\% = 44.1\%$$

d. $$V = \left(\frac{200\text{ k}\Omega\|200\text{ k}\Omega}{(200\text{ k}\Omega\|200\text{ k}\Omega) + 750\text{ k}\Omega}\right)11.\bar{3}\text{ V} = 1.33\text{ V}$$

37. a. Break the circuit between the 5.6 Ω resistor and the voltage source. Insert the ammeter at the break, connecting the red (+) lead of the ammeter to the positive terminal of the voltage source and the black (–) lead to the 5.6 Ω resistor.

b. Measuring I_1

$$I_1(\text{loaded}) = \frac{0.2\text{ V}}{2\ \Omega + 5.6\ \Omega + 6.8\ \Omega\|3.9\ \Omega}$$

$= 19.84\text{ mA}$

Measuring I_2

$$I_1(\text{loaded}) = \frac{0.2\text{ V}}{5.6\ \Omega + (6.8\ \Omega + 2\ \Omega)\|3.9\ \Omega}$$

$= 24.09\text{ mA}$

$$I_2(\text{loaded}) = \left(\frac{3.9\ \Omega}{3.9\ \Omega + 6.8\ \Omega + 2\ \Omega}\right)(24.1\text{ mA}$$

$= 7.40\text{ mA}$

Measuring I_3

$$I_1 = \frac{0.2\text{ V}}{5.6\ \Omega + 6.8\ \Omega\|(3.9\ \Omega + 2\ \Omega)} = 22.83\text{ mA}$$

$$I_3(\text{loaded}) = \left(\frac{6.8\ \Omega}{3.9\ \Omega + 6.8\ \Omega + 2\ \Omega}\right)22.83\text{ mA}$$

$= 12.22\text{ mA}$

c. $$I_{1(NL)} + \frac{0.2\text{ V}}{5.6\ \Omega + 6.8\ \Omega + 3.9\ \Omega} = \frac{0.2\text{ V}}{8.0785\ \Omega}$$

$= 24.76\text{ mA}$

$$I_{2(NL)} = \left(\frac{3.9\ \Omega}{2.9\ \Omega + 6.8\ \Omega}\right)24.76\text{ mA} = 9.02\text{ mA}$$

$$I_{3(NL)} + \left(\frac{6.8\ \Omega}{3.9\ \Omega + 6.8\ \Omega}\right)24.76\text{ mA} = 15.73\text{ mA}$$

Loading(I_1) =19.9%

Loading(I_2) = 18.0%

Loading(I_3) = 22.3%

7.6 Circuit Analysis Using Computers

39.

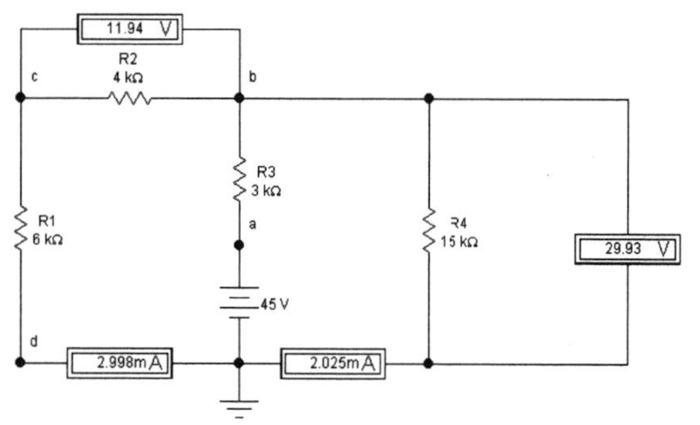

41.

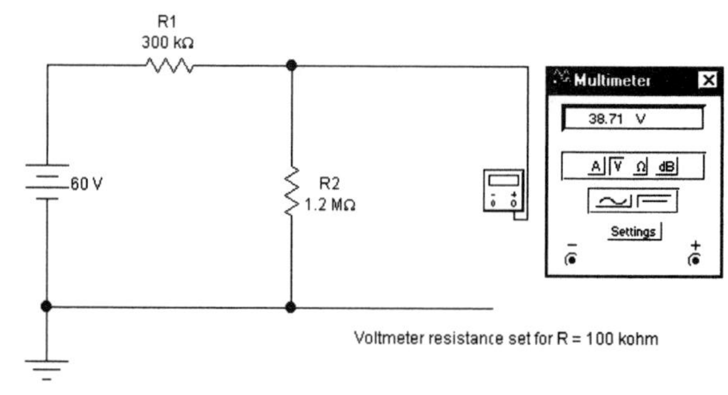

43.

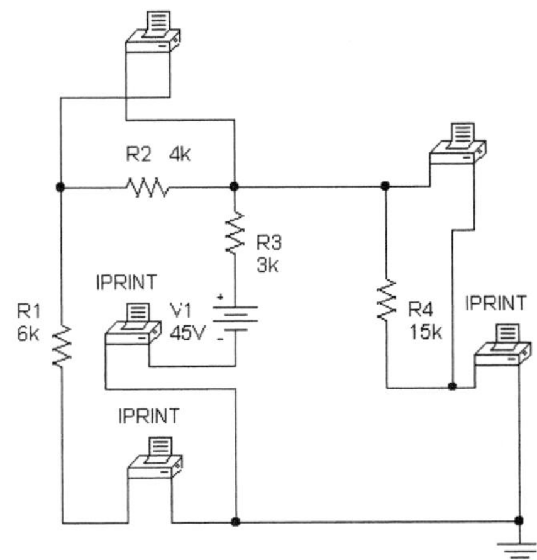
R2 4k
R3
3k
IPRINT
R1
6k
V1
45V
R4
15k
IPRINT
IPRINT

45.

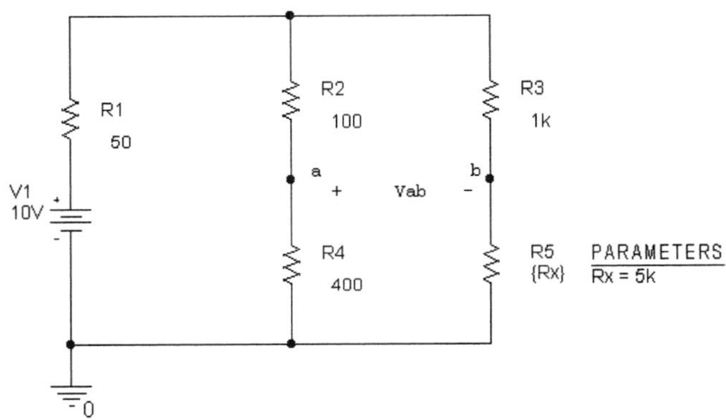
R1
50
V1
10V
R2
100
R3
1k
a
+
Vab
b
-
R4
400
R5
{Rx}
PARAMETERS
Rx = 5k
0

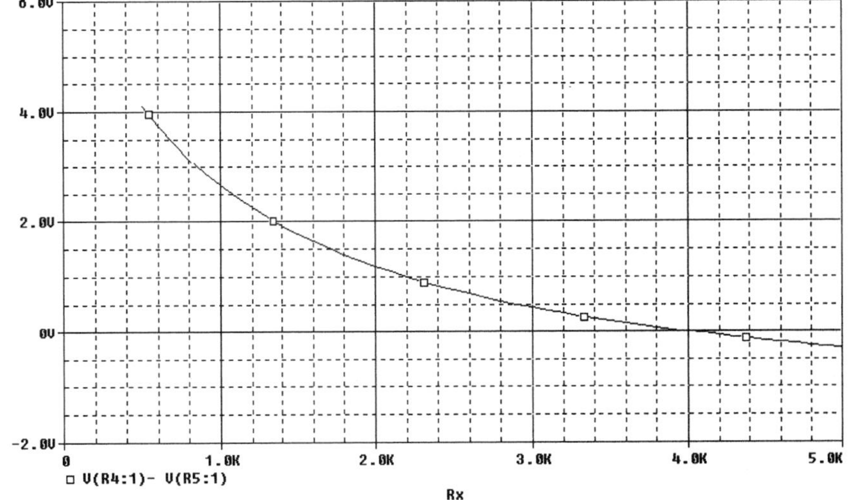
6.0V
4.0V
2.0V
0V
-2.0V
0
1.0K
2.0K
3.0K
4.0K
5.0K
□ V(R4:1)- V(R5:1)
Rx

Chapter

8

Methods of Analysis

8.1 Current Sources

1. $V_S = 18\text{ V} + 20\text{ V} = 38\text{ V}$

3. a. $I_3 = \left(\dfrac{300\ \Omega}{200\ \Omega + 300\ \Omega}\right)20\text{ mA} = 12\text{ mA}$

   b. $V_S = (20\text{ mA})(0.1\text{ k}\Omega) + (12\text{ mA})(0.2\text{ k}\Omega) = 4.4\text{ V}$

   $V_1 = (20\text{ mA})(0.1\text{ k}\Omega) = 2.0\text{ V}$

5. $I_{50\text{k}\Omega} = \dfrac{15\text{ V}}{50\text{ k}\Omega} = 300\ \mu\text{A}$

   $I_{150\text{k}\Omega} = \dfrac{15\text{ V}}{150\text{ k}\Omega} = 100\ \mu\text{A}$

   $I_1 = 300\ \mu\text{A} + 100\ \mu\text{A} = 400\ \mu\text{A}$

   $I_2 = 400\ \mu\text{A} + 100\ \mu\text{A} = 500\ \mu\text{A}$

7. Power provided by voltage source:

   $P = (15\text{ V})(500\ \mu\text{A}) - 7.5\text{ mW}$

   Power dissipated by resistors:

   $P_{150\text{k}\Omega} = (300\ \mu\text{A})^2 50\text{ k}\Omega = 4.5\text{ mW}$

   $P_{150\text{k}\Omega} = (100\ \mu\text{A})^2 150\text{ k}\Omega = 1.5\text{ mW}$

   Power absorbed by current source:

   $P = (0.1\ \mu\text{A})(15\text{ V}) = 1.5\text{ mW}$

   $P_{\text{in}} = 7.5\text{ mW} = \sum P_{\text{out}}$

   Note:

   The current source is taking energy from the circuit rather than providing energy.

8.2 Source Conversions

9. a.

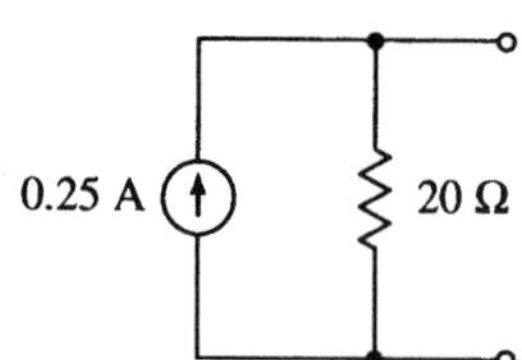

   b.

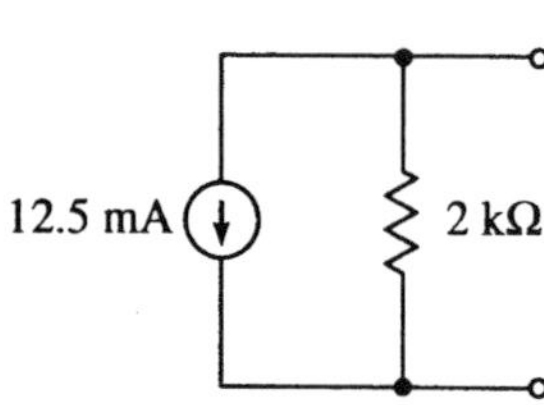

11. a. $I_L = \left(\dfrac{450\ \Omega}{450\ \Omega + 50\ \Omega}\right)8\text{ A} = 7.2\text{ A}$

    b. $E = (8\text{ A})(450\ \Omega) = 3600\text{ V}$

    $I_L = \dfrac{3600\text{ V}}{450\ \Omega + 50\ \Omega} = 7.2\text{ A}$

13. a.

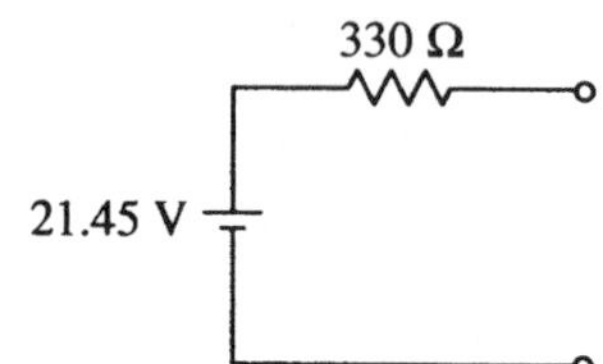

    b. $I = \dfrac{21.45\text{ V} - 16\text{ V}}{330\ \Omega + 470\ \Omega + 100\ \Omega} = 6.0\overline{5}\text{ mA}$

    c. $V_{ab} = (6.0\overline{5})\text{ mA})(0.1\text{ k}\Omega) = 0.60\overline{5}\text{ V}$

8.3 Current Sources in Parallel and Series

15. $I_T = 100\text{ mA} - 50\text{ mA} = 50\text{ mA (down)}$

    $R_T = 3\text{ k}\Omega \| 6\text{ k}\Omega \| 8\text{ k}\Omega = 1.6\text{ k}\Omega$

    $V_2 = -(50\text{ mA})(1.6\text{ k}\Omega) = -80\text{ V}$

    $I_1 = -\left(\dfrac{1.6\text{ k}\Omega}{3\text{ k}\Omega}\right)50\text{ mA} = -26.7\text{ mA}$

17. *a* — 7.2 V — 2.4 kΩ — *b*

    $E = (3\text{ mA})(2.4\text{ k}\Omega) = 7.2\text{ V}$

    $I_3 = \dfrac{8\text{ V} - 7.2\text{ V}}{2.4\text{ k}\Omega + 1.6\text{ k}\Omega + 2.0\text{ k}\Omega} = 0.133\text{ mA}$

    $V_{ab} = -7.2\text{ V} - (0.133\text{ mA})(2.4\text{ k}\Omega) = -7.52\text{ V}$

8.4 Branch Circuit Analysis

19. $(30\ \Omega)I_1 + (6\ \Omega)I_2 + 0I_3 = +15$ V

$0I_1 - (6\ \Omega)I_2 + (20\ \Omega)I_3 = +5$ V

$I_1 - I_2 - I_3 = 0$

D = 900

$I_1 = 0.467$ A

$I_2 = 0.167$ A

$I_3 = 0.300$ A

21. Convert current source into an equivalent voltage source

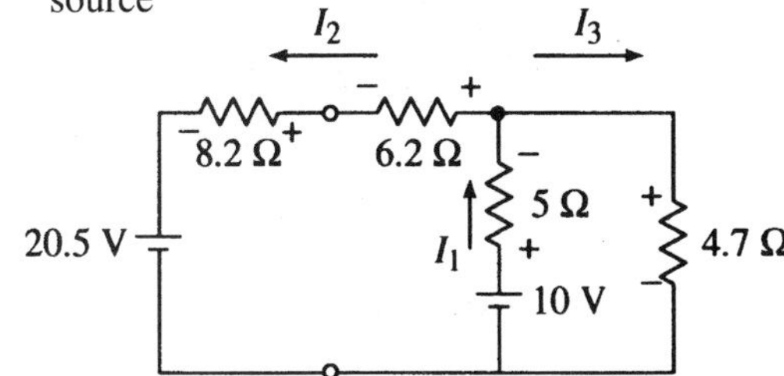

$-(5\ \Omega)I_1 - (14.4\ \Omega)I_2 + 0I_3 = 20.5\ \text{V} - 10\ \text{V} = 10.5$ V

$(5\ \Omega)I_1 + 0I_2 + (4.7\ \Omega)I_3 = +10$ V

$I_1 - I_2 - I_3 = 0$

D = −163.18

$I_1 = 0.580$ A

$I_2 = -0.931$ A

$I_3 = 1.511$ A

23. Convert current source to voltage source

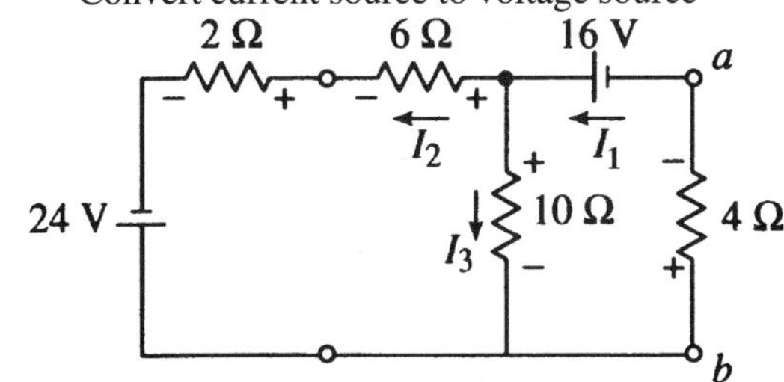

(one possible solution)

a. $4\Omega\, I_1 + 0\Omega\, I_2 + 10\Omega\, I_3 = +16$ V

$0\, I_1 + 8\Omega\, I_2 - 10\Omega\, I_3 = +24$ V

$I_1 - I_2 - I_3 = 0$

b. **D** = −152

$I_1 = 3.47$ A

$I_2 = 3.26$ A

$I_3 = 0.211$ A

c. $V_{ab} = -(4\ \Omega)(3.474\ \text{A}) = -13.89$ V

8.5 Mesh (Loop) Analysis

25. a. $(36\ \Omega)(I1 - (6\ \Omega)I2 = +15$ V

$-(6\ \Omega)I1 + (26\ \Omega)I2 = +5$ V

D = 900

$I_1 = 0.4\overline{6}$ A

$I_2 = 0.300$ A

27.

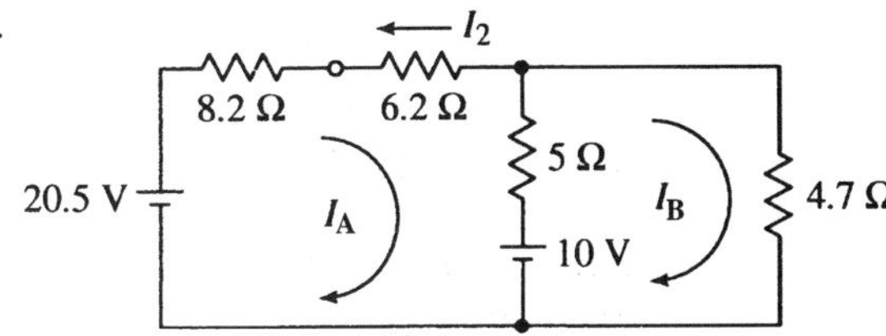

$(19.4\ \Omega)(I_A - (5\ \Omega)I_B = 20.5\ \text{V} - 10\ \text{V} = 10.5$ V

$-(5\ \Omega)I_A + (9.7\ \Omega)I_B = +10$ V

D = 163.18

$I_A = 0.931$ A

$I_2 = -I_A = -0.931$ A

$I_B = 1.511$ A

29. Although the circuit appears to have three loops, it has only two loops. One of the outside connections can be removed without affecting the circuit's operation.

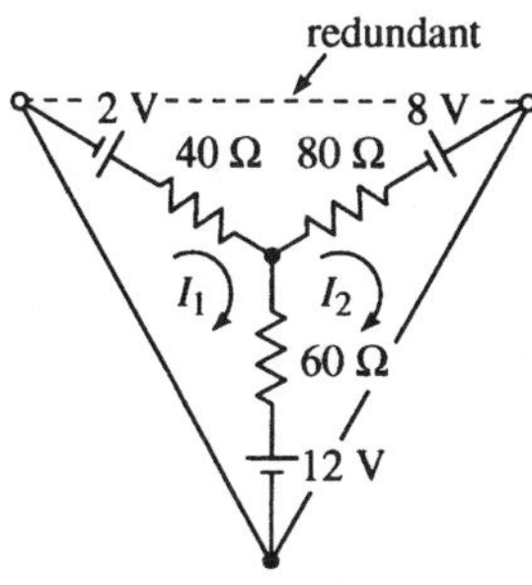

$(100\ \Omega)I_1 - (60\ \Omega)I_2 = -10$ V

$-(60\ \Omega)I_1 + (140\ \Omega)I_2 = +20$ V

D = 10 400

$I_1 = -19.23\ \text{mA} = I$

$I_2 = 134.6$ mA

$V_{ab} = 60\ \Omega(-29.34\ \text{mA} - 134.62\ \text{mA}) + 12$ V

$= +2.77$ V

31. $(10\ \Omega)I_1 - (1\ \Omega)I_2 - (6\ \Omega)I_3 = -6$ V

$-(1\ \Omega)I_1 + (8\ \Omega)I_2 - (3\ \Omega)I_3 = +10$ V

$-(6\ \Omega)I_1 - (3\ \Omega)I_2 + (9\ \Omega)I_3 = +5$ V

D = 297

$I_1 = 0.\overline{49}$ A

$I_2 = 1.\overline{87}$ A

$I_3 = 1.512$ A

8.6 Nodal Analysis

33. $+\left(\frac{1}{2\,\Omega}+\frac{1}{5\,\Omega}\right)V_1-\left(\frac{1}{5\,\Omega}\right)V_2=-5\text{ A}$

$+(0.700\text{ S})V_1-(0.200\text{ S})V_2=-5\text{A}$

$-\left(\frac{1}{5\,\Omega}\right)V_1+\left(\frac{1}{5\,\Omega}+\frac{1}{4\,\Omega}\right)V_2=2\text{ A}$

$-(0.200\text{ S})V_1+(0.450)V_2=2\text{ A}$

$V_1=-6.\overline{72}\text{ V}$

$V_2=+1.\overline{45}\text{ V}$

$\mathbf{D}=0.275$

35. $\left(\frac{1}{2\text{ k}\Omega}\right)V_1-0V_2=3\text{ mA}-6\text{ mA}$

$V_1=(-3\text{ mA})(2\text{ k}\Omega)=-6\text{ V}$

$\left(\frac{1}{5\text{ k}\Omega}+\frac{1}{10\text{ k}\Omega}\right)V_2=6\text{ mA}$

$V_2=(6\text{ mA})(3.33\text{ k}\Omega)=20\text{ V}$

37. Convert voltage sources except E_4 (which has no series resistance) into equivalent current source. Assign current I as shown.

$\left(\frac{1}{3\,\Omega}+\frac{1}{1\,\Omega}+\frac{1}{4\,\Omega}\right)V_a-\left(\frac{1}{3\,\Omega}\right)V_b-\left(\frac{1}{1\,\Omega}\right)V_c$

$=\frac{-2}{3}\text{ A}+4\text{ A}-1.5\text{ A}$

$-\left(\frac{1}{3\,\Omega}\right)V_a+\left(\frac{1}{3\,\Omega}+\frac{1}{6\,\Omega}\right)V_b-\left(\frac{1}{6}\,\Omega\right)V_c=I+\frac{2}{3}\text{ A}$

$-\left(\frac{1}{1}\,\Omega\right)V_a-\left(\frac{1}{6\,\Omega}\right)V_v+\left(\frac{1}{6\,\Omega}+\frac{1}{3\,\Omega}+\frac{1}{1\,\Omega}\right)V_c=-4\text{ A}$

Since $V_b=5$ V, we need to solve for V_a, V_c and I.

The equations are simplified as follows:

$(1.58\overline{3}\text{ S})V_a-(1\text{ S})V_c+0I=3.5\text{ A}$

$-0\overline{3}V_a-0.1\overline{6}V_c-1I=-1.8\overline{3}\text{ A}$

$-(1\text{ S})V_a+(1.5\text{ S})V_c-0I=-3.1\overline{6}\text{ A}$

$V_a=1.51\text{ V}\quad V_c=-1.10\text{ V}\quad I=1.512\text{ A}$

($\mathbf{D}=1.375$)

$V_{6\,\Omega}=V_{bc}=5\text{ V}-(-1.\overline{10}\text{ V})=6.10\text{ V}$

8.7 Delta-Wye (Pi-Tee) Conversion

39. a.

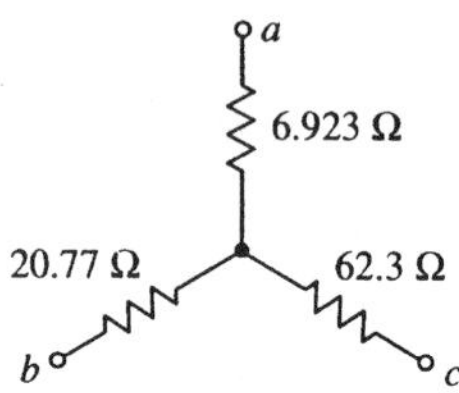

b.

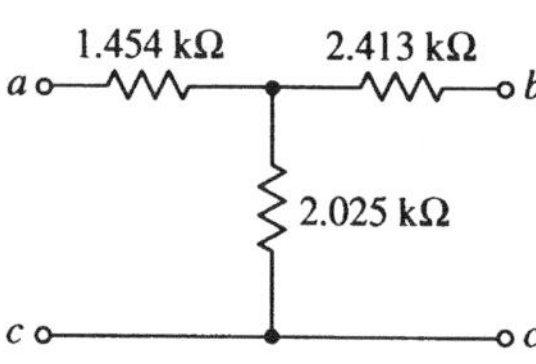

41. a.

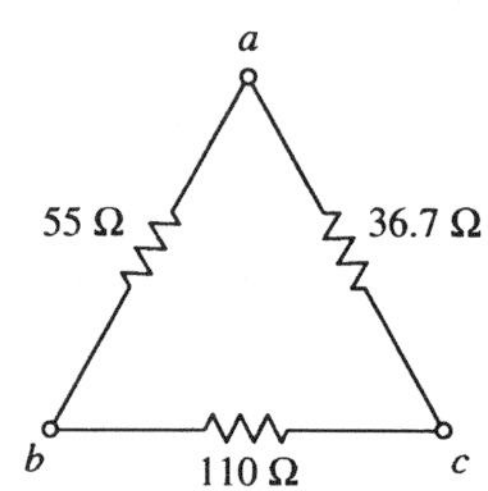

b.

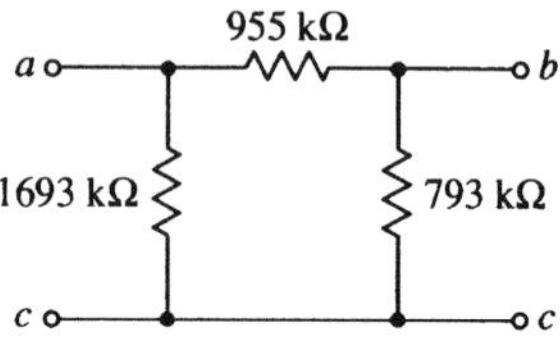

43.

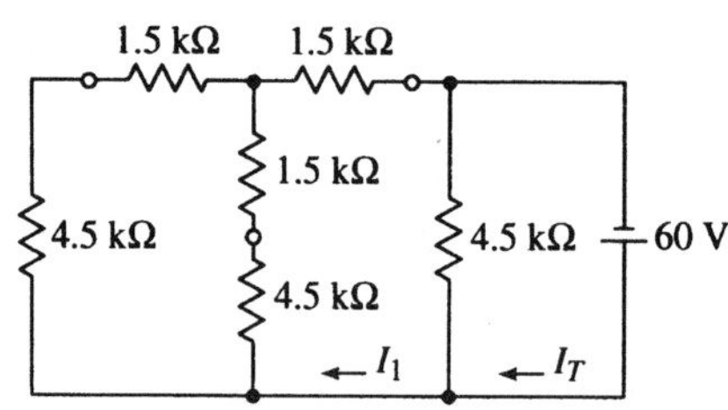

$R_T=4.5\text{ k}\Omega\|[1.5\text{ k}\Omega+(1.5\text{ k}\Omega+4.5\text{ k}\Omega)\|(1.5\text{ k}\Omega+4.5\text{ k}\Omega)]=2.25\text{ k}\Omega$

$I_T=26.\overline{6}\text{ mA}$

$I_1=13.\overline{3}\text{ mA}$

$I=6.\overline{6}\text{ mA}$

45.

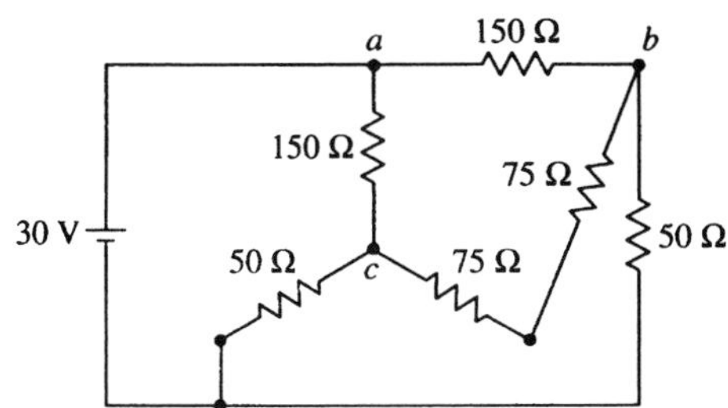

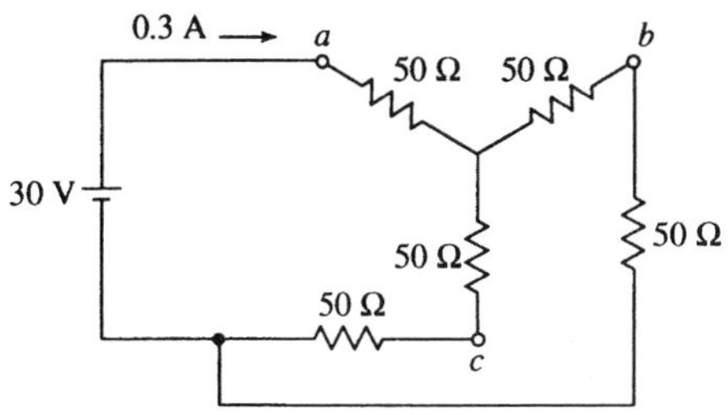

$R_T = 50\ \Omega + (50\ \Omega + 50\ \Omega) \| (50\ \Omega + 50\ \Omega) = 100\ \Omega$

$I = \dfrac{22.5\ \Omega}{150\ \Omega} = 0.15\ \text{A}$

8.8 Bridge Networks

47. a. The bridge is *not* balanced since

$$\frac{12\ \Omega}{18\ \Omega} \neq \frac{6\ \Omega}{6\ \Omega}$$

b. $(18\ \Omega)I_1 = (12\ \Omega)I_2 - (6\ \Omega)I_3 = +15\ \text{V}$

$-(12\ \Omega)I_1 + (54\ \Omega)I_2 - (6\ \Omega)I_3 = 0\ \text{V}$

$-(6\ \Omega)I_1 - (24\ \Omega)I_2 + (36\ \Omega)I_3 = 0\ \text{V}$

c. $I_1 = 1.462\ \text{A}$ $\quad$ $\mathbf{D} = 14\ 040$

$I_2 = 0.615\ \text{A}$

$I_3 = 0.654\ \text{A}$

$I = I_3 - I_2 = 38.5\ \text{mA}$

d. $V_{R_5} = 0.923\ \text{V}$

49. The bridge is balanced, therefore

$I_{R_5} = 0$

$R_T = 100\ \Omega + (100\ \Omega + 300\ \Omega) \| (300\ \Omega + 900\ \Omega)$

$= 400\ \Omega$

$I_{R_S} = \dfrac{24\ \text{V}}{400\ \Omega} = 60\ \text{mA}$

$I_{R_1} = I_{R_3} = \left(\dfrac{1200\ \Omega}{200\ \Omega + 400\ \Omega}\right) 60\ \text{mA} = 45\ \text{mA}$

$I_{R_2} = I_{R_4} = 60\ \text{mA} - 45\ \text{mA} = 15\ \text{mA}$

51.

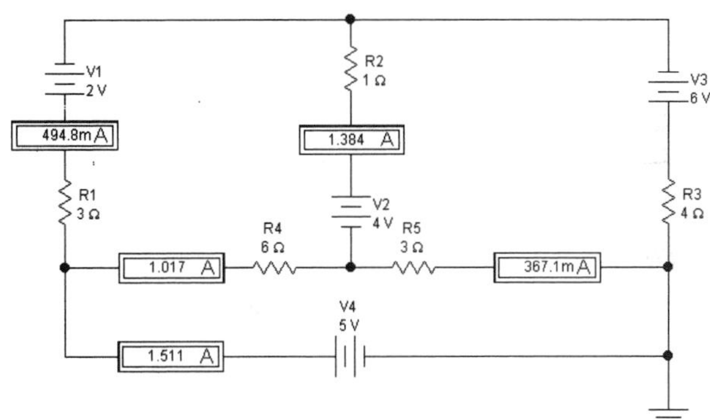

53.

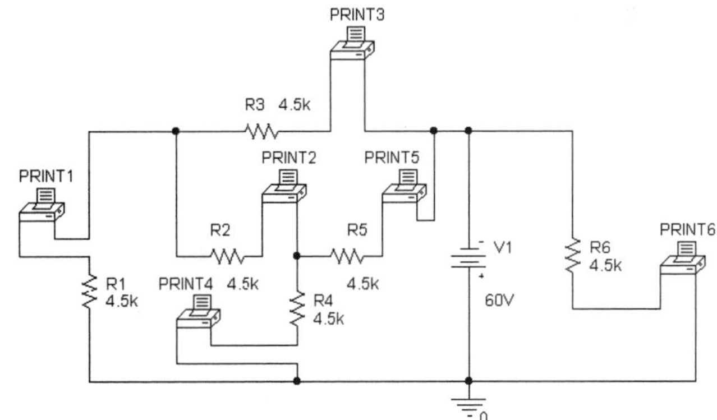

Chapter

9

Network Theorems

9.1 Superposition Theorem

1.

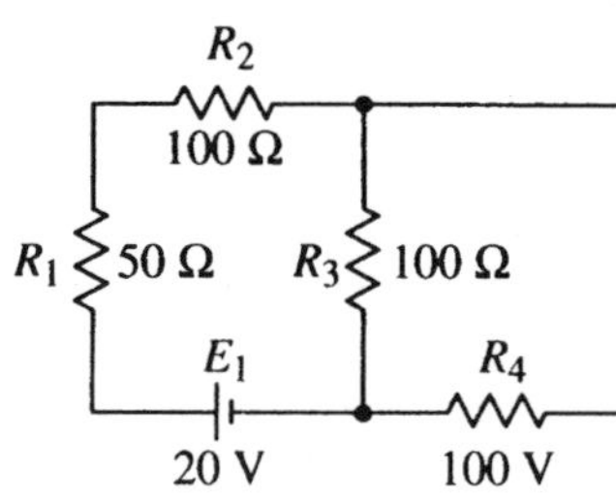

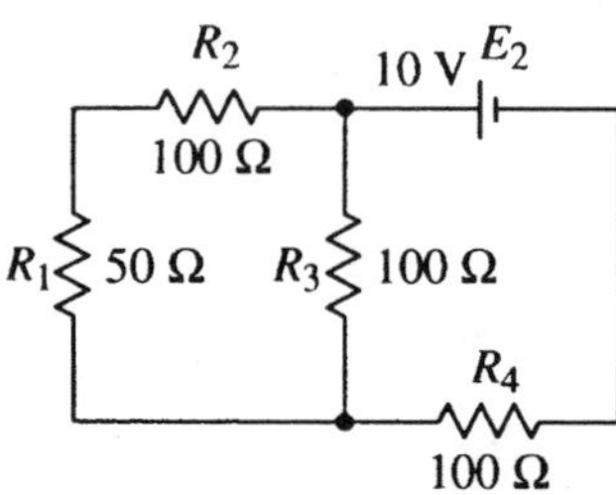

$I_{R_1} = 100 \text{ mA} - 25 \text{ mA} = 75 \text{ mA (up)}$

$I_{R_2} = 75 \text{ mA (right)}$

$I_{R_3} = 50 \text{ mA} + 37.5 \text{ mA} = 87.5 \text{ mA (down)}$

$I_{R_4} = 62.5 \text{ mA} - 50 \text{ mA} = 12.5 \text{ mA (right)}$

3.

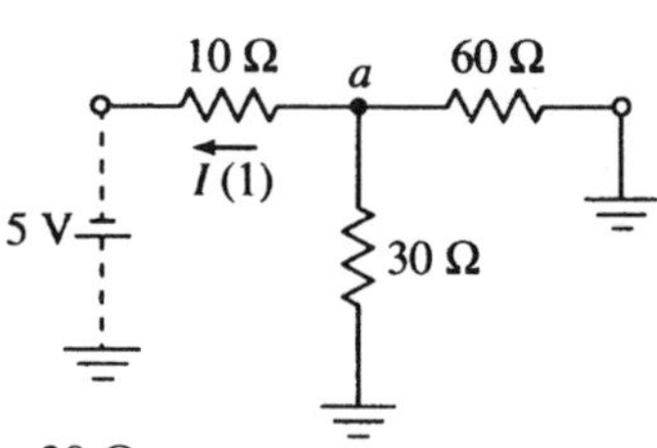

$R_{T_1} = 30\ \Omega$

$I(1) = 0.1\overline{6}\text{ A}$

$V_a(1) = -3.\overline{3}\text{V}$

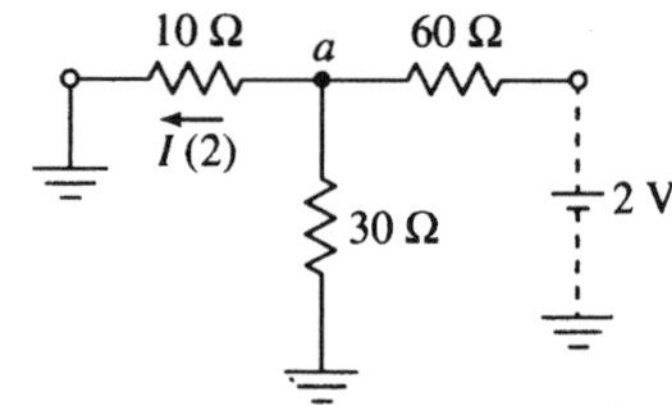

$R_{T_2} = 67.5\ \Omega$

$I(2) = \left(\dfrac{30\ \Omega}{40\ \Omega}\right)29.\overline{629}\text{ mA} = 22.\overline{2}\text{ mA}$

$V_a(2) = +(7.5\ \Omega)(29.629\text{ mA}) = +0.\overline{2}\text{ V}$

$I_1 = 0.1\overline{6}\text{ A} + 0.0\overline{2}\text{ A} = 0.1\overline{8}\text{ A}$

$V_a = -3.\overline{3}\text{ V} + 0.\overline{2}\text{ V} = -3.\overline{1}\text{ V}$

5.

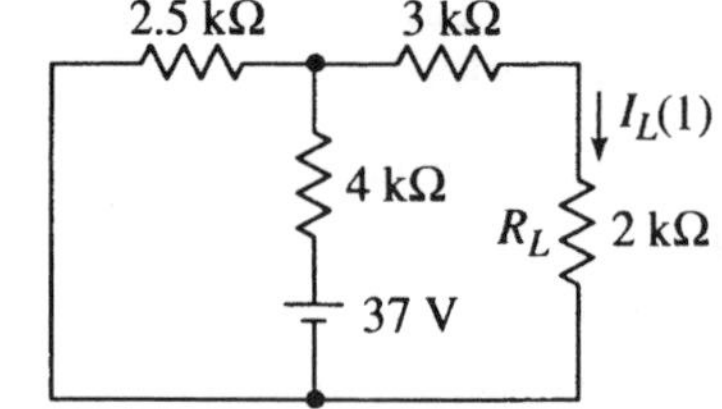

$R_{T_1} = 5.\overline{6}\text{ k}\Omega$

$I_L(1) = \left(\dfrac{2.5\text{ k}\Omega}{7.5\text{ k}\Omega}\right)(6.53\text{ mA}) = 2.18\text{ mA}$

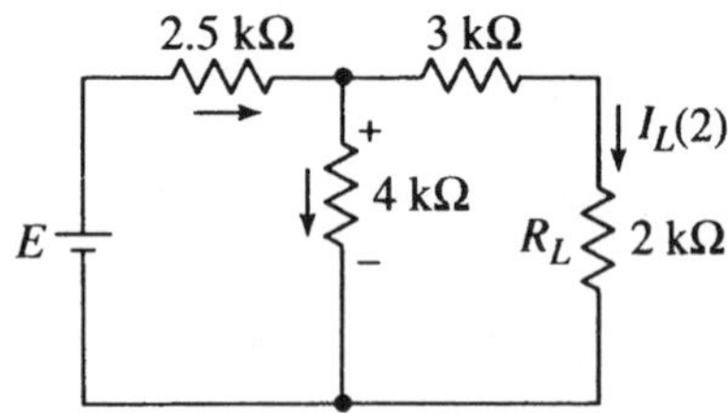

$I_L(2) = 5\text{ mA} - 2.18\text{ mA} = 2.82\text{ mA}$

$V_{4\text{ k}\Omega} = (5\text{ k}\Omega)(2.28\text{ mA}) = 14.1\text{ V}$

$I_{4\text{ k}\Omega} = 3.53\text{ mA}$

$I_{2.5\text{ k}\Omega} = 6.36\text{ mA}$

$E = (6.36\text{ mA})(2.5\text{ k}\Omega) + 14.1\text{ V} = 30\text{ V}$

9.2 Thévenin's Theorem

7. $R_{Th} = 12\ \Omega + 10\ \Omega \| 40\ \Omega = 20\ \Omega$

$E_{Th} = V_{ab(OC)} = \left(\frac{10\ \Omega}{10\ \Omega + 40\ \Omega}\right) 50\ V = 10\ V$

$V_{ab} = \left(\frac{30\ \Omega}{30\ \Omega + 20\ \Omega}\right) 10\ V = +6\ V$

9. $R_{Th} = 1.0\ k\Omega + 6.8\ k\Omega \| 1.2\ k\Omega = 2.02\ k\Omega$

$E_{Th} = V_{ab(OC)} = -\left(\frac{1.2\ k\Omega}{1.2\ k\Omega + 6.8\ k\Omega}\right) 8\ V = -1.20\ V$

$V_{ab} = -\left(\frac{1.5\ k\Omega}{1.5\ k\Omega + 2.02\ k\Omega}\right)(1.20\ V) = -0.511\ V$

11. $R_{Th} = 16\ \Omega$

$V_{ab(OC-1)} = 2.4\ V$

$V_{ab(OC-2)} = (0.2\ A)(16\ \Omega) = 3.2\ V$

$E_{Th} = V_{ab(OC)} = 5.6\ V$

$R_L = 20\ \Omega : V_{ab} = \left(\frac{20\ \Omega}{20\ \Omega + 16\ \Omega}\right) 5.6\ V = 3.11\ V$

$R_L = 50\ \Omega : V_{ab} = \left(\frac{50\ \Omega}{50\ \Omega + 16\ \Omega}\right) 5.6\ V = 4.24\ V$

13. a. $R_{Th} = 35\ \Omega + 20\ \Omega \| 60\ \Omega = 50\ \Omega$

$E_{Th} = \left(\frac{60\ \Omega}{60\ \Omega + 20\ \Omega}\right) 100\ V = 75\ V$

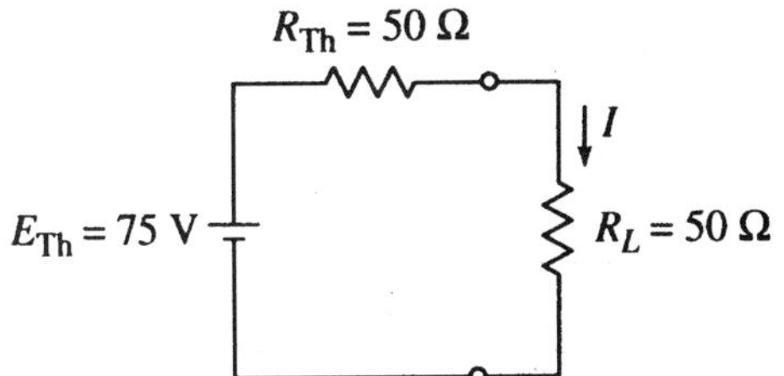

b. $I = \frac{75\ V}{50\ \Omega + 50\ \Omega} = 0.75\ A$

15. a. $R_{Th} = 1.8\ k\Omega + 2\ k\Omega = 3.8\ k\Omega$

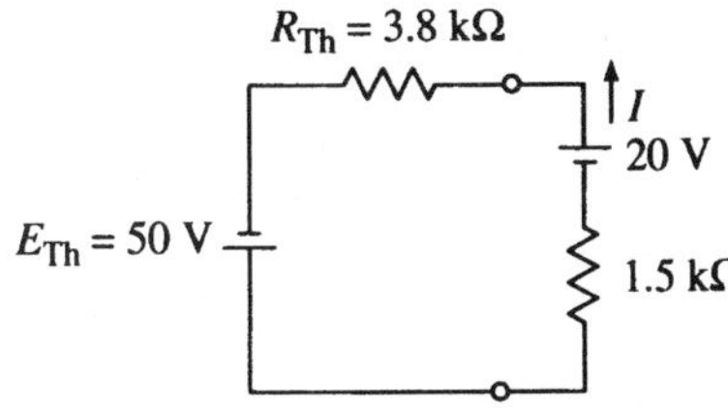

b. $I = \frac{50\ V + 20\ V}{3.8\ k\Omega + 1.5\ k\Omega} = 13.21\ mA$

17. a. $R_{Th} = 15\ k\Omega + 25\ k\Omega + 20\ k\Omega = 60\ k\Omega$

b. $E_{OC}(1) = (3\ mA)(25\ k\Omega) = +75\ V$

$E_{OC}(2) = -(5\ mA)(20\ k\Omega) = -100\ V$

$E_{Th} = 100\ V - 75\ V = 25\ V$

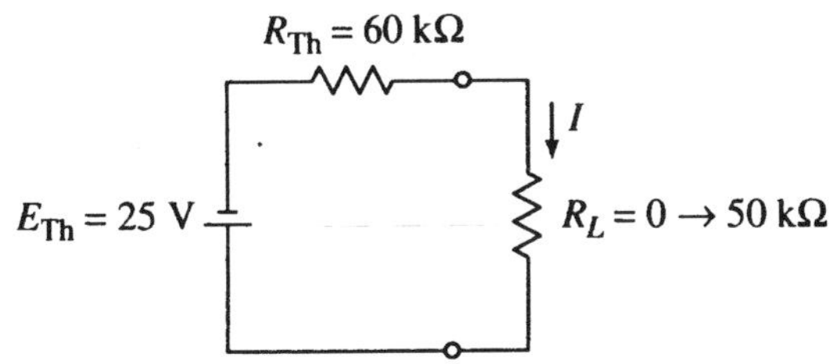

$R_L = 0 : \ I = -0.417\ mA$

$R_L = 10\ k\Omega : \ I = -0.357\ mA$

$R_L = 50\ k\Omega : \ I = -0.227\ mA$

19. a. $R_{Th} = 10\ k\Omega + (16\ k\Omega \| 24\ k\Omega) = 16\ k\Omega$

$E_{TH} = \left(\frac{24\ k\Omega}{24\ k\Omega + 16\ k\Omega}\right)(48\ V) = 28.8\ V$

b. $R_L = 0$:

$I = \frac{28.8\ V}{16\ k\Omega + 0} = 1.80\ mA$

$R_L = 10\ k\Omega$:

$I = \frac{28.8\ V}{16\ k\Omega + 10\ k\Omega} = 1.11\ mA$

$R_L = 50\ k\Omega$:

$I = \frac{28.8\ V}{16\ k\Omega + 50\ k\Omega} = 0.436\ mA$

21. $R_{Th} = 18\ \Omega \| (4\ \Omega + 16\ \Omega \| 16\ \Omega) = 7.2\ \Omega$

Current Source:

$V_{ab}(1) = (300\ mA)(18\ \Omega \| (4\ \Omega + 16\ \Omega) = -2.16\ V$

Voltage Source:

$R_T = 16\ \Omega + 16\ \Omega \| (4\ \Omega + 18\ \Omega) = 25.2632\ \Omega$

$I_T = 316.\bar{6}\ mA$

$I_{18\ \Omega} = \left(\frac{16\ \Omega}{16\ \Omega + 4\ \Omega + 18\ \Omega}\right) 316.\bar{6}\ mA = 133.\bar{3}\ mA$

$V_{ab}(2) = -(133.\bar{3}\ mA)(18\ \Omega) = -2.40\ V$

$E_{Th} = +2.16\ V + 2.40\ V = +4.56\ V$

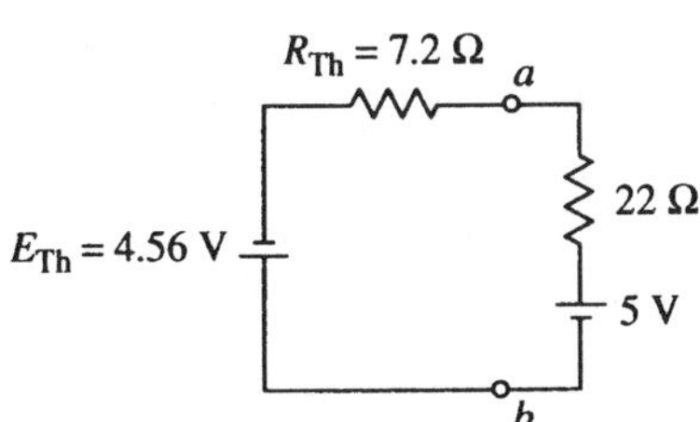

23. a. $R_{Th} = 120\ \Omega + 100\ \Omega \| 400\ \Omega = 200\ \Omega$

$E_{Th} = V_{ab} = -(200\ \Omega)(0.1\ mA) = -20\ V$

b. $I = \frac{20\ V}{200\ \Omega + 160\ \Omega} = 0.0556\ A = 55.6\ mA$

9.3 Norton's Theorem

25. $R_N = 12\ \Omega + 10\ \Omega \| 40\ \Omega = 20\ \Omega$

Shorting terminals *a* and *b*:

$R_T = 45.4\ \Omega$

$I_T = 1.1\ \text{A}$

$$I_{ab} = \left(\frac{10\ \Omega}{10\ \Omega + 12\ \Omega}\right) 1.1\ \text{A} = 0.500\ \text{A}$$

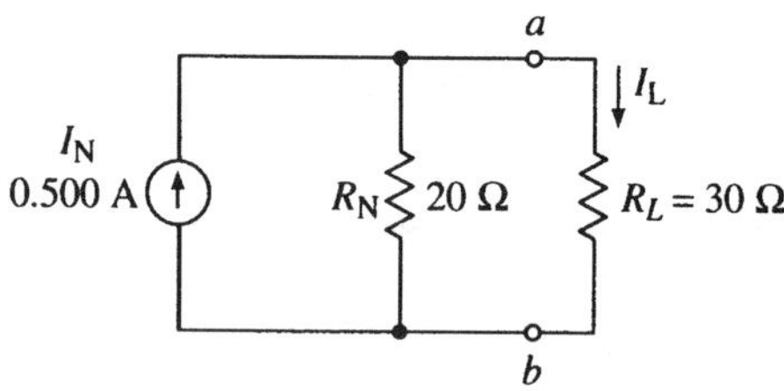

$$I_L = \left(\frac{20\ \Omega}{20\ \Omega + 30\ \Omega}\right)(0.500\ \text{A})\ 0.200\ \text{A}$$

27. $R_N = 1.0\ \text{k}\Omega + 6.8\ \text{k}\Omega \| 1.2\ \text{k}\Omega = 2.02\ \text{k}\Omega$

For voltage source:

$R_T = 1.0\ \text{k}\Omega + 6.8\ \text{k}\Omega + 1.0\ \text{k} \| 1.2\ \text{k}\Omega = 7.34\ \text{k}\Omega$

$$I_T = \frac{8\ \text{V}}{7.34\ \text{k}\Omega} = 1.089\ \text{mA}$$

$$I_{ab} = -\left(\frac{1.2\ \text{k}\Omega}{1.2\ \text{k}\Omega + 1.0\text{k}\Omega}\right)(1.089\ \text{mA}) = -0.595\ \text{mA}$$

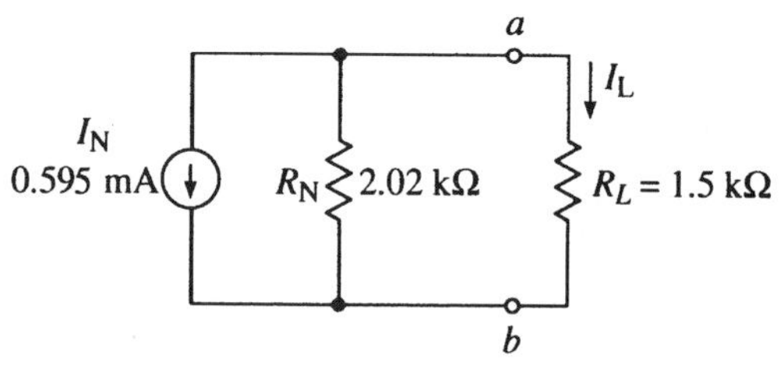

$$I_L = \left(\frac{2.02\ \text{k}\Omega}{2.02\ \text{k}\Omega + 1.5\ \text{k}\Omega}\right)(0.595\ \text{mA}) = 0.341\ \text{mA}$$

29. a. $R_N = 16\ \Omega$

$$I_{ab}(1) = \frac{2.4\ \text{V}}{16\ \Omega} = 0.15\ \text{A}$$

$I_{ab}(2) = 0.2\ \text{A}$

$I_N = 0.15\ \text{A} + 0.2\ \text{A} = 0.35\ \text{A}$

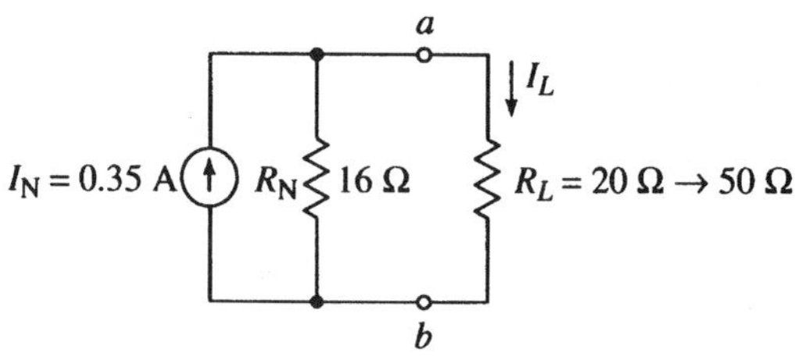

b.
$$R_L = 20\ \Omega : I_L = \left(\frac{16\ \Omega}{16\ \Omega + 20\ \Omega}\right)(0.35\ \text{A}) = 0.156\ \text{A}$$

$$R_L = 50\ \Omega : I_L = \left(\frac{16\ \Omega}{16\ \Omega + 50\ \Omega}\right)(0.35\ \text{A}) = 0.085\ \text{A}$$

31. a. $R_N = 35\ \Omega + 20\ \Omega \| 60\ \Omega = 50\ \Omega$

$R_T = 20\ \Omega + 60\ \Omega \| 35\ \Omega = 42.105\ \Omega$

$I_T = 2.375\ \text{A}$

$$I_N = \left(\frac{60\ \Omega}{60\ \Omega + 35\ \Omega}\right) 2.375\ \text{A} = 1.5\ \text{A}$$

b. $R_N = R_{Th} = 50\ \Omega$

$$I_N = \frac{E_{Th}}{R_{Th}} = \frac{75\ \text{V}}{50\ \Omega} = 1.5\ \text{A}$$

33. a. $R_N = 15\ \text{k}\Omega + 25\ \text{k}\Omega + 20\ \text{k}\Omega = 60\ \text{k}\Omega$

$$I_{ab}(1) = \left(\frac{25\ \text{k}\Omega}{25\ \text{k}\Omega + 35\ \text{k}\Omega}\right)(3\ \text{mA}) = 1.25\ \text{mA}$$

$$I_{ab}(2) = -\left(\frac{20\ \text{k}\Omega}{20\ \text{k}\Omega + 40\ \text{k}\Omega}\right)(5\ \text{mA}) = -1.667\ \text{mA}$$

$I_N = 0.417\ \text{mA}$

b. $R_N = R_{Th} = 60\ \text{k}\Omega$

$$I_N = \frac{25\ \text{V}}{60\ \text{k}\Omega} = 0.417\ \text{mA}$$

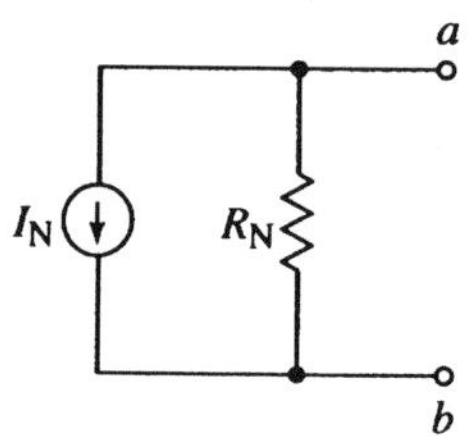

35.

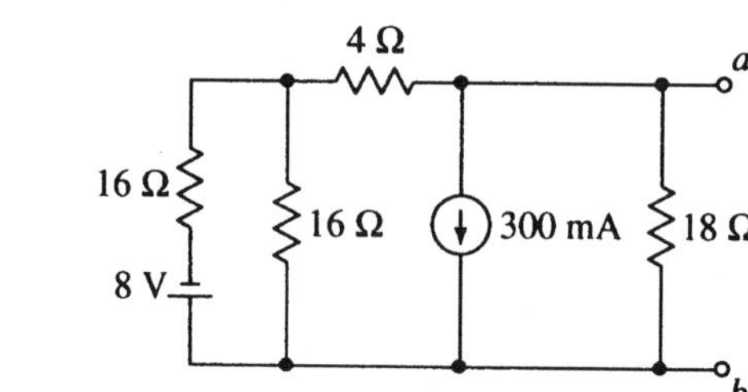

a. $R_N = 18\ \Omega \| [4\ \Omega + 16\ \Omega \| 16\ \Omega] = 7.2\ \Omega$

$R_T(1) = 16\ \Omega + (16\ \Omega \| 4\ \Omega) = 19.2\ \Omega$

$I_T(1) = 0.41\overline{6}\ \text{A}$

$$I_{ab}(1) = -\left(\frac{16\ \Omega}{16\ \Omega + 4\ \Omega}\right)(0.41\overline{6}\ \text{A})$$
$$= -0.333\ \text{A} = -333\ \text{mA}$$

$I_{ab}(2) = -300\ \text{mA}$

$I_N = 300\ \text{mA} + 333\ \text{mA} = 633\ \text{mA}$

b. $R_N = R_{Th} = 7.2\ \Omega$

$$I_N = \frac{E_{Th}}{R_N} = \frac{4.56\ \text{V}}{7.2\ \Omega} = 633\ \text{mA}$$

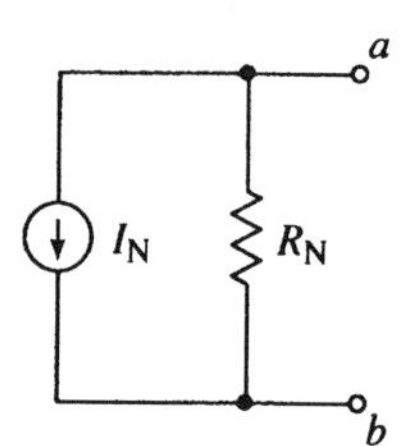

9.4 Maximum Power Transfer Theorem

37. a. $R_L = R_N = R_{Th} = 60\ k\Omega$

b. $V_L - \dfrac{E_{Th}}{2} = 12.5\ V$

$P_{max} = \dfrac{(V_L)^2}{R_L} = 2.60\ mW$

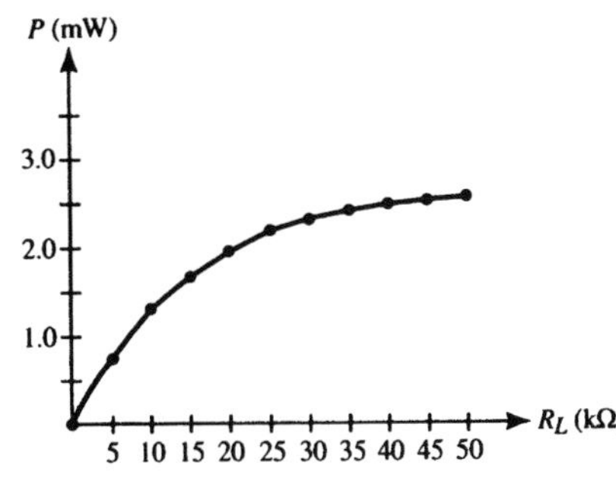

Note: Maximum power is not possible since R_L can only go to 50 kΩ ($P_{max} = 2.58$ mW).

39. a. $R_{Th} = 20\ \Omega + R \| 600\ \Omega = 50\ \Omega$

$\therefore \dfrac{(R)(600\ \Omega)}{R + 600\ \Omega} = 50\ \Omega - 20\ \Omega$

$R(600\ \Omega) = R(30\ \Omega) + (30\ \Omega)(600\ \Omega)$

$570R = 18\ 000\ \Omega$

$R = 31.58\ \Omega$

b. $E_{Th} = \left(\dfrac{31.58\ \Omega}{31.58 + 600\ \Omega}\right) 25\ V = 1.25\ V$

$P_{max} = \dfrac{(1.25\ V)^2}{4(50\ \Omega)} = 7.81\ mW$

41. a. $R_L = R_{Th} = 32\ k\Omega = R_2 \| R_1 = \dfrac{R_1 R_2}{R_1 + R_2}$

For all values in kΩ, where $R_2 = 200 - R_1$:

$32(R_1 + 200 - R_1) = R_1\ (200 - R_1)$

$6400 = 200\ R_1 - R_1^2$

$R_1 = \dfrac{200 \pm 120}{2} = 40{,}160$

$\therefore R_1 = 40\ k\Omega\ \&\ R_2 = 160\ k\Omega$ or

$R_1 = 160\ k\Omega\ \&\ R_2 = 40\ k\Omega$

b. For $R_1 = 40\ k\Omega\ \&\ R_2 = 160\ k\Omega$:

$E_{Th} = 20\ V \qquad P_L = 3.125\ mW$

9.5 Substitution Theorem

43. $V_{ab}(1) = 50\ mA \left(\dfrac{75\Omega}{300\ \Omega}\right)(125\ \Omega) = (50\ mA)(31.25\ \Omega) = 1.56\ V$

$V_{ab}(2) = -\left(\dfrac{125\ \Omega}{100\ \Omega + 125\ \Omega + 75\ \Omega}\right)(10\ V) = -4.1\bar{6}\ V$

$V_{ab} = 2.60\ V$

$I = 20.83\ mA$

$E = 2.60\ V - 1.04\ V = 1.56\ V$

a —[50 Ω, − +, I ←]— E = 1.56 V — b

1.04 V

9.6 Millman's Theorem

45. $R_{eq} = 20\ \Omega \| 30\ \Omega = 12\ \Omega$

$E_{eq} = V_{ab} = \dfrac{\dfrac{20\ V}{30\ \Omega} - \dfrac{10\ V}{20\ \Omega}}{\dfrac{1}{30\ \Omega} + \dfrac{1}{20\ \Omega}}$

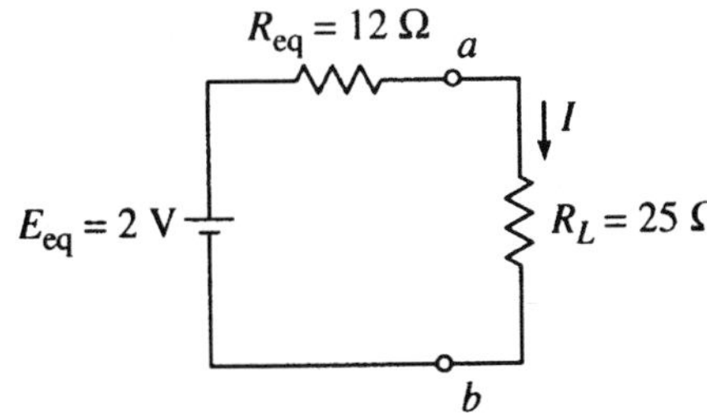

$I = \dfrac{2\ V}{12\ \Omega + 25\ \Omega} = 0.054\ A$

$P_L = (0.054\ A)^2(25\ \Omega) = 0.073\ W$

47. $R_{eq} = 5.6\ k\Omega \| 4.7\ k\Omega \| (3.3\ k\Omega + 1.8\ k\Omega) = 1.702\ k\Omega$

$E_{eq} = V_{ab} = \dfrac{-\dfrac{10\ V}{5.1\ k\Omega} - \dfrac{5\ V}{4.7\ k\Omega} + \dfrac{6\ V}{5.6\ k\Omega}}{\dfrac{1}{5.1\ k\Omega} + \dfrac{1}{4.7\ k\Omega} + \dfrac{1}{5.6\ k\Omega}} = -3.325\ V$

$I = \dfrac{3.325V}{10\ k\Omega + 1.702\ K\Omega} = 0.284\ mA$

$P_L = (0.284\ mA)^2(10\ k\Omega) = 0.807\ mW$

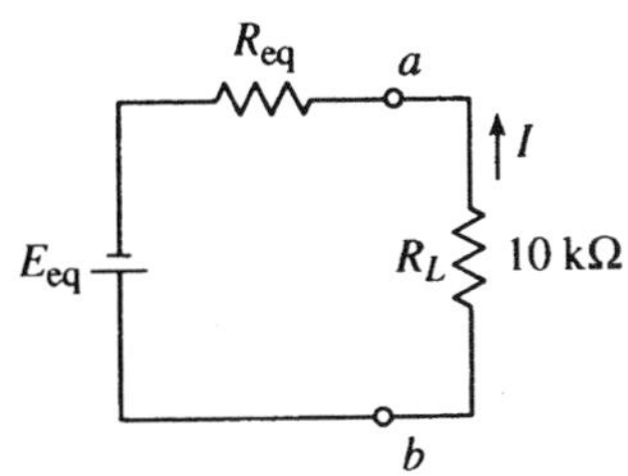

9.7 Reciprocity Theorem

49. a. $R_T = 30\ \Omega + 60\ \Omega \| [22.5\ \Omega + 10\ \Omega \| 30\ \Omega]$

$= 30\ \Omega + 60\ \Omega \| 30\ \Omega$

$= 30\ \Omega + 20\ \Omega = 50\ \Omega$

$I_T = 0.48\ \text{A}$

$$I_1 = \left(\frac{60\ \Omega}{60\ \Omega + 30\ \Omega}\right)(0.48\ \text{A}) = 0.32\ \text{A}$$

$$I = \left(\frac{30\ \Omega}{30\ \Omega + 10\ \Omega}\right)(0.32\ \text{A}) = 0.24\ \text{A}$$

b. Move the voltage source

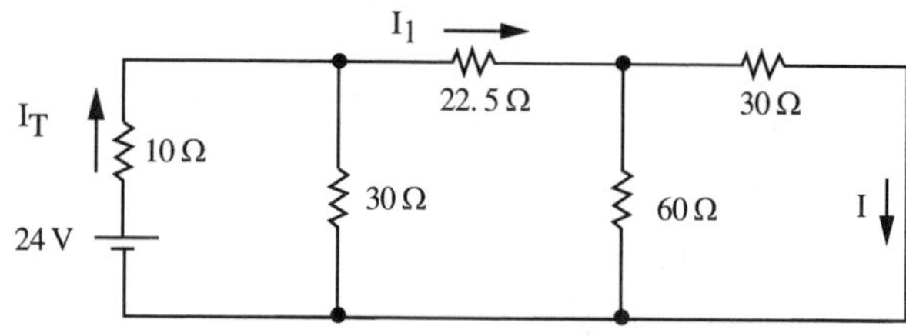

$R_T = 10\ \Omega + 30\ \Omega \| (22.5\ \Omega + 30\ \Omega \| 60\ \Omega)$

$= 10\ \Omega + 30\ \Omega \| 42.5\ \Omega$

$= 27.59\ \Omega$

$$I_T = \frac{24\ \text{V}}{27.59\ \Omega} = 0.87\ \text{A}$$

$$I_1 = \left(\frac{30\ \Omega}{30\ \Omega + 42.5\ \Omega}\right)(0.87\ \text{A}) = 0.36\ \text{A}$$

$$I = \left(\frac{60\ \Omega}{60\ \Omega + 30\ \Omega}\right)(0.36\ \text{A}) = 0.24\ \text{A}$$

Reciprocity applies.

51. a. Convert the current source to a voltage source.

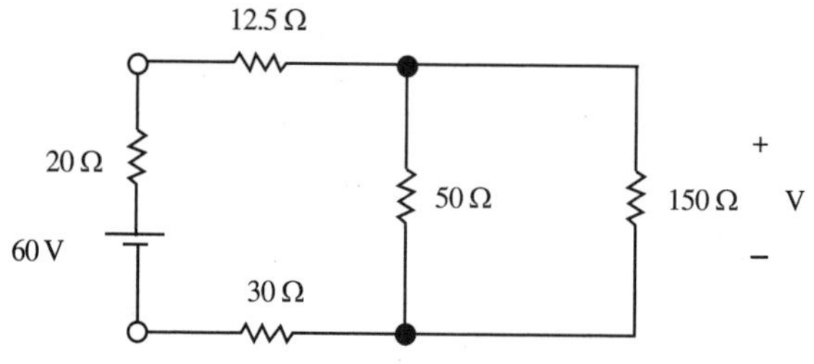

$$V = \frac{(50\ \Omega \| 150\ \Omega)(60\ \text{V})}{20\ \Omega + 30\ \Omega + 12.5\ \Omega + 50\Omega \| 150\ \Omega}$$

$$= \left(\frac{37.5\ \Omega}{100\ \Omega}\right) 60\ \text{V} = 22.5\ \Omega$$

b. Place the 3-A current source across the 150 Ω resistor:

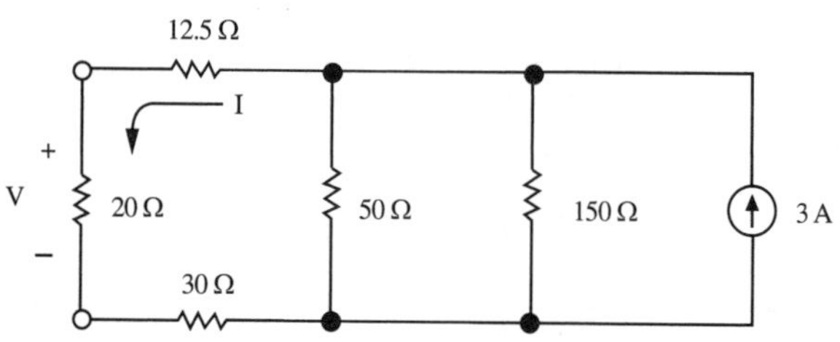

$R_T = 150\ \Omega \| 50\ \Omega \| (12.5\ \Omega + 20\ \Omega + 50\ \Omega) = 23.4\ \Omega$

$$I = \left(\frac{23.4\ \Omega}{62.5\ \Omega}\right) 3\ \text{A} = 1.125\ \text{A}$$

$V = (1.125\ \text{A})(20\ \Omega) = 22.5\ \text{V}$

Reciprocity applies.

9.8 Circuit Analysis Using Computers

53.

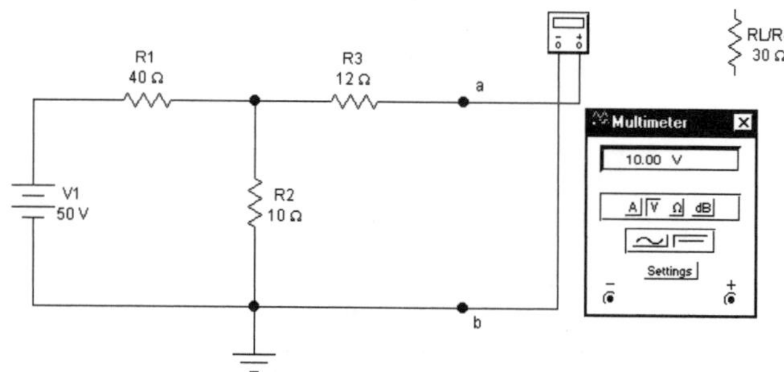

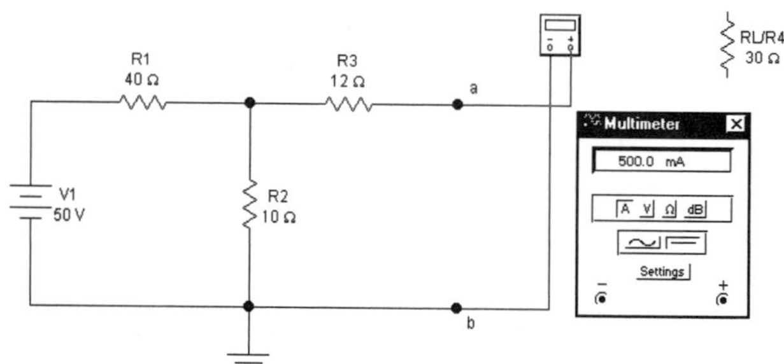

$E_{Th} = 10.0\ \text{V}$

$I_N = 500\ \text{mA} = 0.5\ \text{A}$

$$R_{Th} = R_N = \frac{10.0\ \text{V}}{0.5\ \text{A}} = 20\ \Omega$$

55.

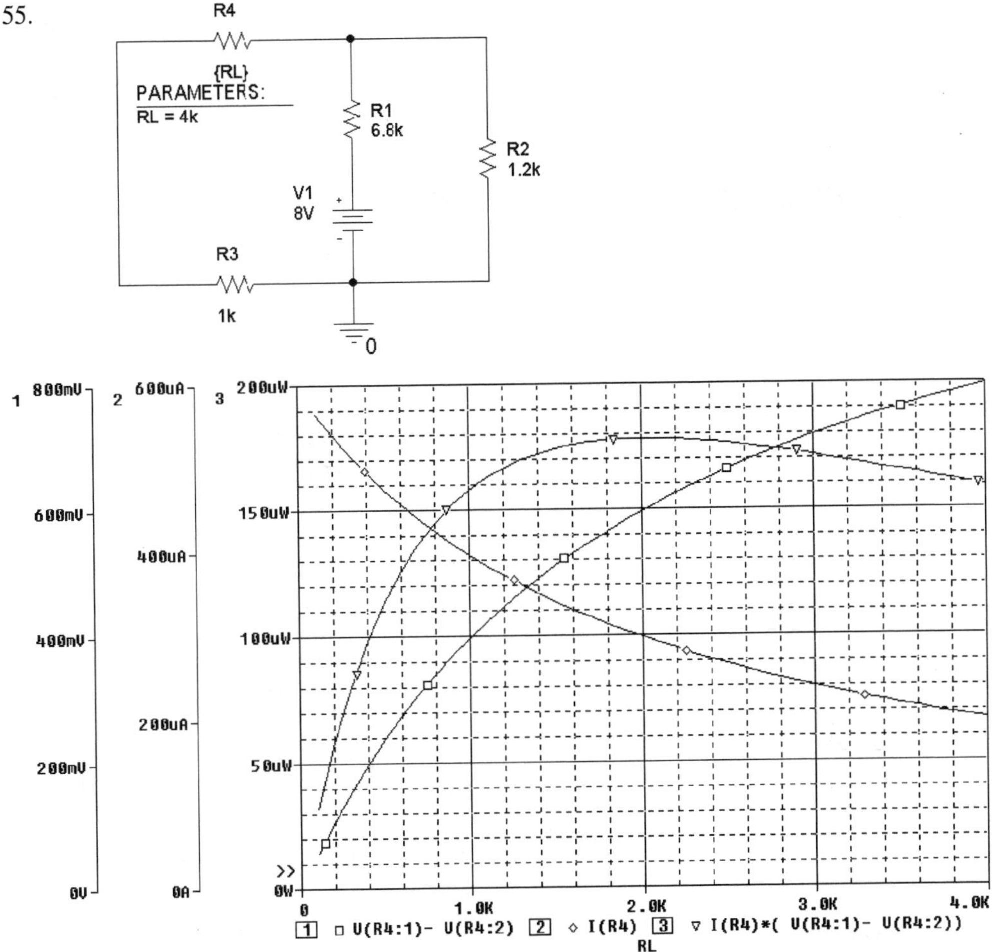

$P_{\max} = 178\ \mu\text{W}$ when $R_L = 2\ \text{k}\Omega$

Chapter

10

Capacitors and Capacitance

10.1 Capacitance

1. a. $Q = CV = (20 \times 10^{-6}\text{F})(40\text{ V}) = 800\,\mu\text{C}$

b. $C = \dfrac{Q}{V} = \dfrac{1000\,\mu\text{C}}{500\text{ V}} = 2\,\mu\text{F}$

c. $Q = (500 \times 10^{-9}\text{F})(200\text{ V}) = 100\,\mu\text{C}$

d. $V = \dfrac{Q}{C} = \dfrac{3 \times 10^{-4}\text{C}}{10 \times 10^{-6}\text{F}} = 30\text{ V}$

e. $V = \dfrac{6 \times 10^{-3}\text{C}}{40 \times 10^{-6}\text{F}} = 150\text{ V}$

f. $C = \dfrac{Q}{V} = \dfrac{1.8 \times 10^{-3}}{1200\text{ V}} = 1.5\,\mu\text{F}$

3. $V = \dfrac{Q}{C} = \dfrac{10 \times 10^{-3}}{50 \times 10^{-6}} = 200\text{ V}$

5. $Q = CV = (5\,\mu\text{F})(84\text{ V}) = 420\,\mu\text{C}$

7. $C = \dfrac{\in A}{d} = \dfrac{\in_r \in_0 A}{d}$ where $\in_r = 5.5$ and $\in_0$
$= 8.854 \times 10^{-12}$ F/m
$A = (0.01\text{ m})(0.015\text{ m}) = 1.5 \times 10^{-4}\text{ m}^2$;
$d = 0.1 \times 10^{-3}$ m
$C = \dfrac{(5.5)(8.854 \times 10^{-12}\text{ F/m})(1.5 \times 10^{-4}\text{ m}^2)}{0.1 \times 10^{-3}\text{ m}}$
$= 73$ pF

9. $C = \dfrac{\in_r \in_0 A}{d} \quad \therefore A = \dfrac{Cd}{\in_r \in_0}$
$= \dfrac{200 \times 10^{-12}\text{ F})(0.1 \times 10^{-3}\text{ m})}{(4)(8.854 \times 10^{-12}\text{ F/m})} = 5.65 \times 10^{-4}\text{ m}^2$

11. $C_2 = \left(\dfrac{\in_2}{\in_1}\right)C_1 = \left(\dfrac{3}{2.1}\right)(33\,\mu\text{F}) = 47.14\,\mu\text{F}$
$V = \dfrac{Q}{C} = \dfrac{55 \times 10^{-4}\text{C}}{47.14\,\mu\text{F}} = 117\text{ V}$

10.3 Electric Fields

13. a. $\mathscr{E} = \dfrac{Q}{4\pi \in r^2} = \dfrac{100 \times 10^{-3}\text{ C}}{4\pi(4)(8.854 \times 10^{-12})(1 \times 10^{-2}\text{ m})^2}$
$= 2.25 \times 10^{12}$ N/C

b. $\mathscr{E}$ varies as $\dfrac{1}{r^2}$ $\therefore$ by $\left(\dfrac{1}{2}\right)^2 = \dfrac{1}{4}.$

Thus, $\mathscr{E} = \dfrac{2.25 \times 10^{12}}{4} = 0.563 \times 10^{12}$ N/C

10.4 Dielectrics

15. Breakdown occurs at 3 kV/mm $\therefore$ $V = (3\text{ kV/mm})(1.5\text{ mm}) = 4.5\text{ kV}$

17. $\mathscr{E}_1 = \dfrac{E_1}{d_1}$ and $\mathscr{E}_2 = \dfrac{E_2}{d_2}$. Take the ratio and solve for E_1.
$E_1 = E_2\left(\dfrac{d_1}{d_2}\right)\left(\dfrac{\mathscr{E}_1}{\mathscr{E}_2}\right) = 500\text{ V}\left(\dfrac{1}{2}\right)\left(\dfrac{40\text{ kV/mm}}{3\text{ kV/mm}}\right)$
$= 3.33$ kV

19. a. The sharp points.

b. The spherical points.

c. The sharp points.

10.5 Nonideal Effects

21. $1\text{ ppm} = \dfrac{25\,\mu\text{F}}{10^6} = 25 \times 10^{-12}\text{ F} = 25\text{ pF}$

$\therefore$ 175 ppm = 4.37 nF $\therefore$ Coefficient = 4.375 nF/°C

$\therefore$ May decrease by (50°C)(4.375 nF/°C) = 219 nF $= 0.219\,\mu$F.

Thus, $C_{new} = 25\,\mu\text{F} - 0.219\,\mu\text{F} \approx 24.8\,\mu\text{F}$.

10.7 Capacitors in Parallel and Series

23. $C_T = C_1 + C_2 + C_3 + C_4 = 10\,\mu F + 12\,\mu F + 22\,\mu F + 33\,\mu F = 77\ \mu F$

25. $\frac{1}{C_T} = \frac{1}{10\,\mu F} + \frac{1}{12\,\mu F} + \frac{1}{22\,\mu F} + \frac{1}{33\,\mu F}$

$= 0.2591 \times 10^6$

$C_T = \frac{1}{0.2591 \times 10^6} = 3.86\,\mu F$

27. (a) $\frac{1}{C_T} = \frac{1}{120\,\mu F} + \frac{1}{12\,\mu F} + \frac{1}{80\,\mu F}$

$\therefore C_T = 9.6\,\mu F$

(b) $C_T = 8\,\mu F + 4\,\mu F + 1\,\mu F = 13\,\mu F$

(c) $C_2 \| C_3 = 5\,\mu F + 4\,\mu F = 9\,\mu F$

$\frac{1}{C_T} = \frac{1}{6\,\mu F} + \frac{1}{9\,\mu F}\ \therefore C_T = 3.6\,\mu F$

(d) Using step by step reduction, capacitances are combined as shown below. Finally from (iii).

$\frac{1}{C_T} = \frac{1}{1\,\mu F} + \frac{1}{2\,\mu F} + \frac{1}{6\,\mu F} + \frac{1}{3\,\mu F}.$

Thus, $C_T = 0.5\,\mu F$.

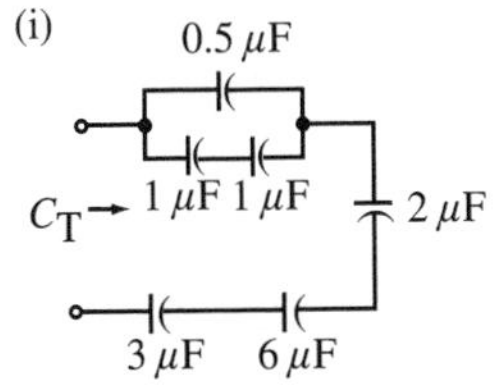

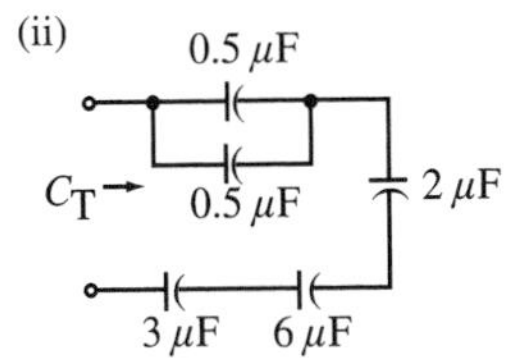

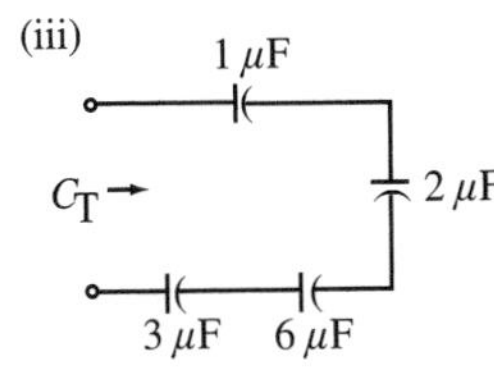

29. $\frac{1}{C_T} = \frac{1}{90\,\mu F} + \frac{1}{10\,\mu F}\ \therefore C_T = 9.0\,\mu F$

30 μF 60 μF 90 μF 10 μF C_T

31. From diagram (b) below, $\frac{1}{20\,\mu F} = \frac{1}{30\,\mu F} + \frac{1}{C_{eq}}$.

Thus, $C_{eq} = 60\,\mu F$.

Denote C_3 in series with C_4 by C_x as shown in (c). Then $60\,\mu F = 40\,\mu F + C_x\ \therefore C_x = 20\,\mu F$.

Now consider (d):

$\frac{1}{20\,\mu F} = \frac{1}{C_3} + \frac{1}{C_4} = \frac{1}{2C_4} + \frac{1}{C_4} = \frac{1.5}{C_4}\ \therefore C_4$

$= 30\,\mu F$ and $C_3 = 2C_4 = 60\,\mu F$.

(a)

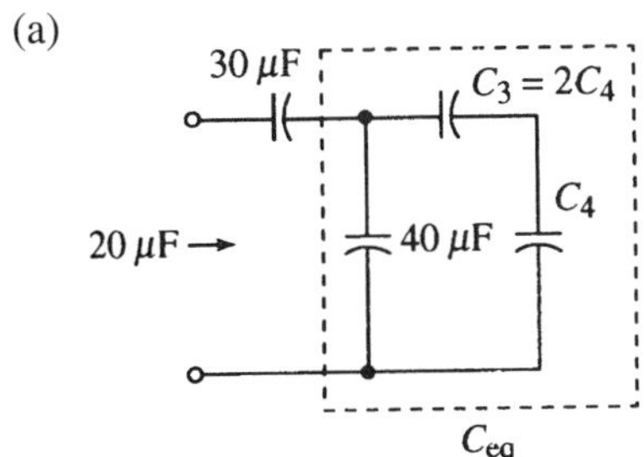

(b)

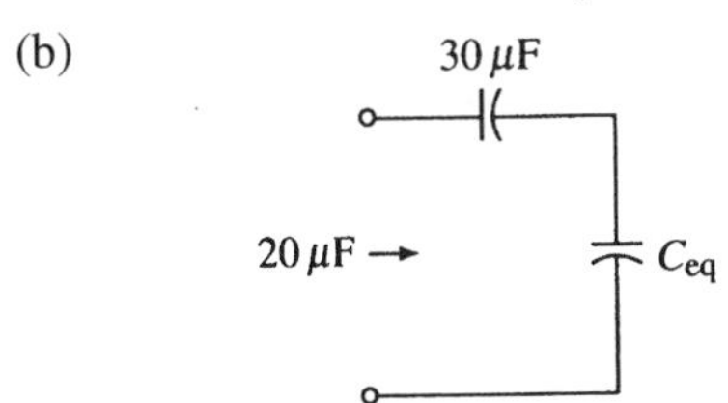

(c)

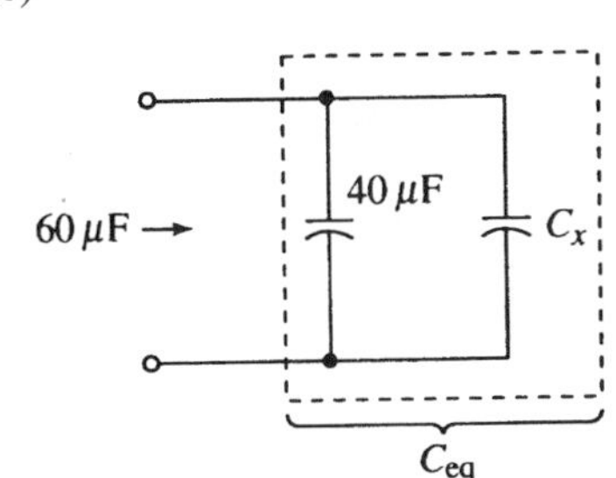

(d)

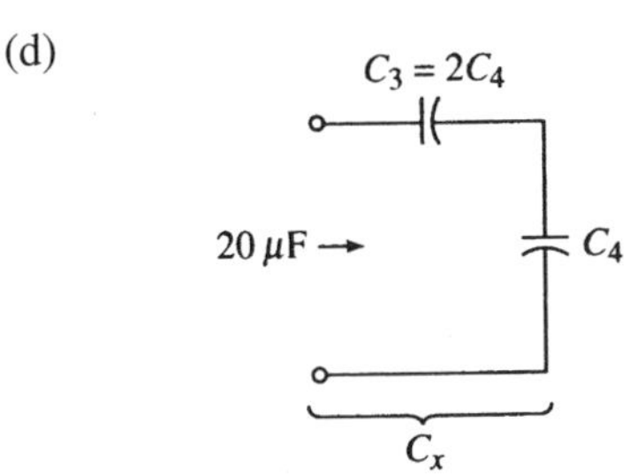

33. Largest when in parallel. $C_T = 22\,\mu F + 47\,\mu F + 2.2\,\mu F + 10\,\mu F = 81.2\,\mu F$

Smallest when in series.

$\frac{1}{C_T} = \frac{1}{22\,\mu F} + \frac{1}{47\,\mu F} + \frac{1}{2.2\,\mu F} + \frac{1}{10\,\mu F}$

$C_T = 1.61\,\mu F$

35. To yield 10.6 μF, the 10 μF capacitor must be connected in parallel with some combination of the 1 μF and 1.5 μF capacitors. Only the connection shown below works.

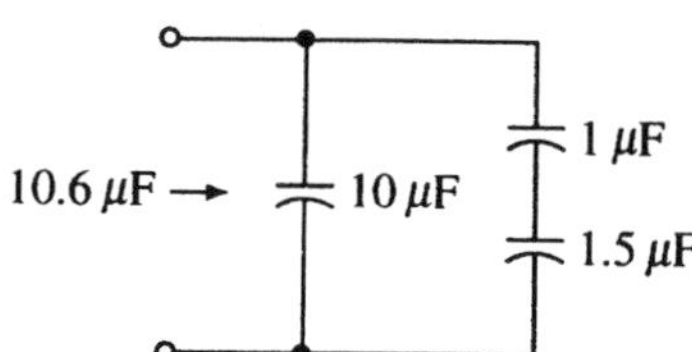

37. a. Consider Figure 10-32(c). Reduce the circuit to that shown below as (b). Then, $\frac{1}{C_T} = \frac{1}{6\,\mu F} + \frac{1}{9\,\mu F}$. Thus $C_T = 3.6\,\mu$F.

$V_1 = \left(\frac{C_T}{C_1}\right)E = \left(\frac{3.6\,\mu F}{6\,\mu F}\right)(100\text{ V}) = 60\text{ V}$

$\therefore V_2 = 40$ V by (KVL).

Voltages are shown in (c).

(a)

(b)

(c)

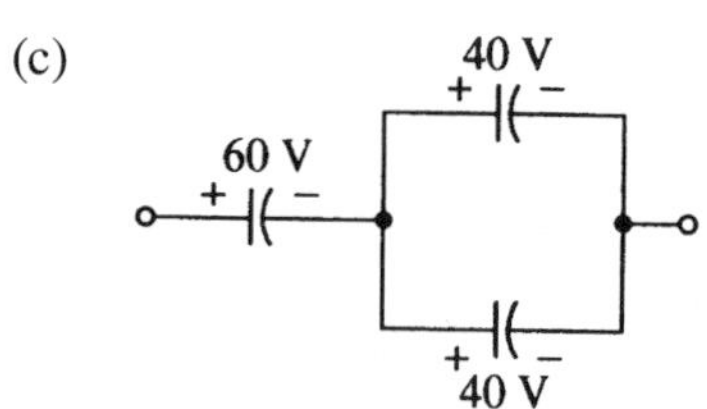

b. Consider Figure 10-33(d). Reduce the circuit to that shown below as (a). To find C_T,

$\frac{1}{C_T} = \frac{1}{1\,\mu F} + \frac{1}{2\,\mu F} + \frac{1}{6\,\mu F} + \frac{1}{3\,\mu F}$.

Thus, $C_T = 0.5\,\mu$F and $V_1 = \left(\frac{C_T}{C_1}\right)E$

$= \left(\frac{0.5\,\mu F}{1\,\mu F}\right)(100\text{ V}) = 50$ V. Similarly, $V_4 = 25$ V, $V_6 = 8.3$ V and $V_5 = 16.7$ V.

Consider again figure 10-33(d). Since $V_1 = 50$ V, the two 1 μF capacitors in series have 50 V across them. Thus, each has 25 volts as shown in (b) in the next column.

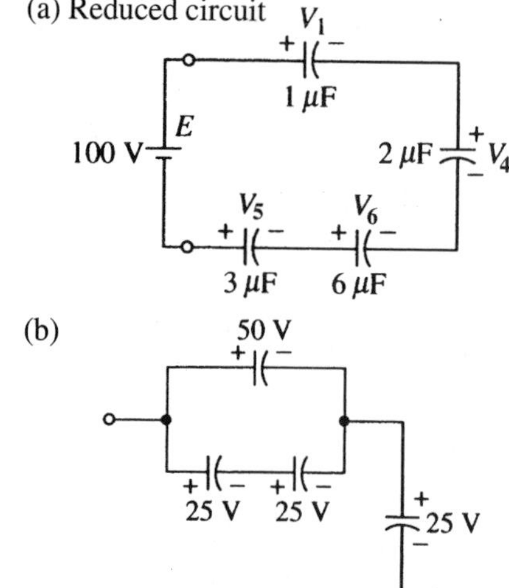

39. For the circuit of Figure 10-39, combine the 35 μF and 25 μF capacitor to yield 60 μF as shown below. Then, $\frac{1}{C_T} = \frac{1}{40\,\mu F} + \frac{1}{16\,\mu F} + \frac{1}{60\,\mu F}$. Thus, $C_T = 9.6\,\mu$F and $V_1 = \left(\frac{C_T}{C_1}\right)E = \left(\frac{9.6\,\mu F}{40\,\mu F}\right)(60\text{ V}) = 14.4$ V.

Similarly, $V_2 = \left(\frac{9.6\,\mu F}{16\,\mu F}\right)(60\text{ V}) = 36$ V; $V_3 =$

$= \left(\frac{9.6\,\mu F}{60\,\mu F}\right)(60\text{ V}) = 9.6$ V

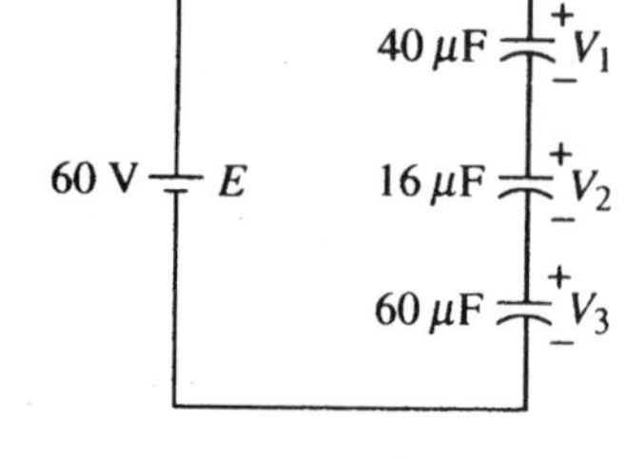

41. The 40 μF capacitor does not affect the solution and can be discarded, yielding the circuit of (a). Now combine C_x with the 1200 μF capacitor to yield C_x' as in (b).

$V_2 = \left(\frac{C_1}{C_2}\right)V_1 = \left(\frac{500\,\mu F}{100\,\mu F}\right)(16\text{ V}) = 80\text{ V}$

$\therefore V_x = 100\text{ V} - 16\text{ V} - 80\text{ V} = 4\text{ V}$

$C_x' = \left(\frac{C_1}{V_x}\right)V_1 = \left(\frac{500\,\mu F}{4\,\mu F}\right)(16\text{ V}) = 2000\,\mu F$

But $C_x' = C_x + 1200\,\mu F$

$\therefore C_x = 800\,\mu F$

(a)

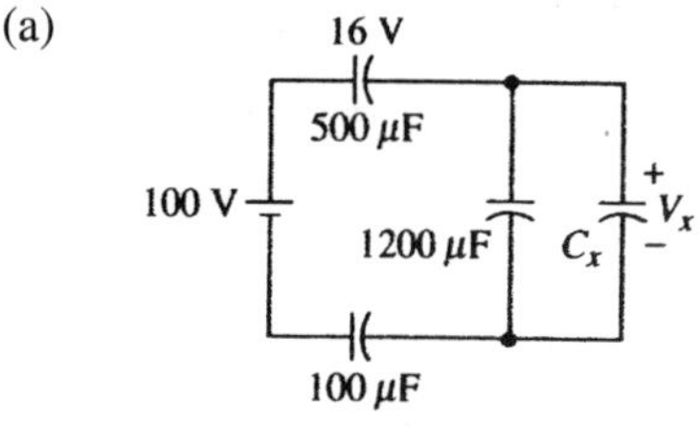

(b)

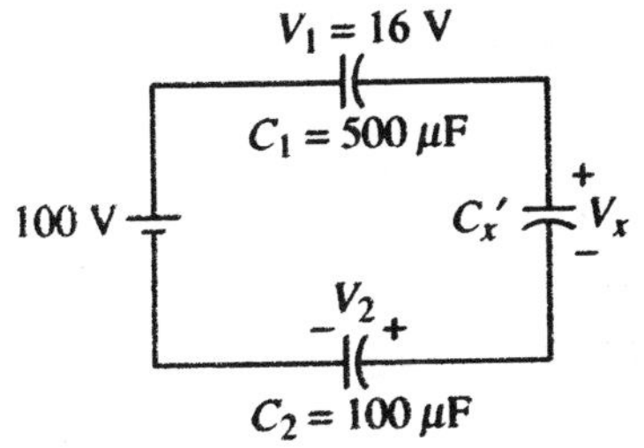

$V_1 = 16$ V, $C_1 = 500\ \mu F$, 100 V, C_x', V_x, V_2, $C_2 = 100\ \mu F$

10.8 Capacitor Voltage and Current

43. $i = C\frac{\Delta v_C}{\Delta t}$

0 ms – 1 ms:

$$i = (5 \times 10^{-6}\text{ F})\left(-\frac{10\text{ V}}{1 \times 10^{-3}\text{ s}}\right) = -50\text{ mA}$$

1 ms – 4 ms:

$$i = (5 \times 10^{-6}\text{ F})\left(\frac{30\text{ V}}{3 \times 10^{-3}\text{ s}}\right) = 50\text{ mA}$$

4 ms – 6 ma:

$$\frac{\Delta v}{\Delta t} = 0 \therefore i = 0\text{ mA}$$

6 ms – 7 ms:

$$i = (5 \times 10^{-6}\text{F})\left(\frac{10\text{ V}}{1 \times 10^{-3}\text{ s}}\right) = 50\text{ mA}$$

7 ms – 9 ms:

$$i = (5 \times 10^{-6}\text{ F})\left(\frac{-30\text{ V}}{2 \times 10^{-3}\text{ s}}\right) = -75\text{ mA}$$

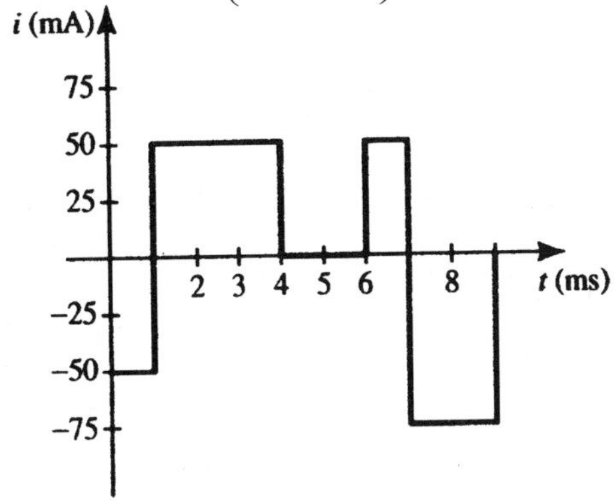

i (mA); 75; 50; 25; –25; –50; –75; 2 3 4 5 6 8 t (ms)

45. $i_C = C\frac{dv_C}{dt}$. Given $C = 4.7\ \mu$F and $v_C = 100e^{-0.05t}$ V.

Thus, $i_C = (4.7 \times 10^{-6})\frac{d}{dt}(100e^{-0.05t})$

$= (4.7 \times 10^{-6})(100)(-0.05e^{-0.05t}) = -23.5e^{-0.05t}\ \mu$A.

10.9 Energy Stored by a Capacitor

47. $W = \frac{1}{2}Cv^2$

t (ms)	v (V)	W (mJ)
0	0	0
2	–10	0.25
4	20	1.0
5	20	1.0
7	30	2.25
9	0	0

Chapter

11

Capacitor Charging, Discharging and Simple Waveshaping Circuits

11.1 Introduction

1. a. $v_C(0^+) = 0$ V;

$$i_C(0^+) = \frac{E}{R} = \frac{20\text{ V}}{4\ \Omega} = 5\text{ A}$$

b. $v_C = E = 20$ V; $i_C = 0$ A

3. a. A short circuit.

b. A voltage source equal to V_0.

c. An open circuit.

d. $i(0^-)$ = current just before $t = 0$ s

$i(0^+)$ = current just after t = 0 s

5. $i(0^+) = \dfrac{E}{R}$ $\therefore E = Ri(0^+) = (5.6\text{ k}\Omega)(2.7\text{ mA})$

$= 15.1$ V

11.2 Capacitor Charging Equations

7. $RC = (500\ \Omega)(25 \times 10^{-6}\text{ F}) = 12.5\text{ ms} : \dfrac{1}{RC} = 80$

a. $v_C = E(1 - e^{-t/RC}) = 45(1 - e^{-80t})$ V

b. $i_C = \dfrac{E}{R}e^{-t/RC} = 90e^{-80t}$ mA

c.

t (ms)	v_C (V)	i_C (mA)
0	0	90
20	35.9	18.2
40	43.2	3.67
60	44.6	0.741
80	44.93	0.150
100	44.98	0.030

Example: At $t = 20$ ms.

$v_C = 45(1 - e^{-80 \times 20 \times 10^{-3}})$
$= 45(1 - e^{-1.6})$
$= 45(0.798)$
$= 35.9$ V

d.

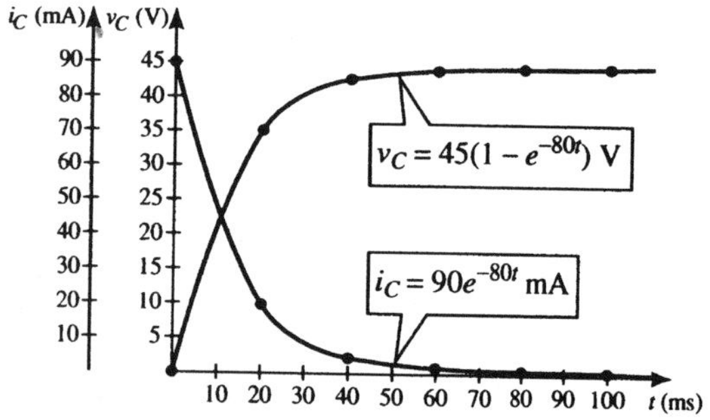

9. For the voltage polarity and current direction shown,
$v_C = E(1 - e^{-t/RC}) = 40(1 - e^{-t/39\text{ ms}})$ V

$$i_C = \frac{40\text{ V}}{3.9\text{ k}\Omega}e^{-t/39\text{ ms}} = 10.3\,e^{-t/39\text{ ms}}\text{ mA}$$

At $t = 50$ ms, $v_C = 40\left(1 - e^{-50\text{ ms}/39\text{ ms}}\right) = 28.9$ V

$i_C = 10.3\,e^{-50\text{ ms}/39\text{ ms}} = 2.86$ mA

11. $\tau = RC = (4\ \Omega)(10\ \mu\text{F}) = 40\ \mu$s
Requires 5τ to charge. $5\tau = 200\ \mu$s.

13. $\tau = RC = (4\ \Omega)(10\ \mu\text{F}) = 40\ \mu$s. The times indicated are thus multiples of τ and Figure 11-15 applies directly. For example, $t = 40\ \mu s = \tau$ and $v_C = (0.632)E = (0.632)(20\text{ V}) = 12.6$ V
Similarly, $i_C = (0.368)(5\text{A}) = 1.84$ A
Continuing in this manner yields

t (μs)	v_C (V)	i_C (A)
0	0	5
40	12.6	1.84
80	17.3	0.675
120	19.0	0.249
160	19.64	0.0915
200	19.86	0.0337

15. $i(0^+) = 3\text{ mA} = \dfrac{75\text{ V}}{R}$ $\therefore R = 25\text{ k}\Omega$

$5\tau = 1\text{ s} \therefore \tau = 0.2\text{ s} = RC$

$$C = \frac{0.2\text{ s}}{R} = \frac{0.2\text{ s}}{25\text{ k}\Omega} = 8\ \mu\text{F}$$

17. Capacitor charges to E. Therefore, $E = 45$ V.

$$i = \frac{E}{R}e^{-t/\tau}$$

At $t = \tau$, $i = 3.678$ mA and $\dfrac{t}{\tau} = 1$.

$$\therefore 3.678\text{ mA} = \frac{45}{R}e^{-1} = \frac{16.55}{R} \text{ and } R = 4.5\text{ k}\Omega$$

$$\tau = \frac{5\text{ ms}}{5} = 1\text{ ms}$$

$$C = \frac{1 \times 10^{-3}\text{ s}}{4.5 \times 10^{3}\ \Omega} = 0.222\ \mu\text{F}$$

19. $$i(0^+) = \frac{E - V_0}{R} = \frac{20\text{ V} - 10\text{ V}}{4\ \Omega} = 2.5\text{ A}$$

11.3 Capacitor with an Initial Voltage

21. a. $v_C = E + (V_0 - E)e^{-t/RC} = 20 + 10e^{-25\,000t}$ V

$\tau = RC = 40\ \mu s$

b. $i = \left(\dfrac{E - V_0}{R}\right)e^{-t/RC} = \dfrac{20\text{ V} - 30\text{ V}}{4\ \Omega}e^{-25\,000t}$

$= -2.5e^{-25\,000t}$ A

c.

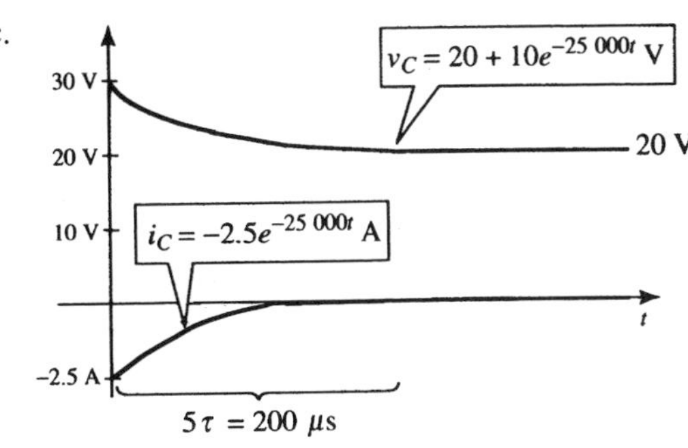

11.4 Capacitor Discharging Equations

23. a. $v_C = V_0e^{-t/RC}$ $\quad RC = (25 \times 10^3\ \Omega)(20 \times 10^{-6}\text{ F}) = 0.5\text{ s}$

$v_C = 50e^{-2t}$ V

b. $i_C = -\dfrac{V_0}{R}e^{-t/RC} = -\dfrac{50\text{ V}}{25\text{ k}\Omega}e^{-2t} = -2e^{-2t}$ mA

c. $\tau = RC = 0.5$ s

d.

t	v_C (V)	i_C (mA)
0	50	–2.0
τ	18.4	–0.736
2τ	6.77	–0.271
3τ	2.49	–0.100
4τ	0.916	–0.037
5τ	0.337	–0.014

e.

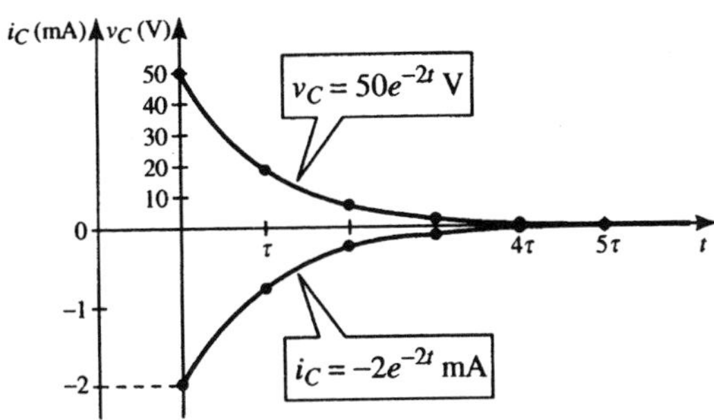

25. $v_C = V_0e^{-t/RC} = 43e^{-t/183.3\text{ ms}}$ V

At 200 ms, $v_C = 43e^{-200\text{ ms}/183.3\text{ ms}} = 14.4$ V

27. a. $V_0 = 200$ V; $I_0 = \dfrac{-V_0}{R} = \dfrac{-200\text{ V}}{16\text{ k}\Omega} = -12.5$ mA

b. $\tau_d = (16 \times 10^3\ \Omega)(0.5 \times 10^{-6}\text{ F}) = 8$ ms

c. $v_C = V_0e^{-t/\tau_d} = 200e^{-125t}$ V

$i_C = \dfrac{-V_0}{R} = {}^{-t/\tau_d} = -12.5e^{-125t}$ mA

11.5 More Complex Circuits

29. Simplifying the circuit yields

26.91 kΩ

v_C + – 6.9 μF 45 V

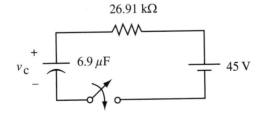

$\tau = RC = (26.91\text{ k}\Omega)(6.9\ \mu\text{F}) = 0.1857$ s

$v_C = E(-e^{-t/\tau}) = 45(1 - e^{-t/0.1857})$ V

At $t = \tau$, $v_C = 45(1 - e^{-1})$ V $= 28.4$ V

From Figure 11-15, at $t = \tau$,

$v_C = (0.632)(45\text{ V}) = 28.4$ V (Same)

31. Combine components and reduce the circuit to that shown in **a.** Now determine its Thévenin equivalent. Consider **b.** Since there are no drops across the 16 Ω and 4 Ω resistors. E_{Th} is the voltage across the 60 Ω resistor. Thus,

$E_{Th} = \left(\dfrac{60\ \Omega}{60\ \Omega + 30\ \Omega}\right)(90\text{ V}) = 60$ V

$R_{Th} = 30\ \Omega \| 60\ \Omega + 16\ \Omega + 4\ \Omega = 40\ \Omega$

$\tau_{Th} = R_{Th}C = (40\ \Omega)(50\ \mu\text{F}) = 2$ ms (a).

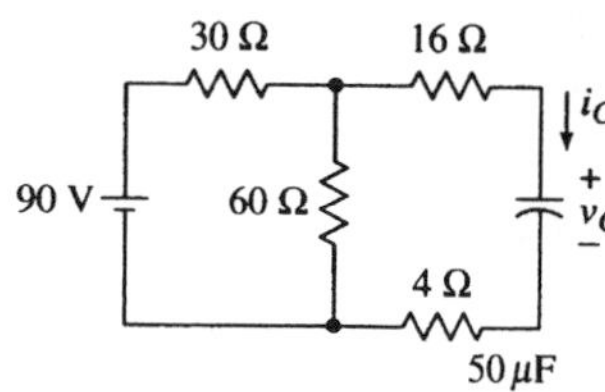

(b).

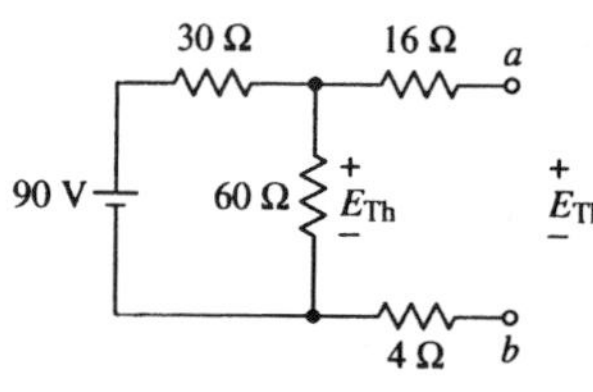

(c).

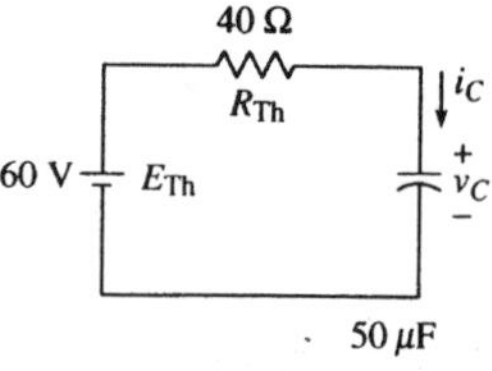

a.

$$v_C = E_{Th}(1 - e^{-t/\tau_{Th}}) = 60(1 - e^{-500t})\text{ V}$$

$$i_C = \frac{E_{Th}}{R_{Th}}e^{-t/\tau_{Th}} = \frac{60\text{ V}}{40\ \Omega}e^{-500t} = 1.5e^{-500t}\text{ A}$$

b. and c.

t (ms)	v_C (V)	i_C (A)
0	0	1.5
2	37.9	0.552
4	51.9	0.203
6	57.0	0.075
8	58.9	0.028
10	59.6	0.010
12	59.9	0.004

Example: At $t = 2$ ms

$v_C = 60(1 - e^{-500 \times 2\text{ ms}}) = 60(1 - e^{-1})\text{ V} = 37.9\text{ V}.$

33. $i(0^+) = 3.6\text{ mA} = \dfrac{E}{R_1 + R_3} = \dfrac{E}{25\text{ k}\Omega} \quad \therefore E = 90\text{ V}$

At the instant the switch is moved to discharge, $i_C = -3\text{ mA} = \dfrac{-V_0}{R_2 + R_3}$ where $V_0 = 90$ V (since the capacitor fully charges). Thus,

$-3\text{ mA} = \dfrac{-90}{R_2 + 15\text{ k}\Omega}$ and $R_2 = 15\text{ k}\Omega$

$5\tau_C = 12.5\text{ s} \quad \therefore \tau_C = 2.5\text{ s}$

$C = \dfrac{\tau_C}{R_1 + R_3} = \dfrac{2.5\text{ s}}{25\text{ k}\Omega} = 100\ \mu\text{F}$

35. Since the circuit is in steady state, a transient analysis is not required. All capacitors are open circuits. Thus,

$I_T = \dfrac{E}{R_T} = \dfrac{80\text{ V}}{160\ \Omega} = 0.5\text{ A}$

$V_{C_1} = 80\text{ V} - (0.5\text{ A})(30\ \Omega) = 65\text{ V}$

$V_{C_2} = (0.5\text{ A})(20\ \Omega) = 10\text{ V}$

$V_{C_3} = (0.5\text{ A})(110\ \Omega) = 55\text{ V}$

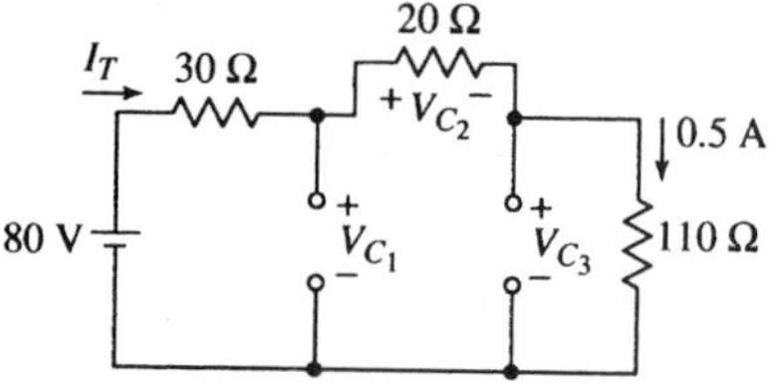

11.6 An RC Timing Application

37. $v_C = E(1 - e^{-t/RC})$

$3.8\text{ V} = 5\text{ V}(1 - e^{-t/RC})$

$\therefore e^{-t/RC} = \dfrac{5 - 3.8}{5} = 0.24$

$\ln(e^{-t/RC}) = \ln(0.24)$

$-\dfrac{t}{RC} = -1.4271$

$\therefore C = \dfrac{t}{1.4271R} = \dfrac{15\text{ s}}{1.427(750\text{ k}\Omega)} = 14\ \mu\text{F}$

11.7 Pulse Response of RC Circuits

39. a. $T = 5\ \mu s$

b. Duty cycle $= \dfrac{t_p}{T} = \times 100\% = \dfrac{2\ \mu s}{5\ \mu s} \times 100\% = 40\%$

c. $\text{PPR} = \dfrac{1}{T} = \dfrac{1}{5 \times 10^{-6}\text{ s}} = 200\ 000$ pulses/s

41. The pulse rises from 0 to 30 V in 1 μs as illustrated in (a). The rise time is the time between the 10% and 90% points. At 10%, $v = 3$ V and at 90%, $v = 27$ V as shown in (b). Using similar triangles,

$$\frac{t_r}{1\ \mu s} = \frac{24\text{ V}}{30\text{ V}} \therefore t_r = 0.8\ \mu s.$$

Similarly, $t_f = 0.8\ \mu s$.

The pulse width is determined at the 50% point. Thus,

$$t_p = \frac{3\ \mu s + 5\ \mu s}{2} = 4\ \mu s$$

(a)

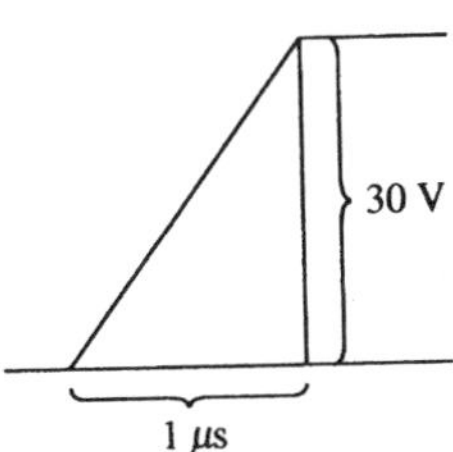

(b)

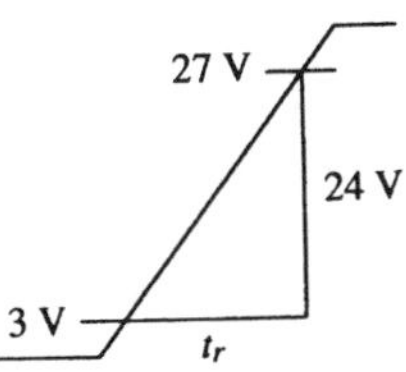

(c)

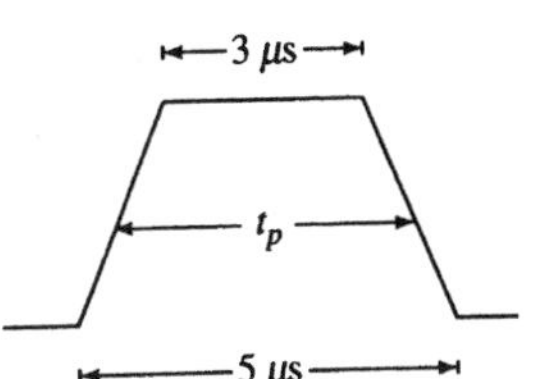

43. $\tau = RC = (150\ \Omega)(20\text{ pF}) = 3$ ns. The output rises exponentially according to

$v_C = E(1 - e^{-t/\tau}) = 100(1 - e^{-t/\tau})$ V

10% is 10 V : 10 V = $100(1 - e^{-t/\tau})$ V

$e^{-t/\tau} = 0.9$ Now take natural log of both sides.

Thus:

$$-\frac{t}{\tau} = -0.105$$

$\therefore t \approx 0.1\tau = 0.3$ ns at the 10% point.

Similarly, $t \approx 2.3\tau = 6.9$ ns at the 90% point.

Thus, $t_r = 6.9$ ns – 0.3 ns = 6.6 ns.

11.8 Transient Analysis Using Computers

Note: For MSM, select *Analysis*, *Transient*, set *Initial Conditions* to Zero, then change the "Minimum number of time points" to a large enough value to get a smooth curve. (For most of the graphs shown here, I used 1000 points.)

45. The MSM solution is shown below. Using the cursor, $v_C = -17.8$ V at $t = 20$ ms.

Check: $v_C = E(1 - e^{-t/RC}) = -25(1 - e^{-t/16\text{ ms}})$ V.

At $t = 20$ ms, $v_C = -25(1 - e^{-1.25}) = -17.8$ V

Thus, agreement is excellent.

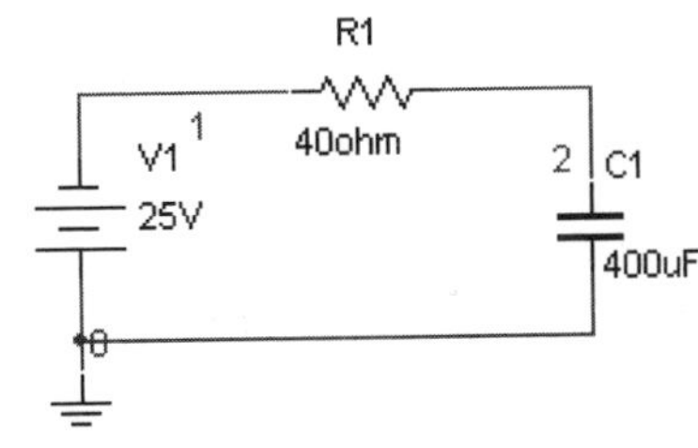

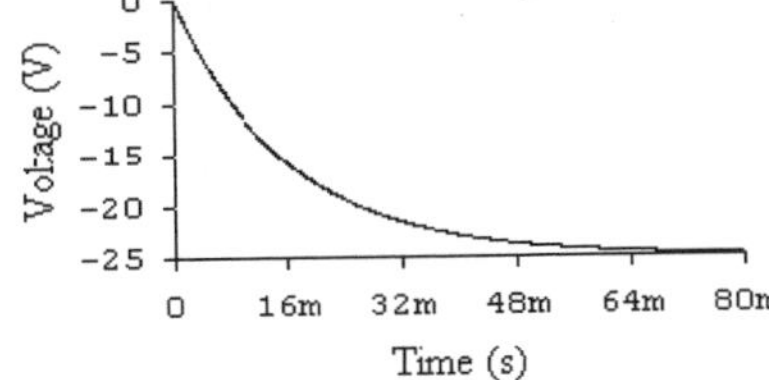

(b) Voltage at Node 2

47. a. Place the ground below the capacitor and graph the capacitor voltage. Using the cursor, you find v_C at $t = 4$ ms is 51.9 V as computed earlier in Problem 31.

b. Move the ground to the intersection of R4 and R5, graph the voltage across R5 and measure the voltage at 4 ms. Using Ohm's law, compute current. It should be 203 mA.

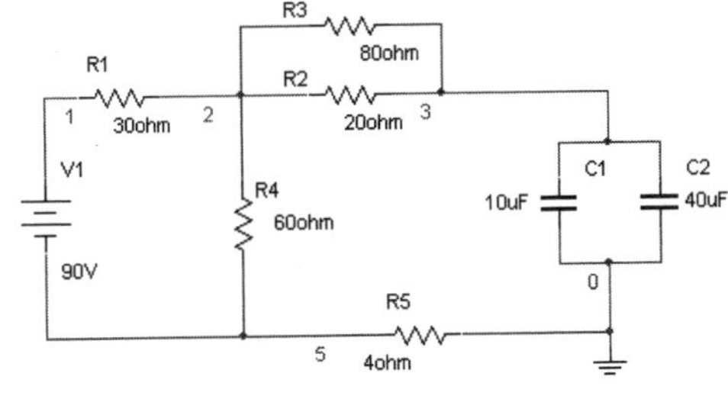

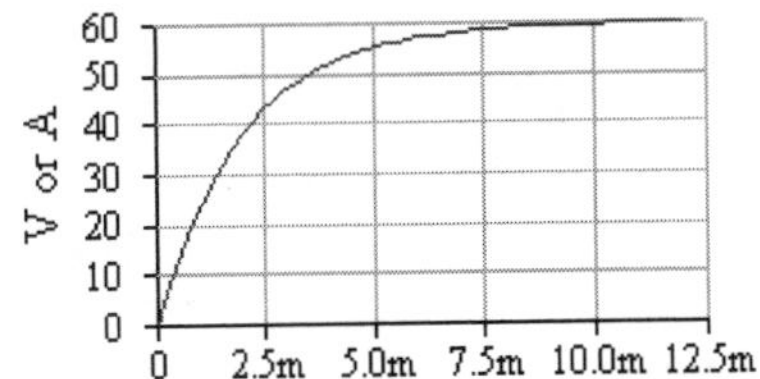

49. The PSpice solution is shown below. Using the cursor, you find $v_C = -17.8$ V and $i_C = -0.179$ A at $t = 20$ ms. Analytic Check: This is the same as Problem 45. Therefore, $v_C = -17.8$ V as determined earlier. For current, $i_C = \frac{E}{R}e^{-t/RC} = -0.625\,e^{-t/16\text{ ms}}$ A. At $t = 20$ ms, $i_C = -0.6255e^{-1.25} = -0.179$ A. Note the excellent agreement in both cases.

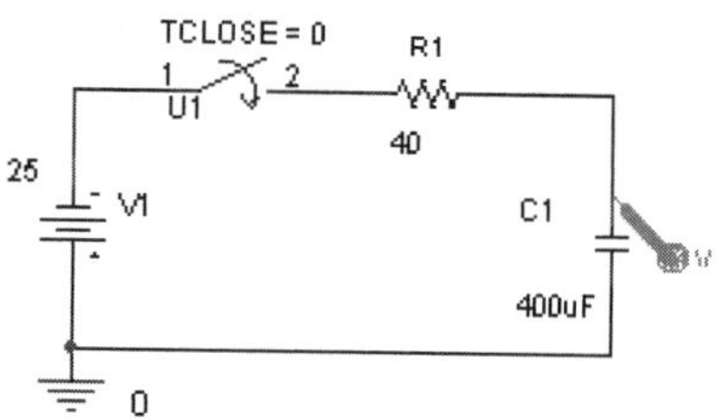

(a) Circuit

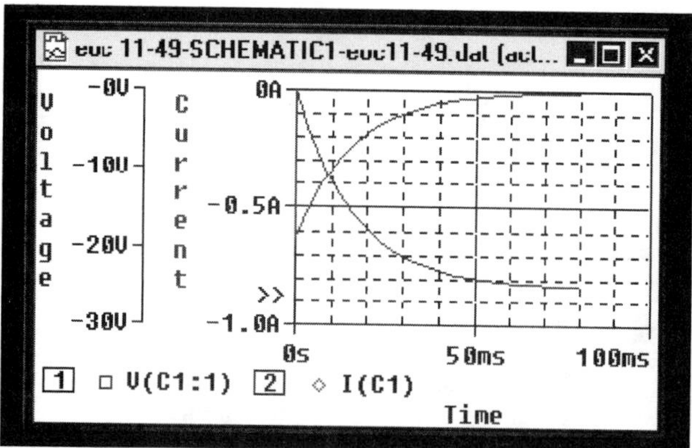

(b) Capacitor voltage and current

51. The PSpice solution is shown below. Using the cursor, read values from the curves at $t = 10$ ms. You should get $v_C = 29.3$ V and $i_C = 0.227$ mA. Check: Convert the current source to a voltage source and simplify the circuit. Equations for the simplified circuit are $v_C = 35(1 - e^{t/5.5\text{ ms}})$V and $i_C = 1.4e^{-t/5.5\text{ ms}}$A. At $t = 10$ ms, these yield 29.3V and 0.227 mA respectively, the same as PSpice.

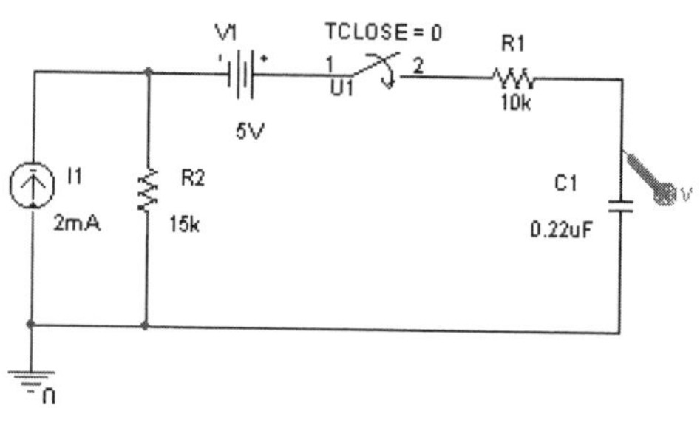

(a) Circuit

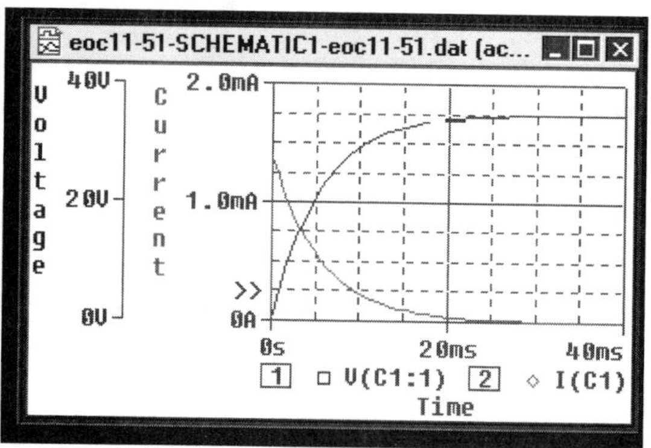

(b) Voltage and current waveforms

53. There are several ways to solve this problem. You can either perform a transient analysis then use the cursor to read values from the graphs after steady state has been reached, or you can solve for steady state values directly (without performing a transient analysis) using either Bias Point analysis or *DC Sweep*. The solution below shows the latter approach. Be sure to set the meters (*IPRINT*, etc) to dc. Following "run", click *View*, open the *Output* File, then scroll. Answers agree with those of Problem 35.

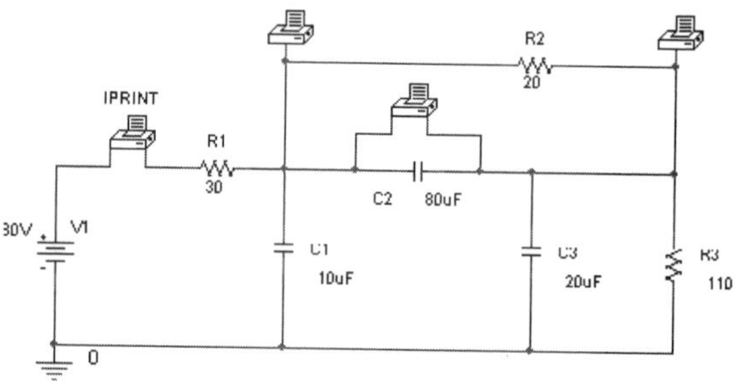

Chapter

12

Magnetism and Magnetic Circuits

12.3 Flux and Flux Density

1. a. A_1

b. $B = \dfrac{\Phi}{A} = \dfrac{28 \times 10^{-3}\ \text{Wb}}{0.02\ \text{m}^2} = 1.4\ \text{T}$

3. Diameter of the toroid cross-section: $d = r_2 - r_1 = 12 - 8 = 4$ cm.

$$A = \frac{\pi d^2}{4} = \frac{\pi}{4}(4 \times 10^{-2}\ \text{m})^2 = 1.2566 \times 10^{-3}\ \text{m}^2$$

$$B = \frac{\Phi}{A} = \frac{628 \times 10^{-6}\ \text{Wb}}{1.2566 \times 10^{-3}\ \text{m}^2} = 0.50\ \text{T}$$

12.5 Air Gaps, Fringing, and Laminated Cases

5. $A = (0.025\ \text{m})(0.04\ \text{m}) = 1 \times 10^{-3}\ \text{m}^2$

$A_{\text{eff}} = (0.85)(1 \times 10^{-3}\ \text{m}^2) = 0.85 \times 10^{-3}\ \text{m}^2$

$\Phi = BA_{\text{eff}} = (1.45\ \text{T})(0.85 \times 10^{-3}\ \text{m}^2) = 1.23 \times 10^{-3}\ \text{Wb}$

12.6 Series Elements and Parallel Elements

7. $\Phi = \Phi_2 + \Phi_3$

$\therefore\ \Phi_2 = \Phi_1 - \Phi_3$

$= 12\ \text{m Wb} - 2\ \text{m Wb} = 10 \times 10^{-3}$

$B_2 = \dfrac{\Phi_2}{A_2} = \dfrac{10 \times 10^{-3}\ \text{Wb}}{0.01\ \text{m}^2}$

$= 1\ \text{T}$

9. $A = (0.02\text{m})(0.03\ \text{m}) = 6 \times 10^{-4}\ \text{m}^2$

Cast Iron: From Figure 12-9, $B = 0.44$T

$\Phi = BA = (0.44\ \text{T})(6 \times 10^{-4}\ \text{m}^2) = 264\ \mu\ \text{Wb}$

Cast Steel: From Figure 12-9, $B = 1.23$ T

$\Phi = BA = (1.23\ \text{T})(6 \times 10^{-4}\ \text{m}^2) = 738\ \mu\text{Wb}$

Sheet steel: From Figure 12-9, $B = 1.43$ T

Effective area $A_{\text{effective}} = (0.94)(6 \times 10^{-4}\ \text{m}^2) = 5.64 \times 10^{-4}\ \text{m}^2$

$\Phi = (1.23\ \text{T})(5.64 \times 10^{-4}\text{m}^2) = 807\ \mu\text{Wb}$

12.8 Magnetic Field Intensity and Magnetization Curves

11. Mean radius $R = \dfrac{r_1 + r_2}{2} = \dfrac{5\ \text{cm} + 7\ \text{cm}}{2} = 0.06\ \text{m}$

Mean path $\ell = 2\pi R = 2\pi(0.06\ \text{m}) = 0.377\ \text{m}$

$H\ell = NI$

$H = N\dfrac{I}{\ell} = \dfrac{(40\ t)(10\ \text{A})}{0.377\ \text{m}} = 1061\ \text{At/m}$

12.9 Ampere's Circuital Law

13. $N_1 I_1 = H_1\ell_1 + H_2\ell_2$

$N_2 I_2 = H_2\ell_2 - H_3\ell_3$

12.10 Series Magnetic Circuits: Given Φ, find NI

15. $\Phi = 0.16$ mWb

$$B = \frac{\Phi}{A} = \frac{0.16 \times 10^{-3}\ \text{Wb}}{3.2 \times 10^{-4}\ \text{m}^2} = 0.5\ \text{T (All sections)}$$

$\therefore$ From Fig. 12-19, $\begin{cases} H_{\text{steel}} = 350\ \text{At/m} \\ H_{\text{iron}} = 1550\ \text{At/m} \end{cases}$

$NI = H_{\text{steel}}\ell_{\text{steel}} + H_{\text{iron}}\ell_{\text{iron}} = (350\ \text{At/m})(0.14\ \text{m}) + (1550\ \text{At/m})(0.06\ \text{m})$

$NI = 142$ At

$$I = \frac{142\ \text{At}}{300\ \text{t}} = 0.47\ \text{A}$$

17.

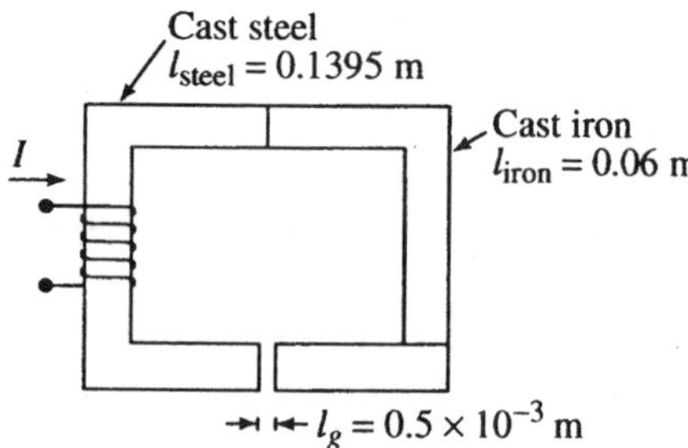

$$B = \frac{0.128 \times 10^{-3}\ \text{Wb}}{3.2 \times 10^{-4}\ \text{m}^2} = 0.4\ \text{T (All sections)}$$

$\therefore$ From Fig 12-19, $\begin{cases} H_{\text{steel}} = 300\ \text{At/m} \\ H_{\text{iron}} = 1060\ \text{At/m} \end{cases}$

$$H_g = \frac{B_g}{\mu_0} = \frac{0.4\ \text{T}}{4\pi \times 10^{-7}} = 318.3 \times 10^3\ \text{At/m}$$

$NI = H_{\text{steel}}\ell_{\text{steel}} + H_{\text{iron}}\ell_{\text{iron}} + H_g\ell_g = (300)(0.1395) + (1060)(0.06) + (318.3 \times 10^3)(0.5 \times 10^{-3})$

$NI = 264.6$ At

$$I = \frac{264.6\ \text{At}}{300\ \text{t}} = 0.88\ \text{A}$$

19. To approximate fringing, add the gap length to each dimension of the cross section at the gap. Thus,
$A_g = (1 + 0.03)(1.5 + 0.03)$
$= 1.576\ \text{cm}^2 = 1.576 \times 10^{-4}\ \text{m}^2$

$\Phi = BA = (0.426\ \text{T})(1.576 \times 10^{-4}\ \text{m}^2) = 67.1\ \mu\text{Wb}$

$$B_{\text{iron}} = \frac{\Phi}{A_{\text{iron}}} = \frac{67.1\ \mu\text{Wb}}{1.5 \times 10^{-4}\ \text{m}^2} = 0.45\ \text{T}$$

From Figure 12-19, $B_{\text{iron}} = 1260$ At/m

$$H_g = \frac{B_g}{\mu_0} = \frac{0.426\ \text{T}}{4\pi \times 10^{-7}} = 339 \times 10^3\ \text{At/m}$$

$\ell_{\text{iron}} = 3.2 + 3.2 - 0.03 + 2\pi(2) = 18.9\ \text{cm} = 0.189\ \text{m}$

Ampere's Law:

$NI = H_{\text{iron}}\ell_{\text{iron}} + H_g\ell_g = (1260)(0.189) + (339 \times 10^3)(0.3 \times 10^{-3}) = 340$ At

$$I = \frac{340\ \text{At}}{600\ \text{t}} = 0.57\ \text{A}$$

21.

$$B = \frac{\Phi}{A} = \frac{30 \times 10^{-6}\ \text{Wb}}{0.5 \times 10^{-4}\ \text{m}^2} = 0.6\ \text{T (Everywhere)}$$

$\therefore$ From Fig 12-19, $\begin{cases} H_{\text{steel}} = 400\ \text{At/m} \\ H_{\text{iron}} = 2675\ \text{At/m} \end{cases}$

$$H_g = \frac{B_g}{\mu_0} = \frac{0.6\ \text{T}}{4\pi \times 10^{-7}} = 477.5 \times 10^3\ \text{At/m}$$

$NI = H_{\text{steel}}\ell_{\text{steel}} + H_{\text{iron}}\ell_{\text{iron}} + H_g\ell_g = (400)(0.08) + (2675)(0.03) + 477.5 \times 10^3)(2 \times 10^{-3})$

$NI = 1067$ At

$$I = \frac{1067\ \text{A}}{2000\ \text{t}} = 0.53\ \text{A}$$

23.

$$\Phi = 35\,000\ \text{lines} \times \frac{1\ \text{Wb}}{10^8\ \text{lines}} = 35 \times 10^{-5}\ \text{Wb}$$

$$B_1 = \frac{\Phi}{A_1} = \frac{35 \times 10^{-5}\ \text{Wb}}{6.452 \times 10^{-4}\ \text{m}^2} = 0.543\ \text{T}$$

$$B_2 = \frac{\Phi}{A_2} = 0.271\ \text{T (Since } A_2 = 2A_1)$$

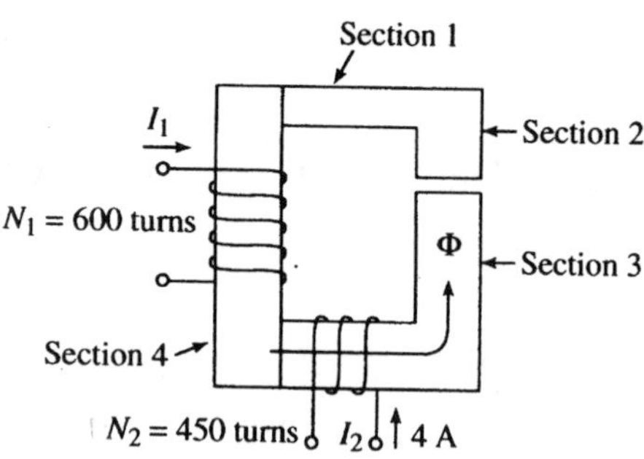

Section 1: Cast iron:
$B_1 = 0.543\ \therefore\ H_1 = 1900$ At/m
$\ell_1 = 0.0508$ m

Section 2: Cast iron:
$B_2 = 0.271\ \text{T}\ \therefore\ H_2 = 700$ At/m
$\ell_2 = 0.0889$ m

Section 3: Cast steel:
$B_3 = 0.271\ \text{T}\ \therefore\ H_3 = 225$ At/m
$\ell_3 = 0.1473$ m

Section 4: Sheet steel:
$B_4 = 0.271\ \text{T}\ \therefore\ H_4 = 75$ At/m
$\ell_4 = 0.1905$ m

Air gap
$B_g = 0.271\ \text{T}\ \therefore\ H_g = 215.7 \times 10^3$ At/m
$\ell_g = 5.08 \times 10^{-3}$ m

$(450)(4) - 600I_1 = H_1\ell_1 + H_2\ell_2 + H_3\ell_3 + H_4\ell_4 + H_g\ell_g = 1302$ AT

$600\,I_1 = 498$ At

$\therefore\ I_1 = 0.83$ A

12.11 Series–Parallel Magnetic Circuits

25. To simplify notation, let $\ell_1 = \ell_{cda}$, $\ell_2 = \ell_{ac}$, and $\ell_3 = \ell_{abc}$.

Thus, $\ell_2 = 0.039 + 0.001 + 0.039 = 0.079$ m.

$$B_3 = \frac{\Phi_3}{A} = \frac{0.2 \times 10^{-3}\ \text{Wb}}{4 \times 10^{-4}\ \text{m}^2} = 0.5\ \text{T}$$

From Fig. 12-19, $H_3 = 340$ At/m

Loop 2: $H_2\ell_2 = H_3\ell_3$

$$\therefore\ H_2 = \frac{H_3\ell_3}{\ell_2} = \frac{(340\ \text{At/m})(0.14\ \text{m})}{0.079\ \text{m}} \approx 603\ \text{At/m}$$

From Fig. 12-19, $B_2 = 0.92$ T

$\therefore\ \Phi_2 = B_2A = (0.92\ \text{T})(4 \times 10^{-4}\ \text{m}^2) = 0.368$ mWb

$\Phi_1 = \Phi_2 + \Phi_3 = 0.2\ \text{mWb} + 0.368\ \text{mWb}$
$= 0.568$ mWb

$$B_1 = \frac{\Phi_1}{A} = \frac{0.568 \times 10^{-3}\ \text{Wb}}{4 \times 10^{-4}\ \text{m}^2} = 1.42\ \text{T}$$

From Fig. 12-19, $H_1 = 2100$ At/m

Ampere's law:

$NI = H_1\ell_1 + H_3\ell_3 = (2100\ \text{At/m})(0.16\ \text{m}) + (350\ \text{At/m})(0.14\ \text{m}) = 385$ At

$$I = \frac{NI}{N} = \frac{385\ \text{At}}{100\ \text{t}} \approx 3.9\ \text{A}$$

12.12 Series Magnetic Circuits: Given NI, Find Φ

27. Mean radius $R = 6\ \text{cm} - 1\ \text{cm} = 5\ \text{cm} = 0.05$ m

$\ell = 2\pi R = 2\,\pi(0.05\ \text{m}) = 0.314$ m

$$H = \frac{NI}{\ell} = \frac{644\ \text{At}}{0.314\ \text{m}} = 2049\ \text{At/m}$$

From Fig 12-19, $B = 1.41$ T

$A = \pi r^2 = \pi(0.01\ \text{m}^2) = 3.14 \times 10^{-4}\ \text{m}^2$

$\Phi = BA = (1.41\ \text{T})(3.14 \times 10^{-4}\ \text{m}^2) = 4.4 \times 10^{-4}$ Wb

12.13 Force Due to an Electromagnet

29.

$$F = \frac{0.5B_g{}^2A}{\mu_0}\ \text{N}$$

$$F = 2\ \text{lb} \times 4.448\frac{\text{N}}{\text{lb}} = 8.896\ \text{N}$$

$A = (0.02\ \text{m})(0.025\ \text{m}) = 5 \times 10^{-4}\ \text{m}^2$

$$B_g{}^2 = \frac{\mu_0\,\text{F}}{0.5\ \text{A}} = \frac{(4\pi \times 10^{-7})(8.896\ \text{N})}{0.5(5 \times 10^{-4}\ \text{m}^2)} = 0.0447\ \text{T}^2$$

$\therefore\ B_g = \sqrt{0.0447\ \text{T}^2} = 0.212$ T

$\Phi = B_gA = (0.212\ \text{T})(5 \times 10^{-4}\ \text{m}^2) = 1.06 \times 10^{-4}$ Wb

Chapter

13

Inductance and Inductors

13.2 Induced Voltage and Inductance

1. $e = N\frac{\Delta\Phi}{\Delta t} = (75 \text{ turns})\left(\frac{3 \text{ Wbs}}{\text{s}}\right) = 225 \text{ V}$

3. Induced voltage is proprotional to the rate of change of current. For case 2, the rate of change of current is $\frac{1}{10}$ that of case 1. Thus,

$v_2 = \frac{1}{10}(v_1) = \frac{1}{10}(60 \text{ V}) = 6.0 \text{ V}$

13.3 Self-Inductance

5. $v_L = L\frac{\Delta i}{\Delta t} = (75 \times 10^{-3} \text{ H})\left(\frac{200 \times 10^{-6} \text{ A}}{0.1 \times 10^{-3} \text{ s}}\right) = 150 \text{ mV}$

7. $v_L = L\frac{\Delta i}{\Delta t}$; $\Delta i = i_2 - i_1 = 5 \text{ A} - 3 \text{ A} = 2 \text{ A}$

$v_L = 180 \text{ V} \therefore 180 \text{ V} = 10 \text{ H}\left(\frac{2 \text{ A}}{\Delta t}\right)$

$\therefore \Delta t = \frac{20}{180} = 0.111 \text{ s}$

9. $A = \frac{\pi d^2}{4} = \frac{\pi}{4}(2 \times 10^{-2} \text{ m})^2 = 3.142 \times 10^{-4} \text{ m}^2$

$L = \frac{\mu_0 N^2 A}{\ell} = \frac{4\pi \times 10^{-7}(200)^2(3.142 \times 10^{-4} \text{ m}^2)}{0.2 \text{ m}}$
$= 79.0 \, \mu\text{H}$

11. $L = \frac{N\Phi}{I} = \frac{N(B_g A_g)}{I} = \frac{N\mu_0 H_g A_g}{I} = \frac{N\mu_0\left(\frac{NI}{\ell_g}\right)A_g}{I}$

$= \frac{\mu_0 N^2 A_g}{\ell_g}$

13.4 Computing Induced Voltage

13. $v_L = L\frac{\Delta i}{\Delta t} \therefore L = \frac{v_L}{\left(\frac{\Delta i}{\Delta t}\right)} = \frac{100 \text{ V}}{\left(\frac{50 \text{ mA}}{2 \text{ ms}}\right)} = 4 \text{ H}$

15\. a. $\Delta i = 1 \text{ A}$ in $\Delta t = 1$ s.

Therefore, $L = \frac{v_L}{\left(\frac{\Delta i}{\Delta t}\right)} = \frac{4 \text{ V}}{1 \text{ A/s}} = 4 \text{ H}$

b.

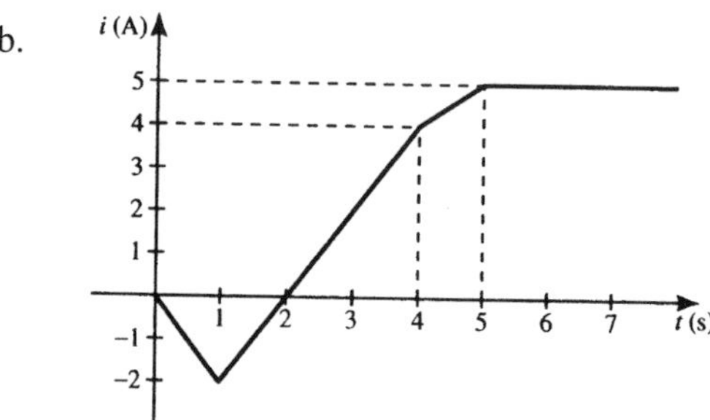

c. Since $v_L = 0$ V from 5 s onward, $\Delta i/\Delta t = 0$ here. Thus, current remains constant at 5 A.

13.5 Inductances in Series and Parallel

17. $L_T = 12 \text{ mH} + 14 \text{ mH} + 22 \text{ mH} + 36 \text{ mH} = 84 \text{ mH}$

19. $\frac{1}{L_T} = \frac{1}{12 \text{ mH}} + \frac{1}{14 \text{ mH}} + \frac{1}{22 \text{ mH}} + \frac{1}{36 \text{ mH}}$

$\therefore L_T = 4.39 \text{ mH}$

21\. a. $L_T = 10 \text{ H} + 5 \text{ H} + 6 \text{ H} = 21 \text{ H}$

b. $\frac{1}{L_T} = \frac{1}{3 \text{ H}} + \frac{1}{6 \text{ H}} \therefore L_T = 2 \text{ H}$

c. $9 \text{ H} \| 18 \text{ H} = \frac{(9 \text{ H} \times 18\text{H})}{9 \text{ H} + 18 \text{ H}} = 6 \text{ H} \therefore L_T$
$= 6 \text{ H} + 14 \text{ H} = 20 \text{ H}$

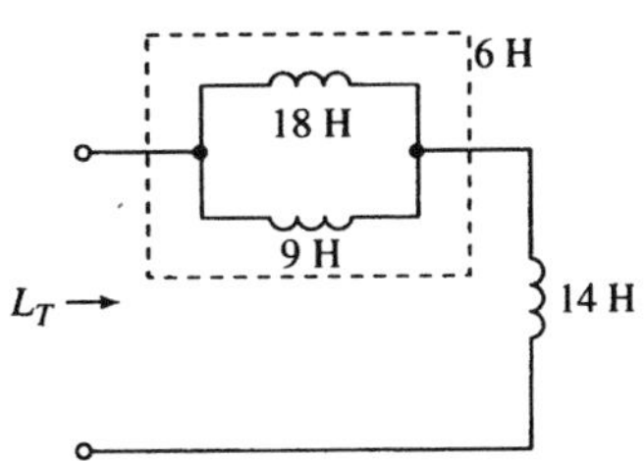

d. Through successive reduction, you get the circuit of (b). Then, 4 H||6 H = 2.4 H. thus, L_T = 1.6 H + 2.4 H = 4 H

(a)

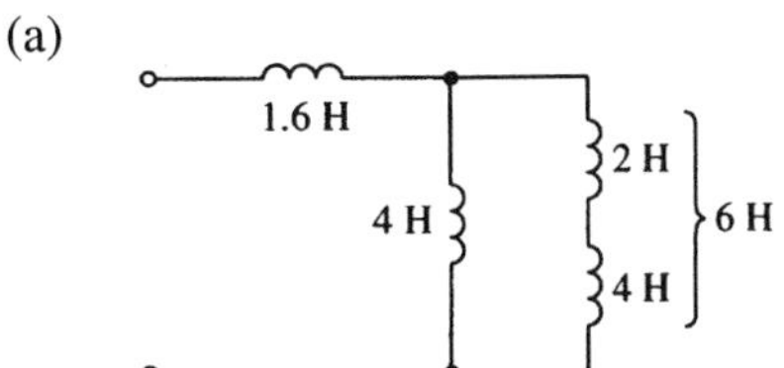

(b)

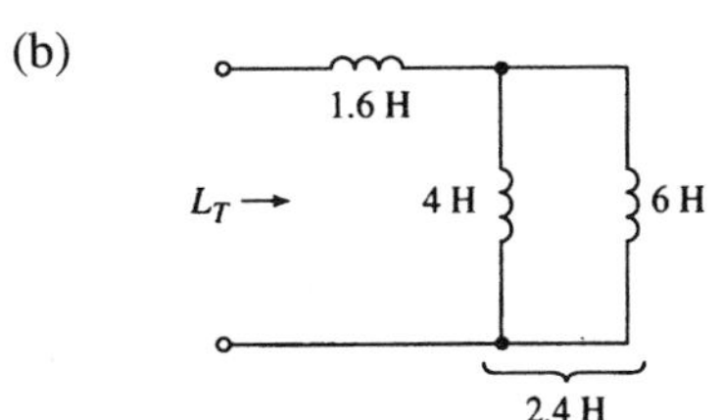

e. Through successive reduction, you get the circuit of (c).

Thus, $L_T = \dfrac{(6\text{ mH})(12\text{ mH})}{6\text{ mH} + 12\text{ mH}} = 4\text{ mH}$

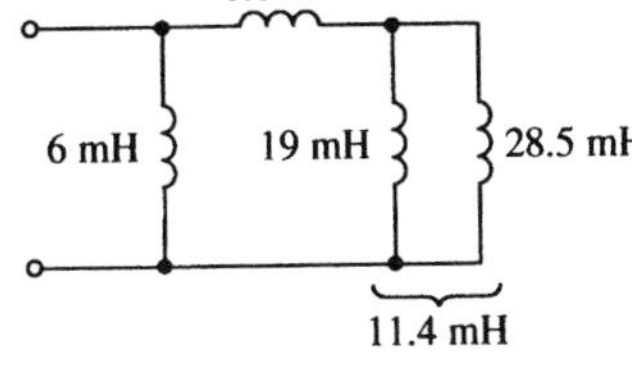

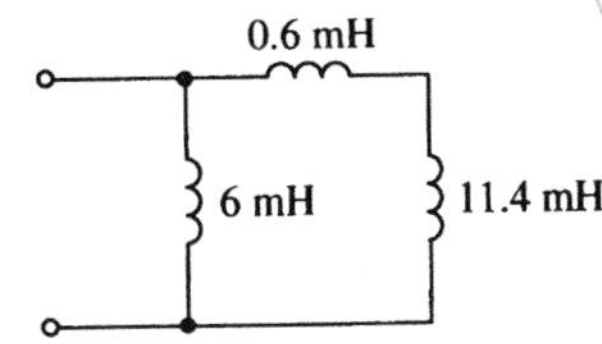

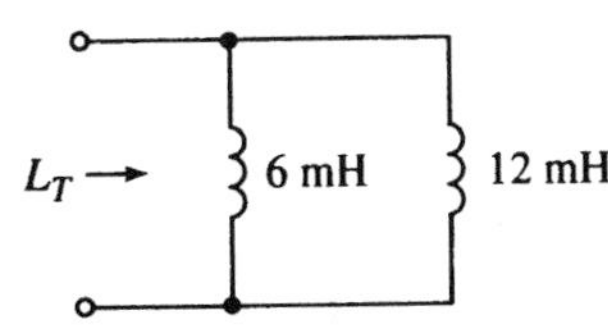

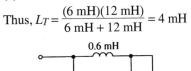

23. $L_T = (30\,\mu\text{H} + 60\,\mu\text{H})\|10\,\mu\text{H} = 90\,\mu\text{H}\|10\,\mu\text{H} = 9\,\mu\text{H}$

25. a. $L_{eq} = L_3 + L_4 = 4L_4 + L_4 = 5L_4$;

$L'_{eq} = 6\text{ H} - 1.5\text{ H} = 4.5\text{ H}$

$11.25\text{ H}\|L_{eq} = 4.5\text{ H}$

$\therefore\ L_{eq} = 7.5\text{ H}$

Thus, $5L_4 = 7.5$ H and $L_4 = 1.5$ H and $L_3 = 4L_4 = 4(1.5\text{ H}) = 6$ H.

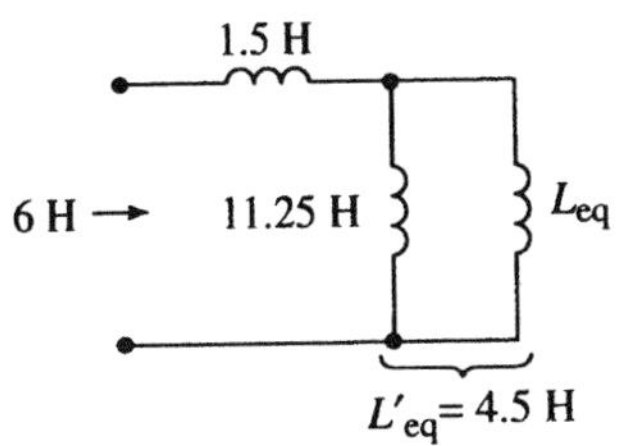

b. Reduce the circuit to that shown below.

$L_{eq} = 12.4\text{ H} - 10.8\text{ H} = 1.6\text{ H}$

$L_{eq} = \dfrac{L_3(4L_3)}{L_3 + 4L_3} = 0.8L_3$

Thus, $L_3 = \dfrac{1.6\text{ H}}{0.8} = 2$ H and $L_4 = 4L_3 = 8$ H

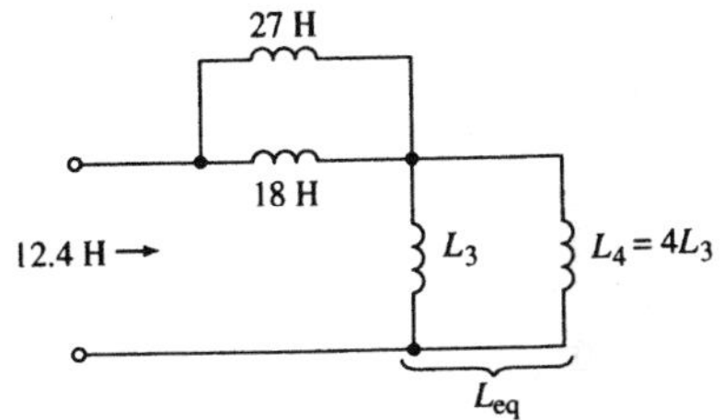

27. 6 H||4 H yields 2.4 H. thus, 4 H = L_x + 2.4 H and L_x = 1.6 H.

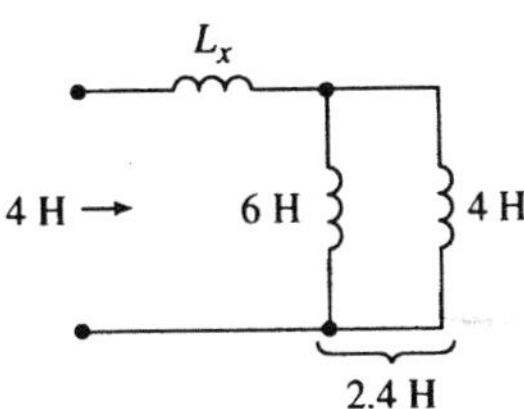

29. Only the circuit below yields L_T = 6 H.

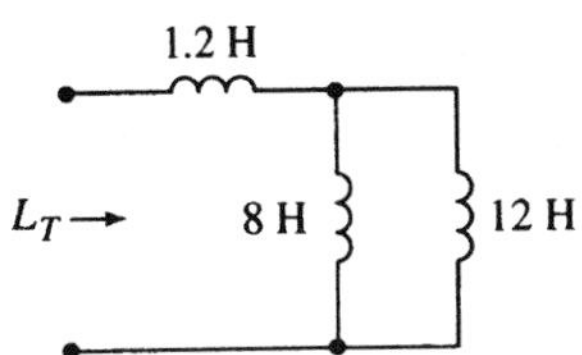

31.

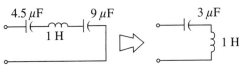

4.5 μF 9 μF 1 H ⇨ 3 μF 1 H

(a)

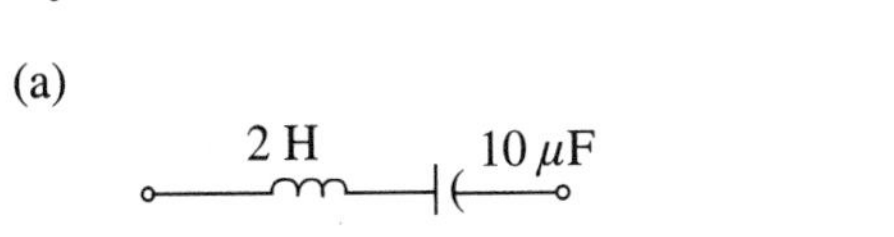

(b)

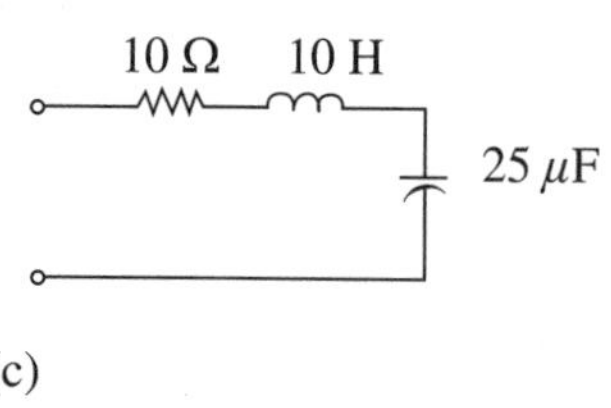

(c)

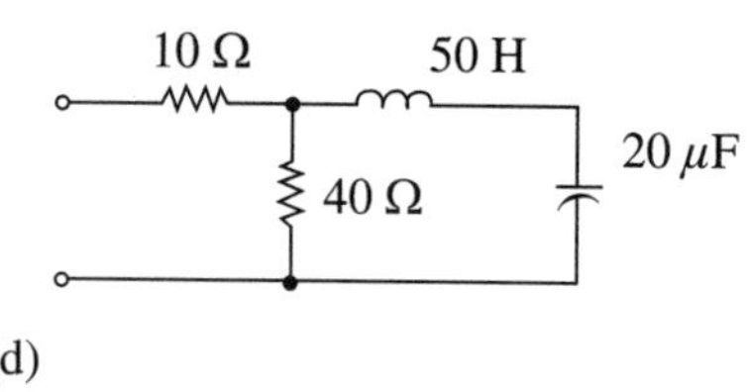

(d)

13.8 Energy Storage by an Inductance

33. Remove the coil and determine the Thévenin equivalent of the circuit.

$E_{Th} = \left(\frac{5\ \Omega}{25\ \Omega}\right)(40\ \text{V}) = 8\ \text{V};\ R_{Th} = 6\ \Omega + 20\ \Omega \| 5\ \Omega = 10\ \Omega$

Replace the inductance with a short. Thus,

$$I_{coil} = \frac{8\ \text{V}}{10\ \Omega + 10\ \Omega} = 0.4\ \text{A}$$

Thus, $W_L = \frac{1}{2}LI_{coil}^2 = \frac{1}{2}(4\ \text{H})(0.4\ \text{A})^2 = 0.32\ \text{J}$

(a)

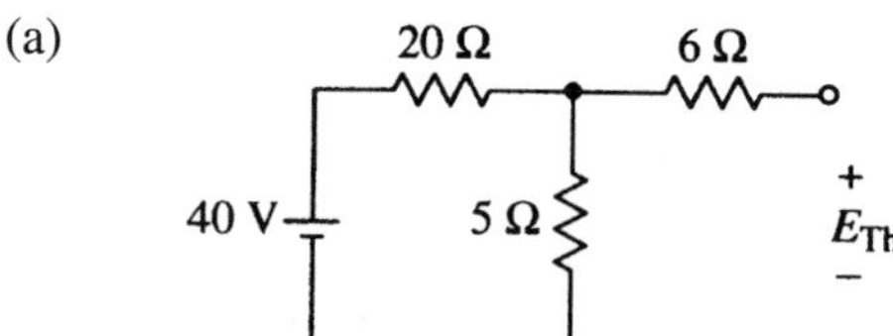

(b)

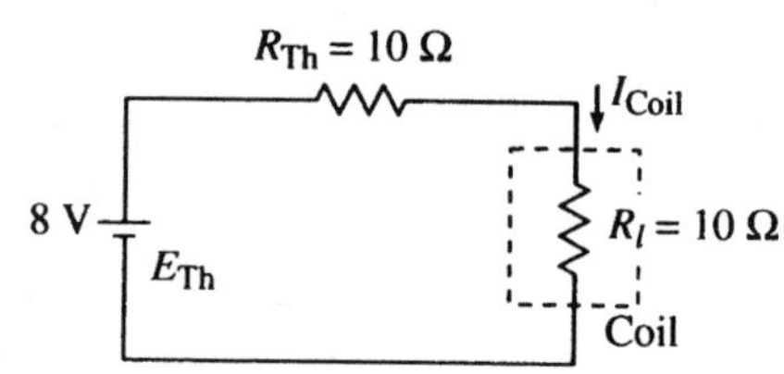

13.9 Inductor Troubleshooting Hints

35. The path contain L_1 and L_2 is open.

Chapter

14

Inductive Transients

14.1 Introduction

1\. a. Open circuit

b. (a) $i_S(0^+) = \dfrac{40\text{ V}}{25\ \Omega} = 1.6\text{ A}$

(b) $i_S(0^+) = \dfrac{60\text{ V}}{10\ \Omega} = 6\text{ A}$

$v_L(0^+) = (6\text{ A})(10\ \Omega) = 60\text{ V}$

(c) $i_S(0^+) = 0\text{ A};\ v_L(0^+) = E$

(d) $i_S(0^+) = \dfrac{90\text{ V}}{30\ \Omega + 15\ \Omega} = 2\text{ A}$

$v_L(0^+) = (2\text{ A})(15\ \Omega) = 30\text{ V}$

3\. Replace inductors with open circuits and capacitors with short circuits as below. This is now a simple dc circuit and may be solved as in previous chapters. Answers are:

$i_1 = 18\text{ A}$	$v_{R_1} = 180\text{ V}$	$v_{C_1} = 0\text{ V}$
$i_2 = 3\text{ A}$	$v_{R_2} = 120\text{ V}$	$v_{L_2} = 28\text{ V}$
$i_3 = 1\text{ A}$	$v_{R_3} = 60\text{ V}$	
$i_4 = i_5 = 2\text{A}$	$v_{R_4} = 32\text{ V}$	
$i_6 = 0\text{ A}$	$v_{R_5} = 28\text{ V}$	
$i_T = 21\text{ A}$	$v_{R_6} = 0\text{ V}$	

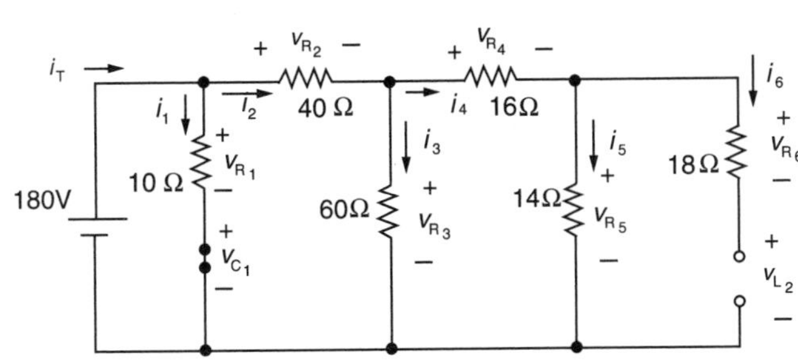

5\. a. $\tau = \dfrac{L}{R} = \dfrac{3\text{ H}}{60\ \Omega} = 0.05\text{ s} = 50\text{ ms}$

b. Current reaches its final value in $5\tau = 250\text{ ms}$.

c. $i_L = \dfrac{E}{R}(1 - e^{-t/\tau}) = \dfrac{180\text{ V}}{60\ \Omega}(1 - e^{-t/0.05\text{ s}})$

$= 3(1 - e^{-20t})\text{ A}$

$v_L = Ee^{-t/\tau} = 180e^{-20t}\text{ V}$

d. At $t = \tau$, $i_L = 3(1 - e^{-1}) = 1.90\text{ A}$

$v_L = 180e^{-1} = 66.2\text{ V}$

Continuing in this manner yields the following table

$t\ (\tau)$	i_L (A)	v_L (V)
0	0	180
τ	1.90	66.2
2τ	2.59	24.4
3τ	2.85	8.96
4τ	2.95	3.30
5τ	2.98	1.21

e.

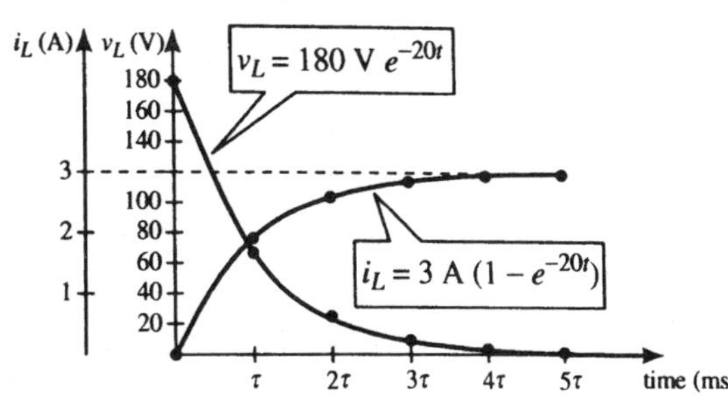

7\. Redrawing and simplifying the circuit yields the circuit below (next page).

a. $\tau = \dfrac{L}{R} = \dfrac{4\text{ H}}{20\ \Omega} = 0.2\text{ s}$

b. $5\tau = 5(0.2\text{ s}) = 1.0\text{ s}$

c. $i_L = \dfrac{E}{R}(1 - e^{-t/\tau}) = \dfrac{20\text{ V}}{20\ \Omega}(1 - e^{-t/0.2}) = 1(1 - e^{-5t})\text{ A}$

$v_L = Ee^{-t/\tau} = 20e^{-5t}\text{ V}$

d. At $t = \tau$

$i_L = 1\text{ A}(1 - e^{-1}) = 0.632\text{ A}$

$v_L = 20\text{ V}e^{-1} = 7.36\text{ V}.$

Thus,

t	i_L (A)	v_L (V)
0	0	20
τ	0.632	7.36
2τ	0.865	2.71
3τ	0.950	0.996
4τ	0.982	0.366
5τ	0.993	0.135

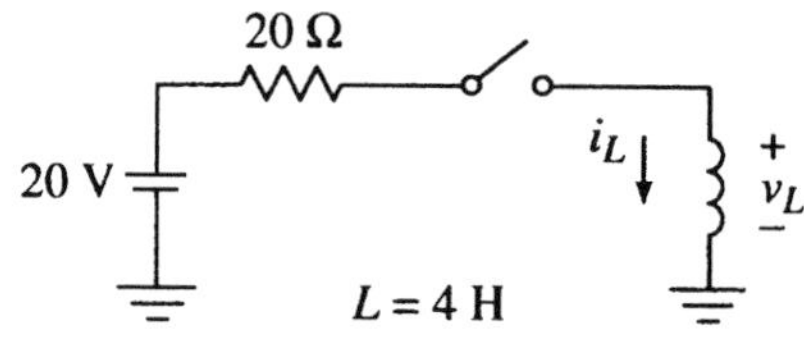

Waveforms are similar to those of Question 5e.

9. Note the relative polarity of E and v_L. Because of this v_L and i_L are negative.

$$i_L = -\frac{E}{R}(1 - e^{-Rt/L}) = -182(1 - e^{-392.9t})\text{ mA}$$

$$v_L = -Ee^{-Rt/L} = -40e^{-392.9t}\text{ V}$$

At $t = 3.4$ ms, $i_L = -182(1 - e^{-1.336}) = -134$ mA

$v_L = -40e^{-1.336} = -10.5$ V

11. $v_L(0^+) = E \therefore E = 80$ V

$$I_{SS} = 4\text{ A} = \frac{E}{R} \therefore R = \frac{80\text{ V}}{4\text{ A}} = 20\ \Omega$$

$5\tau = 0.5$ s $\therefore \tau = 0.1$ s

$$\tau = \frac{L}{R} \therefore L = 0.1(R) = 2\text{ H}$$

13. $v_L = Ee^{-Rt/L} \therefore E = 40$ V

$$I_{SS} = \frac{E}{R} = 10\text{ mA} \therefore R = \frac{40\text{ V}}{10\text{ mA}} = 4\text{ k}\Omega$$

$$\frac{R}{L} = 2000 \therefore L = \frac{R}{2000} = \frac{4000}{2000} = 2\text{ H}$$

14.4 De-Energizing Transients

15. With the switch open,

a. $$\tau = \frac{L}{R_1 + R_2} = \frac{0.5\text{ H}}{250\ \Omega} = 2\text{ ms}$$

b. $i_L = I_0e^{-t/\tau}$

$= 5\text{ A } e^{-500t}$

$v_L = -I_0(R_1 + R_2)e^{-t/\tau}$

$= -(5\text{ A})(250\ \Omega)e^{-500t}$

$= -1250\text{ V}e^{-500t}$

c. At $t = \tau$, $i_L = 5\text{ A } e^{-1} = 1.84$ A

$v_L = -1250\text{ V}e^{-1} = -460$ V.

Similarly for $t = 2\tau$, 3τ, 4τ, and 5τ. Thus,

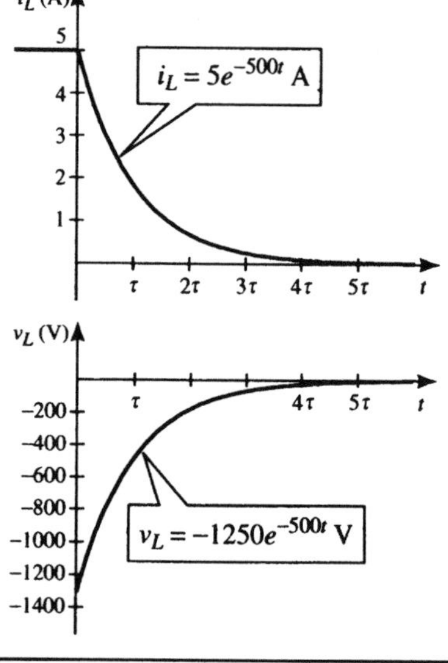

17. $e^{-t/\tau} = e^{-100t}$

$$\therefore \tau = \frac{1}{100} = 10\text{ ms}$$

$\therefore 20\text{ ms} = 2\tau$

At $t = 2\tau$, $v_L = 0.135E$ (Figure 14-10)

$\therefore v_L = (0.135)(-2700\text{ V}) = -365$ V

19. Build-up: $\tau = \frac{5\text{ s}}{5} = 1$ s

$$\tau = \frac{L}{R_1} \therefore R_1 = \frac{L}{\tau} = \frac{20\text{ H}}{1\text{ s}} = 20\ \Omega$$

Decay: $\tau' = \frac{2\text{ s}}{5} = 0.4$ s

$$\tau' = \frac{L}{R_1 + R_2} \Rightarrow 0.4\text{ s} = \frac{20\text{ H}}{20\ \Omega + R_2} \therefore R_2 = 30\ \Omega$$

14.5 More Complex Circuits

21. Simplify the circuit.

$$i_L = \frac{E}{R_T}\left(1 - e^{-R_Tt/L}\right) = 8.216(1 - e^{-54.37t})\text{ A}$$

At $t = 18.4$ ms, $i_L = 8.216(1 - e^{-1}) = 5.19$ A

$R_T = 8.155\ \Omega$
i_L
+
v_L
−
150 mH
E
67 V

23. a. The current decay circuit is shown below.

$$\tau = \frac{L}{R_T} = \frac{0.36\text{ H}}{40.5\text{ k}\Omega} = 8.89\ \mu\text{s}$$

b. From Problem 22, $I_0 = 5$ mA

$i_L = I_0 e^{-t/\tau} = 5e^{-t/8.89\ \mu s}$ mA

$v_L = -i_L R_T = -(5\text{ mA})(40.5\text{ k}\Omega)e^{-t/8.89\ \mu s}$ V

$= -202.5e^{-t/8.89\ \mu s}$ V

c. At $t = 17.8\ \mu$s, $v_L = -202.5e^{-17.8\ \mu s/8.89\ \mu s} = -202.5e^{-2} = -27.3$ V

$i_L = 5e^{-2}$ mA $= 0.675$ mA

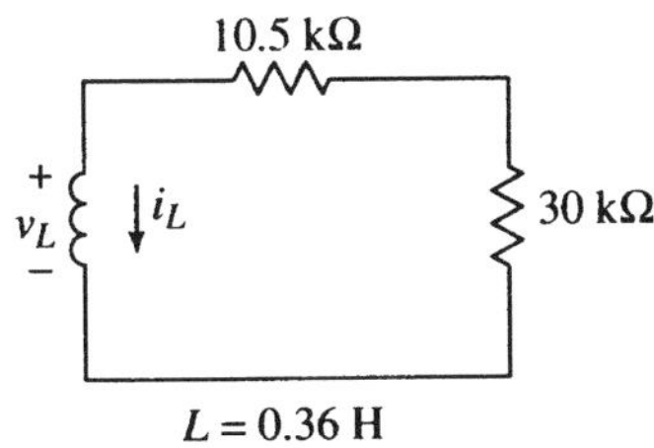

25. Redraw the circuit as in (a), convert the current source to a 100 V source in series with 200 Ω, then combine with the 40 V source to yield the circuit of (b). For the left hand side of (b),

$$E_{Th} = \left(\frac{300\ \Omega}{300\ \Omega + 200\ \Omega}\right)(60\text{ V}) = 36\text{ V}$$

$R_{Th} = 200\ \Omega \| 300\ \Omega = 120\ \Omega.$

The final circuit is shown in (c).

a. $$\tau = \frac{L}{R_1} = \frac{4\text{ H}}{400\ \Omega} = 10\text{ ms}$$

b. $$i_L = \frac{E_{Th}}{R_T}(1 - e^{-t/\tau}) = \frac{36\text{ V}}{400\ \Omega}(1 - e^{-t/10\text{ ms}})$$

$= 90(1 - e^{-t/10\text{ ms}})$ mA

$v_L = E_{Th}\, e^{-t/\tau} = 36e^{-t/10\text{ ms}}$ V

c. At $t = 25$ ms : $v_L = 36e^{-25\text{ ms}/10\text{ ms}} = 36\, e^{-2.5}$

$= 2.96$ V

$i_L = 90(1 - e^{-2.5}) = 82.6$ mA

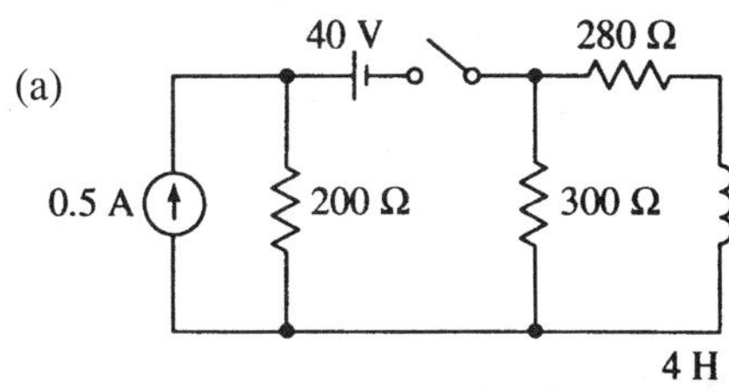

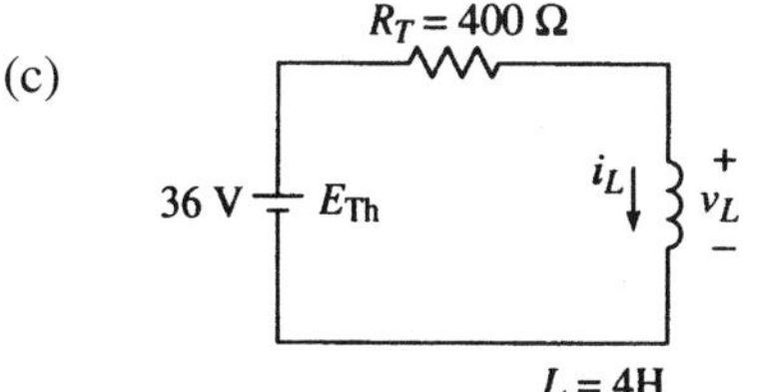

(c)

27. E_{Th} is the circuits open circuit voltage. Therefore, $E_{Th} = 45$ V.

$$I_{sc} = \frac{E_{Th}}{R_{Th}} \therefore R_{Th} = \frac{E_{Th}}{I_{sc}} = \frac{45\text{ V}}{0.15\text{ A}} = 300\ \Omega$$

$$\tau = \frac{L}{R_T} = \frac{0.4\text{ H}}{400\ \Omega} = 1\text{ ms}$$

$$i_L = \frac{E_{Th}}{R_T}(1 - e^{-t/\tau}) = \frac{45\text{ V}}{400\ \Omega}(1 - e^{-t/1\text{ ms}})$$

$= 112.5(1 - e^{-1000t})$ mA

$v_L = E_{Th}\, e^{-t/\tau} = 45e^{-1000t}$ V.

At $t = 2.5$ ms, $i_L = 112.5(1 - e^{-2.5}) = 103$ mA

$v_L = 45e^{-2.5} = 3.69$ V

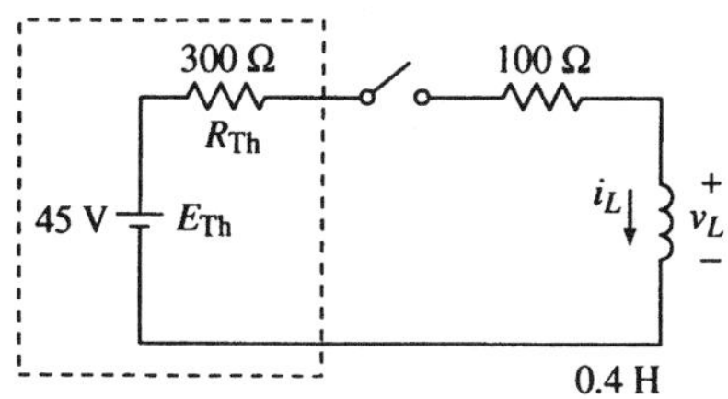

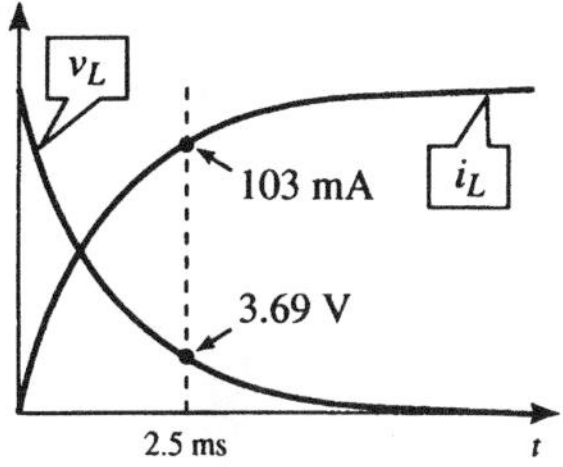

14.6 RL Transients Using Computers (MSM)

Note: For MSM, select *Analysis, Transient,* set *Initial Conditions* to Zero, then change the "Minimum number of time points" to a large enough value to get a smooth curve. (For most of the graphs here, 1000 points were used.)

29. Using the cursor, $v_L = 33.1$ V at $t = 20\ \mu$s. Check: Determine the Thévenin equivalent of the circuit. (You get $R_{Th} = 18$ kΩ and $E_{Th} = 90$ V.) This yields $v_L = 90e^{-t/20\ \mu s}$ V, and at $t = 20\ \mu$s, $v_L = 33.1$ V, the same as MSM.

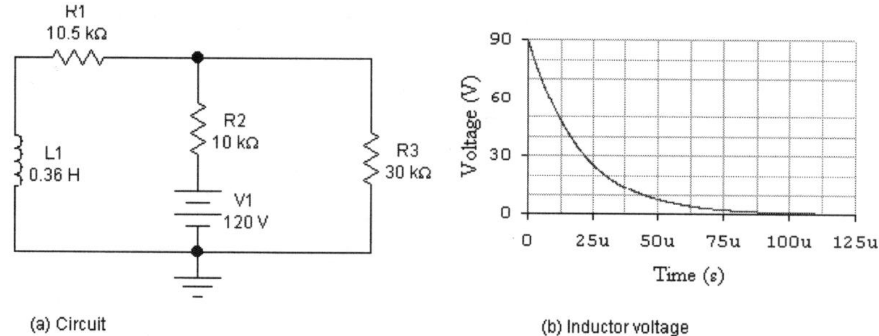

(a) Circuit (b) Inductor voltage

31. From the graph, $v = 138.4$ V at $t = 2$ ms. This yields a current of 138.4 V/30 Ω = 4.61 A. Check: Note that $R2$, $R3$, $R4$ and $L2$ have no effect on the current through the $R1$-$L1$ branch. Thus, the circuit of interest here consists of $V1$, $L1$ and $R1$ only. The current equation is $i_{R_1} = \dfrac{160\text{ V}}{30\ \Omega}(1 - e^{-1000t})$. At $t = 2$ ms, this yields a value of $5.33(1 - e^{-2}) = 4.61$ A, which agrees with MSM.

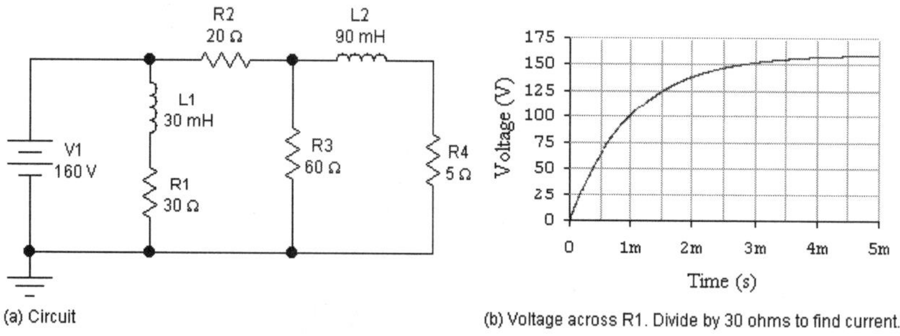

(a) Circuit (b) Voltage across R1. Divide by 30 ohms to find current.

14.6 RL Transients Using Computers (PSPice)

29. Using the cursor, you get approximately 33.5 V at $t = 20\ \mu$s. (For an analytic check, see the MSM solution above.)

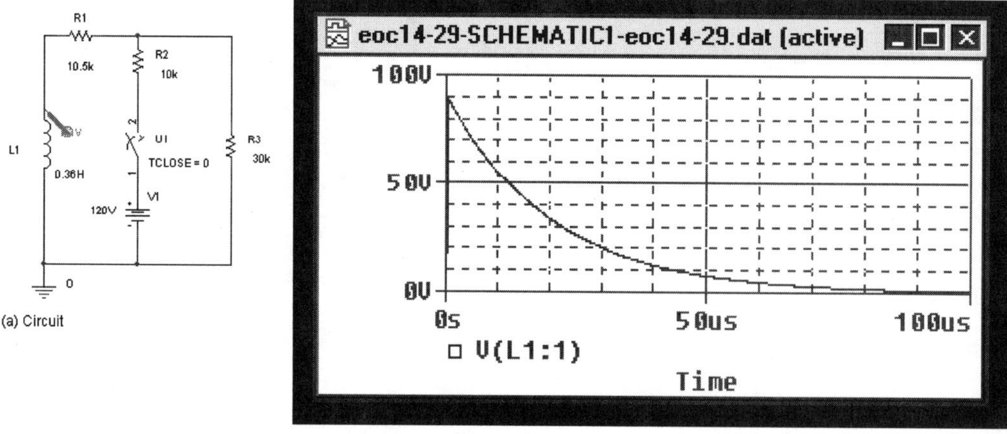

(a) Circuit

(b) Inductor voltage

31. From the graph, $i = 4.61$ A at $t = 2$ ms. (For an analytic check, see MSM solution above.)

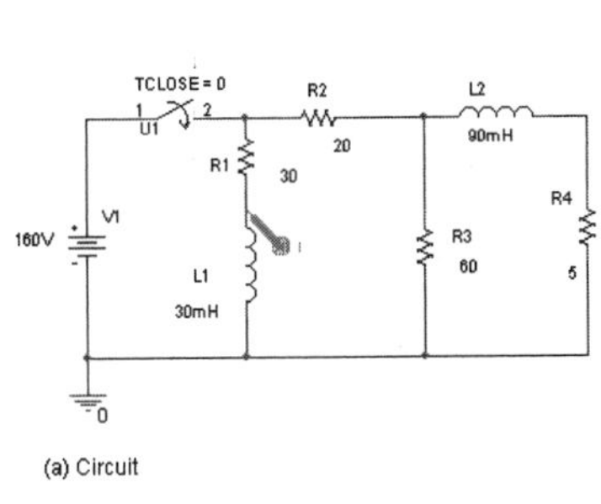

(a) Circuit

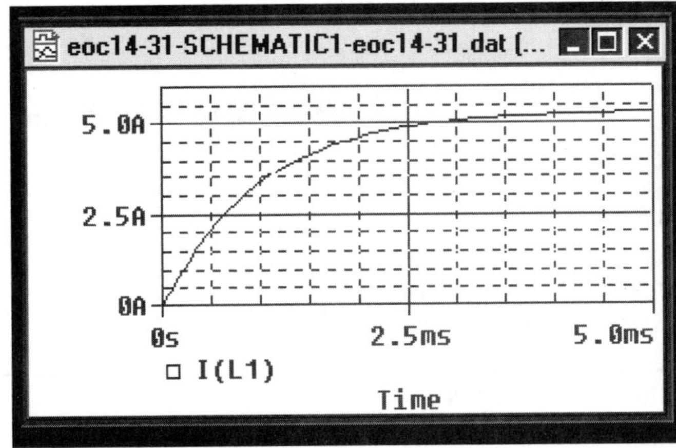

(b) Current through inductor L1

33. The PSpice solution is below. At $t = 25$ ms, $i_L = 0.126$ A. As a check, at $t = 25$ ms, $i_L = (0.632)(0.2\text{ A}) = 0.126$ A (using the Universal curve of Figure 14-10, or the equation for i_L from Example 14-8).

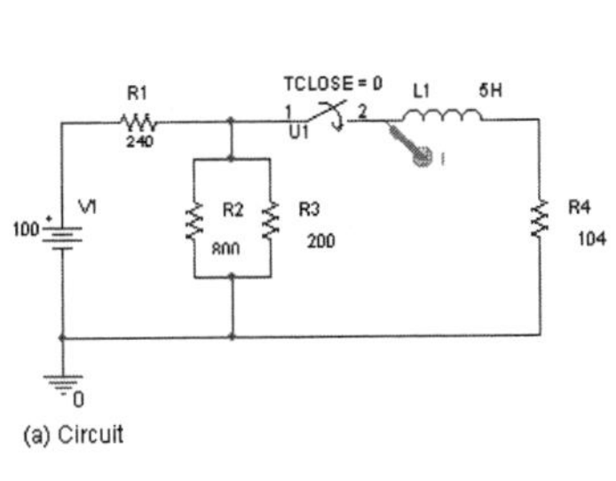

(a) Circuit

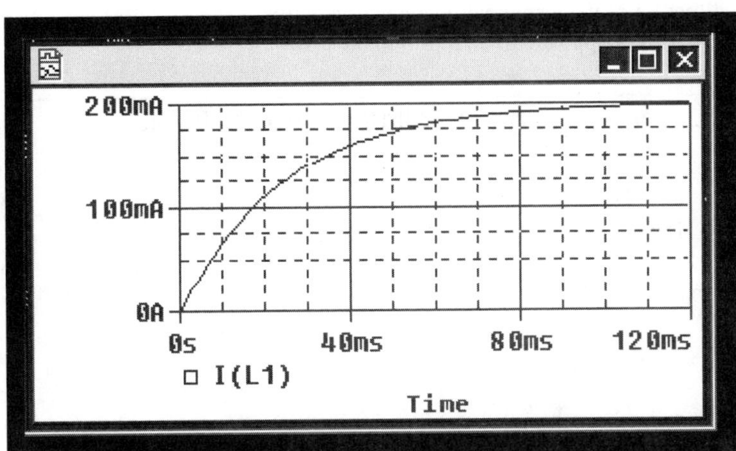

(b) Inductor current

Chapter

15

AC Fundamentals

15.1 Introduction

1. AC voltage is voltage whose polarity cycles alternately between positive and negative. AC current is current whose direction changes cyclically.

15.2 Generating ac Voltages

3. a. A waveform's value at each instant of time.
   b. 0 V, 10 V, 20 V, 20 V, 20 V, 0 V, –20 V, –20 V, 0 V

15.3 Voltage and Current Conventions for ac

5. At each instant, $i = \frac{e}{4\ \text{k}\Omega}$. Thus, currents are 0 mA, 2.5 mA, 5 mA, 5 mA, 5 mA, 0 mA, –5 mA, –5 mA, 0 mA. A positive value means the current is in the direction of the arrow, while a negative value means it is opposite in direction to the arrow.

15.4 Frequency, Period, Amplitude, and Peak Value

7. a. $f = \frac{1}{T} = \frac{1}{0.5\ \text{s}} = 2\ \text{Hz}$
   b. 10 Hz
   c. $T = \frac{80\ \mu\text{s}}{5} = 16\ \mu\text{s} \therefore\ f = 62.5\ \text{kHz}$

9. $T = 7\ \text{ms};\ f = \frac{1}{T} = \frac{1}{7\ \text{ms}} = 142.9\ \text{Hz}$

11. 9 V + 6 V = 15 V; 3 mA + 3 mA = 6 mA.

13. 2 min and 57 s = 177 s. At 847 cycles/s

$$N = \left(\frac{847\ \text{cycles}}{\text{s}}\right) \times 177\ \text{s} = 149\ 919\ \text{cycles}.$$

15. $T_1 = \frac{1}{f_1} = \frac{1}{10\ \text{kHz}} = 100\ \mu\text{s}$

$$T_2 = \frac{T_1}{0.25} = 400\ \mu\text{s} \ \therefore\ f_2 = \frac{f}{400\ \mu\text{s}} = 2500\ \text{Hz}$$

15.5 Angular and Graphic Relationships for Sine Waves

17. $v = 240 \sin 37^\circ\ \text{V} = 144.4\ \text{V}$

19. $v = V_m \sin\alpha \ \therefore V_m = \frac{v}{\sin\alpha} = \frac{50\ \text{V}}{\sin 150} = 100\ \text{V}$

21. $\alpha_{\text{rad}} = \frac{\pi}{180} \times \alpha_{\text{degrees}}$. Thus,
   a. 0.1745
   b. 0.4363
   c. 1.396
   d. 2.618
   e. 6.109
   f. 10.82

23. T = 180 ms ⇒ 360°

$$\therefore\ 30\ \text{ms} = \left(\frac{30\ \text{ms}}{180\ \text{ms}}\right)(360^\circ) = 60^\circ$$

and $i = 50 \sin 60^\circ = 43.3$ A

Similarly,

75 ms ⇒ 150° $i = 50 \sin 150^\circ = 25$ A

140 ms ⇒ 280° $i = 50 \sin 280^\circ = -49.2$ A

315 ms ⇒ 630° $i = 50 \sin 630^\circ = -50$ A

25. $T = \frac{1}{f} = \frac{1}{20\ \text{kHz}} = 50\ \mu\text{s}$

$$5\ \mu\text{s}\left(\frac{360^\circ}{50\ \mu\text{s}}\right) = 36^\circ$$

$50\ \text{V} = V_m \sin 36^\circ$

$$\therefore\ V_m = \frac{50\ \text{V}}{\sin 36^\circ} = 81.5\ \text{V}$$

15.6 Voltages and Currents as Functions of Time

27. a. $\omega = \frac{2\pi}{T} = \frac{2\pi}{100 \times 10^{-9}\text{ s}} = 62.83 \times 10^6$ rad/s

b. $\omega = 2\pi f = 2\pi(30\text{ Hz}) = 188.5$ rad/s

c. $f = \frac{100\text{ cycles}}{4\text{ s}} = 25$ Hz

$\therefore \omega = 2\pi(25) = 157.1$ rad/s

d. $\omega = \frac{2\pi}{T} = \frac{2\pi}{20\text{ ms}} = 314.2$ rad/s

e. $T = \frac{20\text{ ms}}{5} = 4\text{ ms} \quad \omega = \frac{2\pi}{4\text{ ms}} = 1571$ rad/s

29. a. $\omega = 2\pi f = 2\pi(60) = 377$ rad/s

$\therefore v = 170\sin 377t$ V

b. $\omega = \frac{2\pi}{T} = \frac{2\pi}{10\text{ ms}} = 628$ rad/s

$\therefore i = 40\sin 628t\ \mu A$

c. $12\ \mu s\left(\frac{360^\circ}{120\ \mu s}\right) = 36^\circ$

$v = V_m \sin\alpha \therefore 10\text{ V} = V_m \sin 36^\circ$

$\therefore V_m = 17$ V

$\omega = \frac{2\pi}{T} = \frac{2\pi}{120\ \mu s} = 52.4 \times 10^3$ rad/s

$v = V_m \sin\omega t$

$\therefore v = 17\sin 52.4 \times 10^3 t$ V

31. $\omega = \frac{2\pi}{T} = \frac{2\pi}{50\text{ ms}} = 125.7$ rad/s

$V_m = \frac{40\text{ V}}{2} = 20$ V

$\therefore v = 20\sin 125.7t$ V

33. $t = 0$ s:

$i = 47\sin(8260 \times 0)\text{ mA} = 0$ mA.

$t = 80\ \mu s$:

$i = 47\sin 8260(80 \times 10^{-6}\text{ s}) = 47\sin 0.6608$ rad

$= 47\sin 37.86^\circ\text{ mA} = 28.8$ mA

Similarly, at $t = 410\ \mu s$, $i = -11.4$ mA and at $t = 1200\ \mu s$, $i = -22$ mA.

35. a. $\theta = \pi/5 = 36^\circ$. Thus, $i = 5\sin(1000t + 36^\circ)$ mA.

b. $\theta = 180^\circ - 60^\circ = 120^\circ$ and $\omega = \frac{2\pi}{T} = \frac{2\pi}{50\text{ ms}} = 40\pi$

Thus, $i = 10\sin(40\pi t + 120^\circ)$ A.

c. $\theta = \pi/4 = 45^\circ$ and $\omega = 2\pi f = 1800\pi$. Thus, $v = 4\sin(1800\pi t - 45^\circ)$ V.

37. $v = 5\sin(\omega t + 45^\circ)$ where $\omega = 20\pi$ rad/s

$t = 20$ ms: $\omega t = 20\pi(0.02) = 1.2566\text{ rad} = 72^\circ$

$v = 5\sin(72^\circ + 45^\circ) = 5\sin 117^\circ = 4.46$ V

$t = 75$ ms: $\omega t = 20\pi(0.075) = 4.7124\text{ rad} = 270^\circ$

$v = 5\sin(270^\circ + 45^\circ) = 5\sin 315^\circ = -3.54$ V

$t = 90$ ms: $\omega t = 20\pi(0.090) = 5.6549\text{ rad} = 324^\circ$

$v = 5\sin 369^\circ = 0.782$ V

39. $\theta = 90^\circ - 54^\circ = 36^\circ$

$\frac{x}{36^\circ} = \frac{1620\ \mu s}{324^\circ} \therefore x = 180\ \mu s$. Thus, $T = 1800\ \mu s$.

$\omega = \frac{2\pi}{T} = 3491$ rad/s

$v = 100\sin(3491t + 36^\circ)$ V

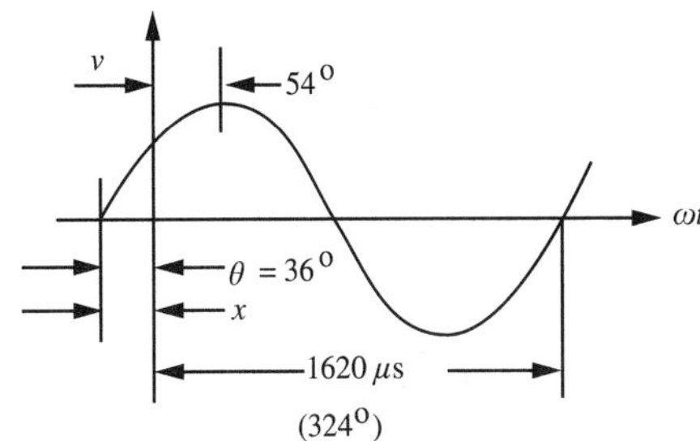

41. Time to 0V: $v = 30\sin(\omega t_1 - 45^\circ)$ reaches zero when $(\omega t_1 - 45^\circ) = 0$. $\therefore \omega t_1 = 45^\circ = \frac{\pi}{4}$ rad and

$t_1 = \frac{\frac{\pi}{4}\text{ rad}}{40\pi\text{ rad/s}} = 6.25$ ms

Time to 23 V: $23 = 30\sin(\omega t_2 - 45^\circ)$

$\therefore \sin(\omega t_2 - 45^\circ) = 0.7667$

$\therefore (\omega t_2 - 45^\circ) = \sin^{-1}(0.7667) = 50.06^\circ$

$\therefore \omega t_2 = 95.06^\circ = 1.659$ rad

$t_2 = \frac{1.659\text{ rad}}{40\pi\text{ rad/s}} = 13.2$ ms

Time to –23V: $-23 = 30\sin(\omega t_3 - 45^\circ)$

Define $x = \omega t_3 - 45^\circ$

$\therefore -23 = 30\sin x \qquad \therefore \sin x = -0.7667$

$x = -50.06^\circ$

This corresponds to point A on the waveform below. However, we want point B. Point B corresponds to $x = 180^\circ + 50.06^\circ = 230.06^\circ$. But $x = \omega t_3 - 45^\circ$. $\therefore \omega t_3 = 275.06^\circ = 4.801$ rad

$\therefore t_3 = 38.2$ ms

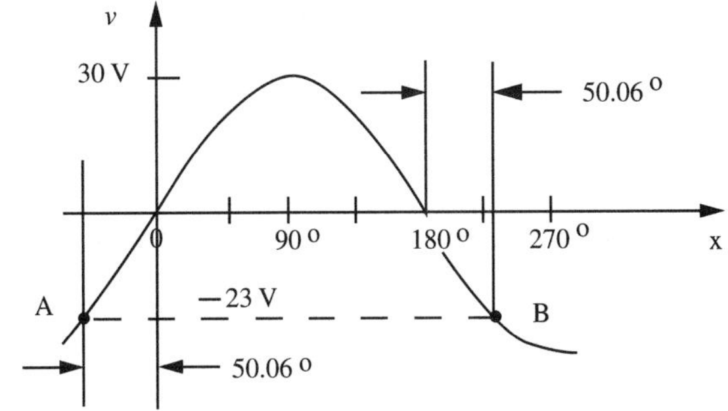

15.7 Introduction to Phasors

43\. a. Current leads by 20°

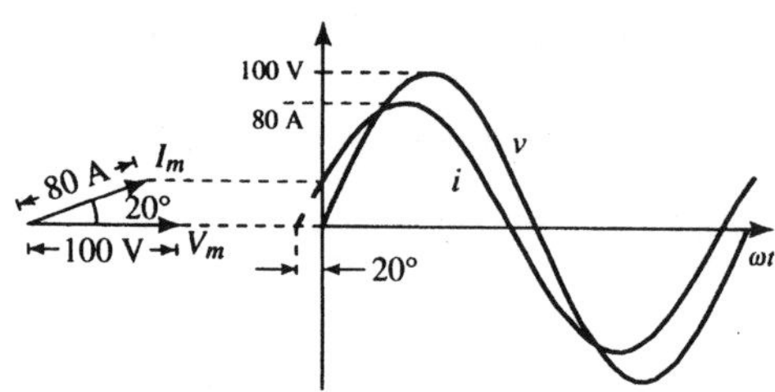

b. They are in phase.

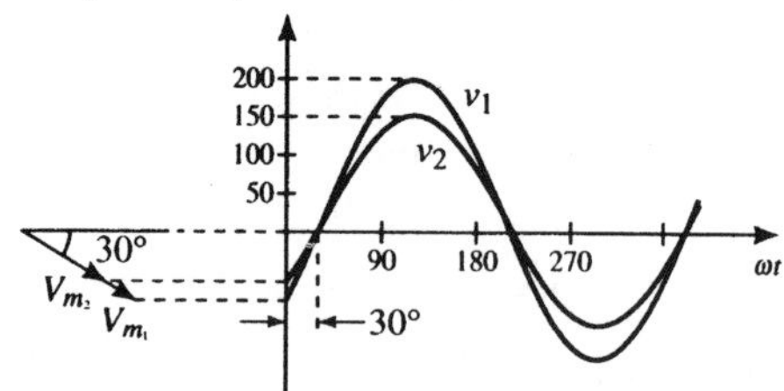

c. i_1 leads by 50°

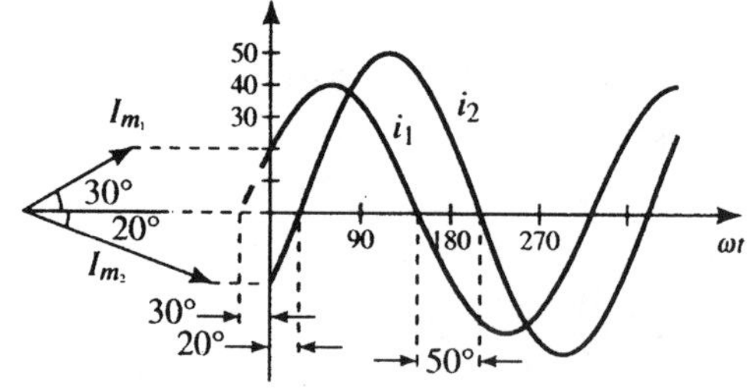

d. Current leads by 60°

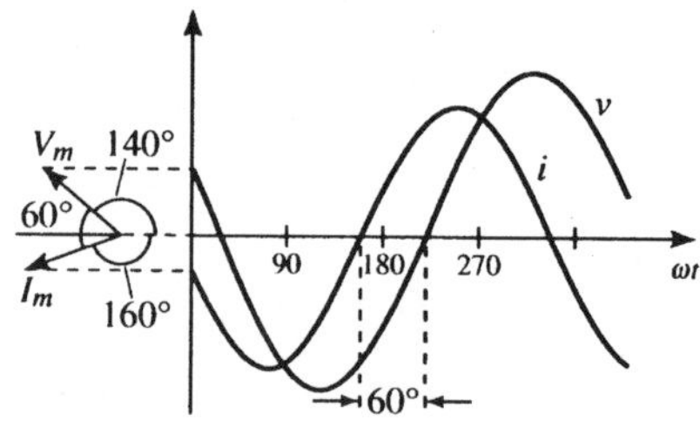

45\. a. If waveform B is projected back to the origin, we see that is passes through zero at $\omega t = 300° - 180° = 120°$. Phasors are shown below. Thus, A leads by 90°.

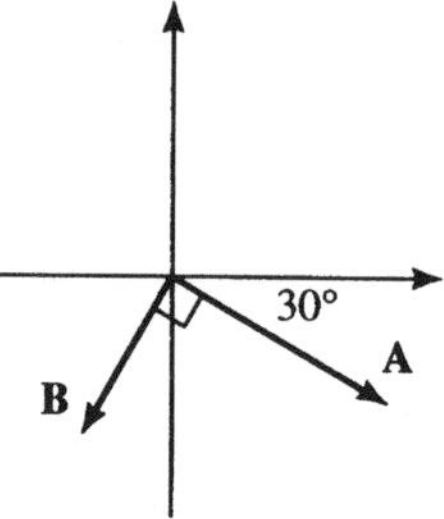

b. If waveform B is projected back to the origin, it has a negative peak at $t = 0$. Phasors are shown below. Thus, A leads by 150°.

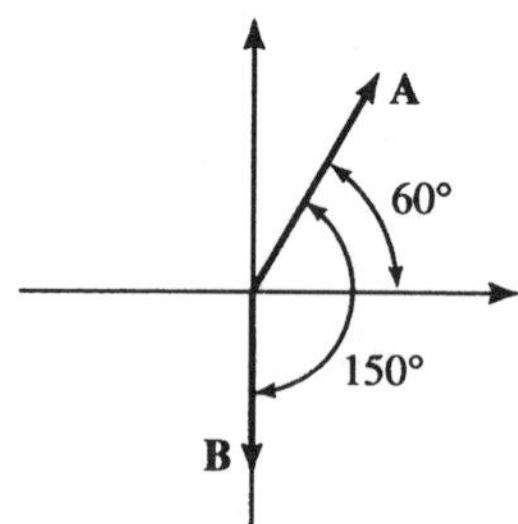

15.8 AC Waveforms and Average Value

47\. Since all are sinusoidal, all have a value of zero.

49\. a. $I_{avg} = \dfrac{(2\times 3) + (2\times 1) - (3\times 1) + (3\times 2)}{10} = 1.1 \text{ A}$

b. $V_{avg} = \dfrac{\frac{1}{2}(100)(20) - (20)(100)}{200} = -5 \text{ V}$

c. $I_{avg} = \dfrac{(2\times 2\pi) - (2\times 2)}{2\pi} = 1.36 \text{ A}$

51\. a. Similar to Figure 15-61(b), except positive peak is 40 V, negative peak is –10 V, and $V_{avg} = 15$ V. $T = 120$ ms.

b. Peak = 15 V + 25 V = 40 V

Negative peak = 15 V – 25 V = –10 V

c. 10 ms ⇒ 30° $v = 15 + 25 \sin 30° = 27.5$ V

Similarly, the other values are 36.7 V, 2.51 V and – 6.65 V.

d. Since the average of a sine wave is zero, the waveform's average is its dc value. Thus, $V_{avg} = 15$ V.

53\. Area under the section from 0 to 2 s is

$$A = \int_0^2 3t^2 dt = \frac{3t^3}{3}\Bigg|_0^2 = (2)^3 = 8 \text{ V-s}$$

Total area $A_T = 8 + (12)(1) - (6)(1) = 14$ V-s

$$V_{avg} = \frac{14 \text{ V–s}}{5 \text{ s}} = 2.80 \text{ V}$$

15.9 Effective Values

55. a. 12 V
b. (0.707)(24 mA) = 17.0 mA
c. $\sqrt{(10\text{ V})^2 + \left(\frac{24\text{ V}}{\sqrt{2}}\right)^2} = 19.7\text{ V}$
d. $\sqrt{(45\text{ V})^2 + \left(\frac{27\text{ V}}{\sqrt{2}}\right)^2} = 48.9\text{ V}$

57. a. $\sqrt{(3\text{ mA})^2 + (4\text{ mA})^2} = 5\text{ mA}$
b. $\sqrt{(15\text{ V})^2 + \left(\frac{25\text{ V}}{\sqrt{2}}\right)^2} = 23.2\text{ V}$

59. a. Square the curve as below. Apply equation 15-30.

$$I = \sqrt{\frac{16 \times 2) + (144 \times 2)}{4}} = 8.94\text{ A}$$

b.

$$V = \sqrt{\frac{(25 \times 1) + (100 \times 2) + (900 \times 1)}{4}} = 16.8\text{ V}$$

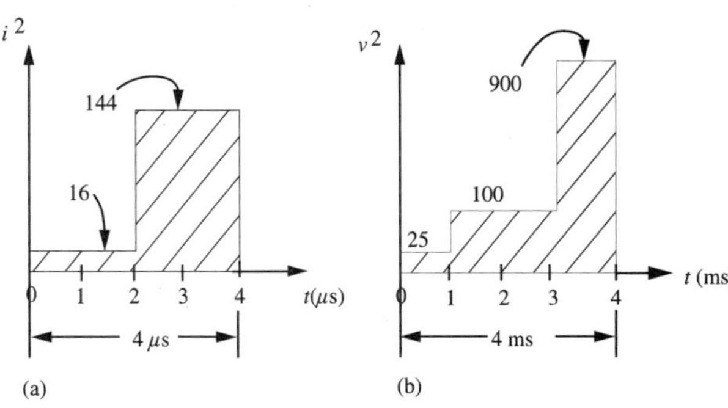

61. Square the curve as in (b). RMS equals the root of the mean of this squared curve.

Thus,

$$V = \sqrt{\frac{576 \times 2}{2}} = 24\text{ V}$$

The waveform has the same effective value as a 24 V battery because its magnitude is always 24 V and rms depends only on magnitude—see curve (a).

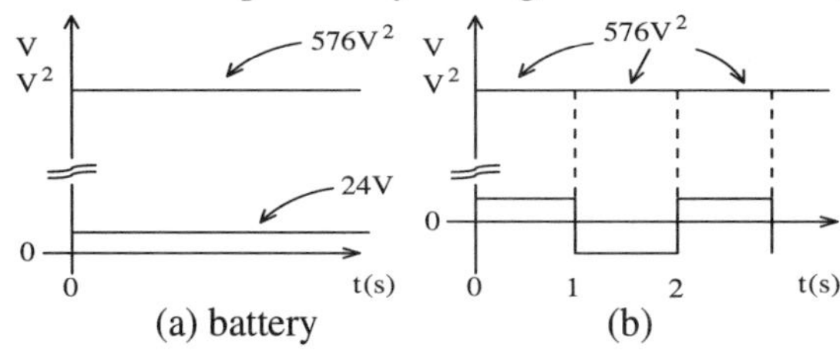

63. See solution of Problem 62 for diagram

$$A_1 = \int_0^3 i^2 dt = \int_0^3 \left(\frac{40}{3}t\right)^2 dt = \left(\frac{40}{3}\right)^2 \int_0^3 t^2 dt$$

$$= \left(\frac{40}{3}\right)^2 \left[\frac{t^3}{3}\right]_0^3 = 1600$$

$$\therefore I_{\text{eff}} = \sqrt{\frac{A_1 + A_2 + A_3}{\text{Base}}} = \sqrt{\frac{1600 + 800 + 3200}{8}}$$

$$= 26.5\text{ mA}$$

15.11 AC Voltage and Current Measurement

65. a. (0.707)(153 V) = 108 V
b. 120 V
c. $V = \sqrt{(10\text{ V})^2 + \left(\frac{15\text{ V}}{\sqrt{2}}\right)^2} = 14.6\text{ V}$
d. (0.707)(597 V) = 422 V

15.12 Circuit Analysis Using Computers

67. $f = \frac{\omega}{2\pi} = \frac{40\pi \text{ rad/s}}{2\pi} = 20 \text{ Hz.}$

PSpice: The PSpice solution is shown below. Use source VSIN and *Transient Analysis* with TSTOP set to 50ms. Use the cursor to determine the time at which $v = 0$. (The answer is 6.25 ms, the same as obtained by theoretical analysis in Problem 41). Similarly, use the cursor to find when $v = 23$ V and -23 V.

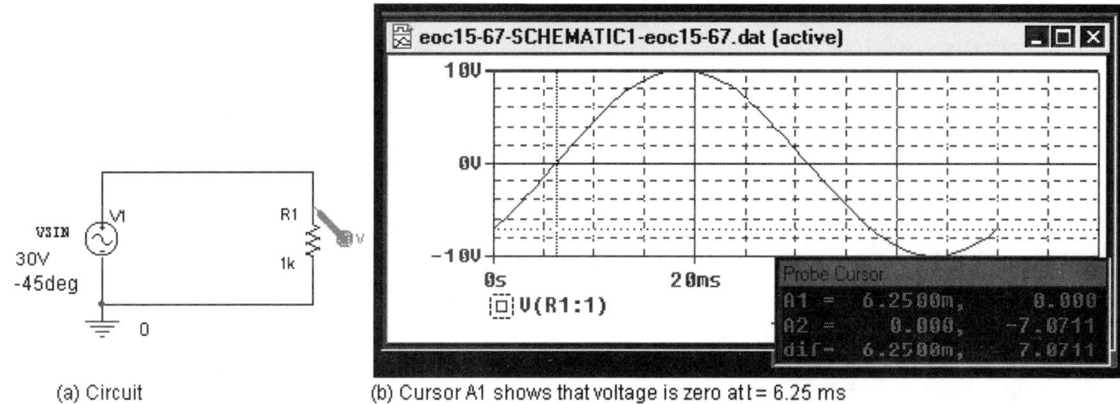

(a) Circuit (b) Cursor A1 shows that voltage is zero at t = 6.25 ms

MSM: The circuit for MSM is similar to that for PSpice. Use Transient Analysis. The waveform is shown below. Via the cursor, determine at what time voltage crosses zero. You should measure about 6.25 ms, the same answer as obtained in Problem 41. Similarly, use the cursor to determine when $v = 23$ V and -23 V.

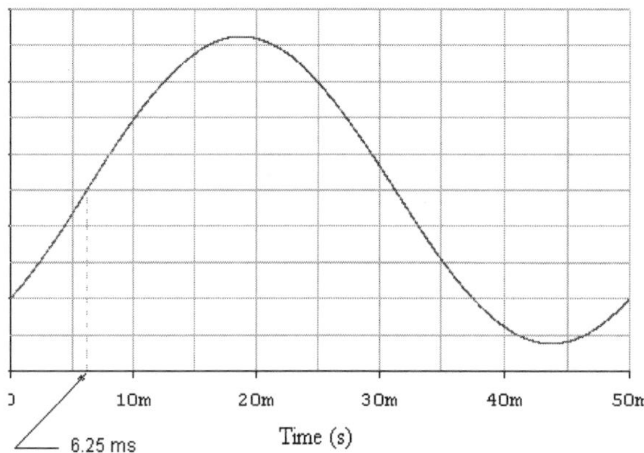

Chapter

16

R, L, and C Elements and the Impedance Concept

16.1 Complex Number Review

1. a. $13\angle 67.4^\circ$
   b. $10.8\angle -33.7^\circ$
   c. $17\angle 118.1^\circ$
   d. $10.8\angle -158.2^\circ$

3.

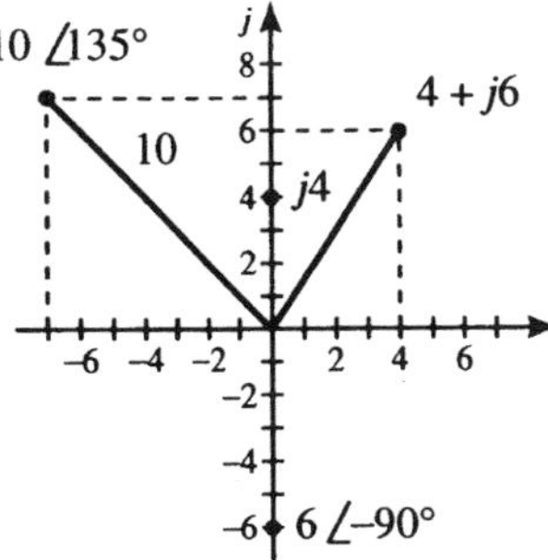

5. a. $(4 + j8) + (3 - j2) = 7 + j6$
   b. $(4 + j8) - (3 - j2) = 1 + j10$
   c. $(4.1 - j7.6) + 12\angle 20^\circ = (4.1 - j7.6) + (11.3 + j4.1) = 15.4 - j3.5$
   d. $2.9\angle 25^\circ - 7.3\angle -5^\circ = (2.628 + j1.226) - (7.272 - j0.636) = -4.64 + j1.86$
   e. $9.2\angle -120^\circ - (2.6 + j4.1) = (-4.60 - j7.967) - (2.6 + j4.1) = -7.20 - j12.1$
   f. $(0.12 - j\,0.16) + (0.08 + j\,0.06) = 0.20 - j\,0.10$

7. a. $(15 - j6) - \left[\dfrac{(13.79 + j11.57) + (12 + j8)}{11 + j11}\right] = (15 - j6) - \left[\dfrac{25.79 + j19.57}{11 + j11}\right] = (15 - j6) - \dfrac{32.37\angle 37.19^\circ}{15.56\angle 45^\circ}$

   $= (15 - j6) - 2.08\angle -7.81 = (15 - j6) - (2.06 - j0.283) = 12.94 - j5.72 = 14.1\angle -23.8^\circ$

   b. $\dfrac{(19.73 + j7.18) - j41}{(36 + j0) + (1 + j12) - (8.43 + j7.07)} = \dfrac{19.73 - j33.82}{28.57 + j4.93} = \dfrac{39.15\angle -59.74^\circ}{28.99\angle 9.79^\circ} = 1.35\angle -69.5^\circ$

   c. $\dfrac{(13.79 + j11.57) - (13.79) - j11.57)}{7 + j12} - \dfrac{(16 + j17) + (10.5 - j18.19)}{4} = \dfrac{j23.14}{7 + j12} - \dfrac{26.5 - j1.19}{4}$

   $= \dfrac{23.14\angle 90^\circ}{13.89\angle 59.74^\circ} - (6.625 - j0.2975) = 1.666\angle 30.26 - (6.625 - j0.2975)$

   $= (1.439 + j0.8395) - (6.625 - j0.2975) = -5.186 + j1.137 = 5.31\angle 167.6^\circ$

16.2 Complex Numbes in ac Analysis

9. a. $e = 10\sin(\omega t + 30^\circ)$ V
   b. $e = 15\sin(\omega t - 10^\circ)$ V

11. a. $\mathbf{E}_1 = 10\text{ V}\angle 30^\circ \quad \mathbf{E}_2 = 15\text{ V}\angle -20^\circ$
    b. $\mathbf{V} = 10\text{ V}\angle 30^\circ - 15\text{ V}\angle -20^\circ = 11.5\text{ V}\angle 118.2^\circ$
    c. $v = 11.5\sin(\omega t + 118.2)$ V
    d.

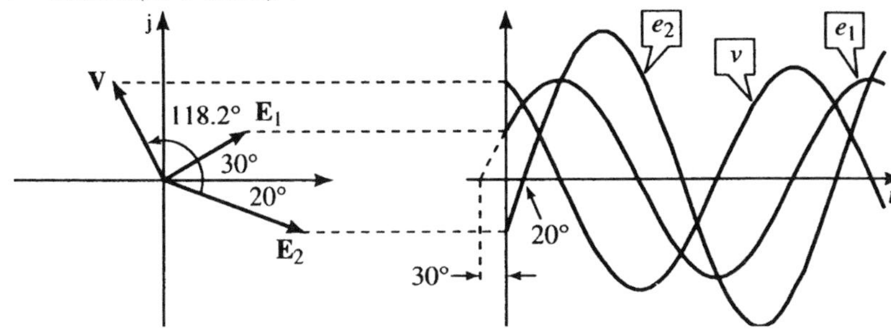

13. a. $\mathbf{I}_1 = (0.707)(25\text{ mA})\angle 36° = 17.7\text{ mA}\angle 36°$

$\mathbf{I}_2$: First, note that $\cos\omega t \Rightarrow \angle 90°$

$\therefore \cos(\omega t - 10°) \Rightarrow \angle 90° - \angle 10° = \angle 80°$

Thus, $\mathbf{I}_2 = 28.3\text{ mA}\angle 80°$

$\mathbf{I}_T = \mathbf{I}_1 + \mathbf{I}_2 = 17.7\angle 36° + 28.3\angle 80°$

$= 42.8\text{ mA}\angle 63.3°$

b. $i_T = \sqrt{2}(42.8)\sin(\omega t + 63.3°)$

$= 60.5\sin(\omega t + 63.3°)\text{ mA}$

15. Similarly to Question 13:

a. $\mathbf{I}_1 = 4.95\text{ mA}\angle 0°$

$\mathbf{I}_2 = 2.83\text{ mA}\angle -90°$

$\mathbf{I}_3 = 4.24\text{ mA}\angle 90°$

$\mathbf{I}_T = 4.95\angle 0° + 2.83\angle -90° + 4.24\angle 90°$

$= 5.15\text{ mA}\angle 15.9°$

b. $i_T = 7.28\sin(\omega t + 15.9°)\text{ mA}$

16.4 to 16.6

17. a. $i = \dfrac{v}{R} = 10\sin\omega t\text{ A}$

b. $i = 10\sin(\omega t + 27°)\text{ A}$

c. $v = Ri = 204\sin(\omega t - 56°)\text{ mV}$

d. $v = Ri = -204\cos(\omega t - 67°)\,\mu\text{V}$

Using the principles of Sec. 15.7, this can be expressed as $v = 204\sin(\omega t - 157°)\mu\text{V}$.

19. a. $v_{R_1} = R_1 i = 147\sin(\omega t + 39°)\text{ V}$

$v_{R_2} = R_2 i = 183.75\sin(\omega t + 39°)\text{ V}$

b. Since these are in phase, they can be added directly in the time domain. Thus,

$v_T = v_{R_1} + v_{R_2} = 330.75\sin(\omega t + 39°)\text{ V}$

$v_T = R_T i = (22.5\text{ k}\Omega)[14.7\sin(\omega t + 39°)\text{ mA}]$

$= 330.75\sin(\omega t + 39°)\text{ V}$ (same)

21. a. $i_L = 5\sin(\omega t - 30°)\text{ A}$

b. $i_L = 5\sin(\omega t - 105°)\text{ A}$

c. $v_L = 10\sin(\omega t + 120°)\text{ V}$

d. $v_L = 10\sin(\omega t + 100°)\text{ V}$

23. a. $I_m = \dfrac{E_m}{X_L} = \dfrac{100\text{ V}}{188.5\ \Omega} = 0.531\text{ A}$

$\omega = 2\pi f = (2\pi)(60\text{ Hz}) = 377\text{ rad/s}$

$\therefore i_L = I_m\sin(\omega t - 90°) = 0.531\sin(377t - 90°)\text{ A}$

b. $I_m = \dfrac{100\text{ V}}{3142\ \Omega} = 31.8\text{ mA}\quad \omega = 6283\text{ rad/s}$

$i_L = 31.8\sin(6283t - 90°)\text{ mA}$

c. $I_m = \dfrac{100\text{ V}}{250\ \Omega} = 0.4\text{ A}$

$\therefore i_L = 0.4\sin(500t - 90°)\text{ A}$

25. a. $X_L = \dfrac{V_m}{I_m} = \dfrac{40\text{ V}}{0.364\text{ A}} = 109.9\ \Omega$

$f = \dfrac{X_L}{2\pi L} = \dfrac{109.9\ \Omega}{2\pi(2\text{ mH})} = 8.74\text{ kHz}$

b. $X_L = \dfrac{40\text{ V}}{250\,\mu\text{A}} = 160\text{ k}\Omega$

$L = \dfrac{160\text{ k}\Omega}{2\pi(500\text{ kHz})} = 50.9\text{ mH}$

$\theta = 40° + 90° = 130°$

27. a. $X_C = \dfrac{1}{\omega C} = \dfrac{1}{(2\pi)(60\text{ Hz})(5\times 10^{-6}\text{ F})} = 530.5\ \Omega$

b. $X_C = \dfrac{1}{(2\pi)(1000\text{ Hz})(5\times 10^{-6}\text{ F})} = 31.83\ \Omega$

c. $X_C = \dfrac{1}{(500\text{ rad/s})(5\times 10^{-6}\text{ F})} = 400\ \Omega$

29. a. $X_C = \dfrac{1}{\omega C} = \dfrac{1}{(377)(50\ \mu\text{F})} = 53.05\ \Omega$

$I_m = \dfrac{V_m}{X_C} = \dfrac{100\text{ V}}{53.05\ \Omega} = 1.89\text{ A}$

Current leads by 90°.

$\therefore i_C = 1.89\sin(377t + 90°)\text{ A}$

b. $X_C = \dfrac{1}{(2\pi)(400)(50\,\mu\text{F})} = 7.96\ \Omega$

$V_m = (10\text{ mA})(7.96\ \Omega) = 79.6\text{ mV}$

Voltage lags by 90°

$\therefore v_C = 79.6\sin(2\pi\times 400t - 150°)\text{ mV}$

16.7 The Impedance Concept

31. a. $\mathbf{Z}_R = 48\ \Omega\angle 0°$

b. $\mathbf{Z}_L = j\omega L = j(2\pi)(60\text{ Hz})(0.1\text{ H}) = j37.7\ \Omega$

c. $\mathbf{Z}_C = -j\dfrac{1}{\omega C} = -j\dfrac{1}{(2000\text{ rad/s})(10\times 10^{-6}\text{ F})} = -j50\ \Omega$

33. a. $\mathbf{V}_R = \mathbf{I}_R\mathbf{Z}_R = (0.5\text{ A}\angle 0°)(50\ \Omega) = 25\text{ V}\angle 0°$

$\mathbf{V}_L = \mathbf{I}_L\mathbf{Z}_L = (0.5\text{ A}\angle 0°)(25\ \Omega\angle 90°) = 12.5\text{ V}\angle 90°$

$\mathbf{V}_C = \mathbf{I}_C\mathbf{Z}_C = (0.5\text{ A}\angle 0°)(10\ \Omega\angle -90°)$

$= 5\text{ V}\angle -90°$

b. $v_R = \sqrt{2}V_R\sin(\omega t + \theta_R) = \sqrt{2}(25\text{ V})\sin(\omega t + 0°)$

$= 35.4\sin\omega t\text{ V}$

$v_L = \sqrt{2}(12.5\text{ V})\sin(\omega t + 90°)$

$= 17.7\sin(\omega t + 90°)\text{ V}$

$v_C = \sqrt{2}(5\text{ V})\sin(\omega t - 90°) = 7.07\sin(\omega t - 90°)\text{ V}$

35. a

$$X_L = \frac{E}{I} = \frac{100\text{ V}}{2\text{ A}} = 50\ \Omega \quad \omega L = 50\ \Omega$$

$$\omega = \frac{X_L}{L} = \frac{50\ \Omega}{0.2\text{ H}} = 250\text{ rad/s}$$

$$f = \frac{\omega}{2\pi} = \frac{250\text{ rad/s}}{2\pi} = 39.8\text{ Hz}$$

b.

$$X_C = \frac{E}{I} = \frac{100\text{ V}}{0.4\text{ A}} = 250\ \Omega$$

$$C = \frac{1}{\omega X_C} = \frac{1}{(2\pi)(100\text{ Hz})(250\ \Omega)} = 6.37\ \mu\text{F}$$

16.8 Computer Analysis of ac Circuits

37. From the MultiSIM solution, $I = 0.045\text{ A} = 45\text{ mA}$.

Verification:

$$X_C = \frac{1}{\omega C} = \frac{1}{(2\pi)(60\text{ Hz})(1\ \mu\text{F})} = 2653\ \Omega$$

Thus, $I = \dfrac{120\text{ V}}{2653\ \Omega} = 45.2\text{ mA}$.

39. Use source VAC. Set IPRINT as indicated. Select *AC Sweep*, set *Start* and *End* frequencies to 50Hz, *Points/Decade* to 1, then run the simulation. Scroll the output. The answer is 1.59 A $\angle -90°$.

Verification:

$X_L = \omega L = 62.83\ \Omega$. $\mathbf{I} = \dfrac{100\text{ V}\angle 0°}{j62.83\ \Omega} = 1.59\text{ A}\angle -90°$.

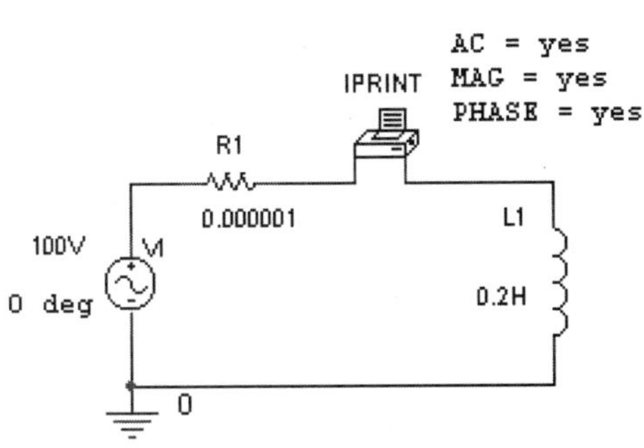

41. Use the circuit of Problem 39, except delete IPRINT, and add a current Marker to monitor inductor current. Select *AC Sweep*, set *Start Frequency* to 1Hz, *End Frequency* to 20Hz, *Total Points* to 100, then run the simulation. With the cursor, measure current at 10 Hz. You should get 7.96 A.

Verification: At 10 Hz, $X_L = 2\pi(10\text{ Hz})(0.2\text{ H}) = 12.57\ \Omega$. Thus, $I = (100\text{ V})/(12.57\ \Omega) = 7.96\text{ A}$

Chapter

17

Power in AC Circuits

17.1 to 17.5 Power to Loads

1. When p_L is positive, power is flowing from the source to the load; when p_L is negative, power is flowing out of the inductor back into the circuit. (This latter happens when the field collapses, returning energy to the circuit.) Between T/4 and $T/2$, power flows out of the inductor.

3. a. $P_1 = \dfrac{V^2}{R_1} = \dfrac{(100\text{ V})^2}{10\ \Omega} = 1000\text{ W} \qquad Q_1 = 0\text{ VAR}$

$P_2 = \dfrac{(100\text{ V})^2}{20\ \Omega} = 500\text{ W} \qquad Q_2 = 0\text{ VAR}$

b. $P_T = P_1 + P_2 = 1500\text{ W} \qquad Q_T = 0\text{ VAR}$

5. $X_c = \dfrac{1}{(377)(40\ \mu\text{F})} = 66.31\ \Omega$

$Q_c = \dfrac{V^2}{X_c} = \dfrac{(100\text{ V})^2}{66.31\ \Omega} = 151\text{ VAR (cap.)}$

7. a. $P = I^2R;\ R = \dfrac{P}{I^2}$

$R = \dfrac{250\text{ W}}{(5\text{ A})^2} = 10\ \Omega$

b. $Q_C = I^2X_C;\ X_C = \dfrac{Q_C}{I^2}$

$X_C = \dfrac{150\text{ VAR}}{(5\text{ A})^2} = 6\ \Omega$

c. $X_C = \dfrac{1}{\omega C}\ \therefore\ C = \dfrac{1}{\omega X_C}$

$C = \dfrac{1}{(2\pi)(100\text{ Hz})(6\ \Omega)} = 265\ \mu\text{F}$

9. $P = \dfrac{V^2}{R}\ \therefore\ V = \sqrt{PR} = \sqrt{(360)(40)} = 120\text{ V}$

$Q_C = \dfrac{V^2}{X_C}\ \therefore\ X_C = \dfrac{V^2}{Q_C} = \dfrac{(120\text{ V})^2}{480\text{ VAR}} = 30\ \Omega$

11. $P = I^2R = (4\text{ A})^2(10\ \Omega) = 160\text{ W}$

$Q_L = I^2X_L = (4\text{ A})^2(40\ \Omega) = 640\text{ VAR (ind.)}$

$Q_C = I^2X_C = (4\text{ A})^2(15\ \Omega) = 240\text{ VAR (cap.)}$

$P_T = P = 160\text{ W}$

$Q_T = Q_L - Q_C = 640 - 240 = 400\text{ VARs (ind.)}$

13. $P_T = P_1 + P_2 + P_3$

$2900\text{ W} = 1200\text{ W} + P_2 + 800\text{ W}\ \therefore\ P_2 = 900\text{ W}$

$Q_T = Q_1 + Q_2 + Q_3$

$1100\text{ VAR} = 1400\text{ VAR} - 600\text{ VAR} + Q_3\ \therefore\ Q_3 = 300\text{ VAR (ind.)}$

15. a. $P = I^2R_T\ \therefore\ R_T = \dfrac{720\text{ W}}{(6\text{ A})^2} = 20\ \Omega$

b. $R_T = 10 + R_2 + 4\ \therefore\ R_2 = 20 - 14 = 6\ \Omega$

c. $Q_T = I^2X_{eq}$

$X_{eq} = \dfrac{Q_T}{I^2} = \dfrac{432\text{ VAR}}{(6\text{ A})^2} = 12\ \Omega$

$X_{eq} = X_L - X_C$

$\therefore\ X_C = X_L - X_{eq} = 20 - 12 = 8\ \Omega$

d. $X_{eq} = \omega L_{eq}$

$\therefore\ L_{eq} = \dfrac{X_{eq}}{\omega} = \dfrac{12\ \Omega}{10\text{ rad/s}} = 1.2\text{ H}$

17.7 The Relationship Between P, Q, and S

17. $S = \sqrt{P^2 + Q^2} = \sqrt{(75\text{ W}^2 + (100\text{ VAR})^2} = 125\ VA$

or $\mathbf{S} = P + jQ = 75\text{ W} + j100\text{ VAR}$

$= 125\text{ VAR}\ \angle 53.1^\circ$

$\therefore\ S = 125\text{ V}$

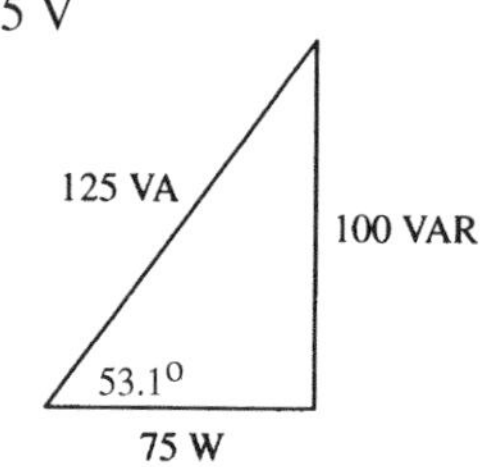

19. $P_T = 100\text{ W} + 300\text{ W} + 10\text{ W} + 40\text{ W} + 700\text{ W} = 1150\text{ W}$

$Q_T = 70\text{ VAR} - 80\text{ VAR} - 60\text{ VAR} = -70\text{ VAR}$

The triangle is shown below: $S = 1152$ VA

1150 W
70 VAR
1152 VA

21. $S_T = VI = (600\text{ V})(30\text{ A}) = 18\ 000\text{ VA}$

$Q_T = 2750\text{ VAR} + 12\ 960\text{ VAR} - 17\ 880\text{ VAR}$

$= -2170\text{ VAR}$

$P_T = \sqrt{S_T^2 - Q_T^2} = \sqrt{(18\ 000)^2 - (2170)^2} = 17\ 869\text{ W}$

$P_R = 17\ 869\text{ W} - 1377\text{ W} - 6915\text{ W} - 7450\text{ W}$

$= 2127\text{ W}$

$$R = \frac{P_R}{I^2} = \frac{2127\text{ W}}{(30\text{ A})^2} = 2.36\ \Omega$$

23. $S_T = 4835\text{ VA}$

$Q_1 = 4608\text{ VAR} - 1912\text{ VAR} = 2696\text{ VAR}$

$P_T = \sqrt{S^2 - Q^2} = 4014\text{ W}$

$P_R = 4014\text{ W} - 1014\text{ W} = 3000\text{ W}$

$$R = \frac{V^2}{P_R} = \frac{(600\text{ V})^2}{3000\text{ W}} = 120\ \Omega$$

17.8 Power Factor

25. a. Load 1:

$\theta = \cos^{-1}(0.8) = 36.9°$

$P_1 = S_1 \cos\theta_1 = (182\text{ VA})(0.8) = 146\text{ W}$

$Q_1 = S_1 \sin\theta_1 = (182\text{ VA}) \sin 36.9° = 109\text{ VAR (ind.)}$

Load 2:

$\theta_2 = \cos^{-1}(0.385) = 67.4°$

$P_2 = S_2 \cos\theta_2 = (772\text{ VA})(0.385) = 297\text{ W}$

$Q_2 = S_2 \sin\theta_2 = 712.5\text{ VAR (cap.)}$

$P_T = 146\text{ W} + 297\text{ W} + 278\text{ W} = 721\text{ W}$

$Q_T = 109\text{ VAR} - 712.5\text{ VAR} + 521\text{ VAR} = -82.5\text{ VAR}$

$S_T = \sqrt{P_T^2 + Q_T^2} = \sqrt{(721)^2 + (82.5)^2} = 726\text{ VA}$

b. $I = \frac{S_T}{V} = \frac{726\text{ VA}}{120\text{ V}} = 6.05\text{ A}$ $\therefore$ Fuse does not blow.

27. a. Connect the capacitor across the load.

b. To correct to unity, you need $Q_C = 10\ 026\text{ VAR}$ (from Problem 26).

$$X_C = \frac{V^2}{Q_C} = \frac{(600\text{ V})^2}{10\ 026\text{ VAR}} = 35.9\ \Omega$$

$$C = \frac{1}{\omega X_C} = \frac{1}{(2\pi)(60\text{ Hz})(35.9\ \Omega)} = 73.9\ \mu\text{F}$$

29. The utility supplies $P = 300 \cos 36° = 242.7$ kW. If corrected to unity, it can supply 300 kW $\therefore$ increase = 57.3 kW.

17.9 AC Power Measurement

31. $P = VI \cos\theta$ where $\theta = 50° - 20° = 30°$

$P = (120\text{ V})(25\text{ A}) \cos 30° = 2598\text{ W}$

17.10 Effective Resistance

33. $$R = \frac{P}{I^2} = \frac{25.6\text{ W}}{(0.4\text{ A})^2} = 160\ \Omega$$

Note that the ohmmeter measures only dc resistance.

17.12 Circuit Analysis Using Computers

35. PSpice waveforms are shown below. Peak power (measured via cursor) is 3.14 W. This can be verified as follows, $X_C = 15.92$ W. Thus, $I_m = \frac{10\text{ V}}{15.92\ \Omega} = 0.628$ A. As indicated in Figure 17-5, peak power is given by the product VI where V and I are the rms values of voltage and current respectively. $V = (0.707)(10\text{ V})$ $= 7.07$ V and $I = (0.707)(0.628\text{ A})$ $= 0.444$ A. Thus, the peak value is $(7.07\text{ V})(0.444\text{ A}) = 3.14$ W, the same as obtained by PSpice.

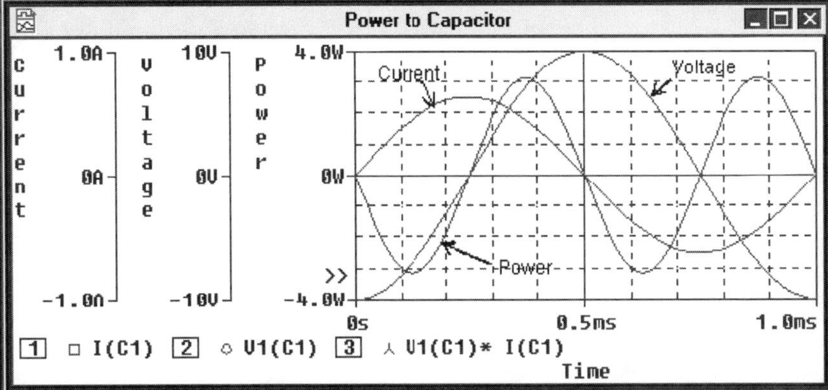

37. a. Voltage across the inductor is given by $v_L = L\frac{di}{dt}$ where $\frac{di}{dt}$ is the slope of the current versus time curve. Between $t = 0$ and $t = 1$ ms, the slope of the current waveform is (2 A)/(1 ms) = 2000 A/s. Voltage is thus $L\frac{di}{dt}$ = (2 mH)(2000 A/s) = 4 V. Similarly, between $t = 1$ ms and $t = 3$ ms, inductor voltage is –4 V, etc. Voltage and current are plotted below, and power (their product, obtained by point by point multiplication) is also shown. Note that power is a saw-tooth wave that oscillates between –8 W and 8 W.

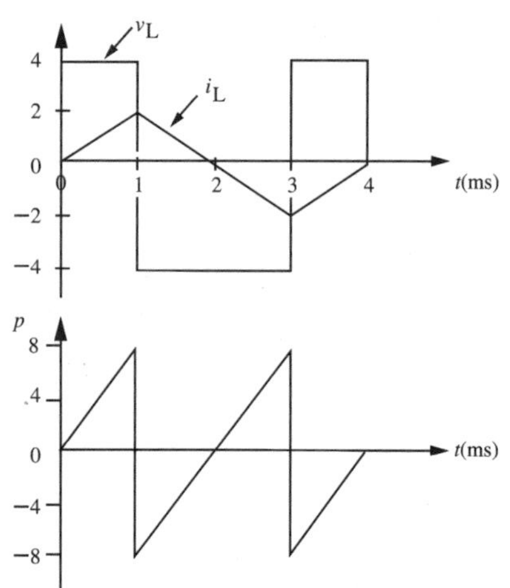

b. The PSpice solution is shown below. Use current source IPWL. It permits you to describe the waveform as straight-line segments. Note however, PSpice descriptions and measurements are based on current into devices, not out. Thus, you must invert the given waveform. To describe the waveform, double click the current source symbol, and in the *Properties Editor*, enter time and current values as follows: $T_1 = 0$, $I_1 = 0$, $T_2 = 1$ms, $I_2 = -2$A, $T_3 =$ 3ms, $I_3 = 2$A and $T_4 = 4$ms, $I_4 = 0$A, then click *Apply*. (PSpice joins the above points via straight lines to create the waveform.) Perform a transient analysis with a TSTOP value of 4ms. Plot voltage, current and power. (Power is the product of the inductor voltage and current as indicated by the PSpice waveform shown.) Note only power is shown here to avoid the clutter of too many waveforms which are hard to see when not in color. Notice the exact agreement with the manual calculation of (a).

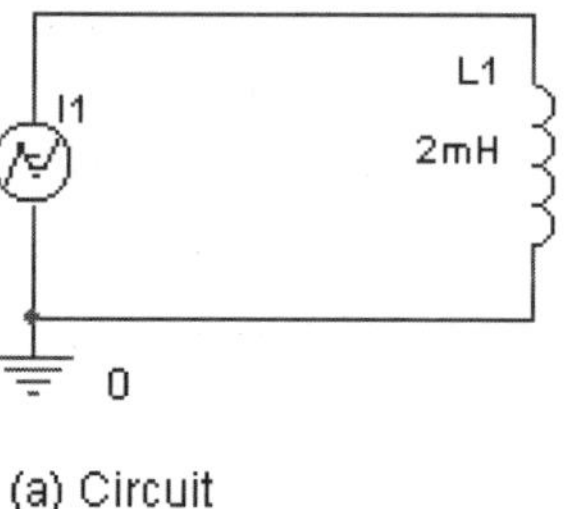

(a) Circuit

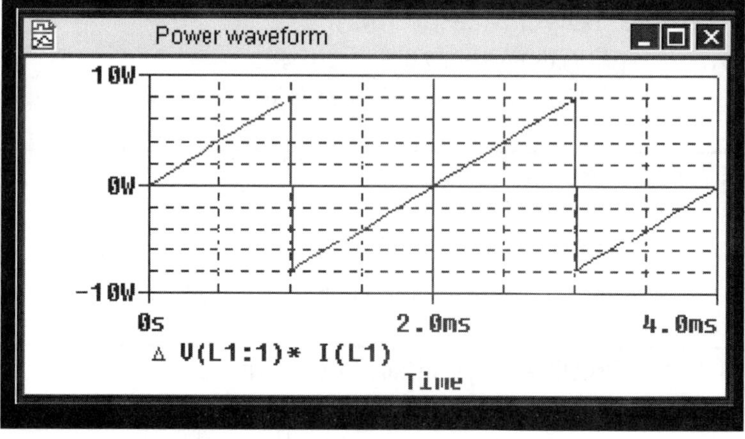

(b) Power waveform

Chapter

18

AC Series-Parallel Circuits

18.1 Ohm's Law for ac Circuits

1. a. $\mathbf{V} = \frac{25}{\sqrt{2}}\angle 0° = 17.68V\angle 0°$

$\mathbf{I} = \frac{17.68\ \text{V}\angle 0°}{200\ \Omega\angle 0°} = 0.0884\ \text{A}\angle 0°$

$i = (0.0884)(\sqrt{2})\sin(\omega t + 0°) = 0.125\ \sin\omega t$

b.

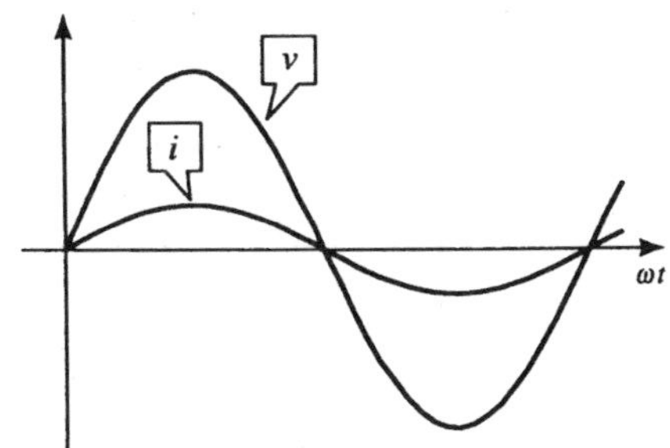

c.

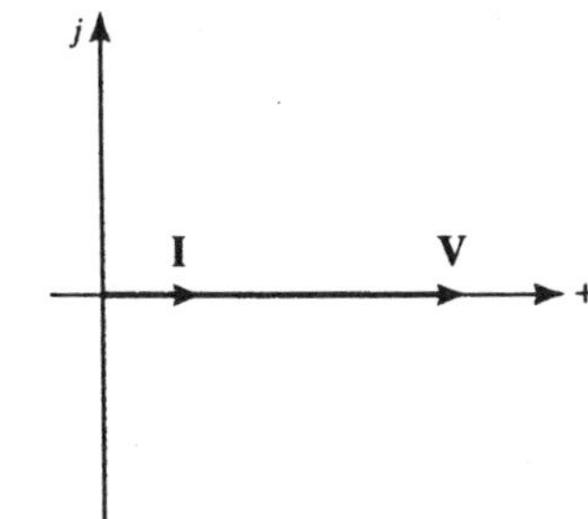

3. a. $\mathbf{I} = \frac{62\ \text{V}\ \angle 30°}{47\ \text{k}\Omega\angle 0°} = 1.319\ \text{mA}\angle 30°$

$i = 1.866 \times 10^{-3}\ \sin(\omega\text{t} + 30°)$

b.

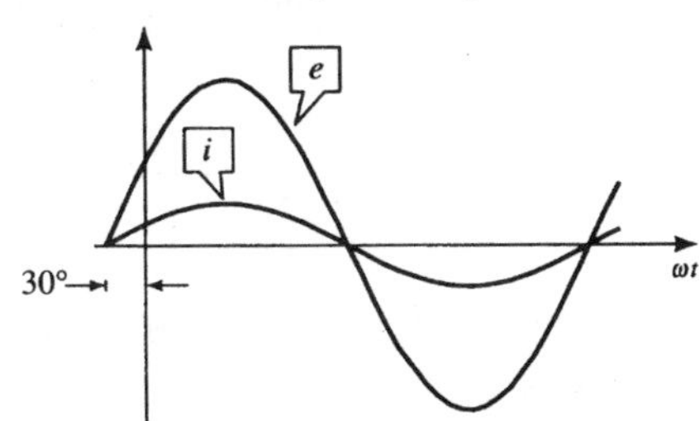

c.

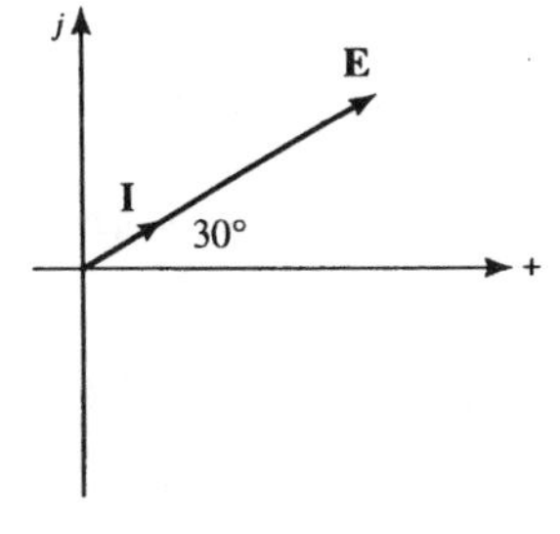

5. a. $\mathbf{I} = \frac{2.0 \times 10^{-3}}{\sqrt{2}}\ \angle 0° = 1.414\ \text{mA}\angle 0°$

$\mathbf{V} = \mathbf{IZ}_C = (1.414\ \text{mA}\angle 0°)(680\ \Omega\angle -90°)$
$= 0.962\ \text{V}\ \angle -90°$

$v = (0.962)(\sqrt{2})\sin(\omega t - 90°) = 1.36\ \sin(\omega t - 90°)$

b.

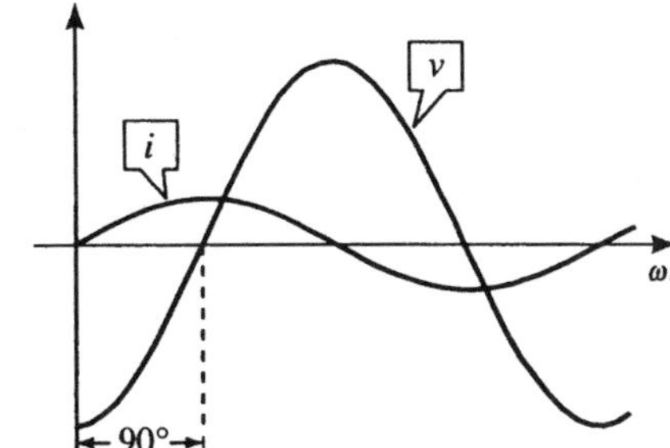

c.

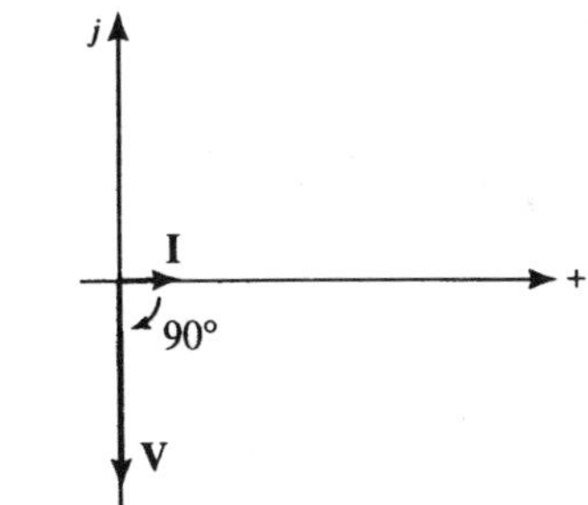

7. a. $X_L = 2\pi fL = 2\pi(1\ \text{kHz})(30\ \text{mH}) = 188.5\ \Omega$

$\mathbf{V} = (5\ \text{A}\angle -60°)(188.5\ \Omega\angle 90°) = 942\ \text{V}\ \angle 30°$

$v = (942)(\sqrt{2})\sin(2000\pi t + 30°)$
$= 1333\ \sin(2000\pi t + 30°)$

b.

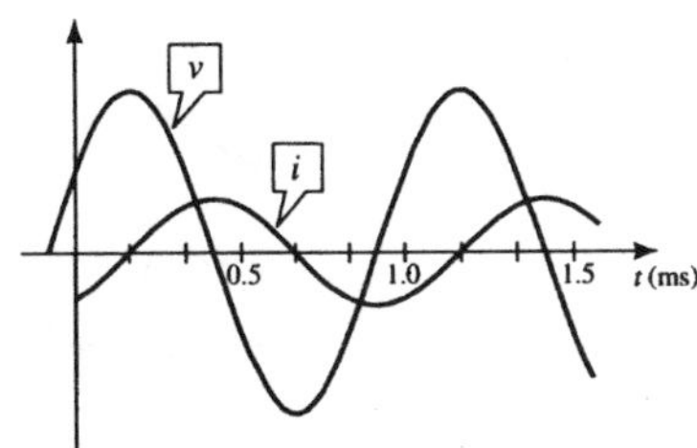

c.

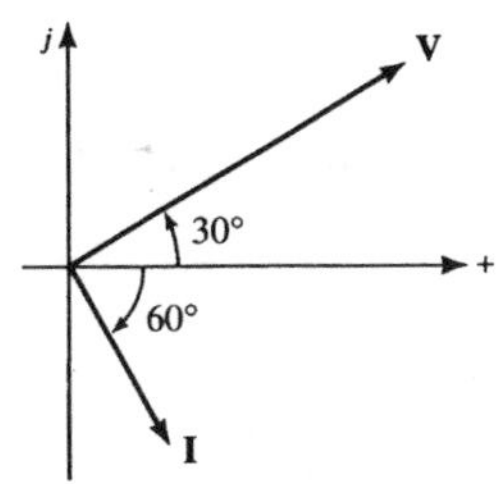

9. a. $\omega = 10\ 000$ rad/s

$$X_C = \frac{1}{(0.01\ \mu\text{F})(10\ \text{krad/s}} = 10\ \text{k}\Omega$$

$$\mathbf{I} = \frac{6.25 \times 10^{-3}}{\sqrt{2}} = 4.42\ \text{mA}\angle -0^\circ$$

$$\mathbf{V} = (4.42\ ma\ \angle 0^\circ)(10\ \text{k}\Omega\angle -90^\circ) = 44.2\ \text{V}\ \angle -90^\circ)$$

$$v = (44.2)(\sqrt{2})\sin(10\ 000t - 90^\circ)$$

b. 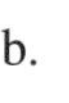

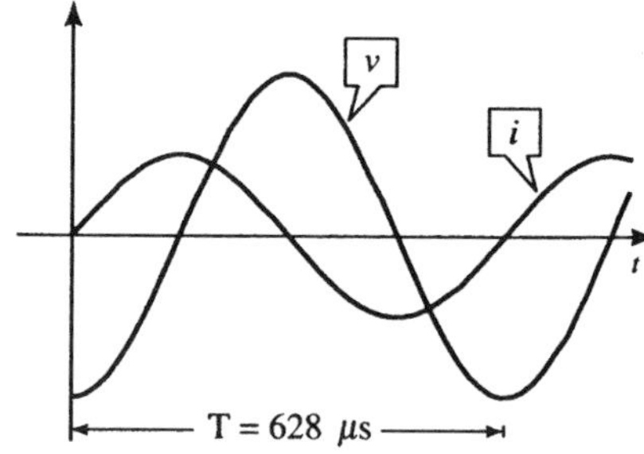

c.

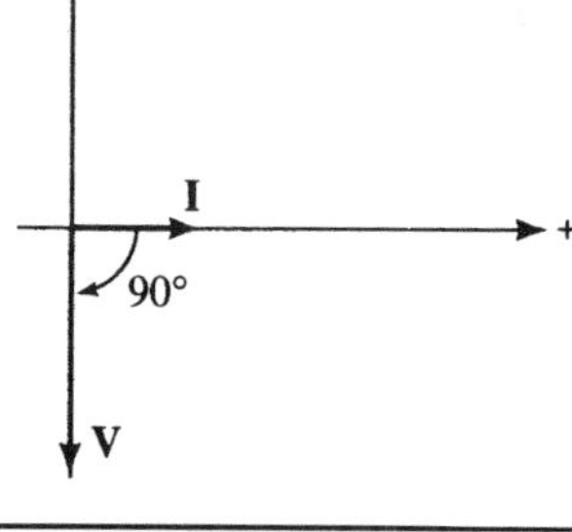

11. a. $i = 22.5 \times 10^{-3}\cos(20\ 000t + 20^\circ)$

$= 22.5 \times 10^{-3}\sin(20\ 000t + 110^\circ)$

$$\mathbf{I} = \frac{22.5}{\sqrt{2}}\ \text{mA}\angle 110^\circ = 15.91\ \text{mA}\angle 110^\circ$$

$X_L = (20\ \text{krad/s})(150\ \text{mH}) = 3\text{k}\Omega$

$\mathbf{V} = (15.91\ \text{mA}\angle 110^\circ)(3\ \text{k}\Omega\angle 90^\circ) = 47.7\ \text{V}\ \angle 200^\circ$
$= 47.7\ \text{V}\ \angle -160^\circ$

$v = (47.7)(\sqrt{2})\sin(20\ 000t - 160^\circ)$

b.

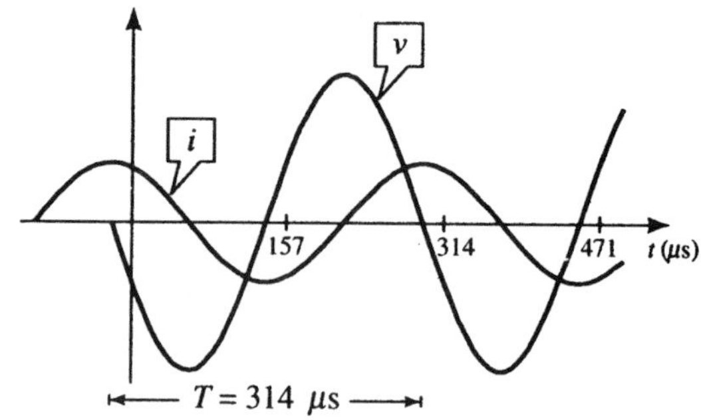

8.2 AC Series Circuit

13. Network a:

$\mathbf{Z}_T = 30\ \Omega - j25\ \Omega + j35\ \Omega = 30\ \Omega + j10\ \Omega$
$= 31.6\ \Omega\angle 18.43^\circ$

Network b:

$\mathbf{Z}_T = 3\ \text{k}\Omega - j1.5\ \text{k}\Omega + j3.3\ \text{k}\Omega + 4.2\ \text{k}\Omega - j5.9\ \text{k}\Omega$
$= 7.2\ \text{kW} - j4.1\ \text{k}\Omega = 8.29\ \text{k}\Omega\angle -29.66^\circ$

15. a. $\mathbf{Z} = (100\ \Omega\angle 30^\circ) - (47\ \Omega + j36\ \Omega)$

$= 39.2\ \Omega + j14\ \Omega = 42.0\ \Omega\angle 19.47^\circ$

b.

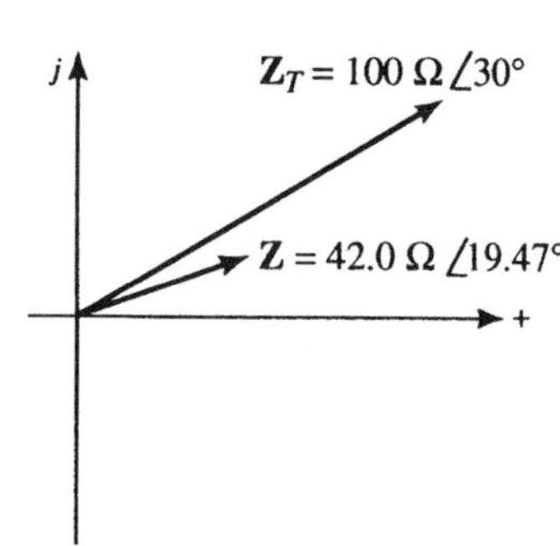

17. $\mathbf{Z}_T = 2\ \text{k}\Omega\angle 15^\circ = 1.932\ \text{k}\Omega + j0.518\ \text{k}\Omega$

$R = 1.932\ \text{k}\Omega$

$X_L = 0.518\ \text{k}\Omega = 518\ \Omega$

$$L = \frac{518\ \Omega}{2\pi(18\ \text{kHz})} = 4.58\ \text{mH}$$

19. $X_L = (2\pi)(1000\ \text{Hz})(20\ \text{mH}) = 125.7\ \Omega$

$\mathbf{Z} = (50\ \Omega\angle 60^\circ) - j125.7\ \Omega - 10\ \Omega$

$= 15\ \Omega - j82.36\ \Omega$

$R = 15\ \Omega$

$$X_C = 82.36\ \Omega\quad C = \frac{1}{(2\pi)(1000\ \text{Hz})(82.4\ \Omega)}$$

$= 1.93\ \mu\text{F}$

21. a. $\mathbf{Z}_T = j20\ \Omega - j50\ \Omega + 40\ \Omega = 40\ \Omega - j30\ \Omega$

$= 50\ \Omega\angle -36.87^\circ$

$$\mathbf{I} = \frac{120\ \text{V}\angle 0^\circ}{50\ \Omega\angle -36.87^\circ} = 2.4\ \text{A}\angle 36.87^\circ$$

$\mathbf{V}_R = (2.4\ \text{A}\angle 36.87^\circ)(40\ \Omega\angle 0^\circ) = 96\ \text{V}\ \angle 36.87^\circ$

$\mathbf{V}_L = (2.4\ \text{A}\angle 36.87^\circ)(20\ \Omega\angle 90^\circ) = 48\ \text{V}\ \angle 126.87^\circ$

$\mathbf{V}_C = (2.4\ \text{A}\angle 36.87^\circ)(50\ \Omega\angle -90^\circ)$

$= 120\ \text{V}\ \angle -53.13^\circ$

b.

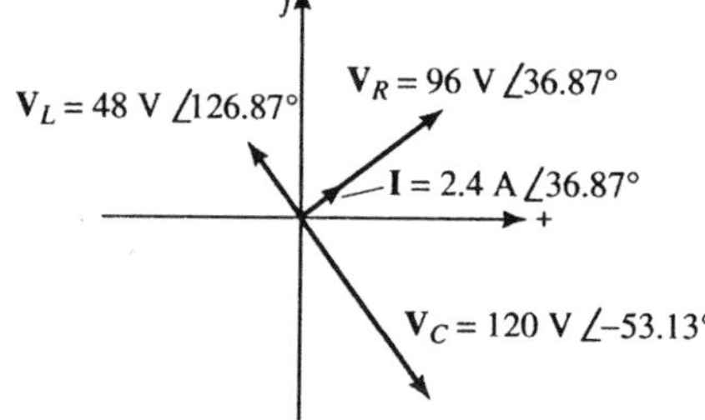

c. $P_R = (2.4\text{ A})^2(40\ \Omega) = 230.4\text{ W}$

d. $P_T = (120\text{ V})(2.4\text{ A})(\cos 36.87^\circ)$

$= 230.4\text{ W}$ (as required)

23. a. $\mathbf{Z}_T = -j47\ \Omega + 36\ \Omega + j20\ \Omega = 36\ \Omega - j27\ \Omega$

$= 45\ \Omega\angle -36.87^\circ$

b. $$\mathbf{E} = \frac{24\text{ V}}{\sqrt{2}} = 16.97\text{ V}\angle 0^\circ$$

$$\mathbf{I} = \frac{16.27\ V\angle 0^\circ}{45\ \Omega\angle -36.87^\circ} = 0.377\text{ A}\angle 36.87^\circ$$

$\mathbf{V}_R = 13.58\text{ V}\angle 36.87^\circ$

$\mathbf{V}_L = 7.54\text{ V}\angle 128.87^\circ$

$\mathbf{V}_C = 17.72\text{ V}\angle -53.13^\circ$

$i = 0.533\sin(\omega t + 36.87^\circ)$

$v_R = 19.20\sin(\omega t + 36.87^\circ)$

$v_L = 10.67\sin(\omega t + 126.87^\circ)$

$v_C = 25.1\sin(\omega t - 53.13^\circ)$

c.

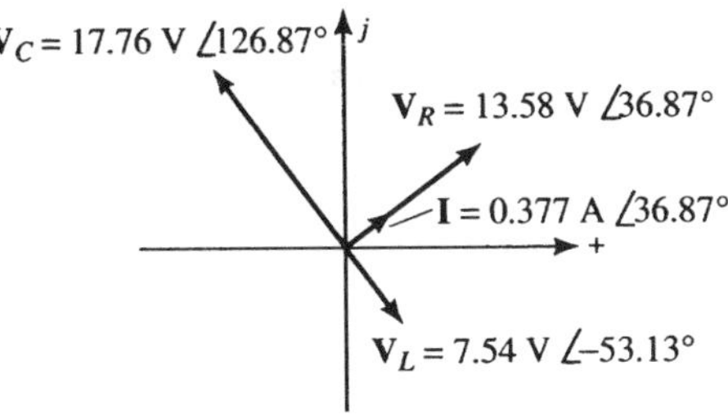

d.

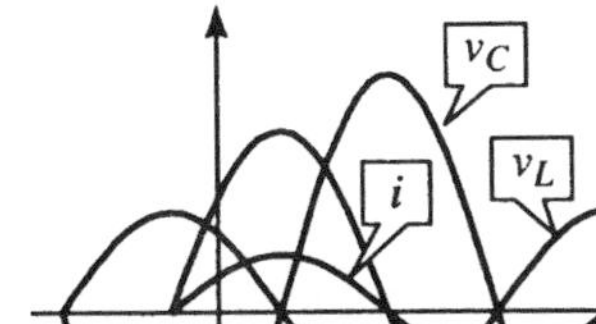

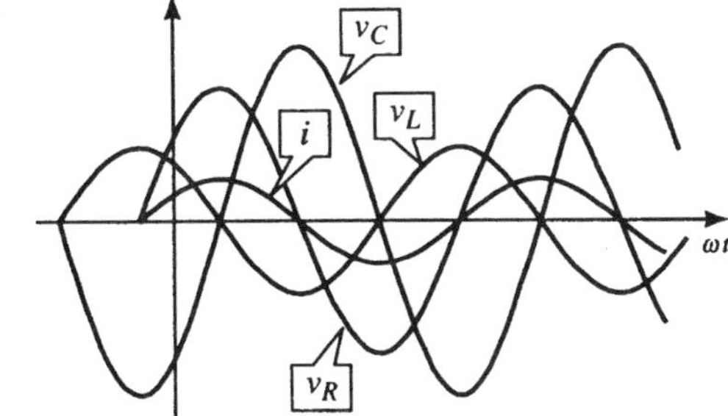

e. $P_R = I^2R = (0.377\text{ A})^2(36\ \Omega) = 5.12\text{ W}$

f. $P_T = (16.97\text{ V})(0.377\text{ A})(\cos 36.87^\circ) = 5.12\text{ W}$ (as in Part **e.**)

18.3 Kirchhoff's Voltage Law and the Voltage Divider Rule

25. network (a)

a. $$\mathbf{V}_R = \left(\frac{30\ \Omega}{30\ \Omega - j25\ \Omega + j35\ \Omega}\right)(10\text{ V}\angle 0^\circ)$$
$= 9.49\text{ V}\angle -18.43^\circ$

$$\mathbf{V}_L = \left(\frac{j35\ \Omega}{30\ \Omega - j25\ \Omega + j35\ \Omega}\right)(10\text{ V}\angle 0^\circ)$$
$= 11.07\text{ V}\angle 71.57^\circ$

$$\mathbf{V}_C = \left(\frac{-j25\ \Omega}{30\ \Omega - j25\ \Omega + j35\ \Omega}\right)(10\text{ V}\angle 0^\circ)$$
$= 7.91\text{ V}\angle -108.43^\circ$

b. $\Sigma\mathbf{V} = 9.49\text{ V}\angle -18.43^\circ + 11.07\text{ V}\angle 71.57^\circ +$
$7.91\text{ V}\angle -108.43^\circ = 10.0\text{ V}\angle 0^\circ = \mathbf{E}$

27. a. $\mathbf{V}_C + \mathbf{V}_L = 250\text{ V}\angle 0^\circ - 125\text{ V}\angle 60^\circ$
$= 216\text{ V}\angle -30^\circ$

$$\mathbf{V}_C = \left(\frac{-j63.3\ \Omega}{-j63.3\ \Omega + j20\ \Omega}\right)(216\text{ V}\angle -30^\circ)$$
$= 317\text{ V}\angle -30^\circ$

$$\mathbf{V}_L = \left(\frac{+j20\ \Omega}{-j63.3\ \Omega + j20\ \Omega}\right)(216\text{ V}\angle -30^\circ)$$
$= 99.8\text{ V}\angle 150^\circ$

b. $$\mathbf{I} = \frac{99.8\text{ V}\angle 150^\circ}{20\ \Omega\angle 90^\circ} = 5.0\text{ A}\angle 60^\circ$$

$$R = \frac{250\text{ V}}{5.0\text{ A}} = 25\ \Omega$$

29. a. $$\mathbf{I} = \frac{4\text{ V}\angle -20^\circ}{20\ \Omega} = 0.20\text{ A}\angle -20^\circ$$

$\mathbf{V}_C = (0.20\text{ A}\angle -20^\circ)(30\ \Omega\angle -90^\circ)$
$= 6.0\text{ V}\angle -110^\circ$

b. $\mathbf{V}_Z = 10\text{ V}\angle 30^\circ - 4\text{ V}\angle -20^\circ - 6\text{ V}\angle -110^\circ$
$= 13.87\text{ V}\angle 59.92^\circ$

c. $$\mathbf{Z} = \frac{13.87\text{ V}\angle 59.92^\circ}{0.2\text{ A}\angle -20^\circ} = 69.4\ \Omega\angle 79.92^\circ$$
$= 12.14\ \Omega + j68.3\ \Omega$

d. $P_T = I^2R_T = (0.20\text{ A})^2(20\ \Omega + 12.14\ \Omega)$
$= 1.286\text{ W}$

or

$P_T = EI\cos\theta = (10\text{ V})(0.2\text{ A})\cos 50^\circ = 1.286\text{ W}$

18.4 AC Parallel Circuits

31. network (a)

$$\mathbf{Y}_T = \frac{1}{200\ \Omega} + \frac{1}{j500\ \Omega} + \frac{1}{-j460\ \Omega} = 0.005\text{ S}\angle 1.99^\circ$$

$\mathbf{Z}_T = 199.9\ \Omega\angle -1.99^\circ$

network (b)

$$\mathbf{Y}_T = \frac{1}{500\ \Omega} + \frac{1}{-j3\text{ k}\Omega} + \frac{1}{-j6\text{ k}\Omega} = 2.06\text{ mS}\angle 14.04^\circ$$

$\mathbf{Z}_T = 485\ \Omega\angle -14.04^\circ = 470.6\ \Omega - j117.65\ \Omega$

33. a. $\mathbf{Y}_T = \dfrac{1}{200\Omega} + \dfrac{1}{j500\ \Omega} + \dfrac{1}{-j0.8\ k\Omega} = 255\ \mu S\angle 78.69^\circ$

$\mathbf{Z}_T = 3922\ \Omega\angle -78.69$

$\mathbf{I}_T = \dfrac{10\ V\angle 0^\circ}{3.922\ k\Omega\angle -78.69^\circ} = 2.55 mA\angle 78.69^\circ$

$\mathbf{I}_1 = \dfrac{10\ V\angle 0^\circ}{20\ k\Omega} = 0.5\ mA\angle 0^\circ$

$\mathbf{I}_2 = \dfrac{10\ V\angle -0^\circ}{1k\Omega\angle 90^\circ} = 10\ mA\angle -90^\circ$

$I_3 = \dfrac{10\ V\angle 0^\circ}{0.8\ k\Omega\angle -90^\circ} = 12.5\ mA\angle 90^\circ$

b.

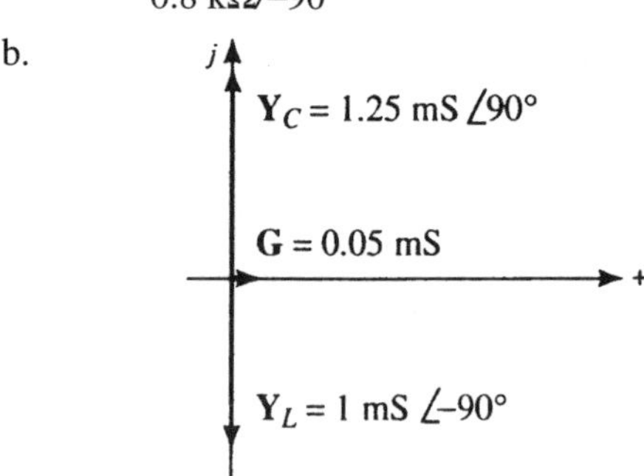

c.

j

$\mathbf{I}_3 = 12.5$ mA ∠90°

$\mathbf{I}_1 = 0.5$ mA

+

$\mathbf{E} = 10$ V ∠0°

$\mathbf{I}_2 = 10$ mA ∠–90°

d. $P_R = \dfrac{(10\ V)^2}{20\ k\Omega} = 5.00\ mW$

e. $F_P = \cos 78.69^\circ = 0.1961$ leading

$P_T = (10\ V)(2.55\ mA)(0.1961)$

$= 5.00$ mW (same as Part **d.**)

35. a. $\mathbf{Y}_T = \dfrac{1}{(3\ k\Omega + j4\ k\Omega)} + \dfrac{1}{(6\ k\Omega - j8\ k\Omega)}$

$= 197.0\ \mu S \angle -23.96^\circ$

$\mathbf{Z}_T = 5.08\ k\Omega\angle 23.96^\circ$

b. $\mathbf{V} = (30\ mA\ \angle 0^\circ)(5.08\ k\Omega\angle 23.96^\circ)$

$= 152.3\ V\ \angle 23.96^\circ)$

37. $\mathbf{Y}_T = \mathbf{Y}_1 + \mathbf{Y}_2$

$\mathbf{Y}_2 = \mathbf{Y}_T - \mathbf{Y}_1$

$= \dfrac{1}{4\ \Omega\angle 60^\circ} - \dfrac{1}{2\ \Omega - j5\ \Omega} = 0.3929\ S\ \angle -81.80^\circ$

$\mathbf{Z}_2 = 2.545\ \Omega\ \angle 81.80^\circ = 0.3629\ \Omega + j2.5189\ \Omega$

18.5 Kirchhoff's Current Law and the Current Divider Rule

39. network (a)

$\mathbf{I}_R = \left(\dfrac{199.9\ \Omega\angle -1.992^\circ}{200\ \Omega\angle 0^\circ}\right)(10\ mA\ \angle -30^\circ)$

$= 9.995\ mA\ \angle -31.99^\circ$

$\mathbf{I}_L = \left(\dfrac{199.9\ \Omega\angle -1.992^\circ}{500\ \Omega\angle 90^\circ}\right)(10\ mA\ \angle -30^\circ)$

$= 3.998\ mA\ \angle -121.99^\circ$

$I_C = \left(\dfrac{199.9\ \Omega\ \angle -1.992^\circ}{460\ \Omega\angle -90^\circ}\right)(10\ mA\ \angle -30^\circ)$

$= 4.346\ mA\ \angle 58.01^\circ$

network (b)

$\mathbf{I}_R = \left(\dfrac{485\ \Omega\angle -14.04^\circ}{500\ \Omega}\right)(10\ mA\angle -30^\circ)$

$= 9.70\ mA\ \angle -44.04^\circ$

$\mathbf{I}_{C1} = \left(\dfrac{485\ \Omega\angle -14.04^\circ}{3\ \Omega - 90^\circ}\right)(10\ mA\angle -30^\circ)$

$= 1.617\ mA\ \angle 45.96^\circ$

$\mathbf{I}_{C2} = \left(\dfrac{485\ \Omega\angle -14.04^\circ}{6\ k\Omega\angle -90^\circ}\right)(10\ mA\angle -30^\circ)$

$= 0.808\ mA\ \angle 45.96^\circ$

41. $\mathbf{Y}_T = 70.71\ \mu S\angle 45^\circ$

$\mathbf{Z}_T = 14.14\ k\Omega\angle -45^\circ$

$\mathbf{I}_L = \left(\dfrac{14.14\ k\Omega\angle -45^\circ}{5\ k\Omega\angle 90^\circ}\right)(1\ mA\angle 0^\circ)$

$= 2.83 mA\angle -135^\circ$

$\mathbf{I}_C = 3.54\ mA\angle 45^\circ$

$\mathbf{I}_R = 0.707\ mA\angle -45^\circ$

$\Sigma \mathbf{I}_{out} = 2.83\ mA\angle -135^\circ + 3.54\ mA\angle 45^\circ +$
$0.070\ mA\angle -45^\circ = 1.00\ mA\angle 0^\circ = \Sigma \mathbf{I}_{in}$

43. a. $\mathbf{I} = \mathbf{I}_L + \mathbf{I}_R$

$8\ A\angle\theta = 5\ A\angle 0^\circ + \mathbf{I}_R$

$\mathbf{V}_R = \mathbf{V}_L = (5\ A\angle 0^\circ)(50\ \Omega\angle 90^\circ) = 250\ V\ \angle 90^\circ$

We know that $\mathbf{V}_R$ is in phase with $\mathbf{I}_R$, and so $\mathbf{I}_R$ has a phase angle of 90°.

However, $8\ A = \sqrt{(5\ A)^2 + (I_R)^2}$

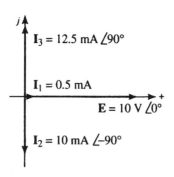

$I_R = \sqrt{64 - 25} = 6.245$ A
$\mathbf{I}_R = 6.245$ A$\angle 90°$.

b. $R = \dfrac{250 \text{ V}\angle 90°}{6.245 \text{ A}\angle 90°} = 40.03\ \Omega$

c. $\mathbf{I} = 5 \text{ A}\angle 0° + 6.245 \text{ A}\angle 90° = 8.00 \text{ A}\angle 51.32°$

18.6 Series-Parallel Circuits

45. a. $\mathbf{Z}_T = j5\ \Omega + (-j30\ \Omega)\|(60\ \Omega)$
$= j5\ \Omega + (12\ \Omega + j24\ OMEGA)$
$= 12\ \Omega + j29\ \Omega = 31.38\ \Omega\angle 67.52°$

$\mathbf{I}_L = \dfrac{120 \text{ V}\angle 0°}{31.38\ \Omega\angle 67.52°} = 3.824 \text{ A}\angle -67.52°$

$\mathbf{I}_C = \left(\dfrac{60\ \Omega}{60\ \Omega - j30\ \Omega}\right)(3.824 \text{ A}\angle -67.52°)$
$= 3.4119 \text{ A}\angle -40.96°$

$\mathbf{I}_R = \left(\dfrac{-j30\ \Omega}{-j30\ \Omega + 60\ \Omega}\right)(3.824 \text{ A}\angle -67.52°)$
$= 1.710 \text{ A}\angle -130.96°$

b.

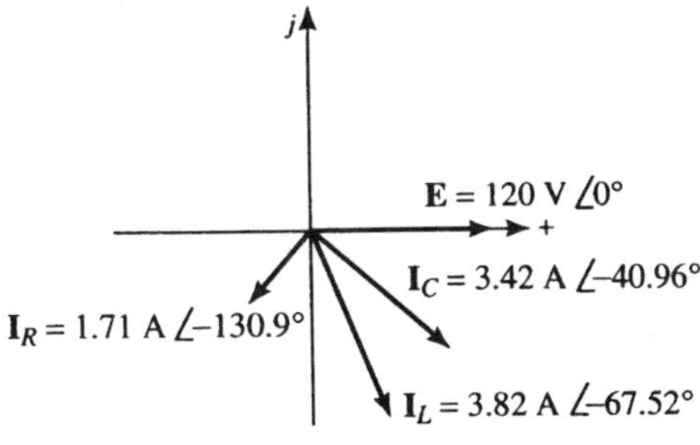

c. $P_R = (1.7099 \text{ A})^2(60\ \Omega) = 175.4$ W

d. $P_T = (120 \text{ V})(3.824 \text{ A})(\cos 67.52°) = 175.4$ W (as required)

47. a. $\mathbf{Z}_T = 3\ \Omega + (2\ \Omega + j6\ \Omega)\|(4\ \Omega - j6\ \Omega)$
$= 3\ \Omega + 7.\bar{3}\ \Omega + j2\ \Omega = 10.\bar{3}\ \Omega + j2\ \Omega$
$= 10.53\ \Omega\angle 10.95°$

$\mathbf{I}_T = \dfrac{20 \text{ V}\angle 0°}{10.53\ \Omega\angle 10.95°} = 1.900 \text{ A}\angle -10.95°$

$\mathbf{I}_1 = \left(\dfrac{7.\bar{3}\ \Omega + j2\ \Omega}{2\ \Omega + j6\ \Omega}\right)(1.900 \text{ A} - 10.95°)$
$= 2.28 \text{ A}\angle -67.26°$

$\mathbf{I}_2 = \left(\dfrac{7.\bar{3}\ \Omega + j2\ \Omega}{(4\ \Omega - j6\ \Omega}\right)(1.900 \text{ A}\angle -10.95°)$
$= 2.00 \text{ A}\angle +60.61°$

b. $\mathbf{V}_{ab} = -(j6\ \Omega)(2.28 \text{ A}\angle -67.26°) +$
$(4\ \Omega)(2.00 \text{ A}\angle 60.61°) = 8.87 \text{ V}\ \angle 169.06°$

49. a. $\mathbf{Y}_T = \dfrac{1}{10 \text{ k}\Omega} + \dfrac{1}{-j10 \text{ k}\Omega} + \dfrac{1}{3 \text{ k}\Omega + j9 \text{ k}\Omega}$
$= 0.133 \text{ mS}+j0$

$\mathbf{Z}_T = 7.5\ \text{k}\Omega$

$\mathbf{I}_1 = \left(\dfrac{7.5 \text{ k}\Omega}{10 \text{ k}\Omega}\right)(1 \text{ mA}\angle 0°) = 0.75 \text{ mA}\angle 0°$

$\mathbf{I}_2 = \left(\dfrac{7.5 \text{ k}\Omega}{-j10 \text{ k}\Omega}\right)(1 \text{ mA}\angle 0°) = 0.7906 \text{ mA}\angle -71.57°$

$\mathbf{I}_3 = \left(\dfrac{7.5 \text{ k}\Omega}{3 \text{ k}\Omega = j9 \text{ k}\Omega}\right)(1 \text{ mA}\ \angle 0°) = 0.7906 \text{ mA}\angle -71.57°$

b. $\mathbf{V} = -(0.7906 \text{ mA}\angle -71.57°) = (9 \text{ k}\Omega\angle\ 90°$
$= 7.12 \text{ V}\ \angle -161.57°$

18.7 Frequency Effects

51. $\omega_C = \dfrac{1}{(50 \text{ k}\Omega)(0.01\ \mu\text{F})} = 2000$ rad/s

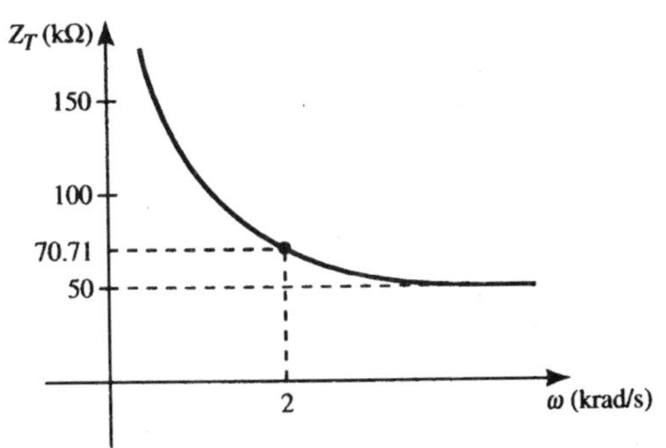

53. $\omega_C = \dfrac{1}{(100 \text{ k}\Omega)(0.47\ \mu\text{F})} = 21.277$ rad/s

$f_C = \dfrac{21.277 \text{ rad/s}}{2\pi \text{ rad}} = 3.39$ Hz

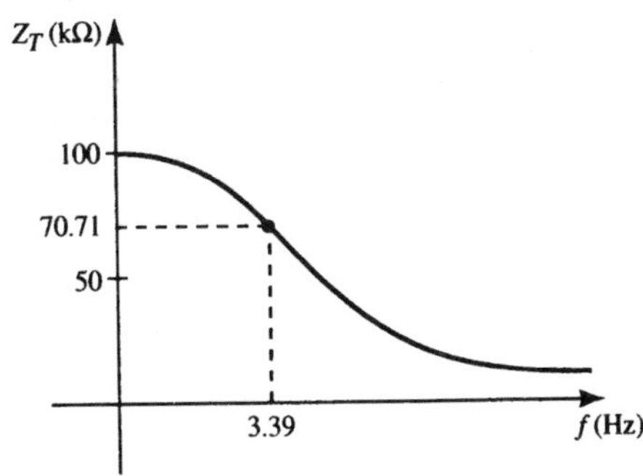

18.8 Applications

55. network (a)

$\mathbf{Z}_T = 2.5\text{ k}\Omega + 30\text{k}\Omega \| j10\text{ k}\Omega$

$= 2.5\text{ k}\Omega + 9.487\text{ k}\Omega\angle 71{,}57°$

$= 10.55\text{ k}\Omega\angle 58.57°$

$= 5.5\text{ k}\Omega + j9.0\text{ k}\Omega$

5.5 kΩ j9.0 kΩ

network (b)

$$\mathbf{Y}_T = \frac{1}{270\ \Omega - j90\ \Omega} + \frac{1}{j300\ \Omega}$$

$= 0.00\overline{3}\text{ S} - j0.00\overline{2}\text{ S}$

$\mathbf{Z}_T = 207.7\ \Omega + j138.5\ \Omega$

207.7 kΩ j138.5 kΩ

57. at $\omega = 1$ krad/s: $X_L = 100\ \Omega$

$X_C = 10\ \Omega$

$$\mathbf{Y}_T = \frac{1}{100\ \Omega - j100\ \Omega} + \frac{1}{100\ \Omega + j100\ \Omega}$$

$= (0.005\text{ S} + j0.005\text{ S}) + (0.005\text{ S} - j0.005\text{ S})$

$= 0.01\text{ S}$

$\mathbf{Z}_T = 100\ \Omega$

at $\omega = 10$ krad/s: $X_L = 1000\ \Omega$

$X_C = 10\ \Omega$

$$\mathbf{Y}_T = \frac{1}{(100\ \Omega - j10\ \Omega)} + \frac{1}{(100\ \Omega + j1000\ \Omega)}$$

$= (0.009\overline{900}\text{ S} + j0.000\overline{9900}\text{ S}) + (0.0000\overline{9900}\text{ S} -$
$-j0.000\overline{9900}\text{ S})$

$= 0.01\text{ S}$

$\mathbf{Z}_T = 100\ \Omega$

18.9 Circuit Analysis Using Computers

59.

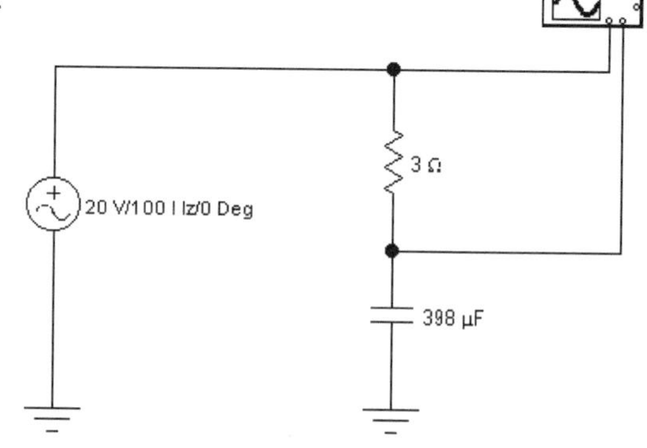

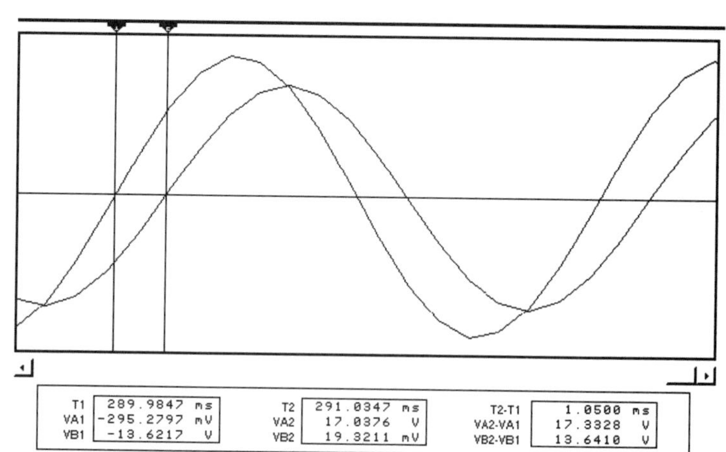

$v_C = 22.5\text{ V}_p$ (capacitor voltage)

$$\theta = \left(\frac{1.05\text{ms}}{10\text{ms}}\right)360° = -37.8°$$

$$\mathbf{V}_C = \frac{22.5\text{V}}{\sqrt{2}}\angle -37.8° = 15.9\text{V}\angle -37.8°$$

b.

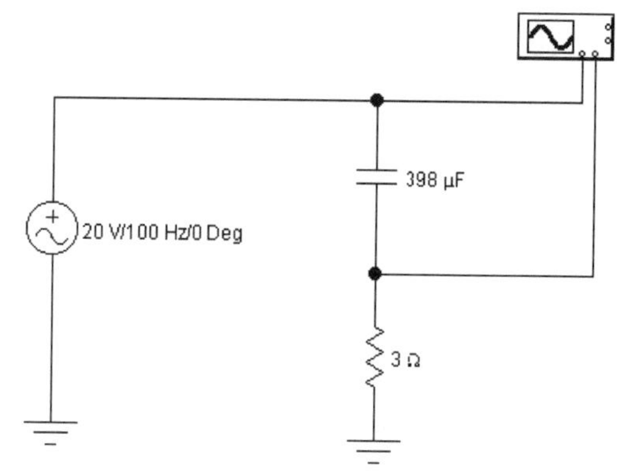

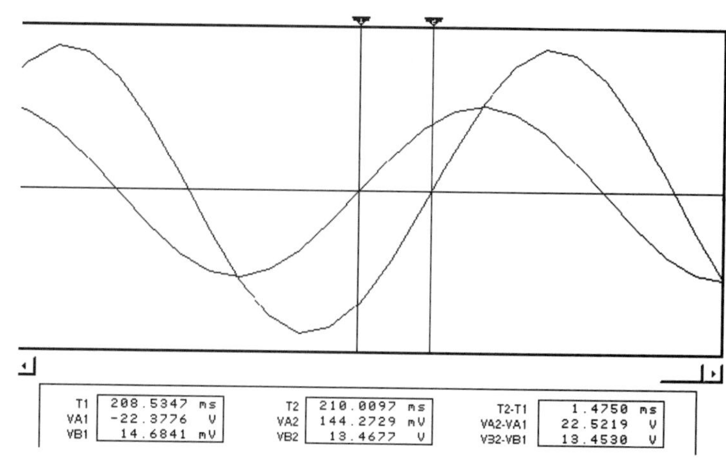

$v_R = 17.11\ V_p$ (resistor voltage)

$$\theta = +\left(\frac{1.475\ \text{ms}}{10\text{ms}}\right)360^\circ = 53.1^\circ$$

$$\mathbf{V}_R = \frac{17.11\text{V}}{\sqrt{2}}\angle 53.1^\circ = 12.1\text{V}\angle 53.1^\circ$$

$$\mathbf{I} = \frac{12.1\text{V}\angle 53.1^\circ}{3\Omega} = 4.03\text{A}\angle 53.1^\circ$$

c. These results are consistent with those in Example 18-8.

61.

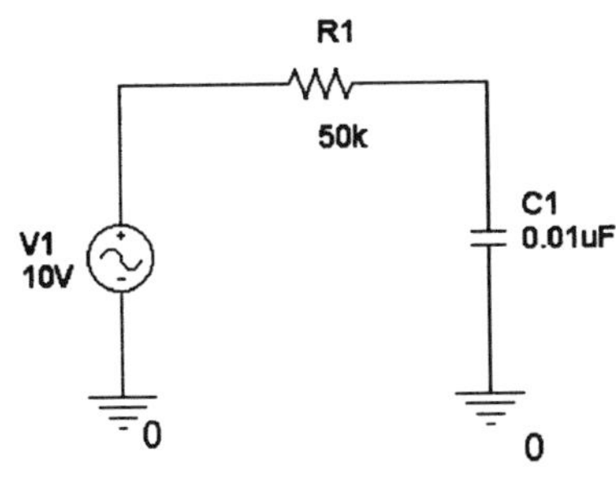

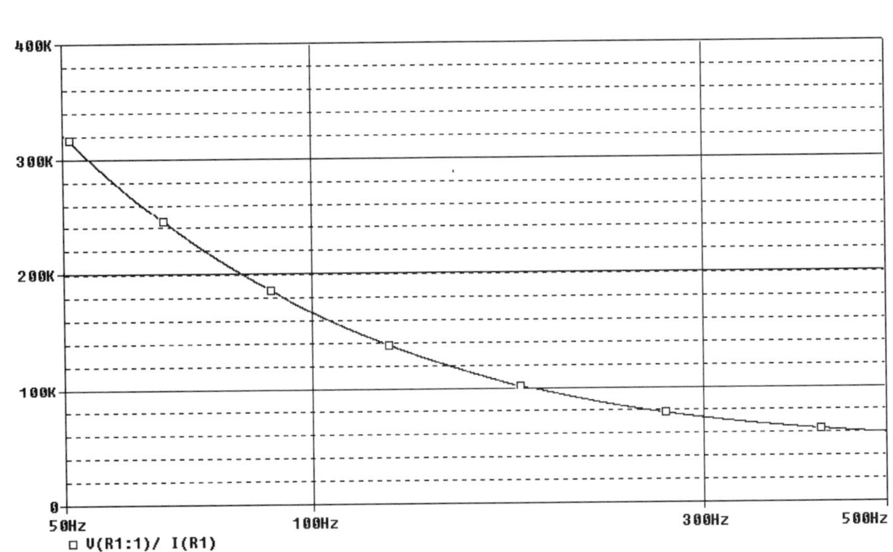

63.

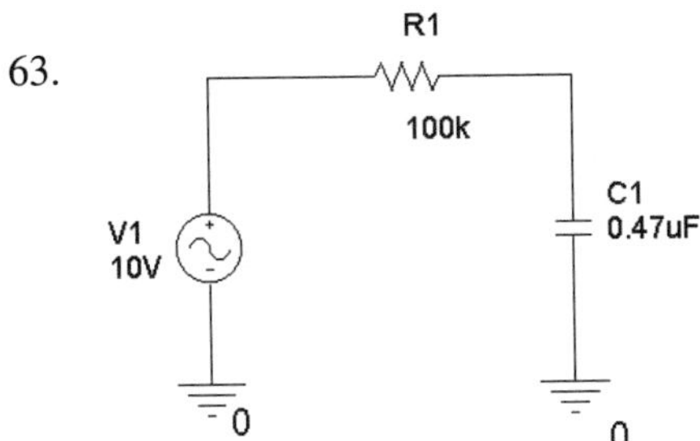

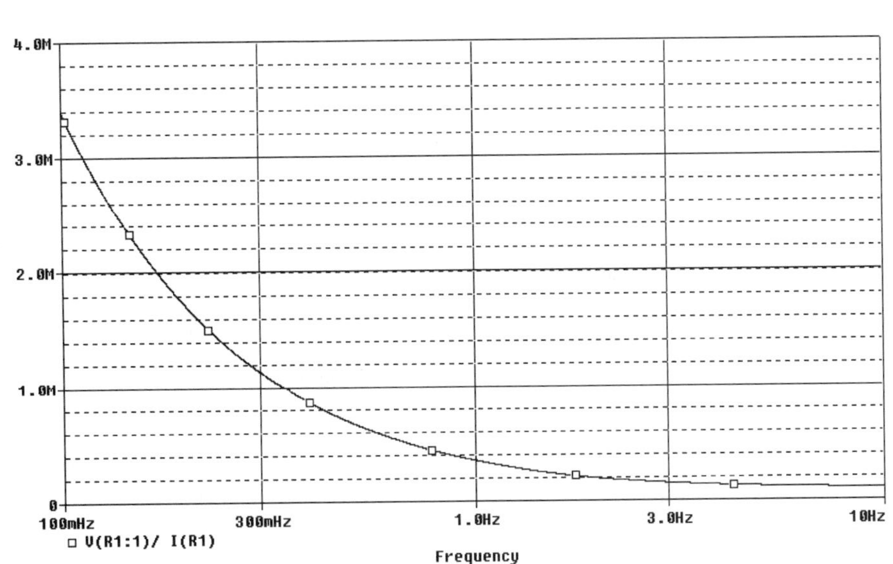

Chapter

19

Methods of AC Analysis

19.1 Dependent Sources

1. $R_T = 25\text{ k}\Omega \| 5\text{ k}\Omega = 4.1\bar{6}\text{ k}\Omega$

$\mathbf{V} = -(60\mathbf{I})(4.1\bar{6}\text{ k}\Omega) = -(250\text{ k}\Omega)\mathbf{I}$

a. $\mathbf{V} = -(250\text{ k}\Omega)(20\ \mu\text{A}\angle -180^\circ) = 5.00\text{ V}\angle 180^\circ$
$= -5.00\text{ V}$

b. $\mathbf{V} = -(250\text{ k}\Omega)(50\ \mu\text{A}\angle -180^\circ) = 12.50\text{ V}\angle 0^\circ$

c. $\mathbf{V} = -(250\text{ k}\Omega)(60\ \mu\text{A}\angle 60^\circ) = 15.00\text{ V}\angle -120^\circ$

3. $$\mathbf{V} = -(800\ \Omega)\mathbf{I}\left(\frac{10\text{ k}\Omega}{10\text{ k}\Omega + 40\text{ k}\Omega}\right) = -(160\ \Omega)\mathbf{I}$$

a. $\mathbf{V} = -(160\ \Omega)(20\ \mu\text{A}\angle 0^\circ) = 3.20\text{ mV}\angle -180^\circ$

b. $\mathbf{V} = -(160\ \Omega)(50\ \mu\text{A}\angle -180^\circ) = 8.00\text{ mV}\angle 0^\circ$

c. $\mathbf{V} = -(160\ \Omega)(60\ \mu\text{A}\angle 60^\circ) = 9.60\text{ mV}\angle -120^\circ$

5. $R_T = 30\text{ k}\Omega \| 20\text{ k}\Omega = 12\text{ k}\Omega$

$$\mathbf{I} = \frac{10\text{ mV}\angle 30^\circ}{2\text{ k}\Omega} = 50\ \mu\text{A}\angle 30^\circ$$

$\mathbf{V}_0 = -(103\mathbf{I})(12\text{ k}\Omega) = -(1.560\text{ M}\Omega)\mathbf{I}$

$\mathbf{V}_0 = -(1.560\text{ M}\Omega)(5.0\ \mu\text{A}\angle 30^\circ) = 7.80\text{ V}\angle -120^\circ$

19.2 Source Conversion

7. circuit (a)

$\mathbf{E} = 30\text{ mA}\angle 0^\circ)(1.8\text{ k}\Omega) = 54\text{ V}\angle 0^\circ$

$$\mathbf{V}_L = \left(\frac{600\ \Omega}{600\ \Omega + 1800\ \Omega}\right)(54\text{ V}\angle 0^\circ) = 13.5\text{ V}\angle 0^\circ$$

circuit (b)

$\mathbf{E} = (2\text{ mA}\angle 30^\circ)(225\ \Omega\angle -90^\circ) = 450\text{ mV}\angle -60^\circ$

$$\mathbf{V}_L = \left(\frac{1000\ \Omega}{1000\ \Omega - j225\ \Omega}\right)(450\text{ mV}\angle -60^\circ)$$
$= 439\text{ mV}\angle -47.32^\circ$

9. a. $$\mathbf{I} = \frac{30\text{ mV}\angle 0^\circ}{2\text{ k}\Omega + 6\text{ k}\Omega} = 3.75\ \mu\text{A}\angle 0^\circ$$

$R_T = 10\text{ k}\Omega \| 50\text{ k}\Omega = 8.\bar{3}\text{ k}\Omega$

$\mathbf{V} = -(150\mathbf{I})(8.\bar{3}\text{ k}\Omega) = (1250\text{ k}\Omega)\mathbf{I}$
$= -(1250\text{ k}\Omega)(3.75\ \mu\text{A}\angle 0^\circ) = 4.69\text{ V}\angle 180^\circ$

b. $\mathbf{E} = (150\mathbf{I})(50\text{ k}\Omega) = (7.5\text{ M}\Omega)\mathbf{I}$

$$\mathbf{V} = -\left(\frac{10\text{ k}\Omega}{10\text{ k}\Omega + 50\text{ k}\Omega}\right)(7.5\text{ M}\Omega)(3.75\ \mu\text{A}\angle 0^\circ)$$
$= 4.69\text{ V}\angle 180^\circ$ (as expected)

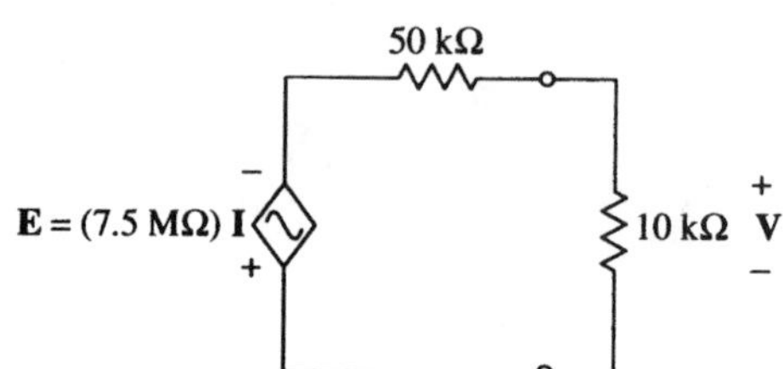

19.3 Mesh (Loop) Analysis

11. a. $(j5\ \Omega - j3\ \Omega + 4\ \Omega)\,\mathbf{I}_1 - (4\ \Omega)\,\mathbf{I}_2 = 20\text{ V}\angle 0^\circ$

$-(4\ \Omega)\mathbf{I}_1 + (4\ \Omega + 2\ \Omega - j8\ \Omega + j12\ \Omega)\mathbf{I}_2 = -30\text{ V}\angle 30^\circ - 20\text{ V}\angle 0^\circ$

$(4\ \Omega + j2\ \Omega)\mathbf{I}_1 - (4\ \Omega)\mathbf{I}_2 = 20\text{ V}\angle 0^\circ$

$-(4\ \Omega)\mathbf{I}_1 + (6\ \Omega + j4\ \Omega)\mathbf{I}_2 = 48.366\text{ V}\angle -161.93^\circ$

b. $$\mathbf{D} = \begin{vmatrix} 4+j2 & -4 \\ -4 & 6+j4 \end{vmatrix} = j28 = 28\angle 90^\circ$$

$$\mathbf{I}_1 = \frac{\begin{vmatrix} 20 & -4 \\ 48.4\text{ V}\angle -161.3^\circ & 6+j4 \end{vmatrix}}{\mathbf{D}} = \frac{66.979\text{ A}\angle 162.63^\circ}{28\angle 90^\circ} = 2.392\text{ A}\angle 72.63^\circ$$

$$\mathbf{I}_2 = \frac{\begin{vmatrix} 4+j2 & 20 \\ -4 & 48.4\text{ V}\angle -161.93^\circ \end{vmatrix}}{\mathbf{D}} = \frac{168.988\text{ A}\angle -115.94^\circ}{28\angle 90^\circ} = 6.035\text{ A}\angle 154.06^\circ$$

c. $\mathbf{I} = 2.392\text{ A}\angle 72.63^\circ - 6.035\text{ A}\angle 154.06^\circ = 6.152\text{ A}\angle -3.33^\circ$

13. a.

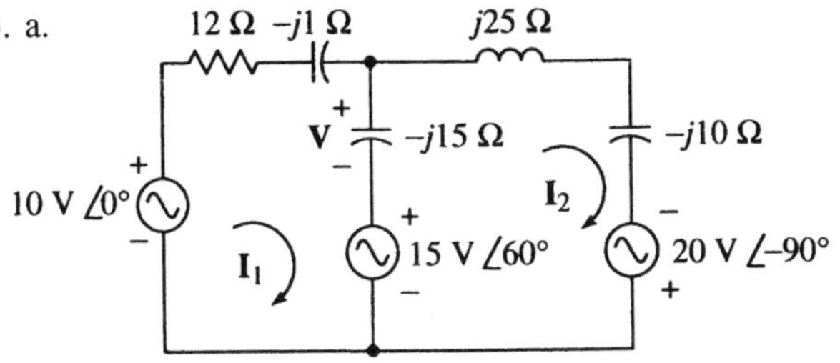

$(12\ \Omega - j16\ \Omega)\mathbf{I}_1 - (-j15\ \Omega)\mathbf{I}_2 = -15\text{ V}\angle 60° + 10\text{ V}\angle 0°$

$-(-j15\ \Omega)\mathbf{I}_1 + (j25\ \Omega - j10\ \Omega - j15\ \Omega)\mathbf{I}_2 = 20\text{ V}\angle -90° + 15\text{ V}\angle 60°$

$(12\ \Omega - j16\ \Omega)\mathbf{I}_1 + (j15\ \Omega)\mathbf{I}_2 = 13.23\text{ V}\angle -79.11°$

$(j15\ \Omega)\mathbf{I}_1 + 0\mathbf{I}_2 = 10.27\text{ V}\angle -43.06°$

b. $\mathbf{I}_1 = \dfrac{10.27\text{ V}\angle -43.06°}{15\ \Omega\angle 90°} = 0.684\text{ A}\angle -133.06°$

$\mathbf{I}_2 = (13.23\text{ V}\angle -79.11°) - \dfrac{(12\ \Omega - j16\ \Omega)(0.684\text{ A}\angle -133.06°)}{j15\ \Omega} = 1.443\text{ A}\angle -131.93°$

c. $\mathbf{I} = 0.684\text{ A}\angle -133.06° - 1.443\text{ A}\angle -131.93° = 0.759\text{ A}\angle 49.09°$

$\mathbf{V} = (15\ \Omega\angle -90°)(0.759\text{ A}\angle 49.09°) = 11.39\text{ V}\angle -40.91°$

15.

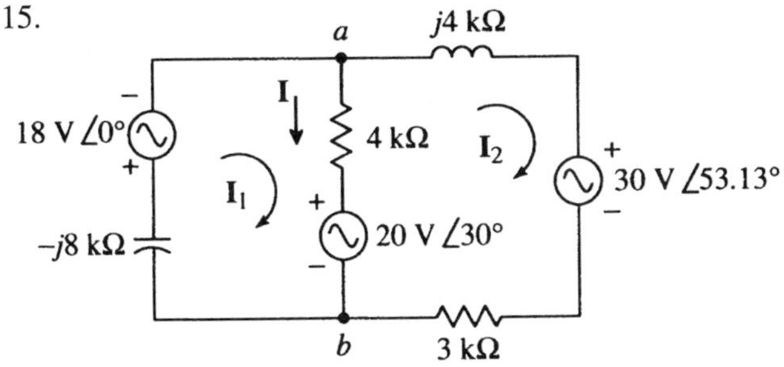

$(4\text{ k}\Omega - j8\text{ k}\Omega)\mathbf{I}_1 - (4\text{ k}\Omega)\mathbf{I}_2 = -20\text{ V}\angle 30° - 18\text{ V}\angle 0°$

$-(4\text{ k}\Omega)\mathbf{I}_1 + (7\text{ k}\Omega + j4\text{ k}\Omega)\mathbf{I}_2 = -30\text{ V}\angle 53.13° + 20\text{ V}\angle 30°$

$(4\text{ k}\Omega - j8\text{ k}\Omega)\mathbf{I}_1 - (4\text{ k}\Omega)\mathbf{I}_2 = 36.7\text{ V}\angle -164.19°$

$-(4\text{ k}\Omega)\mathbf{I}_1 + (7\text{ k}\Omega + j4\text{ k}\Omega)\mathbf{I}_2 = 14.0\text{ V} - 92.78°$

$$\mathbf{D} = \begin{vmatrix} 4\text{ k}\Omega - j8\text{ k}\Omega & -4\text{ k}\Omega \\ -4\text{ k}\Omega & 7\text{ k}\Omega + j4\text{ k}\Omega \end{vmatrix} = 59.5\text{ mS}\angle -42.27°$$

$$\mathbf{I}_1 = \frac{\begin{vmatrix} 36.7\angle -164.19° & -4\text{ k}\Omega \\ 14.0\text{ V}\angle -92.78° & 7\text{ k}\Omega + j4\text{ k}\Omega \end{vmatrix}}{\mathbf{D}} = 5.72\text{ mA}\angle -85.88°$$

$$\mathbf{I}_2 = \frac{\begin{vmatrix} 4\text{ k}\Omega - j8\text{ k}\Omega & 36.7\text{ V}\angle -164.19° \\ -4\text{ k}\Omega & 14.0\text{ V}\angle -92.78° \end{vmatrix}}{\mathbf{D}} = 4.57\text{ mA}\angle -118.24°$$

$\mathbf{I}_1 - \mathbf{I}_2 = 3.07\text{ mA}\angle -33.13°$

$\mathbf{V} = \mathbf{V}_{ab} = 27.8\text{ V}\angle 6.79°$

$\mathbf{I} = 6.95\text{ mA}\angle 6.79°$

19.4 Nodal Analysis

17. a. $\left(\dfrac{1}{3\ \Omega} + \dfrac{1}{-j4\ \Omega}\right)\mathbf{V}_1 - \left(\dfrac{1}{-j4\ \Omega}\right)\mathbf{V}_2 = 2\text{ A}\angle 0° - 3\text{ A}\angle 90°$

$-\left(\dfrac{1}{-j4\ \Omega}\right)\mathbf{V}_1 + \left(\dfrac{1}{-j4\ \Omega} + \dfrac{1}{j6\ \Omega}\right)\mathbf{V}_2 = 3\text{ A}\angle 90° - 4\text{ A}\angle -90°$

$(0.41\bar{6}\text{ S}\angle 38.87°)\mathbf{V}_1 - (0.25\text{ S}\angle 90°)\mathbf{V}_2 = 3.60555\text{ A}\angle -56.31°$

$-(0.25\text{ S}\angle 90^\circ)\mathbf{V}_1 + (0.08\overline{3}\text{ S}\angle 90^\circ)\mathbf{V}_2 = 7.00\text{ A}\angle 90^\circ$

b. $\mathbf{D} = \begin{vmatrix} 0.41\overline{6}\angle 36.87^\circ & 0.25\angle -90^\circ \\ 0.25\angle -90^\circ & 0.08\overline{3}\angle 90^\circ \end{vmatrix} = 0.050077\angle 33.69^\circ = 0.041\overline{6} + j0.02\overline{7}$

$$\mathbf{V}_1 = \frac{\begin{vmatrix} 3.606\angle -56.31^\circ & 0.25\text{ S}\angle -90^\circ \\ 7.00\angle 90^\circ & 0.08\overline{3}\text{ S}\angle 90^\circ \end{vmatrix}}{0.041\overline{6} + j0.02\overline{7}} = 30.1\text{ V}\angle 139.97^\circ$$

$$\mathbf{V}_2 = \frac{\begin{vmatrix} 0.41\overline{6}\text{ S}\angle 36.87^\circ & 3.606\angle -56.31^\circ \\ 0.25\text{ S}\angle -90^\circ & 7.00\angle 90^\circ \end{vmatrix}}{0.041\overline{6} + j0.02\overline{7}} = 60.0\text{ V}\angle 75.75^\circ$$

c. $\mathbf{I} = \dfrac{(30.1\text{ V}\angle 139.97^\circ) - (60.0\text{ V}\angle 75.75^\circ)}{4\ \Omega\angle -90^\circ} = 13.54\text{ A}\angle -44.31^\circ$

19.

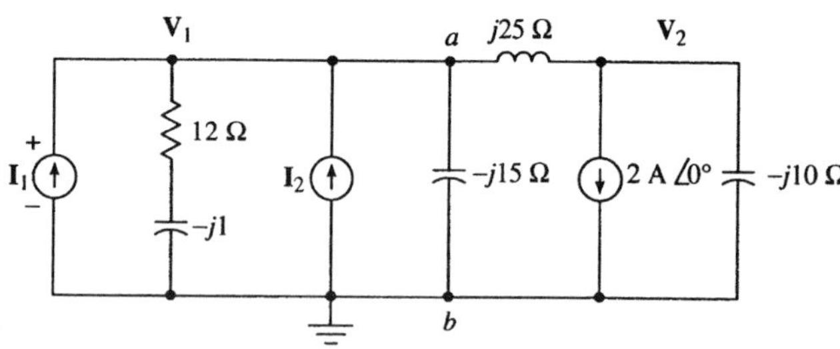

a. $\mathbf{I}_1 = \dfrac{10\text{ V}\angle 0^\circ}{12\ \Omega - j1\ \Omega} = 0.830\text{ A}\angle 4.76^\circ \quad \mathbf{I}_2 = \dfrac{15\text{ V}\angle 60^\circ}{-j15\ \Omega} = 1.0\text{ A}\angle 150^\circ$

$$\left(\frac{1}{12\ \Omega - j1\ \Omega} + \frac{1}{j25\ \Omega} + \frac{1}{j25\ \Omega}\right)\mathbf{V}_1 - \left(\frac{1}{j25\ \Omega}\right)\mathbf{V}_2 = \mathbf{I}_1 + \mathbf{I}_2$$

$$-\left(\frac{1}{j25\ \Omega}\right)\mathbf{V}_1 + \left(\frac{1}{j25\ \Omega} + \frac{1}{-j10\ \Omega}\right)\mathbf{V}_2 = -2.\text{ A}\angle 0^\circ$$

$(0.0893055\text{ S}\angle 22.08^\circ)\mathbf{V}_1 + (0.04\text{ S}\angle 90^\circ)\mathbf{V}_2 = 0.57021\text{ A}\angle 93.86^\circ$

$(0.04\text{ S}\angle 90^\circ)\mathbf{V}_1 + (0.06\text{ S}\angle 90^\circ)\mathbf{V}_2 = 2.0\text{ A}\angle +180^\circ$

$\mathbf{D} = 0.0049826\angle 94.77^\circ$

b. $$\mathbf{V}_1 = \frac{\begin{vmatrix} 0.57021\angle 93.86^\circ & 0.4\text{ S}\angle 90^\circ \\ 2\angle 180^\circ & 0.06\text{ S}\angle 90^\circ \end{vmatrix}}{0.0049826\angle 94.77^\circ} = 17.03\text{ V}\angle 18.95^\circ$$

$$\mathbf{V}_2 = \frac{\begin{vmatrix} 0.0893055\text{ S}\angle 22.08^\circ & 0.57021\angle 93.86^\circ \\ 0.04\text{ S}\angle 90^\circ & 2\angle 180^\circ \end{vmatrix}}{\mathbf{D}} = 31.5\text{ V}\angle 109.91^\circ$$

c. $\mathbf{V} = 17.03\text{ V}\angle 18.95^\circ - 15.00\text{ V}\angle 60^\circ = 11.39\text{ V}\angle -40.91^\circ$

21.

$\mathbf{I}_1 = \dfrac{18\text{ V}\angle 0^\circ}{8\text{ k}\Omega\angle -90^\circ} = 2.25\text{ mA}\angle 90^\circ$

$\mathbf{I}_2 = \dfrac{30\text{ V}\angle 53.13^\circ}{3\text{ k}\Omega + j4\text{ k}\Omega} = 6.0\text{ mA}\angle 0^\circ$

$$\left(\frac{1}{-j8\text{ k}\Omega} + \frac{1}{4\text{ k}\Omega} + \frac{1}{3\text{ k}\Omega + j4\text{ k}\Omega}\right)\mathbf{V}$$
$= 5\text{ mA}\angle 30^\circ + 6.0\text{ mA}\angle 0^\circ - 2.25\text{ mA}\angle 90^\circ$

$(0.37165\ \mu\text{S}\angle -5.40^\circ)\mathbf{V} = 10.33\text{ mA}\angle 1.39^\circ$

$\mathbf{V} = 27.8\text{ V}\angle 6.79^\circ$

$\mathbf{I} = 6.95\text{ mA}\angle 6.79^\circ$

(Same results as Problem 15)

19.5 Delta-to-Wye and Wye-to-Delta Conversions

23. network (a)

$$\mathbf{Z}_1 = \frac{(810\ \Omega\angle-90^\circ)(270\ \Omega)}{270\ \Omega + j90\ \Omega - j810\ \Omega} = 284.4\ \Omega\angle-20.56^\circ$$

$$\mathbf{Z}_2 = \frac{(810\ \Omega\angle90^\circ)(90\ \Omega\angle90^\circ)}{270\ \Omega - j720\ \Omega} = 94.8\ \Omega\angle69.44^\circ$$

$$\mathbf{Z}_3 = \frac{(90\ \Omega\angle90^\circ)(270\ \Omega)}{270\ \Omega - j720\ \Omega} = 31.6\ \Omega\angle159.44^\circ$$

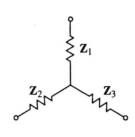

network (b)

$$\mathbf{Z}_1 = \frac{(36\ \text{k}\Omega)(18\ \text{k}\Omega)}{36\ \text{k}\Omega + 18\ \text{k}\Omega - j9\ \text{k}\Omega} = 11.84\ \text{k}\Omega\angle9.46^\circ$$

$$\mathbf{Z}_2 = \frac{(36\ \text{k}\Omega)(-j9\ \text{k}\Omega)}{54\ \text{k}\Omega - j9\ \text{k}\Omega}) = 5.92\ \text{k}\Omega\angle-80.54^\circ$$

$$\mathbf{Z}_3 = \frac{(18\ \text{k}\Omega)(-j9\ \text{k}\Omega)}{54\ \text{k}\Omega - j9\ \text{k}\Omega} = 2.96\ \text{k}\Omega\angle-80.54^\circ$$

25. Convert "Y" to Δ:

$$\mathbf{Z}_A = \frac{(6\ \Omega\angle90^\circ)(2\ \Omega\angle-90^\circ) + (6\ \Omega\angle90^\circ)(18\ \Omega)+(2\ \Omega\angle-90^\circ)(18\ \Omega)}{18\ \Omega}$$

$$= \frac{72.99\ \Omega\angle80.54^\circ}{18} = 4.06\ \Omega\angle80.54^\circ$$

$$\mathbf{Z}_B = \frac{72.99\ \Omega\angle80.54^\circ}{2\angle-90^\circ} = 36.5\ \Omega\angle170.54^\circ$$

$$\mathbf{Z}_C = \frac{72.99\ \Omega\angle80.54^\circ}{6\angle90^\circ} = 12.17\ \Omega\angle-9.46^\circ$$

$$\mathbf{Z}_1 = 5\ \Omega \| \mathbf{Z}_A = 2.92\ \Omega\angle45.32^\circ$$

$$\mathbf{Z}_2 = j10\ \Omega \| \mathbf{Z}_C = 8.44\ \Omega\angle46.85^\circ$$

$$\mathbf{Z}_T = (-j15\ \Omega)\|\mathbf{Z}_B\|[(5\ \Omega)\|(\mathbf{Z}_A) + (j10\ \Omega)\|\mathbf{Z}_C] = 29.7\ \Omega\angle2.82^\circ$$

$$\mathbf{I} = \frac{10\ \text{V}\ \angle0^\circ}{29.7\ \Omega\angle2.82^\circ} = 0.337\ \text{A}\angle-2.82^\circ$$

27. Convert the "Y" to a "Δ."

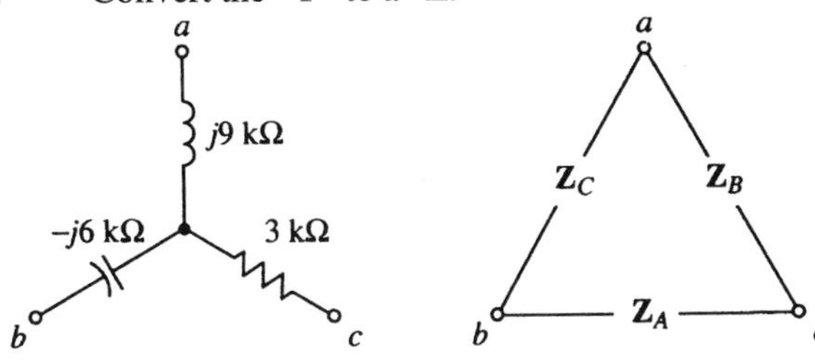

$$\mathbf{Z}_A = \frac{(6\ \text{k}\Omega\angle-90^\circ)(3\ \text{k}\Omega) + (6\ \text{k}\Omega\angle-90^\circ)(9\ \text{k}\Omega\angle90^\circ) + (9\ \text{k}\Omega\angle90^\circ)(3\ \text{k}\Omega)}{9\ \text{k}\Omega\angle90^\circ} = 1\ \text{kW} - j6\ \text{k}\Omega$$

$$\mathbf{Z}_B = \frac{54\ \text{k}\Omega + j9\ \text{k}\Omega}{-j6} = -1.5\ \text{k}\Omega + j9\ \text{k}\Omega$$

$$\mathbf{Z}_C = \frac{54\ \text{k}\Omega + j9\ \text{k}\Omega}{3} = 18\ \text{k}\Omega + j3\ \text{k}\Omega$$

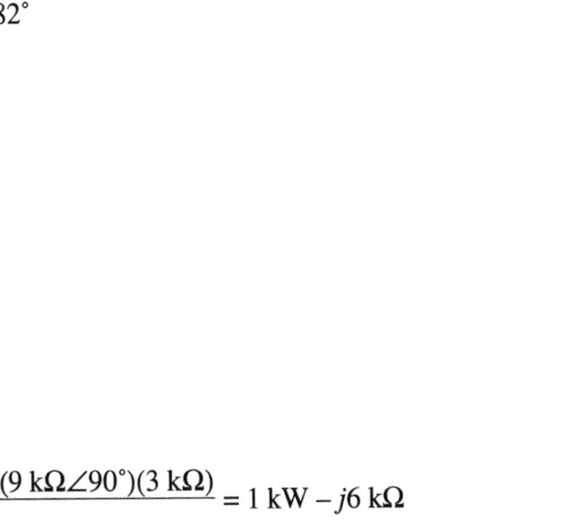

$$\mathbf{Z}_T = (-j3\ \text{k}\Omega)\|(18\ \text{k}\Omega + j3\ \text{k}\Omega)\|(\mathbf{Z}_1 + \mathbf{Z}_2)$$

$$\mathbf{Z}_1 = 2\ \Omega\|(-1.5\ \Omega + j9\ \Omega) = 2.02\ \text{k}\Omega\angle12.64^\circ$$

$$\mathbf{Z}_2 = (j6\ \text{k}\Omega)\|(1\ \text{k}\Omega - j6\ \text{k}\Omega) = 36.5\ \text{k}\Omega\angle9.462^\circ$$

$$\mathbf{Z}_1 + \mathbf{Z}_2 = 38.5\ \text{k}\Omega\angle9.629^\circ$$

$$\mathbf{Z}_T = 3.03\ \Omega\angle-76.02^\circ$$

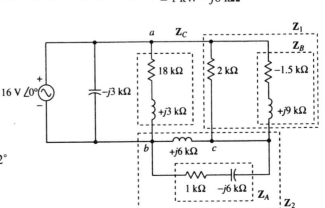

$$\mathbf{I}=\frac{16\text{ V}\angle 0^\circ}{3.033\ \Omega\angle -76.02^\circ}=5.28\text{ A}\angle 76.02^\circ$$

$$\mathbf{V}_{ac}=\left(\frac{\mathbf{Z}_1}{\mathbf{Z}_1+\mathbf{Z}_2}\right)(16\text{ V}\angle 0^\circ)=0.841\text{ V}\angle 3.011^\circ$$

$$\mathbf{I}_{2\text{ k}\Omega}=\frac{\mathbf{V}_{ac}}{2\text{ k}\Omega}=0.320\text{ A}\angle 3.011^\circ$$

$$\mathbf{I}_1=\mathbf{I}-\mathbf{I}_{-j3\text{ k}\Omega}-\mathbf{I}2\text{ k}\Omega=5.28\text{ A}\angle 76.02^\circ-5.33\text{ A}\angle 90^\circ-0.42\text{A}\angle 3.011^\circ=0.887\text{ A}\angle -15.42^\circ$$

19.6 Bridge Networks

29. a. $$\frac{2\ \Omega-j4\ \Omega}{\mathbf{Z}_2}-\frac{2\ \Omega}{3\ \Omega-j1\ \Omega}$$

$$\mathbf{Z}_2=\frac{(2\ \Omega-j4\ \Omega)(3\ \Omega-j1\ \Omega)}{2\ \Omega}$$

$$=1\ \Omega-j7\ \Omega=7.071\ \Omega\angle -81.87^\circ$$

b. $$\mathbf{I}=\frac{500\text{ mV}\angle 0^\circ}{(2\ \Omega-j4\ \Omega+2\ \Omega)\|(1\ \Omega-j7\ \Omega+3\ \Omega-j1\ \Omega)}$$

$$=\frac{500\text{ mV}\angle 0^\circ}{(4\ \Omega-j4\ \Omega)\|(4\ \Omega-j8\ \Omega)}$$

$$=\frac{500\text{ mV}\angle 0^\circ}{3.51\ \Omega\angle -52.125^\circ}$$

$$=142.5\text{ mA}\angle 52.13^\circ$$

31. $\omega=2000\pi$ rad/s

$$X_C=\frac{1}{(2000\pi)(0.2\ \mu\text{F})}=796\ \Omega$$

$$X_L=(2000\pi)(100\text{ mH})=628\ \Omega$$

$$\mathbf{Z}_1=-j796\ \Omega\|100\text{ k}\Omega=796\ \Omega\angle -89.54^\circ$$

$$\mathbf{Z}_4=5\ \Omega+j628\ \Omega=628\ \Omega\angle 89.54^\circ$$

$$\frac{\mathbf{Z}_1}{\mathbf{Z}_2}\overset{?}{=}\frac{\mathbf{Z}_3}{\mathbf{Z}_4}$$

$$\frac{796\ \Omega\angle -89.54^\circ}{1000\ \Omega}\overset{?}{=}\frac{500\ \Omega}{628\ \Omega\angle 89.54^\circ}$$

$0.796\angle -89.54^\circ=0.796\angle -89.54^\circ$ (as required)

33. $$\frac{\mathbf{Z}_1}{\mathbf{Z}_2}=\frac{\mathbf{Z}_3}{\mathbf{Z}_4}$$

$$\frac{\dfrac{\left(\dfrac{1}{j\omega C_1}\right)(R_1)}{\dfrac{1}{j\omega C_1}R_1}}{R_2}=\frac{\dfrac{1}{j\omega C_3}}{R_x+\dfrac{1}{j\omega C_x}}$$

$$\frac{\dfrac{R_1}{1+j\omega R_1C_1}}{R_2}=\frac{\dfrac{\dfrac{1}{C_3}}{1+j\omega C_xR_x}}{C_x}$$

$$\frac{R_1}{R_2+j\omega R_1R_2C_1}=\frac{C_x}{C_3+j\omega C_xR_xC_3}$$

$$\frac{R_2+j\omega R_1R_2C_1}{R_1}=\frac{C_3+j\omega C_xR_xC_3}{C_x}$$

$$\frac{R_2}{R_1}=\frac{C_3}{C_x}\quad R_2C_1=R_xC_3$$

35. $$X_C=\frac{1}{(2\pi)(1000\text{ Hz})(0.01\ \mu\text{F})}=15.92\text{ k}\Omega$$

$$X_L=(2\pi)(1000\text{ Hz})(500\text{ mH})=3.14\text{ k}\Omega$$

$$\frac{R_1-j15.92\text{ k}\Omega}{1\text{ k}\Omega}=\frac{R_3}{50\ \Omega+j3.14\text{ k}\Omega}$$

$$\frac{R_1}{R_3}-\frac{j15.92\text{ k}\Omega}{R_3}=\frac{1\text{ k}\Omega}{50\ \Omega+j3.14\text{ k}\Omega}=0.00506-j0.31823$$

$$R_3=\frac{15.92\text{ k}\Omega}{0.318}=50.0\text{ k}\Omega$$

$$R_1=(0.00506)(50.0\text{ k}\Omega)=253.3\ \Omega$$

19.7 Computer Analysis

37.

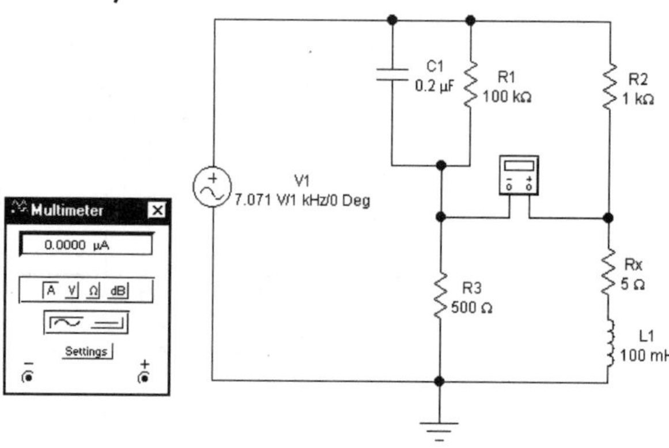

39.

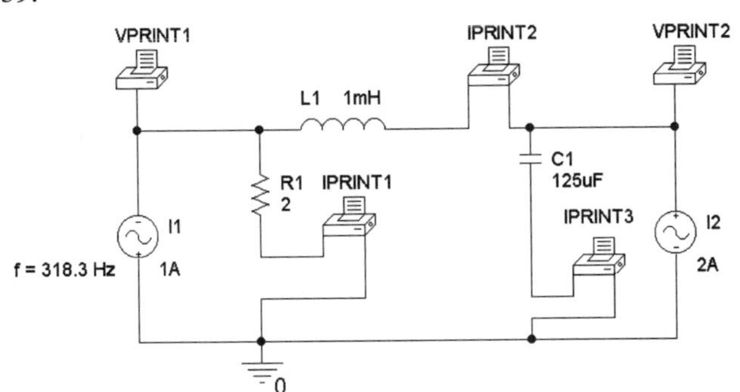

$\mathbf{V}_1 = 4.24\ \text{V}\angle\ 135^\circ$

$\mathbf{V}_2 = 6.32\ \text{V}\angle{-161.6^\circ}$

$\mathbf{I}_1 = 2.12\ \text{A}\angle 135^\circ$

$\mathbf{I}_2 = 2.92\ \text{A}\angle{-30.96^\circ}$

$\mathbf{I}_3 = 1.581\ \text{A}\angle{-71.56^\circ}$

41.

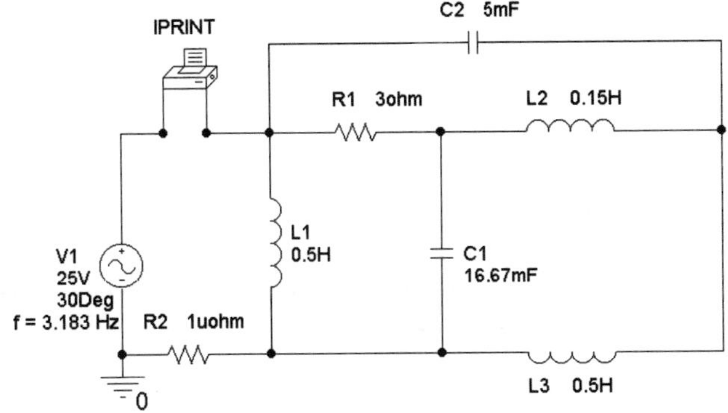

$\mathbf{I} = 2.89\ \text{A}\angle 75^\circ$

Chapter

20

AC Network Theorems

20.1 Superposition Theorem—Independent Sources

1. current source:

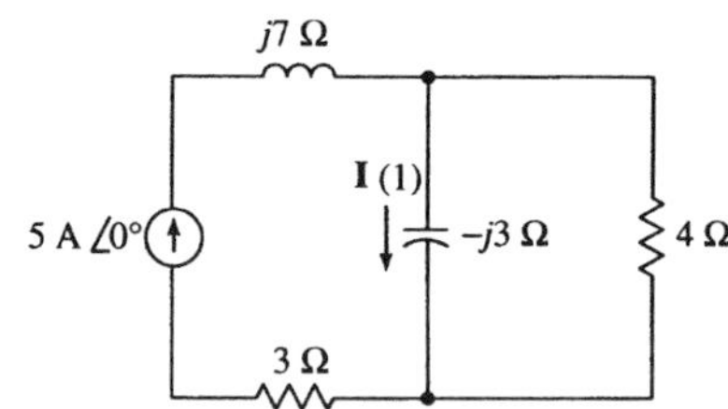

$\mathbf{I}(1) = \left(\dfrac{4\ \Omega}{4\ \Omega - j3\ \Omega}\right)(5\ \text{A}\angle 0°) = 4\ \text{A}\angle 36.87°$

voltage source:

$\mathbf{I}(2) = \dfrac{5\ \text{V}\ \angle 90°}{4\ \Omega - j3\ \Omega} = 1\ \text{A}\angle 126.87°$

$\mathbf{I} = 4\ \text{A}\angle 36.87° + 1\ \text{A}\angle 126.87° = 4.12\ \text{A}\angle 50.88°$

3. Current source:

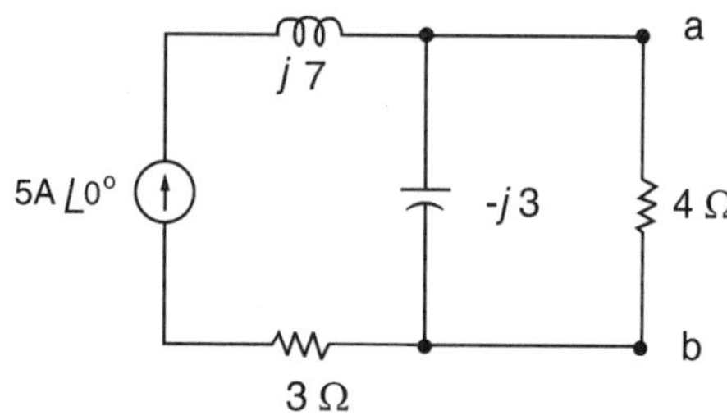

$\mathbf{V}_{ab(1)} = (5\ \text{A}\angle 0°)(-j3\Omega \| 4\ \Omega)\ = 12\ \text{V}\ \angle -53.13°$

Voltage source:

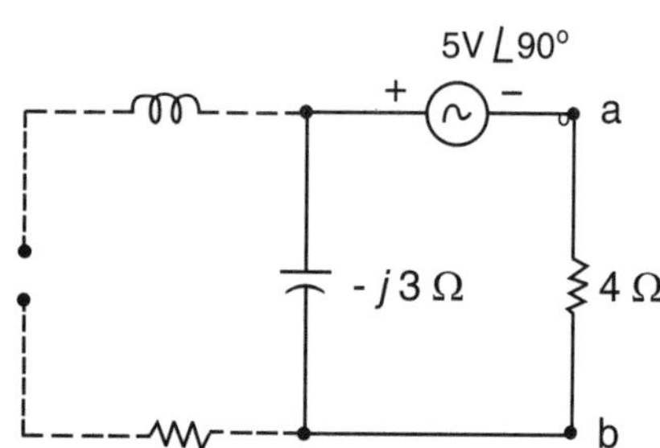

$\mathbf{V}_{ab(2)} = -\left(\dfrac{4\ \Omega}{4\ \Omega - j3\ \Omega}\right) 5\ \text{V}\ \angle 90° = 4\ \text{V}\ \angle -53.13°$

$\mathbf{V}_{ab} = \mathbf{V}_{ab(1)} + \mathbf{V}_{ab(2)} = 16\ \text{V}\ \angle -53.13°$

5. a. voltage source:

$\mathbf{Z}_T = (300\ \Omega \| j600\ \Omega) - j100\ \Omega + (j200\ \Omega \| 100\ \Omega)$
$= 268\ \Omega\angle 28.57° - j100\ \Omega + 89.443\ \Omega\angle 26.57°$
$= 326\ \Omega\angle 10.62° = 320\ \Omega + j60\ \Omega$

$\mathbf{V}(1)\left(\dfrac{80\ \Omega + j40\ \Omega}{320\ \Omega + j60\ \Omega}\right)(10\ \text{V}\ \angle 0°) = 2.75\ \text{V}\ \angle 15.95°$

current source:

$\mathbf{Z}_T = [(300\ \Omega \| j600\ \Omega) - j100\ \Omega \| \text{j}\ j\ 200\ \Omega \| 100\ \Omega$
$= (240\ \Omega + j20\ \Omega) \| 80\ \Omega + j40\ \Omega)$
$= 66.2\ \Omega\angle 20.71°$

$\mathbf{V}(2) = (0.2\ \text{A}\angle 20°)(66.2\ \Omega\angle 20.71°)$
$= 13.23\ \text{V}\ \angle 40.71°$

$\mathbf{V}\ = \mathbf{V}(1) + \mathbf{V}_2 = 15.77\ \text{V}\ \angle 36.52°$

b. $P_{100\ \Omega} = \dfrac{(17.77\ \text{V})^2}{100\ \Omega} = 2.49\ \text{W}$

assuming superposition applies for power.

$P(1) = \dfrac{(2.75\ \text{V})^2}{100\ \Omega} = 0.0755\ \text{W}$

$P(2) = \dfrac{(13.23\ \text{V})^2}{100\ \Omega} = 1.751\ \text{W}$

$P(1) + P(2) = 1.83\ \text{W} \neq P_{100\ \Omega} = 2.49\ \text{W}$

Superposition does not apply for power.

7. Voltage source #1:

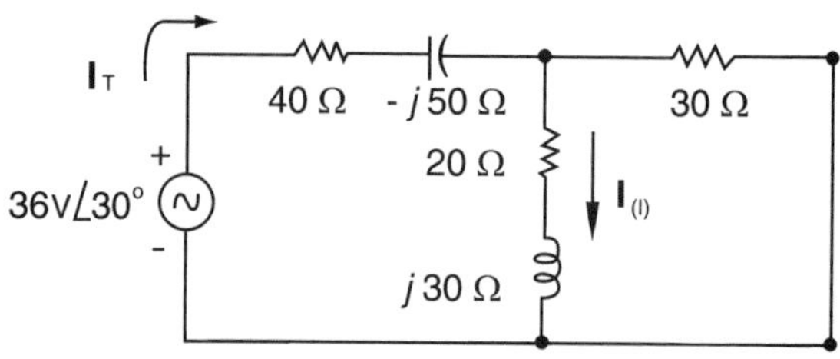

$\mathbf{Z}_T = 40\ \Omega - j50\ \Omega + 30\ \Omega \| (20\ \Omega + j30\ \Omega)$
$= 70.6\ \Omega\angle -36.54°$

$\mathbf{I}_T = \dfrac{36\ \text{V}\ \angle 30°}{70.6\ \Omega\angle -36.54°} = 0.510\ \text{A}\angle 66.54°$

$\mathbf{I}_1 = \left(\dfrac{30\ \Omega}{50\ \Omega + j30\ \Omega}\right)(0.510\ \text{A}\angle 66.54°)$
$= 0.262\ \text{A}\angle 35.57°$

Voltage source #2:

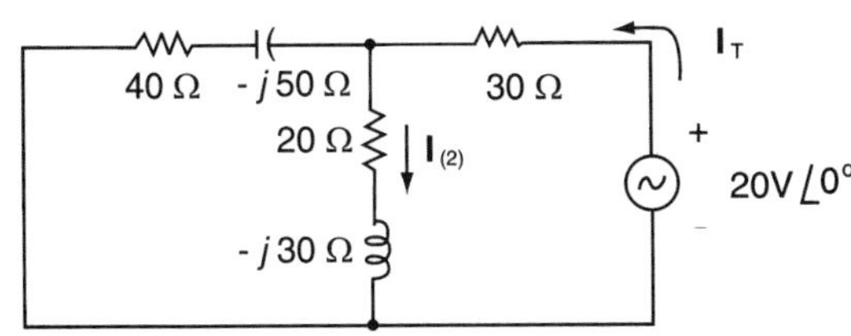

$\mathbf{Z}_T = 30\ \Omega + (20\ \Omega + j30\ \Omega) \| (40\ \Omega - j50\ \Omega)$

$= 65.1\ \Omega\angle 12.86^\circ$

$\mathbf{I}_T = \dfrac{20\ \text{V}\ \angle 0^\circ}{65.1\ \Omega\angle 12.86^\circ)} = 0.307\ \text{A}\angle{-12.86^\circ}$

$\mathbf{I}_{(2)} = \left(\dfrac{40\ \Omega - j50\ \Omega}{60\ \Omega - j20\ \Omega}\right)(0.307\ \text{A}\angle - 12.86^\circ)$

$= 0.311\ \text{A}\angle - 45.77^\circ$

$\mathbf{I} = \mathbf{I}_{(1)} + \mathbf{I}_{(2)} = 0.436\ \text{A}\angle - 9.27^\circ$

9. Voltage source #1:

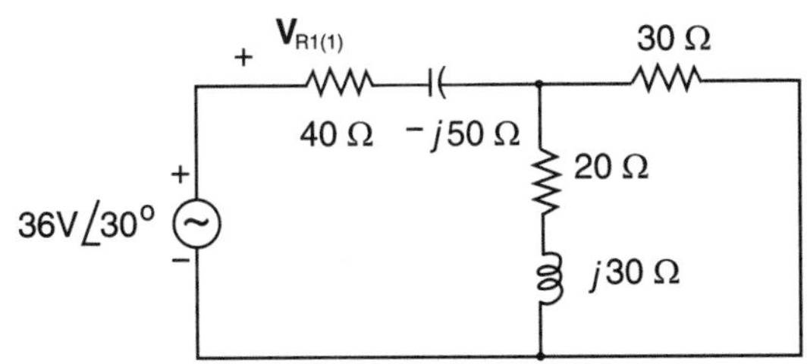

$\mathbf{V}_{R1(1)} = \dfrac{(40\ \Omega)(36\ \text{V}\ \angle 30^\circ)}{40\ \Omega - j50\ \Omega + 30\ \Omega \| (20\ \Omega + j30\Omega)}$

$= 20.4\ \text{V}\ \angle 66.54^\circ$

Voltage source #2:

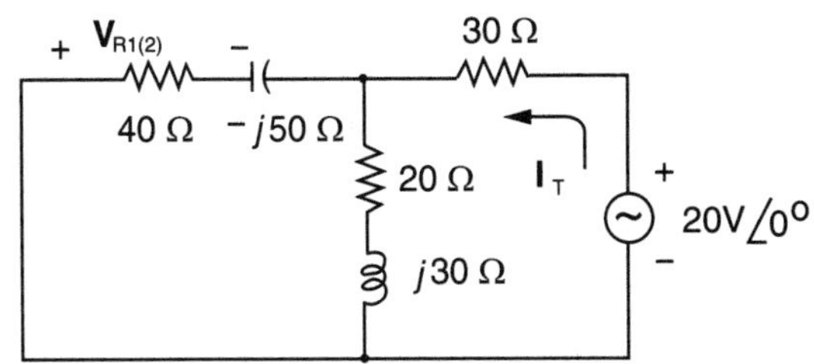

$\mathbf{Z}_T = 30\ \Omega + (40\ \Omega - j50\ \Omega) \| (20\ \Omega + j30\ \Omega)$

$= 65.1\ \Omega\angle\ 12.86^\circ$

$\mathbf{I}_T = \dfrac{20\ \text{V}\ \angle 0^\circ}{65.1\ \Omega\angle 12.86^\circ} = 0.307\ \text{A}\angle - 12.86^\circ$

$\mathbf{I}_{R1} = \left(\dfrac{20\ \Omega + j30\ \Omega}{60\ \Omega - j20\ \Omega}\right) 0.307\ \text{A}\angle - 12.86^\circ$

$= 0.175\ \text{A}\angle 61.88^\circ$

$\mathbf{V}_{R1(2)} = -(0.175\ \text{A}\angle 61.88^\circ)(40\ \Omega)$

$= 7.00\ \text{V}\ \angle - 118.12^\circ$

$\mathbf{V}_{R1} = \mathbf{V}_{R1(1)} + \mathbf{V}_{R1(2)} = 13.42\ \text{V}\ \angle 68.96^\circ$

$\mathbf{V}_{R1} = 18.97 \sin(\omega t + 68.96^\circ)$

20.2 Superposition Theorem—Dependent Sources

11. a. ◇ (4.0 ms)(100 mV ∠0°) = 400 μA∠0°

$\mathbf{V}_L(1) = \text{V}_{ab}(1)$

$= -(400\ \mu\text{A}\angle 0^\circ)(20\ \text{k}\Omega \| - j40\ \text{k}\Omega \| 40\ \text{k}\Omega)$

$= -(400\ \mu\text{A}\angle 0^\circ)(12.64911\ \text{k}\Omega\angle - 18.43^\circ)$

$= 5.06\ \text{V}\ \angle 161.57^\circ$

Independent source:

$\mathbf{Z}_T = 20\ \text{k}\Omega + 40\ \text{k}\Omega \| - j40\ \text{k}\Omega$

$= 44.7\ \text{k}\Omega\angle - 26.57^\circ$

$\mathbf{V}_L(2) = \left(\dfrac{40\ \text{k}\Omega \| - j40\ \text{k}\Omega}{\mathbf{Z}_T}\right)(6\ \text{V}\ \angle 0^\circ)$

$= 3.79\ \text{V}\ \angle - 18.43^\circ$

$\mathbf{V}_L = \mathbf{V}_L(1) + \mathbf{V}_L(2) = 1.265\ \text{V}\ \angle 161.57^\circ$

b. $\mathbf{V}_L(1) = 10.12\ \text{V}\ \angle 161.57^\circ$

$\mathbf{V}_L = \mathbf{V}_L(1) + \mathbf{V}_L(2) = 6.32\ \text{V}\ \angle 161.57^\circ$

13. Dependent current source:

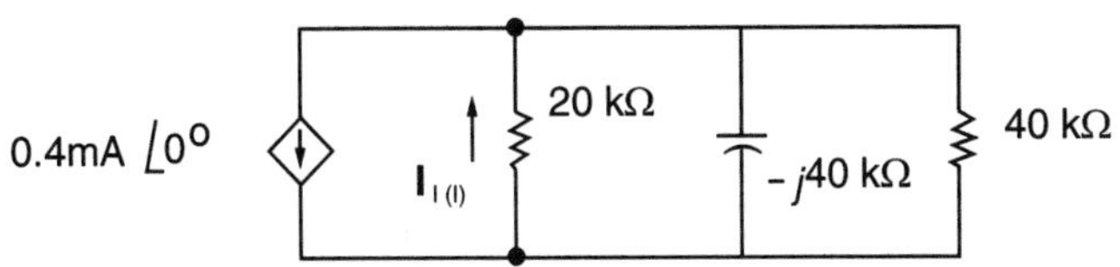

$\mathbf{Z}_T = 20\ \text{k}\Omega \| {-j40}\ \text{k}\Omega \| 40\ \text{k}\Omega = 12\ \text{k}\Omega - j4\text{k}\Omega$

$\mathbf{I}_{1(1)} = \left(\dfrac{12 - j4}{20}\right)(0.4\ \text{mA}\angle 0^\circ)$

$= 0.253\ \text{mA}\angle - 18.43^\circ$

Independent voltage source:

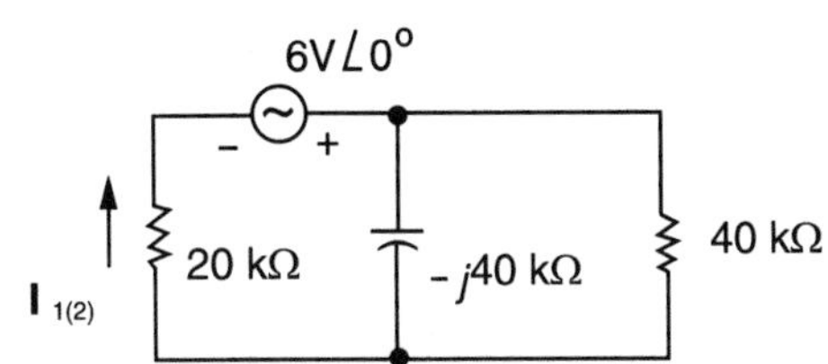

$\mathbf{Z}_T = 20\text{ k}\Omega + 40\text{ k}\Omega \| -j40\text{ k}\Omega = 40\text{ k}\Omega - j20\text{k}\Omega$

$\mathbf{I}_{1(2)} = \dfrac{6\text{ V}\angle 0^\circ}{40\text{ k}\Omega - j20\text{ k}\Omega} = 0.134\text{ mA}\angle 26.57^\circ$

$\mathbf{I} = \mathbf{I}_{1(1)} + \mathbf{I}_{1(2)} = 0.361\text{ mA}\angle -3.18^\circ$

15. $\mathbf{I}_L = \mathbf{I} + 20\mathbf{I} = 21\mathbf{I} = \dfrac{\mathbf{V}_L}{80\ \Omega}$ (1)

$\mathbf{V}_L = 10\text{ V}\angle 0^\circ - (20\ \Omega)\mathbf{I}$ (2)

From (1) $\mathbf{I} = \dfrac{\mathbf{V}_L}{(21)(80\ \Omega)}$

Substituting into (2) we get:

$\mathbf{V}_L = 10\text{ V}\angle 0^\circ - 20\ \Omega\left(\dfrac{\mathbf{V}_L}{1680\ \Omega}\right)$

$\mathbf{V}_L(1 + 0.0119) = 10\text{ V}\angle 0^\circ$

$\mathbf{V}_L = 9.88\text{ V}\angle 0^\circ$

17. Voltage source #1:

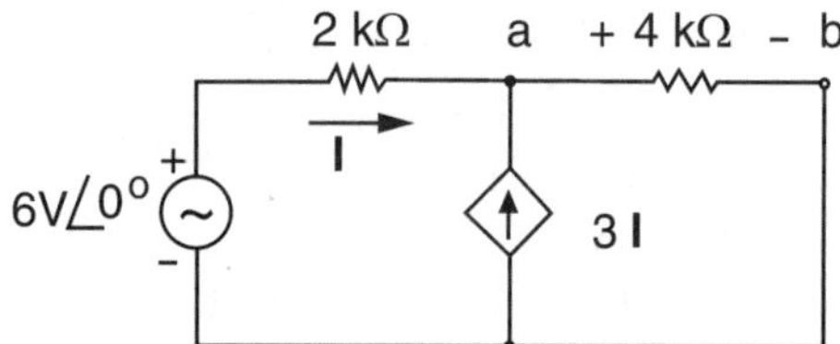

$\mathbf{V}_{ab} = (4\ \mathbf{I})(4\text{ k}\Omega)$

$6\text{ V}\angle 0^\circ = 2\text{ k}\Omega\mathbf{I} + 4\text{ k}\Omega(4\ \mathbf{I})$

$\mathbf{I} = \dfrac{6\text{ V}\angle 0^\circ}{18\text{ k}\Omega} = 0.333\text{ mA}\angle 0^\circ$

$\mathbf{V}_{ab(1)} = (4\text{ k}\Omega)(0.333\text{ mA}\angle 0^\circ) = 5.33\text{ V}\angle 0^\circ$

Voltage source #2:

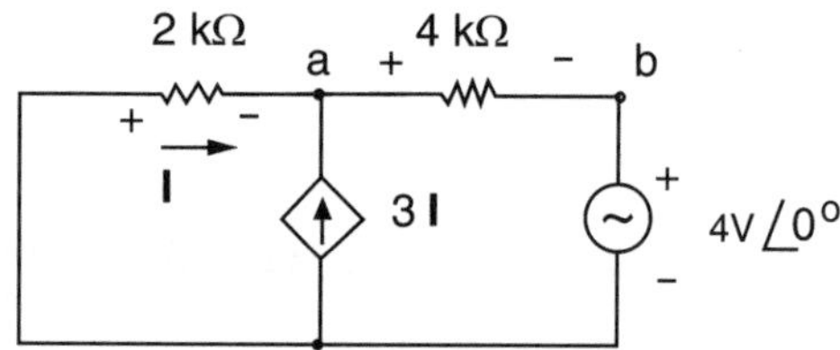

$4\text{ V}\angle 0^\circ = -(4\ \mathbf{I})(4\text{ k}\Omega) - \mathbf{I}(2\text{ k}\Omega) = -(18\text{ k}\Omega)\mathbf{I}$

$\mathbf{I} = -\dfrac{4\text{ V}\angle 0^\circ}{18\text{ k}\Omega} = -0.222\text{ mA}$

$\mathbf{V}_{ab(2)} = (4\text{ k}\Omega)(4)(-0.222\text{ mA}) = -3.56\text{ V}$

$\mathbf{V}_{ab} = \mathbf{V}_{ab(1)} + \mathbf{V}_{ab(2)} = 1.78\text{ V}\angle 0^\circ$

20.3 Thévenin's Theorem—Independent Sources

19. $\mathbf{Z}_{Th} = -j3\ \Omega$

$\mathbf{V}_{ab} = \mathbf{E}_{Th} = (5\text{ A}\angle 0^\circ)(3\ \Omega\angle -90^\circ) - 5\text{ V}\angle 90^\circ$
$= 20\text{ V}\angle -90^\circ$

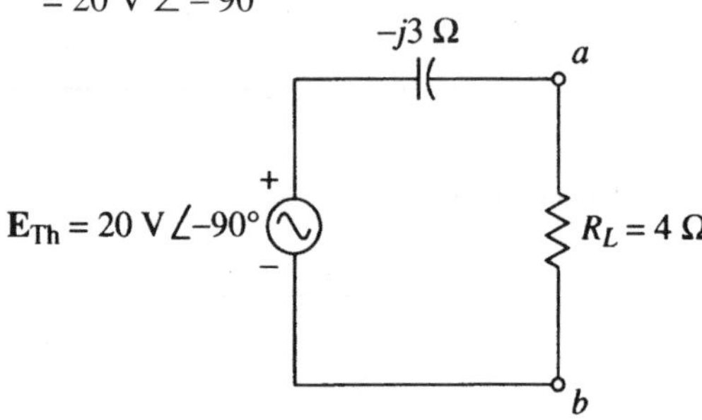

21. a.

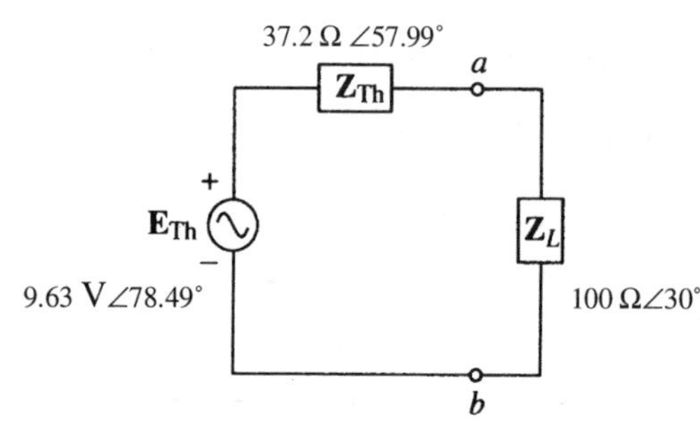

$X_C = \dfrac{1}{(2\pi)(5\text{ kHz})(1\ \mu\text{F})} = 31.8\ \Omega$

$X_L = (2\pi)(5\text{ kHz})(1\text{ mH}) = 31.4\ \Omega$

$\mathbf{Z}_{Th} = j31.4\ \Omega \| (50\ \Omega - j31.8\ \Omega) = 37.2\ \Omega\angle 57.99^\circ$

$\mathbf{V}_{ab}(1) = \left(\dfrac{j31.4\ \Omega}{50\ \Omega + j31.4\ \Omega - j31.8\ \Omega}\right)(10\text{ V}\angle 0^\circ)$

$= 6.28\text{ V}\angle 90.48^\circ$

$\mathbf{V}_{ab}(2) = (100\text{ mA}\angle 0^\circ)(37.2\ \Omega\angle 57.99^\circ)$

$= 3.72\text{ V}\angle 57.99^\circ$

$\mathbf{V}_{ab} = \mathbf{V}_{ab}(1) + \mathbf{V}_{ab}(2) = 9.63\text{ V}\angle 78.49^\circ = \mathbf{E}_{Th}$

$\mathbf{I} = \dfrac{9.63\text{ V}\angle 78.49^\circ}{37.2\ \Omega\angle 57.99^\circ + 100\ \Omega\angle 30^\circ}$
$= 0.0719\text{ A}\angle 41.00^\circ$

$P = I^2 Z_L \cos 30^\circ = 0.447\text{ W}$

23.

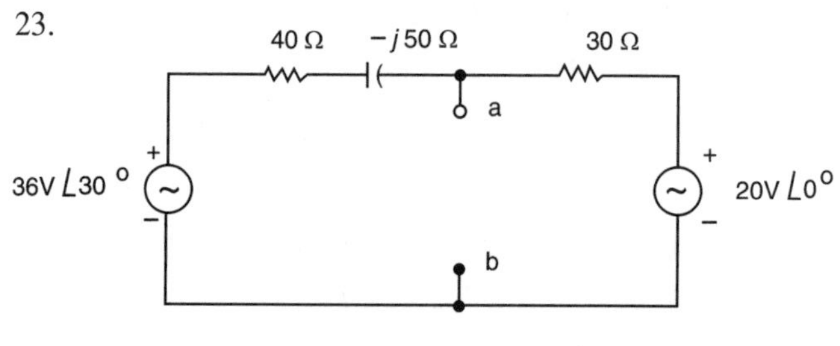

$\mathbf{V}_{ab} = 30\ \Omega\left(\dfrac{36\text{ V}\angle 30^\circ - 20\text{ V}\angle 0^\circ}{40\ \Omega + 30\ \Omega - j50\ \Omega}\right) + 20\text{ V}\angle 0^\circ$

$= 20.9\text{ V}\angle 20.69^\circ = \mathbf{E}_{Th}$

$\mathbf{Z}_{Th} = 30\ \Omega \| (40\ \Omega - j50\Omega) = 22.33\ \Omega\angle -15.80^\circ$

25.

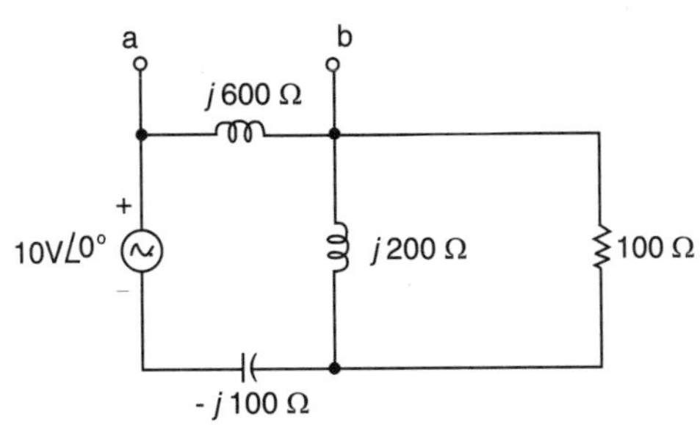

$\mathbf{Z}_{Th} = j600\ \Omega \| (-j100\ \Omega + 100\ \Omega \| j200\ \Omega)$
$= 109.9\ \Omega\angle -28.44^\circ$
voltage source:
$\mathbf{V}_{ab(1)}$
$$= \left(\frac{j600\ \Omega}{-j100\ \Omega + j600\ \Omega + 100\ \Omega \| j200\ \Omega}\right) 10\ \text{V}\ \angle 0^\circ$$
$= 10.99\ \text{V}\ \angle 8.43^\circ$
current source:

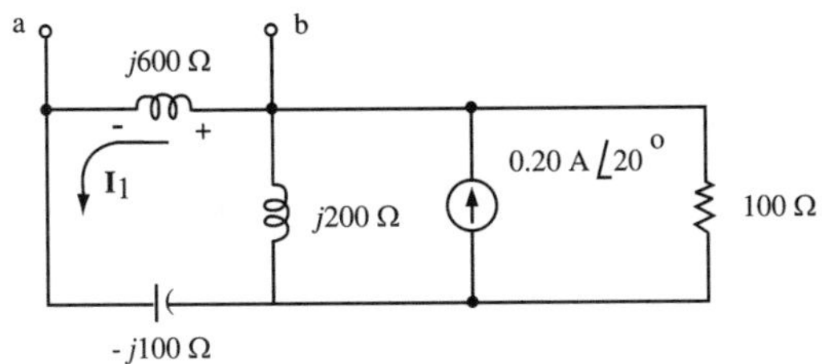

$\mathbf{Z}_T = j500\ \Omega \| j200\ \Omega \| 100\ \Omega = 81.9\ \Omega\angle 34.99^\circ$
$$\mathbf{I}_1 = \left(\frac{81.92\ \Omega\angle 34.99^\circ}{j500\ \Omega}\right)(0.20\ \text{A}\angle 20^\circ)$$
$= 0.0328\ \text{A}\angle -35.01^\circ$
$\mathbf{V}_{ab}(2) = -(j600\ \Omega)(0.0328\ \text{A}\angle -35.01^\circ)$
$= 19.66\ \text{V}\ \angle -125.01^\circ$
$\mathbf{E}_{Th} = \mathbf{V}_{ab} = \mathbf{V}_{ab}(1) + \mathbf{V}_{ab}(2) = 14.50\ \text{V}\ \angle -91.61^\circ$

27. a.

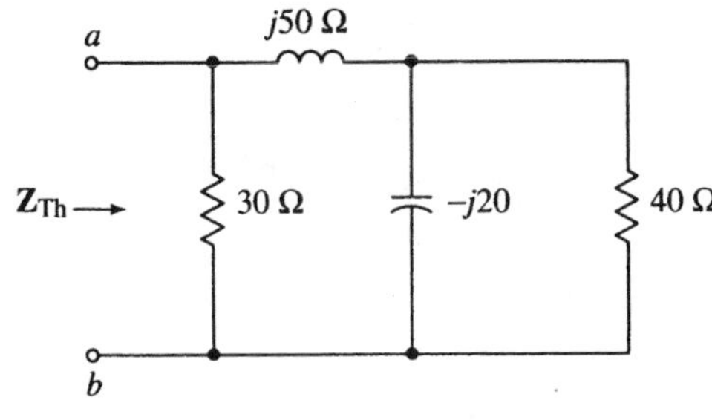

$\mathbf{Z}_{Th} = 30\ \Omega \| (j50\ \Omega + 40\ \Omega \| -j20\ \Omega)$
$= 20.6\ \Omega\angle 34.94^\circ$

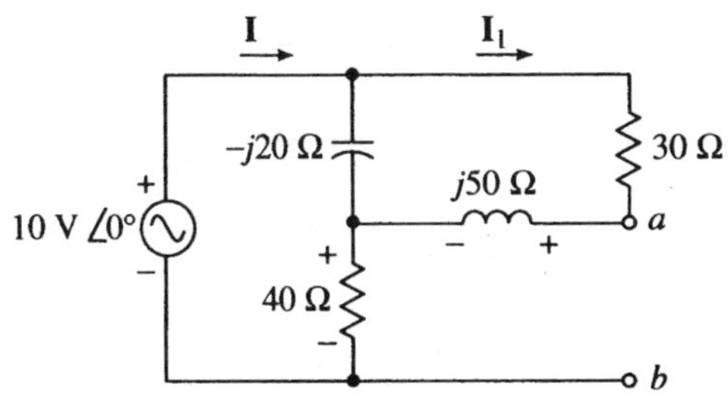

$\mathbf{Z}_T = 40\ \Omega + (-j20\ \Omega) \| (30\ \Omega + j50\ \Omega)$
$= 40\ \Omega + 27.5\ \Omega\angle -75.96^\circ = 53.7\ \Omega\angle -29.74^\circ$
$\mathbf{I} = 0.1861\ \text{A}\angle 29.74^\circ$
$\mathbf{I}_1 = 0.0877\ \text{A}\angle -105.26^\circ$
$\mathbf{E}_{Th} = (j50\ \Omega)\mathbf{I}_1 + (40\ \Omega)\mathbf{I} = 10.99\ \text{V}\ \angle 13.36^\circ$

b.

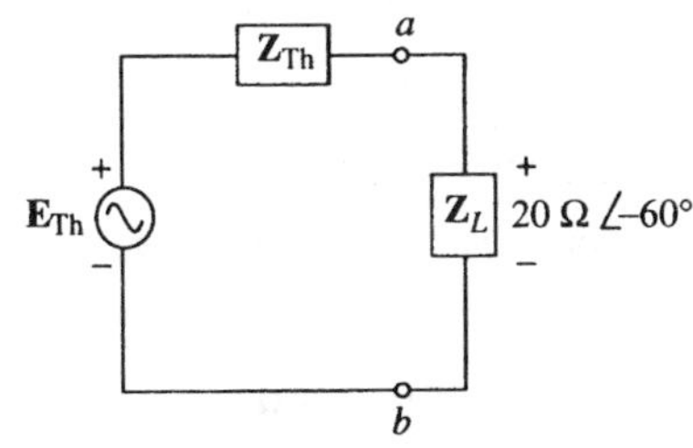

$\mathbf{V}_L = \mathbf{V}_{ab}$
$$= \left(\frac{20\ \Omega\angle -60^\circ}{20\ \Omega\angle 60^\circ + 20.55\ \Omega\angle 34.93^\circ}\right)(10.99\ \text{V}\ \angle 13.36^\circ)$$
$= 8.02\ \text{V}\ \angle -34.96^\circ$

$$P_L = \frac{(8.02\ \text{V})^2}{20\ \Omega}\cos 60^\circ = 1.607\ \text{W}$$

20.4 Norton's Theorem—Independent Sources

29. $\mathbf{Z}_N = -j3\ \Omega = 3\ \Omega\angle -90^\circ$
Current source:

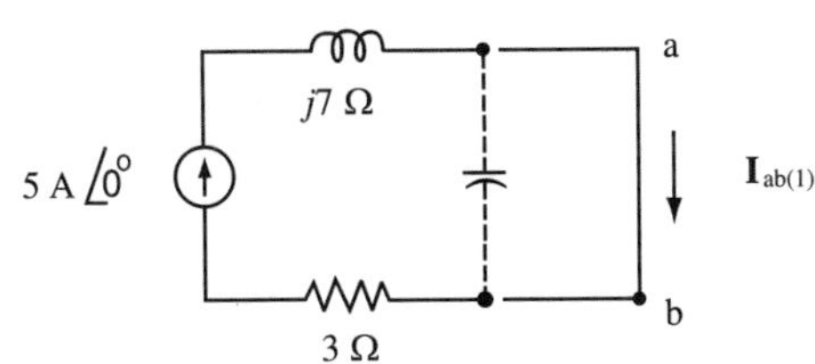

$\mathbf{I}_{ab(1)} = 5\ \text{A}\angle 0^\circ$
Voltage source:

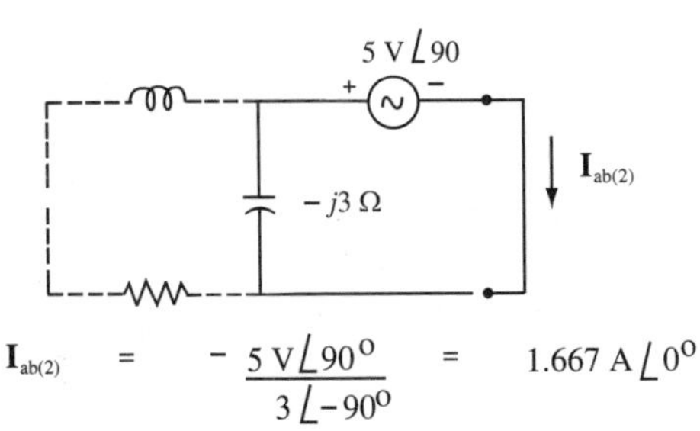

$$\mathbf{I}_{ab(2)} = -\frac{5\ \text{V}\angle 90^\circ}{3\angle -90^\circ} = 1.667\ \text{A}\angle 0^\circ$$

$$\mathbf{I}_{ab(2)} = \frac{-5\ \text{V}\ \angle 90^\circ}{3\ \Omega\angle -90^\circ} = 1.667\ \text{A}\angle 0^\circ$$
$\mathbf{I}_N = \mathbf{I}_{ab(1)} + \mathbf{I}_{ab(2)} = 6.67\ \text{A}\angle 0^\circ$

31. a. $\mathbf{Z}_N = 30\ \Omega \| (40\ \Omega - j50\ \Omega) = 22.3\ \Omega\angle -15.80°$

voltage source #1:

$$\mathbf{I}_{ab(1)} = \frac{36\ \text{V}\ \angle 0°}{40\ \Omega - j50\ \Omega} = 0.562\ \text{A}\angle 81.34°$$

voltage source #2:

$$\mathbf{I}_{ab(2)} = \frac{20\ \text{V}\ \angle 0°}{30\ \Omega} = 0.67\ \text{A}\angle 0°$$

$\mathbf{I}_N = \mathbf{I}_{ab} = \mathbf{I}_{ab(1)} + \mathbf{I}_{ab(2)} = 0.935\ \text{A}\angle 36.49°$

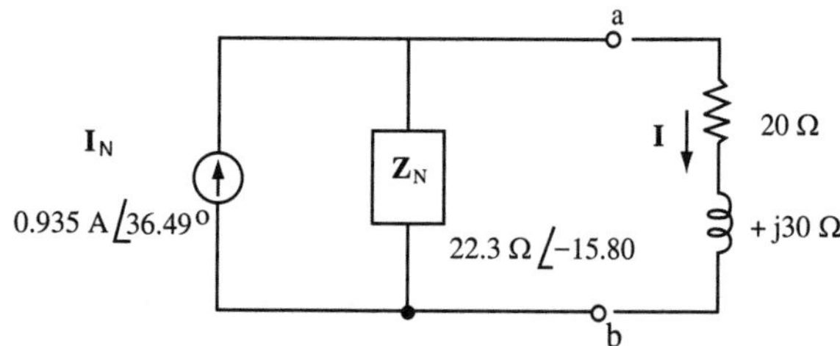

b. $$\mathbf{I} = \left(\frac{22.3\ \Omega\angle -15.80°}{22.3\ \Omega\angle -15.80 + 20\ \Omega + j30\ \Omega}\right) 0.935\ \text{A}\angle 36.49° = 0.436\ \text{A}\angle -9.27°$$

c. $P = (0.436\ \text{A})^2(20\ \Omega) = 3.80\ \text{W}$

33. a.

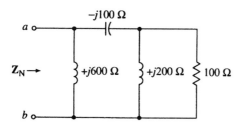

$\mathbf{Z}_N = +j600\ \Omega \| [-j100\ \Omega + (j200\ \Omega \| 100\ \Omega)] = +j600\ \Omega \| (80\ \Omega - j60\ \Omega) = 109.9\ \Omega\angle -28.44°$

Voltage source:

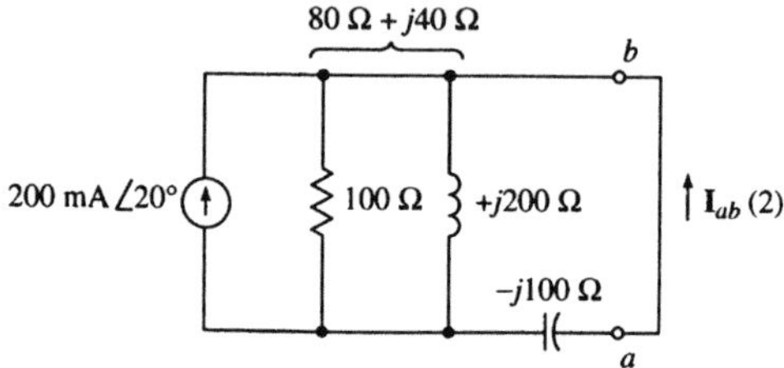

$$\mathbf{I}_{ab(1)} = \frac{10\ \text{V}\ \angle 0°}{80\ \Omega + j40\ \Omega - j100\ \Omega} = 0.1\ \text{A}\angle 36.87°$$

Current source:

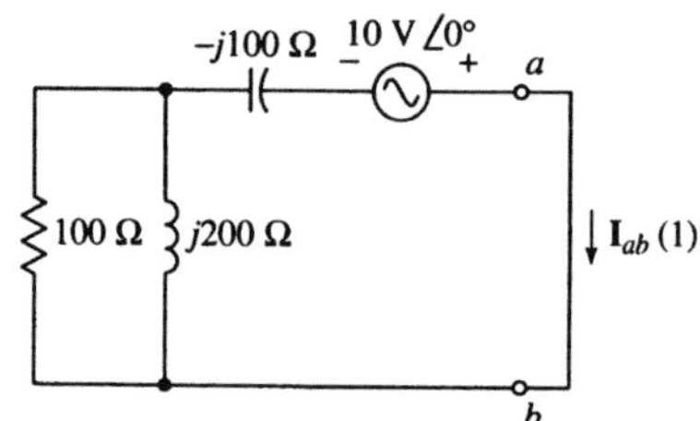

$$\mathbf{I}_{ab(2)} = (-0.2 \text{ A}\angle 20^\circ)\left(\frac{80\ \Omega + j40\ \Omega}{80\ \Omega + j40\ \Omega - j100\ \Omega}\right) = 0.1789 \text{ A}\angle -96.57^\circ$$

$$\mathbf{I}_N = \mathbf{I}_{ab} = \mathbf{I}_{ab(1)} + \mathbf{I}_{ab(2)} = 0.1319 \text{ A}\angle -63.17^\circ$$

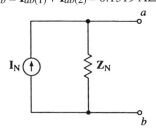

b. $$\mathbf{I}_L = \left(\frac{109.9\ \Omega\angle -28.44^\circ}{109.9\ \Omega\angle -28.44^\circ + 300\ \Omega\angle 0^\circ}\right)\cdot(0.1319 \text{ A}\angle -63.17^\circ) = 36.2 \text{ mA}\angle -84.09^\circ$$

c. $P_L = (0.0362)^2(300\ \Omega) = 0.394$ W

35. $$X_C = \frac{1}{2\pi(2 \text{ kHz})(1\ \mu\text{F})} = 79.6\ \Omega$$

$X_L = 2\pi(2 \text{ kHz})(1 \text{ mH}) = 12.57\ \Omega$

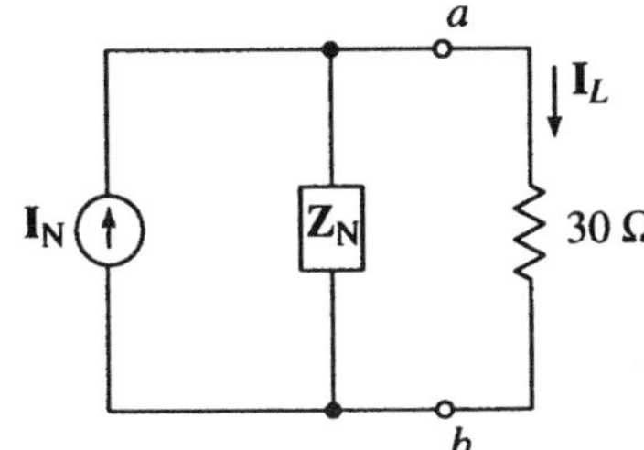

a. $\mathbf{Z}_N = j12.57\ \Omega \| (50\ \Omega - j79.6\ \Omega) = 14.13\ \Omega\angle 85.41^\circ$

Voltage source:

$$\mathbf{I}_{ab(1)} = \frac{10 \text{ V}\angle 0^\circ}{50\ \Omega - j79.6\ \Omega} = 0.1064 \text{ A}\angle 57.86^\circ$$

Current source:

$\mathbf{I}_{ab(2)} = 0.100 \text{ A}\angle 0^\circ$

$\mathbf{I}_N = \mathbf{I}_{ab(1)} + \mathbf{I}_{ab(2)} = 0.1806 \text{ A}\angle 29.91^\circ$

b. $$\mathbf{I}_L = \left(\frac{14.13\ \Omega\angle 85.41^\circ}{14.13\ \Omega\angle 85.41^\circ + 30\ \Omega}\right)(0.1807 \text{ A}\angle 29.92^\circ)$$

$= 0.0747 \text{ A}\angle 90.99^\circ$

20.5 Thévenin's and Norton's Theorems for Dependent Sources

37. a. $\mathbf{Z}_{Th} = -j40\ \text{k}\Omega \| 20\ \text{k}\Omega = 16\ \text{k}\Omega - j8\ \text{k}\Omega$

Dependent current source:

$\mathbf{V}_{ab(1)} = -(4.0 \text{ mS})(100 \text{ mV}\angle 0^\circ)(20\ \text{k}\Omega \| -j40\ \text{k}\Omega)$

$= 7.16 \text{ V}\angle 153.43^\circ$

Voltage source:

$$\mathbf{V}_{ab(2)} = \left(\frac{-j40\ \text{k}\Omega}{20\ \text{k}\Omega - j40\ \text{k}\Omega}\right)(6 \text{ V}\angle 0^\circ)$$

$= 5.367 \text{ V}\angle -26.57^\circ$

$\mathbf{E}_{Th} = \mathbf{V}_{ab}(1) + \mathbf{V}_{ab}(2) = 1.789 \text{ V}\angle 153.43^\circ$

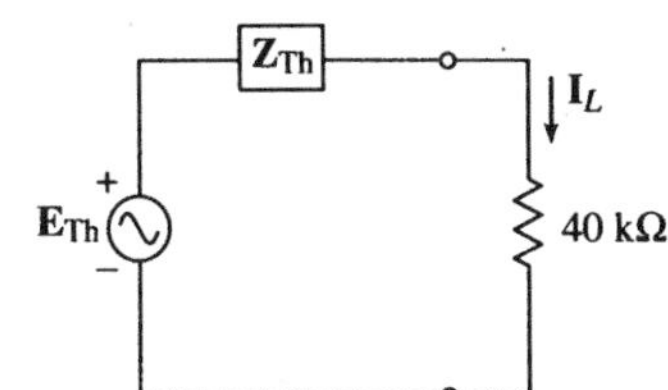

b. $$\mathbf{I}_L = \frac{1.789 \text{ V}\angle 153.43^\circ}{16\ \text{k}\Omega - j8\ \text{k}\Omega + 40\ \text{k}\Omega} = 31.6\ \mu\text{A}\angle 161.56^\circ$$

c. $P_L = (31.6\ \mu\text{A})^2(40\ \text{k}\Omega) = 0.04 \text{ mW} = 40\ \mu\Omega$

39.

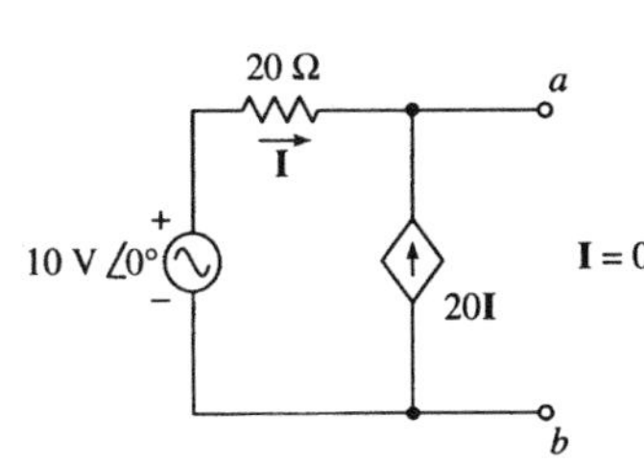

$\mathbf{V}_{ab} = 10 \text{ V}\angle 0^\circ = \mathbf{E}_{Th}$

$\mathbf{I}_{ab} = 21\mathbf{I}$

$$\mathbf{I} = \frac{10 \text{ V}\angle 0^\circ}{20\ \Omega} = 0.5 \text{ A}\angle 0^\circ$$

$\mathbf{I}_{ab} = 10.5 \text{ A}\angle 0^\circ = \mathbf{I}_N$

$$\mathbf{Z}_{Th} = \mathbf{Z}_N = \frac{10 \text{ V}\angle 0^\circ}{10.5 \text{ A}\angle 0^\circ} = 0.952\ \Omega$$

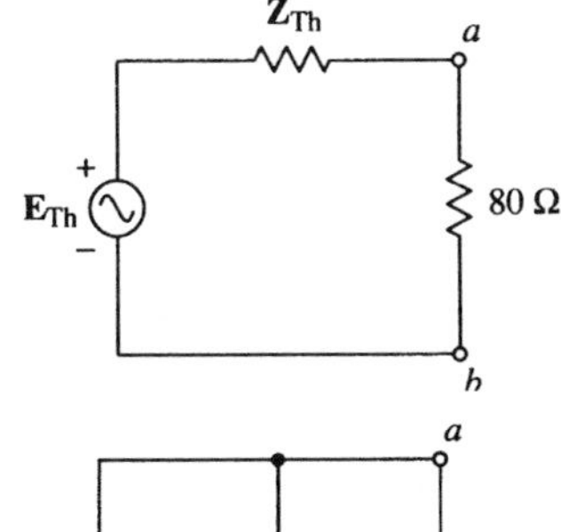

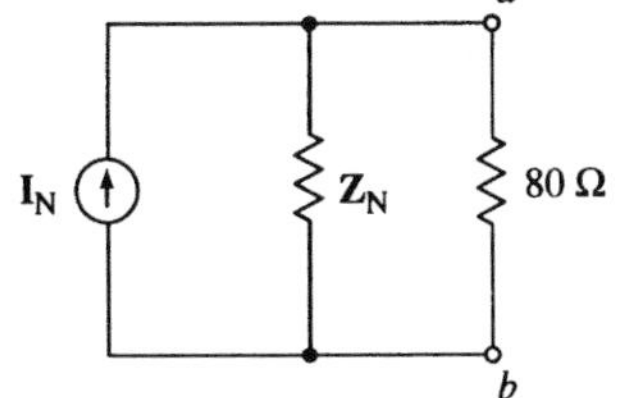

20.6 Maximum Power Transfer Theorem

41. a. $\mathbf{Z}_{Th} = (24\ \Omega \| -j16\ \Omega) + j8\ \Omega$
$= 13.31\ \Omega\angle -56.31^\circ + j8\ \Omega = 8\ \Omega\angle -22.62^\circ$

Voltage source:

$$\mathbf{V}_{ab}(1) = \left(\frac{-j16\ \Omega}{24\ \Omega - j16\ \Omega}\right)(36\ \text{V}\ \angle 0^\circ)$$
$$= 19.97\ \text{V}\ \angle -56.31^\circ$$

Current source:

$\mathbf{V}_{ab}(2) = -(j8\ \Omega)(2\ \text{A}\angle 0^\circ) = 16\ \text{V}\ \angle -90^\circ$

$\mathbf{E}_{Th} = \mathbf{V}_{ab} = 19.77\ \text{V}\ \angle -56.31^\circ + 16\ \text{V}\ \angle -90^\circ$
$= 34.4\ \text{V}\ \angle -71.24^\circ$

For maximum power $\mathbf{Z}_L = 8\ \Omega\angle\ 22.62^\circ$

b. $$\mathbf{I}_L = \frac{34.4\ \text{V}\ \angle -71.24^\circ}{8\ \Omega\angle -22.62^\circ + 8\ \Omega\angle +22.62^\circ}$$
$= 2.33\ \text{A}\angle -71.24^\circ$

$P_{max} = (2.33\ \text{A})^2(8\ \Omega)\cos 22.62^\circ = 40.1\bar{6}\ \text{W}$

43. a.

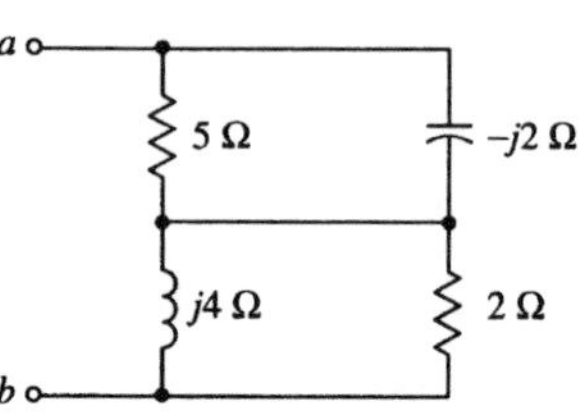

$\mathbf{Z}_{Th} = (5\ \Omega \| -j2\ \Omega) + (j4\ \Omega \| 2\ \Omega)$
$= (1.857\ \Omega\angle -68.20^\circ) + (1.789\ \Omega\angle 26.57^\circ)$
$= 2.47\ \Omega\angle -21.98^\circ$

$6\ \text{V}\ \angle 0^\circ$ source:

$$\mathbf{V}_{ab}(1) = \left(\frac{-j2\ \Omega}{5\ \Omega - j2\ \Omega}\right)(6\ \text{V}\ \angle 0^\circ)$$
$$-\left(\frac{2\ \Omega}{(2\ \Omega + j4\ \Omega}\right)(6\ \text{V}\ \angle 0^\circ) = 0.498\ \text{V}\ \angle 138.37^\circ$$

$8\ \text{V}\ \angle 30^\circ$ source:

$$\mathbf{V}_{ab}(2) = \left(\frac{2\ \Omega}{2\ \Omega + j4\ \Omega}\right)(8\ \text{V}\ \angle 30^\circ)$$
$$= 3.58\ \text{V}\ \angle -33.43^\circ$$

$\mathbf{E}_{Th} = \mathbf{V}_{ab} = \mathbf{V}_{ab}(1) + \mathbf{V}_{ab}(2) = 3.09\ \text{V}\ \angle -32.12^\circ$

b. $\mathbf{Z}_L = 2.47\ \Omega\angle 21.98^\circ$

$$\mathbf{I}_L = \frac{3.09\ \text{V}\ \angle -32.12^\circ}{2..47\ \Omega\angle -21.98^\circ + 2.47\ \Omega\angle 21.98^\circ}$$
$= 0.674\ \text{A}\angle -21.12^\circ$

c. $P_{max} = (0.674\ \text{A})^2(2.47\ \Omega)\cos 21.98^\circ = 1.039\ \text{W}$

45. $\mathbf{Z}_{Th} = (-j5\ \Omega) \| (10\ \Omega - j20\ \Omega) = 4.15\ \Omega\angle -85.24^\circ$
$\mathbf{Z}_L = 4.15\ \Omega\angle 85.24^\circ$

47. From Problem 21, the Thévenin equivalent is:

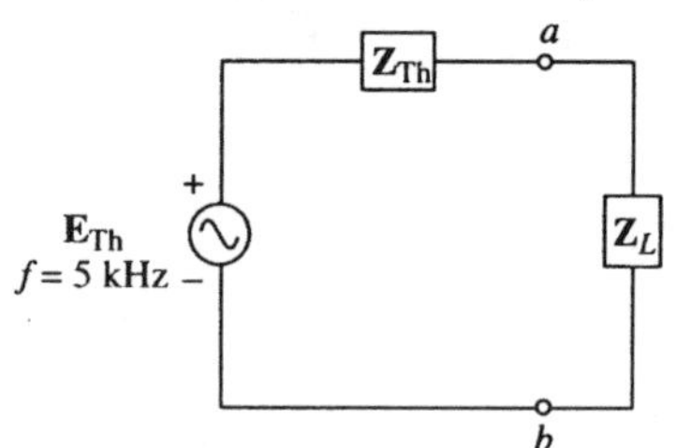

$\mathbf{E}_{Th} = 9.63\ \text{V}\ \angle 78.49^\circ$
$\mathbf{Z}_{Th} = 37.2\ \Omega\angle 57.99^\circ$

a. For maximum power, $\mathbf{Z}_L = 37.24\ \Omega\angle -57.99^\circ$.

b. For relative maximum power,
$R_L = \sqrt{R_{Th}^2 + (X_{Th} - X_L)^2}$
$= \sqrt{(19.74\ \Omega)^2 + (0.25\ \Omega)^2}$
$= 19.74\ \Omega$

c. $$X_C = \frac{1}{(2\pi)(5\ \text{kHz})(1\ \mu\text{F})} = = 31.8\ \Omega$$

$$\mathbf{I} = \frac{9.634\ \text{V}\ \angle 78.49^\circ}{37.24\ \Omega\angle 57.99^\circ + 19.74\ \Omega - j31.8\ \Omega}$$
$= 0.244\ \text{A}\angle 78.86^\circ$

$P_L = I^2R = (0.244\ \text{A})^2(19.74\ \Omega) = 1.176\ \text{W}$

20.7 Circuit Analysis Using Computers

4

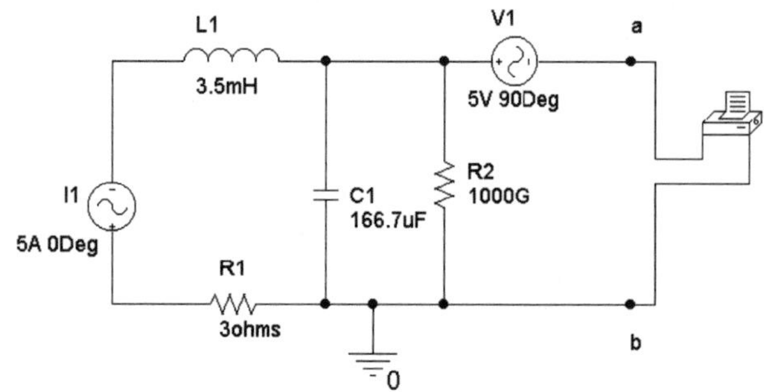

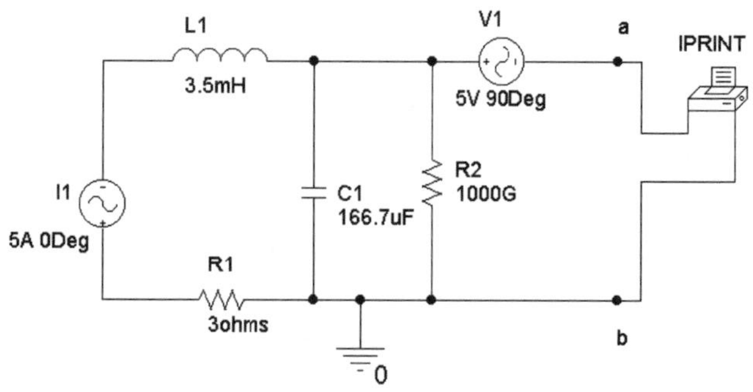

$\mathbf{E}_{Th} = 20\ \text{V}\ \angle -90^\circ$

$\mathbf{I}_N = 6.67\ \text{A}\angle 0^\circ$

$\mathbf{Z}_{Th} = \mathbf{Z}_N = 3.00\ \Omega\angle -90^\circ$

51.

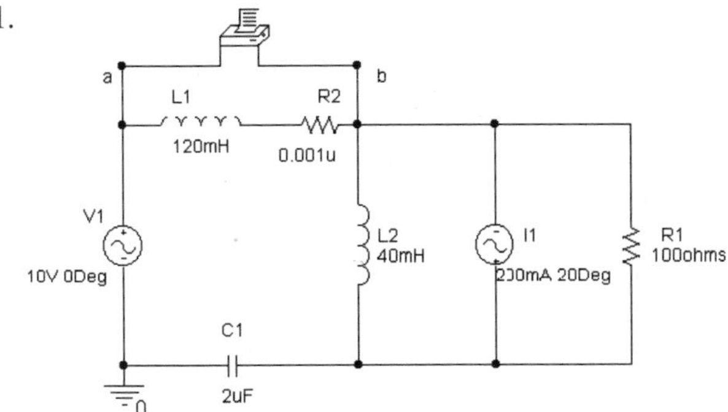

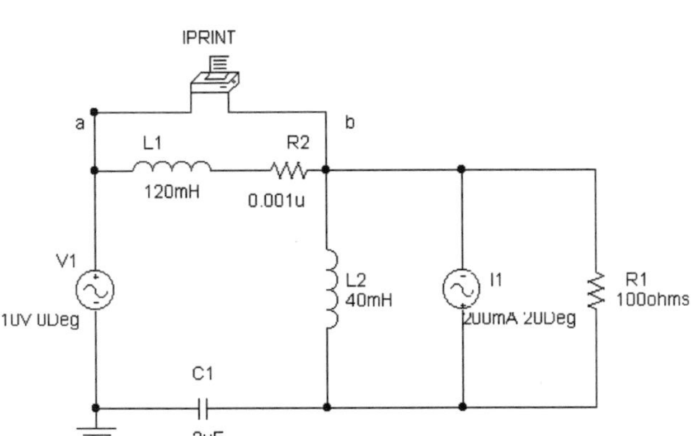

$\mathbf{E}_{Th} = 14.50 \text{ V} \angle -91.61^\circ$

$\mathbf{I}_N = 0.1319 \text{ A} \angle -63.17^\circ$

$\mathbf{Z}_{Th} = \mathbf{Z}_N = 109.9\ \Omega \angle -28.44^\circ$

53.

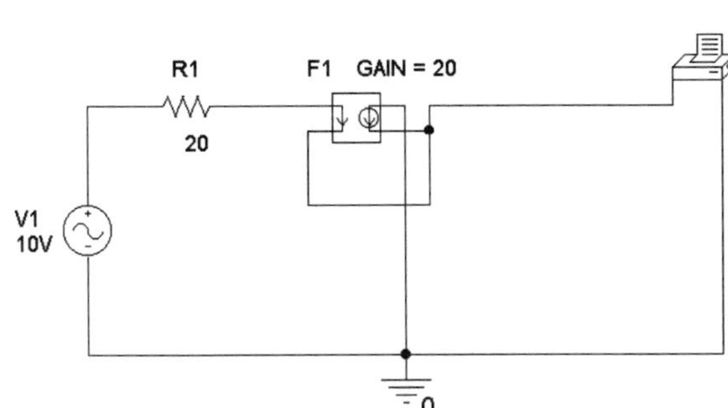

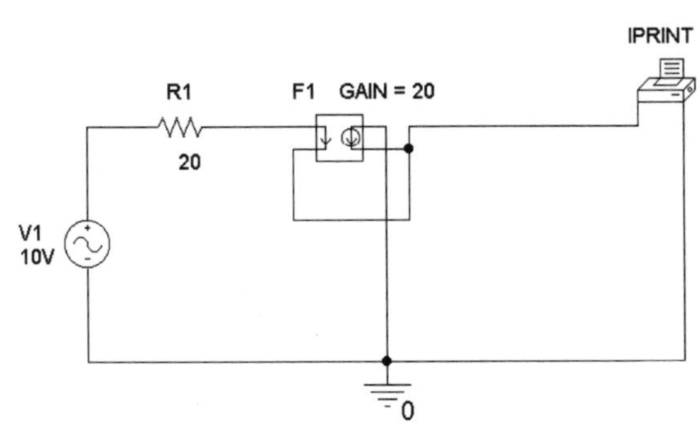

$\mathbf{E}_{Th} = 10 \text{ V} \angle 0^\circ$

$\mathbf{I}_N = 10.5 \text{ A} \angle 0^\circ$

$\mathbf{Z}_N = \mathbf{Z}_{Th} = 0.952\ \Omega \angle 0^\circ$

55.

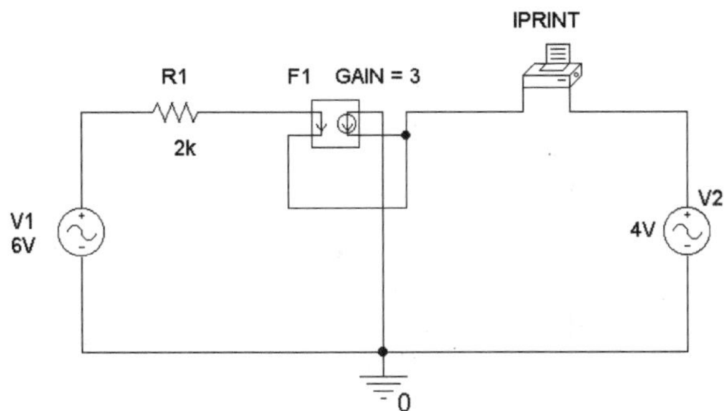

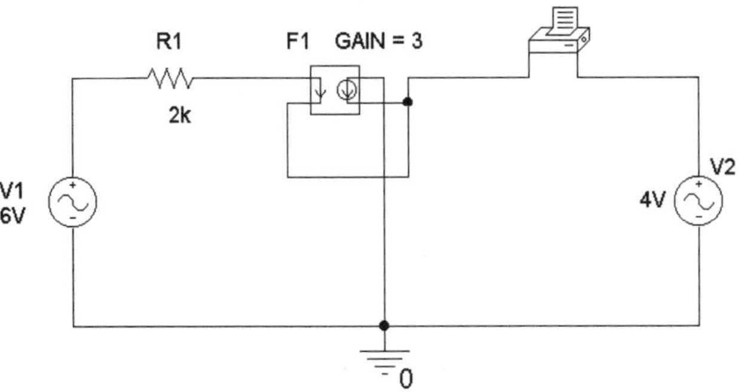

$\mathbf{E}_{Th} = 2 \text{ V} \angle 0^\circ$

$\mathbf{I}_N = 4 \text{ mA} \angle 0^\circ$

$\mathbf{Z}_N = 500\ \Omega \angle 0^\circ$

57.

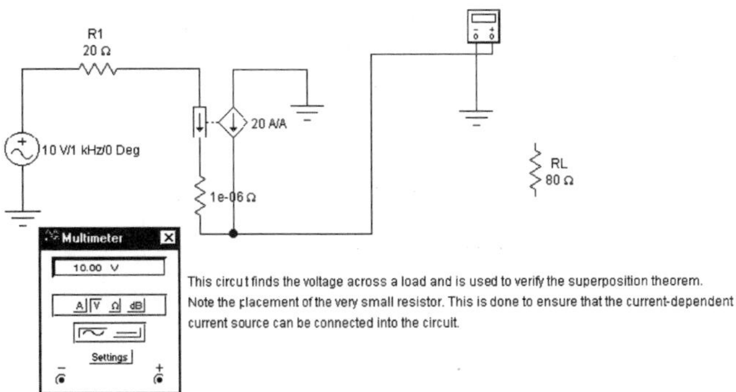

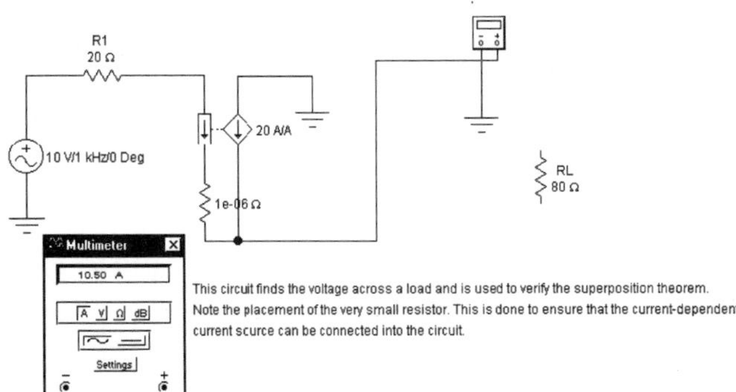

$$\mathbf{Z}_{Th} = \frac{10 \text{ V}}{10.5 \text{ A}} = 0.952\ \Omega$$

$\mathbf{E}_{Th} = 10 \text{ V}$

59.

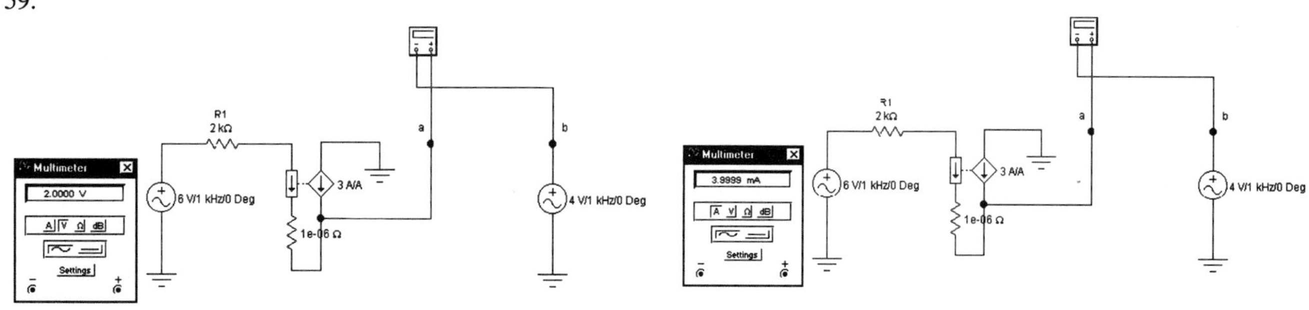

$$\mathbf{Z}_N = \frac{2.0\text{ V}}{4\text{ mA}} = 0.5\text{ k}\Omega$$

$$\mathbf{I}_N = 4.0\text{ mA}$$

Chapter

21

Resonance

21.1 Series Resonance

1. a. $\omega_S = \dfrac{1}{\sqrt{(100\text{ mH})(0.68\ \mu\text{F})}} = 3835\text{ rad/s}$

$f_S = \dfrac{3835\text{ rad/s}}{2\pi\text{ rad}} = 610.3\text{ Hz}$

b. $\mathbf{I} = \dfrac{10\text{ V}\angle 0°}{50\ \Omega + 15\ \Omega} = 153.8\text{ mA}\angle 0°$

c. $\mathbf{V}_R = (50\ \Omega)(153.8\text{ mA}\angle 0°) = 7.69\text{ V}\angle 0°$

$X_L = X_C = (3835\text{ rad/s})(100\text{ mH}) = 383.5\ \Omega$

$\mathbf{V}_C = (383.5\ \Omega\angle -90°)(153.8\text{ mA}\angle 0°)$
$= 59.0\text{ V}\angle -90°$

$\mathbf{V}_L = (15\ \Omega + j383.5\ \Omega)(153.8\text{ mA}\angle 0°)$
$= 59.03\text{ V}\angle 87.67°$

d. $P_L = (0.1538\text{ A})^2(15\ \Omega) = 0.355\text{ W}$

3. a. $R = \dfrac{625\text{ mV}}{25\text{ mA}} = 5.0\ \Omega$

$C = \dfrac{1}{4\pi^2(25\text{ kHz})^2(10\text{ mH})} = 4.05\text{ nF}$

b. $P = (0.025\text{ A})^2(5.0\ \Omega) = 3.13\text{ mW}$

c. $X_C = X_L = (2\pi)(25\text{ kHz})(10\text{ mH}) = 1.57\text{ k}\Omega$

$\mathbf{V}_C = (1.57\text{ k}\Omega\angle -90°)(25\text{ mA}\angle 0°)$
$= 39.3\text{ V}\angle -90°$

$\mathbf{V}_L = (1.57\text{ k}\Omega\angle 90°)(25\text{ mA}\angle 0°) = 39.3\text{ V}\angle 90°$

$\mathbf{V}_R = \mathbf{E} = 0.625\text{ V}\angle 0°$

d. $v_C = 55.5\sin(50\ 000\pi\tau - 90°)$

$v_L = 55.5\sin(50\ 000\pi\tau + 90°)$

$v_R = 0.884\sin(50\ 000\pi\tau)$

21.2 Quality Factor, Q

5. a. $\omega_S = \dfrac{1}{\sqrt{(10\text{ mH})(400\text{ pF})}} = 500\text{ krad/s}$

$f_S = \dfrac{500\text{ krad/s}}{2\pi} = 79.6\text{ kHz}$

b. $X_L = (500\text{ krad/s})(10\text{ mH}) = 5\text{ k}\Omega = X_C$

$R_{\text{coil}} = \dfrac{5\text{ k}\Omega}{50} = 100\ \Omega$

$\mathbf{Z}_T = 100\ \Omega + 100\ \Omega = 200\ \Omega$

c. $\mathbf{I} = \dfrac{2\text{ V}\angle 0°}{200\ \Omega} = 10\text{ mA}\angle 0°$

d. $\mathbf{V}_R = (10\text{ mA}\angle 0°)(100\ \Omega) = 1\text{ V}\angle 0°$

$\mathbf{V}_C = (10\text{ mA}\angle 0°)(5\text{ k}\Omega\angle -90°) = 50\text{ V}\angle -90°$

$\mathbf{V}_L = (10\text{ mA}\angle 0°)(100\ \Omega + j5000\Omega)$

$= 50.01\text{ V}\angle +88.85°$

e. $P_T = (2\text{ V})(10\text{ mA}) = 20\text{ mW}$

$Q_C = (10\text{ mA})^2(5\text{ k}\Omega) = 500\text{ mVAR}$ (capacitive)

$Q_L = (10\text{ mA})^2(5\text{ k}\Omega) = 500\text{ mVAR}$ (inductive)

f. $Q_S = \dfrac{500\text{ mVAR}}{20\text{ mW}} = 25$

7. a. $C = \dfrac{1}{(50\text{ krad/s})^2(5\text{ mH})} = 0.08\ \mu\text{F}$

$X_C = X_L = (500\text{ krad/s})(5\text{ mH}) = 250\ \Omega$

$R_T = \dfrac{250\ \Omega}{25} = 10\ \Omega$

$R = 10\ \Omega - 3.6\ \Omega = 6.4\ \Omega$

b. $P_T = \dfrac{(2.5\text{ V})^2}{10\ \Omega} = 0.625\text{ W}$

c. $\mathbf{V}_L = \dfrac{3.6\ \Omega + j250\ \Omega}{10\ \Omega\angle 0°} = 62.5\text{ V}\angle 89.17°$

21.3 Impedance of a Series Resonant Circuit

9. a. $\omega_S = \dfrac{1}{\sqrt{(1.25\ \mu\text{F})(12.5\text{ mH})}} = 8000\text{ rad/s}$

b.

ω_S (rad/s)	$\mathbf{Z}_T (\Omega)$
800	$10 - j990 = 990\ \Omega\angle -89.42°$
1600	$10 - j480 = 480\ \Omega\angle -88.81°$
4000	$10 - j150 = 150.3\ \Omega\angle -86.19°$
8000	$10 = 10\ \Omega\angle 0°$
16 000	$10 + j150 = 150.3\ \Omega\angle 86.19°$
40 000	$10 + j480 = 480\ \Omega\angle 88.81°$
80 000	$10 + j990 = 990\ \Omega\angle 89.42°$

c.

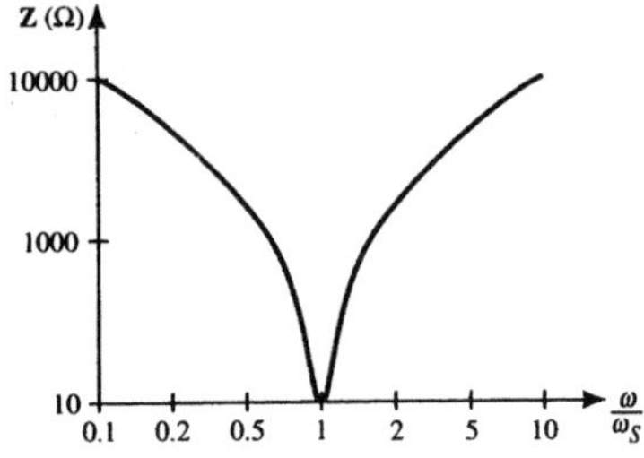

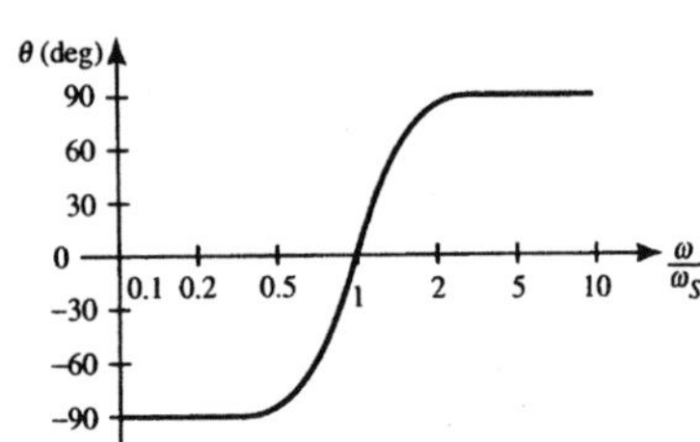

d.

ω(rad/s)	I
800	20.2 mA
1600	41.7 mA
4000	133.1 mA
8000	2 A
16 000	133.1 mA
40 000	41.7 mA
80 000	20.2 mA

e.

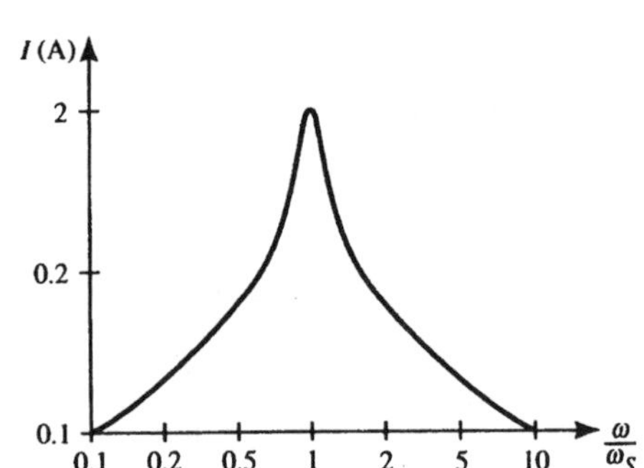

21.4 Power, Bandwidth, and Selectivity of a Series Resonant Circuit

11. a. $\omega_S = \dfrac{1}{\sqrt{(200\text{ mH})(0.36\,\mu\text{F})}} = 3727\text{ rad/s}$

$X_C = X_L = (3727\text{ rad/s})(200\text{ mH}) = 745\ \Omega$

$Q = \dfrac{745\ \Omega}{100\ \Omega} = 7.45$

$BW = \dfrac{3727\text{ rad/s}}{7.45} = 500\text{ rad/s}$

b. $P_{\max} = \dfrac{120\text{ V})^2}{100\ \Omega} = 144\text{ W}$

c. $\omega_1 \approx 3727\text{ rad/s} - \dfrac{500\text{ rad/s}}{2} = 3477\text{ rad/s}$

$\omega_2 \approx 3477\text{ rad/s} + 500\text{ rad/s} = 3977\text{ rad/s}$

d. $\omega_1 = \dfrac{-(100\ \Omega)(0.36\,\mu\text{F}) + \sqrt{[(100\ \Omega)(0.36\,\mu\text{F})]^2 + 4(0.36\,\mu\text{F})(200\text{ mH})}}{2(200\text{ mH})(0.36\,\mu\text{F})} = 3485\text{ rad/s}$

$\omega_2 = 3485\text{ rad/s} + 500\text{ rad/s} = 3985\text{ rad/s}$

e. The results were close, although the approximation will yield some errors if used in further calculations. The errors would be less if Q were larger.

f. $\mathbf{I}_1 + \dfrac{120\text{ V}}{100\ \Omega - j797\ \Omega + j697\ \Omega} = 0.849\text{ A}\angle 45^\circ \quad P = 72\text{ W}$

13. a. $C = \dfrac{1}{4\pi^2(200\text{ kHz})^2(10\text{ mH})} = 63.325\text{ pF}$

$X_C = X_L = 2\pi(200\text{ kHz})(10\text{ mH}) = 12.566\text{ k}\Omega$

$Q = \dfrac{200\text{ kHz}}{16\text{ kHz}} = 12.5$

$R = \dfrac{12.566\text{ k}\Omega}{12.5} = 1005\ \Omega$

b. $\mathbf{V} = 25\text{ V}\angle 0^\circ$

$P = \dfrac{(25\text{ V})^2}{1\text{ k}\Omega} = 0.625\text{ W}$

c. $\mathbf{V} = \left(\dfrac{12.566\text{ k}\Omega\angle 90^\circ}{1.005\text{ k}\Omega\angle 0^\circ}\right)(25\text{ V}\angle 0^\circ) = 312.5\text{ V}\angle 90^\circ$

$v_O = 442\sin(400\pi \times 10^3 t + 90^\circ)$

21.5 Series-to-Parallel RL and RC Conversion

15. circuit (a)

a. $X_L = (1000 \text{ rad/s})(240 \text{ MH}) = 240\ \Omega$

$Q = \dfrac{240\ \Omega}{10\ \Omega} = 24$

b. $R_P = 10\ \Omega(1 + 24^2) = 5770\ \Omega$

$X_{LP} = \dfrac{5770\ \Omega}{24} = 240\ \Omega$

c. $X_L = (10 \text{ krad/s})(240 \text{ mH}) = 2400\ \Omega$

$Q = \dfrac{2400\ \Omega}{10\ \Omega} = 240$

$R_P \cong 10\ \Omega(240)^2 = 576 \text{ k}\Omega$

$X_{LP} \cong \dfrac{576 \text{ k}\Omega}{240} = 2400\ \Omega$

circuit (b)

a. $X_L = 100\ \Omega$

$Q = 1$

b. $R_P = 100\ \Omega(1 + 1^2) = 200\ \Omega$

$X_{LP} = 200\ \Omega$

c. $X_L = 1000\ \Omega$

$Q = 10$

$R_P = 100\ \Omega(1 + 10^2) = 10.1 \text{ k}\Omega$

$X_{LP} = 1.01 \text{ k}\Omega$

circuit (c)

a. $X_L = (1000 \text{ rad/s})(25 \text{ mH}) = 25\ \Omega$

$Q = \dfrac{25\ \Omega}{2\ \Omega} = 12.5$

b. $R_P = (2\ \Omega)(1 + 12.5^2) = 314.5\ \Omega$

$X_{LP} = \dfrac{314.5\ \Omega}{12.5} = 25.16\ \Omega$

c. $X_L = 250\ \Omega$

$Q = 125$

$R_P = 31.25 \text{ k}\Omega$

$X_{LP} = 250\ \Omega$

17. circuit (a)

$Q = \dfrac{300\ \Omega}{20\ \Omega} = 15$

$R_P \cong (20 \text{ W})(15^2) = 4500\ \Omega$

$X_{CP} \cong 300\ \Omega$

circuit (b)

$Q = \dfrac{90\ \Omega}{45\ \Omega} = 2$

$R_P = 45\ \Omega(1 + 2^2) = 225\ \Omega$

$X_{CP} = \dfrac{225\ \Omega}{2} = 112.5\ \Omega$

circuit (c)

$Q = \dfrac{2500\ \Omega}{500\ \Omega} = 5$

$R_P = 500\ \Omega(1 + 5^2) = 13 \text{ k}\Omega$

$X_{CP} + \dfrac{13 \text{ k}\Omega}{5} = 2600\ \Omega$

19. circuit (a)

$Q = \dfrac{68 \text{ k}\Omega}{17 \text{ k}\Omega} = 4$

$R_S = \dfrac{68 \text{ k}\Omega}{(1 + 4^2)} = 4 \text{ k}\Omega$

$X_{LS} = (4)(4 \text{ k}\Omega) = 16 \text{ k}\Omega$

circuit (b)

$Q = \dfrac{4 \text{ k}\Omega}{12 \text{ k}\Omega} = 0.333$

$R_S = \dfrac{4 \text{ k}\Omega}{1 + (0.333)^2} = 3.6 \text{ k}\Omega$

$X_{CS} = (0.333)(3.6 \text{ k}\Omega) = 1.2 \text{ k}\Omega$

circuit (c)

$Q = 100$

$R_S \cong \dfrac{100 \text{ k}\Omega}{(100)^2} = 10\ \Omega$

$X_{LS} = (10\ \Omega)(100) = 1 \text{ k}\Omega$

21. $R_P = R_S(1 + Q^2)$

$Q = \sqrt{\dfrac{R_P}{R_S} - 1} = \sqrt{\dfrac{600\ \Omega}{300\ \Omega} - 1} = 1$

$X_{LS} = 300\ \Omega \qquad L_S = \dfrac{300\ \Omega}{250 \text{ krad/s}} = 1.2 \text{ mH}$

$X_{LP} = 600\ \Omega \qquad L_P = \dfrac{600\ \Omega}{250 \text{ krad/s}} = 2.4 \text{ mH}$

21.6 Parallel Resonance

23. a. $\omega_P = \dfrac{1}{\sqrt{(12.5 \text{ nF})(200 \text{ mH})}} = 20 \text{ krad/s}$

b.

ω	$\mathbf{Z}_T$	V
2 krad/s	$0.404 \text{ k}\Omega\angle +88.84°$	$0.808 \text{ V } \angle 88.84°$
4 krad/s	$0.833 \text{ k}\Omega\angle 87.61°$	$1.666 \text{ V } \angle 87.61°$
10 krad/s	$2.643 \text{ k}\Omega\angle 82.41°$	$5.286 \text{ V } \angle 82.41°$
20 krad/s	$20 \text{ k}\Omega\angle 0°$	$40 \text{ V } \angle 0°$
40 krad/s	$2.643 \text{ k}\Omega\angle -82.41°$	$5286 \text{ V } \angle -82.41$
100 krad/s	$0.833 \text{ krad/s } \angle -87.61°$	$1.666 \text{ V } \angle -87.61$
200 krad/s	$0.404 \text{ k}\Omega\angle -88.84°$	$0.808 \text{ V } \angle 88.84$

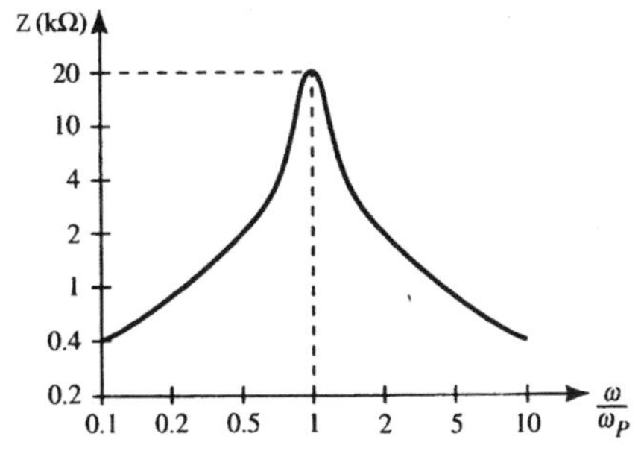

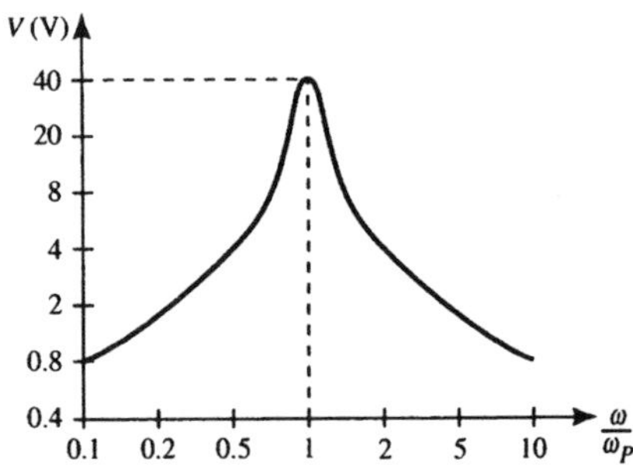

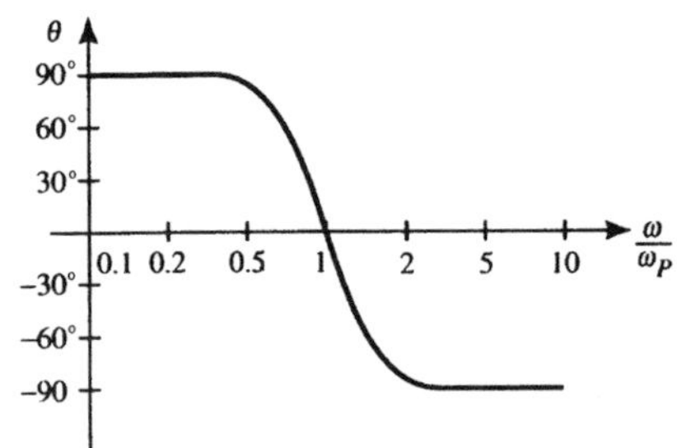

25. a. $\omega_P = \dfrac{1}{\sqrt{(25 \text{ mH})(25 \text{ nF})}}\sqrt{1 - \dfrac{(133\ \Omega)^2(25 \text{ nF})}{25 \text{ mH}}}$

$= (40\ \ 000 \text{ rad/s})(0.9911) = 39.6 \text{ krad/s}$

$f_P = \dfrac{39.6 \text{ krad/s}}{2\pi} = 6310 \text{ Hz}$

b. $X_{LS} = (39.6 \text{ krad/s})(25 \text{ mH}) = 991\ \Omega$

$Q_{\text{coil}} = \dfrac{991\ \Omega}{133\ \Omega} = 7.452$

$R_P = (133\ \Omega)(1 + 7.452^2) = 7519\ \Omega$

$X_{LP} = \dfrac{7519\ \Omega}{7.542} = 1009\ \Omega = X_C$

$R_{\text{eq}} = 7519\ \Omega \| 60 \text{ k}\Omega = 6682\ \Omega$

$Q = \dfrac{6682\ \Omega}{1009\ \Omega} = 6.622$

c. $\mathbf{V} = (100 \text{ mA}\angle 0^\circ)(6682\ \Omega) = 668.2 \text{ V } \angle 0^\circ$

$\mathbf{I}_R = 11.14 \text{ mA}\angle 0^\circ$

$\mathbf{I}_L = \dfrac{668.2 \text{ V } \angle 0^\circ}{133\ \Omega + j991\ \Omega} = 668.3 \text{ mA}\angle -82.36^\circ$

$\mathbf{I}_C = 662.2 \text{ mA}\angle 90^\circ$

d. $P_T = (100 \text{ mA})^2(6682\ \Omega) = 66.82 \text{ W}$

e. $\text{BW} = \dfrac{396 \text{ krad/s}}{6.622} = 5.98 \text{ krad/s}$

$\text{BW} = \dfrac{6310 \text{ Hz}}{6.622} = 952 \text{ Hz}$

f.

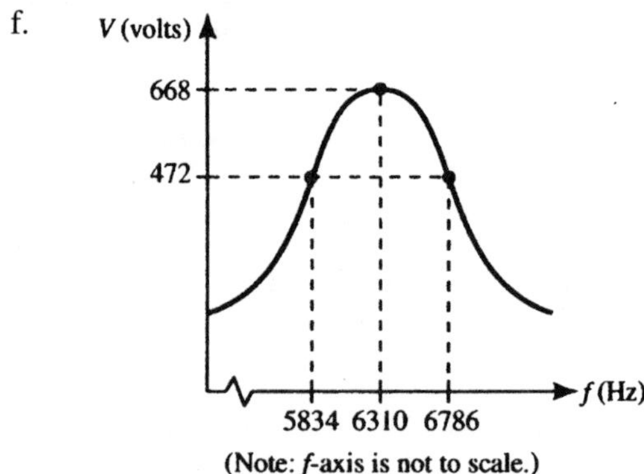

27. $X_L = 2\pi(50 \text{ kHz})(25 \text{ mH}) = 7854\ \Omega$

$Q_{\text{coil}} = \dfrac{7854\ \Omega}{100\ \Omega} = 78.54$

$X_{LP} \approx X_L = 7854\ \Omega = X_C$

$R_P \approx (78.54)^2(100\ \Omega) = 616.95 \text{ k}\Omega$

$Q = \dfrac{50 \text{ kHz}}{10 \text{ kHz}} = 5.0$

$R_{\text{eq}} = (7854\ \Omega)(5.0) = 39.270 \text{ k}\Omega$

$\dfrac{1}{R_1} = \dfrac{1}{39.27 \text{ k}\Omega} - \dfrac{1}{616.95 \text{ k}\Omega} = 23.84\ \mu\text{S}$

$R_1 = 41.94 \text{ k}\Omega$

$C = \dfrac{1}{2\pi(50 \text{ kHz})(7854\ \Omega)} = 405 \text{ pF}$

$\mathbf{I}_L = (1 \text{ mA}\angle 0^\circ)\dfrac{(39.27 \text{ k}\Omega)}{100\ \Omega + j7854\ \Omega}$

$= 5.0 \text{ mA}\angle -89.27^\circ$

29. a. $X_{LP} = 1000\ \Omega$ for resonance

But $X_{LP} = \dfrac{X_{LS}^2 + R_S^2}{X_{LS}}$

$1000\ \Omega = \dfrac{X_{LS}^2 + (300\ \Omega)^2}{X_{LS}}$

$X_{LS}^2 - 1000\, X_{LS} + 90{,}000 = 0$

Solving the quadratic equation gives

$X_{LS} = 100\ \Omega,\ 900\ \Omega$

$X_{LS} = 900\ \Omega$ is the better answer (more selective)

b. $Q_{\text{coil}} = \dfrac{900\ \Omega}{300\ \Omega} = 3.0$

$R_P = (1000\ \Omega)(3) = 3000\ \Omega$

$R_{\text{eq}} = 3000\ \Omega \| 6000\ \Omega = 2000\ \Omega$

$Q = \dfrac{2000\ \Omega}{1000\ \Omega} = 2.0$

c. $\text{BW} = \dfrac{2000 \text{ rad/s}}{2.0} = 1000 \text{ rad/s}$

d. $C \dfrac{1}{(2000 \text{ rad/s})(1000\ \Omega)} = 500 \text{ nF}$

$L = \dfrac{900\ \Omega}{2000 \text{ rad/s}} = 0.450 \text{ H}$

e. $\mathbf{V}_C = (50 \text{ mA}\angle 0^\circ)(2000\ \Omega) = 100 \text{ V } \angle 0^\circ$

21.7 Circuit Analysis Using Computers

31.

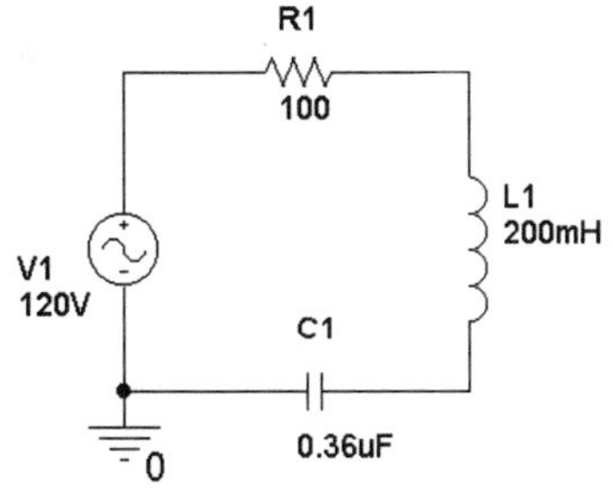

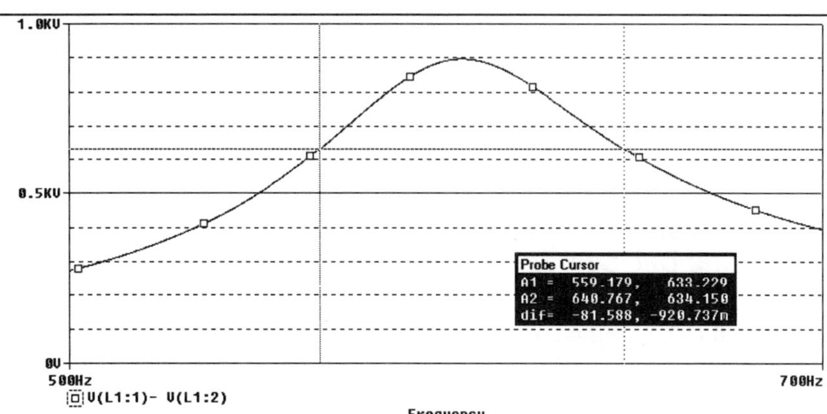

33.

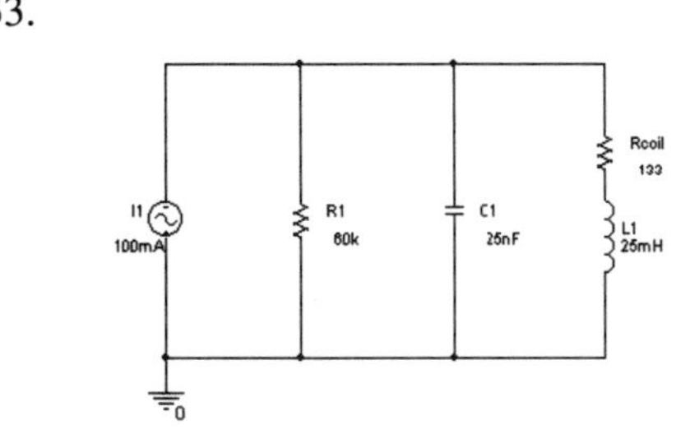

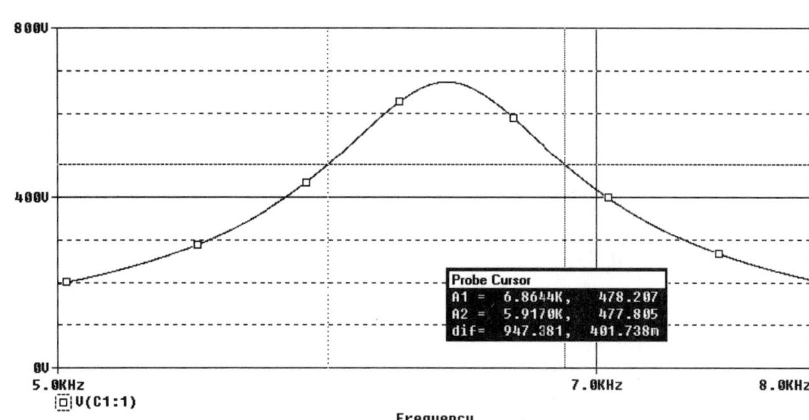

35.

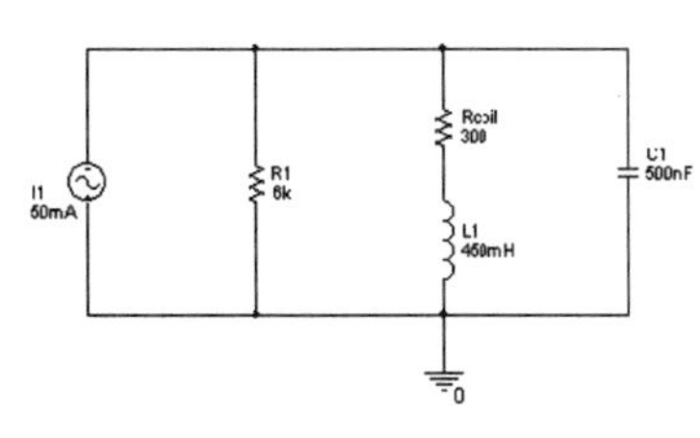

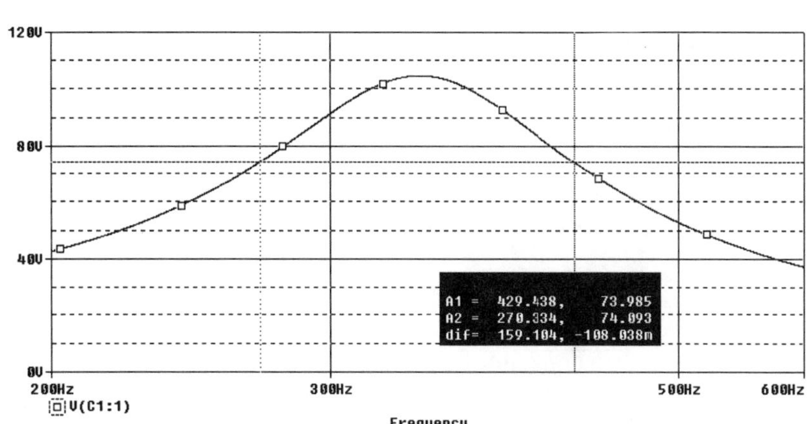

Chapter

22

Filters and the Bode Plot

22.1 The Decibel

1. a. $$A_p = \frac{2.4\text{ W}}{1.2\text{ mW}} = 2000\ (33.0\text{ db})$$

b. $$A_p = \frac{700\text{ mW}}{3.5\ \mu\text{W}} = 200\,000\ (53.0\text{ dB})$$

c. $$A_p = \frac{12\ \mu\text{W}}{6.\text{ pW}} = 2 \times 10^6\ (63.0\text{ dB})$$

d. $$A_p = \frac{1.0\text{ W}}{2.5\text{ mW}} = 400\ (26.0\text{ dB})$$

3. a. $$P_{in} = \frac{(2\text{ mV})^2}{2\text{ k}\Omega} = 2 \times 10^{-9}\text{ W} = 2\text{ nW}$$

$$V_{out} = \sqrt{(10\ \Omega)(100\text{ mW})} = 1\text{ V}$$

$$A_p = \frac{100\text{ mW}}{2\text{ nW}} = 50 \times 10^6\ (77.0\text{ dB})$$

$$A_v = \frac{1\text{ V}}{2\text{ mV}} = 500\ (54.0\text{ dB})$$

b. $$V_{in} = \sqrt{(2\text{ k}\Omega)(16\ \mu\text{W})} = 0.1789\text{ V}$$

$$P_{out} = \frac{(40\text{ mV})^2}{10\ \Omega} = 160\ \mu\text{W}$$

$$A_p = \frac{(160\ \mu\text{W}}{16\ \mu\text{W}} = 10\ (10\text{ dB})$$

$$A_v = \frac{40\text{ mV}}{178.9\text{ mV}} = 0.2236\ (-13.0\text{ dB})$$

c. $$P_{in} = \frac{(3\text{ mV})^2}{2\text{ k}\Omega} = 4.5\text{ nW}$$

$$V_{out} = \sqrt{(10\ \Omega)(60\text{ mW})} = 0.7746\text{ V}$$

$$A_p = \frac{60\text{ mW}}{4.5\text{ nW}} = 13.3 \times 10^6\ (71.25\text{ db})$$

$$A_v = \frac{0.7746\text{ V}}{3\text{ mV}} = 258.2\ (48.24\text{ dB})$$

d. $$V_{in} = \sqrt{(2\text{ k}\Omega)(2\text{ pW})} = 63.246\mu\text{V}$$

$$P_{out} = \frac{(80\text{ mV})^2}{10\ \Omega} = 640\ \mu\text{W}$$

$$A_p = \frac{640\ \mu\text{W}}{2\text{ pW}} = 320 \times 10^6\ (85.05\text{ dB})$$

$$A_v = \frac{80\text{ mV}}{63.2\ \mu\text{V}} = 1265\ (62.04\text{ dB})$$

5. $$P_{in} = \frac{(250\text{ mV})^2}{5\text{ k}\Omega} = 12.5\ \mu\text{W}$$

$$A_p = 10^{35/10} = 3162$$

$$P_{out} = (12.5\ \mu\text{W})(3162) = 39.53\text{ mW}$$

$$V_{out} = \sqrt{(39.53\text{ mW})(250\ \Omega)} = 3.1436\text{ V}$$

$$A_v = \frac{3.1436\text{ V}}{250\text{ mV}} = 12.57$$

$$A_v(\text{dB}) = 21.99\text{ dB}$$

7. a. $$P = 10\log\frac{50\text{ mW}}{1\text{ mW}} = 17\text{ dBm } (-13\text{ dBW})$$

b. $$P = 10\log\frac{1\text{ W}}{1\text{ mW}} = 30\text{ dBm } (0\text{ dBW})$$

c. $$P = 10\log\frac{400\text{ nW}}{1\text{ mW}} = -34\text{ dBm } (-64\text{ dBW})$$

d. $$P = 10\log\frac{250\text{ pW}}{1\text{ mW}} = -66\text{ dBm } (-96\text{ dBW})$$

9. a. $P = (1\text{ mW})(10^{23.5/10}) = 0.2239\text{ W}$

b. $P = (1\text{ W})(10^{-45.2/10}) = 30.2\ \mu\text{W}$

c. $P = (1\text{ mW})(10^{-83/10}) = 5.012\text{ pW}$

d. $P = (1\text{ W})(10^{33/10}) = 1995\text{ W}$

11. a. $$20\log\frac{2.00\text{ V}}{1.0\text{ V}} = 6.02\text{ dBV}$$

b. $$20\log\frac{0.034\text{ V}}{1.0\text{ V}} = -29.4\text{ dBV}$$

c. $$20\log\frac{24.0\text{ V}}{1.0\text{ V}} = 27.6\text{ dBV}$$

d. $$20\log\frac{58.2 \times 10^{-6}\text{ V}}{1\text{ V}} = -84.7\text{ dBV}$$

13. a. $V = (1\text{ V})10^{-2.5/20} = 0.750\text{ V}$

b. $V = (1\text{ V})10^{6.0/20} = 2.00\text{ V}$

c. $V = (1\text{ V})10^{-22.4/20} = 0.0759\text{ V}$

d. $V = (1\text{ V})10^{10/20} = 3.16\text{ V}$

15. $$V = 30\text{ V}_{p\text{-}p} \equiv \frac{30\text{ V}}{2\sqrt{2}} = 10.6\text{ V}_{rms}$$

$$V \equiv 20\log\frac{10.6\text{ V}}{1\text{ V}} = 20.5\text{ dBV}$$

22.2 Multistage Systems

17. $A_{P1} = 10 \log 200 = 23.01 \text{ dB}$

$A_{P3} = 10 \log 16 = 12.04 \text{ dB}$

$P_{in} = 10 \log \frac{16\ \mu\text{W}}{1 \text{ mW}} = -17.96 \text{ dBm}$

$P_1 = -17.96 \text{ dBM} + 23.01 \text{ dB} = 5.05 \text{ dBm}$

$P_2 = 5.05 \text{ dBm} - 3.0 \text{ dB} = 2.05 \text{ dBm}$

$P_{out} = 2.05 \text{ dBm} + 12.04 \text{ dB} = 14.09 \text{ dBm}$

$P_{out} = (1 \text{ mW})(10^{14.09/10}) = 25.6 \text{ mW}$

19. $P_2 = 10\log \frac{140 \text{ mW}}{1 \text{ mW}} = 21.5 \text{ dBm}$

$P_{out} = 21.5 \text{ dBm} + 6 \text{ dB} = 27.5 \text{ dBm}$

$P_1 = 21.5 \text{ dBm} + 4 \text{ dB} = 25.5 \text{ dBm}$

$A_{P1} = 10 \log 10\ 000 = 40 \text{ dB}$

$P_{in} = 25.5 \text{ dBm} - 40 \text{ dB} = -14.5 \text{ dBm}$

$P_{out} = (1 \text{ mW})(10^{27.5/10}) = 0.557 \text{ W}$

$V_{out} = \sqrt{(0.557 \text{ W})(5 \text{ k}\Omega)} = 52.8 \text{ W}$

21.

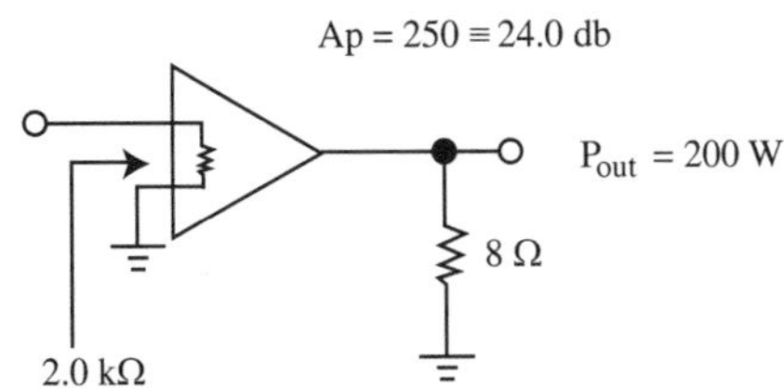

a. $\left[P_{out}\right]_{dBm} = 10 \log \frac{200 \text{ W}}{1 \text{ mW}} = 53.0 \text{ dBm}$

$\left[P_{in}\right]_{dBm} = 29.0 \text{ dBm} \equiv 0.8 \text{ W}$

b. $V_{out} = \sqrt{P_{out} R_L} = \sqrt{(200 \text{ W})(8\ \Omega)} = 40.0 \text{ V}_{rms}$

$V_{in} = \sqrt{(0.8 \text{ W})(2000\ \Omega)} = 40.0\ V_{rms}$

c. $\left[V_{out}\right]_{dBV} = 20 \log \frac{40 \text{ V}}{1 \text{ V}} = 32.0 \text{ dBV}$

$\left[V_{in}\right]_{dBV} = 20 \log \frac{40 \text{ V}}{1 \text{ V}} = 32.0 \text{ dBV}$

d. $A_v = 20 \log \frac{V_{out}}{V_{in}} = 20 \log 1 = 0 \text{ dB}$

22.3 Simple RC and RL Transfer Functions

23. a. $\omega_C = \frac{1}{0.001 \text{ s}} = 1000 \text{ rad/s}$

$f_C = \frac{1000 \text{ rad/s}}{2\pi} = 159.2 \text{ Hz}$

b.

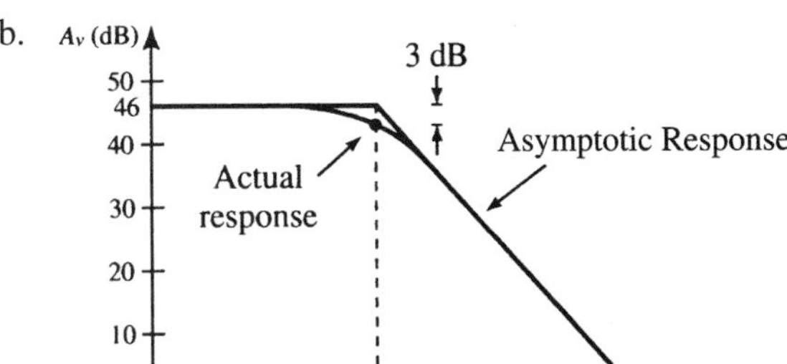

c.

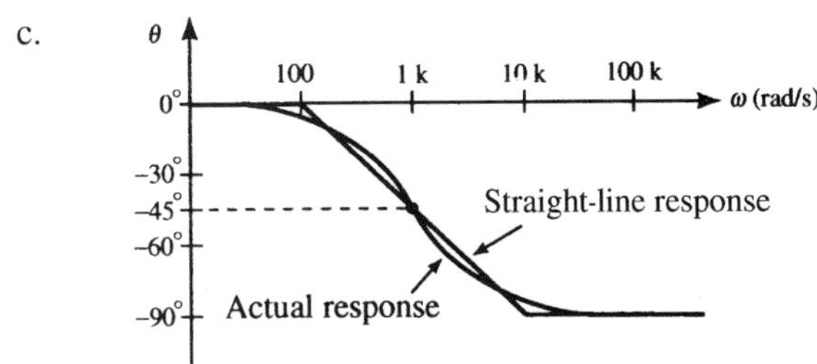

25. a.

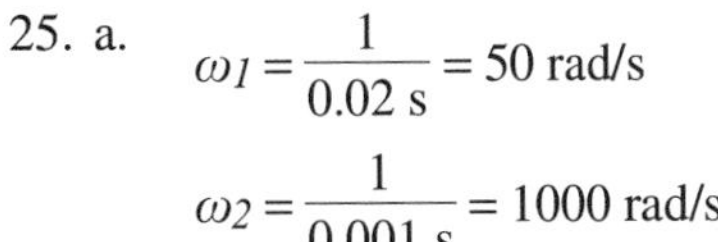

$\omega_1 = \frac{1}{0.02 \text{ s}} = 50 \text{ rad/s}$

$\omega_2 = \frac{1}{0.001 \text{ s}} = 1000 \text{ rad/s}$

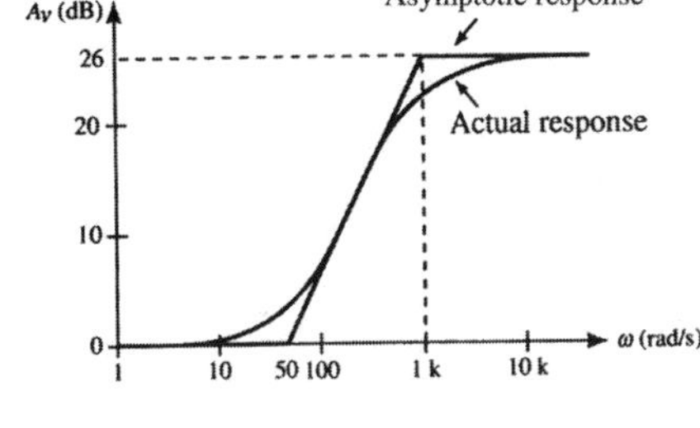

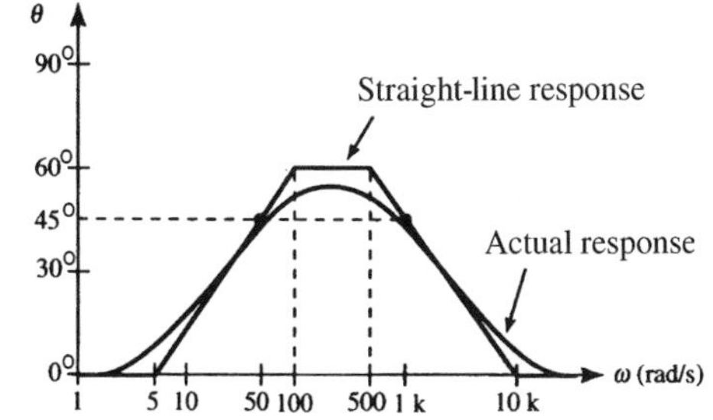

27. a. $\omega c = 50$ rad/s

$f_C = 7.958$ Hz

b.

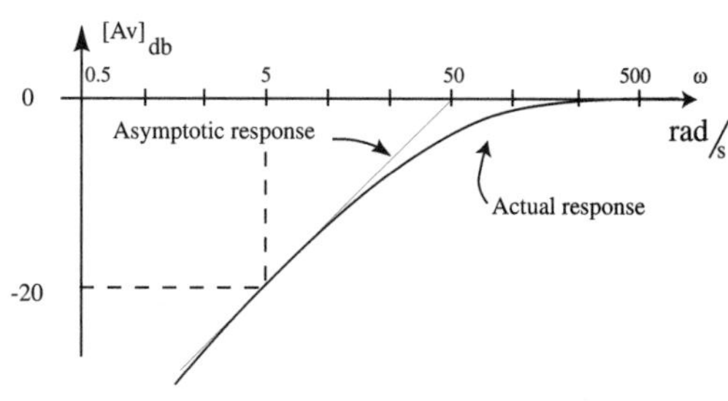

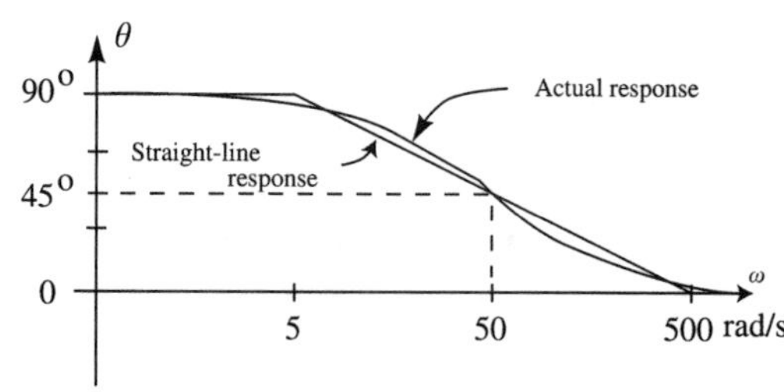

22.4 The Low-Pass Filter Circuit

29.

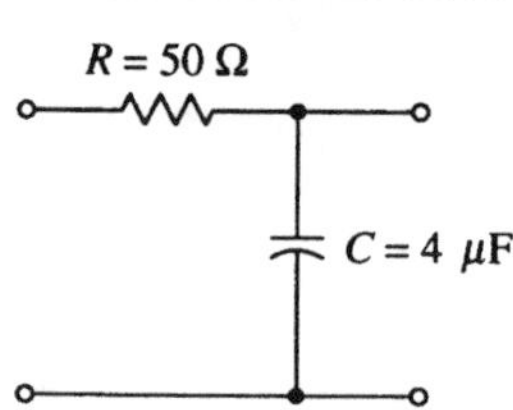

$$\tau = \frac{1}{5 \text{ krad/s}} = 0.2 \text{ ms}$$

$$R = \frac{0.2 \text{ ms}}{4\,\mu\text{F}} = 50\ \Omega$$

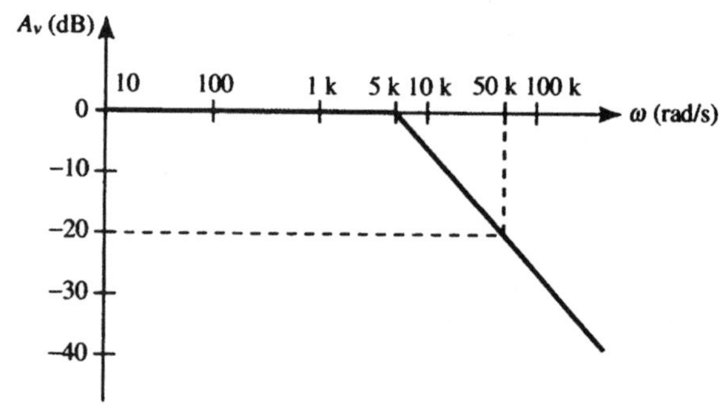

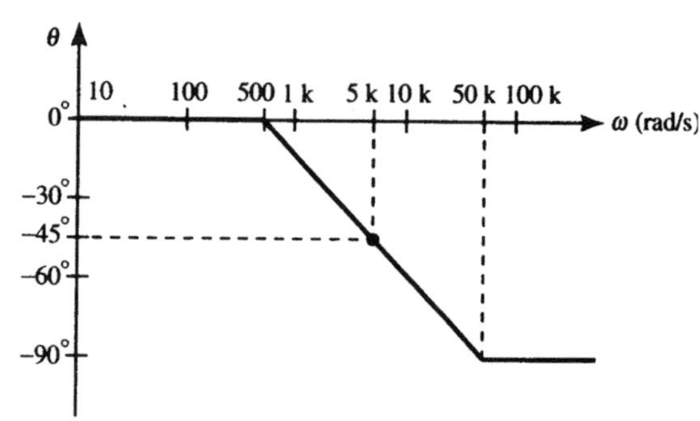

31.

$$\tau = \frac{1}{50 \text{ krad/s}} = 20\ \mu\text{s}$$

$$\tau = \frac{L}{R} \quad R = \frac{L}{\tau} = \frac{25 \text{ mH}}{20\ \mu\text{s}} = 1250\ \Omega$$

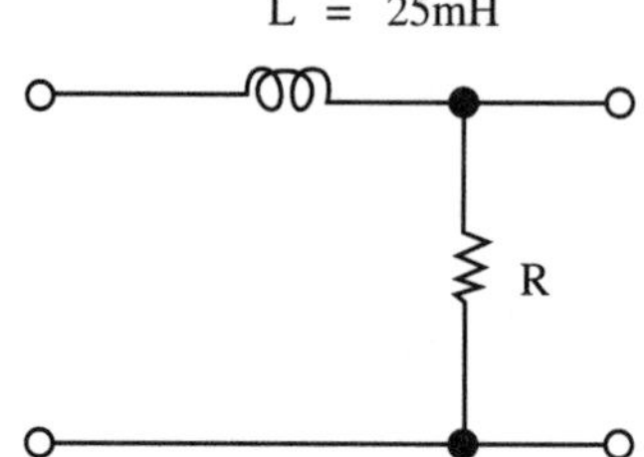

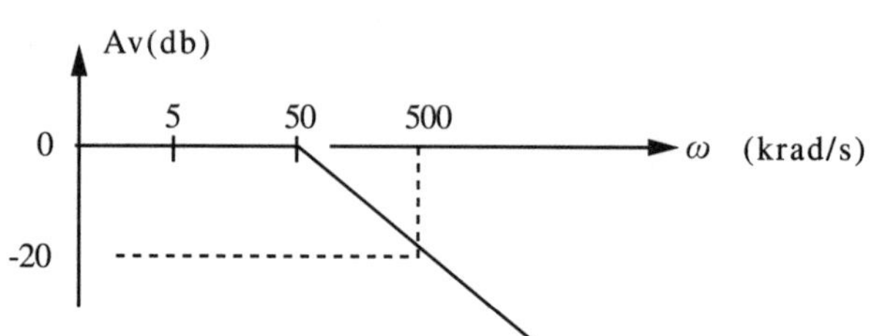

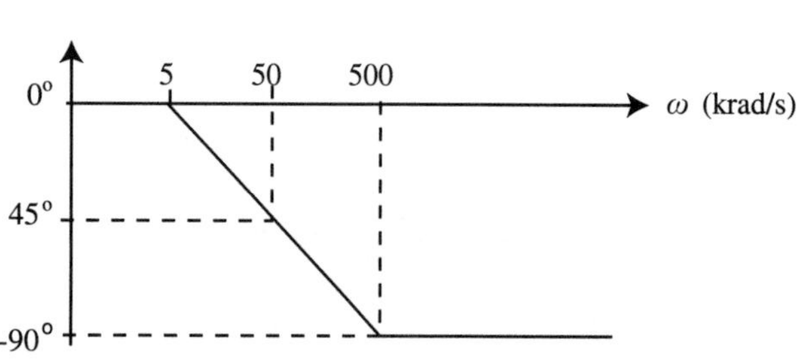

33.

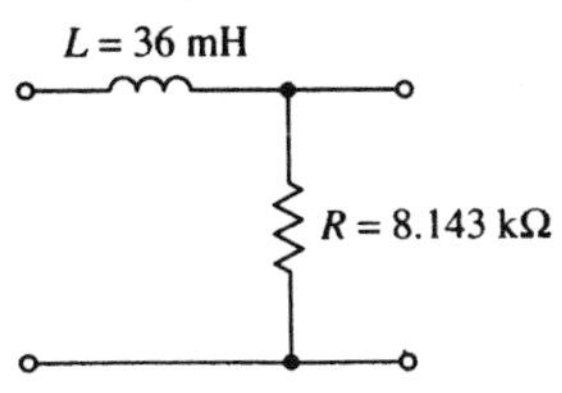

$\omega = 2\pi\,(36\text{ kHz}) = 226\text{ krad/s}$

$\tau = 4.43\ \mu s$

$$R = \frac{36\text{ mH}}{4.42\ \mu s} = 8.14\text{ k}\Omega$$

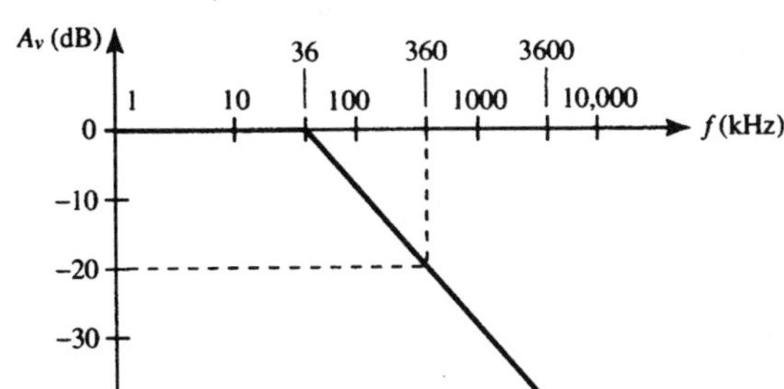

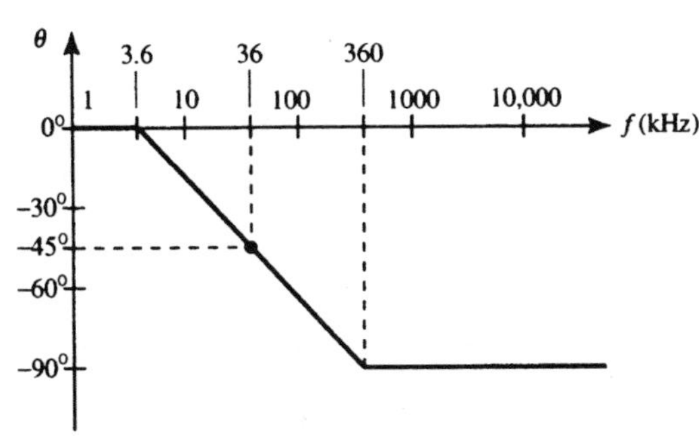

35.

$$T.F. = \frac{R_2 + \mathbf{Z}_C}{R_1 + R_2 + \mathbf{Z}_C}$$

$$= \frac{R_2 + \dfrac{1}{j\omega C}}{R_1 + R_2 + \dfrac{1}{j\omega C}}$$

$$= \frac{1 + j\omega R_2 C}{1 + j\omega (R_1 + R_2)C}$$

$$T.F. = \frac{1 + j0.00003\omega}{1 + j0.00006\omega}$$

$\omega_1 = 16.67\text{ krad/s}$

$\omega_2 = 33.33\text{ krad/s}$

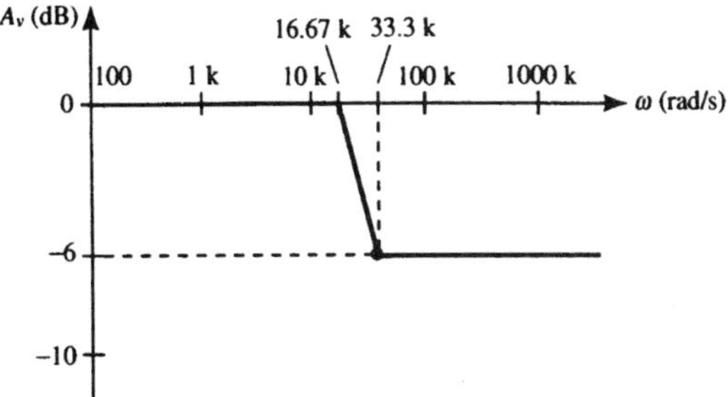

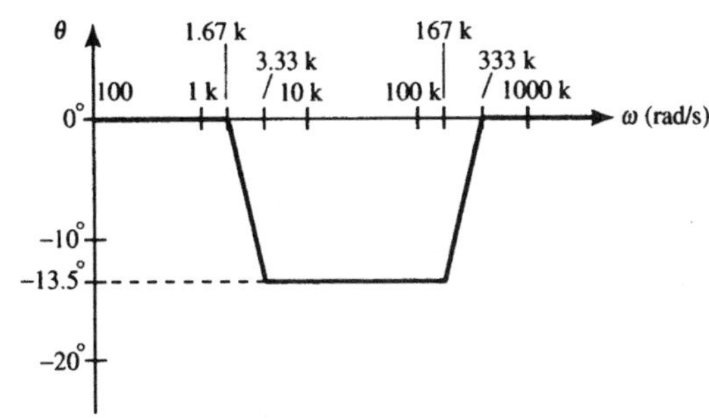

22.5 The High-Pass Filter

37.

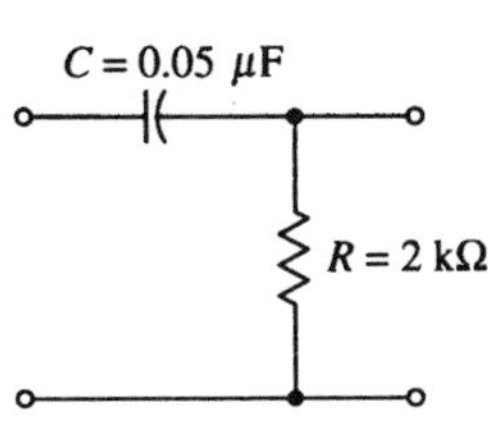

$$\tau = \frac{1}{100\text{ krad/s}} = 100\ \mu s$$

$$R = \frac{100\ \mu s}{0.05\ \mu F} = 2\text{ k}\Omega$$

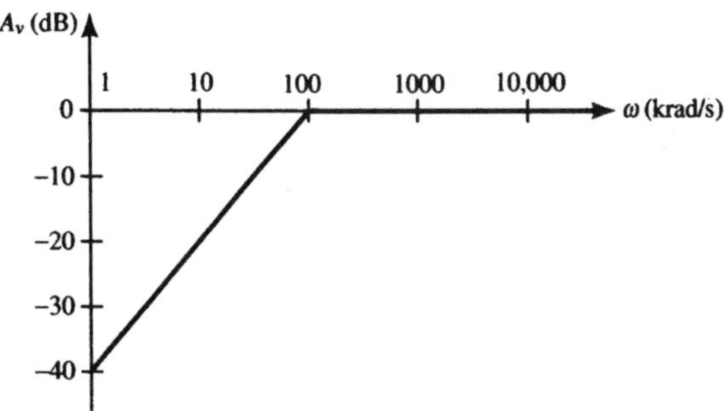

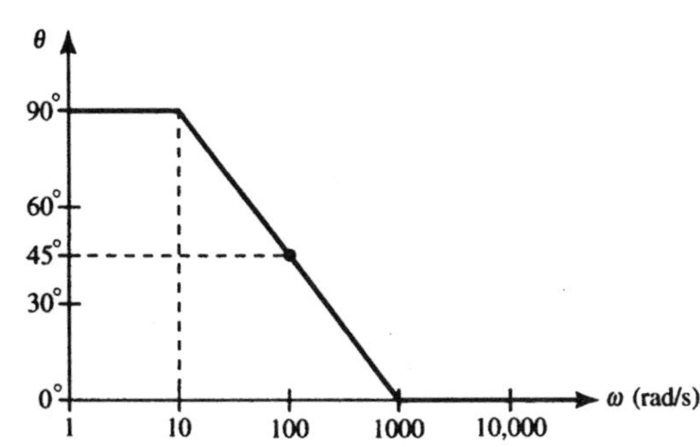

39.

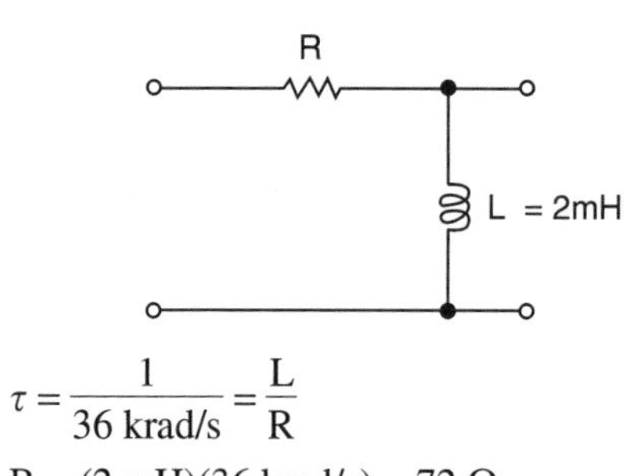

$$\tau = \frac{1}{36\ \text{krad/s}} = \frac{L}{R}$$

R = (2 mH)(36 krad/s) = 72 Ω

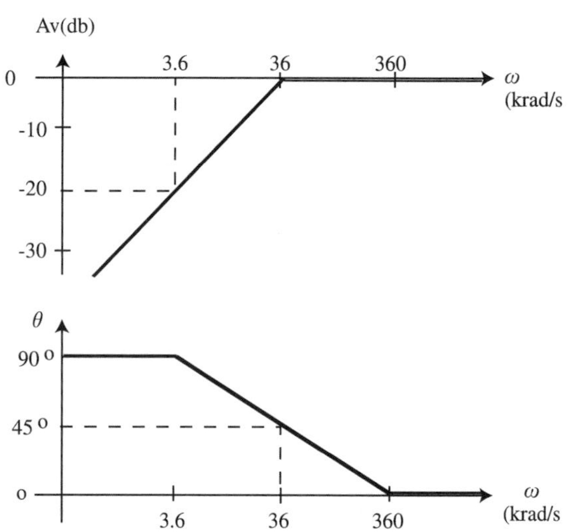

41. a. $$\text{TF} = \frac{R_2}{R_1 + R_2 + \frac{1}{sC}} = \frac{sR_2C}{(R_1 + R_2)sC + 1}$$

$$\text{TF} = \frac{j\omega 0.0064}{1 + j\omega 0.008}$$

b. $$\omega_1 = \frac{1}{0.008\ \text{s}} = 125\ \text{rad/s}$$

$$\omega_2 = \frac{1}{0.0064\ \text{s}} = 156.25\ \text{rad/s}$$

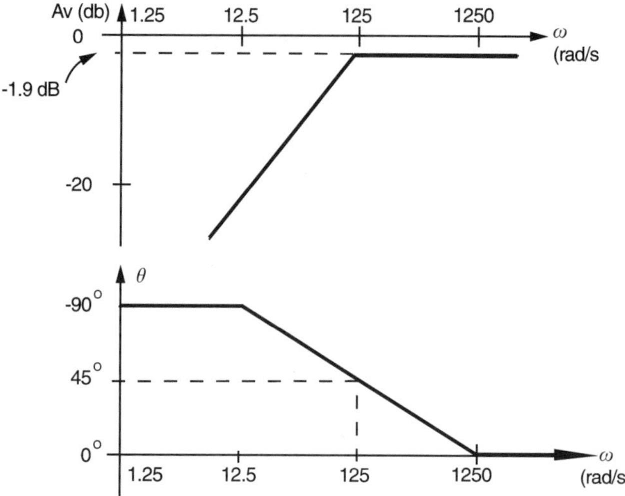

22.6 The Band-Pass Filter

43. a. Low-pass filter:

$\tau = (200\ \Omega)(0.01\ \mu\text{F}) = 2\ \mu\text{s}$

$\omega_C = 500$ krad/s (79.6 kHz)

High-pass filter:

$\tau = (200\ \Omega)(0.2\ \mu\text{F}) = 40\ \mu\text{s}$

$\omega_C = 25$ krad/s (3.98 kHz)

BW = 500 krad/s – 25 krad/s

= 475 krad/s (75.6 kHz)

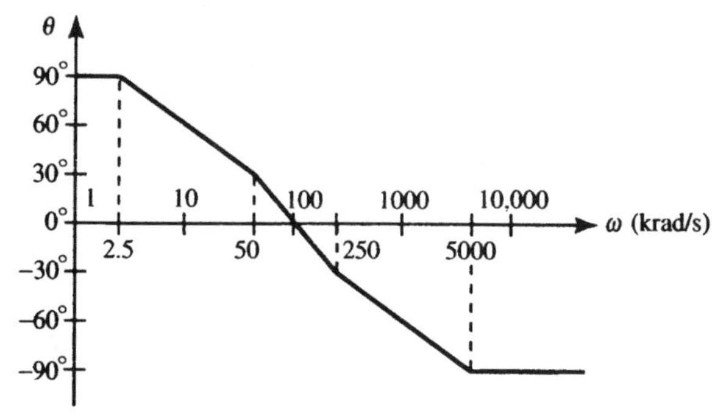

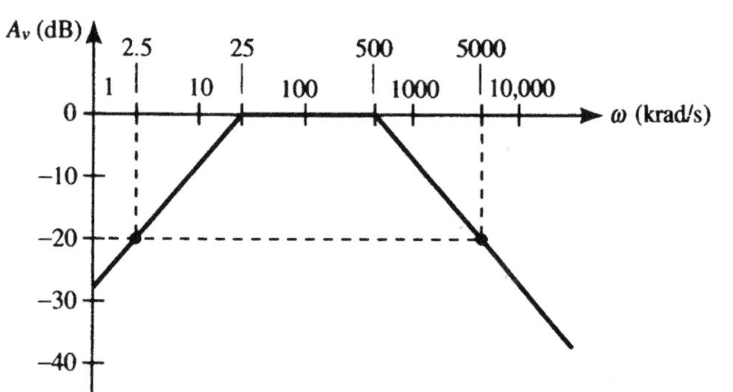

45.

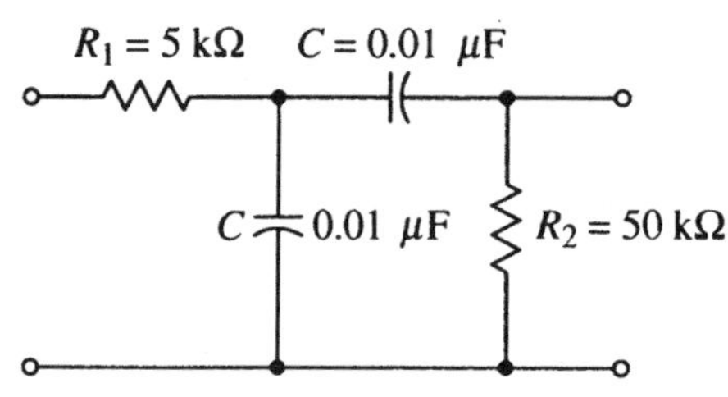

a. $\omega_L : \tau_L = \dfrac{1}{2\text{ krad}} = 500\ \mu s$

$R_2 = \dfrac{500\ \mu s}{0.01\ \mu F} = 50\ k\Omega$

$\omega_H : \tau_H = \dfrac{1}{20\text{ krad}} = 50\ \mu s$

$R_1 = \dfrac{50\ \mu s}{0.01\ \mu F} = 5\ k\Omega$

b.

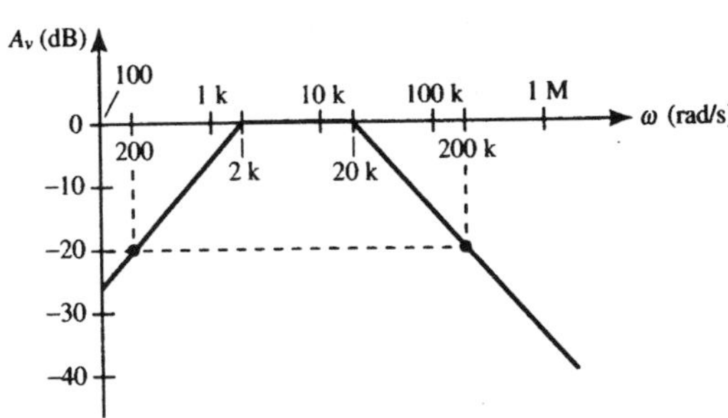

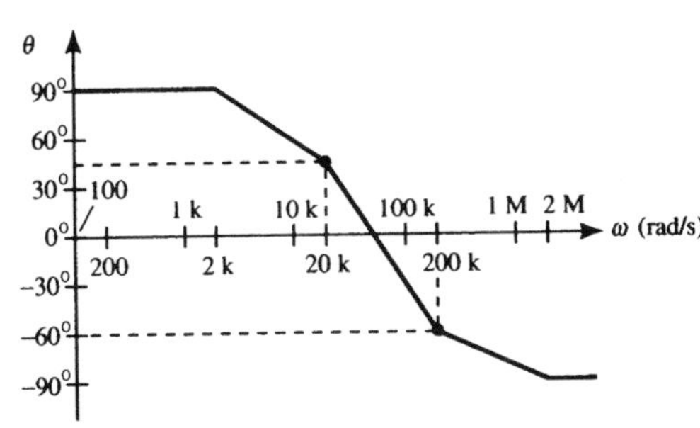

c. The actual cut-off frequencies will be close to the designed values since the break frequencies are separated by one decade.

47\. a. $\omega = \dfrac{1}{\sqrt{(10\text{ mH})(1\ \mu F)}} = 10\text{ krad/s }(1.59\text{ kHz})$

$X_L = (10\text{ krad/s})(10\text{ mH}) = 100\ \Omega$

b. $Q = \dfrac{X_{LS}}{R_s} = \dfrac{100\ \Omega}{10\ \Omega} = 10$

c. $BW = \dfrac{10\text{ krad/s}}{10} = 1\text{ krads/s}$

$\omega_1 \cong 9.5\text{krad/s} \quad (f_1 \cong 1.51\text{ kHz})$

$\omega_2 \cong 10.5\text{krad/s} \quad (f_2 \cong 1.67\text{ kHz})$

d. At resonance

$V_{out} = \dfrac{10\ \Omega}{250\ \Omega} V_{in}$

$\left[A_v\right]_{dB} = 20\log\dfrac{10}{250} = -28.0\text{ dB}$

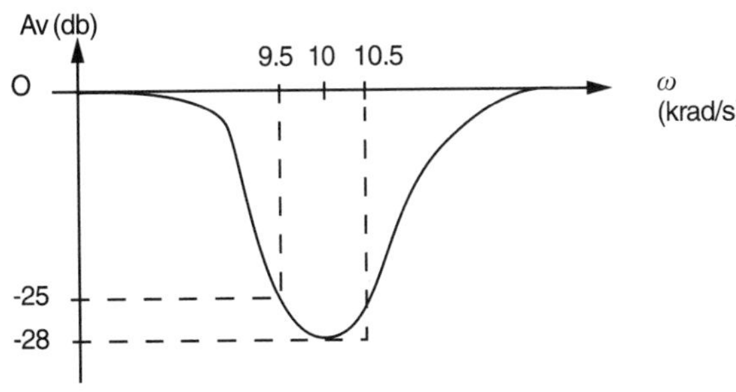

49\. a. $\omega_0 \cong \dfrac{1}{\sqrt{LC}} = 10\text{ krad / s} \equiv 1592\text{ Hz}$

b. $Q_{coil} = \dfrac{\omega L}{R_1} = 100$

c. At the resonant frequency, the impedance of the "tank circuit" is

$R_p = Q^2 R_s = 10\ k\Omega$

By using the voltage divider rule,

$A_v = \dfrac{10\ \Omega}{10\ k\Omega} = 0.001$ and so

$[A_v]_{dB} = 20\log 0.001 = -60\text{ dB}$

d. At $\omega = 0$, $A_v = \dfrac{10\ \Omega}{11\ \Omega} = 0.909 \equiv -0.83\text{ dB}$

and

as $\omega \to \infty$, $A_v = 1 \equiv 0\text{ dB}$

e. $\text{BW} = \dfrac{10\text{krad / s}}{100} = 100\text{ rad / s }(\equiv 16\text{ Hz})$

$\omega_1 = 9.950\text{ krad / s }(1584\text{ Hz})$

$\omega_2 = 10.050\text{ krad / s }(1600\text{ Hz})$

22.8 Circuit Analysis Using Computers

51.

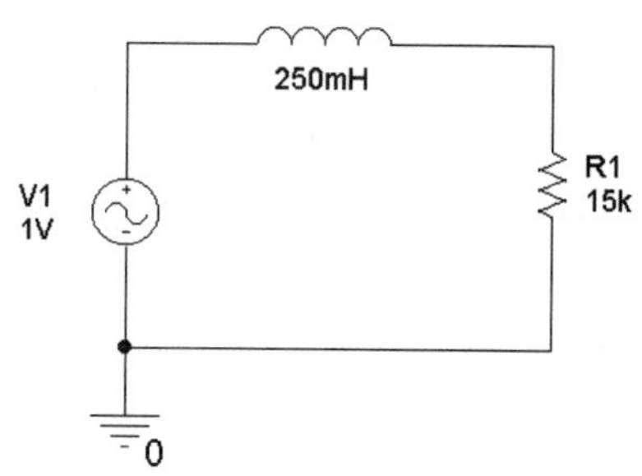

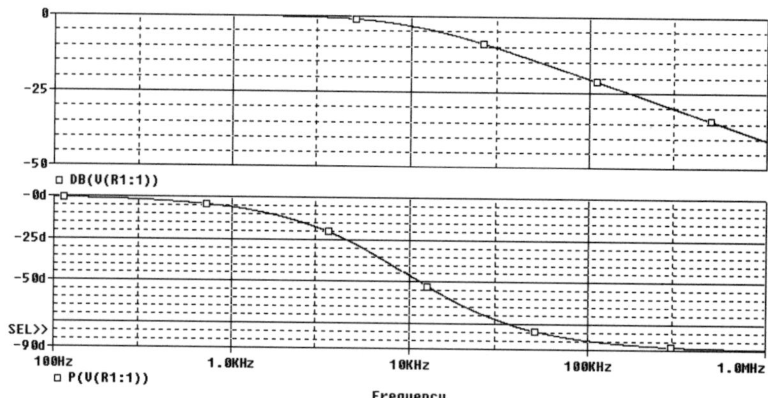

53.

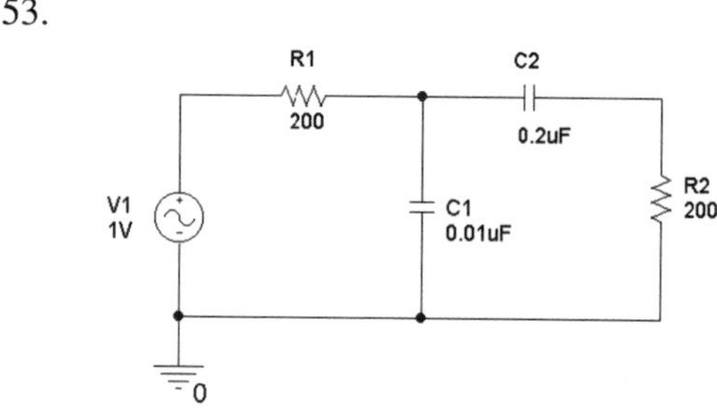

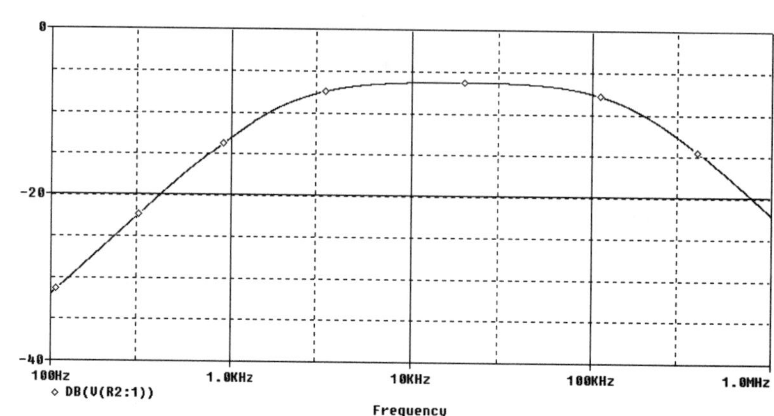

55.

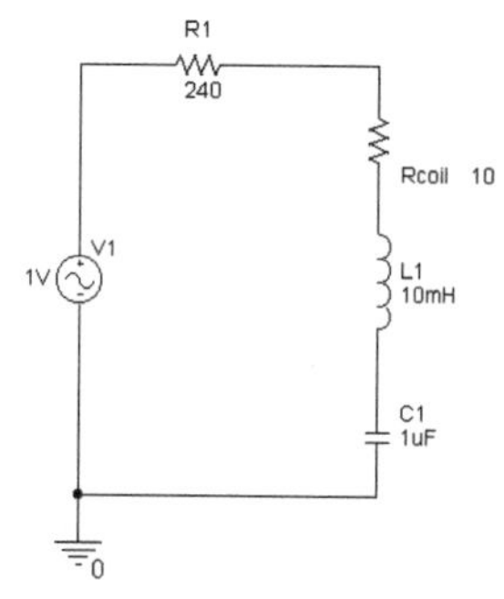

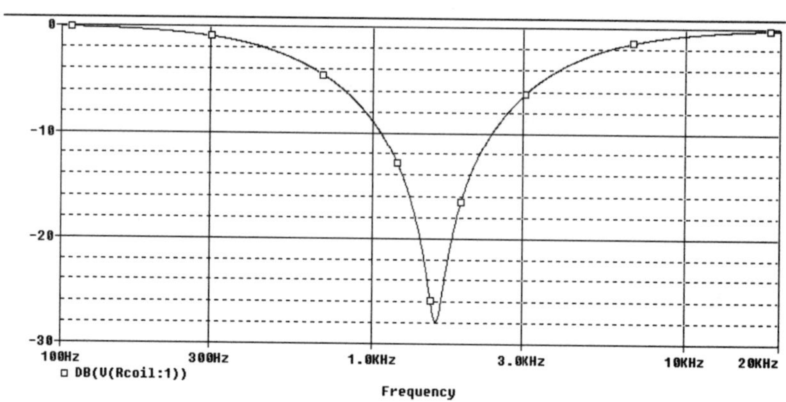

57.

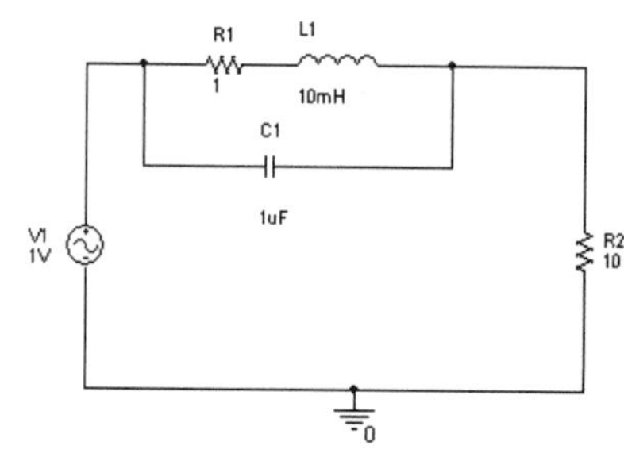

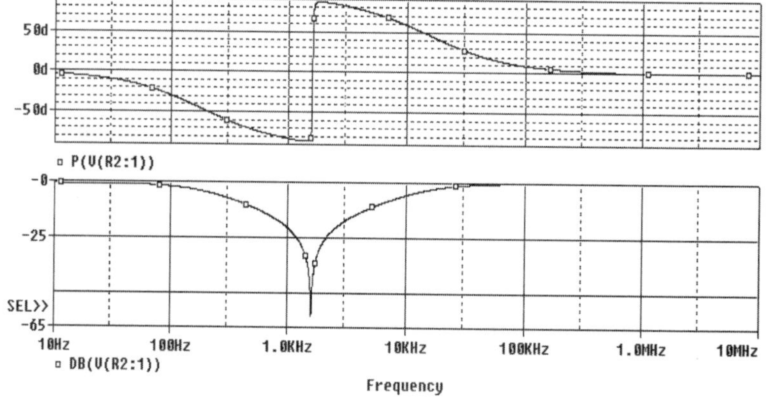

59.

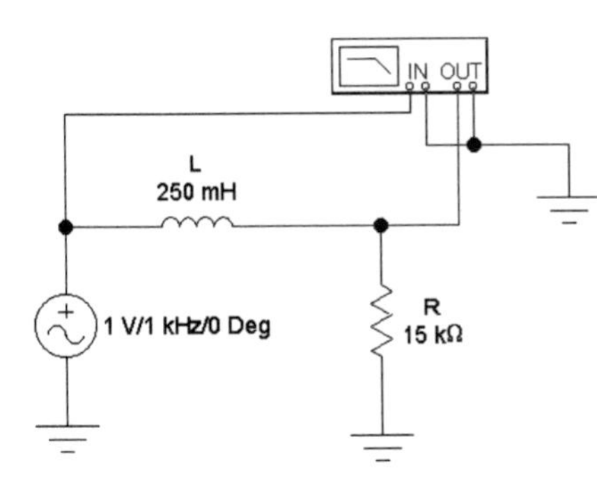
IN OUT
L
250 mH
1 V/1 kHz/0 Deg
R
15 kΩ

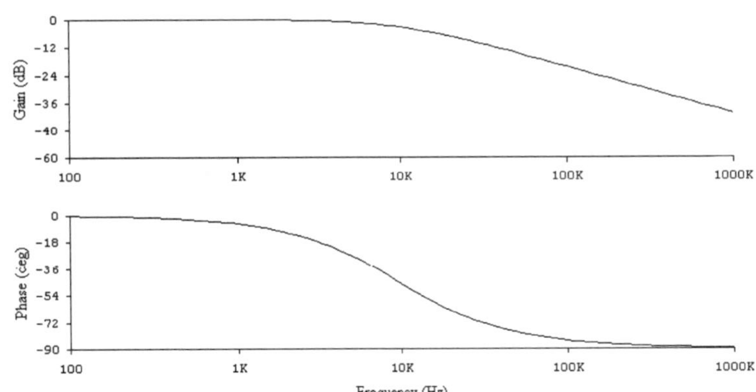
Gain (dB)
Phase (deg)
Frequency (Hz)

61.

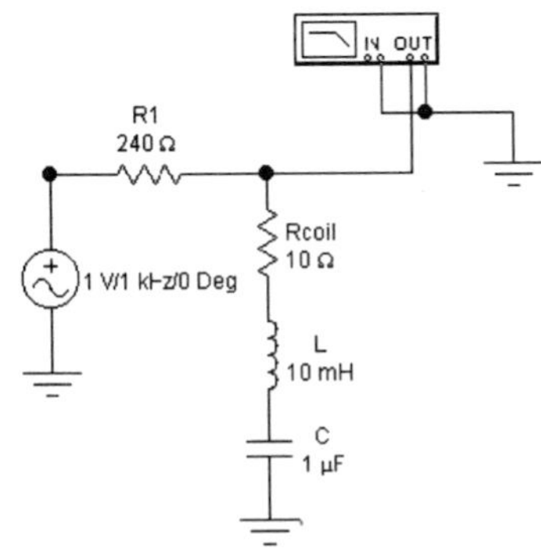
IN OUT
R1
240 Ω
Rcoil
10 Ω
1 V/1 kHz/0 Deg
L
10 mH
C
1 µF

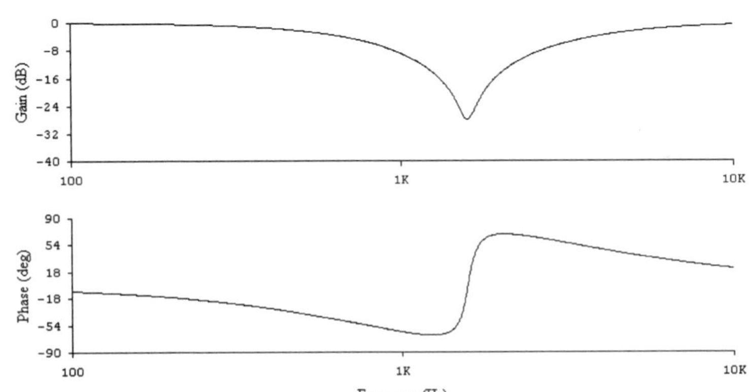
Gain (dB)
Phase (deg)
Frequency (Hz)

63.

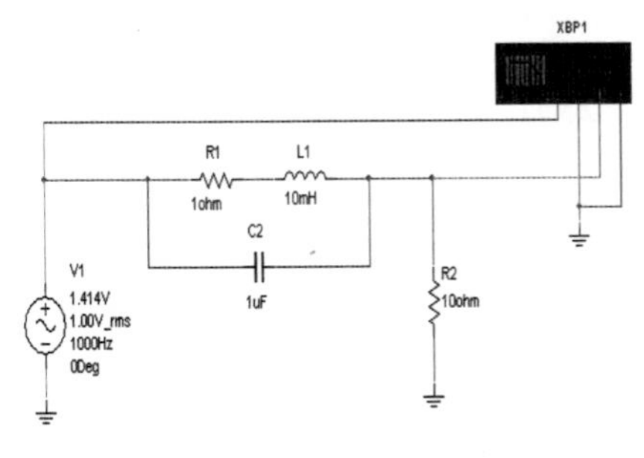
XBP1
R1
1ohm
L1
10mH
C2
1uF
V1
1.414V
1.00V_rms
1000Hz
0Deg
R2
10ohm

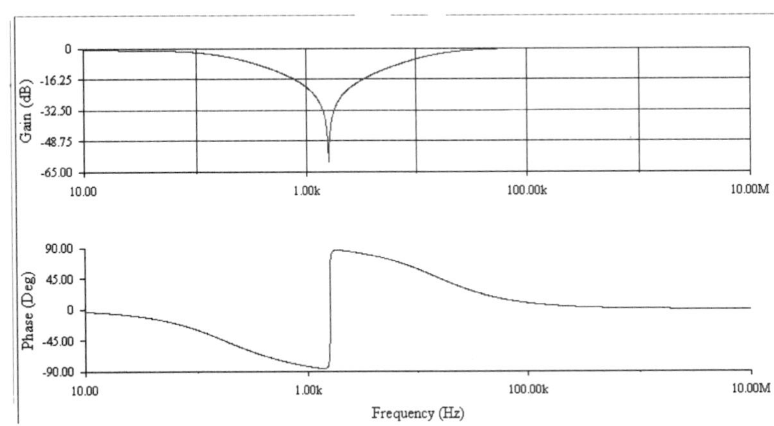
Gain (dB)
Phase (Deg)
Frequency (Hz)

Chapter

23

Transformers and Coupled Circuits

23.1 Introduction

1. (a)

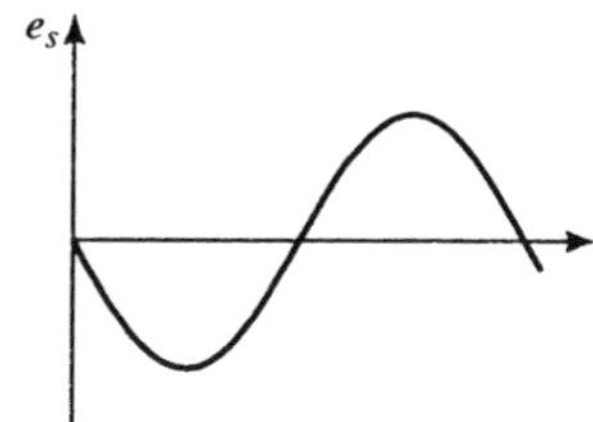

(b)

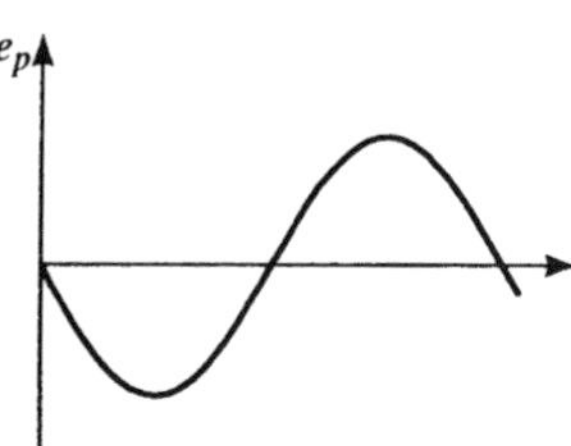

23.2 Iron-Core Transformers: The Ideal Model

3. a. Step-up

b. $a = \dfrac{N_p}{N_s} = \dfrac{1000}{4000} = 0.25$

$e_p = ae_s = (0.25)(100 \sin\omega t) = 25 \sin\omega t$ V

c. $E_p = aE_s = (0.25)(24\text{ V}) = 6$ V

d. $\mathbf{E}_s = \dfrac{\mathbf{E}_p}{a} = \dfrac{24\text{ V}\angle 0°}{0.25} = 96\text{ V}\angle 0°$

e. $\mathbf{E}_s = \dfrac{-\mathbf{E}_p}{a} = \dfrac{-800\text{ V}\angle 0°}{0.25} = 3200\text{ V}\angle 180°$

5.

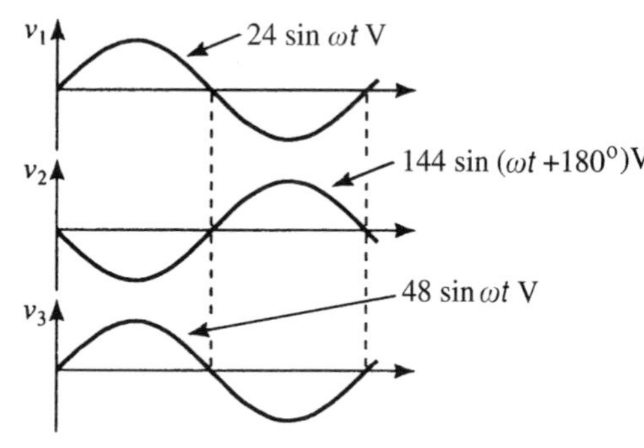

7. a.
$\mathbf{I}_L = a\mathbf{I}_p = a\mathbf{I}_g = (0.5)(2\text{ A}\angle 120°) = 1\text{ A}\angle 20°$

b. $\mathbf{V}_L = \dfrac{\mathbf{E}_p}{a} = \dfrac{\mathbf{E}_g}{a} = \dfrac{240\text{ V}\angle 0°}{0.5} = 480\text{ V}\angle 0°$

c. $\mathbf{Z}_L = \dfrac{\mathbf{V}_L}{\mathbf{I}_L} = \dfrac{480\text{ V}\angle 0°}{1\text{ A}\angle 20°} = 480\ \Omega\angle -20°$

9. a.
$\mathbf{I}_L = a\mathbf{I}_p = a\mathbf{I}_g = (4)(4\text{ A}\angle 30°) = 16\text{ A}\angle 30°$
$\mathbf{V}_L = \mathbf{I}_L\mathbf{Z}_L = (16\text{ A}\angle 30°)(10\ \Omega\angle -53.1°) = 160\text{ V}\angle -23.1°$

b. $\mathbf{E}_g = a\mathbf{V}_L = (4)(160\text{ V}\angle -23.1°) = 640\text{ V}\angle -23.1°$

23.3 Reflected Impedance

11. a. $\mathbf{Z}_p = a^2\mathbf{Z}_L = (2)^2(10\ \Omega - j20\ \Omega) = 40\ \Omega - j80\ \Omega$

b. $a = \dfrac{N_p}{N_s} = \dfrac{100}{200} = 0.5$

$\mathbf{Z}_p = (0.5)^2(5\ \Omega + j8\ \Omega) = 1.25\ \Omega + j2\ \Omega$

13. $\mathbf{Z}_p = a^2\mathbf{Z}_L \therefore a^2 = \dfrac{\mathbf{Z}_p}{\mathbf{Z}_L} = \dfrac{62.5 - j125}{10 - j20} = 6.25$

$\therefore a = 2.5$

15. a. $\mathbf{Z}_T = (4\ \Omega + j6\ \Omega) + a^2\mathbf{Z}_L$
$= (4\ \Omega + j6\ \Omega) + (3)^2(2\ \Omega)$
$= 4\ \Omega + j6\ \Omega + 18\ \Omega$
$= 22\ \Omega + j6\ \Omega$

b. $\mathbf{Z}_T = 2\ \Omega + j3\ \Omega + a_1^2\,[a_2^2\,\mathbf{Z}_L]$
$= 2\ \Omega + j3\ \Omega + (4)^2[(0.5)^2(6\ \Omega)]$
$= 2\ \Omega + j3\ \Omega + (16)(0.25)(6)$
$= 26\ \Omega + j3\ \Omega$

23.4 Transformer Power Ratings

17. $I_p = \frac{I_s}{a} = \frac{3\text{ A}}{0.2} = 15\text{ A}$

$S = V_p I_p = (7200\text{ V})(15\text{ A}) = 108\text{ kVA}$

23.5 Transformer Applications

19. a.

$I_{\text{Load 1}} = \frac{P_1}{V_1} = \frac{1200}{120\text{ V}} = 10\text{ A}$

$I_{\text{Load 2}} = \frac{P_2}{V_2} = \frac{1500\text{ W}}{120\text{ V}} = 12.5\text{ A}$

$I_{\text{Load 3}} = \frac{P_3}{V_3} = \frac{2400\text{ W}}{240\text{ V}} = 10\text{ A}$

Since all loads are resistive, currents are in phase. Thus, $I_1 = I_{\text{Load 1}} + I_{\text{Load 3}} = 10\text{ A} + 10\text{ A} = 20\text{ A}$.

b. $I_2 = I_{\text{Load 2}} + I_{\text{Load 3}} = 12.5\text{ A} + 10\text{ A} = 22.5\text{ A}$

c. $I_N = |I_{\text{Load 1}} - I_{\text{Load 2}}| = |10\text{ A} - 12.5\text{ A}| = 2.5\text{ A}$

d. $P_{\text{in}} = P_{\text{out}} \therefore 7200 I_p = 5100\text{ W} \therefore I_p = \frac{5100\text{ W}}{7200\text{ V}}$

$= 0.708\text{ A}$

21. Part 1: The circuit is shown in (a). Reflect the load as in (b). (Note that this is not a matched load.) the voltage across the reflected load is

$V'_{\text{Load}} = \left(\frac{100\ \Omega}{125\ \Omega}\right)(10\text{ V}) = 8\text{ V}$

Power to reflected load $= \frac{(8\text{ V})^2}{100\ \Omega} = 0.64\text{ W}$

Since the transformer is deemed lossless, $P_{speaker} = 0.64\text{ W}$

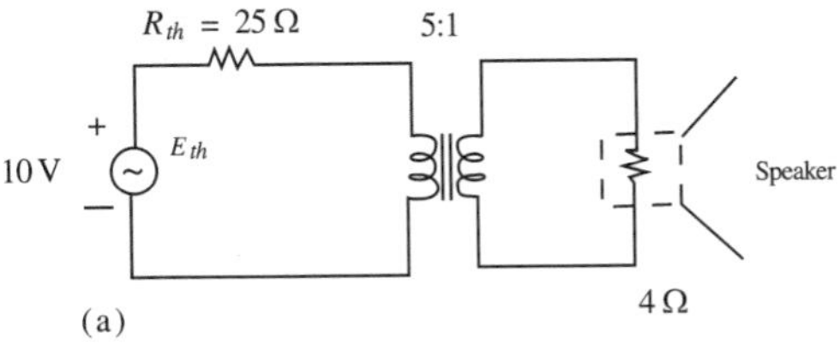

(a)

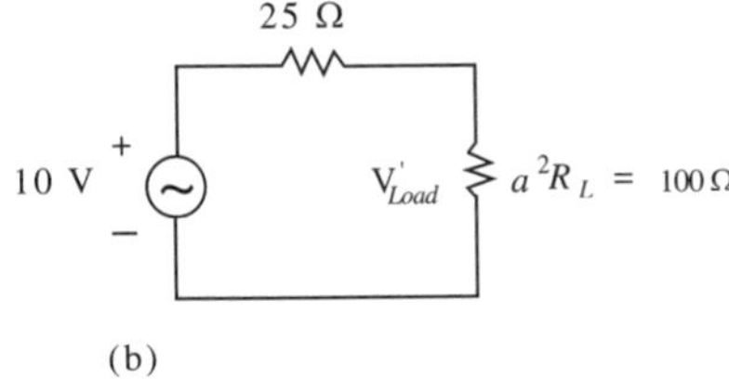

(b)

Part 2: This problem can be solved intuitively or by formal means. First, the intuitive solution. Consider the following diagram. One can see that if $R_L' = 25\ \Omega$, then half the voltage drops across it and $P_L' = \frac{(5\text{ V})^2}{25\ \Omega} = 1\text{W}$ as we are looking for. This then is the solution.

Since $R_L' = a^2 R_L$, $a^2 = 25\ \Omega/4\ \Omega$, and $a = 2.5$. Alternatively, you can apply basic circuit principles as follows:

$P_L' = \frac{V_x^2}{R_L'} = 1\text{ W} \quad \therefore V_x^2 = (1)\,R_L'$ and $V_x = \sqrt{R_L'}$

$\text{VDR}: V_x = \left[\frac{R_L'}{R_L' + 25}\right](10\text{ V})$

Thus: $V_x(R_L' + 25) = 10\,R_L'$

$\sqrt{R_L'}\,(R_L' + 25) = 10\,R_L'$

Square both sides. Result is a quadratic.

$(R_L')^2 - 50\,R_L' + 625 = 0$

Solution is $R_L' = 25\ \Omega$ as above.

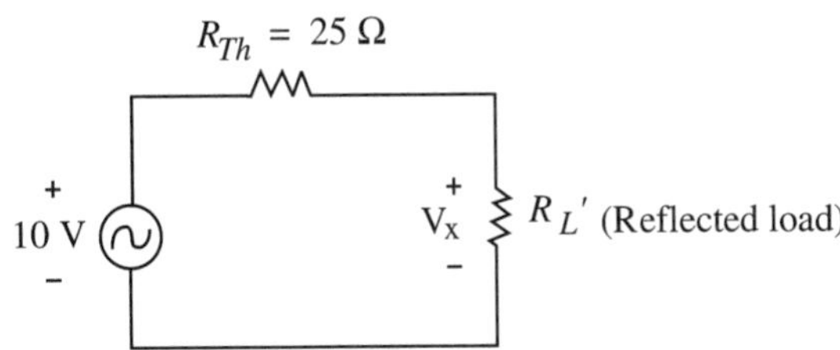

$R_L' = a^2 R_L$

23. $\frac{\mathbf{E}_1}{\mathbf{E}_2} = 2 \therefore \mathbf{E}_2 = \frac{\mathbf{E}_1}{2} = \frac{120\text{ V}\angle 0^\circ}{2} = 60\text{ V}\angle 0^\circ$

Similarly, $\mathbf{E}_3 = 24\text{ V}\angle 0^\circ$

$\mathbf{I}_2 = \frac{\mathbf{E}_2}{\mathbf{Z}_2} = \frac{60\text{ V}\angle 0^\circ}{20\ \Omega\angle 50^\circ} = 3\text{ A}\angle -50^\circ$

$\mathbf{I}_3 = \frac{24\text{ V}\angle 0^\circ}{12 + j4} = 1.90\text{ A}\angle -18.4^\circ$

$\mathbf{I}_p = \frac{\mathbf{I}_2}{a_2} + \frac{\mathbf{I}_3}{a_3} = \frac{3\text{ A}\angle -50^\circ}{2} + \frac{1.90\text{ A}\angle -18.4^\circ}{5}$

$\mathbf{I}_p = 1.83\text{ A}\angle -43.8^\circ$

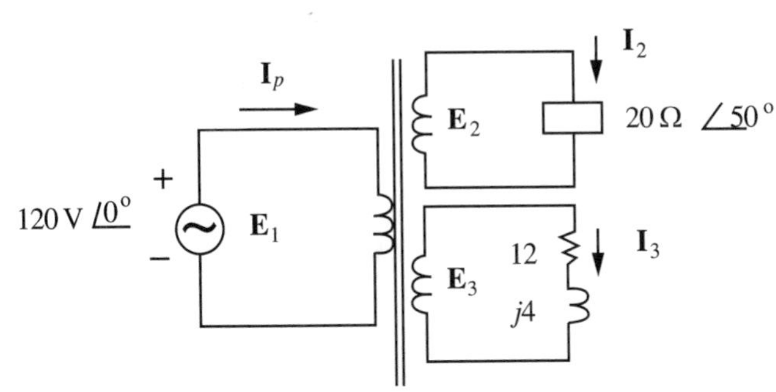

23.6 Practical Iron-Core Transformers

25. a. $R_{eq} = R_p + a^2R_s = 4\ \Omega + (10)^2(0.02) = 6\ \Omega$

$X_{eq} = X_p + a^2X_s = 4\ \Omega + (10)^2(0.02) = 6\ \Omega$

$a^2\mathbf{Z}_L = (10)^2(4\ \Omega + j4\ \Omega) = 400\ \Omega + j400\ \Omega$

b. $\mathbf{I}_g = \dfrac{\mathbf{E}_g}{\mathbf{Z}_T} = \dfrac{1220\text{ V}\angle 0^\circ}{406\ \Omega + j406\ \Omega} = 2.125\text{ A}\angle -45^\circ$

$\mathbf{I}_L = a\mathbf{I}_g = (10)(2.125\angle -45^\circ) = 21.25\text{ A}\angle -45^\circ$

$\mathbf{V}_L = \mathbf{I}_L\mathbf{Z}_L = (21.25\text{ A}\angle -45^\circ)(4\ \Omega + j4\ \Omega)$
$= 120.2\text{ V}\angle 0^\circ$

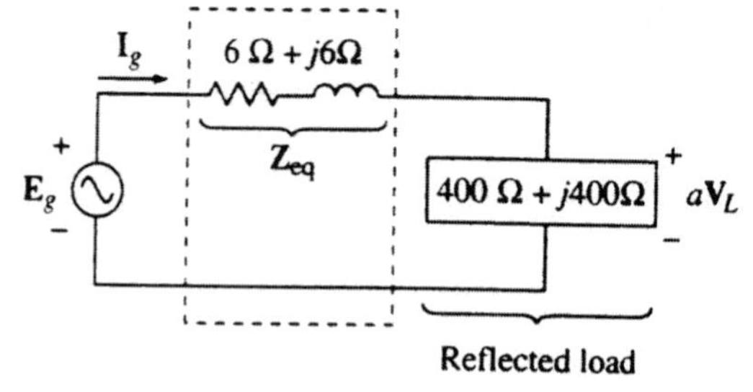

27. $P_{loss} = P_{copper} + P_{core} = 450\text{ W} + 280\text{ W} = 730\text{ W}$

$P_{in} = P_{out} + P_{loss} = 48\ 000\text{ W} + 730\text{ W} = 48\ 730\text{ W}$

$\eta = \dfrac{P_{out}}{P_{in}} \times 100\% = \left(\dfrac{48\ 000\text{ W}}{48\ 730\text{ W}}\right) \times 100 = 98.5\%$

23.9 Loosely Coupled Circuits

29. a. Minus
b. Minus
c. Minus

31. $k = \dfrac{M}{\sqrt{L_1L_2}} \quad \therefore 0.6 = \dfrac{0.8\text{ H}}{\sqrt{(2\text{ H})L_2}}$

Square both sides and solve for $L_2 = 0.889$ H

33. $v_{11} = L_1\dfrac{di_1}{dt} = 25 \times 10^{-3}\dfrac{d}{dt}\left(10e^{-500t}\right)\text{V}$

$= 250 \times 10^{-3}\dfrac{d}{dt}\left(e^{-500t}\right)\text{V}$

$= (0.250)(-500)e^{-500t}\text{ V}$

$\therefore \quad v_{11} = -125e^{-500t}\text{ V}$

At $t = 1$ ms, $v_{11} = -125(e^{-0.5}) = -75.8$ V

$v_{21} = M\dfrac{di_1}{dt} = (0.8 \times 10^{-3})\dfrac{d}{dt}\left(10e^{-500t}\right)\text{V}$

$\therefore v_{21} = -4e^{-500t}\text{ V}$

At $t = 1$ ms, $v_{21} = -4e^{-0.5} = -2.43$ V

Note that the actual polarity of v_{21} is indeterminate since no dots are shown.

35. $L_T = (L_1 + L_4 + 2M_{14}) + (L_2 + L_3 - 2M_{23})$
$= (1\text{ H} + 4\text{ H} + 2\text{ H}) + (6\text{H} + 1.5\text{ H} - 4\text{ H})$
$= 10.5$ H

37. $M = k\sqrt{L_1L_2} = (0.8)\sqrt{(250)(40)} = 80$ mH

$L_{eq} = \dfrac{L_1L_2 - M^2}{L_1 + L_2 \pm 2M}$ (Eq. 24–19)

Since both dots are at the same ends of the coils, use the minus sign. Thus,

$L_{eq} = \dfrac{(250)(40) - (80)^2}{250 + 40 - 2(80)}\text{ mH} = 27.69\text{ mH}$

$\mathbf{I} = \dfrac{\mathbf{E}}{\mathbf{Z}_{eq}} = \dfrac{120\text{ V}\angle 0^\circ}{j(2\pi)(60\text{ Hz})(27.69\text{ mH})} = 11.5\text{ A}\angle -90^\circ$

23.10 Magnetically Coupled Circuits with AC Excitation

39. Loop 1:

$100\angle 0^\circ - 4\mathbf{I}_1 - (-j10)\mathbf{I}_1 - j\omega L_1\mathbf{I}_1 - j\omega M\mathbf{I}_2 - (-j8)\mathbf{I}_1 + (-j8)\mathbf{I}_2 = 0$

$\therefore (4 + j22)\mathbf{I}_1 + j13\mathbf{I}_2 = 100\angle 0^\circ \quad (1)$

Loop 2:

$-j\omega L_2\mathbf{I}_2 - (-j8)\mathbf{I}_2 + (-j8)\mathbf{I}_1 - j\omega M\mathbf{I}_1 = 0$

$\therefore j13\mathbf{I}_1 + j12\mathbf{I}_2 = 0 \quad (2)$

Solution: $\left.\begin{matrix}\mathbf{I}_1 = 11.3\text{ A}\angle -63.2^\circ \\ \mathbf{I}_2 = 12.2\text{ A}\angle 116.8^\circ\end{matrix}\right\}$ Bonus. (These were not asked for.)

41. To simplify the thought process, let the current through coil 2 be denoted as $\mathbf{I}_3$ where $\mathbf{I}_3 = \mathbf{I}_1 - \mathbf{I}_2$. Write KVL for each loop in turn. Thus,

Loop 1:

$\mathbf{E} - \mathbf{I}_1(R_1 + j\omega L_1) - \underbrace{j\omega M\mathbf{I}_3}_{\text{Mutual voltage in coil 1}} - j\omega L_2\mathbf{I}_3 - \underbrace{j\omega M\mathbf{I}_1}_{\text{Mutual voltage in coil 2}} = 0$

Substituting values and gathering terms yields
$(10 + j84)\mathbf{I}_1 - j62\mathbf{I}_2 = 120\text{ V}\angle 0^\circ$

Loop 2:

$j\omega L_2\mathbf{I}_3 + j\omega M\mathbf{I}_1 - \mathbf{I}_2R_2 - \mathbf{I}_2(-jX_C) = 0$

Substituting values and simplifying yields

$-j62\mathbf{I}_1 + 15\mathbf{I}_2 = 0$

Bonus: $\mathbf{I}_1 = 0.430\text{ A}\angle -17.5^\circ$

$\mathbf{I}_2 = 1.78\text{ A}\angle 72.5^\circ$

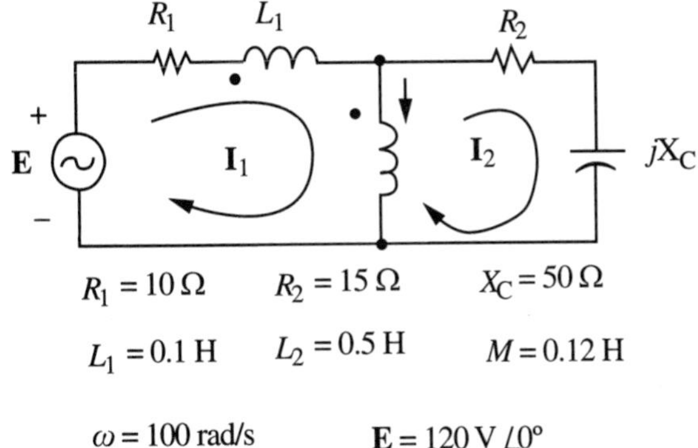

23.12 Circuit Analysis Using Computers (MSM)

43. Create the circuit at right. Set all meters for AC. For the transformer, use the virtual model and set its turns ratio to 4. Set other parameters as noted in the text. Energize the circuit using MSM's power ON/OFF switch. Verification: An analytic solution (see PSpice Problem 43 below) yields voltage and current magnitudes of $V_{load} = 30$ V, $I_{load} = 1.87$ A and $I_P = 0.468$ A.

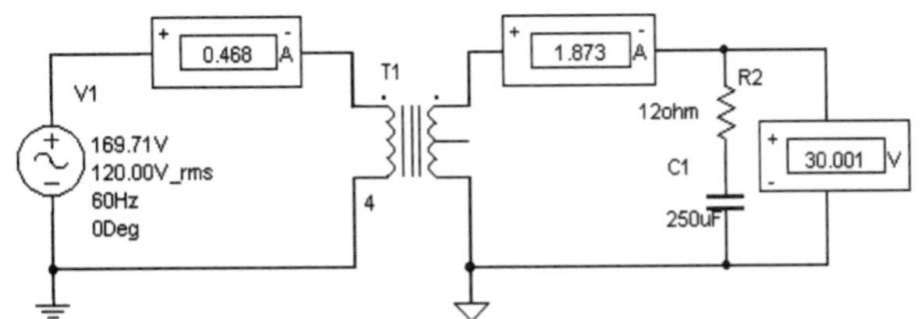

23.12 Circuit Analysis Using Computers (PSpice)

Annotating Schematics: If you want to annotate your schematics by adding text, click **Place** on the menu bar, then click **Text** and key in the text you want.

43. Use source VAC with its voltage set to 120V. (If you want the phase angle of the source to show on the screen, use **Place** and **Text** as noted above.) (Resistor R_1 is needed to avoid a source-inductor loop.) Set all meters for AC, MAG and PHASE. Use XFRM_LINEAR for the transformer. (Since the transformer is considered ideal, set its coefficient of coupling to 1 and make L_1 and L_2 very large, but related by $L_2 = L_1/a^2$ as described in the text. For example, I used $L_1 = 16000$ and $L_2 = 1000$, which yields a turns ratio of 4.) Select AC Sweep and enter 60 for Start and End frequencies. Following simulation, scroll the output for the

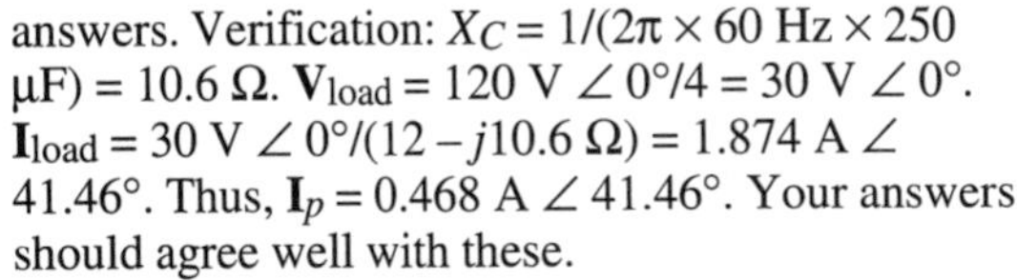
answers. Verification: $X_C = 1/(2\pi \times 60\ \text{Hz} \times 250\ \mu\text{F}) = 10.6\ \Omega$. $\mathbf{V}_{load} = 120\ \text{V} \angle 0°/4 = 30\ \text{V} \angle 0°$. $\mathbf{I}_{load} = 30\ \text{V} \angle 0°/(12 - j10.6\ \Omega) = 1.874\ \text{A} \angle 41.46°$. Thus, $\mathbf{I}_p = 0.468\ \text{A} \angle 41.46°$. Your answers should agree well with these.

45. Create the circuit below. (The low value resistors are necessary to avoid inductor loops.) Use source VAC. (See comments in Problem 43 regarding schematic annotation.) Set the meter for AC, MAG and PHASE. Use XFRM_LINEAR. Double click it and set values as given. Select AC Sweep and enter 60 for Start and End frequencies. Following simulation, scroll the output. Answers should agree with the solution to Problem 37.

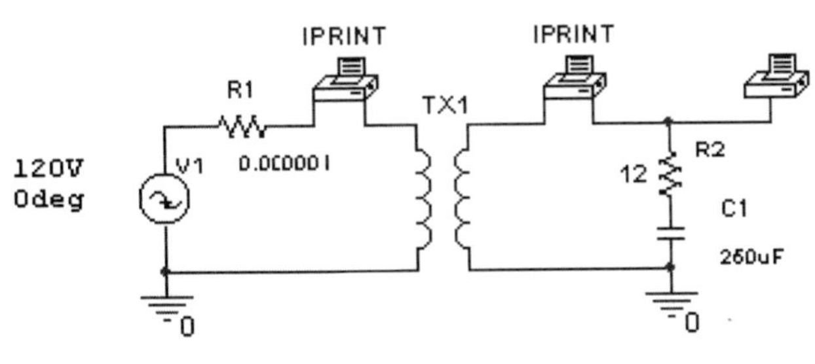

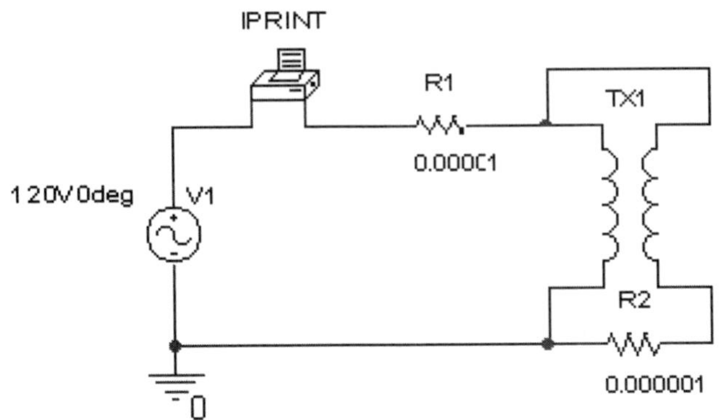

47. Create the circuit below. Use source VAC and transformer XFRM_LINEAR. (See comments in Problem 43 regarding schematic annotation.) Set all meters for AC, MAG and PHASE. Compute the coefficient of coupling *k* for the transformer using equation 24-16. (You should get 0.5367. However, because of the position of the dots, you must make *k* negative. Thus, enter –0.5367 for the coefficient of coupling.) Compute frequency as $f = \omega/2\pi$ = 15.9155 Hz. Select AC Sweep and enter 15.9155Hz for Start and End frequencies. (Note: Enter all digits shown for *f* and *k* to avoid round-off error.) Following simulation, scroll the output. Answers should agree with the solution to Practice Problem 8.

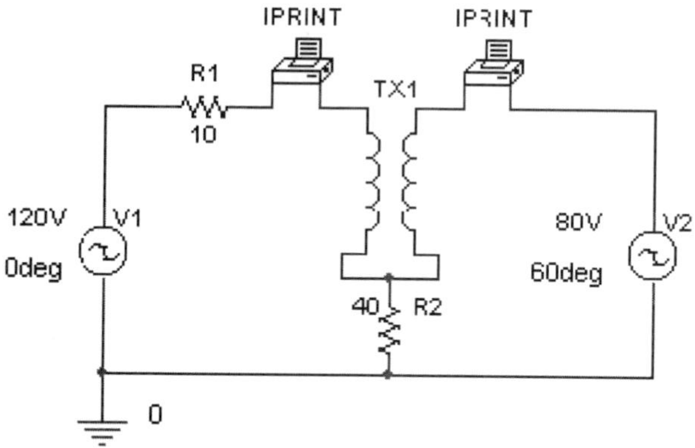

Chapter

24

Three-Phase Systems

24.2 Basic Three-Phase Circuit Connections

1. a. $\mathbf{I}_A = \dfrac{\mathbf{E}_{AA'}}{\mathbf{Z}} = \dfrac{120\text{ V}\angle 0^\circ}{15\ \Omega\angle 30^\circ} = 8\text{ A}\angle -30^\circ$

$\mathbf{I}_B = \dfrac{\mathbf{E}_{BB'}}{\mathbf{Z}} = \dfrac{120\text{ V}\angle -120^\circ}{15\ \Omega\angle 30^\circ} = 8\text{ A}\angle -150^\circ$

$\mathbf{I}_C = \dfrac{\mathbf{E}_{CC'}}{\mathbf{A}} = \dfrac{120\text{ V}\angle 120^\circ}{15\ \Omega\angle 30^\circ} = 8\text{ A}\angle 90^\circ$

b. $\mathbf{I}_A + \mathbf{I}_B + \mathbf{I}_C = 8\angle -30^\circ + 8\angle -150^\circ + 8\angle 90^\circ$
$= (6.93 - j4) + (-6.93 - j4) + (0 + j8)$
$= 0\text{ A}$ (Yes)

3. Sequence is ACB

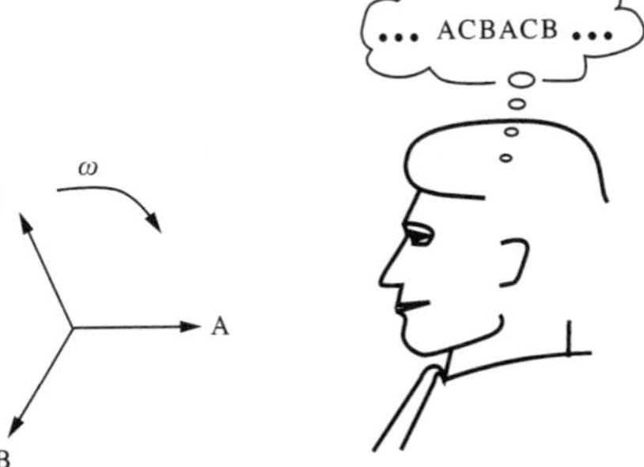

24.3 Basic Three-Phase Relationships

5. a. $\mathbf{V}_{ab} = 208\text{ V}\angle 45^\circ \qquad \mathbf{V}_{ca} = 208\text{ V}\angle 165^\circ$

b. $\mathbf{V}_{an} = \dfrac{\mathbf{V}_{ab}}{\sqrt{3}\angle 30^\circ} = \dfrac{208\text{ V}\angle 45^\circ}{\sqrt{3}\angle 30^\circ} = 120\text{ V}\angle 15^\circ$

$\mathbf{V}_{bn} = 120\text{ V}\angle -105^\circ \quad \mathbf{V}_{cn} = 120\text{ V}\angle 135^\circ$

c.

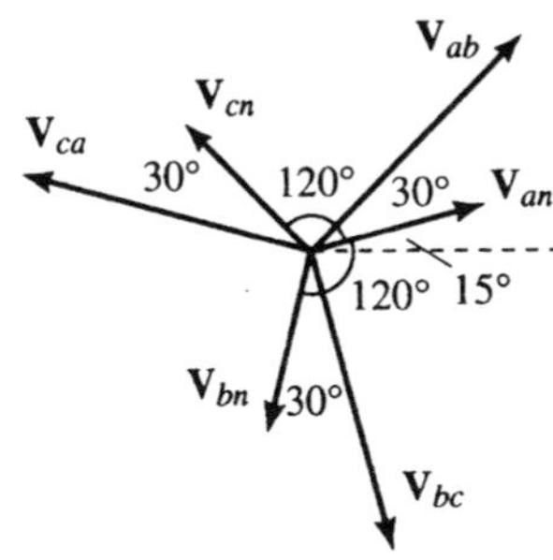

7. a. $\mathbf{I}_a = \dfrac{\mathbf{V}_{an}}{\mathbf{Z}_{an}} = \dfrac{347\text{ V}\angle 15^\circ}{12\ \Omega + j9\ \Omega} = 23.1\text{ A}\angle -21.9^\circ$

$\mathbf{I}_b = \dfrac{\mathbf{V}_{bn}}{\mathbf{Z}_{bn}} = \dfrac{347\angle -105^\circ}{12 + j9} = 23.1\text{ A}\angle -141.9^\circ$

$\mathbf{I}_c = \dfrac{\mathbf{V}_{cn}}{\mathbf{Z}_{cn}} = \dfrac{347\angle 135^\circ}{12 + j9} = 23.1\text{ A}\angle 98.1^\circ$

You can also obtain $\mathbf{I}_b$ from $\mathbf{I}_a$ by subtracting 120° from its angle. Thus, $\mathbf{I}_b = 23.1\text{ A}\angle -141.9^\circ$. Similarly, $\mathbf{I}_c$ is found by adding 120° to the angle of $\mathbf{I}_a$. Thus, $\mathbf{I}_c = 23.1\text{ A}\angle 98.1^\circ$.

9. $\mathbf{V}_{cn} = 120\text{ V}\angle 160^\circ \quad \therefore \quad \mathbf{V}_{an} = 120\text{ V}\angle 40^\circ$

$\mathbf{I}_a = \dfrac{\mathbf{V}_{an}}{\mathbf{Z}_{an}} = \dfrac{120\text{ V}\angle 40^\circ}{14.7\ \Omega\angle 16^\circ} = 8.16\text{ A}\angle 24^\circ$

$\therefore\ \mathbf{I}_b = 8.16\text{ A}\angle -96^\circ$ and $\mathbf{I}_c = 8.16\text{ A}\angle 144^\circ$

11. $\mathbf{I}_{ab} = \dfrac{\mathbf{V}_{ab}}{\mathbf{Z}_{ab}} = \dfrac{480\text{ V}\angle 0^\circ}{20\ \Omega - j15\ \Omega} = 19.2\text{ A}\angle 36.9^\circ$

$\therefore\ \mathbf{I}_{bc} = 19.2\text{ A}\angle -83.1^\circ$

$\mathbf{I}_{ca} = 19.2\text{ A}\angle 156.9^\circ$

$\mathbf{I}_a = \sqrt{3}\mathbf{I}_{ab}\angle -30^\circ$
$= \sqrt{3}(19.2\text{ A})\ \underline{\angle 36.9^\circ - 30^\circ}$
$= 33.3\text{ A}\angle 6.9^\circ$

$\therefore\ \mathbf{I}_b = 33.3\text{ A}\angle -113.1^\circ \qquad \mathbf{I}_c = 33.3\text{ A}\angle 126.9^\circ$

13. $\mathbf{V}_{ab} = \mathbf{I}_{ab}\mathbf{Z}_{ab}$
$= (10\text{ A}\angle -21^\circ)(20\ \Omega - j15\ \Omega)$
$= 250\text{ V}\angle -57.9^\circ$

$\therefore\ \mathbf{V}_{bc} = 250\text{ V}\angle -177.9^\circ$

$\mathbf{V}_{ca} = 250\text{ V}\angle 62.1^\circ$

15. $V_{an} = \dfrac{600\text{ V}}{\sqrt{3}} = 346\text{ V} \ \therefore\ \mathbf{V}_{an} = 346\text{ V}\angle 0^\circ$

$\mathbf{I}_a = \dfrac{\mathbf{V}_{an}}{\mathbf{Z}_{an}} = \dfrac{346\text{ V}\angle 0^\circ}{24\ \Omega\angle 33^\circ} = 14.4\text{ A}\angle -33^\circ$

$\therefore\ \mathbf{I}_b = 14.4\text{ A}\angle -153^\circ$ and $\mathbf{I}_c = 14.4\text{ A}\angle 87^\circ$

17. a. $\mathbf{V}_{an} = \dfrac{\mathbf{V}_{ab}}{\sqrt{3}\angle 30^\circ} = \dfrac{208\text{ V}\angle 30^\circ}{\sqrt{3}\angle 30^\circ} = 120\text{ V}\angle 0^\circ$

$\mathbf{Z}_{an} = \dfrac{\mathbf{V}_{an}}{\mathbf{I}_a} = \dfrac{120\text{ V}\angle 0^\circ}{24\text{ A}\angle 40^\circ} = 5\ \Omega\angle -40^\circ$
$= 3.83\ \Omega - j3.21\ \Omega$

$R_{an} = 3.83\ \Omega$

$C_{an} = \frac{1}{\omega X_{an}} = \frac{1}{(2\pi)(60)(3.21)} = 826\ \mu F$

b. $\mathbf{V}_{bc} = 208\angle -30^\circ$ ∴ $\mathbf{V}_{ab} = 208\angle 90^\circ$ and $\mathbf{V}_{an} = 120\text{ V }\angle 60^\circ$

$\mathbf{I}_c = 12\text{ A}\angle 140^\circ$ ∴ $\mathbf{I}_a = 12\text{ A}\angle 20^\circ$

$\therefore \mathbf{Z}_{an} = \frac{\mathbf{V}_{an}}{\mathbf{I}_a} = \frac{120\text{ V }\angle 60^\circ}{12\text{ A}\angle 20^\circ}$

$= 10\ \Omega\angle 40^\circ = 7.66\ \Omega + j6.43$

$R_{an} = 7.66\ \Omega \quad L = \frac{X_{an}}{\omega} = \frac{6.43}{(2\pi)(60)} = 17.1\text{ mH}$

19. a. $\mathbf{I}_{bc} = 4.5\text{ A}\angle -85^\circ$

∴ $\mathbf{I}_{ab} = 4.5\text{ A}\angle 35^\circ$ and $\mathbf{I}_{ca} = 4.5\text{ A}\angle 155^\circ$

b. $\mathbf{I}_a = \sqrt{3}\mathbf{I}_{ab}\angle -30^\circ$ ∴ $\mathbf{I}_a = 7.79\text{ A}\angle 5^\circ$

$\mathbf{I}_b = 7.79\text{ A}\angle -115^\circ$

$\mathbf{I}_c = 7.79\text{ A}\angle 125^\circ$

c. $\mathbf{Z}_{ab} = \frac{\mathbf{V}_{ab}}{\mathbf{I}_{ab}} = \frac{240\text{ V }\angle 0^\circ}{4.5\text{ A}\angle 35^\circ} = 55.33\ \Omega\angle -35^\circ$

$= 43.7 - j30.6$

$\therefore R_{ab} = 43.7\ \Omega \quad C_{ab} = \frac{1}{\omega X_{ab}} = \frac{1}{(2\pi)(60)(30.6)}$

$= 86.7\ \mu F$

24.4 Examples

21. a. Convert to the single phase equivalent as below. Thus,

$\mathbf{I}_a = \frac{\mathbf{V}_{an}}{\mathbf{Z}_{an}} = \frac{120\text{ V }\angle 0^\circ}{12\ \Omega + j9\ \Omega} = 8\text{ A}\angle -36.87^\circ$

$\mathbf{E}_{AN} = \mathbf{I}_a\mathbf{Z}_{\text{line}} + \mathbf{V}_{an} = (8\text{ A}\angle -36.87^\circ)(0.1\ \Omega + j0.3\ \Omega) + 120\text{ V }\angle 0^\circ = 122.1\ \angle 0.676^\circ$

b. $\mathbf{E}_{AB} = \sqrt{3}\mathbf{E}_{AN}\angle 30^\circ = 212\text{ V }\angle 30.676^\circ$.

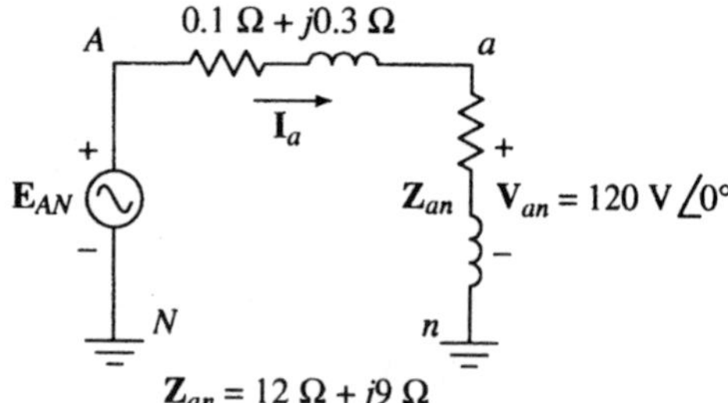

$\mathbf{I}_a = \frac{\mathbf{V}_{an}}{\mathbf{Z}_{an}} = \frac{346.4\text{ V }\angle 0^\circ}{12\ \Omega + j9\ \Omega} = 23.09\text{ A}\angle -36.87^\circ$

$\mathbf{E}_{AN} = \mathbf{I}_a\mathbf{Z}_{\text{line}} + \mathbf{V}_{an}$
$= (23.09\ \angle -36.87^\circ)(0.15 + j0.25) + 346.4\ \angle 0^\circ$
$= 352.6\ \angle 0.413^\circ$

$\mathbf{E}_{AB} = \sqrt{3}\mathbf{E}_{AN}\angle 30^\circ = 611\text{ V }\angle 30.4^\circ$

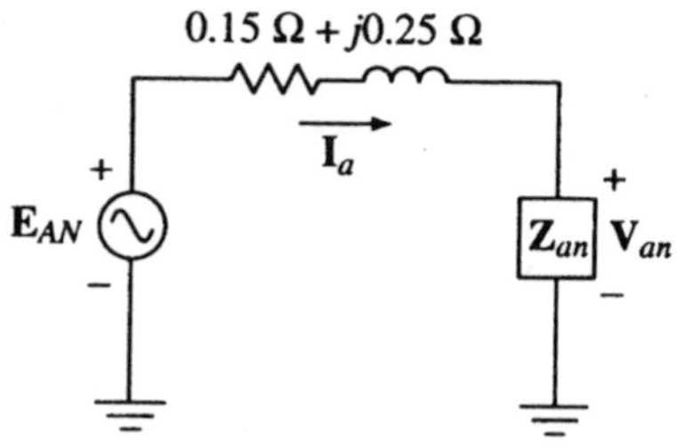

23. $\mathbf{Z}_{an} = \frac{\mathbf{Z}_{ab}}{3} = \frac{20\ \Omega - j15\ \Omega}{3} = 8.33\ \Omega\angle -36.9^\circ$

$\mathbf{I}_a = \frac{\mathbf{V}_{an}}{\mathbf{Z}_{an}} = \frac{\mathbf{E}_{AN}}{\mathbf{Z}_{an}} = \frac{120\text{ V }\angle -10^\circ}{8.33\ \Omega\angle -36.9^\circ} = 14.4\text{ A}\angle 26.9^\circ$

∴ $\mathbf{I}_b = 14.4\text{ A}\angle -93.1^\circ$ and $\mathbf{I}_c = 14.4\text{ A}\angle 146.9^\circ$

25. $\mathbf{Z}_{an} = \frac{\mathbf{Z}_{ab}}{3} = \frac{20\ \Omega - j15\ \Omega}{3} = 6.667\ \Omega - j5\ \Omega$

$\mathbf{I}_a = \frac{\mathbf{E}_{AN}}{\mathbf{Z}_{\text{line}} + \mathbf{Z}_{an}} = \frac{120\text{ V }\angle 0^\circ}{(0.15 + j0.25) + (6.667 - j5)}$
$= 14.4\text{ A}\angle 34.9^\circ$

∴ $\mathbf{I}_b = 14.4\text{ A}\angle -85.1^\circ \qquad \mathbf{I}_c = 14.4\text{ A}\angle 154.9^\circ$

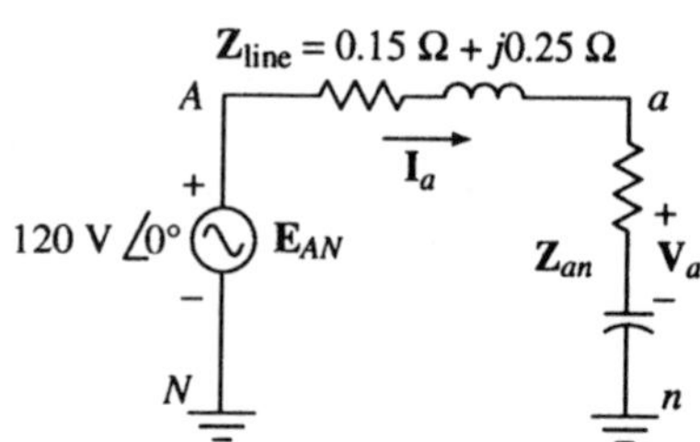

27. The single phase equivalent is shown below.

$\mathbf{V}_{an} = \frac{\mathbf{V}_{ab}}{\sqrt{3}\angle 30^\circ} = \frac{600\text{ V }\angle 30^\circ}{\sqrt{3}\angle 30^\circ} = 346.4\text{ V }\angle 0^\circ$

29. a. Convert the Δ load to a Y as in Problem 24. The line-to-neutral voltage is then

$\mathbf{V}_{a'n'} = \frac{\mathbf{V}_{a'b'}}{\sqrt{3}\angle 30^\circ} = \frac{480\text{ V }\angle 30^\circ}{\sqrt{3}\angle 30^\circ} = 277.1\text{ V }\angle 0^\circ$.

The single phase equivalent is the same as Problem 28 except

$\mathbf{V}_{an} = \mathbf{V}_{a'n'} = 277.1\text{ V }\angle 0^\circ$.

b. $\mathbf{I}_a = \frac{\mathbf{V}_{an}}{\mathbf{Z}_Y} = \frac{277.1\text{ V }\angle 0^\circ}{12\ \Omega + j9\ \Omega} = 18.47\text{ A}\angle -36.87^\circ$

$\mathbf{I}_{a'} = \frac{\mathbf{V}_{an}}{\mathbf{Z}_{Y'}} = \frac{277.1\text{ V }\angle 0^\circ}{9\ \Omega + j12\ \Omega} = 18.47\text{ A}\angle -53.13^\circ$

$\mathbf{I}_A = \mathbf{I}_a + \mathbf{I}_{a'} = 36.57\text{ A}\angle -45^\circ$

$\mathbf{E}_{AN} = \mathbf{I}_A\mathbf{Z}_{\text{line}} + V_{an}$
$= (36.57\text{ A}\angle -45^\circ)(0.1\ \Omega + j0.1\ \Omega) + 277.1\text{ V }\angle 0^\circ$
$= 282.3\text{ V }\angle 0^\circ$

$\mathbf{E}_{AB} = \sqrt{3}\mathbf{E}_{AN}\angle 30^\circ = 489\text{ V }\angle 30^\circ$

31. $\mathbf{V}_{a'b'} = \mathbf{I}_{a'b'}\mathbf{Z}_{a'b'} = (40\text{ A}\angle 73.13^\circ)(9\ \Omega - \text{j}12\ \Omega)$
$= 600\text{ V }\angle 20^\circ$

$\mathbf{V}_{ab} = \mathbf{V}_{a'b'}$ and $\mathbf{V}_{an}$

$= \frac{\mathbf{V}_{ab}}{\sqrt{3}\angle 30^\circ} = \frac{600\text{ V }\angle 20^\circ}{\sqrt{3}\angle 30^\circ} = 346\text{ V }\angle -10^\circ$

24.5 Power in a Balanced System

33. $V_\phi = 207.8$ V. (Use this instead of the nominal value of 208 V in order to facilitate comparing solutions.)

$$P_\phi = \frac{(207.8\text{ V})^2}{500\ \Omega} = 86.4\text{ W}$$

$P_T = 3P_\phi = 259$ W

$Q_\phi = 0$ VAR $\therefore Q_T = 0$ VAR

$S_\phi = 86.4$ VA $\qquad S_T = 259$ VA (since Q = 0)

35. $V_L = \sqrt{3}(120) = 207.8$ V; $I_L = 8$ A

$P_T = \sqrt{3}V_L I_L \cos\theta_\phi = \sqrt{3}(207.8)(8)\cos 36.87° = 2303$ W

$Q_T = \sqrt{3}V_L I_L \sin\theta_\phi = \sqrt{3}(207.8)(8)\sin 36.87° = 1728$ VAR

$S_T = \sqrt{3}V_L I_L = \sqrt{3}(207.8)(8) = 2879$ VA

Slight differences are due to round-off errors.

37. $I_L = \sqrt{3}I_\phi = 14.41$ A

$P_T = \sqrt{3}V_L I_L \cos\theta_\phi = \sqrt{3}(208\text{ V})(14.41\text{ A})\cos 36.87° = 4153$ W

$Q_T = \sqrt{3}(208\text{ V})(14.41\text{ A})\sin 36.87° = 3115$ VAR

$S_T = \sqrt{3}(208\text{ V})(14.41\text{ A}) = 5191$ VA

Slight differences are due to round-off errors.

39. $\mathbf{Z}_\phi = 12 + j6 = 13.42\ \angle 26.56°$

$$I_\phi = \frac{V_\phi}{Z_\phi} = \frac{600\text{ V}}{13.42\ \Omega} = 44.72\text{ A}$$

$P_T = 3I^2_\phi R_\phi = 3[(44.72\text{A})^2(12\Omega)] = 72$ kW

$Q_T = 3I^2_\phi X_\phi = 3[(44.72\text{A})^2(6\Omega)] = 36$ kVAR (ind.)

$S_T = 3V_\phi I_\phi = 3[(600\text{ V})(44.72\text{ A})] = 80.5$ kVA

$F_p = \cos 26.56° = 0.894$

41. $$I_\phi = \frac{V_\phi}{Z_\phi} = \frac{480}{15\ \Omega} = 32\text{ A}$$

$P_T = 3V_\phi I_\phi \cos\theta_\phi = 3(480\text{ V})(32\text{ A})\cos 53.13° = 27.7$ kW

$Q_T = 3V_\phi I_\phi \sin\theta_\phi = 3(480\text{ V})(32\text{ A})\sin 53.13° = 36.9$ kVAR (ind.)

$S_T = 3V_\phi I_\phi = 3(480\text{ V})(32\text{ A}) = 46.1$ kVA

$F_p = \cos\theta_\phi = \cos 53.13° = 0.60$

43. $S_T = \sqrt{P_T^2 + Q_T^2} = \sqrt{(1200\text{ W})^2 + (750\text{ VAR})^2} = 1415$ VA

$$I_a = I_L = \frac{S_T}{\sqrt{3}V_L} = \frac{1415\text{ VA}}{\sqrt{3}(208\text{ V})} = 3.93\text{ A}$$

$$\theta_\phi = \tan^{-1}\left(\frac{Q_T}{P_T}\right) = \tan^{-1}\left(\frac{750}{1200}\right) = 32°$$

Choose V_{an} as reference: $V_{an} = 120\text{ V}\angle 0°$

Current lags by 32°. Therefore, $I_a = 3.93\text{ A}\angle -32°$.

45. $$X_C = \frac{1}{\omega C} = \frac{1}{(2\pi)(60\text{ Hz})(120\ \mu\text{F})} = 22.1\ \Omega$$

$$Q_C = \frac{V_\phi^2}{X_C} = \frac{(575\text{ V}/\sqrt{3})^2}{22.1\ \Omega} = 4.987\text{ kVAR}$$

$P_T = 31.08$ kW (from Problem 44)

$Q_T = 19.26\text{ kVAR} - 4.987\text{ kVAR} = 14.27$ kVAR

$$\theta = \tan^{-1}\left(\frac{Q_T}{P_T}\right) = \tan^{-1}\left(\frac{14.27}{31.08}\right) = 24.7°$$

$F_p = \cos 24.7° = 0.909$

24.6 Measuring Power in Three-Phase Circuits

47. a. See Figure 24-29 of text.

b. $\mathbf{Z}_\phi = 12\ \Omega + j9\ \Omega = 15\ \Omega\angle 36.87°$: $I_\phi = \dfrac{V_\phi}{Z_\phi} = \dfrac{120\text{ V}}{15\ \Omega} = 8$ A

Each meter reads the same. Thus,

$W_1 = W_2 = W_3 = V_\phi I_\phi \cos\theta_\phi = (120\text{ V})(8\text{ A})\cos 36.87° = 768$ W.

c. $P_T = W_1 + W_2 + W_3 = 2304$ W

49. a.

$$\mathbf{I}_a = \frac{\mathbf{V}_{an}}{\mathbf{Z}_{an}} = \frac{120\text{ V}\angle 0°}{20\ \Omega + j5\ \Omega} = 5.82\text{ A}\angle -14.0°$$

$\mathbf{I}_b = 5.82\text{ A}\angle -134.0° \qquad \mathbf{I}_c = 5.82\text{ A}\angle 106.0°$

b. $P_\phi = V_\phi I_\phi \cos\theta_\phi = (120\text{ V})(5.82\text{ A})\cos 14° = 678$ W

$P_T = 3P_\phi = 2034$ W

c. $W_1 = V_{ac}I_a\cos\theta_1$ where θ_1 is angle between $\mathbf{V}_{ac}$ and $\mathbf{I}_a$

$\mathbf{V}_{ac} = -\mathbf{V}_{ca} = -207.8\text{ V}\angle 150° = 207.8\text{ V}\angle -30°$

$\mathbf{I}_a = 5.82\text{ A}\angle -14°\ \therefore \theta_1 = 30° - 14° = 16°$

$W_1 = (207.8\text{ V})(5.82\text{ A})\cos 16° = 1163$ W

$W_2 = V_{bc}I_b\cos\theta_2 \qquad \mathbf{V}_{bc}$ is at −90°

$\mathbf{I}_b$ is at − 134°

$\therefore \theta_2 = 44°$.

$W_2 = (207.8\text{ V})(5.82\text{ A})\cos 44° = 870$ W

d. $W_1 + W_2 = 2033$ W. Agrees with 2034 W from (b).

51. a. $F_p = \cos 14.0 = 0.970$

b. $$\tan\theta_\phi = \sqrt{3}\left(\frac{P_h - P_\ell}{P_h + P_\ell}\right) = \sqrt{3}\left(\frac{1163 - 870}{1163 + 870}\right) = 0.2496$$

$\therefore \theta_\phi = 14.0°$

$F_p = \cos 14.0° = 0.970$

24.7 Unbalanced Systems

53. a.

$$\mathbf{I}_{ab} = \frac{\mathbf{V}_{ab}}{\mathbf{Z}_{ab}} = \frac{240 \text{ V} \angle 0^\circ}{60\ \Omega} = 4 \text{ A}\angle 0^\circ$$

$$\mathbf{I}_{bc} = \frac{\mathbf{V}_{bc}}{\mathbf{Z}_{bc}} = \frac{240 \text{ V} \angle -120^\circ}{80\ \Omega + j60\ \Omega} = 2.4 \text{ A}\angle -156.9^\circ$$

$$\mathbf{I}_{ca} = \frac{\mathbf{V}_{ca}}{\mathbf{Z}_{ca}} = \frac{240 \text{ V} \angle 120^\circ}{50\ \Omega - j60\ \Omega} = 3.07 \text{ A}\angle 170.2^\circ$$

$KCL: \mathbf{I}_a = \mathbf{I}_{ab} - \mathbf{I}_{ca} = 4 \text{ A}\angle 0^\circ - 3.07 \text{ A}\angle 170.2^\circ = 7.04 \text{ A}\angle -4.25^\circ$

$\mathbf{I}_b = \mathbf{I}_{bc} - \mathbf{I}_{ab} = 2.4 \text{ A}\angle -156.9^\circ - 4 \text{ A}\angle 0^\circ = 6.28 \text{ A}\angle -171.4^\circ$

$\mathbf{I}_c = \mathbf{I}_{ca} - \mathbf{I}_{bc} = 3.07 \text{ A}\angle 170.2^\circ - 2.4 \text{ A}\angle -156.9^\circ = 1.68 \text{ A}\angle 119.2^\circ$

b.

$P_{ab} = I_{ab}^2 R_{ab} = (4 \text{ A})^2 (60\ \Omega) = 960 \text{ W}$

$P_{bc} = I_{bc}^2 R_{bc} = (2.4 \text{ A})^2 (80\ \Omega) = 461 \text{ W}$

$P_{ca} = I_{ca}^2 R_{ca} = (3.07 \text{ A})^2 (50\ \Omega) = 471 \text{ W}$

$P_T = 960 + 461 + 471 = 1892 \text{ W}$

55. a.

$$\mathbf{I}_a = \frac{\mathbf{V}_{an}}{\mathbf{Z}_{an}} = \frac{120 \text{ V} \angle 0^\circ}{18\ \Omega} = 6.67 \text{ A}\angle 0^\circ$$

$$\mathbf{I}_b = \frac{\mathbf{V}_{bn}}{\mathbf{Z}_{bn}} = \frac{120 \text{ V} \angle -120^\circ}{40\ \Omega - j20\ \Omega} = 2.68 \text{ A}\angle -93.4^\circ$$

$$\mathbf{I}_c = \frac{\mathbf{V}_{cn}}{\mathbf{Z}_{cn}} = \frac{120 \text{ V} \angle 120^\circ}{30\ \Omega + j40\ \Omega} = 2.4 \text{ A}\angle 66.9^\circ$$

b. $\mathbf{I}_n = \mathbf{I}_a + \mathbf{I}_b + \mathbf{I}_c = 6.67\angle 0^\circ + 2.68\angle -93.4^\circ + 2.4\angle 66.9^\circ = 7.46 \text{ A}\angle -3.62^\circ$

c. $P_{an} = I_a^2 R_{an} = (6.67 \text{ A})^2 (18\ \Omega) = 800 \text{ W}$

$P_{bn} = I_b^2 R_{bn} = (2.68 \text{ A})^2 (40\ \Omega) = 287 \text{ W}$

$P_{cn} = I_c^2 R_{cn} = (2.4 \text{ A})^2 (30\ \Omega) = 173 \text{ W}$

d. $P_T = 800 \text{ W} + 287 \text{ W} + 173 \text{ W} = 1260 \text{ W}$

57. a. $\mathbf{V}_{an} = \mathbf{I}_a \mathbf{Z}_{an} = (1.94 \text{ A}\angle -0.737^\circ)(18\ \Omega) = 34.9 \text{ V}\angle -0.737^\circ$

$\mathbf{V}_{bn} = \mathbf{I}_b \mathbf{Z}_{bn} = (4.0 \text{ A}\angle -117.7^\circ)(40\ \Omega - j20\ \Omega) = 179 \text{ V}\angle -144^\circ$

$\mathbf{V}_{cn} = \mathbf{I}_c \mathbf{Z}_{cn} = (3.57 \text{ A}\angle 91.4^\circ)(30\ \Omega + j40\ \Omega) = 178 \text{ V}\angle 145^\circ$

b. $KVL: \mathbf{E}_{AN} - \mathbf{V}_{an} - \mathbf{V}_{nN} = 0$

$\therefore\ \mathbf{V}_{nN} = \mathbf{E}_{AN} - \mathbf{V}_{an} = 120 \text{ V}\angle 0^\circ - 34.9 \text{ V}\angle -0.737^\circ = 85.0 \text{ V}\angle 0.302^\circ$

24.9 Circuit Analysis Using Computers (MSM)

Notes

1. When assigning angles for sources, remember that MultiSIM does not accept angles with a minus sign. Thus, –30° must be entered as 330°. In addition, for MultiSIM 2001 users, recall Note 2, page 525, Chapter 15.

2. Don't forget to convert inductive reactance to henries. Thus, $L = X_L/\omega$. Similarly for capacitive reactance.

59. Build the circuit as shown. Set all meters for AC. Energize the circuit using MSM's power ON/OFF switch. Answers should agree with those of Problem 11.

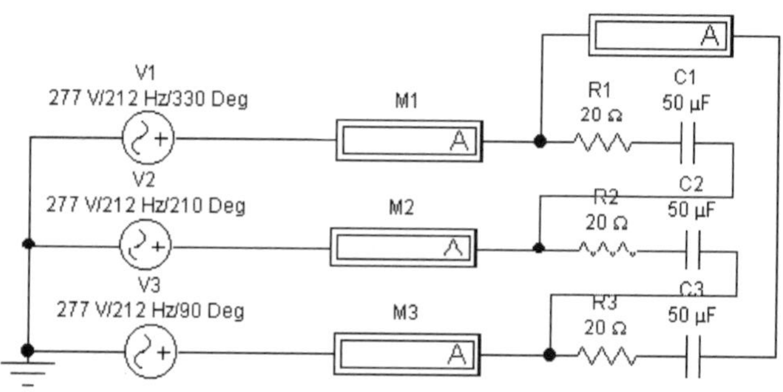

61. Create the circuit as shown. Be sure to set all meters for AC. Set $f = \omega/2\pi = 159.155$ Hz. Energize the circuit using MSM's power ON/OFF switch. Verification: Compare your answers to Problem 55.

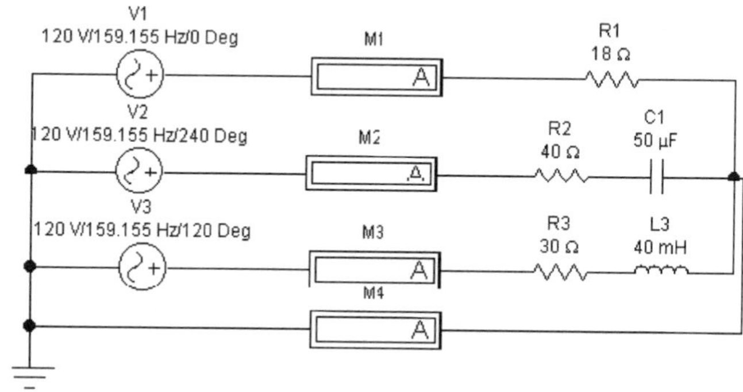

24.9 Circuit Analysis Using Computers (PSpice)

Note

The extra text on these diagrams was placed by clicking *Place* on the menu bar, then *Text*. It is optional.

59. Create the circuit as shown using source VAC. Set all meters for AC, MAG and PHASE. Use AC Sweep with Start and End frequencies set to 212Hz. Following simulation, scroll the output. Answers should agree with those of Problem 11.

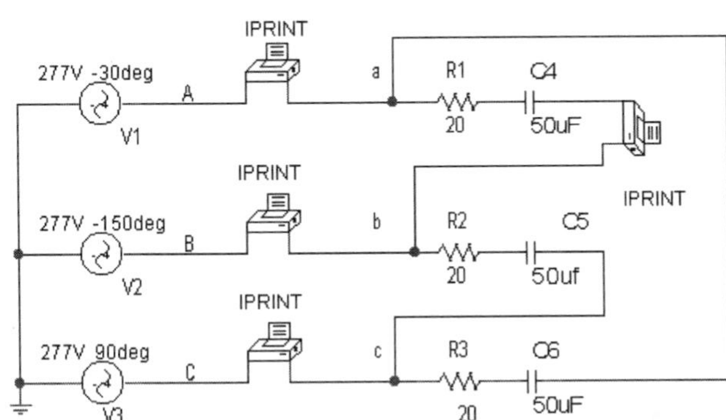

61. Create the circuit shown. Use source VAC and AC Sweep. Set Start and End frequencies to $f = \omega/2\pi =$ 159.155 Hz. Run the simulation and scroll the output file for answers. Verification: Compare your answers to Problem 55.

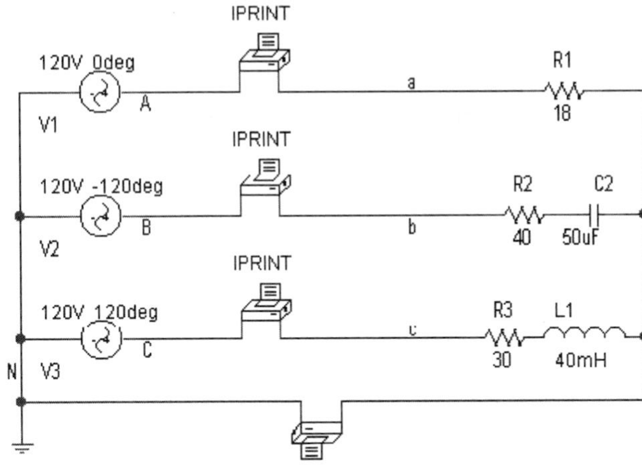

Chapter

25

Nonsinusoidal Waveforms

25.1 Fourier Series

1. a. $V_{dc} = 15$ V

$V_{ac} = 15\ V_p \equiv 10.607\ V_{rms}$

$V_{rms} = \sqrt{337.5\ V} = 18.37$ V

b. $$P = \frac{V_{rms}^2}{R} = \frac{(18.37\ V)^2}{50\ \Omega} = 6.75\ W$$

3. a. $V_{dc} = -10$ V

$V_{ac} = 20\ V_p = 14.14\ V_p$

Vsubrms $= \sqrt{300\ V^2} = 17.32$ V

b. $$P = \frac{(17.32\ V)^2}{2.5\ k\Omega} = 0.12\ W$$

5. $v(t) = 2 - 2t \qquad 0 < t < 1$ s

$$a_0 = \frac{1}{1}\int_{t=0}^{t=1} (2-2t)dt = \left(2t - \frac{2t^2}{2}\right)\Bigg|_0^1 = 2(1) - 1(1)^2 = 1\ V$$

$$a_n = \frac{2}{1}\int_{t=0}^{t=1} (2-2t)\cos(n\omega t)dt = 2(2)\left[\int_0^1 \cos(n\omega t)dt - \int_0^1 t\cos(n\omega t)dt\right]$$

$$= \left(\frac{4\sin(n\omega t)}{n\omega}\right)\Bigg|_0^1 - 4\left(\frac{\cos(n\omega t)}{n^2\omega^2} + \frac{x\sin(n\omega t)}{n\omega}\right)\Bigg|_0^1$$

But $\omega = \dfrac{2\pi}{T} = 2\pi$

$$a_n = 0 - \left(\frac{4\cos(2\pi\, n)}{(2\pi)^2 n^2} - \frac{4\cos(0)}{(2\pi)^2 n^2)}\right) = 0$$

$$b_n = \frac{2}{1}\int_0^1 (2-2t)\sin(n\omega t)dt$$

$$= (2)(2)\left[\int_0^1 \sin(n\omega t)dt - \int_0^1 t\sin(n\omega t)dt\right]$$

$$= \left(\frac{4\cos(n\omega t)}{n\omega}\right)\Bigg|_0^1 - 4\left(\frac{\sin(n\omega t)}{n^2\omega^2} - \frac{t\cos(n\omega t)}{n\omega}\right)\Bigg|_0^1$$

But $\omega = \dfrac{2\pi}{T} = 2\pi$

$$b_n = (0-0) - 4\left[\left(0 - \frac{1}{2\pi\, n}\right) - 0\right] = \frac{2}{\pi n}$$

$$v(t) = 1 + \frac{2}{\pi}\sin(\omega t) + \frac{2}{2\pi}\sin(2\omega t) + \frac{2}{3\pi}\sin(3\omega t) + \frac{2}{4\pi}\sin(4\omega t) + \ldots$$

Refer to Figure 25-11: (checking)

$$v(t) = 2\ V - 2v(t) = 2\ V - \left[\frac{2\ V}{2} - \frac{2\ V}{n\pi}\sum_{n=1}^{\infty} \sin(n\omega t)\right]$$

7. $T = 4$ ms $\qquad \omega = \dfrac{2\pi}{4\text{ ms}} = 500\pi$ rad/s

$$v(t) = \frac{32}{\pi}\sin(500\pi t) - \frac{32}{2\pi}\sin(1000\pi t) + \frac{32}{3\pi}\sin(1500\pi t) - \frac{32}{3\pi}\sin(2000\pi t) + \ldots$$
$$= 10.19\sin(500\pi t) - 5.09\sin(1000\pi t) + 3.40\sin(1500\pi t) - 2.55\sin(2000\pi t) + \ldots$$

9. $\omega = 100\pi$ rad/s

$$v(t) = \frac{10}{\pi} + 5\sin(\omega t) - \frac{20}{\pi}\left[\frac{\cos(2\omega t)}{3} + \frac{\text{cost}(4\omega t)}{15}\ldots\right]$$
$$= 3.183 + 5\sin(\omega t) - 2\cos(2\omega t) - 0.42\cos(4\omega t) - \ldots$$

11. $T = 34 - 10 = 24$ ms

$t = 2$ ms

$$\theta = \frac{2\text{ ms}}{24\text{ ms}} \times 360^\circ = 30^\circ$$

$$\omega = \frac{2\pi}{T} = 83.\overline{3}\pi \text{ rad/s}$$

$$v(t) = \frac{32}{\pi}\sin(\omega t + 30^\circ) + \frac{32}{3\pi}\sin[3(\omega t + 30^\circ)] + \frac{32}{5\pi}\sin[5(\omega t + 30^\circ)] + \frac{32}{7\pi}\sin[7(\omega t + 30^\circ)] + \ldots$$

13. a.

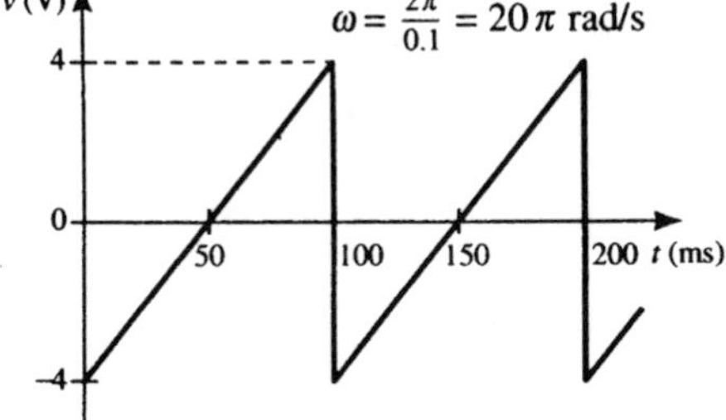

b.
$$v_1 = -\frac{16}{\pi}\sin\omega t - \frac{16}{3\pi}\sin 3\omega t - \frac{16}{5\pi}\sin 5\omega t \ldots$$
$$v_2 = +\frac{8}{\pi}\sin\omega t - \frac{8}{2\pi}\sin 2\omega t + \frac{8}{3\pi}\sin 3\omega t - \ldots$$

c.
$$v = v_1 + v_2 = -\frac{8}{\pi}\sin\omega t - \frac{8}{2\pi}\sin 2\omega t - \frac{8}{3\pi}\sin 3\omega t - \ldots$$

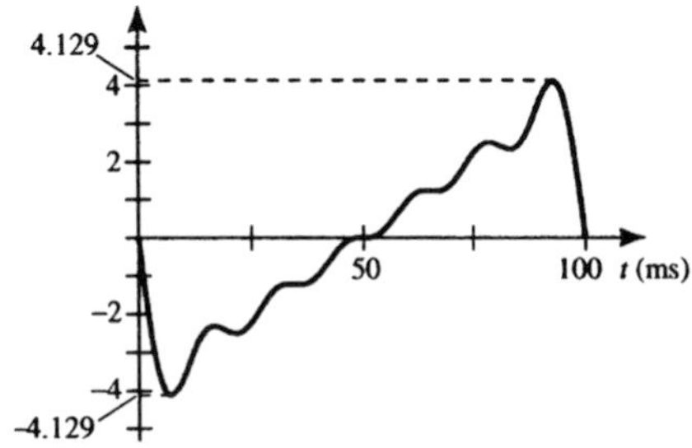

15. a.

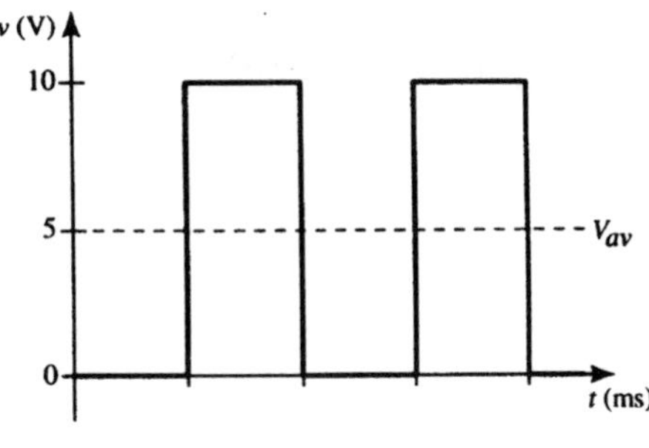

b. $V_{av} = 5$ Vdc

From Figure 25-11 $\qquad$ ($T = 100$ ms)

c.
$$v_1 = 5 - \frac{10}{\pi}\sin\omega t - \frac{10}{2\pi}\sin(2\omega t) - \frac{10}{3\pi}\sin(3\omega t)$$

From Figure 25-10 $\qquad$ ($T = 100$ ms)

$$v_2 = \frac{-10}{\pi}\sin\omega t + \frac{10}{2\pi}\sin(2\omega t) - \frac{10}{3\pi}\sin(3\omega t)$$

d.
$$v_1 + v_2 = 5 - \frac{20}{\pi}\sin\omega t - \frac{20}{3\pi}\sin(3\omega t) - \frac{20}{5\pi}\sin(5\omega t) - \ldots$$

17.

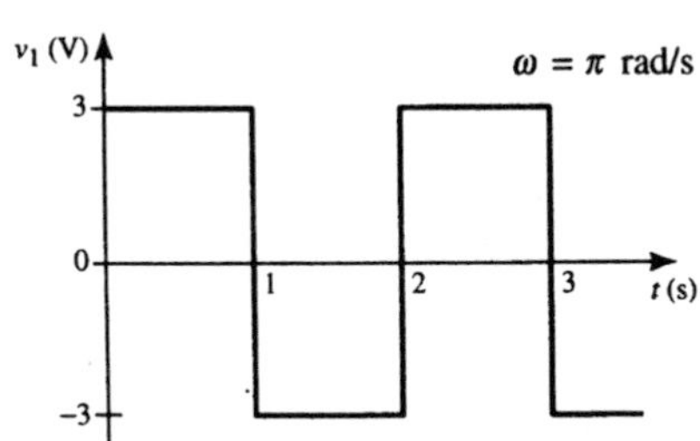

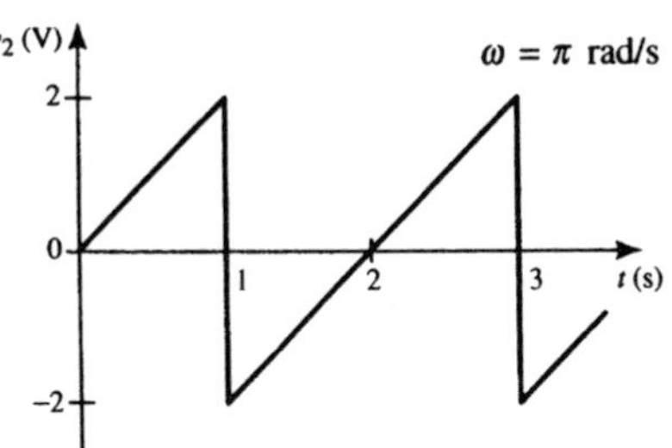

$$v_1 = \frac{12}{\pi}\sin\omega t + \frac{12}{3\pi}\sin(3\omega t) + \frac{12}{5\pi}\sin(5\omega t) + \ldots$$
$$v_2 = \frac{4}{\pi}\sin\omega t - \frac{4}{2\pi}\sin(2\omega t) + \frac{4}{3\pi}\sin(3\omega t) - \ldots$$
$$v_1 + v_2 = \frac{16}{\pi}\sin\omega t - \frac{4}{2\pi}\sin(2\omega t) + \frac{16}{3\pi}\sin(3\omega t) - \ldots$$

25.3 Frequency Spectrum

19. $V_{dc} = 0$

$$V_1 = \frac{32}{\pi}V_p \equiv \frac{32}{\pi\sqrt{2}} = 7.20\ \text{V}_{\text{rms}}$$

$$V_2 = \frac{32}{2\pi}V_p \equiv \frac{32}{2\pi\sqrt{2}} = 3.60\ \text{V}_{\text{rms}}$$

$$V_3 = \frac{32}{3\pi}V_p \equiv \frac{32}{3\pi\sqrt{2}} = 2.40\ \text{V}_{\text{rms}}$$

$$V_4 = \frac{32}{4\pi}V_p \equiv \frac{32}{4\pi\sqrt{2}} = 1.80\ \text{V}_{\text{rms}}$$

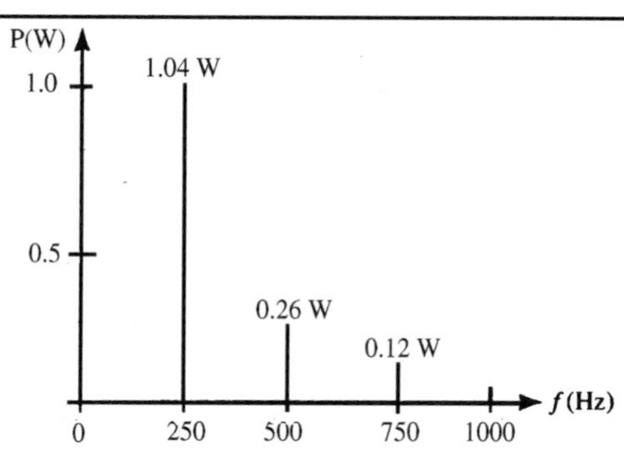

$$\text{V}_{\text{rms}} = \sqrt{0^2 + (7.20\ \text{V})^2 + (3.60\ \text{V})^2 + (2.40\ \text{V})^2 + (1.80\ \text{V})^2} = 8.59\ \text{V}_{\text{rms}}$$

$$P = \frac{(8.59\ \text{V})^2}{50\ \Omega} = 1.477\ \text{W}$$

21. $V_0 = \frac{10}{\pi} = 3.18\ \text{V}$

$$V_1\ (\text{rms}) = \frac{5\ \text{V}}{\sqrt{2}} = 3.54\ \text{V}$$

$$V_2\ (\text{rms}) = \frac{20\ \text{V}}{\pi\sqrt{2}} = 4.50\ \text{V}$$

$$V_3\ (\text{rms}) = \frac{20\ \text{V}}{15\pi\sqrt{2}} = 0.300\ \text{V}$$

$$V_4\ (\text{rms}) = \frac{20\ \text{V}}{35\pi\sqrt{2}} = 0.129\ \text{V}$$

$$P_0 = \frac{(3.18\ \text{V})^2}{50\ \Omega} = 203\ \text{mW}\ (23.1\ \text{dBm})$$

$$P_1 = \frac{(3.54\ \text{V})^2}{50\ \Omega} = 250\ \text{mW}\ (24.0\ \text{dBm})$$

$$P_2 = \frac{(4.50\ \text{V})^2}{50\ \Omega} = 405\ \text{mW}\ (26.1\ \text{dBm})$$

$$P_3 = \frac{(0.300\ \text{V})^2}{50\ \Omega} = 1.80\ \text{mW}\ (2.56\ \text{dBm})$$

$$P_4 = \frac{(0.129\ \text{V})^2}{50\ \Omega} = 0.33\ \text{mW}\ (-4.80\ \text{dBm})$$

25.4 Circuit Response to a Nonsinusoidal Waveform

23. $T = 1.0\ \text{ms}$ $\quad f = 1\ \text{kHz}$

From Fig. 25-13:

$$v_1 = 0.5 + \frac{4}{\pi}\sin\omega t + \frac{4}{3\pi}\sin(3\omega t) + \frac{4}{5\pi}\sin(5\omega t) + \frac{4}{7\pi}\sin(7\omega t)$$

a. $V_0(\text{dc}) = 0.5\ \text{V}$

b. $V_1 = \frac{4\ \text{V}}{\pi}(10^{-3/20}) = 0.90\ \text{V}_p$

$\theta_1 = -45°$

$V_3 = \frac{4\ \text{V}}{3\pi}(10^{-9.5/20}) = 0.14\ \text{V}_p$

$\theta_3 = -63°$

$V_5 = \frac{4\ \text{V}}{5\pi}(10^{-14/20}) = 0.5\ \text{V}_p$

$\theta_5 = -79°$

$V_7 = \frac{4\ \text{V}}{7\pi}(10^{-16.5/20}) = 0.03\ \text{V}_p$

$\theta_7 = -82°$

25.5 Circuit Analysis Using Computers

25.

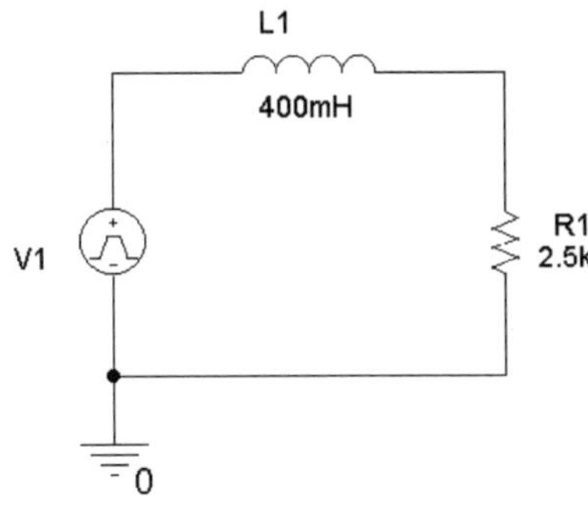

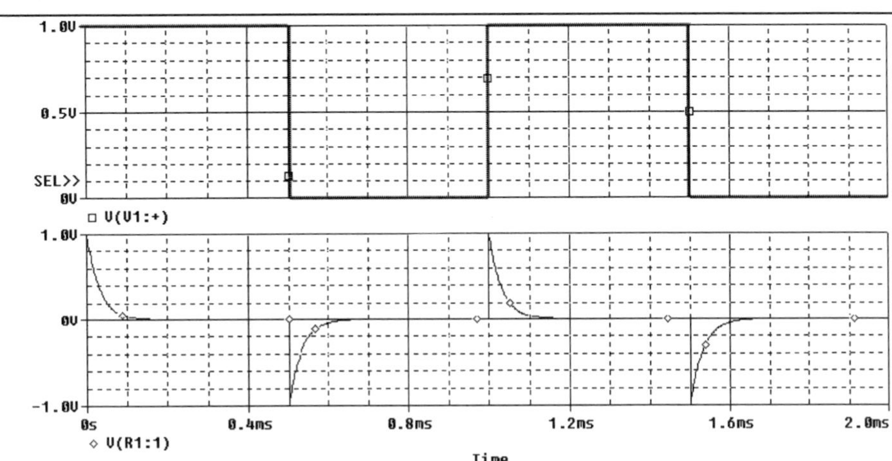

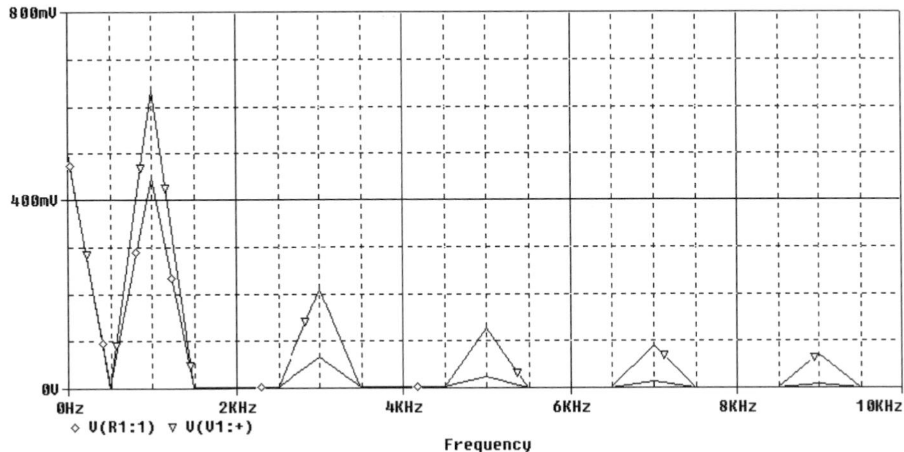

Answers to Selected Odd-Numbered Questions,

Chapters 24–31

CIRCUIT ANALYSIS WITH DEVICES: THEORY AND PRACTICE

Chapter

24

Introduction to Semiconductors

24.1 Semiconductor Basics

1. An electron in the valence (i.e., the last occupied) shell of an atom.
3. Gold is a conductor. Thus, same as Figure 24-3(c).
5. See Figure 24-3. It is smaller than that of an insulator but larger than that of a conductor.
7. a. 6 b. 4 c. tetravalent (has 4 electrons in valence shell)

24.2 Conduction in Semiconductors

9. a. Resistance increases as temperature increases. Metals, e.g., copper.
   b. Resistance decreases as temperature increases. Semiconductors, e.g., silicon.
11. As described in the text.

24.3 Doping

13. a. trivalent b. pentavalent
15. Holes
17. Electrons
19. Antimony is a pentavalent material – thus, it has one more valence electron than is needed for bonding (similar to what we showed in Figure 24-8). If externally applied energy (e.g. heat) causes the electron to escape, it will not leave behind a hole, since it isn't needed for bonding anyway.

24.4 The p-n Junction

21. 0.7 V
23. 0 V

24.5 The Biased p-n Junction

25. The depletion region is formed when free electrons from the *n*-material diffuse across the junction, leaving atoms of the *n*-material near the junction with a deficiency of electrons and atoms of the *p*-material with an excess as indicated in Figure 24-14.When a forward biased source is connected, electrons injected into the *n*-material are propelled toward the junction, replacing some of those originally lost; similarly from the *p*-side, holes are propelled toward the junction, replacing some of those originally lost. As more and more of the ions near the junction have their lost charges replaced, the depletion region narrows.
27. Majority
29. 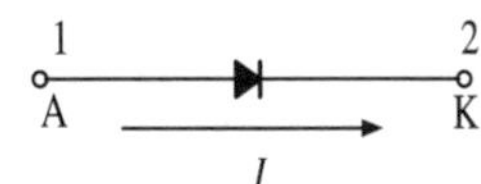

Chapter

25

Diode Theory and Application

25.1 Diode Models

1. a. The diode is reverse biased. Thus, $I_D = 0$ A and $V_D = 27$ V.

   b. Since the diode is assumed ideal, $V_D = 0$ V.

   $R_T = 2.5\ \text{k}\Omega + 6\ \text{k}\Omega \| 3\ \text{k}\Omega = 4.5\ \text{k}\Omega$.

   Thus, $I_D = \dfrac{18\ \text{V}}{4.5\ \text{k}\Omega} = 4$ mA.

3. When the coil is energized as in (a), the diode is reverse biased and draws no current. At the instant the switch is opened, an induced voltage occurs because of the falling current. As indicated in (b), its polarity is reversed and thus, the diode is forward biased and conducts. Now, instead of getting a huge voltage spike, the diode limits coil voltage to one diode drop (about 0.7 V for silicon) as indicated in (c).

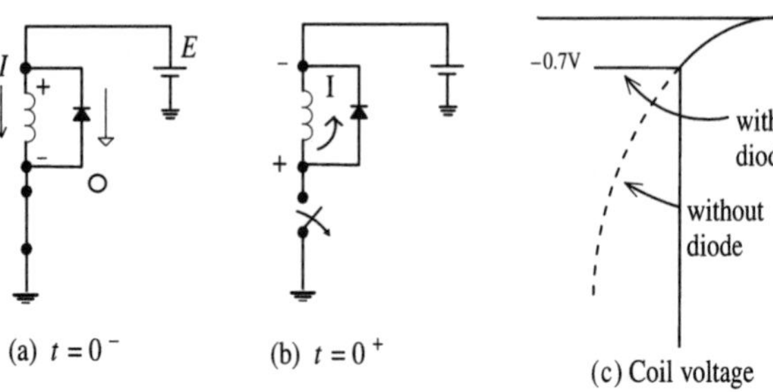

(a) $t = 0^-$ (b) $t = 0^+$ (c) Coil voltage

5. a. Diode is reverse biased, thus

   $I_D = 0$ A and $V_D = 27$ V.

   b. $I_D = \dfrac{E - V_D}{R_T} = \dfrac{18\ \text{V} - 0.7\ \text{V}}{4.5\ \text{k}\Omega} = 3.84$ mA

7. a. Remove the diode branch as shown in Figure (a) and find the Thévenin equivalent.

   $R_{Th} = 600\ \Omega \| 200\ \Omega \| 300\ \Omega = 100\ \Omega$.

   $E_{Th} = \dfrac{300\Omega}{400\Omega} \times 45\ \text{V} = 30$ V. Replace the diode branch with the diode equivalent as shown in (b).

   Thus, $I_D = \dfrac{E_{Th} - V_D}{R_T} = \dfrac{30\ \text{V} - 0.7\ \text{V}}{120\ \Omega} = 0.244$ A

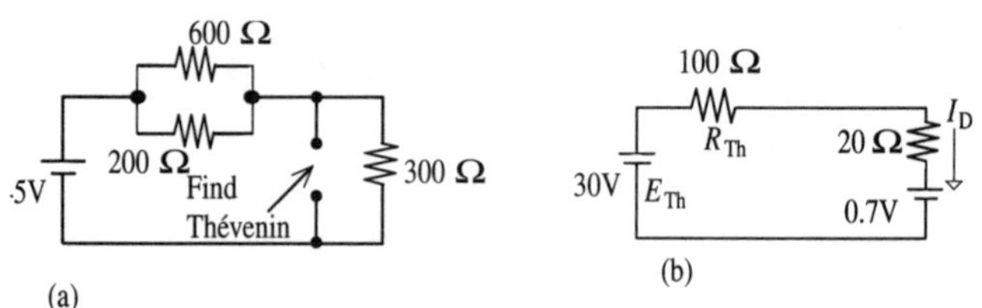

(a) (b)

   b. Remove the diode/10 V branch and determine the Thévenin equivalent. As indicated in (b), $E_{Th} = 28$ V and $R_{Th} = 900\ \Omega$. Thus,

   $I_D = \dfrac{28\ \text{V} - 0.7\ \text{V} - 10\ \text{V}}{900\ \Omega} = 19.2$ mA

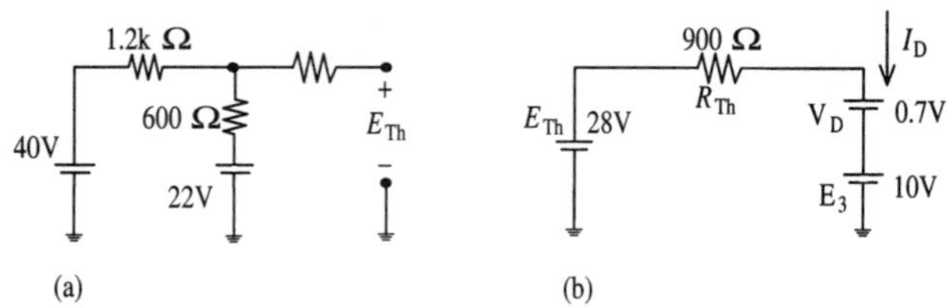

(a) (b)

25.2 to 25.4 Diode Characteristic Curve, Data Sheets, Temperature Considerations, etc.

9. At $I_D = 12$ mA, $V_D = 0.88$ V. Thus, $E = (12\ \text{mA})(1.8\ \text{k}\Omega) + 0.88\ \text{V} = 22.48$ V

11. The peak inverse voltage seen by the diode is $\sqrt{2}$ (35 V) = 49.5 V. Choose the 1N4004 to achieve a safety margin.

13. $\Delta T = 110°\text{C} - 75°\text{C} = 35°\text{C}$. Thus, derate the diode by $35°\text{C} \times 8.5\ \text{mA/°C} = 0.3$ A. Thus, you can draw 1.0 A − 0.3 A = 0.7 A at 110°C.

15. $\Delta V_B = 0.76\ \text{V} - 0.73\ \text{V} = 0.03$ V. V_B rises about 2.5 mV/°C drop in temperature. Thus,

    $\Delta T = \dfrac{0.03\ \text{V}}{2.5\ \text{mV/°C}} = 12°\text{C}$, yielding 25°C − 12°C = 13°C.

17. Leakage current doubles for every 10°C rise. Here is the history of current versus temperature. Thus, the answer is 55°C.

25°C	125nA
35°C	250nA
45°C	500nA
55°C	1.0μA

25.5 The Zener Diode

19. From Figure (a), $E_{Th} = \frac{600\ \Omega}{682\ \Omega} \times 24\ V = 21.1\ V$ and $R_{Th} = 600 \| 82 = 72.1\ \Omega$. Add back the zener as in (b). $I_Z = \frac{21.1\ V - 18\ V}{72.1\ \Omega} = 43.2\ mA$. $P_D = V_Z I_Z =$ (18 V)(43.2 mA) = 777 mW.
$I_L = \frac{V_L}{R_L} = \frac{18\ V}{600\ \Omega} = 30\ mA.$

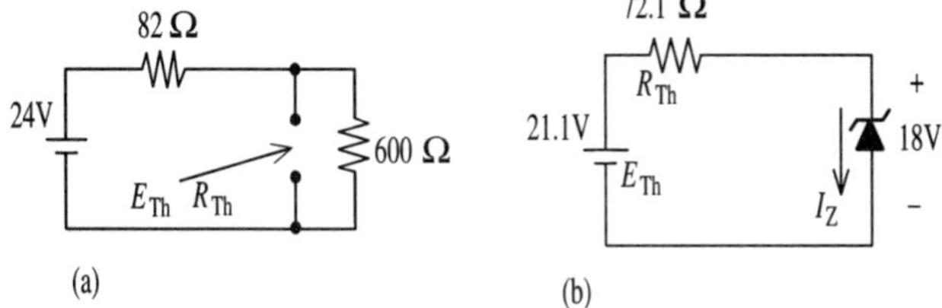

21. From Figure 25-56,
$E = V_Z + R_1 \times I_R = 18\ V + 150\Omega \times I_R$ which shows that E is minimum when I_R is minimum. But $I_R = I_Z + I_L = I_Z + 37.5\ mA$. Thus, E is minimum when $I_Z = I_{ZK}$. Similarly, E is maximum when $I_Z = I_{ZM}$. These two cases are represented below in (a) and (b) respectively. Note that for the1N4746A, $I_{ZK} = 0.25\ mA$ and $I_{ZM} = 50\ mA$.

From (a): $I_R = I_{ZK} + I_L = 0.25\ mA + 37.5\ mA = 37.75\ mA$.

$E_{min} = 18\ V + (37.75\ mA)(150\ \Omega) = 23.6\ V$

From (b): $I_R = I_{ZM} + I_L = 50\ mA + 37.5\ mA = 87.5\ mA$.

$E_{max} = 18\ V + (87.5\ mA)(150\ \Omega) = 31.2\ V$

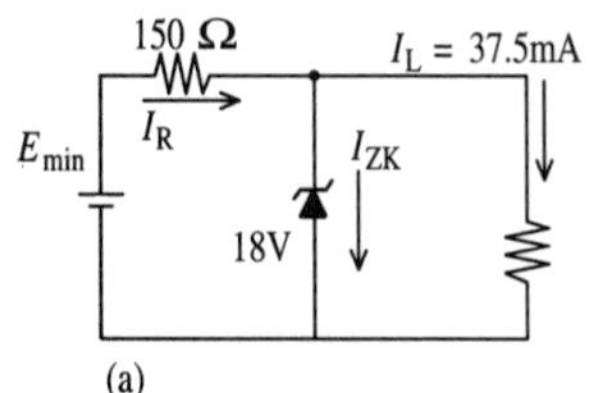

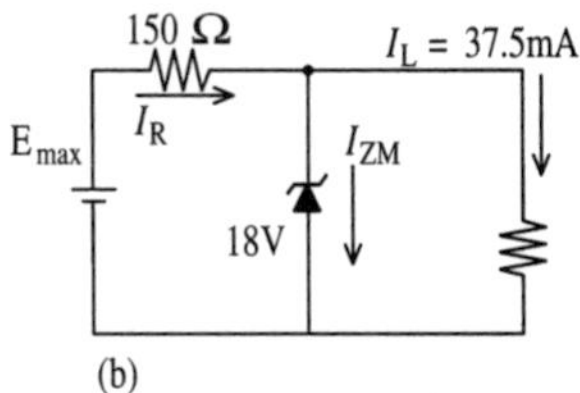

23. As in Problem 21, E is minimum when $I_Z = I_{ZK}$. However, which value of load current should we use to go with it when computing E_{min}? A little reflection (as summarized in the note below) tells us that we should use max current (i.e., $I_L = 50\ mA$). Consider diagram (a). KVL yields $E_{min} = 10\ V + (50.25\ mA)(120\ \Omega) = 16.0\ V$. E_{max} is calculated using I_{ZM} and min I_L as indicated in (b). KVL yields $E_{max} = 10\ V + (111\ mA)(120\ \Omega) = 23.3\ V$.

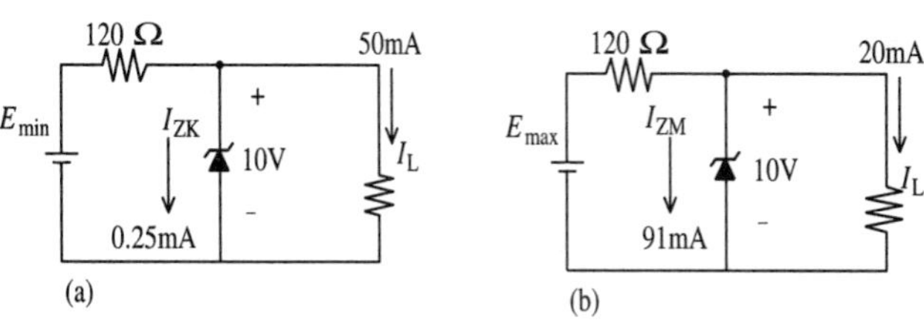

Note What if you incorrectly choose min I_L for calculating E_{min}? If you do, you get $E_{min} = 10\ V + (20.25\ mA)(120\ \Omega) = 12.4\ V$. But, if the source voltage is set at 12.4, load voltage will drop to 12.4 V – (50.25 mA)(120 Ω) = 6.37 V at $I_L = 50\ mA$. This, you can see, is below the knee of the zener voltage curve and you will thus lose regulation—i.e., this is not a valid solution. Similar reasoning shows that you need to use I_{ZM} and min I_L to compute E_{max}.

25. From the data sheet, we see that 17 mA corresponds to I_{ZT}. Thus, $V_Z = V_{ZT} = 15\ V$ at $I_Z = 17\ mA$. Zener voltage is given by $V_Z = V_{ZT} + Z_{ZT} \times \Delta I_Z$. From the data sheet, $Z_{ZT} = 14\ \Omega$. Thus, at 1 mA, $V_Z = 15\ V + (14\ \Omega)(1\ mA - 17\ mA) = 14.8\ V$, and at 55 mA, $V_Z = 15\ V + (14\ \Omega)(55\ mA - 17\ mA) = 15.5\ V$.

27. Waveforms are shown below.

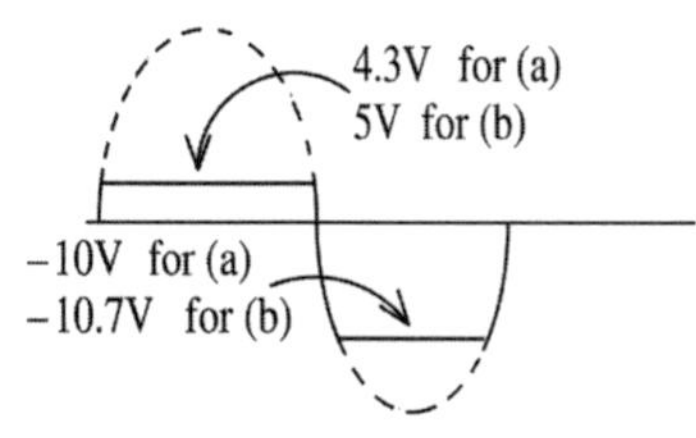

25.7 Half-Wave and Full-Wave Rectifier Circuits

29. Secondary rms voltage is 120/5 = 24 V. Thus, $E_m = \sqrt{2}(24\text{ V}) = 33.9$ V. Subtracting the diode drop yields $V_m = 33.0 - 0.7 = 32.3$ V. Thus, $I_m = V_m/R_L = 4.74$ A and $I_{dc} = 0.318 I_m = 1.51$ A. The maximum reverse voltage seen by the diode is 33.9 V.

25.8 Power Supply Filtering

31. $$V_{dc} = \frac{V_m}{1 + \dfrac{T}{2R_LC}} = \frac{32.54}{1 + \dfrac{8.33\text{ ms}}{2(430\ \Omega)(330\ \mu\text{F})}} = 31.6\text{ V}$$

33. $$V_{r_{pp}} = \frac{2V_m}{1 + \dfrac{2R_LC}{T}} = \frac{2(20\text{ V})}{1 + \dfrac{2(650\ \Omega)(330\ \mu\text{F})}{8.33\text{ ms}}} = 0.762\text{ V}$$

35. $$V_{r_{pp}} = \frac{I_{dc}T}{C} = \frac{(20\text{ mA})(8.33\text{ ms})}{220\ \mu\text{F}} = 0.758\text{ V}$$

$$V_{dc} = V_m - \frac{V_{r_{pp}}}{2} = 20\text{ V} - \frac{0.758\text{ V}}{2} = 19.6\text{ V}$$

37. $V_{dc} = V_m - \dfrac{V_{r_{pp}}}{2}$. Thus

$V_{r_{pp}} = 2(V_m - V_{dc}) = 2(20\text{ V} - 19\text{ V}) = 2$ V.

$V_{r_{pp}} = \dfrac{I_{dc}T}{C} = 2\text{ V} = \dfrac{(500\text{ mA})(8.33\text{ ms})}{C}$. Solving for C yields $C = 2083\ \mu$F.

39. $r = \dfrac{T}{2\sqrt{3}R_LC}$. Thus, $0.03 = \dfrac{8.33\text{ ms}}{2\sqrt{3}(400\ \Omega)C}$. Solving yields $C = 200\ \mu$F.

$$V_{r_{pp}} = \frac{2V_m}{1 + \dfrac{2R_LC}{T}} = \frac{2(20\text{ V})}{1 + \dfrac{2(400\ \Omega)(200\ \mu\text{F})}{8.33\text{ ms}}} = 1.98\text{ V}$$

$$V_{dc} = V_m - \frac{V_{r_{pp}}}{2} = 20 - \frac{1.98}{2} = 19.0\text{ V}$$

Thus, $V_{rms} = (0.03)(19.0\text{ V}) = 0.57$ V

41.

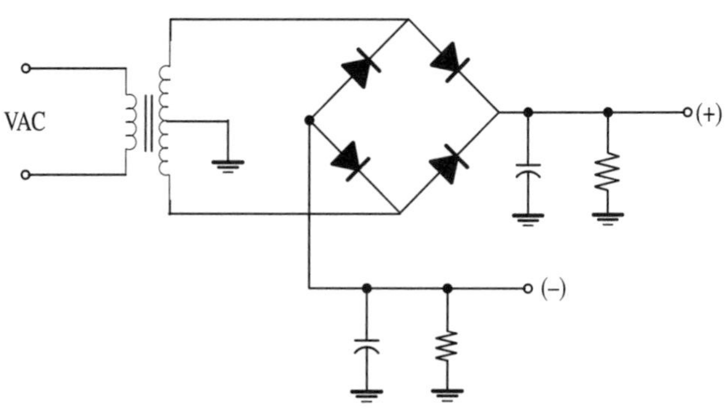

25.9 Computer Analysis (MultiSIM and PSpice)

43. Using a value of $V_F = 0.74$ V for the diode drop yields $V_m = 10 - 0.74 = 9.26$ V.

$$V_{r_{pp}} = \frac{2V_m}{1 + \dfrac{2R_LC}{T}} = \frac{2(9.26\text{ V})}{1 + \dfrac{2(100\ \Omega)(940\ \mu\text{F})}{16.67\text{ ms}}} = 1.51\text{ V}$$

$$V_{dc} = V_m - \frac{V_{r_{pp}}}{2} = 9.26 - \frac{1.51}{2} = 8.51\text{ V}$$

45. Using a value of $V_F = 0.74$ V for the diode drop yields $V_m = 10 - 2(0.74) = 8.52$V.

$$V_{r_{pp}} = \frac{2V_m}{1 + \dfrac{2R_LC}{T}} = \frac{2(8.52\text{ V})}{1 + \dfrac{2(100\ \Omega)(940\ \mu\text{F})}{8.33\text{ ms}}} = 0.723\text{ V}$$

$$V_{dc} = V_m - \frac{V_{r_{pp}}}{2} = 8.52 - \frac{0.723}{2} = 8.16\text{ V}$$

Chapter

26

Basic Transistor Theory

26-2 Transistor Operation

1. $I_B = 4.55\text{ mA} - 4.50\text{ mA} = 0.05\text{ mA} = 50\ \mu\text{A}$

$$\alpha = \frac{4.50\text{ mA}}{4.55\text{ mA}} = 0.989$$

$$\beta = \frac{4.50\text{ mA}}{0.05\text{ mA}} = 90$$

3. $$I_B = \frac{5.00\text{ mA}}{120} = 0.0417\text{ mA}$$

$I_E = 5.00\text{ mA} + 0.0417\text{ mA} = 5.04\text{ mA}$

$$\alpha = \frac{5.00\text{ mA}}{5.04\text{ mA}} = 0.9917$$

5. $$\alpha = \frac{100}{101} = 0.990$$

$I_C = (4.94\text{ mA})(0.990) = 4.89\text{ mA}$

$$I_B = \frac{4.94\text{ mA}}{101} = 0.0489\text{ mA}$$

7. $$\alpha = \frac{I_C}{I_E} \rightarrow I_E = \frac{I_C}{\alpha}$$

$$\beta = \frac{I_C}{I_B}$$

$I_E = I_C + I_B$

$$\frac{I_C}{\alpha} = \beta I_B + I_B$$

$$\frac{\beta I_B}{\alpha} = (\beta + 1)\ I_B$$

$$\alpha = \frac{\beta}{\beta + 1}$$

26.3 Transistor Specifications

9. $V_{(BR)EBO} = 6.0\text{ V}$

emitter - base breakdown voltage (with open collector). $I_E = 10\ \mu\text{A}$, $I_C = 0$

26.4 Collector Characteristic Curves

11. $$\beta = \frac{5.5\text{ mA}}{50\ \mu\text{A}} = 110$$

13. $$\beta = \frac{8.0\text{ mA}}{74\ \mu\text{A}} = 108$$

15. Saturation

26.5 dc Load Line

17. a.

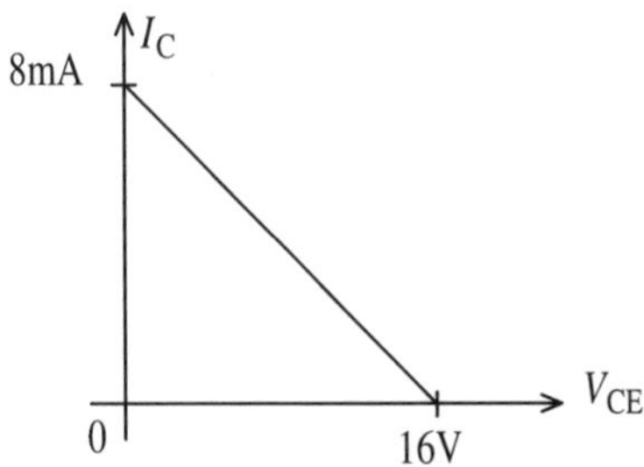

b. $$I_B = \frac{5.0\text{ V} - 0.7\text{ V}}{100\text{ k}\Omega} = 43.0\ \mu\text{A}$$

$I_C = 4.5\text{ mA}$

$$\beta = \frac{4.5\text{ mA}}{43\ \mu\text{A}} = 105$$

c. $$I_B = \frac{5.0\text{ V} - 0.7\text{ V}}{200\text{ k}\Omega} = 21.5\ \mu\text{A}$$

$I_C = 2.5\text{ mA}$

$$\beta = \frac{2.5\text{ mA}}{21.5\ \mu\text{A}} = 116$$

d. $I_B = \dfrac{5.0\text{ V} - 0.7\text{ V}}{20\text{ k}\Omega} = 0.215\text{ mA}$

$I_C \cong 8.0\text{ mA}$

β cannot be determined since the transistor is in saturation.

e. The transistor moves closer to cutoff.

19. a. b. c. } Student answers may vary.

d. The slope becomes less negative. Also the saturation current decreases in magnitude.

26.6 Transistor Biasing

21. a. $I_{C(SAT)} = \dfrac{16\text{ V}}{2\text{ k}\Omega} = 8\text{ mA}$

b. $I_B = \dfrac{16\text{ V} - 0.7\text{ V}}{620\text{ k}\Omega} = 24.67\ \mu\text{A}$

$I_C = (120)(24.67\ \mu\text{A}) = 2.96\text{ mA}$

$I_E = 2.96\text{ mA} + 0.02467\text{ mA} = 2.99\text{ mA}$

$V_{CE} = 16\text{ V} - (2\text{ k}\Omega)(2.96\text{ mA}) = 10.08\text{ V}$

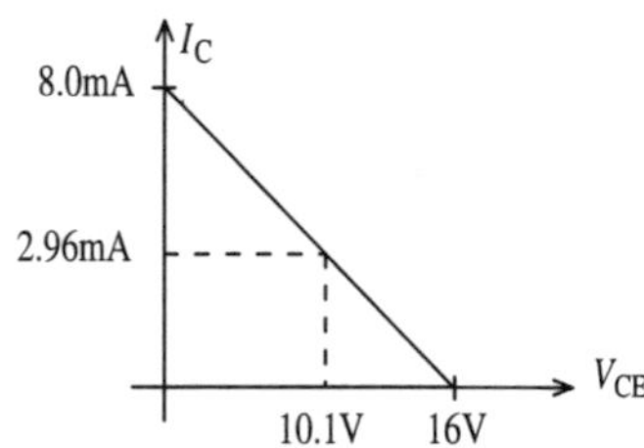

23. a. $I_{C(SAT)} = \dfrac{24\text{ V}}{3.9\text{ k}\Omega} = 6.15\text{ mA}$

b. $I_B = \dfrac{24\text{ V} - 0.7\text{ V}}{1.2\text{ M}\Omega} = 19.4\ \mu\text{A}$

$I_C = (150)(19.417\ \mu\text{A}) = 2.91\text{ mA}$

$I_E = 2.913 + 0.0194\text{ mA} = 2.93\text{ mA}$

$V_{CE} = 24\text{ V} - (2.9\text{ mA})(3.9\text{ k}\Omega) = 12.64\text{ V}$

c.

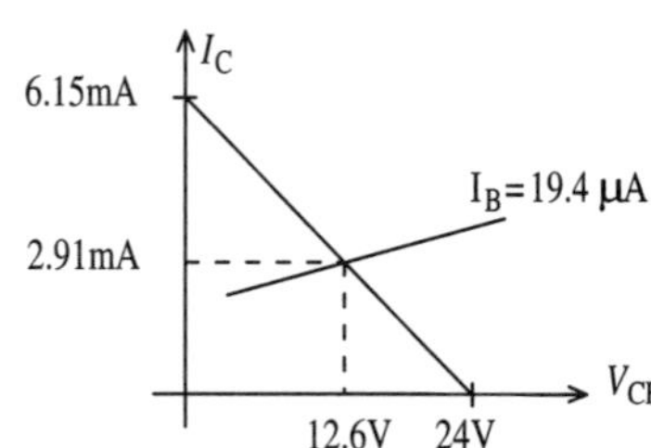

25. a. $I_{C(SAT)} = \dfrac{22\text{ V}}{3.9\text{ k}\Omega + 1.0\text{ k}\Omega} = 4.49\text{ mA}$

b. $(1.5\text{ M}\Omega)\ I_B + 0.7\text{ V} + (1.0\text{ k}\Omega)\ I_E = 22\text{ V}$

$I_B = 12.9\ \mu\text{A}$

$I_C = (12.9\ \mu\text{A})(150) = 1.935\text{ mA}$

$I_E = 1.948\text{ mA}$

$V_{CE} = 22\text{ V} - (3.9\text{ k}\Omega)(1.935\text{ mA}) - (1.0\text{ k}\Omega)$
$(1.948\text{ mA}) = 12.5\text{ V}$

c.

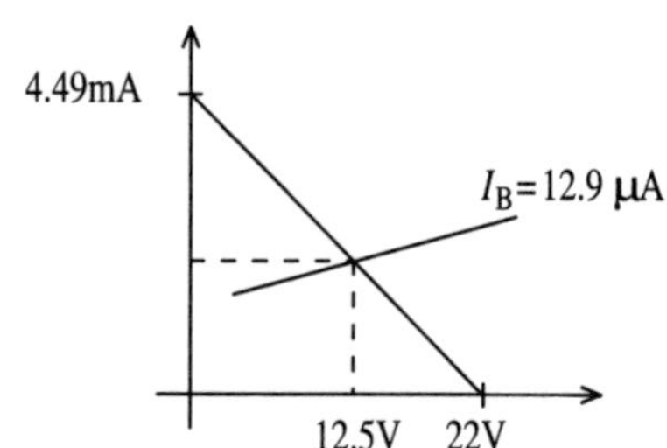

27. a. $I_{C(SAT)} = \dfrac{20\text{ V}}{2.0\text{ k}\Omega} = 10.0\text{ mA}$

b. $(2.0\text{ k}\Omega)(I) + (270\text{ k}\Omega)\ I_B + 0.7\text{ V} = 20\text{ V}$

$I = 126\ I_B$

$I_B = \dfrac{20\text{ V} - 0.7\text{ V}}{(252\text{ k}\Omega) + (270\text{ k}\Omega)} = 36.97\ \mu\text{A}$

$I_C = (125)(36.97\ \mu\text{A}) = 4.62\text{ mA}$

$I_E = I = 4.66\text{ mA}$

$V_{CE} = 20\text{ V} - (2.0\text{ k}\Omega)(4.66\text{ mA}) = 10.68\text{ V}$

c.

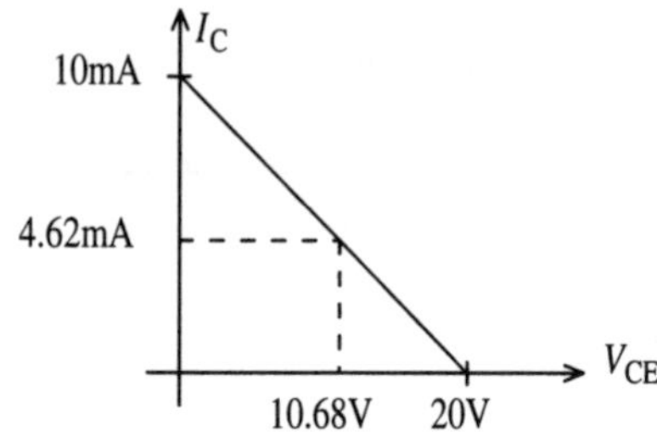

29. a. $I_{C(SAT)} = \dfrac{20\text{ V}}{2.0\text{ k}\Omega + 2.0\text{ k}\Omega} = 5.0\text{ mA}$

b. $20\text{ V} = (2.0\text{ k}\Omega)\ I_E + 0.7\text{ V} + (1.0\text{ M}\Omega)\ I_B$

$I_E = 161\ I_B$

$I_B = \dfrac{20\text{ V} - 0.7\text{ V}}{322\text{ k}\Omega + 1000\text{ k}\Omega} = 14.6\ \mu\text{A}$

$I_C = (160)(14.599\ \mu\text{A}) = 2.34\text{ mA}$

$I_E = 2.35\text{ mA}$

c. $V_{CE} = -10.60\text{ V}$

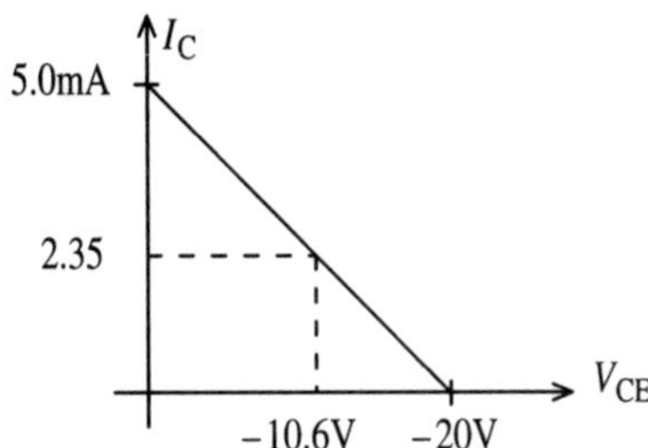

31. a. $I_{C(SAT)} = \dfrac{16\text{ V}}{1.5\text{ k}\Omega + 0.510\text{ k}\Omega} = 7.96\text{ mA}$

b. $R_{BB} = 33\text{ k}\Omega \,//\, 5.1\text{ k}\Omega = 4.42\text{ k}\Omega$

$V_{BB} = \dfrac{5.1\text{ k}\Omega}{33\text{ k}\Omega + 5.1\text{ k}\Omega} \times 16\text{ V} = 2.14\text{ V}$

$2.14\text{ V} = (4.42\text{ k}\Omega)\, I_B + 0.7\text{ V} + (0.510\text{ k}\Omega)\, I_E$

$I_E = 121\, I_B$

$I_B = \dfrac{1.44\text{ V}}{4.41\text{ k}\Omega + 61.71\text{ k}\Omega} = 21.8\ \mu\text{A}$

$I_C = (120)(21.80\ \mu\text{A}) = 2.616\text{ mA} \cong I_E$

$V_{CE} = 16\text{ V} - (2.616\text{ mA})(1.5\text{ k}\Omega + 0.510\text{ k}\Omega)$

$= 10.74\text{ V}$

c.

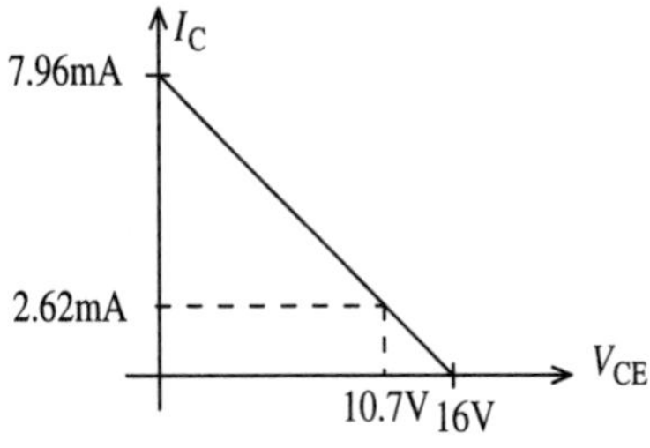

33. a. $I_{C(SAT)} = 7.96\text{ mA}$

b. $R_{BB} = 44.2\text{ k}\Omega$

$V_{BB} = 2.14\text{ V}$

$I_B = \dfrac{2.1417 - 0.7\text{ V}}{44.173\text{ k}\Omega + 61.71\text{ k}\Omega} = 13.6\ \mu\text{A}$

$I_C = (120)(13.6\ \mu\text{A}) = 1.63\text{ mA} \cong I_E$

$V_{CE} \cong 16\text{ V} - (1.63\text{ mA})(1.5\text{ k}\Omega + 0.510\text{ k}\Omega)$

$= 12.72\text{ V}$

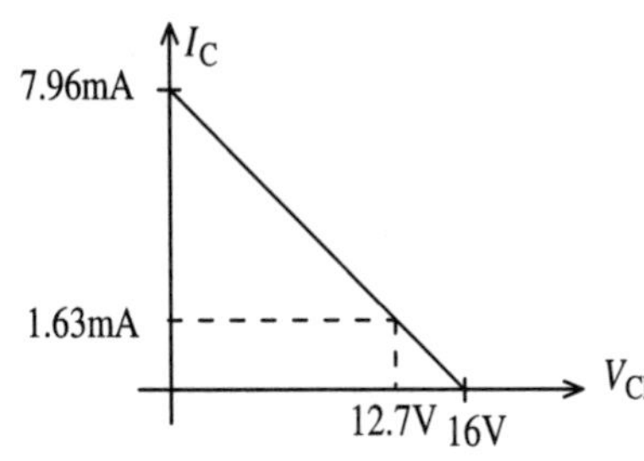

35. a. $I_{C(SAT)} = 7.96\text{ mA}$

b. $V_B \simeq 2.14\text{ V}$

$V_E \simeq 1.44\text{ V}$

$I_E \simeq \dfrac{1.44\text{ V}}{0.51\text{ k}\Omega} = 2.82\text{ mA} \cong I_C$

$V_{CE} \cong 16\text{ V} - (2.82\text{ mA})(1.5\text{ k}\Omega + 0.51\text{ k}\Omega)$

$= 10.32\text{ V}$

37. a. $I_{C(SAT)} = \dfrac{30\text{ V}}{3.9\text{ k}\Omega + 1.0\text{ k}\Omega} = 6.12\text{ mA}$

$V_B \simeq \left(\dfrac{8.2\text{ k}\Omega}{62\text{ k}\Omega + 8.2\text{ k}\Omega}\right)(-30\text{ V}) = -3.50\text{ V}$

$V_E \simeq 3.50 - 0.7\text{ V} = -2.80\text{ V}$

$I_E \simeq -30\text{ V} + (2.80\text{ mA})(3.9\text{ k}\Omega + 1.0\text{ k}\Omega)$

$= -16.26\text{ V}$

39. Worst case $\beta = 100$

$R_C + R_E = \dfrac{20\text{ V}}{8.0\text{ mA}} = 2.5\text{ k}\Omega,\ R_E = R_{C/4}$

$1.25\, R_C = 2.5\text{ k}\Omega \qquad R_C = 2\text{ k}\Omega \qquad R_E = 0.5\text{ k}\Omega$

$V_E = (0.5\text{ k}\Omega)(4\text{ mA}) = 2\text{ V}$

$V_B = 2\text{ V} + 0.7\text{ V} = 2.7\text{ V}$

Let $R_2 = \dfrac{1}{10}(100)\, 0.5\text{ k}\Omega = 5\text{ k}\Omega$

$I = \dfrac{2.7\text{ V}}{5\text{ k}\Omega} = 0.54\text{ mA} \qquad I_B \simeq 0$

$R_1 = \dfrac{20\text{ V} - 2.7\text{ V}}{0.54\text{ mA}} = 32.0\text{ k}\Omega$

41. a. $I_{C(SAT)} = \dfrac{10\text{ V} + 20\text{ V}}{2.0\text{ k}\Omega + 2.0\text{ k}\Omega} = 7.5\text{ mA}$

b. $I_E = \dfrac{10\text{ V} - 0.7\text{ V}}{2.0\text{ k}\Omega} = 4.65\text{ mA} \simeq I_C$

$I_B = \dfrac{4.65\text{ mA}}{121} = 38.4\ \mu\text{A}$

$V_{CE} = (4.65\text{ mA})(2.0\text{ k}\Omega + 2.0\text{ k}\Omega) - 30\text{ V}$

$= 11.4\text{ V}$

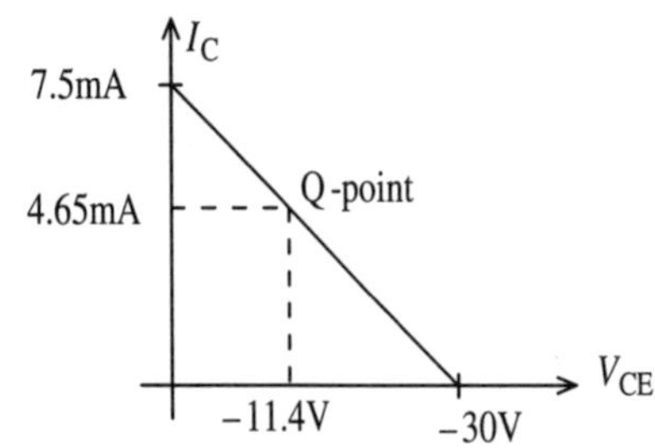

26.7 The Transistor Switch

43. a. $I_{C(SAT)} = \dfrac{8\text{ V} - 1.6\text{ V}}{430\ \Omega} = 14.88\text{ mA}$

b. $I_B = \dfrac{5\text{ V} - 0.7\text{ V}}{33\text{ k}\Omega} = 0.1303\text{ mA}$

$I_C = (120)(0.1303\text{ mA}) = 15.64\text{ mA}$

But I_C cannot exceed 14.9 mA ($I_{C(SAT)}$). Therefore

$I_C = 14.9\text{ mA}$

c. $V_{out} \simeq 0\text{ V}$

d. $I_C = 0\text{ mA}$

e. $V_{out} = 8\text{ V}$

26.8 Testing a Transistor with a Multimeter.

45. Pin 2 must be the Base
Pin 3 must be the Emitter
Pin 1 → Collector
Transistor is pnp

47. Pin 1 → base
Pin 3 → emitter
Pin 2 → collector
Transistor is pnp

26.9 Junction Field Effect Transistor Construction and Operation

49. a. p - channel

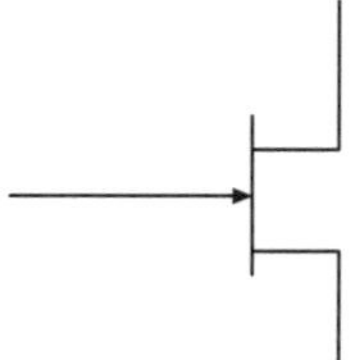

b. $I_D = 8\text{ mA}\left(1 - \dfrac{-3\text{ V}}{-5\text{ V}}\right)^2 = 1.28\text{ mA}$

c. $I_D = 8\text{ mA}\left(1 - \dfrac{-2\text{ V}}{-5\text{ V}}\right)^2 = 2.88\text{ mA}$

d. Since current will remain at zero if V_{GS} is more negative that $V_{GS} = -5\text{ V}$.

$I_D = 0$

26.10 JFET Biasing

51. Exact method.

$V_{GS} + R_S I_S = 0 \qquad I_S = I_D$

(1.) $V_{GS} = -(0.91\text{ k}\Omega)\, I_D$

(2.) $I_D = I_{DSS}\left(1 - \dfrac{V_{GS}}{V_{GS(OFF)}}\right)^2$

$-\dfrac{V_{GS}}{0.91} = 8\left(1 - \dfrac{V_{GS}}{-4}\right)^2$

$-1.0989\ V_{GS} = 8\left(1 + 0.5\ V_{GS} + \dfrac{V_{GS}^2}{16}\right)$

$0.5\ V_{GS}^2 = 5.0989\ V_{GS} + 8 = 0$

$V_{GS} = -5.0989 \pm \dfrac{\sqrt{(5.0989)^2 - 4(0.5)(8)}}{2(0.5)} =$

$-8.26\text{ V}, -1.937\text{ V}$

$I_D = I_S = 2.15\text{ mA}$

$V_{DSQ} = 16\text{ V} - (2.15\text{ mA})(1.8\text{ k}\Omega + 0.91\text{ k}\Omega)$
$= 10.17\text{ V}$

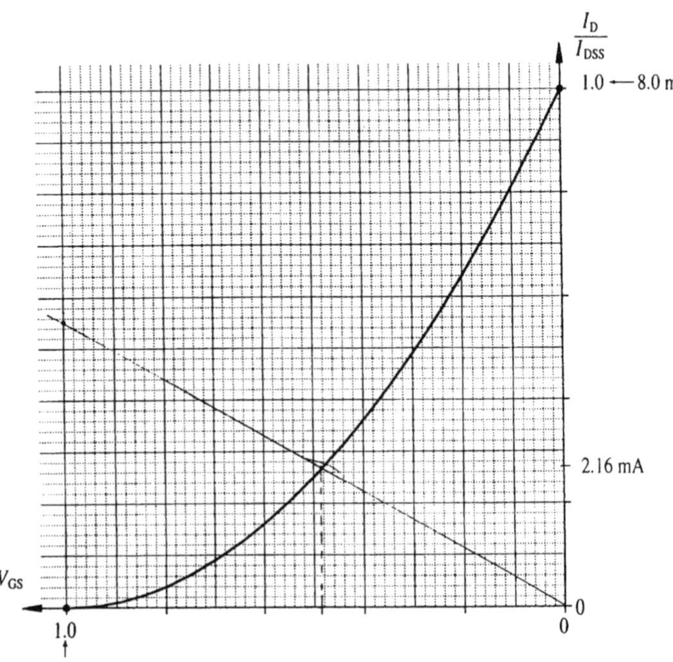

53. Exact method:

$$V_G = \frac{1\ \text{M}\Omega}{6.7\ \text{M}\Omega + 1\ \text{M}\Omega} \times 16\ \text{V} = 2.0779\ \text{V}$$

$V_G = V_{GS} + R_S I_S \qquad I_S = I_D$

$2.08\ \text{V} = V_{GS} + (2.0\ \text{k}\Omega) I_D$

$$I_D = \frac{2.08 - V_{GS}}{2} \qquad ①$$

$$I_D = 8\left(1 - \frac{V_{GS}}{-4}\right)^2$$

$$= 8\left(1 + 0.5\ V_{GS} + \frac{V_{GS}^2}{16}\right)$$

$$I_D = 0.5\ V_{GS}^2 + 4\ V_{GS} + 8 \qquad ②$$

From ① and ②:

$1.03896 - 0.5\ V_{GS} = 0.5\ V_{GS}^2 + 4\ V_{GS} + 8$

$0.5\ V_{GS}^{\ 2} + 4.5\ V_{GS} + 6.91 = 0$

$$V_{GS} = -4.5 \pm \frac{\sqrt{(4.5)^2 - 4(0.5)(6.91)}}{2(0.5)}$$

$= -7.0155\ \text{V}, -1.9845\ \text{V}$

$I_D = 2.032\ \text{mA}$

$V_{DSQ} = 16\ \text{V} - (2.032\ \text{mA})(3.9\ \text{k}\Omega + 2.0\ \text{k}\Omega)$

$= 4.01\ \text{V}$

26.11 MOSFETS

55. Exact method:

a.

$$V_G = \frac{200\ \text{k}\Omega}{1800\ \text{k}\Omega + 200\ \text{k}\Omega} \times 20\ \text{V} = 2.00\ \text{V}$$

$V_G = V_{GS} + R_S I_S \qquad I_S = I_D$

$2.00\ \text{V} = V_{GS} + (0.47\ \text{k}\Omega)\ I_D$

$$I_D = \frac{2 - V_{GS}}{0.47} \qquad ①$$

$$I_D = 10\left(1 + \frac{V_{GS}}{+5}\right)^2 \qquad ②$$

Combining:

$$\frac{2 - V_{GS}}{0.47} = 10\left(1 + 0.4\ V_{GS} + \frac{V_{GS}^2}{25}\right)$$

$$2 - V_{GS} = 4.7\left(1 + 0.4\ V_{GS} + \frac{V_{GS}^2}{25}\right)$$

$= 4.7 + 1.88\ V_{GS} + 0.188\ V_{GS}^2$

$0.188\ V_{GS}^2 + 2.88\ V_{GS} + 2.7 = 0$

$$V_{GS} = -2.88 \pm \frac{\sqrt{2.88^2 - 4(0.188)(2.7)}}{2(0.188)}$$

$= -14.316\ \text{V}, -1.00320\ \text{V}$

$I_D = 6.3898\ \text{mA}$

b. The MOSFET is in its *depletion* mode.

c. $V_{DSQ} = 20\ \text{V} - (6.39\ \text{mA})(1.5\ \text{k}\Omega + 0.47\ \text{k}\Omega)$

$= 7.412\ \text{V}$

57.

$I_D = k\ (V_{GS} - V_{GS(th)})^2$

$20\ \text{mA} = k\ (12\ \text{V} - 2.0\ \text{V})^2$

$$k = \frac{20\ \text{mA}}{100\ \text{V}^2} = 0.0002\ \frac{\text{A}}{\text{V}^2} \qquad \left(\text{or } 0.2\ \frac{\text{mA}}{\text{V}^2}\right)$$

$$I_D = \left(0.2\ \frac{\text{mA}}{\text{V}^2}\right)\left(V_{GS} - 2.0\ \text{V}\right)^2$$

59.

$V_{GS} = V_{DS} \qquad \text{since } I_G = 0$

$$I_D = \left(0.2\ \frac{\text{mA}}{\text{V}^2}\right)\left(V_{GS} - 2.0\ \text{V}\right)^2 \qquad ①$$

and $V_{GS} = V_{DS} = V_{DD} - I_D R_D$

$V_{GS} = 20\ \text{V} - I_D(0.68\ \text{k}\Omega)$

$$I_D = \frac{20\ \text{V} - V_{GS}}{0.68\ \text{k}\Omega} \qquad ②$$

$$(0.2)(V_{GS}^2 - 4\ V_{GS} + 4) = \frac{20 - V_{GS}}{0.68}$$

$0.136\ V_{GS}^2 - 0.544\ V_{GS} + 0.544 = 20 - V_{GS}$

$0.136\ V_{GS}^2 + 0.456\ V_{GS} - 19.456 = 0$

$$V_{GS} = \frac{-0.456 \pm \sqrt{(0.456)^2 + (4)(0.136)(19.456)}}{2(0.136)}$$

$= -13.75\ \text{V}, 10.40\ \text{mA}$

$I_D = 14.12\ \text{mA} \qquad V_{DSQ} = 10.4\ \text{V}$

26.12 Troubleshooting a Transistor Circuit

61. Meter 1 indicates there is no base current. This will be the result of the base-emitter being an open circuit.

Meter 2 satisfies the same diagnosis.

The absence of base current means there is no collector current ($I_C = 0$ as indicated by Meter 3).

Consequently, the transistor is cut off as indicated by Meter 4.

26.13 Computer Analysis of Transistor Circuits

63. $V_B = 0.7$ V
    $I_{CQ} = 4.023$ mA
    $I_{EQ} = 4.029$ mA
    $V_{CEQ} = 7.951$ V
    $V_{BEQ} = 0.700$ V

    $\beta = 160$ (EWB)

    The circuit is dependent on the value of β and so varies significantly from one circuit to the next.

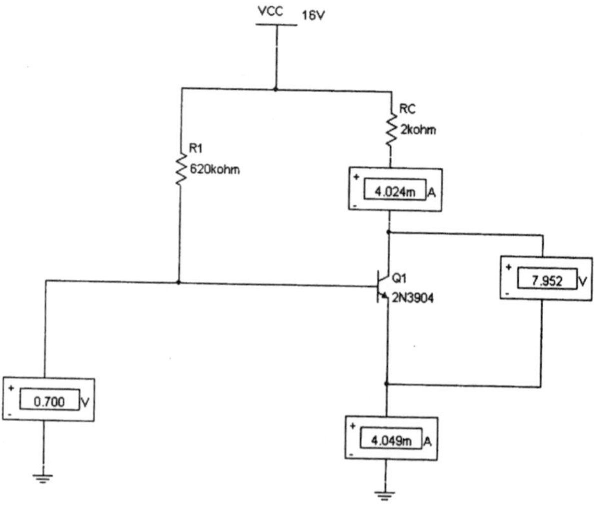

Discrepancies in the bias conditions are due to variations in the transistors' betas.

65. $V_B = 0.680$V
    $I_{CQ} = 2.007$ V
    $I_{EQ} = 2.021$ mA
    $V_{CEQ} = 12.150$ V
    $V_{BEQ} = 0.680$ V

    $I_B = 0.011$ mA
    $\beta = 182$

    The results compare quite well to Problem 25.

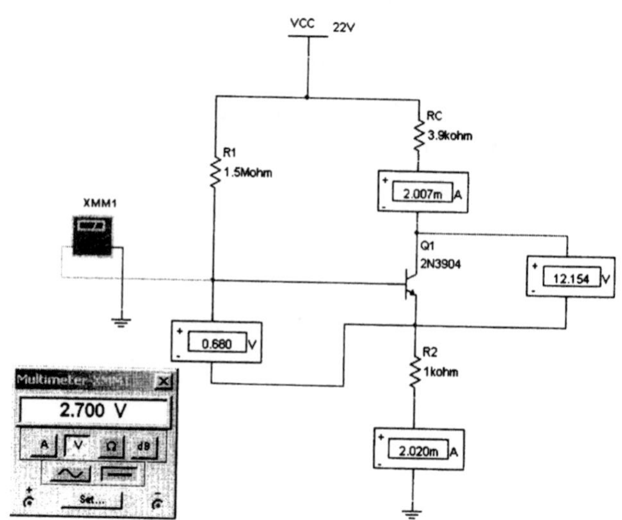

Discrepancies in the bias conditions are due to variations in the transistors' betas.

67.

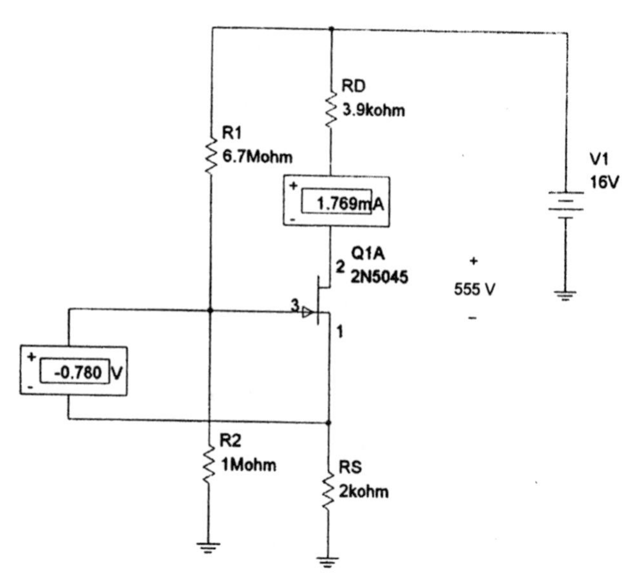

Compare to results of Problem 53.

$I_D = 2.032$ mA
$V_{GS} = -1.9845$
$V_{DSQ} = 5.559$ V

$V_{GSQ} = -0.780$ V
$I_{DQ} = 1.769$ mA
$V_{DSQ} = 5.559$ V

The results differ from those of Problem 53 due to variation in $V_{GS_{OFF}}$ and I_{DSS}.

Discrepancies in the bias conditions are due to variations in I_{DSS} and $V_{GS(OFF)}$

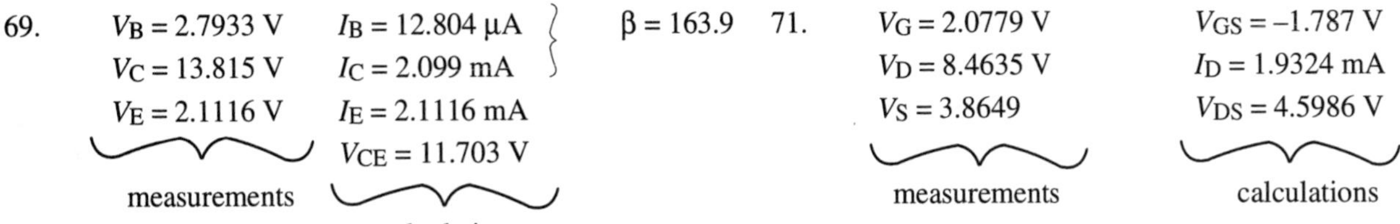

69. $V_B = 2.7933$ V, $V_C = 13.815$ V, $V_E = 2.1116$ V (measurements)

$I_B = 12.804\ \mu A$, $I_C = 2.099$ mA, $I_E = 2.1116$ mA, $V_{CE} = 11.703$ V (calculations)

$\beta = 163.9$

The results are similar to Problem 25.

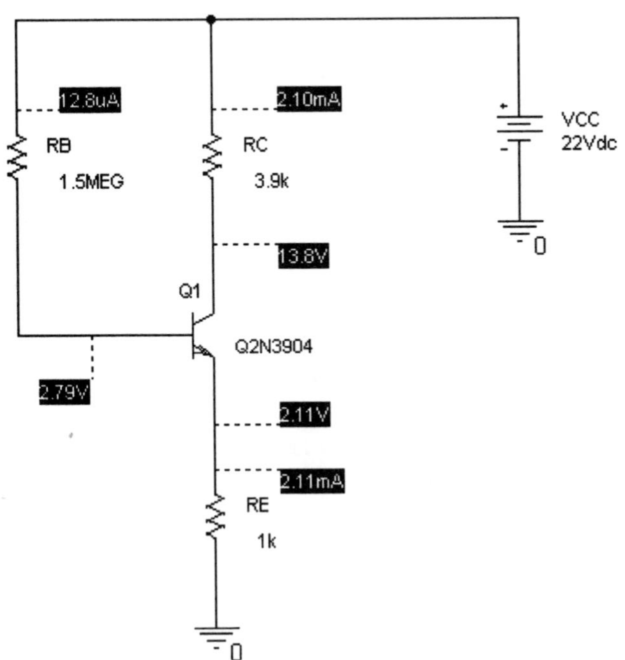

Discrepancies in the bias conditions are due to variations in the transistors' betas.

71. $V_G = 2.0779$ V, $V_D = 8.4635$ V, $V_S = 3.8649$ (measurements)

$V_{GS} = -1.787$ V, $I_D = 1.9324$ mA, $V_{DS} = 4.5986$ V (calculations)

These results are consistent with those of Problem 53. Variations are due to using a different transistor, which has different $V_{GS(OFF)}$ and I_{DSS}.

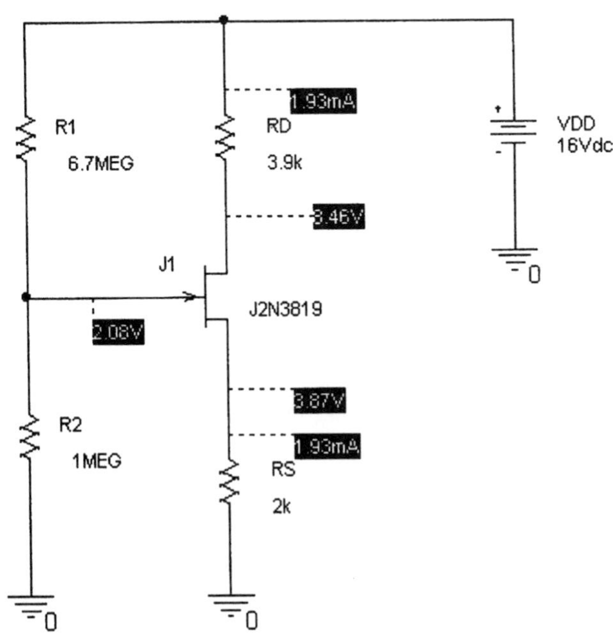

Discrepancies in the bias conditions are due to variations in I_{DSS} and $V_{GS\ (OFF)}$.

Chapter

27

Transistor Amplifiers

27.1 The Use of Capacitors in Amplifier Circuits

1. a. $X_C = \dfrac{1}{2\pi f C}$

But $X_C \le \dfrac{1}{10} R$ where $R = 1200\ \Omega + 800\ \Omega$

$= 2000\ \Omega$

$X_C \le 200\ \Omega$

Let $X_C = 200\ \Omega$

Therefore $200\ \Omega = \dfrac{1}{2\ \Omega(100\text{ Hz})\ C}$

$C_{min} = 7.96\ \mu\text{F}$

b. (*i*) $v_{in} = \left| \dfrac{800\ \Omega}{800\ \Omega + 1200\ \Omega - j\ 200\ \Omega} \right| \times 5\text{ mV}$

$= 1.990\text{ mV}$

(*ii*) At 20 kHz, $X_C = 1.00\ \Omega$

$v_{in} = \left| \dfrac{800\ \Omega}{800\ \Omega + 1200\ \Omega - j\ 1} \right| \times 5\text{ mV}$

$= 2.000\text{ mV}$

3.

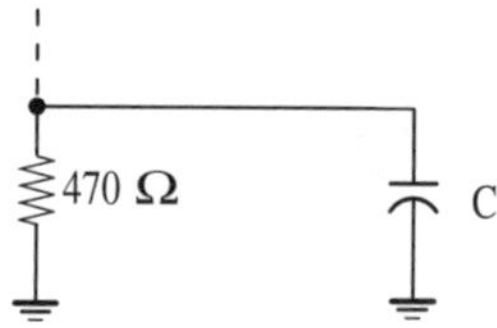

$X_C \le 47\ \Omega$

Let $X_C = 47\ \Omega$

$C = \dfrac{1}{2\ \pi f X_C}$

$= \dfrac{1}{2\ \pi\ (500\text{ Hz})(47\ \Omega)}$

$= 74.5\text{ mF (minimum)}$

27.4 The Common-Emitter Amplifier

5.

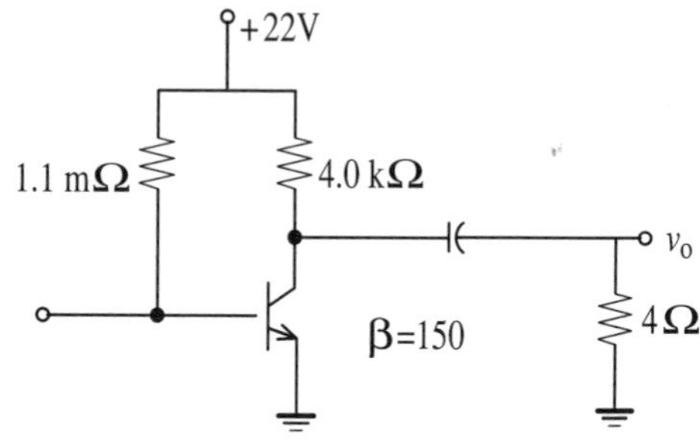

a. $I_B = 19.36\ \mu\text{A}$

$I_C = 2.905\text{ mA}$

$V_{CE} = 10.38\text{ V}$

b.

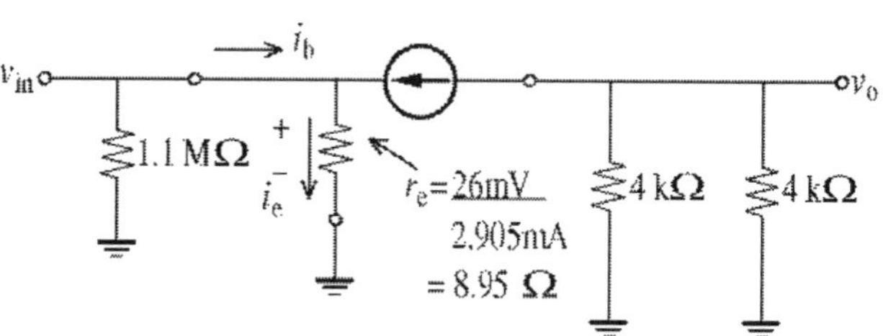

c. $A_v = \dfrac{-(150\ i_b)(4\text{ k}\Omega\ //\ 4\text{ k}\Omega)}{+(151\ i_b)(8.95)} = -222$

$z_{in} = 1350\ \Omega$

$z_{out} = 4\text{ k}\Omega$

$A_i = \dfrac{|A_v|\ z_{in}}{R_L} = 74.9$

7.

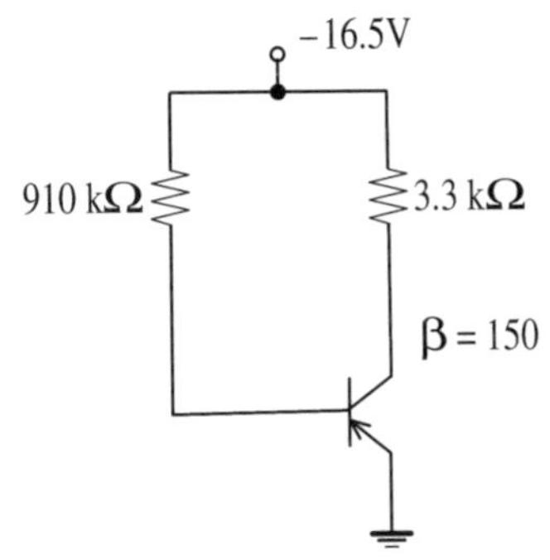

a. $I_B = \dfrac{16.5\text{ V} - 0.7\text{ V}}{910\text{ k}\Omega} = 17.36\ \mu\text{A}$

$I_C = (150)(17.36\ \mu\text{A}) = 2.60\text{ mA}$

$V_{CE} = -16.5\text{ V} + (2.60\text{ mA})(3.3\text{ k}\Omega) = -7.91\text{ V}$

b. $h_{fe} \simeq 160 \qquad h_{ie} \simeq 1600\ \Omega$

c.

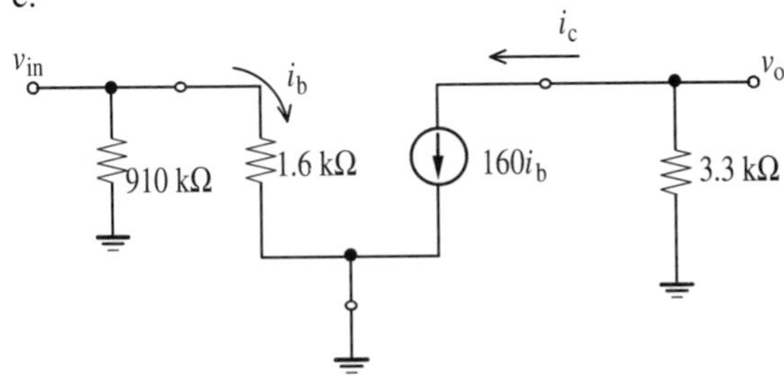

d. $z_{in} = 910\text{ k}\Omega \,//\, 1.6\text{ k}\Omega = 1.597\text{ k}\Omega$

$A_v = \dfrac{-(160\, i_b)(3.3\text{ k}\Omega)}{(1.6\text{ k}\Omega)\, i_b} = -330$

$z_{out} \simeq 3.3\text{ k}\Omega$

$A_i = \dfrac{|\,330\,|(1.597\text{ k}\Omega)}{3.3\text{ k}\Omega} = 159.7$

9. a. $I_B = \dfrac{24\text{ V} - 0.7\text{ V}}{1.2\text{ M}\Omega} = 19.42\ \mu\text{A}$

$I_C = (150)(19.417\ \mu\text{A}) = 2.91\text{ mA}$

$V_{CE} = 24\text{ V} - (2.9125\text{ mA})(3.9\text{ k}\Omega) = 12.64\text{ V}$

b.

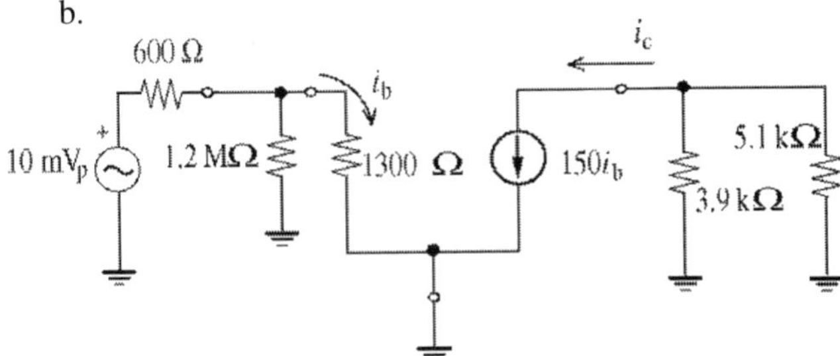

c. $A_v = \dfrac{-(150 i_b)(3.9\text{ k}\Omega \,//\, 5.1\text{ k}\Omega)}{i_b(1.3\text{ k}\Omega)} = -255$

$z_{in} = 1.2\text{ M}\Omega \,//\, 1.3\text{ k}\Omega = 1.299\text{ k}\Omega$

$z_{out} \simeq 3.9\text{ k}\Omega$

$A_i = \dfrac{|\,255\,|\,(1.29859\text{k}\Omega)}{5.1\text{ k}\Omega} = 64.9$

d. $v_{in} = \dfrac{1.29859\text{ k}\Omega}{0.6\text{ k}\Omega + 1.299\text{ k}\Omega} \times 10\text{ mV}_p = 6.84\text{ mV}_p$

$V_{out} = 1.744\text{ V}_p$

e.

1.744V
6.84mV
250
500 μs
t(μs)

11. a. $I_B\,(1.2\text{ M}\Omega) + 0.7\text{ V} + I_E\,(1\text{ k}\Omega) = 23\text{ V}$

$I_B = \dfrac{22.3\text{ V}}{1.2\text{ M}\Omega + 0.161\text{ M}\Omega} = 16.40\ \mu\text{A}$

$I_C = 2.62\text{ mA}$

$V_{CE} = 23\text{ V} - (4.7\text{ k}\Omega)(2.62\text{ mA}) = 10.67\text{ V}$

b. $r_e = \dfrac{26\text{ mV}}{2.62\text{ mA}} = 9.91\ \Omega$

c. $A_v = -\dfrac{(160)(4.7\text{ k}\Omega)}{(161)(1.00991\text{ k}\Omega)} = -4.625$

$Z_{in} = [(161)(1.00991\text{ k}\Omega)] \,//\, 1200\text{ k}\Omega$

$= 143.19\text{ k}\Omega$

$z_{out} \simeq 4.7\text{ k}\Omega$

$A_i = \dfrac{(4.625)(143.19\text{ k}\Omega)}{4.7\text{ k}\Omega} = 141$

13. a. $I_B\,(780\text{ k}\Omega) + 0.7\text{ V} + I_E\,(1\text{ k}\Omega) = 8\text{ V}$

$I_E = 151\, I_B$

$I_B = \dfrac{17.3\text{ V}}{780\text{ k}\Omega + 151\text{ k}\Omega} = 18.58\ \mu\text{A}$

$I_C = (150)(18.58\ \mu\text{A}) = 2.79\text{ mA}$

$V_{CE} = 18\text{ V} - (4.3\text{ k}\Omega + 1\text{k}\Omega)(2.79\text{ mA})$

$= -3.23\text{ V}$

b.

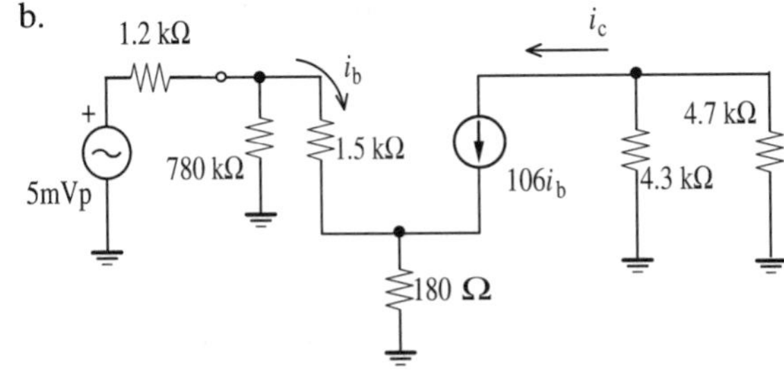

c. $A_v = -\dfrac{(160\, i_b)(4.3\text{ k}\Omega \,//\, 4.7\text{ k}\Omega)}{(1.5\text{ k}\Omega) i_b + (161\, i_b)(180\ \Omega)} = -11.79$

$z_{in} = (780\text{ k}\Omega) \,//\, (1.5\text{ k}\Omega + (161)(0.18\text{ k}\Omega))$

$= 29.33\text{ k}\Omega$

$z_{out} \approx 4.3\text{ k}\Omega$

$A_i = \dfrac{(11.79)(29.33\text{ k}\Omega)}{4.7\text{ k}\Omega} = 73.6$

d. $v_{\text{in}} = \left(\dfrac{29.33\ \text{k}\Omega}{29.33\ \text{k}\Omega + 1.2\ \text{k}\Omega}\right) 5\ \text{mV}_\text{p} = 4.80\ \text{mV}_\text{p}$

$v_{\text{out}} = (11.7877)(4.803\ \text{mV}) = 56.6\ \text{mV}_\text{p}$

15. a.

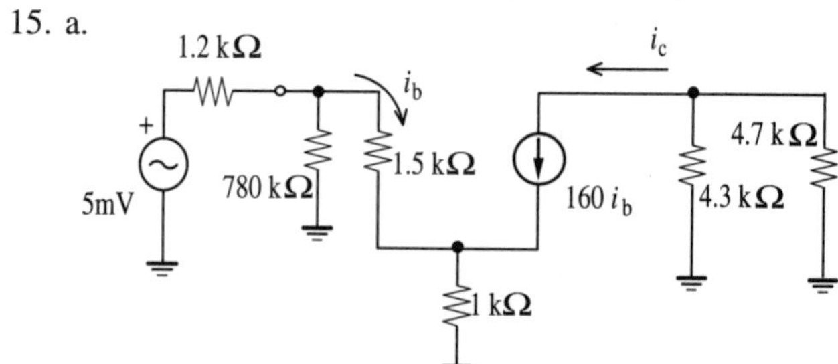

b. $A_\text{v} = \dfrac{-(160\ i_\text{b})(4.3\ \text{k}\Omega\ //\ 4.7\ \text{k}\Omega)}{i_\text{b}\ 1.5\ \text{k}\Omega + 161\ i_\text{b}\ (1.0\ \text{k}\Omega)} = -2.211$

$z_{\text{in}} = 780\ \text{k}\Omega\ //\ (1.5\ \text{k}\Omega + 161 \times 1\ \text{k}\Omega)$
$= 134.5\ \text{k}\Omega$

$z_{\text{out}} \cong 4.3\ \text{k}\Omega$

$A_\text{i} = \dfrac{(2.211)(134.5\ \text{k}\Omega)}{4.7\ \text{k}\Omega} = 63.3$

c. $v_{\text{in}} = \left(\dfrac{134.5\ \text{k}\Omega}{134.5\ \text{k}\Omega + 1.2\ \text{k}\Omega}\right)(5\ \text{mV}_\text{p}) = 4.96\ \text{mV}_\text{p}$

$v_{\text{out}} = (4.9558\ \text{mV}_\text{p})(2.211) = 10.96\ \text{mV}_\text{p}$

27.5 The ac Load Line

17. a. $V_\text{B} = \left(\dfrac{4.7\ \text{k}\Omega}{4.7\ \text{k}\Omega + 47\ \text{k}\Omega}\right) 16\ \text{V} = 1.4\overline{5}\ \text{V}$

$V_\text{E} = 0.75\overline{45}\ \text{V}$

$I_\text{E} = \dfrac{0.755\ \text{V}}{0.39\ \text{k}\Omega} = 1.934\ \text{mA} \simeq I_\text{C}$

$V_{\text{CE}} = 16\ \text{V} - (1.935\ \text{mA})(3.9\ \text{k}\Omega + 0.39\ \text{k}\Omega)$
$= 7.70\ \text{V}$

b. $r_\text{e} = \dfrac{26\ \text{mV}}{1.935\ \text{mA}} = 13.43\ \Omega$

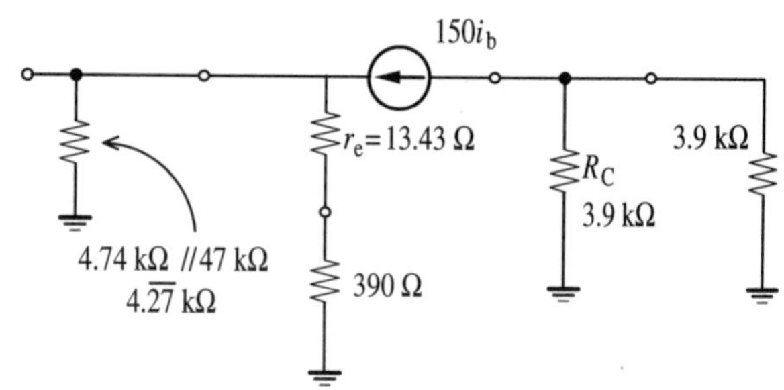

$A_\text{v} = -\dfrac{(150\ i_\text{b})(3.9\ \text{k}\Omega\ //\ 3.9\ \text{k}\Omega)}{151\ i_\text{b}\ (13.4366\ \Omega + 390\ \Omega)} = -4.80$

$z_{\text{in}} = 4.7\ \text{k}\Omega\ //\ 47\ \text{k}\Omega\ //\ (151)(13.4 + 390\ \Omega)$
$= 3992.7\ \Omega$

$z_{\text{out}} \simeq 3.9\ \text{k}\Omega$

$A_\text{i} = \dfrac{(4.80)(3.9927\ \text{k}\Omega)}{3.9\ \text{k}\Omega} = 4.91$

19. a. $V_\text{B} = \left(\dfrac{8.2\ \text{k}\Omega}{8.2\ \text{k}\Omega + 51\ \text{k}\Omega}\right) \times (-18.8\ \text{V}) = -2.60\ \text{V}$

$V_\text{E} = -2.604\ \text{V} + 0.7\ \text{V} = -1.904\ \text{V}$

$I_\text{E} = \dfrac{1.904\ \text{V}}{180\ \Omega + 670\ \Omega} = 2.24\ \text{mA} \simeq I_\text{C}$

$V_{\text{CE}} = -18.8\ \text{V} + (2.24\ \text{mA})(3.3\ \text{k}\Omega + 0.18\ \text{k}\Omega + 0.67\ \text{k}\Omega) = -9.50\ \text{V}$

b. $h_{ie} \simeq 2.0\ \text{k}\Omega$ $\quad h_{\text{fe}} \simeq 150$

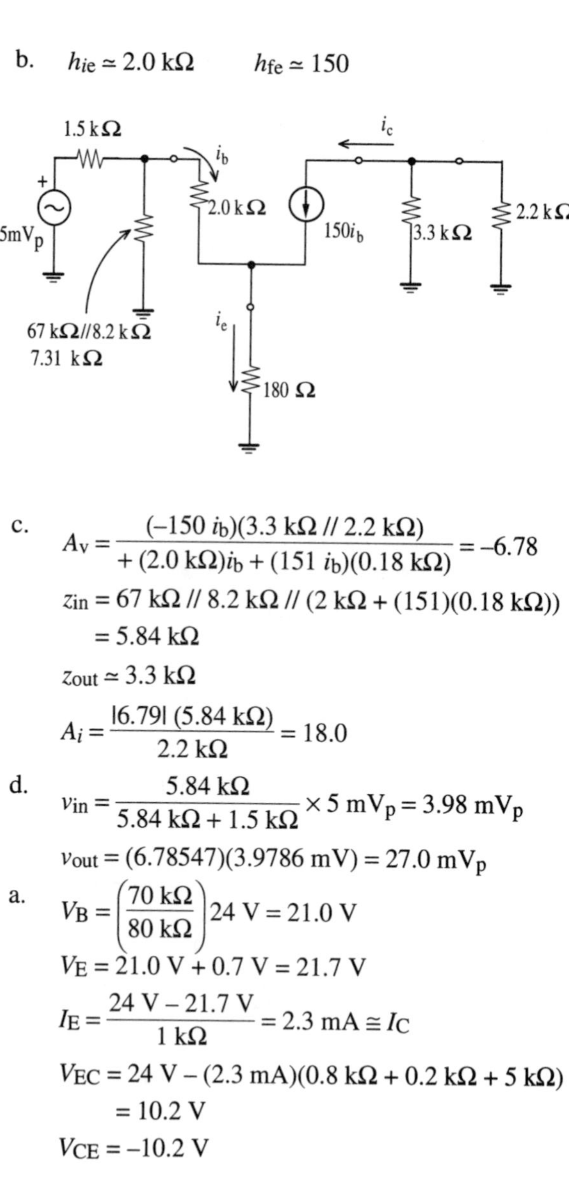

c. $A_\text{v} = \dfrac{(-150\ i_\text{b})(3.3\ \text{k}\Omega\ //\ 2.2\ \text{k}\Omega)}{+ (2.0\ \text{k}\Omega) i_\text{b} + (151\ i_\text{b})(0.18\ \text{k}\Omega)} = -6.78$

$z_{\text{in}} = 67\ \text{k}\Omega\ //\ 8.2\ \text{k}\Omega\ //\ (2\ \text{k}\Omega + (151)(0.18\ \text{k}\Omega))$
$= 5.84\ \text{k}\Omega$

$z_{\text{out}} \simeq 3.3\ \text{k}\Omega$

$A_i = \dfrac{|6.79|\ (5.84\ \text{k}\Omega)}{2.2\ \text{k}\Omega} = 18.0$

d. $v_{\text{in}} = \dfrac{5.84\ \text{k}\Omega}{5.84\ \text{k}\Omega + 1.5\ \text{k}\Omega} \times 5\ \text{mV}_\text{p} = 3.98\ \text{mV}_\text{p}$

$v_{\text{out}} = (6.78547)(3.9786\ \text{mV}) = 27.0\ \text{mV}_\text{p}$

21. a. $V_\text{B} = \left(\dfrac{70\ \text{k}\Omega}{80\ \text{k}\Omega}\right) 24\ \text{V} = 21.0\ \text{V}$

$V_\text{E} = 21.0\ \text{V} + 0.7\ \text{V} = 21.7\ \text{V}$

$I_\text{E} = \dfrac{24\ \text{V} - 21.7\ \text{V}}{1\ \text{k}\Omega} = 2.3\ \text{mA} \cong I_\text{C}$

$V_{\text{EC}} = 24\ \text{V} - (2.3\ \text{mA})(0.8\ \text{k}\Omega + 0.2\ \text{k}\Omega + 5\ \text{k}\Omega)$
$= 10.2\ \text{V}$

$V_{\text{CE}} = -10.2\ \text{V}$

b. $r_\text{e} = \dfrac{26\ \text{mV}}{2.3\ \text{mA}} = 11.30\ \Omega$

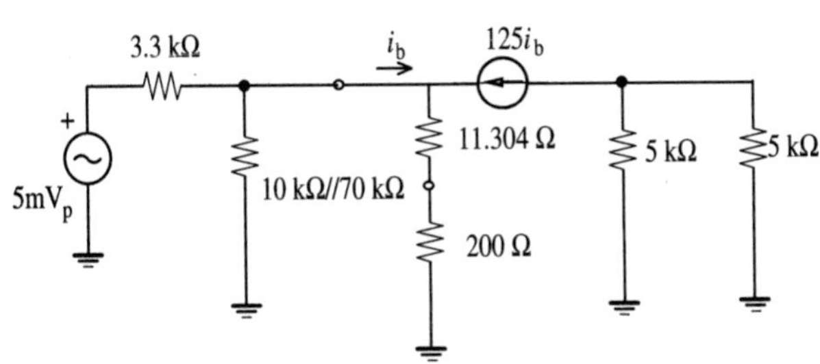

$$\Delta_V = \frac{-(125\ i_b)(5\ k\Omega\ //\ 5\ k\Omega)}{+(126\ i_b)(11.304\ \Omega + 200\ \Omega)} = -11.7$$

$z_{in} = 10\ k\Omega\ //\ 70\ k\Omega\ //\ \{\ (151)(11.304\ \Omega + 200\ \Omega)\ \}$
$= 6.87\ k\Omega$

$z_{out} \simeq 5\ k\Omega \qquad A_i = \dfrac{(11.737)(6.87)}{5} = 16.13$

$v_{in} = \left(\dfrac{6.87\ k\Omega}{6.87\ k\Omega + 3.3\ k\Omega}\right) 5\ mV_p = 3.38\ mV_p$

$v_{out} = (3.38)(-11.7) = 39.6\ mV$

23. a. $I_B = \dfrac{19.3\ V}{1.2\ M\Omega} = 16.08\ \mu A$

$I_{CQ} = (150)(16.08\overline{3}\ \mu A) = 2.41\ mA$

$v_{CEQ} = 20\ V - (2.41\ mA)(4\ k\Omega) = 10.35\ V$

b.

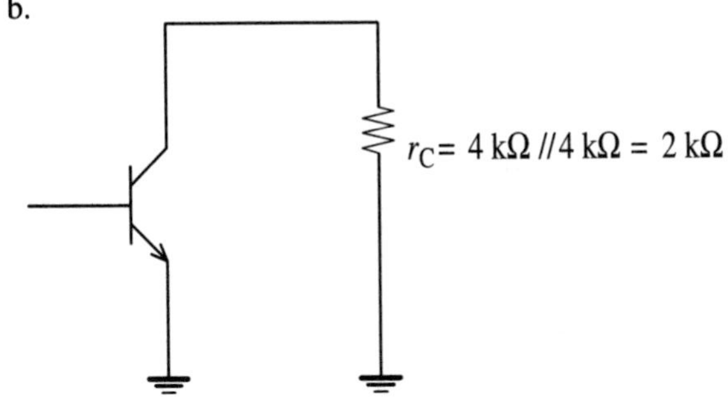

c. $I_{C(DC-SAT)} = \dfrac{20\ V}{4\ k\Omega} = 5\ mA$

$v_{CE\ (DC-OFF)} = 20\ V$

$I_{C(AC-SAT)} = I_{CQ} + \dfrac{V_{CEQ}}{r_C}$

$= 2.4125\ mA + \dfrac{10.35\ V}{2\ k\Omega} = 7.59\ mA$

$V_{CE(AC-OFF)} = V_{CEQ} + I_{CQ}\, r_C$
$= 10.35\ V + (2.4125\ mA)(2\ k\Omega)$
$= 15.175\ V$

d.

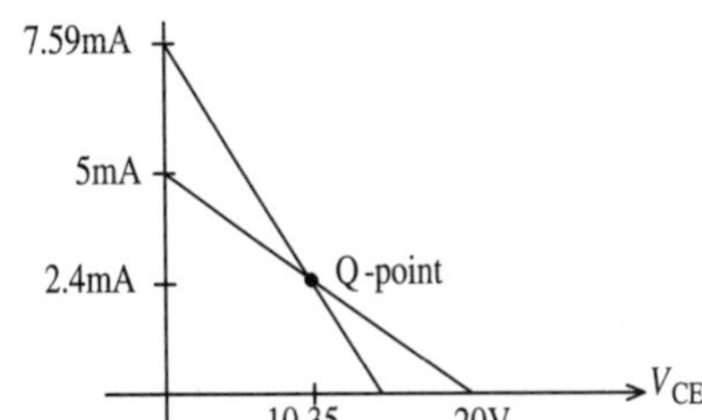

$v_{CE(MAX)} = 2(15.175\ V - 10.35) = 9.65\ V_{p\text{-}p}$

$I_{C(MAX)} = 2(2.4125\ mA) = 4.825\ mA_{p\text{-}p}$

25. a. $V_B = \left(\dfrac{8.7\ k\Omega}{8.7\ k\Omega + 58\ k\Omega}\right)(-19.2\ V) = 2.50\ V$

$V_E = 1.804\ V$

$I_E = \dfrac{1.804\ V}{0.85\ k\Omega} = 2.12\ mA \simeq I_C$

$V_{CE} = -19.2\ V + (2.12\ mA)(3.9\ k\Omega + 0.75\ k\Omega + 0.1\ k\Omega) = -9.12\ V$

$V_{CE(DC-OFF)} = -19.2\ V$

$I_{C(DC-SAT)} = \dfrac{19.2\ V}{3.9\ k\Omega + 0.85\ k\Omega} = 4.04\ mA$

$r_C = 5.1\ k\Omega\ //\ 3.9\ k\Omega = 2.21\ k\Omega \qquad r_E = 0.75\ k\Omega$

$I_{C(AC-SAT)} = I_{CQ} + \dfrac{V_{CEQ}}{r_C + r_E} = 2.12\ mA + \dfrac{9.2\ V}{2.96\ k\Omega}$
$= 5.202\ mA$

$V_{CE(AC-OFF)} = -9.12\ V - (2.12\ mA)(2.96\ k\Omega)$
$= -15.40\ V$

$V_{CE(MAX)} = (15.40\ V - 9.12\ V)(2) = 12.59\ V_{p\text{-}p}$

$I_{C(MAX)} = (2.12276)(2) = 4.25\ mA_{p\text{-}p}$

27. a. $I_{C(SAT)} = \dfrac{18\ V}{4.3\ k\Omega + 0.18\ k\Omega + 0.82\ k\Omega} = 3.4\ mA$

$V_{CE(OFF)} = -18\ V$

$I_{CQ} = 2.79\ mA \qquad V_{CEQ} = -3.23\ V$

$r_C = 4.3\ k\Omega\ //\ 4.7\ k\Omega = 2.25\ k\Omega$

$r_E = 180\ \Omega$

b. $I_{C(AC-SAT)} = 2.79\ mA + \dfrac{3.23\ V}{2.42\overline{5}\ k\Omega} = 4.12\ mA$

$V_{CE(AC-OFF)} = -3.23\ V - (2.79\ mA)(2.42\overline{5}\ k\Omega)$
$= -10.00\ V$

c. $v_{CE(MAX)} = 2(3.23\ V) = 6.46\ V_{p\text{-}p}$

$i_{C(MAX)} = (4.122\ mA - 2.79\ mA)(2) = 2.66\ mA_{p\text{-}p}$

d. $v_{in(MAX)} = \dfrac{v_{CE(MAX)}}{A_v} = \dfrac{6.46\ V_{p-p}}{11.79} = 0.548\ V_{p-p}$

↑ from Prob. 13

27-6 The Common-Collector Amplifier

29. a. $(67\text{ k}\Omega)\,I_B + 0.7\text{ V} + (0.47\text{ k}\Omega)\,I_E = 16\text{ V}$

$I_E = 121\,I_B$

$$I_B = \frac{15.3\text{ V}}{67\text{ k}\Omega + 56.87\text{ k}\Omega} = 123.52\ \mu\text{A}$$

$I_C = (120)(0.124\text{ mA}) = 14.8220\text{ mA}$

$V_{CE} = 16\text{ V} - (14.82\text{ mA})(0.47\text{ k}\Omega) = 9.03\text{ V}$

$$r_e = \frac{26\text{ mV}}{14.82\text{ mA}} = 1.754\ \Omega$$

b.

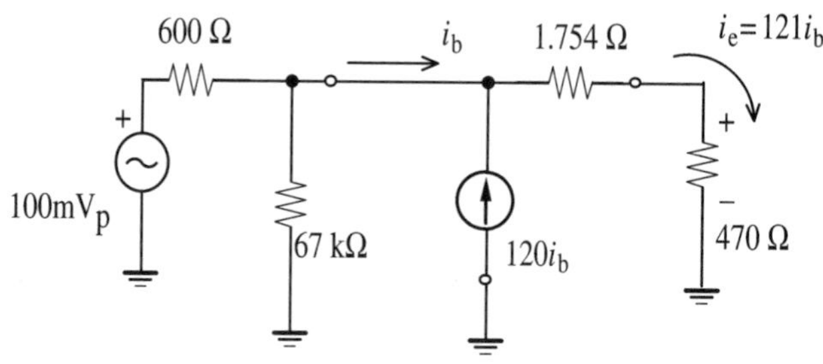

$$A_v = \frac{+(121\,i_b)(470\ \Omega)}{+(121\,i_b)(471.754\ \Omega)} = 0.996$$

$$z_{in} = \frac{(121\,i_b)(471.754\ \Omega)}{i_b} = 57.082\text{ k}\Omega\ //\ 67\text{ k}\Omega$$

$= 30.8\text{ k}\Omega$

$$Z_{out} = 1.754\ \Omega + \frac{600\ \Omega}{120} = 6.75\ \Omega$$

$$A_i = \frac{(0.9963)(30.82\text{ k}\Omega)}{0.47\text{ k}\Omega} = 65.3$$

$A_p = (0.9963)(65.3) = 65.1$

31. a. $$V_B = \left(\frac{15\text{ k}\Omega}{15\text{ k}\Omega + 15\text{ k}\Omega}\right)16\text{ V} = 8.0\text{ V}$$

$V_E = 7.3\text{ V}$

$$I_E = \frac{7.3\text{ V}}{1.5\text{ k}\Omega} = 4.867\text{ mA} \simeq I_C$$

$V_{CE} = 16\text{ V} - 7.3\text{ V} = 8.7\text{ V}$

b. $$r_e = \frac{26\text{ mV}}{4.867\text{ mA}} = 5.34\ \Omega$$

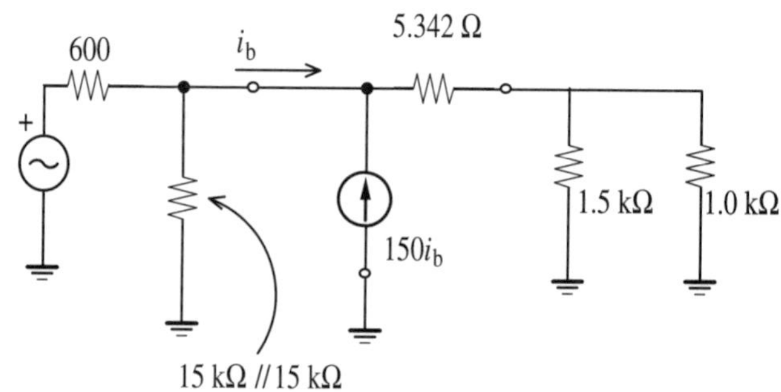

$$A_v = \frac{(151\,i_b)(1.5\text{ k}\Omega\ //\ 1.0\text{ k}\Omega)}{(151\,i_b)(5.3212\ \Omega + 1.5\text{ k}\Omega\ //\ 1.0\text{ k}\Omega)}$$

$= 0.991$

$z_{in} = 15\text{ k}\Omega\ //\ 15\text{ k}\Omega\ //\ \{(151)(605.342\ \Omega)\}$

$= 6.93\text{ k}\Omega$

$$z_{out} = 1.5\text{ k}\Omega\ //\left(5.342\ \Omega + \frac{600\ \Omega}{150}\right) = 9.28\ \Omega$$

$$A_i = \frac{(0.9912)(6.931\text{ k}\Omega)}{1\text{ k}\Omega} = 6.87$$

$A_p = (0.9912)(6.87) = 6.810$

33. a. $h_{ie} \cong 1600\ \Omega$ $\quad h_{re} \cong 1.1 \times 10^{-4}$

$h_{fe} \simeq 150$ $\quad h_{oe} \simeq 20\ \mu\text{S}$

b.

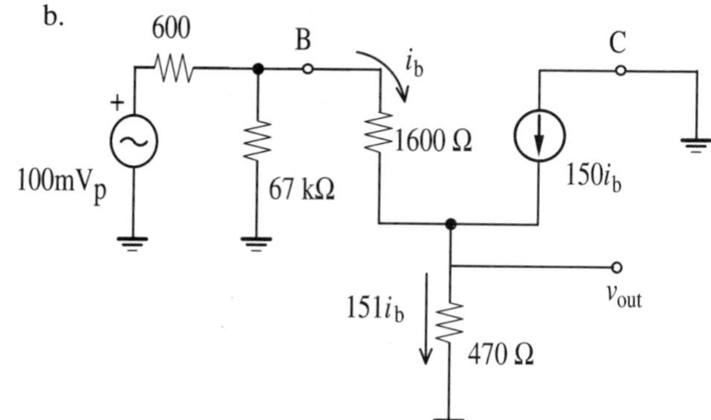

c. $$A_v = \frac{(151\,i_b)(470\ \Omega)}{1600\ \Omega i_b + (151\,i_b)(470\ \Omega)} = 0.978$$

$z_{in} = 67\text{ k}\Omega\ //\ [1600\ \Omega + (151)(470\ \Omega)]$

$= 34.8\text{ k}\Omega$

$$z_{out} = 470\ \Omega\ //\left[\frac{600\ \Omega + 1600\ \Omega}{151}\right] = 14.13\ \Omega$$

$$A_i = \frac{(0.9780)(34.837\text{ k}\Omega)}{0.47\text{ k}\Omega} = 72.5$$

$A_p = (0.9780)(72.49) = 70.9$

35. a. $h_{ie} \simeq 2200\ \Omega$ $\quad h_{re} \simeq 1.1 \times 10^{-4}$

$h_{fe} \simeq 140$ $\quad h_{oe} \simeq 12\ \mu\text{S}$

b.

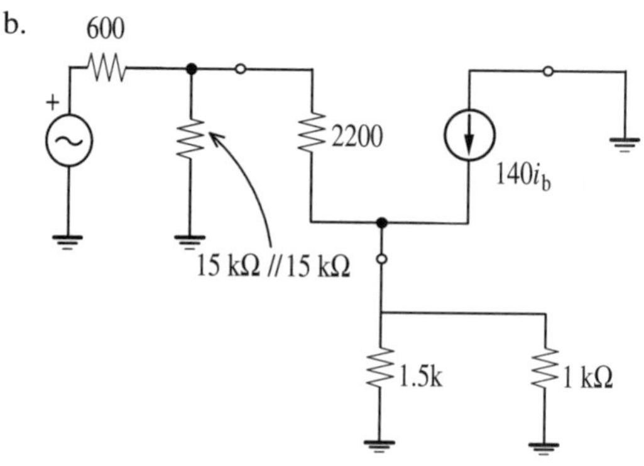

c. $A_V = \frac{(141\, i_b)(1.5\text{ k}\Omega // 1\text{ k}\Omega)}{i_b\,(2.2\text{ k}\Omega) + (141\, i_b)(1.5\text{ k}\Omega // 1\text{ k}\Omega)} = 0.97$

$z_{in} = 15\text{ k}\Omega // 15\text{ k}\Omega // [2.2\text{ k}\Omega + 141\,(0.6\text{ k}\Omega)]$

$= 6.90\text{ k}\Omega$

$z_{out} = 1.5\text{ k}\Omega // \left[\frac{600\ \Omega + 2200\ \Omega}{141}\right] = 19.60\ \Omega$

$A_i = \frac{(0.9747)(6.903\text{ k}\Omega)}{1\text{ k}\Omega} = 6.72$

$A_p = (0.9747)(6.728) = 6.56$

27-7 The FET Small-Signal Model

37. a. $g_{mo} = \frac{2(7.5\text{ mA})}{4.0\text{ V}} = 3.75\text{ mS}$

$g_m = 3.75\text{ mS}\left(1 - \frac{-2.0\text{ V}}{-4.0\text{ V}}\right) = 1.875\text{ mS}$

b. $g_m = 3.75\text{ mS}\left(1 - \frac{-3.0\text{ V}}{-4.0\text{ V}}\right) = 0.9375\text{ mS}$

c. $I_D = 7.5\text{ mA}\left(1 - \frac{V_{GS}}{-4\text{ V}}\right)^2$

$V_{GS} = (-4\text{ V})\left(1 - \sqrt{\frac{6.0\text{ mA}}{7.5\text{ mA}}}\right) = -0.42229\text{ V}$

$g_m = 3.75\text{ mS}\left(1 - \frac{-0.42229\text{ V}}{-4\text{ V}}\right) = 3.354\text{ mS}$

39. a. $10\text{ mA} = k\,(4.0\text{ V} - 2.5\text{ V})^2$

$k = 4.\overline{44}\ \frac{\text{mA}}{\text{V}^2}$

$g_m = 2\left(4.44\ \frac{\text{mA}}{\text{V}^2}\right)(3.0\text{ V} - 2.5\text{ V}) = 4.44\text{ mS}$

b. $g_m = 2\left(4.44\ \frac{\text{mA}}{\text{V}^2}\right)(4.0\text{ V} - 2.5\text{ V}) = 13.\overline{3}\text{ mS}$

c. $6.0\text{ mA} = 4.44\ \frac{\text{mA}}{\text{V}^2}\,(V_{GS} - 2.5\text{ V})^2$

$V_{GS} - 2.5\text{ V} = \sqrt{\frac{6.0\text{ mA}}{4.44\text{ mA}}}$

$V_{GS} = 3.6619\text{ V}$

$g_m = 2\left(4.44\ \frac{\text{mA}}{\text{V}^2}\right)(3.6619\text{ V} - 2.5\text{ V}) = 10.32\text{ mS}$

d. $g_m = 14.6\text{ mS}$ $\quad (V_{GS} = 4.14\text{ V})$

27-8 The Common-Source Amplifier

41. a. $V_{GS} + I_D R_S = 0$

$I_D = -\frac{V_{GS}}{0.75\text{ k}\Omega}$ ①

$I_D = 10\text{ mA}\left(1 + \frac{V_{GS}}{+5\text{ V}}\right)^2$ ②

$-\frac{V_{GS}}{0.75} = 10\left(1 + 0.4\,V_{GS} + \frac{V_{GS}^2}{25}\right)$

$-V_{GS} = 7.5 + 3\,V_{GS} + 0.3\,V_{GS}^2$

$0.3\,V_{GS}^2 + 4\,V_{GS} + 7.5 = 0$

$V_{GSQ} = -4 \pm \frac{\sqrt{4^2 - (4)(0.3)(7.5)}}{2(0.3)} = -2.26\text{ V}$

$I_{DQ} = 3.0\text{ mA}$

$V_{DSQ} = 22\text{ V} - 3.009\text{ mA}\,(2.2\text{ k}\Omega + 0.75\text{ k}\Omega)$

$= 13.12\text{ V}$

b. $g_{mo} = \left|\frac{2\,I_{DSS}}{V_{GS(OFF)}}\right| = 4.0\text{ mS}$

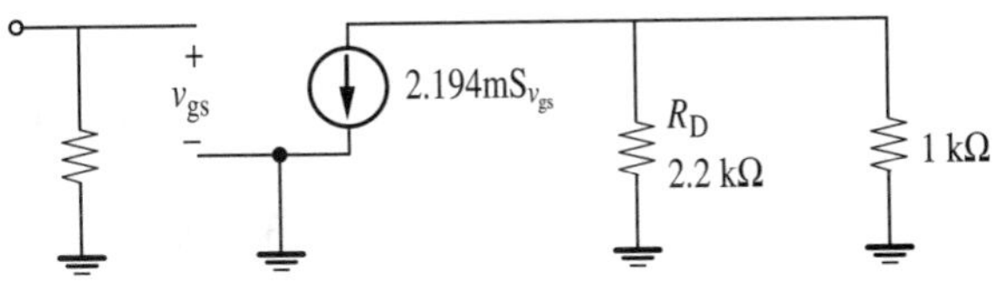

$g_{mo} = 4.0\text{ mS}\left(1 - \frac{-2.257\text{ V}}{-5.0\text{ V}}\right) = 2.19\text{ mS}$

$A_V = \frac{-(2.194\text{ mS}v_{gs})(2.2\text{ k}\Omega // 1\text{ k}\Omega)}{v_{gs}} = -1.51$

$z_{in} = 1\text{ M}\Omega$

$z_{out} \simeq 2.2\text{ k}\Omega$

43. a. $V_G = \left(\frac{100\text{ k}\Omega}{490\text{ k}\Omega}\right)25\text{ V} = 5.10\text{ V}$

$5.10204\text{ V} = V_{GS} + (2.2\text{ k}\Omega)\,I_D$

$I_D = 2.3191 - 0.4545\,V_{GS}$ ①

$I_D = 8\left(1 + \frac{V_{GS}}{+4}\right)^2$ ②

$2.3191 - 0.4545\,V_{GS} = 8 + 4\,V_{GS} + 0.5\,V_{GS}^2$

$0.5\,V_{GS}^2 + 4.4545\,V_{GS} + 5.6809 = 0$

$V_{GS} = \frac{-4.4545 \pm \sqrt{(4.4545)^2 - 4(0.5)(5.6809)}}{2(0.5)}$

$= -1.542\text{ V}$

$I_{DQ} = 3.02\text{ mA}$

$V_{DSQ} = 25\text{ V} - (3.0201\text{ mA})(3.3\text{ k}\Omega + 2.2\text{ k}\Omega)$

$= 8.389\text{ V}$

b. $g_{mo} = 4\text{ mS}$ $\quad g_m = 2.46$

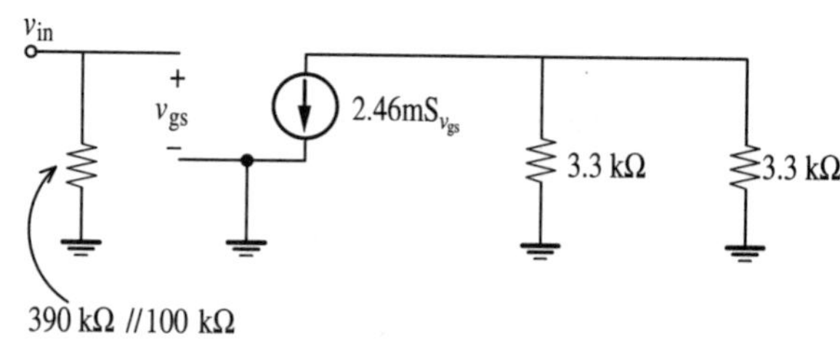

$$A_v = \frac{-(2.46v_{gs})(3.3\text{ k}\Omega\ //\ 3.3\text{ k}\Omega)}{v_{gs}} = -4.055$$

$z_{in} = 390\text{ k}\Omega\ //\ 100\text{ k}\Omega = 79.6\text{ k}\Omega$

$z_{out} \simeq 3.3\text{ k}\Omega$

45. a. $V_{GS} - (0.57\text{ k}\Omega)\,I_D = 0$

$I_D = 1.75439\,V_{GS}$ $\qquad I_{DQ} = 2.128\text{ mA}$

$I_D = 6\left(1 - \frac{V_{GS}}{3}\right)^2$ $\qquad V_{DSQ} = -10.104\text{ V}$

$$1.75439\,V_{GS} = 6 - 4\,V_{GS} + \frac{2\,V_{GS}^2}{3}$$

$$0.66\overline{6}\,V_{GS}^2 - 5.75439\,V_{GS} + 6 = 0$$

$$V_{GS} = \frac{5.75439 \pm \sqrt{(5.75439)^2 - 4(0.66\overline{6})(6)}}{2(0.66\overline{6})}$$

$= 1.213\text{ V}$

b. $g_{mo} = \frac{2(6\text{ mA})}{3\text{ V}} = 4.0\text{ mS}$

$g_m = 4.0\text{ mS}\left(1 - \frac{1.213\text{ V}}{3\text{ V}}\right) = 2.382\text{ mS}$

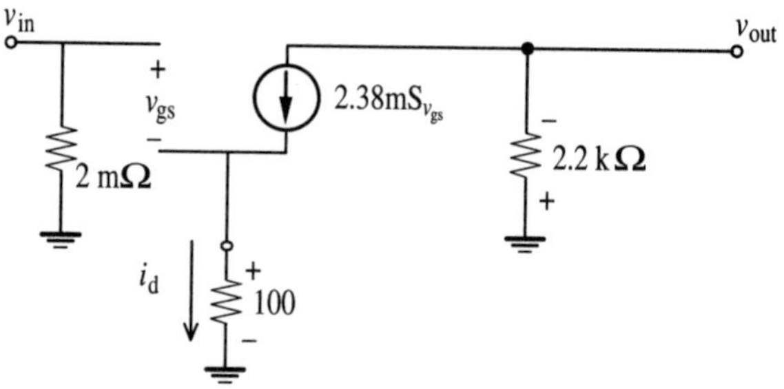

$$A_v = \frac{-(2.38\text{ mS})\,v_{gs}\,(2.2\text{ k}\Omega)}{v_{gs} + (2.38\text{ mS})\,v_{gs}\,(0.1\text{ k}\Omega)} = -4.23$$

$z_{in} = 2\text{ M}\Omega$

$z_{out} \simeq 2.2\text{ k}\Omega$

27.9 The Common-Drain (Source Follower) Amplifier

47. a. $V_{GS} + (1\text{ k}\Omega)\,I_D = 0$

$I_D = -V_{GS}$ ① $\qquad I_D = 2.5\text{ mA}$

$I_D = 10\left(1 + \frac{V_{GS}^2}{+5\text{ V}}\right)^2$ ② $\qquad V_{DSQ} = 17.5\text{ V}$

$$-V_{GS} = 10 + 4\,V_{GS} + 0.4\,V_{GS}^2$$

$$0.4\,V_{GS}^2 + 5\,V_{GS} + 10 = 0$$

$$V_{GS} = \frac{-5 \pm \sqrt{5^2 - 4(0.4)(10)}}{2(0.4)}$$

$= -2.5\text{ V}$

b. $g_{mo} = \frac{2(10\text{ mA})}{5\text{ mV}} = 4.0\text{ mS}$

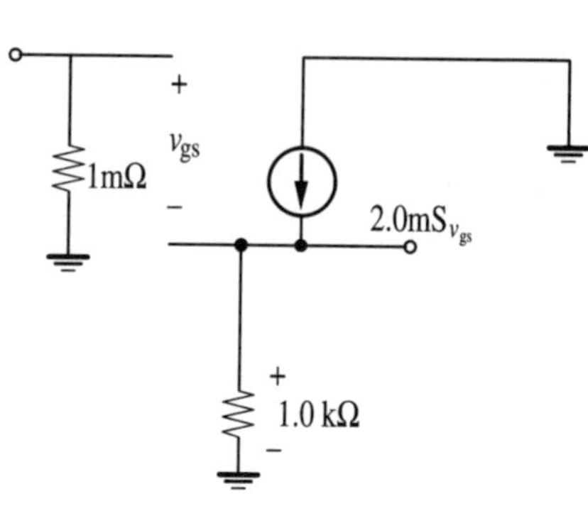

$g_m = 4.0\text{ mS}\left(1 - \frac{-2.5}{-5\text{ V}}\right) = 2.0\text{ mS}$

$$A_V = \frac{(2.0\text{ mS}v_{gs})(1\text{ k}\Omega)}{v_{gs} + (2.0\text{ mS})v_{gs}(1\text{ k}\Omega)} = 0.667$$

$z_{out} = 1.0\text{ k}\Omega\ //\left(\frac{1}{2.0\text{ mS}}\right) = 333\ \Omega$

$z_{in} = 1\text{ M}\Omega$

49. a. $V_G = \left(\frac{220\text{ k}\Omega}{1040\text{ k}\Omega}\right)(-20\text{ V}) = -4.23077\text{ V}$

$V_{GS} - (0.82\text{ k}\Omega)\,I_D = -4.23\text{ V}$

$I_D = +\frac{4.23 + V_{GS}}{0.82\text{ k}\Omega}$ ①

$I_D = 7.5\text{ mA}\left(1 - \frac{V_{GS}}{4}\right)^2$ ②

$$5.15947 + 1.21951\,V_{GS} = 7.5\left(1 - 0.5\,V_{GS} + \frac{V_{GS}^2}{16}\right)$$

$$= 7.5 - 3.75\,V_{GS} + 0.46875\,V_{GS}^2$$

$$0.46875\,V_{GS}^2 - 4.96951\,V_{GS} + 2.34053 = 0$$

$V_{GS} = 0.49506\text{ V}$ $\qquad V_{DS} = 4.7219\text{ V}$

b. $g_{mo} = \frac{2\,(7.5\text{ mA})}{4\text{ V}} = 3.75\text{ mS}$ $\qquad I_{DQ} = 5.76\text{ mA}$

$g_m = 3.75\text{ mS}\left(1 - \frac{0.49506}{4}\right) = 3.29\text{ mS}$

c.

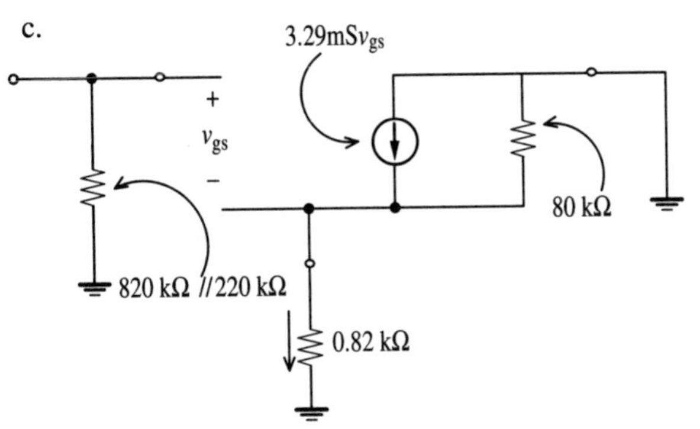

$$A_V = \frac{(0.82\ \text{k}\Omega)(3.29\ \text{mS}\ v_{gs})}{v_{gs} + 0.82\ \text{k}\Omega\ (3.29\ \text{mS}\ v_{gs})} = 0.730$$

$$z_{in} = 820\ \text{k}\Omega\ //\ 220\ \text{k}\Omega = 173.46\ \text{k}\Omega$$

$$z_{out} = 0.82\ \text{k}\Omega\ //\ r_d\ //\ \frac{1}{g_m} = 221\ \Omega$$

27.10 Troubleshooting a Transistor Amplifier Circuit

51. The emitter bypass capacitor is effectively an open circuit. This could be due to poor soldering or an internal fault.

53.

+24V
3.9 kΩ
5.1 kΩ
I_B = 19.4μA
I_C = 2.91mA

Treat transistor as a current source $I = 2.91$mA

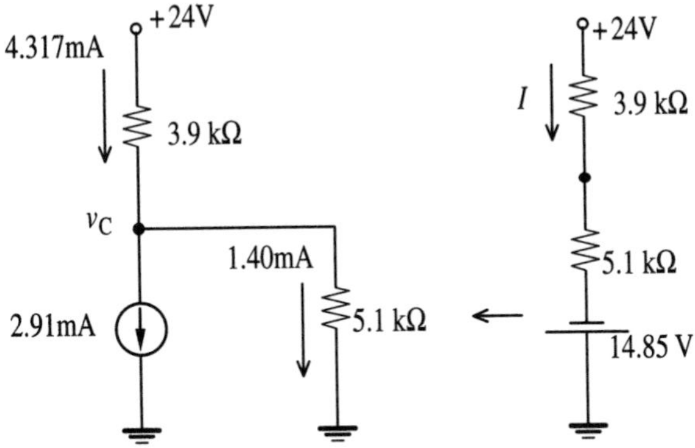

$$I = \frac{38.854\ \text{V}}{3.9\ \text{k}\Omega + 5.1\ \text{k}\Omega} = 4.317\ \text{mA}$$

$$V_C = V_{CE} = 7.163\ \text{V}$$

a. *i.* I_C remains constant, $I_C = 2.9125$ mA but V_{CE} drops to about $V_{CE} = 7.163$ V

ii. The voltage gain would remain about the same.

b. *i.* The operating point *won't change.*

ii. $A_V = \dfrac{-(150)(3.9\ \text{k}\Omega)\ i_b}{i_b\ 1.3\ \text{k}\Omega} = -450$ (increases)

55. The capacitor may cause excessive noise. The capacitor may explode.

27.11 Computer Analysis of Transistor Amplifier Circuit

57.

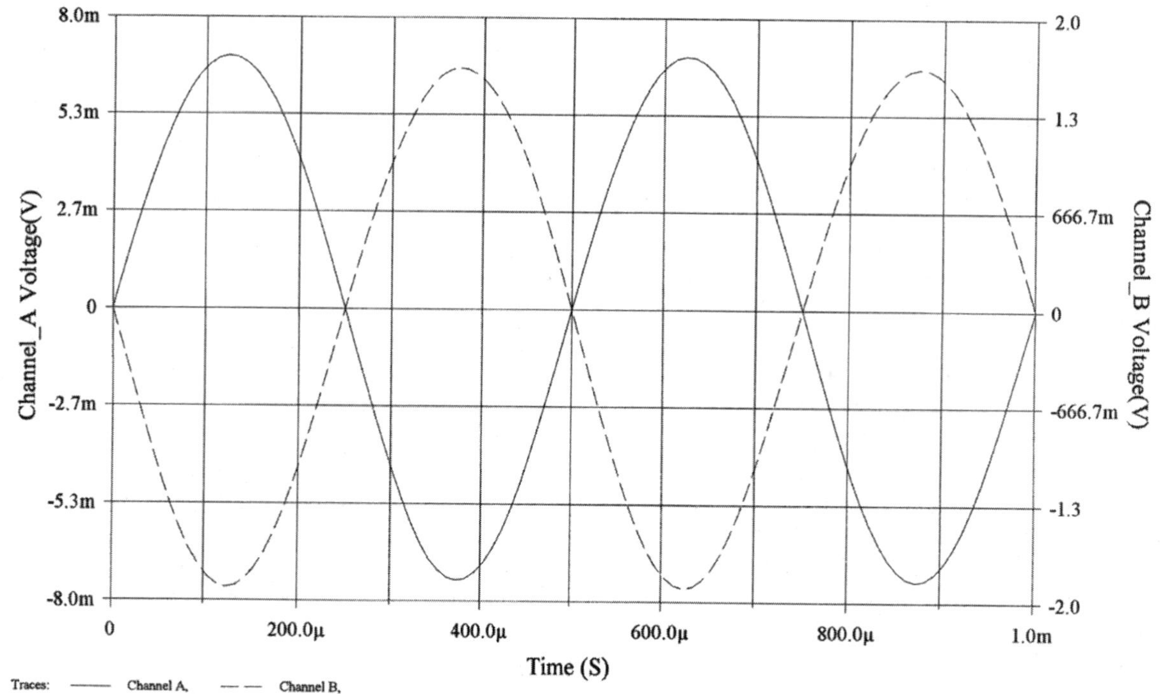

$$A_V = -\frac{1.645 \text{ V}}{6.94 \text{ mV}} = -237$$

59.

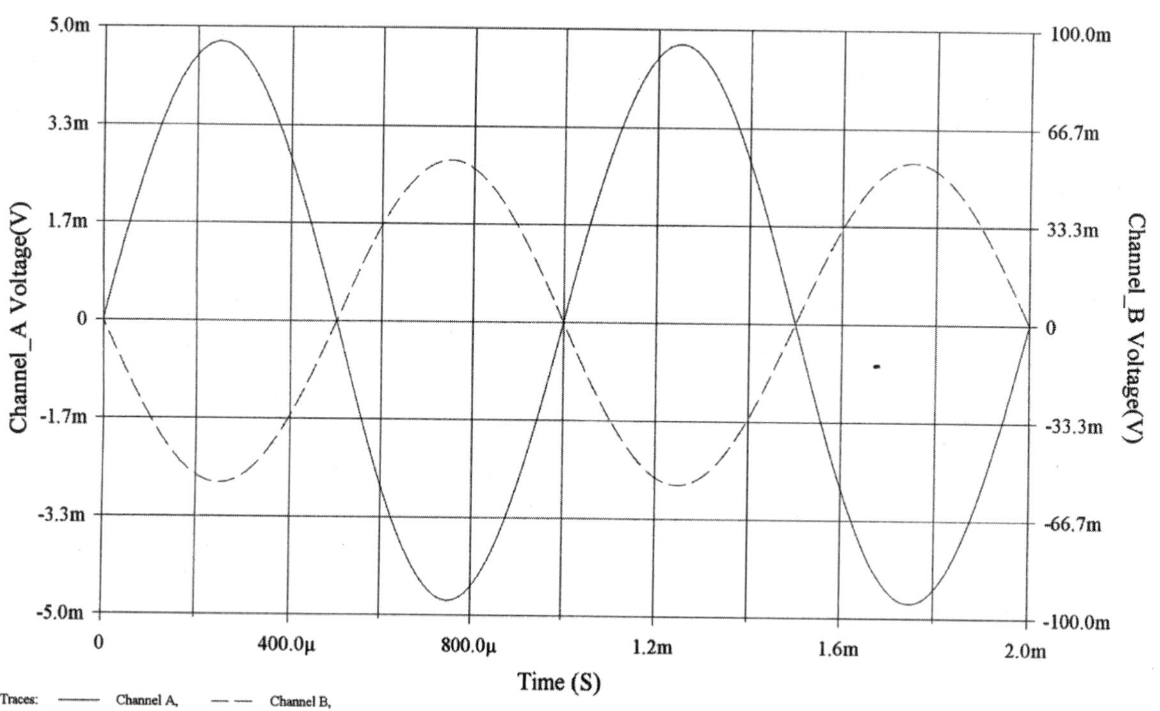

$$A_V = -\frac{55.1 \text{ mV}}{4.75 \text{ mV}} = -11.6$$

61.

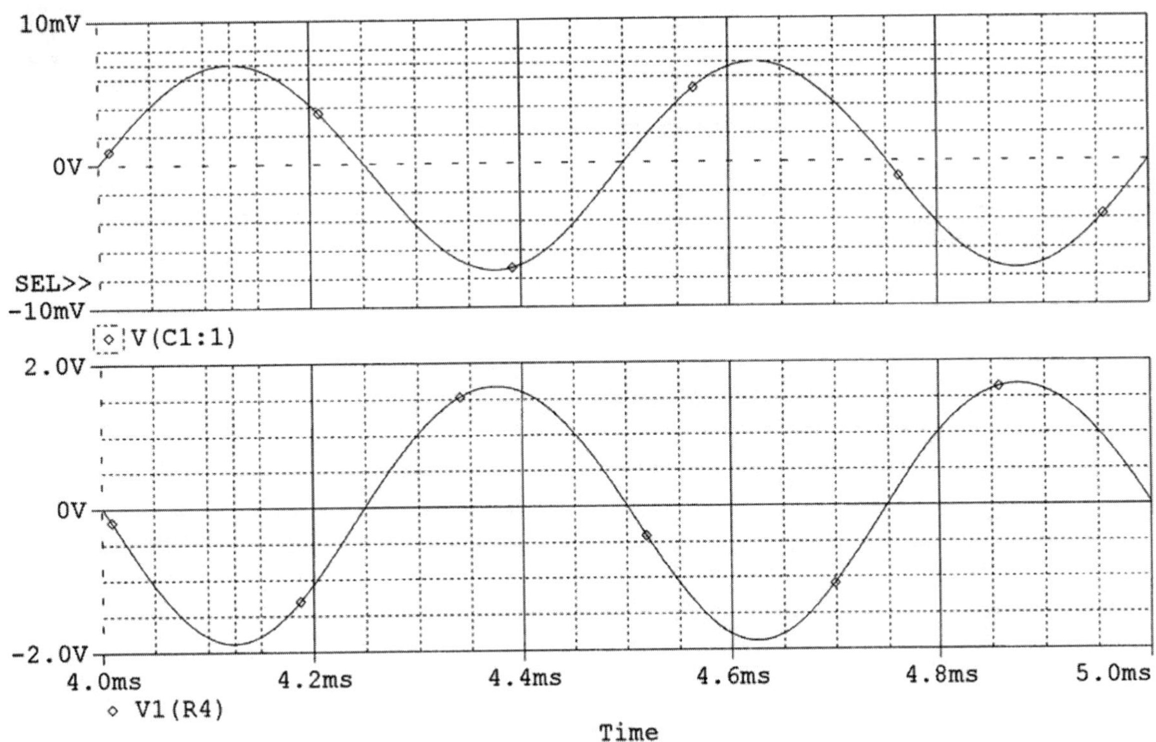

$$A_V = -\frac{1.675\text{ V}}{6.96\text{ mV}} = -241$$

63.

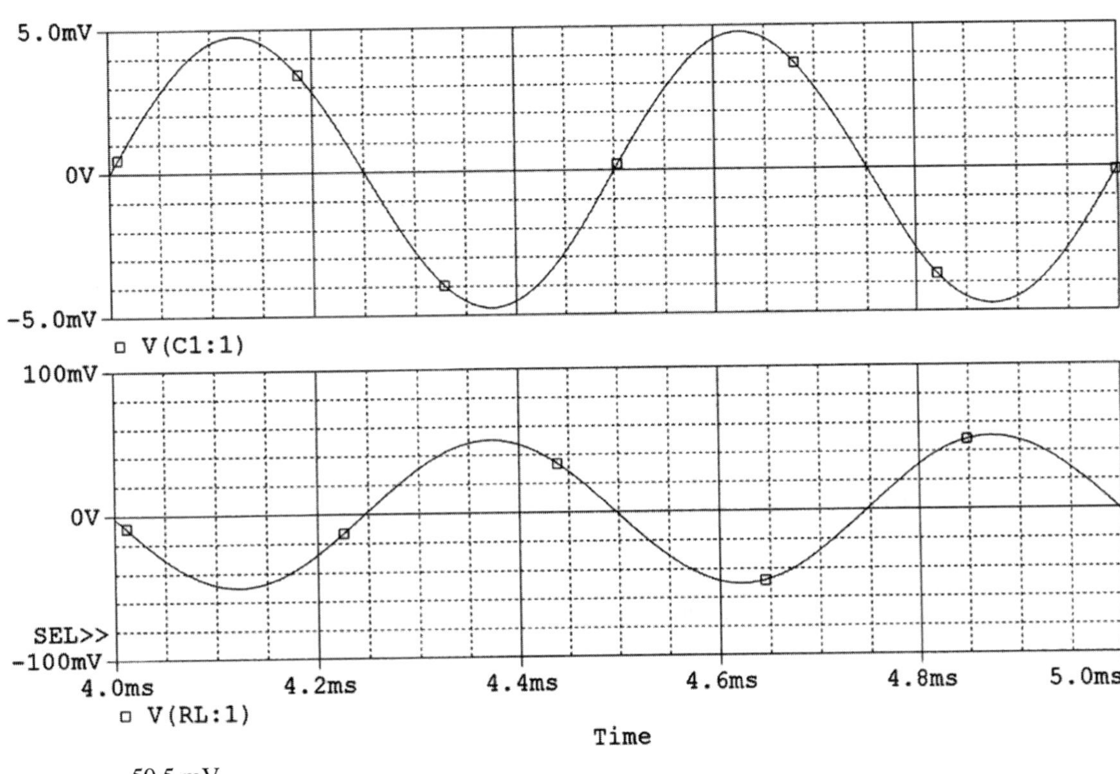

$$A_V = -\frac{50.5\text{ mV}}{4.73\text{ mV}} = -10.7$$

Chapter

28

Operational Amplifiers

28.1 Introduction to the Operational Amplifier

1. Very high open-loop gain.
   Very high input impedance.
   Very low output impedance.

28.2 The Differential Amplifier and Common-Mode Signals

3. $V_E = -0.7\text{ V}$

$$I_E = \frac{-0.7\text{ V} - (-15\text{ V})}{2.7\text{ k}\Omega} = 5.30\text{ mA}$$

$$I_{C1} = I_{C2} = \frac{I_E}{2} = 2.65\text{ mA}$$

$$V_{C1} = 15\text{ V} - (2.65\text{ mA})(2.2\text{ k}\Omega) = 9.17\text{ V}$$

5. $$[\text{CMRR}]_{\text{dB}} = 20\log\frac{200}{0.01} = 86.0\text{ dB}$$

7. $$\text{CMRR} = 10^{80/20} = 10{,}000 = \frac{A_{vd}}{A_{vc}}$$

$$A_{vc} = \frac{A_{vd}}{10{,}000} = 0.02$$

$$V_{S(\text{input})} = \frac{10\ V_{p\text{-}p}}{200} = 50\text{ mV}_{p\text{-}p}$$

$$V_{N(\text{output})} = \frac{10\text{ mV}_{p\text{-}p}}{1000} = 10\text{ mV}_{p\text{-}p}$$

$$V_{N(\text{input})} = \frac{10\text{ mV}_{p\text{-}p}}{0.02} = 0.5\ V_{p\text{-}p} = V_{CM}$$

28.4 The Inverting Amplifier

9. $$A_v = -\frac{R_F}{R_1} = -5.0$$

$$z_{in} = R_1 = 20\text{ k}\Omega$$

$$z_{out} = \left(1 - A_{vc1}\right)\left(\frac{R_{out}}{A_{vol}}\right) = (1+5)\left(\frac{75\ \Omega}{200{,}000}\right) = 2.25\text{ m}\Omega$$

11. $R_1 = 12\text{ k}\Omega$

$R_F = (5)(12\text{ k}\Omega) = 60\text{ k}\Omega$

28.5 Non-inverting Amplifier

13. $$A_v = \frac{R_F}{R_1} + 1 = 6.0$$

$$z_{in} = \left(1 + \frac{A_{vol}}{A_{vcl}}\right)R_{in} = \left(1 + \frac{200{,}000}{6}\right)2\text{ M}\Omega = 66.67\text{ G}\Omega$$

$$z_{out} = \left(\frac{A_{vcl}}{A_{vol}}\right)R_{out} = \left(\frac{6}{200{,}000}\right)75\ \Omega = 2.25\text{ m}\Omega$$

$$V_{out} = (6.0)(-2.0\text{ V}) = -12.0\text{ V}$$

15. Select $R_1 = 10\text{ k}\Omega$ $\quad R_F = 4R_1 = 40\text{ k}\Omega$

17. $$A_V = \left(\frac{R_F}{R_1}\right) = 1$$

$$z_{in} = \left(1 + \frac{200{,}000}{1}\right)2\text{ M}\Omega = 400\text{ G}\Omega$$

$$z_{out} = \left(\frac{1}{200{,}000}\right)75\ \Omega = 375\ \mu\Omega$$

28.6 Op-Amp Specifications

19. $$A_v = \left(1 + \frac{1}{1}\right) = 2$$

$$V_{out} = (2)(2\text{ mV}) = 4\text{ mV}$$

21. $I_B = \dfrac{60 \text{ nA} + 40 \text{ nA}}{2} = 50 \text{ nA}$

$I_{OS} = 60 \text{ nA} - 40 \text{ nA} = 20 \text{ nA}$

23. $0.5 \text{ V} = (1 \text{ M}\Omega)\ I_{B(-)}\left(\dfrac{20 \text{ k}\Omega}{1 \text{ k}\Omega} + 1\right) + 20 \text{ k}\Omega\ I_{B(-)}$

$= 21 \text{ M}\Omega\ I_{B(-)} + 20 \text{ k}\Omega\ I_{B(-)}$

$I_{B(-1)} = \dfrac{0.5 \text{ V}}{21.02 \text{ M}\Omega} = 23.79 \text{ nA}$

25. $\text{BW} = \dfrac{1 \times 10^6 \text{ Hz}}{5} = 200 \text{ kHz}$

27. $\text{BW} = 1 \times 10^6 \text{ Hz}$

29. Slew rate $= 2\ \pi f A$

$f = \dfrac{0.5 \text{ V}/\mu\text{s}}{(2\pi)(1 \text{ V})} = 79.58 \text{ kHz}$

31. $R_C = R_1 \,//\, R_F = 20 \text{ k}\Omega \,//\, 100 \text{ k}\Omega = 16.67 \text{ k}\Omega$

28.7 Troubleshooting an Op-Amp Circuit

33. R_F might be shorted.
The power supply may have failed.

28.8 Computer Analysis of Op-Amp Circuits

35.

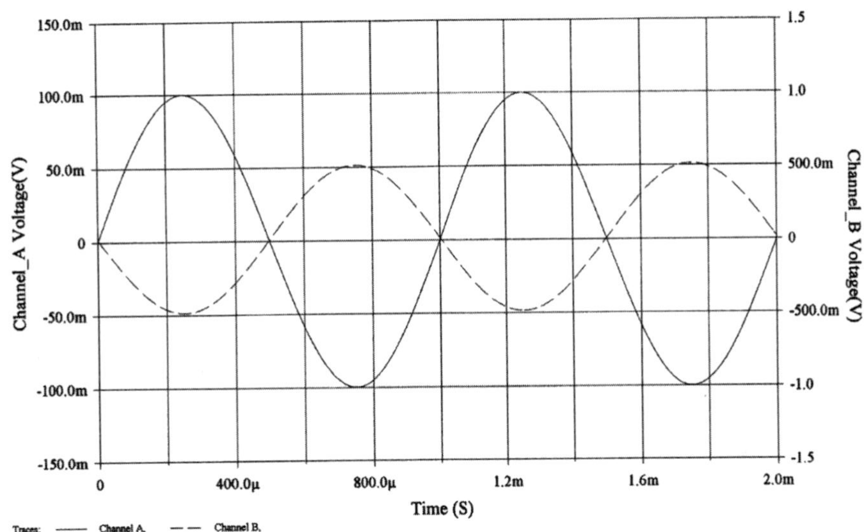

$A_V = -\dfrac{513 \text{ mV}}{100 \text{ mV}} = -5.13$

37.

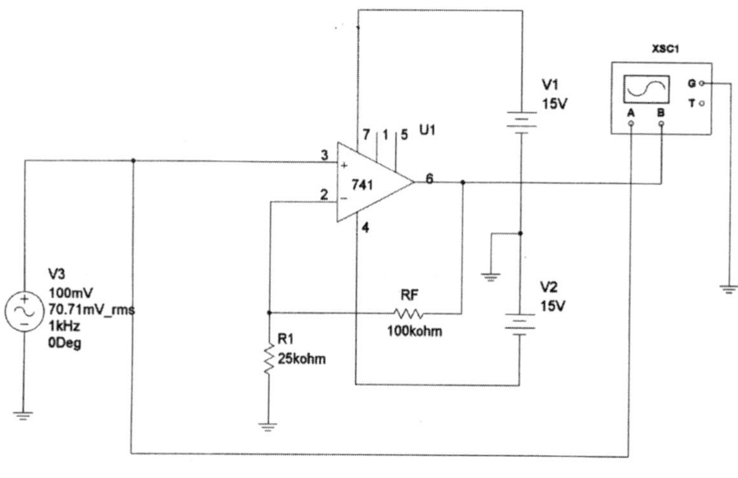

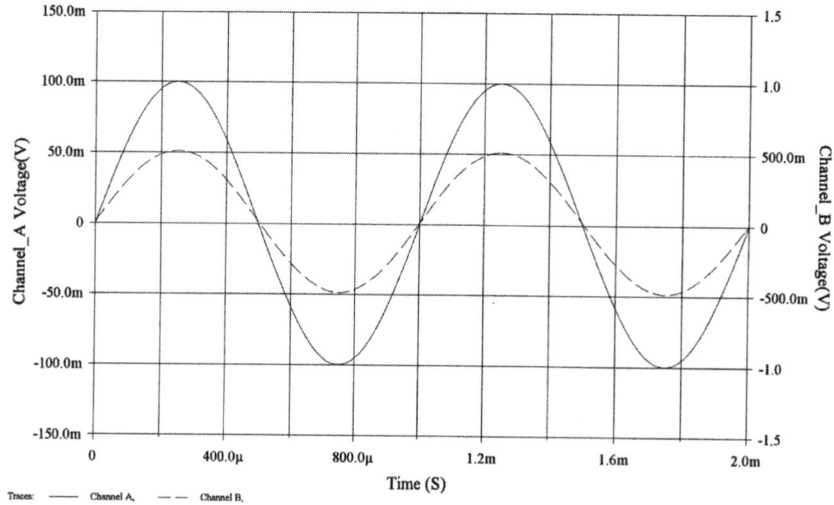

$$A_V = +\frac{512\text{ mV}}{100\text{ mV}} = +5.12$$

39.

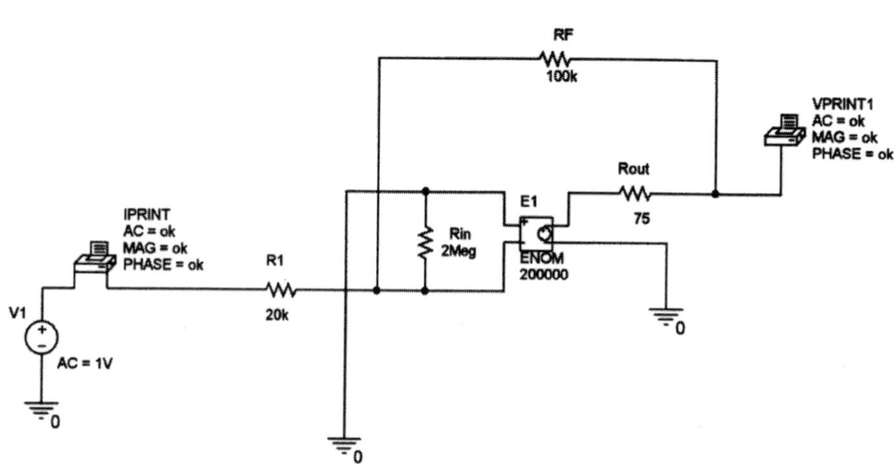

From the output file, we have

$$z_{in} = \frac{1.00\text{ V}}{5.00 \times 10^{-5}\text{ A}} = 20\text{ k}\Omega \qquad z_{out} = \frac{5.00\text{ V}}{2.204 \times 10^{3}\text{ A}} = 2.27\text{ m}\Omega$$

41.

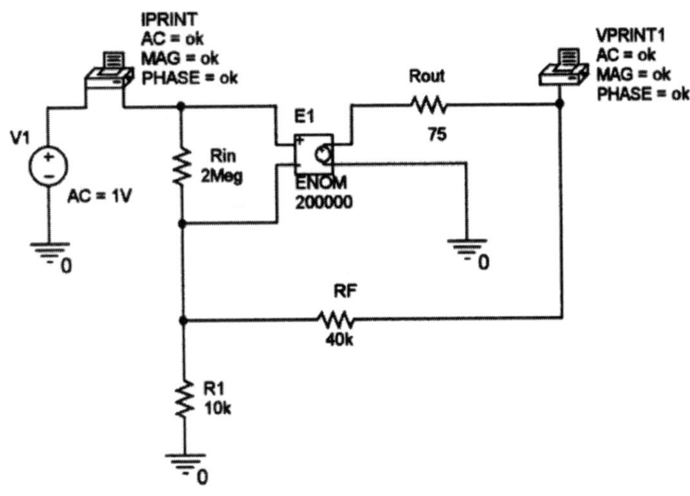

From the output file:

$$z_{in} = \frac{1.00 \text{ V}}{1.252 \times 10^{-11} \text{ A}} = 79.9 \text{ G}\Omega \qquad z_{out} = \frac{5.00 \text{ V}}{2.656 \times 10^{3} \text{ A}} = 1.88 \text{ m}\Omega$$

Chapter

29

Applications of Op-Amps

29.1 Comparators

1. at $v_{in} = 3$ V (= V_{REF}) $t = 6$ ms

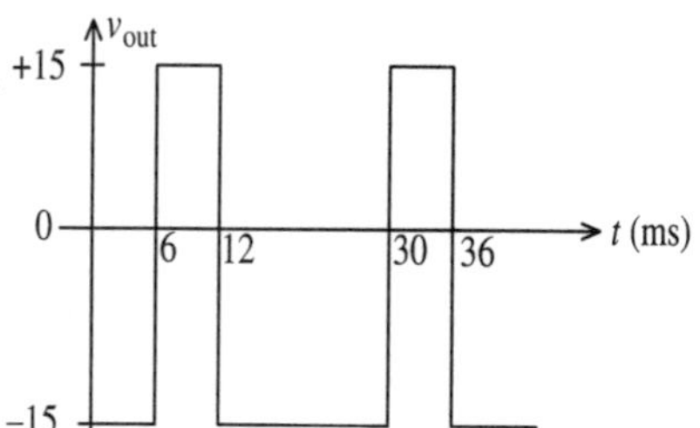

3. at $v_{in} = -4$ V $t = 12 \text{ ms} + \left(\frac{1}{3}\right)(12 \text{ ms}) = 16 \text{ ms}$

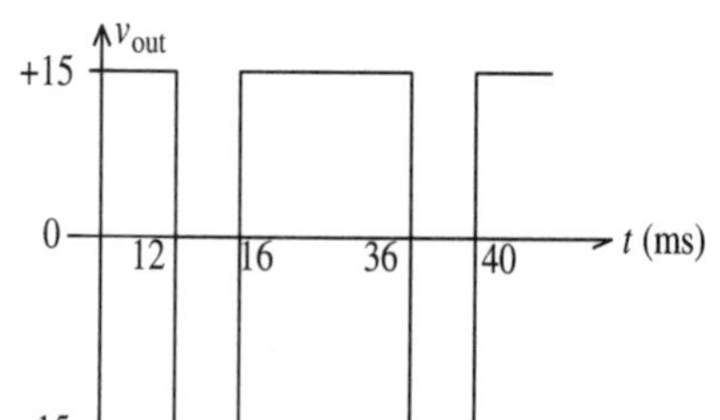

5.

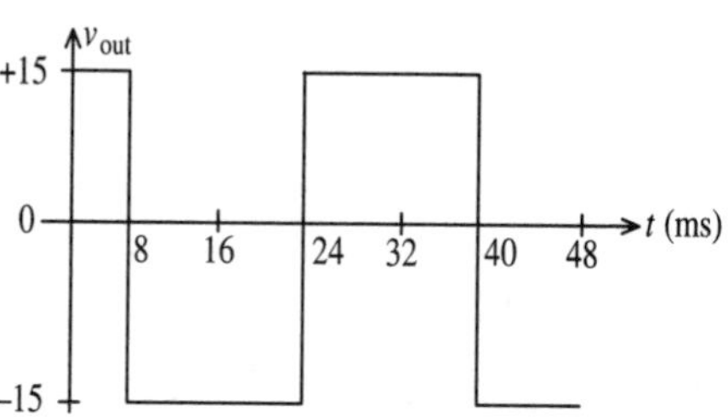

7. at $v_{in} = -2$ V $t = 35.2$ μs and $t = 60.8$ μs

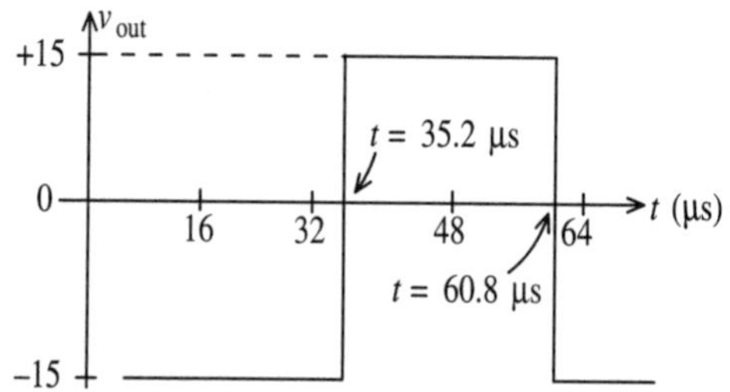

9. a. LED1 will be on whenever $v_{in} > 10$ V
   b. LED2 will be on whenever $v_{in} > 5$ V

29.2 Voltage Summing Amplifier

11.

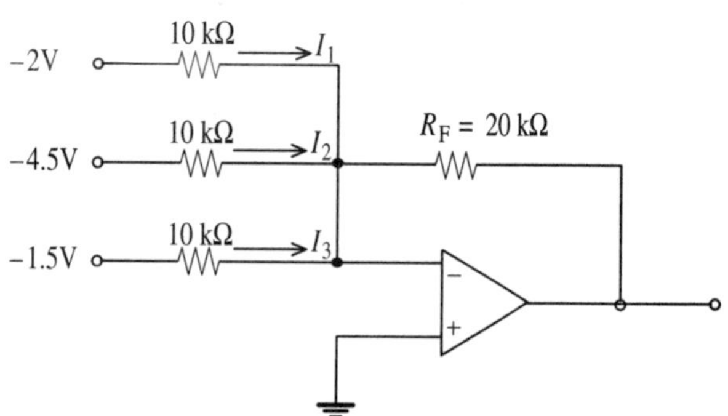

a. $I_1 = -\dfrac{2\text{ V}}{10\text{ k}\Omega} = -0.2 \text{ mA}$

$I_2 = \dfrac{4.5\text{ V}}{10\text{ k}\Omega} = +0.45 \text{ mA}$

$I_3 = -\dfrac{1.5\text{ V}}{10\text{ k}\Omega} = -0.15 \text{ mA}$

$I_F = 0.10$ mA

b. $V_{out} = -(0.10 \text{ mA})(20 \text{ k}\Omega) = -2.0 \text{ V}$

13.

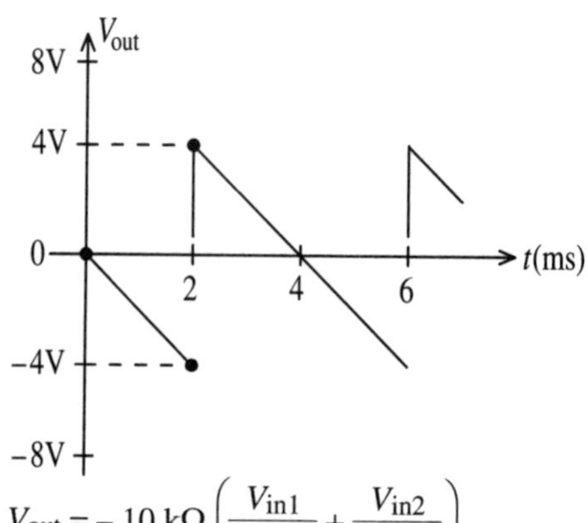

$$V_{out} = -10 \text{ k}\Omega\left(\frac{V_{in1}}{10\text{ k}\Omega} + \frac{V_{in2}}{10\text{ k}\Omega}\right)$$

$$= -(V_{in1} + V_{in2})$$

29.3 Integrators and Differentiators

15. $t = \frac{T}{2} = 1\text{ ms}$ ← charging time

$v_{out} = -\frac{1}{(10\text{ k}\Omega)(0.05\ \mu\text{F})}$

$(2.0\text{ V})(1\text{ ms}) = -4.0\text{ V}$ assumes $V_O = 0\text{ V}$

therefore $4.0\ V_{p\text{-}p}$

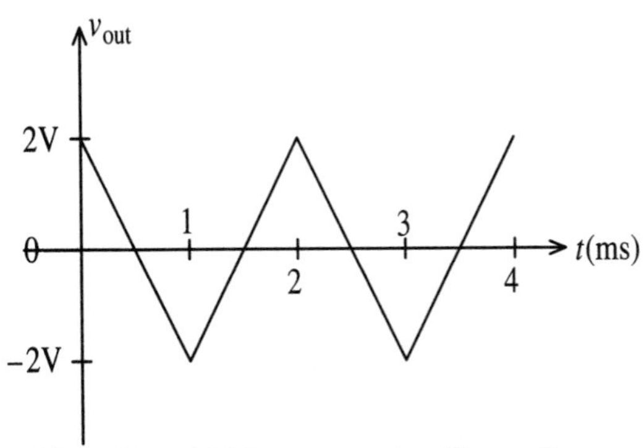

Note: $R_F = 1\text{ M}\Omega$ removes the offset voltage.

17. With power supplies of ± 15 V, the maximum peak-to-peak output is + 30 V.

Therefore

$30\text{ V} = \frac{(V_p)(1\text{ ms})}{(10\text{ k}\Omega)(0.05\ \mu\text{F})}$

$V_p = 15\text{ V}$

19. $v(t) = 2000\frac{\text{V}}{\text{s}}t - 2\text{ V}$

$v_{out} = -(10\text{ k}\Omega)(250\text{ nF})\left(2000\frac{\text{V}}{\text{s}}\right)$

$= -0.5\text{ V}$

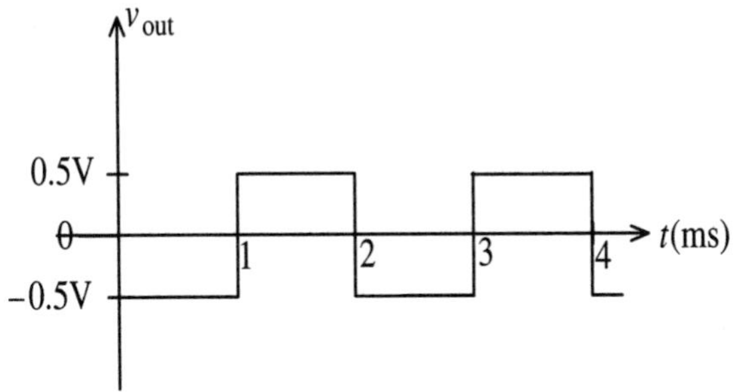

21. ① $(10\text{ k}\Omega)(250\text{ nF}) = (10^4)(R_{in})(C_F)$

② $(10\text{ k}\Omega)(C_F) = (R_{in})(250\text{ nF})$

$C_F = \frac{2.5 \times 10^{-7}}{R_{in}}$ ①

$C_F = (2.5 \times 10^{-11})(R_{in})$ ②

$R_{in} = \sqrt{\frac{2.5 \times 10^{-7}}{2.5 \times 10^{-11}}} = 100\ \Omega$

$C_F = 2.5 \times 10^{-9}\text{ F} = 2.5\text{ nF}$

29.4 Instrumentation Amplifiers

23. $I_1 = 1\ \mu\text{A (right)} = I_3$

$I_2 = 1\ \mu\text{A (left)} = I_4$

$v_{out} = 1\ \mu\text{A}\ (2)(510\text{ k}\Omega) = 1.02\text{ V}$

25. $V_{R1} = V_{R4} = \left(\frac{100.002}{200.002}\right)30\text{ V} = 15.00015\text{ V}$

$v_{in1} = 15.00015\text{ V} - 15.000\text{ V} = +150\ \mu\text{V}$

$v_{in2} = 15\text{ V} - 15.00015\text{ V} = -150\ \mu\text{V}$

$A_v = \frac{680\text{ k}\Omega}{10\text{ k}\Omega} = 68$

$v_{out} = -(68)(0.300\text{ mV}) = -20.4\text{ mV}$

29.5 Active Filters

27. $\omega = (2\pi)(10\text{ kHz}) = 62.832\text{ krad/s}$

$R_1C = \tau = \frac{1}{\omega} = 15.915\ \mu\text{s}$

$R_1 = \frac{15.915\ \mu\text{s}}{0.01\ \mu\text{F}} = 1591.549\ \Omega$

$R_F = (10)(1592) = 15.915\text{ k}\Omega$

$R_2 = \frac{1}{\frac{1}{R_1} - \frac{1}{R_F}} = 1768.388\ \Omega$

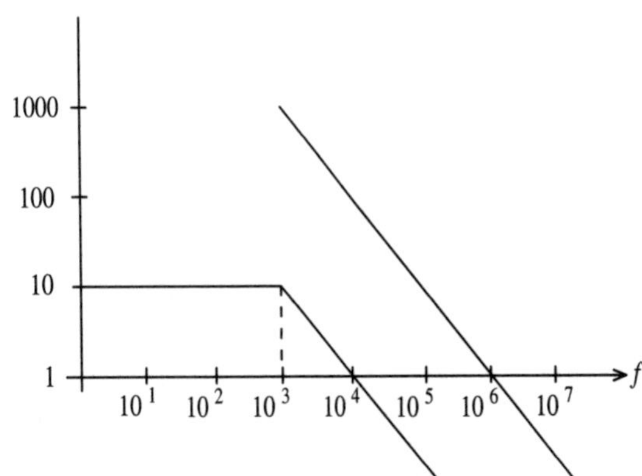

29. $f_c = \dfrac{1}{2\pi(4\text{ k}\Omega)(0.4\ \mu\text{F})} = 99.47\text{ Hz}$

$V_- = V_{in}$ $\qquad I_2 = \dfrac{V_{in}}{6\text{ k}\Omega} = I_F$

$V_{out} = (18\text{ k}\Omega)\left(\dfrac{V_{in}}{6\text{ k}\Omega}\right) = 3\ V_{in} \equiv 9.54\text{ dB}$

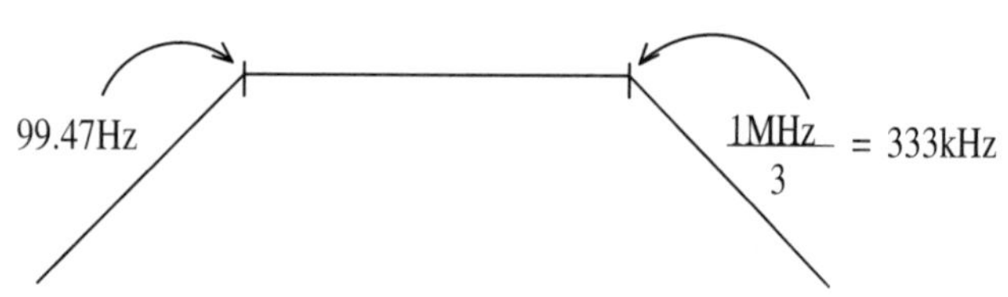

31.

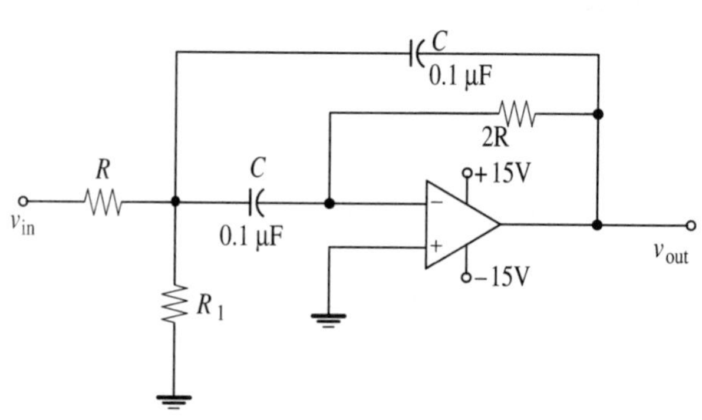

$f_o = 800\text{ Hz}$ $\qquad f_o = \dfrac{0.1125}{RC}\sqrt{1+\dfrac{R}{R_1}}$

$\text{BW} = 80\text{ Hz}$ $\qquad \text{BW} = \dfrac{0.1591}{RC}$

$R = \dfrac{0.1591}{(80\text{ Hz})(0.1\ \mu\text{F})} = 19.888\text{ k}\Omega$

$800 = \dfrac{0.1125}{(19.9\text{ k}\Omega)(0.1\ \mu\text{F})}\sqrt{1+\dfrac{19.9\text{ k}\Omega}{R_1}}$

$1 + \dfrac{19.9\text{ k}\Omega}{R_1} = 200$

$R_1 = 99.94\ \Omega$

29.6 Voltage Regulation

33. For $E = 40$ V: $\quad R_{Th} = 100\ \Omega\ //\ 50\ \Omega = 33.33\ \Omega$

$E_{Th} = \left(\dfrac{50\ \Omega}{150\ \Omega}\right)40\text{ V} = 13.33\text{ V}$

$V_{out} = 10\text{ V} + 7\ \Omega\left(\dfrac{13.33\text{ V}}{40.33\ \Omega}\right)$

$= 12.314\text{ V}$

\+ 10V −

7Ω

For $E = 60$ V: $\quad E_{Th} = \left(\dfrac{50\ \Omega}{150\ \Omega}\right)60\text{ V} = 20\text{ V}$

$V_{out} = 10\text{ V} + 7\ \Omega\left(\dfrac{20\text{ V}}{40.33\ \Omega}\right)$

$= 13.471\text{ V}$

$\%\text{ line regulation} = \dfrac{\Delta V_{out}}{\Delta V_{in}} \times 100\ \% = 5.79\ \%$

35. For $R_L = 50\ \Omega$: $\quad R_{Th} = 33.33\ \Omega$, $E_{Th} = 20$ V

$V_{out} = 13.471$ V

For $R_L = 100\ \Omega$: $\quad R_{Th} = 50\ \Omega$, $E_{Th} = 30$ V

$V_{out} = 10\text{ V} + 7\ \Omega\left(\dfrac{30\text{ V}}{57\ \Omega}\right) = 13.684\text{ V}$

Load regulation =

$\dfrac{13.684\text{ V} - 13.471\text{ V}}{13.471\text{ V}} \times 100\ \% = 1.58\ \%$

37. a. Note: Keep current through zener $I_Z \geq 10$ mA. Therefore, minimum output voltage is

$V_{out\,(min)} = V_Z + (10\text{ mA})(330\ \Omega) = 6.6\text{ V}$

Maximum regulated output voltage is

$V_{out\,(max)} = 28\text{ V} - 3\text{ V} = 25\text{ V}$

b. When $V_{out} = 6.6$ V

$I_{2k} = \dfrac{6.6\text{ V}}{4\text{ k}\Omega} = 1.65\text{ mA}$

$I_{330\,\Omega} = 10\text{ mA}$

$V_{CE} = 28\text{ V} - 6.6\text{ V} = 21.4\text{ V}$

$P = (21.4\text{ V})(11.65\text{ mA}) = 0.249\text{ W}$

Note: The power will increase when a load is connected across the output terminals.

39. $[\text{ ripple rejection }]\text{ dB} = 20\log\dfrac{V_{r(in)}}{V_{r(out)}}$

$= 20\log\left(\dfrac{2.0\text{ V}_{p\text{–}p}}{4.0\text{ mV}_{p\text{–}p}}\right)$

$= 53.98\text{ dB}$

29.7 Computer Analysis

41.

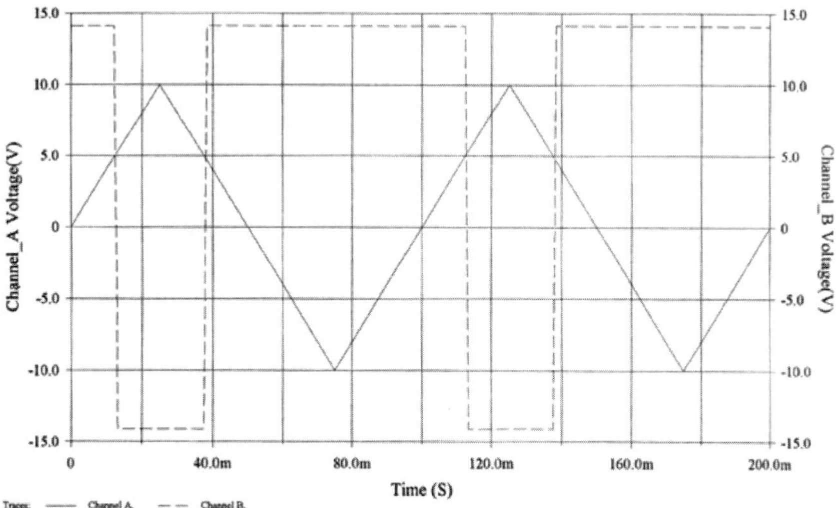

43.

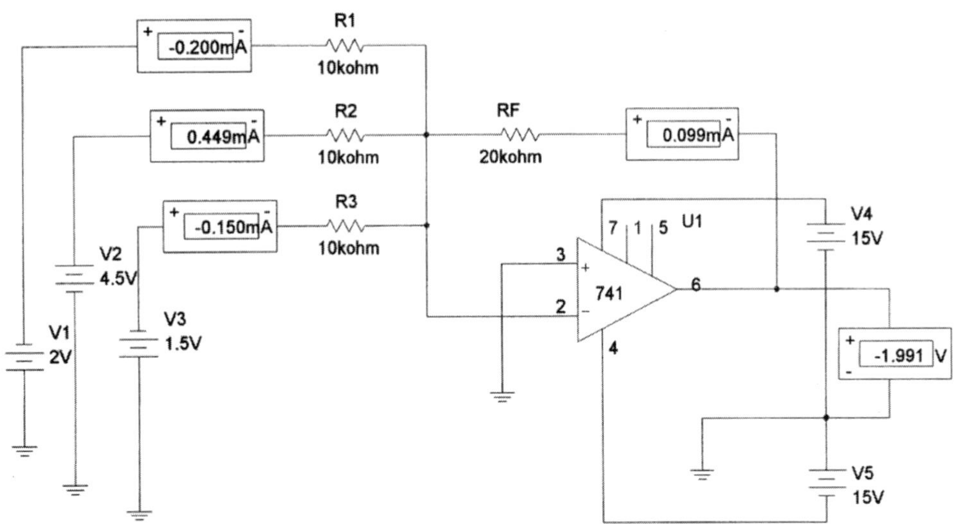

45.

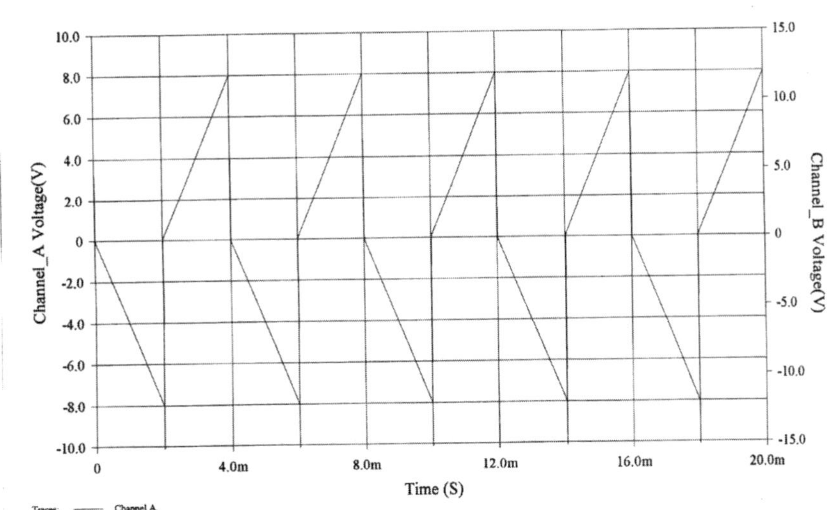

47.

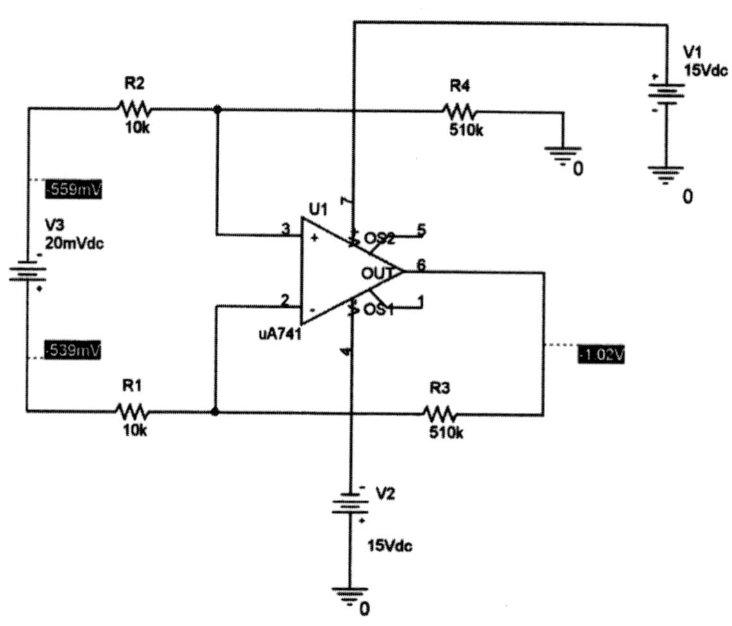

The result is the same as the value obtained in problem 23.

49.

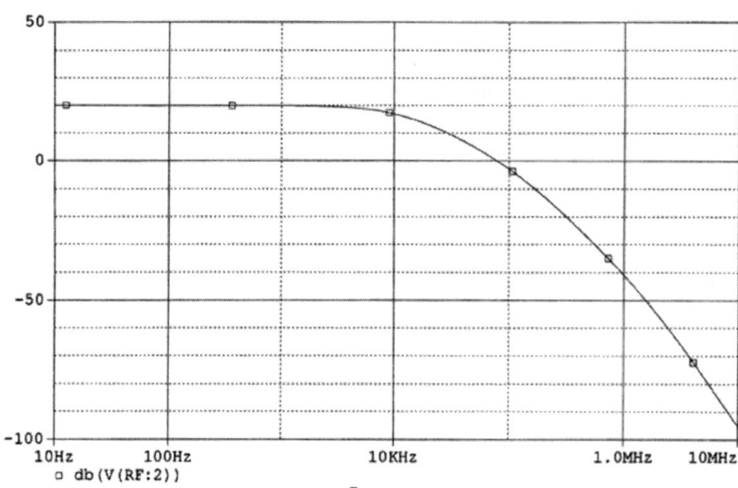

Chapter

30

Oscillators

30.1 Basics of Feedback

1. $$B = \frac{10\ \text{k}\Omega}{100\ \text{k}\Omega} = 0.1$$

$$A_{\text{vcl}} = \frac{500}{1 + (500)(0.1)} = 9.80$$

30.2 The Relaxation Oscillator

3. a. $$V_{(+)} = \pm\left(\frac{3\ \text{k}\Omega}{5\ \text{k}\Omega}\right)15\ \text{V} = \pm 9.0\ \text{V}$$

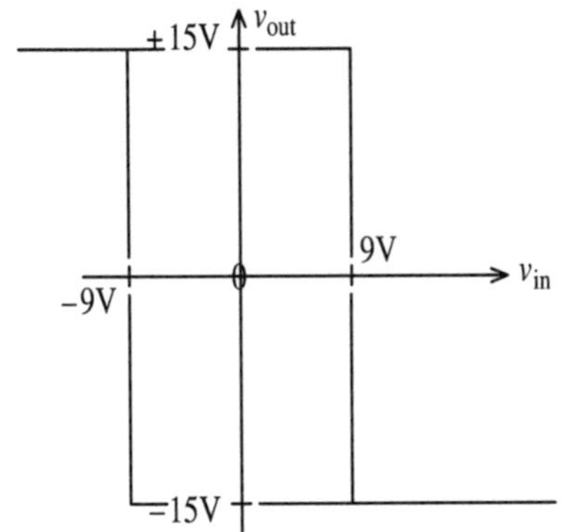

b.

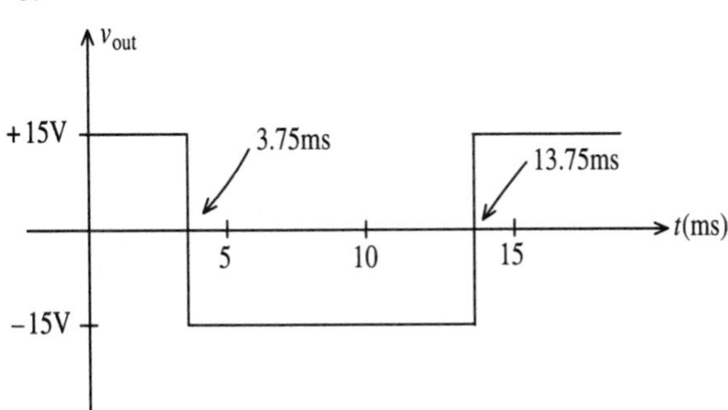

5. $$V_{\text{REF}} = \left(\frac{3\ \text{k}\Omega}{5\ \text{k}\Omega}\right)10\ \text{V} = +6\ \text{V}$$

$$V_{\text{UTP}} = \frac{R_{\text{in}}\,(V_{\text{SAT}} - V_{\text{REF}})}{R_{\text{in}} + R_{\text{F}}} + V_{\text{REF}}$$

$$= \frac{(10\ \text{k}\Omega)(15\ \text{V} - 6\ \text{V})}{20\ \text{k}\Omega} + 6\ \text{V} = 10.5\ \text{V}$$

$$V_{\text{LTP}} = \frac{R_{\text{in}}\,(-V_{\text{SAT}} - V_{\text{REF}})}{R_{\text{in}} + R_{\text{F}}}$$

$$= \frac{(10\ \text{k}\Omega)(-15\ \text{V} - 6\ \text{V})}{20\ \text{k}\Omega} + 6\ \text{V} = -4.5\ \text{V}$$

$$v_{\text{in}} = 10.5\ \text{V at } t = \left(\frac{10.5}{12}\right)5 = 4.375\ \text{ms}$$

$$v_{\text{in}} = -4.5\ \text{V at } t = \left(\frac{4.5}{12}\right)5 + 10\ \text{ms} = 11.875\ \text{ms}$$

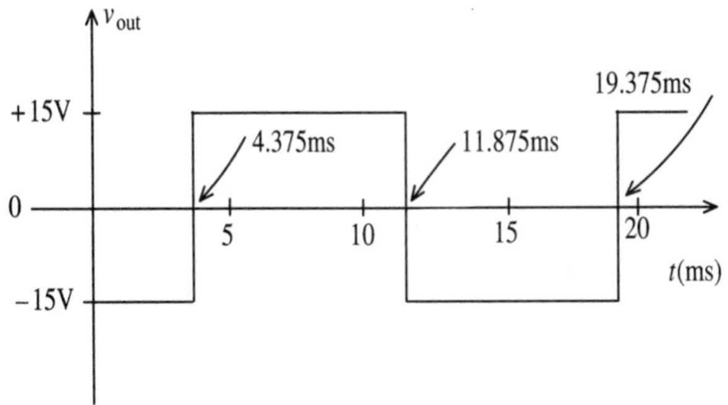

7. $$V_{\text{REF}} = \left(\frac{2\ \text{k}\Omega}{2\ \text{k}\Omega + 3\ \text{k}\Omega}\right)12\ \text{V} = \pm 4.8\ \text{V}$$

$v_C = 9.6\ V_{\text{p-p}}$

$$T = 2(20\ \text{k}\Omega)(0.2\ \mu\text{F})\ \ln\left(1 + \frac{2(2\ \text{k}\Omega)}{3\ \text{k}\Omega}\right)$$

$$= 6.778\ \text{ms}$$

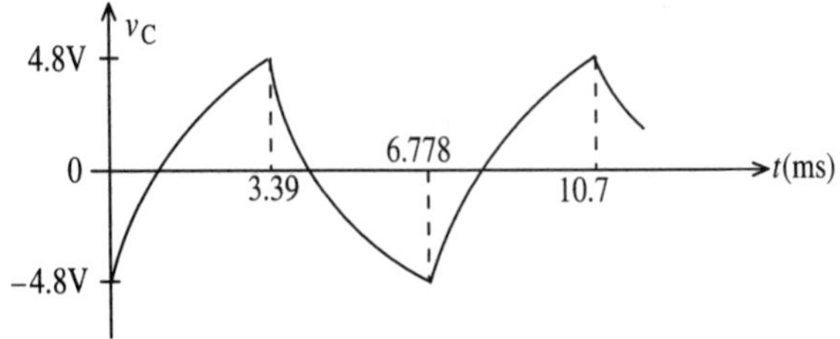

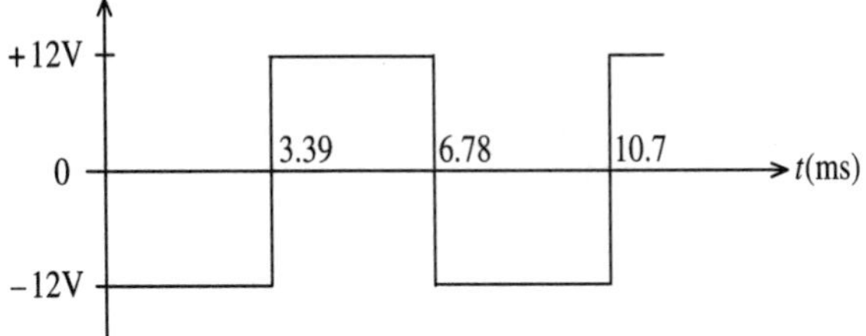

30.3 The Wien Bridge Oscillator

9. a. $R_F = 2\,R_{in} = 2(10\text{ k}\Omega) = 20\text{ k}\Omega$

b. $$f_o = \frac{1}{2\,\pi\,\sqrt{R_1R_2C_1C_2}} = 72.34\text{ Hz}$$

11. $(R_1 = 2\,R_2)$

$$B = \frac{R_2}{2\,R_2 + R_2 + R_2} = \frac{1}{4}$$

$A = 4$

30.4 The Phase - Shift Oscillator

13. a. $$f_o = \frac{1}{2\,\pi\,\sqrt{6}\,(1.5\text{ k}\Omega)(0.047\ \mu\text{F})} = 921\text{ Hz}$$

b. $R_{F2} = 29\,(1.5\text{ k}\Omega) - 33\text{ k}\Omega = 10.5\text{ k}\Omega$

c. $R_C = R_F = 43.5\text{ k}\Omega$

d. $$\text{BW} = \frac{2\times10^6\text{ Hz}}{29} = 68.97\text{ kHz}$$

15. $$R = \frac{1}{2\,\pi\,\sqrt{6}\,(4000\text{ Hz})(0.047\ \mu\text{F})} = 346\ \Omega$$

$R_F = 10.023\text{ k}\Omega = R_C$

30.5 LC Oscillators

17. Colpitts oscillator

$$f_o = \frac{1}{2\,\pi\,\sqrt{(50\ \mu\text{H})\dfrac{(100\text{ nF})(100\text{ nF})}{(100\text{ nF}+100\text{ nF})}}} = 100.658\text{ kHz}$$

30.6 Crystal Oscillators

19. When the crystal is subjected to mechanical pressure, an electric field is developed at right angle to the applied pressure. Conversely, if an electric field is applied, the material will deflect at right angle to the electric field.

21.

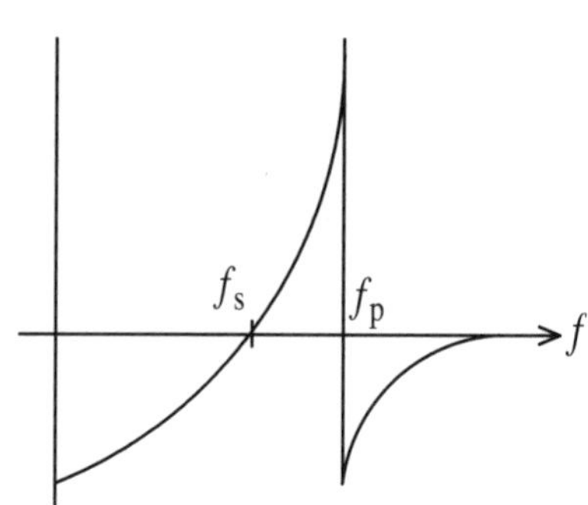

30.7 The 555 Timer

23. a. $v_{out} = V_{CC}$ (≡ "1")

The discharge transistor will be OFF.

b. $v_{out} = 0\text{V}$ (≡ "0")

The discharge transistor will be ON.

25. $T_1 = (\ln 2)\,R_BC$

$$R_B = \frac{0.25\text{ s}}{\ln 2(1.0\ \mu\text{F})} = 360.674\text{ k}\Omega$$

$T_2 = (\ln 2)(R_A + R_B)\,C$

$$R_A = \frac{0.75\text{ s}}{\ln 2(1.0\ \mu\text{F})} - 360.674\text{ k}\Omega = 721.348\text{ k}\Omega$$

27.

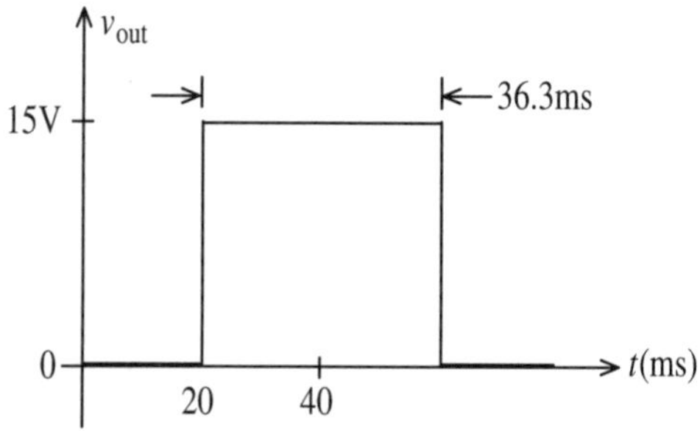

$T_W = 1.10\,R_AC$

$=(1.10)(330\text{ k}\Omega)(0.1\ \mu\text{F})$

$= 36.3\text{ ms}$

30.8 The Voltage Controlled Oscillator—VCO

29. Wiper at 0%:

$$V_C = \left(\frac{33\ \text{k}\Omega}{33\ \text{k}\Omega + 5\ \text{k}\Omega + 0.47\ \text{k}\Omega}\right)20\ \text{V} = 17.16\ \text{V}$$

$$f = \frac{2.4(20\ \text{V} - 17.2\ \text{V})}{(10\ \text{k}\Omega)(1\ \text{nF})(20\ \text{V})} = 34.1\ \text{kHz}$$

Wiper at 50%:

$$V_C = \left(\frac{33\ \text{k}\Omega + 2.5\ \text{k}\Omega}{38.47\ \text{k}\Omega}\right)20\ \text{V} = 18.46\ \text{V}$$

$$f = \frac{2.4(20\ \text{V} - 18.5\ \text{V})}{0.0002} = 18.53\ \text{kHz}$$

Wiper at 100%:

$$V_C = \left(\frac{33\ \text{k}\Omega + 5\ \text{k}\Omega}{38.47\ \text{k}\Omega}\right)20\ \text{V} = 19.76\ \text{V}$$

$$f = \frac{2.4(20\ \text{V} - 19.8\ \text{V})}{0.0002} = 2.93\ \text{kHz}$$

30.9 Computer Analysis

31.

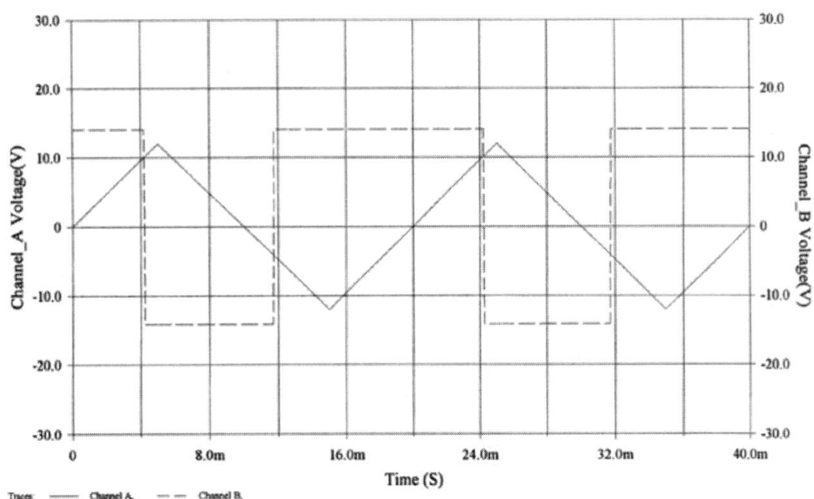

33.

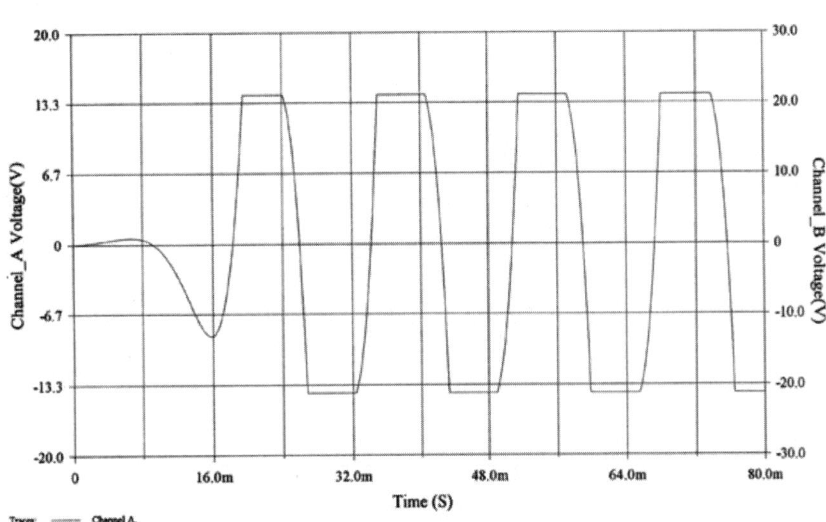

$T = 16.53$ ms $\quad f = 60.5$ Hz

35.

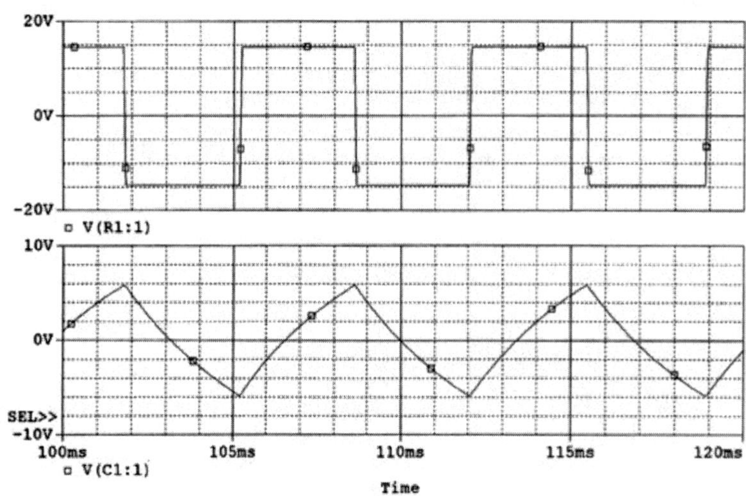

$T = 6.84$ ms $f = 146$ Hz

37.

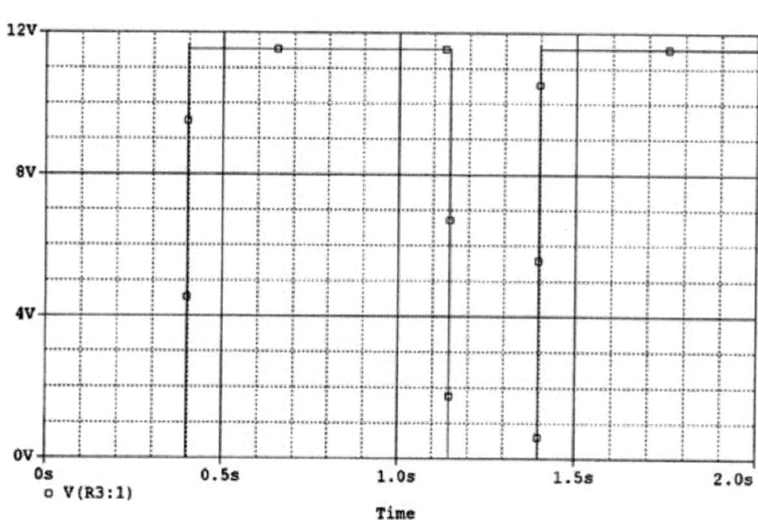

$T_1 = 0.25$ s

$T_2 = 0.75$ s

Chapter

31

Thyristors and Optical Devices

31.2 Triggering Devices

1. a. $V_P = \eta\, V_{BB} + V_D$

$$\eta = \frac{V_P - V_D}{V_{BB}} = \frac{10\text{ V} - 0.6\text{ V}}{15\text{ V}} = 0.62\overline{6}$$

$$f = \frac{1}{(6.8\text{ k}\Omega)(0.56\text{ }\mu\text{F})\ln\left(\frac{1}{1-0.627}\right)}$$

$= 266.53$ Hz

b. $R_{BB} = \dfrac{15\text{ V}}{2.4\text{ mA}} - 0.22\text{ k}\Omega - 0.047\text{ k}\Omega = 5.983\text{ k}\Omega$

c.

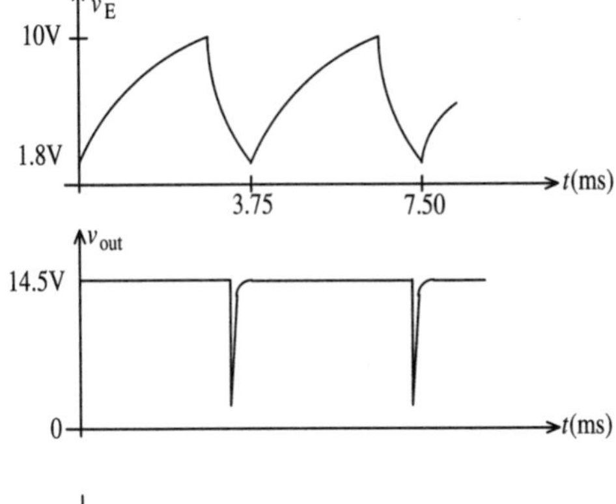

3. Select a suitable capacitor. e.g. $C = 0.01$ μF

$$R = \frac{1}{(8000\text{ Hz})(0.01\text{ }\mu\text{F})\ln\left(\frac{1}{1-0.627}\right)}$$

$= 12.688$ kΩ

Note: Any combination $RC = 0.127$ ms will work!

31.3 Silicon-Controlled Rectifiers (SCRs)

5.

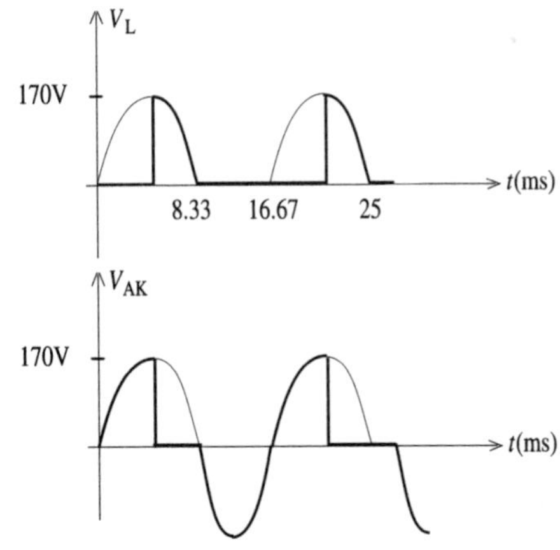

7.

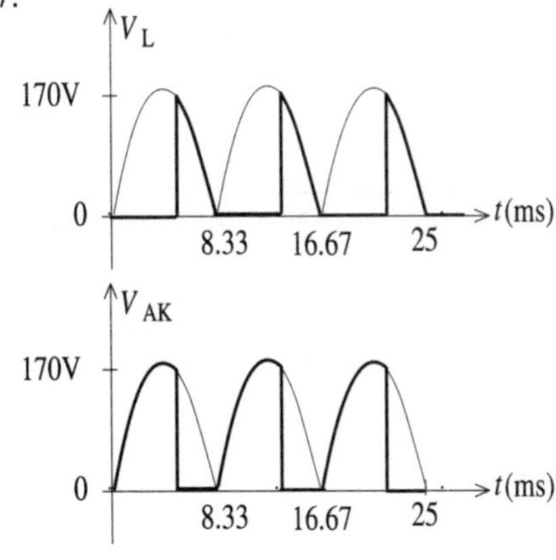

31.4 Triacs

9.

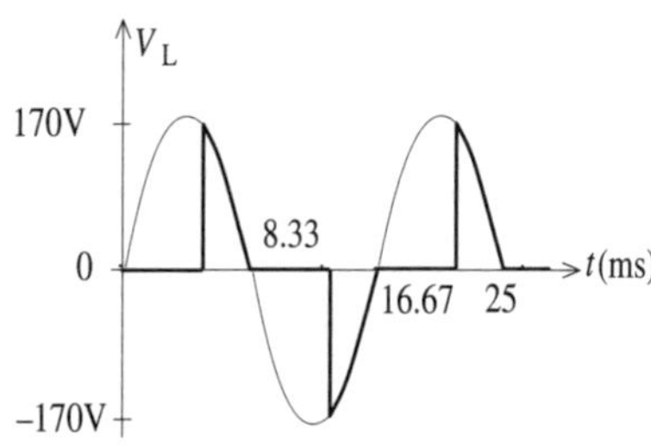

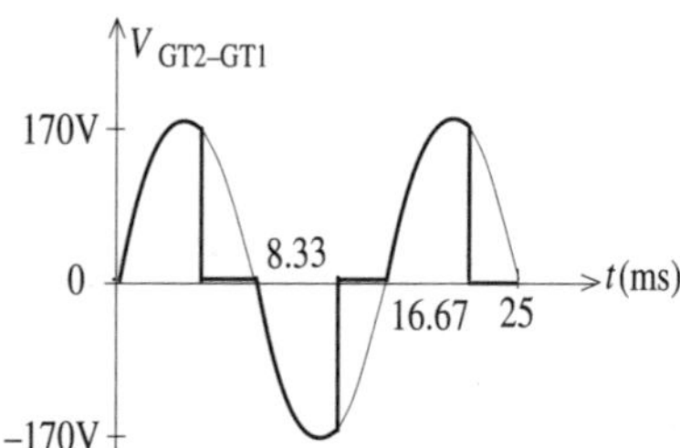

31.5 Power Control Fundamentals

11. At 45° : $\frac{V_{rms}}{V} \cong 0.478$

$V_{rms} = (0.478)(\sqrt{2})(120\text{ V})$

$= 81.119\text{ V}$

$P = \frac{V_{rms})^2}{150\ \Omega} = 43.87\ W$

or $P_{max} = \frac{(120\text{ V})^2}{150\ \Omega} = 96\text{ W}$

$\frac{P}{P_{max}} \cong 0.455$ $\quad P = 43.68\text{ W}$

13. At $\theta = 60°$: $\frac{V_{rms}}{V} \cong 0.635$

$V_{rms} \cong (0.635\sqrt{2})(240\text{ V}) = 215.53\text{ V}$

$P = \frac{(215.53\text{ V})^2}{20\ \Omega} = 2323\text{ W}$

or $P_{max} = \frac{(240\text{ V})^2}{20\ \Omega} = 2800\text{ W}$

$\frac{P}{P_{max}} \cong 0.807$ $\quad P \cong 2324\text{ W}$

15. $\frac{P}{P_{max}} = \frac{0.2\text{ hp}}{0.5\text{ hp}} = 0.4 \qquad \theta = 120°$

17. $V_{rms} = \sqrt{\left(\frac{1}{2\pi}\right)\int_{\pi/4}^{\pi} (V\sin\theta)^2\, d\theta}$

$= V\sqrt{\left(\frac{1}{2\pi}\right)\left[\frac{\theta}{2} - \frac{1}{4}\sin 2\theta\right]_{\pi/4}^{\pi}}$

$= V\sqrt{\left(\frac{1}{2\pi}\right)\left[\left(\frac{\pi}{2} - \frac{1}{4}\sin 2\pi\right) - \left(\frac{\pi}{8} - \frac{1}{4}\sin\frac{\pi}{2}\right)\right]}$

$= V\sqrt{\left(\frac{1}{2\pi}\right)\left(\frac{\pi}{2} - \frac{\pi}{8} + \frac{1}{4}\right)} = 80.9\text{ V}$

31.6 Introduction to Optical Devices

19. $f = \frac{c}{\lambda} = \frac{3.00 \times 10^8\text{ m/s}}{550 \times 10^{-9}\text{ m}} = 5.45 \times 10^{14}\text{ Hz}$

21.

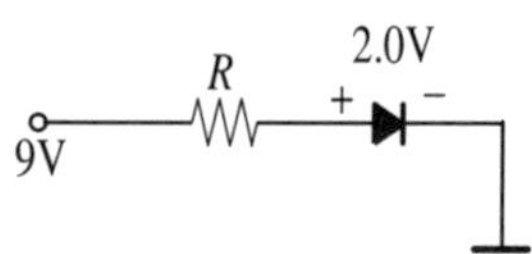

$R = \frac{9\text{ V} - 2\text{ V}}{20\text{ mA}} = 350\ \Omega$

31.8 Optocouplers

23. $$I_F = \frac{15\text{ V} - 1.4\text{ V}}{1.5\text{ k}\Omega} = 9.06\text{ mA}$$

$I_C = (0.4)\ I_F = 3.626\text{ mA}$

a. When $v_{in} = 0$, $I_F = 0 = I_C$ $\quad v_{out} = +20\text{ V}$

b. When $v_{in} = +15\text{ V}$, $I_F = 9.0\overline{6}\text{ mA}$ $\quad I_C = 3.62\overline{6}\text{ mA}$

$v_{out} = 20\text{ V} - (3.62\overline{6}\text{ mA})\ (1.8\text{ k}\Omega) = 13.47\text{ V}$

c.

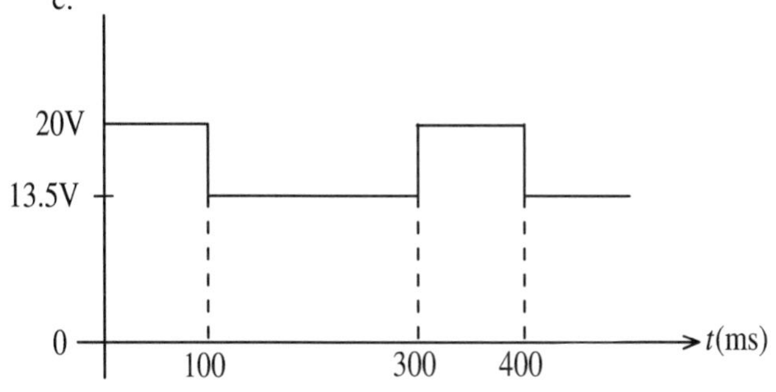

31.9 Semiconductor LASERs

25. Light Amplification through Stimulated Emission of Radiation.

31.10 Computer Analysis

27. MultiSIM 2001 does not permit simulation of this circuit.

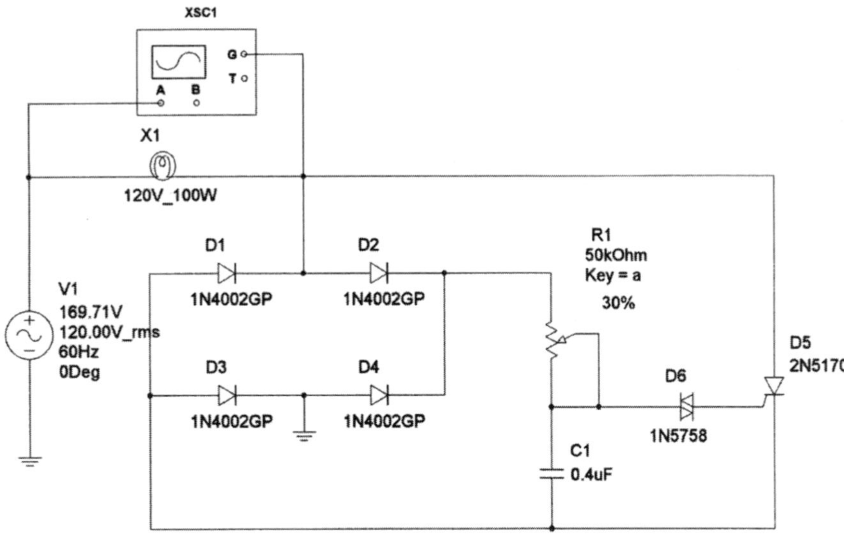

Answers to Selected Even-Numbered Questions

CHAPTER

1

Introduction

1.3 Converting Units

2. a. $27\,\cancel{\text{ft}} \times \dfrac{0.3048 \text{ m}}{\cancel{\text{ft}}} = 8.23 \text{ m}$

b. $2.3\,\cancel{\text{yd}} \times \dfrac{0.914\,\cancel{\text{m}}}{\cancel{\text{yd}}} \times \dfrac{100 \text{ cm}}{\cancel{\text{m}}} = 210.2 \text{ cm}$

c. $\text{C} = \dfrac{5}{9}(\text{F} - 32^\circ) = \dfrac{5}{9}(36^\circ - 32^\circ) = 2.22^\circ \text{ C}$

d. $18\,\cancel{\text{gallons}} \times \dfrac{3.785 \text{ liters}}{\cancel{\text{gallon}}} = 68.1 \text{ liters}$

e. $100\,\cancel{\text{ft}}^2 \times \dfrac{(0.3048)^2 \text{ m}^2}{\cancel{\text{ft}}^2} = 9.29 \text{ m}^2$

f. $124\,\cancel{\text{in}}^2 \times \dfrac{6.452 \times 10^{-4} \text{m}^2}{\cancel{\text{in}}^2} = 0.08 \text{ m}^2$

g. $47\,\cancel{\text{lb}} \times \dfrac{4.448 \text{ N}}{\cancel{\text{lb}}} = 209.1 \text{ N}$

4. $\dfrac{300\,\cancel{\text{rev}}}{\cancel{\text{min}}} \times \dfrac{\frac{1}{60}\,\cancel{\text{min}}}{\text{s}} \times \dfrac{360 \text{ deg}}{\cancel{\text{rev}}} = 1800 \text{ deg/s}$

6. $\dfrac{8 \text{ pages}}{\cancel{\text{min}}} \times \dfrac{60\,\cancel{\text{min}}}{\cancel{\text{h}}} \times \dfrac{1}{10}\,\cancel{\text{h}} = 48 \text{ pages}$

8. $\text{Circum} = 2\,\pi\,\text{r} = 2\,\pi\,(3963\,\cancel{\text{mi}}) \times \dfrac{1.609 \text{ km}}{\cancel{\text{mi}}}$

$= 40\,065 \text{ km}$

10. $16\,\cancel{\text{hand}} \times \dfrac{4\,\cancel{\text{in}}}{\cancel{\text{hand}}} \times \dfrac{1 \text{ m}}{39.37\,\cancel{\text{in}}} = 1.63 \text{ m} = 163 \text{ cm}$

12. $d = \dfrac{circumference}{\pi} = \dfrac{47 \text{ in}}{\pi} = 14.96 \text{ in}$

$d = 14.96\,\cancel{\text{in}} \times \dfrac{1 \text{ m}}{39.37\,\cancel{\text{in}}} = 0.380 \text{ m}$

$t = \dfrac{\text{distance}}{\text{velocity}} = \dfrac{0.380\,\cancel{\text{m}}}{0.12\,\cancel{\text{m}}/\text{s}} = 3.17 \text{ s}$

14. $238\,857\,\cancel{\text{mi}} \times \dfrac{1.609\,\cancel{\text{km}}}{\cancel{\text{mi}}} \times \dfrac{1000 \text{ m}}{\cancel{\text{km}}}$

$= 384\,320\,913 \text{ m}$

$t = \dfrac{384\,320\,913\,\cancel{\text{m}}}{299\,792\,458\,\cancel{\text{m}}/\text{s}} = 1.28 \text{ s}$

16. $\dfrac{2 \text{ mi}}{\text{h}} \times \dfrac{12}{60}\text{ h} + \dfrac{4\text{mi}}{\text{h}} \times 0.75 \text{ h} + \dfrac{5 \text{ mi}}{\text{h}} \times \dfrac{15}{60}\text{ h} = 4.65 \text{ mi}$

18. $\dfrac{1.5 \text{ mi}}{\text{h}} \times \dfrac{16}{60}\text{ h} + \dfrac{3.5 \text{ mi}}{\text{h}} \times t_2 + \dfrac{3 \text{ mi}}{\text{h}} \times \dfrac{12}{60}\text{ h} = 1.7 \text{ mi}$

$t_2 = 0.2 \text{ h} = 12 \text{ min}$

20. $1 \text{ hp} = \dfrac{550\,\cancel{\text{ft-lbs}}}{\text{s}} \times \dfrac{0.3048 \text{ m}}{\cancel{\text{ft}}} \times \dfrac{4.448 \text{ N}}{\cancel{\text{lb}}}$

$= \dfrac{746 \text{ N–m}}{\text{s}} = 746 \text{ J/s} = 746 \text{ W}$

1.4 Power of Ten Notation

22. a. 1.76×10^3

b. 3.78×10^1

c. 2.1×10^2

d. 1.065×10^{-10}

e. 1.25×10^2

f. 2.76×10^{-5}

24. a. $123.7 + 0.05 + 1.259 = 125.0$

b. $0.723 + 0.001 = 0.724$

c. $8695 - 383 = 8312$

d. $4.52 + 6.97 = 11.49$

26. a. $(0.452 \times 10^3)\,(6.73 \times 10^4) = 3.042 \times 10^7$

b. $(0.985 \times 10^{-2})\,(4.7 \times 10^3) = 4.630 \times 10^1$

c. $\dfrac{8.92 \times 10^{-2}}{6.73 \times 10^{-5}} = 1.325 \times 10^3$

d. $1.240 \times 10^1 - 0.236 \times 10^1 = 1.004 \times 10^1$

e. $(1.27)^3 + \dfrac{47.9}{(0.8)^2} = 7.689 \times 10^1$

f. $(-6.43 \times 10^{-1})^3 = -2.658 \times 10^{-1}$

g. $(0.05)\,(1.6 \times 10^4) = 8.000 \times 10^2$

h. $\dfrac{-0.3}{1.5 \times 10^{-4}} = -2.000 \times 10^3$

i. $\dfrac{(4.5 \times 10^{-3})^2 \times (729)^{1/3}}{(3.5 \times 10^4)^2\{[(8.72 \times 10^{-3})(47)^3] - 356\}}$

$= 2.708 \times 10^{-16}$

28. a. 349 000

b. 15.1

c. 0.02346

d. 0.0697

e. 4578.697

f. 0.0000697

30. 8.999×10^{-31} kg

32. $(299\ 792.458 \times 10^3 \text{ m/s})(1.2 \times 10^{-8} \text{ s}) = 3.598\text{m}$

34. $365 \cancel{\text{days}} \times \frac{24 \cancel{\text{h}}}{\cancel{\text{day}}} \times \frac{3600 \cancel{\text{s}}}{\cancel{\text{h}}} \times \frac{299\ 792.458 \text{ km}}{\cancel{\text{s}}}$

$= 9.45 \times 10^{12} \text{ km}$

36. $m_1 = \frac{4\,\pi\, r^3}{3} \times \text{density} = \frac{4\pi}{3}\left(5000 \text{ mi} \times \frac{1609\text{m}}{\text{mi}}\right)^3 \times \frac{25 \text{ kg}}{\text{m}^3}$

$m_1 = 5.453 \times 10^{22} \text{ kg}$

$m_2 = \frac{4\pi}{3}\left(10000 \times 10^3\text{m}\right)^3 \times \frac{12 \text{ kg}}{\text{m}^3} = 5.0265 \times 10^{22} \text{ kg}$

$F = 6.6726 \times 10^{-11} \frac{(5.453 \times 10^{22})(5.0265 \times 10^{22})}{\left(100000 \text{ mi} \times \frac{1609\text{m}}{\text{mi}}\right)^2} \text{ N} = 70.6 \times 10^{17} \text{ N}$

1.5 Prefixes

38. a. mA
    b. kV
    c. MW
    d. μs
    e. μm
    f. ms
    g. nA

40. a. 0.156 V
    b. 150 μV
    c. 47 000 W
    d. 57 kW
    e. 35 kV
    f. 35.7 μA

42. a. $700\,\mu\text{A} - 0.4 \text{ mA} = 700\,\mu\text{A} - 400\,\mu\text{A} = 300\,\mu\text{A}$ or
    $700\,\mu\text{A} - 0.4 \text{ mA} = 0.7 \text{ mA} - 0.4 \text{ mA} = 0.3 \text{ mA}$
    b. $600 \text{ MW} + 300 \times 10^4\text{W} = 600 \text{ MW} + 3 \text{ MW}$
    $= 603 \text{ MW}$

44. $1.15 \times 10^5 \text{ V} = 115 \times 10^3 \text{ V} = 115 \text{ kV}$

46. $I_4 = 1.25 \text{ mA} + 350\ \mu\text{A} + 250 \times 10^{-5} \text{ A}$
    $= 1.25 \text{ mA} + 0.35 \text{ mA} + 2.50 \text{ mA}$
    $= 4.10 \text{ mA}$

48. $39 \text{ mmfd} = 39\ \mu\mu\text{F} = 39 \times 10^{-6} \times 10^{-6} \text{ F}$
    $= 39 \times 10^{-12} \text{ F} = 39 \text{ pF}$

50. a. $0.045 \cancel{\text{C}} \times \frac{6.24 \times 10^{18} \text{electrons}}{\cancel{\text{C}}}$
    $= 2.81 \times 10^{17}$ electrons
    b. $\frac{9.36 \times 10^{19} \cancel{\text{electrons}}}{\text{s}} \times \frac{1.602 \text{ C}}{\cancel{\text{electron}}} = 15 \text{ C/s}$
    $\therefore \frac{15\text{C}}{\cancel{\text{s}}} \times 20\ \mu\cancel{\text{s}} = 300\ \mu\text{C}$

1.7 Circuit Diagrams

52.

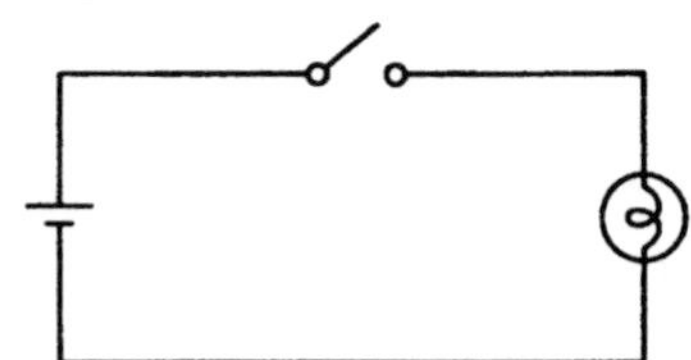

CHAPTER

2

Voltage and Current

2.1 Atomic Theory

2. a. Force is proportional to the product of charges. Therefore, the force increases by a factor of four.

   b. Force is inversely proportional to distance squared. Therefore, the force falls off to $\left(\frac{1}{3}\right)^2 = \frac{1}{9}$ of its original value.

4. The material with one valence electron.

6. a. It oxidizes less than other materials and makes better electrical contact.

   b. It is light in weight and is used for overhead power transmission lines.

2.2 The Unit of Electrical Charge: The Coulomb

8. a. $F = \frac{9 \times 10^9 (1 \times 10^{-6}\text{ C})(7 \times 10^{-6}\text{ C})}{(10 \times 10^{-3})^2}$
   $= 630\text{ N (repulsive)}$

   b. $F = \frac{9 \times 10^9 (8 \times 10^{-6})(4 \times 10^{-6})}{(0.12)^2}$
   $= 20\text{ N (attractive)}$

   c. $F = \frac{9 \times 10^9 (1.602 \times 10^{-19})^2}{(12 \times 10^{-8})^2}$
   $= 1.60 \times 10^{-14}\text{ N (repulsive)}$

   d. $F = \frac{9 \times 10^9 (1.602 \times 10^{-19})^2}{(5.3 \times 10^{-11})^2}$
   $= 8.22 \times 10^{-8}\text{ N (attractive)}$

   e. Neutron is uncharged $\therefore F = 0$

10. $F = \frac{(9 \times 10^9)(1)(1)}{(0.25)^2} = 144 \times 10^9\text{ N}$
    $144 \times 10^9\text{ N} \times \frac{1\text{ lb}}{4.448\text{ N}} \times \frac{1\text{ ton}}{2000\text{ lb}}$
    $= 16.2$ million tons

12. $1.63 \times 10^{-6}\text{ C} \times \frac{6.24 \times 10^{18}\text{ electrons}}{\text{C}}$
    $= 10.2 \times 10^{12}$ electrons

14. $47 \times 10^{-6}\text{ C} \times \frac{6.24 \times 10^{18}\text{electrons}}{\text{C}}$
    $= 293 \times 10^{12}$ electrons

16. When you slide off the chair, you strip electrons from their parent atoms. This leaves you with a net charge. Since the other person is uncharged, a potential difference exists and a shock results.

2.3 Voltage

18. $Q = 9.36 \times 10^{19}\text{ electrons} \times \frac{1.602 \times 10^{-19}\text{C}}{\text{electron}} = 15\text{ C}$

    $V = \frac{W}{Q} = \frac{600\text{ J}}{15\text{C}} = 40\text{ V}$

20. $W = QV = (20 \times 10^{-3}\text{ C})(70.3\text{V}) = 1.41\text{ J}$

22. $W = QV = (1.6 \times 10^{-19}\text{ C})(100\text{ V}) = 1.6 \times 10^{-17}\text{ J}$

2.4 Current

24. $I = \frac{Q}{t} = \frac{27\text{ C}}{9\text{s}} = 3\text{ A}$

26. $Q = It = (4\text{ A})(7 \times 10^{-3}\text{ s}) = 28\text{ mC}$

28. $t = \frac{Q}{I} = \frac{100 \times 10^{-6}\text{ C}}{25 \times 10^{-3}\text{ A}} = 4\text{ ms}$

30. a. $q_1 = 10(5) + 4 = 54\text{ C}$

    b. $q_2 = 10(8) + 4 = 84\text{ C}$

    c. $\Delta q = 30\text{ C}; \Delta t = 3\text{ s}$
    $\therefore I = \frac{\Delta q}{\Delta t} = \frac{30\text{ C}}{3\text{s}} = 10\text{ A}$

32. $Q = 312 \times 10^{19}\text{ electrons} = 500\text{ C}$
    $t = \frac{Q}{I} = \frac{500\text{ C}}{8\text{A}} = 62.5\text{ s}$

2.5 Practical DC Voltage Sources

34. DC current is current that always flows in one direction while dc voltage is voltage that does not change polarity. AC current is current that alternately changes direction while ac voltage is voltage whose polarity alternately cycles between positive and negative.

36. Charging current

Secondary battery

Battery charger

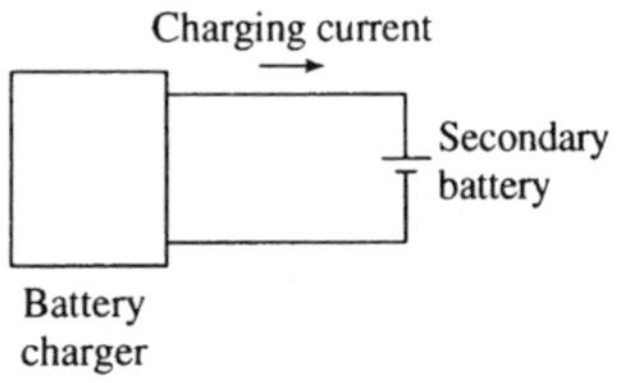

You can't charge a primary battery.

38. The capacity of the battery at the various current drains is as follows:

At 10 mA: Capacity = (10 mA)(525 h) = 5250 mAh

At 50 mA: Capacity = (50 mA)(125 h) = 6250 mAh

At 100 mA: Capacity = (100 mA)(57 h) = 5700 mAh

The capacity varies somewhat with drain, but is relatively constant. It seems to optimized for a current drain around the 50 mA region.

40. At 25°C, Capacity = (1.5 A)(17 h) = 25.5 Ah

At 5°C, Capacity = (0.9)(25.5) = 22.95 Ah

$$\text{Life} = \frac{22.95 \text{ Ah}}{0.8\text{A}} = 28.7 \text{ h}$$

2.6 Measuring Voltage and Current

42. a. 25 V
    b. 25 V
    c. 14 V
    d. –6 V

44. Voltage appears "across" components

2.7 Switches, Fuses, and Circuit Breakers

46.

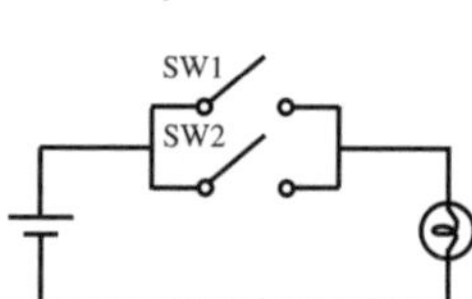

CHAPTER

3

Resistance

3.1 Resistance of Conductors

2. $L = 200 \text{ ft} = 200 \text{ ft}\left(\dfrac{0.3048\text{m}}{1\text{ft}}\right) = 60.96 \text{ m}$

a. $A = (0.25 \text{ in.})(0.25 \text{ in.})$

$= (0.0625 \text{ sq. in.})\left(\dfrac{2.54 \times 10^{-2} \text{ m}}{1\text{in.}}\right)^2$

$= 4.032 \times 10^{-5} \text{ m}^2$

$$R = \frac{12.30 \times 10^{-8}\Omega\cdot\text{m})(60.96 \text{ m})}{4.032 \times 10^{-5} \text{ m}^2} = 0.186\ \Omega$$

b. $A = \dfrac{\pi(0.125 \text{ in.})^2}{4}\left(\dfrac{2.54 \times 10^{-2} \text{ m}}{1\text{in.}}\right)^2$

$= 7.917 \times 10^{-6} \text{ m}^2$

$$R = \frac{12.30 \times 10^{-8}\Omega\cdot\text{m})(60.96 \text{ m}}{7.917 \times 10^{-6} \text{ m}^2} = 0.947\ \Omega$$

c. $A = (0.125 \text{ in.})(4.0 \text{ in.})\left(\dfrac{2.54 \times 10^{-2} \text{ m}}{1\text{in.}}\right)^2$

$= 3.226 \times 10^{-4} \text{ m}^2$

$$R = \frac{(12.30 \times 10^{-8}\ \Omega\cdot\text{m})(60.96 \text{ m})}{3.226 \times 10^{-4} \text{ m}^2} = 23.2 \text{ m}\Omega$$

4. $A = \dfrac{\pi(1.0 \times 10^{-3} \text{ m})^2}{4} = 7.853 \times 10^{-7} \text{ m}^2$

$$L = \frac{(2.0\ \Omega)(7.853 \times 10^{-7} \text{ m}^{2)}}{99.72 \times 10^{-8}\Omega\cdot\text{m}} = 1.58 \text{ m}$$

6. $R_2 = \dfrac{\rho L_2}{A_2} = \dfrac{\rho(4L_1)}{\left(\dfrac{A_1}{4}\right)} = \dfrac{16\rho L_1}{A_1} = 16R_1$

$R_2 = 16(20\ \Omega) = 320\ \Omega$

8. $A = \dfrac{\pi(0.4 \times 10^{-3} \text{ m})^2}{4} = 1.256 \times 10^{-7} \text{ m}^2$

$$\rho = \frac{357\Omega)(1.256 \times 10^{-7} \text{ m}^{2)}}{200\text{m}} = 22.4 \times 10^{-8}\Omega\cdot\text{m}$$

Material is lead.

10. a. $A = \dfrac{\pi(0.030 \text{ in.})^2}{4}\left(\dfrac{2.54 \times 10^{-2} \text{ m}}{1\text{in.}}\right)^2$

$= 4.560 \times 10^{-7} \text{ m}^2 \equiv 0.456 \text{ mm}^2$

b. $L = \dfrac{(2500\ \Omega)(4.560 \times 10^{-7} \text{ m}^2)}{12.30 \times 10^{-8}\ \Omega\cdot\text{m}} = 9270 \text{ m}$

3.2 Electrical Wire Tables

12. $L = 250 \text{ m} = 250 \text{ m}\left(\dfrac{1 \text{ ft}}{0.3048 \text{ m}}\right) = 820 \text{ ft}$

AWG 8: $R = (0.6281\dfrac{\Omega}{1000 \text{ ft}})\ (820 \text{ ft}) = 0.515\ \Omega$

AWG 2: $R = (0.1563\dfrac{\Omega}{1000\text{ft}})\ (820 \text{ ft}) = 0.128\ \Omega$

The diameter of AWG 8 is $\dfrac{3.264\text{mm}}{6.543\text{mm}} = 0.499$ (approximately half) of the diameter of AWG 2.

The resistance of AWG 8 is $\dfrac{0.515\ \Omega}{0.128\ \Omega} = 4.02$ (approximately 4 times) the diameter of AWG 2.

14. AWG 8: 40 A

AWG 4: 80 A

AWG 2: 160 A

16. AWG 26: 0.75 A

AWG 36: 0.075 A ≅ 80 mA

3.3 Resistance of Wires — Circular Mils

18. a. $A = 256 \text{ CM} = 256 \text{ CM}\left(\dfrac{\pi}{4}\dfrac{\text{sq mil}}{4 \text{ CM}}\right) = 201 \text{ sq mil}$

$$A = \frac{\pi\left[(0.016 \text{ in.})\left(\dfrac{25.4 \text{ mm}}{1 \text{ in.}}\right)\right]^2}{4} = 0.130 \text{ mm}^2$$

b. $A = 6200 \text{ CM} = 6200 \text{ CM}\left(\dfrac{\pi}{4}\dfrac{\text{sq mil}}{\text{CM}}\right) = 4870 \text{ sq mil}$

$$A = \frac{\pi(2.0 \text{ mm})^2}{4} = 3.14 \text{ mm}^2$$

c. $A = (250 \text{ mil})(6000 \text{ mil})$
$= 1\,500\,000 \text{ sq mil}$
$A = (0.25 \text{ in.})(6.0 \text{ in.})$
$= (0.25 \text{ in.})\left(\frac{25.4 \text{ mm}}{\text{in.}}\right)^2 (6.0 \text{ in.}) = 968 \text{ mm}^2$

20. a. $d = \sqrt{250 \text{ CM}} = 15.8 \text{ mil}$
$\equiv 0.0158 \text{ in.}$
$\equiv 0.402 \text{ mm}$

b. $d = \sqrt{1000 \text{ CM}} = 31.6 \text{ mil}$
$\equiv 0.0316 \text{ in.}$
$\equiv 0.803 \text{ mm}$

c. $d = \sqrt{250\,000 \text{ CM}} = 500 \text{ mil}$
$\equiv 0.500 \text{ in.}$
$\equiv 12.7 \text{ mm}$

d. $d = \sqrt{750\,000 \text{ CM}} = 866 \text{ mil}$
$\equiv 0.866 \text{ in.}$
$\equiv 22.0 \text{ mm}$

22. a. $A = \dfrac{\left(600 \frac{\text{CM}\cdot\Omega}{\text{ft}}\right)(200 \text{ ft})}{0.500\ \Omega}$
$= 240\,000 \text{ CM} \equiv 1.88 \times 10^5 \text{ sq mil}$

b. $d = \sqrt{240\,000 \text{ CM}} = 490 \text{ mil} \equiv 0.490 \text{ in.}$

24. a. $A = (30 \text{ mil})^2 = 900 \text{ CM} \equiv 707 \text{ sq mil}$

b. $L = \dfrac{(2500\ \Omega)(900 \text{ CM})}{74.0 \text{ (CM}\cdot\Omega)/\text{ft}} = 30\,400 \text{ ft } (\equiv 9270 \text{ m})$

3.4 Temperature Effects

26. At 20°C:
$R_1 = \left(\frac{2.52\Omega}{1000 \text{ ft}}\right)(200 \text{ ft})(2) = 1.008\ \Omega$
At –40°C:
$R = \dfrac{-40^\circ - (-234.5^\circ)}{20^\circ - (-234.5^\circ)}(1.008\ \Omega) = 0.770\ \Omega$
At +90°C:
$R = \dfrac{90^\circ - (-234.5^\circ)}{20^\circ - (234.5^\circ)}(1.008\ \Omega) = 1.285\ \Omega$

28. a. The material has a negative temperature coefficient since it has a lower resistance at a higher temperature.

b. $\alpha_1 = \dfrac{\left(\frac{R_2}{R_1} - 1\right)}{T_2 - T_1} = \dfrac{\left(\frac{150\ \Omega}{100\ \Omega} - 1\right)}{-25^\circ\text{C} - 20^\circ\text{C}}$
$= -0.00111(^\circ\text{C})^{-1}$

c. at 0°C:
$R_{0^\circ\text{C}} = 100\ \Omega\ [1 + (-0.0111(^\circ\text{C})^{-1})(0^\circ\text{C} - 20^\circ\text{C})]$
$= 122\ \Omega$
at –40°C:
$R_{-40^\circ\text{C}} = 100\ \Omega\ [1 + (-0.0111(^\circ\text{C})^{-1})(-40^\circ\text{C} - 20^\circ\text{C})]$
$= 167\ \Omega$

30. $R_{300^\circ\text{C}} = 500\ \Omega\ [1 + (-0.075(^\circ\text{C})^{-1})(30^\circ\text{C} - 20^\circ\text{C})]$
$= 125\ \Omega$

32.

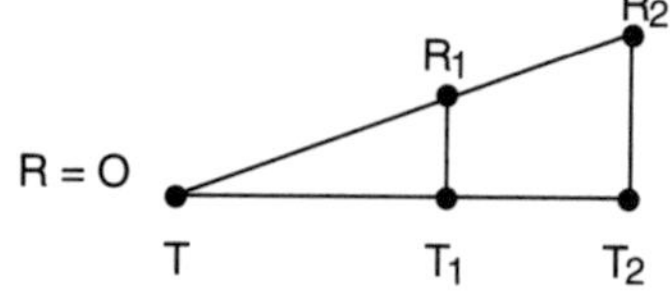

$m = \dfrac{R_2 - R_1}{T_2 - T_1}$

$\alpha_1 = \dfrac{m}{R_1} = \dfrac{R_2 - R_1}{R_1(T_2 - T_1)}$

$R_2 = \alpha_1 R_1 (T_2 - T_1) + R_1$

$R_2 = R_1\ [\ 1 + \alpha_1 (T_2 - T_1)]$

3.5 Types of Resistors

34. $R_{ab} = 200 \text{ k}\Omega - 50 \text{ k}\Omega = 150 \text{ k}\Omega$

3.6 Color Coding of Resistors

36. a. orange orange orange gold red

b. gray red brown silver

c. brown green black

d. red violet green gold

3.7 Measuring Resistance — The Ohmmeter

38. When the contacts of a switch are closed, the resistance is very low ($R \sim 0\ \Omega \equiv$ short circuit).

    When the contacts of a switch are opened, the resistance is extremely high ($R \to \infty\ \Omega \equiv$ open circuit).

40. The component is not faulty if it is a diode.

3.9 Photoconductive Cells

42. a. ~ 18 kΩ
    b. ~ 4.5 kΩ
    c. ~ 700 kΩ

3.11 Conductance

44. a. $$R = \frac{1}{62.5 \times 10^{-6}\ \text{S}} = 16\ 000\ \Omega \equiv 16\ \text{k}\Omega$$

    b. $$R = \frac{1}{2500 \times 10^{-3}\ \text{S}} = 0.4\ \Omega$$

    c. $$R = \frac{1}{5.75 \times 10^{-3}\ \text{S}} = 174\ \Omega$$

    d. $$R \frac{1}{25.0\ \text{S}} = 0.04\ \Omega \equiv 40\ \text{m}\Omega$$

46. $A = (4.0\ \text{in.})(0.25\ \text{in.}) = (4000\ \text{mil})(250\ \text{mil}) = 1 \times 10^6\ \text{sq mil} \equiv 1.273 \times 10^6\ \text{CM}$

    $$R = \frac{(17.0(\text{CM}\cdot\Omega/\text{ft})(200\ \text{ft})}{1.273 \times 10^6 \text{CM}} = 0.00267\ \Omega$$

    $$G = \frac{1}{0.00267\ \Omega} = 374\ \text{S}$$

    As temperature increases, conductance decreases (since resistance goes up).

CHAPTER

4

Ohm's Law, Power, and Energy

4.1 Ohm's Law

2. a. $R = \frac{E}{I} = \frac{50\text{ V}}{2.5\text{ A}} = 20\Omega$

b. $\frac{37.5\text{ V}}{1 \times 10^{-3}\text{ A}} = 37.5\text{ k}\Omega$

c. $\frac{2 \times 10^{3}\text{ V}}{0.1 \times 10^{3}\text{ A}} = 20\ \Omega$

d. $\frac{4 \times 10^{3}\text{ V}}{8 \times 10^{-4}\text{ A}} = 5\text{ M}\Omega$

4. $I = \frac{E}{R} = \frac{120\text{ V}}{48\ \Omega} = 2.5\text{ A}$

6. $V = IR = (3 \times 10^{-3}\text{ A})(20 \times 10^{3}\ \Omega) = 60\text{ V}$

8. $V = (50 \times 10^{-3}\text{ A})(240\ \Omega) = 12\text{ V}$

10. $R = \frac{E}{I} = \frac{12\text{ V}}{36\text{ mA}} = 0.333\text{ k}\Omega$

a. $I = \frac{18\text{ V}}{0.333\text{ k}\Omega} = 54\text{ mA}$

b. $\frac{4\text{ V}}{0.333\text{ k}\Omega} = 12\text{ mA}$

12. a. $R = 56\ \Omega \qquad I = \frac{28\text{ V}}{56\ \Omega} = 0.5\text{ A}$

b. $I = \frac{312\text{ V}}{56\ \Omega} = 5.57\text{ A}$

$\therefore$ Fuse blows and meter indicates 0

14. a. $R = 1000\ \Omega \qquad I = \frac{20\text{ V}}{1000\ \Omega} = 20\text{ mA}$

b. $R_{max} = 1000 + 10\% = 1100\ \Omega$

$\therefore I_{min} = \frac{20\text{ V}}{1100\ \Omega} = 18.2\text{ mA}$

$R_{min} = 1000 - 10\% = 900\ \Omega$

$I_{max} = \frac{20\text{ V}}{900\ \Omega} = 22.2\text{ mA}$

16. $R = \frac{V}{I} = \frac{9.6\text{ V}}{1.75\text{ A}} = 5.486\ \Omega$

The wire is AWG #22, 16.2Ω/1000 ft.

$\therefore \ell = \left(\frac{5.486\ \Omega}{16.2\ \Omega}\right)(1000\text{ ft}) = 338.6\text{ ft} = 103\text{ m}$

18.

E	2.5kΩ I(mA)	5kΩ I(mA)
0	0	0
5	2	1
10	4	2
15	6	3
20	8	4
25	10	5

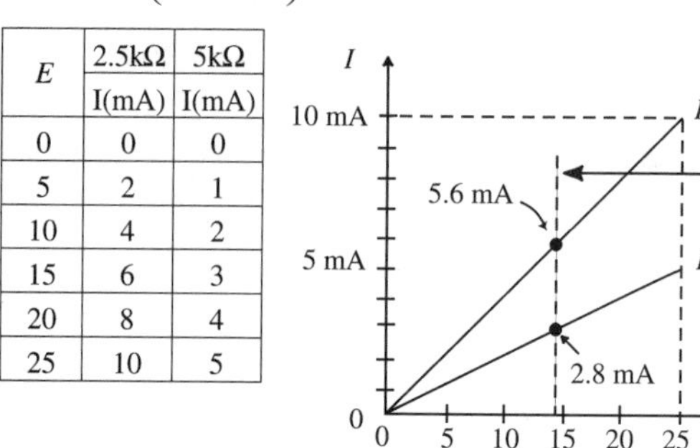

20. $I_{old} = \frac{E}{R} \qquad I_{new} = \frac{4E}{\left(\frac{R}{2}\right)} = 8\frac{E}{R} = 8\ I_{old}$

$I_{old} = \frac{I_{new}}{8} = \frac{24\text{ A}}{8} = 3\text{ A}$

22.

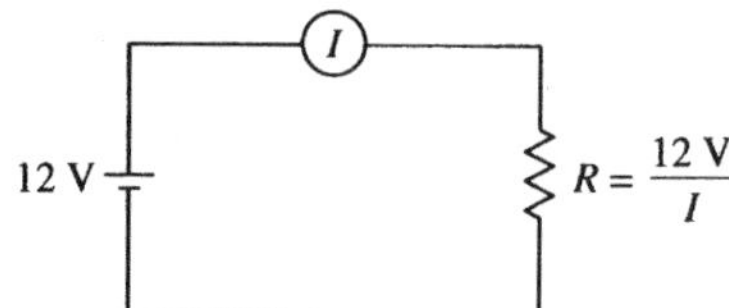

24. $R = \frac{48\text{ V}}{0.5\text{ A}} = 96\ \Omega$

#40 wire: 1080 Ω/1000 ft = 1.08 Ω/ft

$\therefore \ell = \frac{96\ \Omega}{1.08\ \Omega/\text{ft}} = 88.9\text{ ft} = 27.1\text{ m}$

4.2 Voltage Polarity and Current Direction

26. a. 0.75 A

b. –0.75 A

c. –0.75 A

d. –0.75 A

4.3 Power

28. $t = \frac{W}{P} = \frac{1470\text{ J}}{100\text{ W}} = 14.7\text{ s}$

30. $P = \frac{V^2}{R}\ \therefore R = \frac{V^2}{P} = \frac{(120\text{ V})^2}{960\text{ W}} = 15\ \Omega$

$I = \frac{V}{R} = \frac{120\text{ V}}{15\ \Omega} = 8\text{ A}$

32. $R = \frac{P}{I^2} = \frac{15\text{ W}}{(0.125)^2} = 960\ \Omega$

34. $P = \frac{V^2}{R}\ \therefore V^2 = PR = (90\text{ W})(10\Omega) = 900$

$\therefore V = 30\text{ V}$

36. $R = 2.2\text{ k}\Omega \pm 5\% = 2200 \pm 110\ \Omega$

$P_{min} = \frac{V^2}{R_{max}} = \frac{(12\text{ V})^2}{2310\ \Omega} = 62.3\text{ mW}$

$P_{max} = \frac{V^2}{R_{min}} = \frac{(12\text{ V})^2}{2090\ \Omega} = 68.9\text{ mW}$

38. a. $I = \frac{P}{E} = \frac{8\text{ W}}{12\text{ V}} = 0.667\text{ A}$

b. $R = \frac{V^2}{P} = \frac{(12\text{ V})^2}{36\text{ W}} = 4\ \Omega$

40. $P_T = 6(100\text{ W}) + 1200\text{ W} + 1500\text{ W} + 900\text{ W}$

$= 4200\text{ W}$

$I = \frac{4200\text{ W}}{120\text{ V}} = 35\text{ A}$

Therefore, the fuse "blows."

42. a. $P = \frac{V^2}{R} = \frac{(75\text{ V})^2}{560\ \Omega} = 10\text{ W}$ Yes

b. $P = I^2R = (4\text{ A})^2(3\ \Omega) = 48\text{ W}$ Yes

c. $P = VI = (40\text{ V})(0.25\text{ mA}) = 0.01\text{ W}$ No

44. $R_1 = \frac{V^2}{P_1} = \frac{(24\text{ V})^2}{192\text{ W}} = 3\ \Omega$ @ 20°C

Using the principles of Chapter 3 (see below).

$R_2 = \frac{224.5°}{254.5°}(3\ \Omega) = 2.646\ \Omega$ @ –10°C

$\therefore P_2 = \frac{(24\text{ V})^2}{2.646\ \Omega} = 218W$

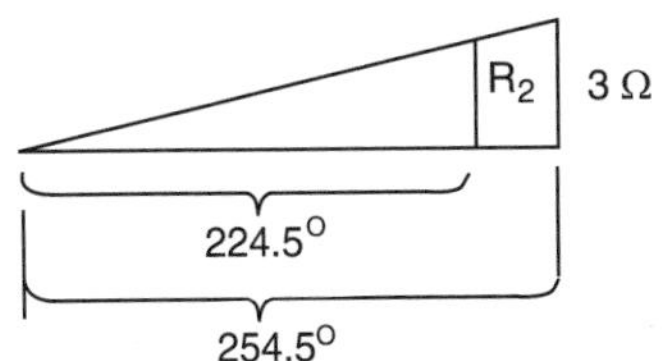

4.4 Power Direction Convention

46. a. →

b. →

c. $P = (12\text{V})\ (4.5\text{A})$

$= 54\text{W}$

48. $P = VI = (120\text{ V})(20\text{ mA}) = 2.4\text{ W}$

$W = Pt = (2.4\text{ W})\left(365\ \cancel{d} \times \frac{24\text{ h}}{\cancel{d}}\right) = 21\ 024\text{ Wh}$

$= 21.02\text{ kWh}$

Cost = (21.02 kWh)($0.09) = $1.89

50. $W = (400\text{ W})\left(\frac{15}{60}\right) + (200\text{ W})\left(\frac{30}{60}\right) = 200\text{ Wh per h}$

$W_T = \frac{200 \times 24\text{ h} \times 365}{1000} = 1752\text{ kWh}$

Cost = (1752 kWh)($0.10/kWh) = $175.20

52. $W = \frac{\text{Cost}}{\text{Cost/kWh}} = \frac{\$1.20}{\$0.08} = 15\text{ kWh}$

$P = \frac{W}{t} = \frac{15\ 000\text{ Wh}}{50\text{ h}} = 300\text{ W}$

$I = \frac{P}{V} = \frac{300\text{ W}}{120\text{ V}} = 2.5\text{ A}$

4.6 Efficiency

54. a. $P_{out} = \eta\ P_{in} = (0.85)(690\text{ W}) = 586.5\text{ W}$

b. $\frac{586.5\text{ W}}{746\text{ W/hp}} = 0.786\text{ hp}$

56. Losses = 6% $\therefore 0.06\ P_{in} = 18\text{ W}$

$\therefore P_{in} = 300\text{ W}$

$P_{out} = \eta\ P_{in} = 0.94(300\text{ W}) = 282\text{ W}$

58. a. $P_{in} = (240\text{ V})(4.5\text{ A}) = 1080\text{ W}$

$P_{out} = 3.6 \times 10^6\text{ J/h} = 3.6 \times 10^6 \frac{J}{\cancel{h}} \times \frac{1\ \cancel{h}}{3600\text{ s}}$

$= 1000\text{ J/s} = 1000\text{ W}$

$\eta = \frac{P_{out}}{P_{in}} \times 100\% = \frac{1000}{1080} \times 100\% = 92.6\%$

b. $W = (1080\text{ W})\frac{6\text{ h}}{\cancel{d}} \times 365\ \cancel{d} = 2.365 \times 10^6\text{ Wh}$

Cost = (2365 kWh)($0.09/kWh) = $212.87

60. $P_{out} = (3.8\text{ hp})\ (746\frac{\text{W}}{\text{hp}}) = 2835\text{ W}$

$P_{in} = \frac{2835}{0.87} = 3259\text{ W}$

$P_{in} = VI\ \therefore I = \frac{3259\text{ W}}{120\text{ V}} = 27.2\text{ A}$

62. For two devices as below.

$\eta_1 \times \eta_2 = \frac{\cancel{P_2}}{P_{in}} \times \frac{P_{out}}{\cancel{P_2}} = \frac{P_{out}}{P_{in}} = \eta_T.$

Continuing in this manner yields

$\eta_T = \eta_1 \times \eta_2 \times \ldots \times \eta_n.$

$P_{in} \rightarrow \boxed{\eta_1} \xrightarrow{P_2} \boxed{\eta_2} \rightarrow P_{out}$

64. $I = \frac{1600\text{ W}}{120\text{ V}} = 13.3\text{ A.}$ No.

66. New Machine:

$P_{in} = \frac{27\text{ kW}}{0.87} = 31.035\text{ kW}$

$W_{in} = (31.035\text{ kW})(8.7\text{ h}) = 270\text{ kWh per day}$

$$W_{in(Total)} = \frac{270\text{ kWh}}{\not{d}} \times 320\not{d} = 86\,400\text{ kWh}$$

Cost = \$8640

Old Machine:

$$P_{in} = \frac{27\text{ kW}}{0.72} = 37.5\text{ kW}$$

$$W_{in} = (37.5\text{ kW})(8.7\text{ h}) = 326.25\text{ kWh per day}$$

$$W_{in(Total)} = (326.25)(320) = 104\,400\text{ kWh}$$

Cost = \$10 440.00

Difference: \$1800.00

4.7 Nonlinear and Dynamic Resistance

68. a. $R_{dynamic} = \dfrac{\Delta V}{\Delta I} = \dfrac{40\text{ V}}{4\text{ A}} = 10\ \Omega$

b. $R_{dynamic} = \dfrac{\Delta V}{\Delta I} = \dfrac{40\text{ V}}{1\text{ A}} = 40\ \Omega$

c. $\Delta I = \dfrac{\Delta V}{R_{dynamic}} = \dfrac{10\text{ V}}{10\ \Omega} = 1\text{ A}$

d. $\Delta I = \dfrac{\Delta V}{R_{dynamic}} = \dfrac{20\text{ V}}{40\ \Omega} = 0.5\text{ A}$

4.8 Computer-Aided Circuit Analysis

70. Following the procedure of Sec. 4.8, create the circuit below. To run the simulation, click the MSM power ON/OFF switch. Note that the current is slightly smaller than expected. This is because the internal resistance of the ammeter defaults to 1 mΩ, which is a bit high for this circuit. Double click the ammeter symbol and set its internal resistance to 1 $\mu\Omega$. You now get the expected answer.

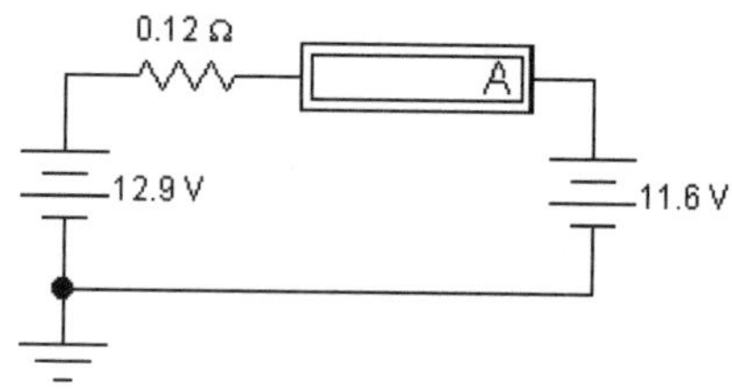

72. Let us use the Bias Point method. Following the procedure that you used to create Figure 4-29, use source VDC and build the circuit on your screen. (For Name, use problem 4-72 or a suitable name of your choosing.) Double click the default source voltage and set it to 40 V. Double click the resistor default value and set it to 20 ohms. Click the New Simulation profile icon and select Bias Point Analysis, then click OK. Click the Run icon. Following simulation, close the inactive window that appears, then click the Bias Point Current Display icon. After confirming the result, change to the next voltage/resistance pair by double clicking the source voltage and the resistor values in turn and updating them. Finally, click the run icon to run a new simulation.

If you wish, you can add ammeter IPRINT as in Figure 4-30 and repeat the solution using the DC Sweep method. We will leave this as an exercise.

74. Create the circuit following the procedure outlined for the analysis of Figure 4-32. (You do not need to set a value for the voltage on the screen, as the voltages that you enter when you set the sweep values will override it.) Include a current marker as in Figure 4-31. Now click the "New Simulation Profile" icon, enter an appropriate name, select DC Sweep, set the Source Voltage Name to V1, select Linear sweep, enter –10V for the start value, 10V for the end value and 1V for the increment. Click OK. Run the simulation and the following plot appears. Values can be read via the cursor. Negative values for current mean that the actual current is in the direction opposite to the reference arrow.

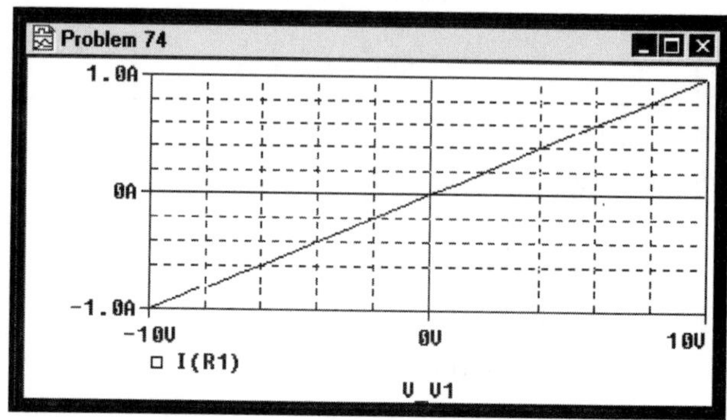

NOTE: PSpice graphic screens are printed in reversed image (i.e, in negative format) throughout this manual for improved readability.

CHAPTER

5

Series Circuits

5.2 Kirchoff's Voltage Law

2. a. −72V

   b. +160V

4. a. −0.75 A

   b. +0.75 A

6. circuit (a)

   $V_2 = (2\ \Omega)(2\ A) = 4\ V$

   $V_1 = 16\ V - 2\ V - 4\ V = 10\ V$

   $V_3 = 16\ V$

   circuit (b)

   $V_1 = \dfrac{40\ W}{4\ A} = 10\ V$

   $V_2 = 6\ V - 2\ V = 4\ V$

   $V_3 = 10\ V + 6\ V - 4\ V = 12\ V$

8. $V_3 = (40\ mA)(1.5\ k\Omega) = 60\ V$

   $V_1 = 100\ V - 30\ V - 60\ V = 10\ V$

5.3 Resistors in Series

10. circuit (a)

    $R_T = 10\ \Omega + 22\ \Omega + 47\ \Omega + 15\ \Omega = 94\ \Omega$

    circuit (b)

    $R_1 = R_2 = R_3 = 12\ k\Omega$

    $R_T = 3(12\ k\Omega) = 36\ k\Omega$

    circuit (c)

    $R_T = R_1 + R_2 + R_3$

    $36\ \Omega = 2\ R_2 + R_2 + 3(2R_2)$

    $R_2 = \dfrac{36\ \Omega}{9} = 4\ \Omega$

    $R_1 = 8\ \Omega,\ R_3 = 24\ \Omega$

12. circuit 1:

    a. $I = \dfrac{90\ V}{12\ k\Omega} = 7.5\ mA$

    b. $P_T = (90\ V)\ (7.5\ mA) = 675\ mW$

    c.

    d. $R = 12\ k\Omega - (1\ k\Omega + 4\ k\Omega + 3\ k\Omega) = 4\ k\Omega$

    e. $V_{1\ k\Omega} = (7.5\ mA)(1\ k\Omega) = 7.5\ V$

    $V_{4\ k\Omega} = (7.5\ mA)(4\ k\Omega) = 30\ V$

    $V_{3\ k\Omega} = (7.5\ mA)(3\ k\Omega) = 22.5\ V$

    $V_R = (7.5\ mA)(4\ k\Omega) = 30\ V$

    f. $P_{1\ k\Omega} = (7.5\ V)(7.5\ mA) = 56.25\ mW$

    $P_{4\ k\Omega} = (30\ V)(7.5\ mA) = 225\ mW$

    $P_{3\ k\Omega} = (22.5\ V)(7.5\ mA) = 168.75\ mW$

    $P_R = P_{4\ k\Omega} = 225\ mW$

    $P_T = 56.25\ mW + 225\ mW + 168.75\ mW + 225\ mW = 675\ mW$ (as required)

    circuit 2:

    a. $I = \dfrac{25\ V}{800\ \Omega} = 31.25\ mA$

    b. $P_T = (25\ V)(31.25\ mA) = 0.78125\ W$

    c.

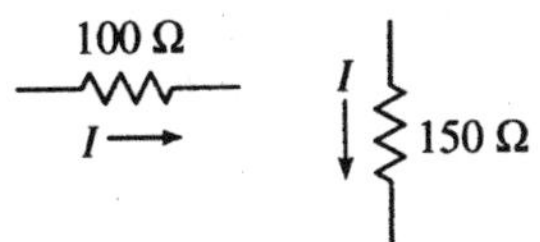

    d. $R = 800\ \Omega - (100\ \Omega + 150\ \Omega + 300\ \ \Omega) = 250\ \Omega$

    e. $V_{100\ \Omega} = (100\ \Omega)(31.25\ mA) = 3.125\ V$

    $V_{150\ \Omega} = (150\ \Omega)(31.25\ mA) = 4.6875\ V$

    $V_{300\ \Omega} = (300\Omega)(31.25\ mA) = 9.375\ V$

    $V_R = (250\ \Omega)(31.25\ mA) = 7.8125\ V$

    f. $P_{100\ \Omega} = (3.125\ V)(31.25\ mA) = 97.66\ mW$

    $P_{150\ \Omega} = (4.6875\ V)(31.25\ mA) = 146.48\ mW$

    $P_{300\ \Omega} = (9.375\ V)(31.25\ mA) = 292.97\ mW$

    $P_R = (7.8125\ V)(31.25\ mA) = 244.14\ mW$

    $P_T = 97.66\ mW + 146.48\ mW + 292.97\ mW + 244.12\ mW = 781.25\ mW$ (as reqired)

14. a. $R_T = \dfrac{45\ V}{2.5\ mA} = 18\ k\Omega$

    b. $R_2 = 18\ k\Omega - (5.6\ k\Omega + 3.3\ k\Omega) = 9.1\ k\Omega$

    c. $V_1 = (3.3\ k\Omega)(2.5\ mA) = 8.25\ V$

    $V_2 = (9.1\ k\Omega)(2.5\ mA) = 22.75\ V$

$V_3 = (5.6\text{ k}\Omega)(2.5\text{ mA}) = 14.0\text{ V}$

d. $P_1 = (2.5\text{ mA})^2(3.3\text{ k}\Omega) = 20.625\text{ mW}$

$P_2 = (2.5\text{ mA})^2(9.1\text{ k}\Omega) = 56.875\text{ mW}$

$P_3 = (2.5\text{ mA})^2(5.6\text{ k}\Omega) = 35\text{ mW}$

16. a. $V_2 + V_3 = 3.6\text{ V} - 2.2\text{ V} = 1.4\text{ V}$

$V_2 = \left(\frac{40\ \Omega}{30\ \Omega + 40\ \Omega}\right)1.4\text{ V} = 0.8\text{ V}$

$V_3 = 1.4\text{ V} - 0.8\text{ V} = 0.6\text{ V}$

b. $I = \frac{0.6\text{ V}}{30\ \Omega} = 20\text{ mA}$

c. $R_1 = \frac{2.2\text{ V}}{20\text{ mA}} = 110\ \Omega$

18. a. $R_T = 1.8\text{ k}\Omega + 3.3\text{ k}\Omega + 10\text{ k}\Omega + 8.2\text{ k}\Omega = 23.3\text{ k}\Omega$

b. $I = \frac{180\text{ V}}{23.3\text{ k}\Omega} = 7.73\text{ mA}$

c. $V_1 = (7.73\text{ mA})(1.8\text{ k}\Omega) = 13.91\text{ V}$

$V_2 = (7.73\text{ mA})(3.3\text{ k}\Omega) = 25.49\text{ V}$

$V_3 = (7.73\text{ mA})(10\text{ k}\Omega) = 77.25\text{ V}$

$V_4 = (7.73\text{ mA})(8.2\text{ k}\Omega) = 63.35\text{ V}$

d. $\Sigma V = 13.91\text{ V} + 25.49\text{ V} + 77.25\text{ V} + 63.35\text{ V}$
$= 180\text{ V}$ (as required)

e. $P_1 = (7.73\text{ mA})^2(1.8\text{ k}\Omega) = 107.4\text{ mW}$

$P_2 = (7.73\text{ mA})^2(3.3\text{ k}\Omega) = 196.9\text{ mW}$

$P_3 = (7.73\text{ mA})^2(10\text{ k}\Omega) = 596.8\text{ mW}$

$P_4 = (7.73\text{ mA})^2(8.2\text{ k}\Omega) = 489.4\text{ mW}$

f. R_1: $\frac{1}{8}$ W

R_2: $\frac{1}{4}$ W

R_3: 1 W

R_4: $\frac{1}{2}$ W

g. $P_T = (180\text{ V})(7.73\text{ mA}) = 1390.6\text{ mW}$

$\Sigma P = 107.4\text{ mW} + 196.9\text{ mW} + 596.8\text{ mW} + 489.4\text{ mW} = 1390.5\text{ mW} = P_T$ (as required)

20. a. $V_3 = (3\text{ mA})(8\text{ k}\Omega) = 24\text{ V}$

$V_2 = 36\text{ V}$ (given)

$V_1 = 72\text{ V} - (24\text{ V} + 36\text{ V}) = 12\text{ V}$

b. $R_1 = \frac{12\text{ V}}{3\text{ mA}} = 4\text{ k}\Omega$

$R_2 = \frac{36\text{ V}}{3\text{ mA}} = 12\text{ k}\Omega$

c. $P_1 = (3\text{ mA})^2(4\text{ k}\Omega) = 36\text{ mW}$

$P_2 = (3\text{ mA})^2(12\text{ k}\Omega) = 108\text{ mW}$

$P_3 = (3\text{ mA})^2(8\text{ k}\Omega) = 72\text{ mW}$

5.5 Interchanging Series Components

22. circuit (a)

$E_T = (2\text{ mA})(12\text{ k}\Omega + 6\text{ k}\Omega + 3\text{ k}\Omega) = 42\text{ V}$

$E = 42\text{ V} + 14\text{ V} = 56\text{ V}$

E 56 V

circuit (b)

$I = \sqrt{\frac{135\text{ mW}}{150\ \Omega}} = 30\text{ mA}$

$E_T = (30\text{ mA})(85\ \Omega + 150\ \Omega + 25\ \Omega) = 7.8\text{ V}$

$E = 7.8\text{ V} - 1.9\text{ V} - 3.3\text{ V} = 2.6\text{ V}$

E 2.6 V

circuit (c)

$I = \frac{3.3\text{ V}}{330\text{ k}\Omega} = 10\ \mu\text{A}$

$E_T = (10\ \mu\text{A})(330\text{ k}\Omega + 390\text{ k}\Omega + 120\text{ k}\Omega) = 8.4\text{ V}$

$E = 8.4\text{ V} + 6\text{ V} + 4\text{ V} = 18.4\text{ V}$

E
18.4 V

5.6 Voltage Divider Rule

24. $R_1 = 12\text{ k}\Omega$

$R_2 = 47\text{ k}\Omega$

$R_3 = 6500\ \Omega$

$V_1 = \left(\frac{12\text{ k}\Omega}{12\text{ k}\Omega + 47\ \Omega + 6.5\text{ k}\Omega}\right)14.2\text{ V} = 2.60\text{ V}$

$V_2 = \left(\frac{47\text{ k}\Omega}{65.5\text{ k}\Omega}\right)14.2\text{ V} = 10.19\text{ V}$

$V_3 = \left(\frac{6.5\text{ k}\Omega}{65.5\text{ k}\Omega}\right)14.2\text{ V} = 1.41\text{ V}$

$\Sigma V = 2.60\text{ V} + 10.19\text{ V} + 1.41\text{ V}$
$= 14.2\text{ V}$ (as required)

circuit (b)

$V_1 = \left(\frac{1.36\ \Omega}{430\ \Omega + 100\ \Omega + 1.36\ \Omega}\right)62\text{ V} = 0.16\text{ V}$

$$V_2 = \left(\frac{430\ \Omega}{531.36\ \Omega}\right) 62\ \text{V} = 50.17\ \text{V}$$

$$V_3 = \left(\frac{100\ \Omega}{531.36\ \Omega}\right) 62\ \text{V} = 11.67\ \text{V}$$

$\Sigma\ V = 0.16\ \text{V} + 50.17\ \text{V} + 11.67\ \text{V}$

$= 62\ \text{V}$ (as required)

26. circuit (a)

a. $V_{R1} + V_{R3} = 100\ \text{V} - 36\ \text{V} - 27\ \text{V} = 37\ \text{V}$

$V_{R1} + 4V_{R1} = 37\ \text{V}$

$V_{R1} = 7.4\ \text{V}$

$$I = \frac{36\ \text{V}}{25\ \text{k}\Omega} = 1.44\ \text{mA}$$

$$R_1 = \frac{7.4\ \text{V}}{1.44\ \text{mA}} = 5.139\ \text{k}\Omega$$

$R_3 = 4(5.139\ \text{k}\Omega) = 20.56\ \text{k}\Omega$

$$R_4 = \frac{27\ \text{V}}{1.44\ \text{mA}} = 18.75\ \text{k}\Omega$$

b. $V_{R1} = 7.4\ \text{V}$ $\quad V_{R3} = 4(7.4\ \text{V}) = 29.6\ \text{V}$

c. $P_1 = (1.44\ \text{mA})(7.4\ \text{V}) = 10.656\ \text{mW}$

$$P_2 = \frac{(36\ \text{V})^2}{25\ \text{k}\Omega} = 51.84\ \text{mW}$$

$P_3 = (1.44\ \text{mA})(29.6\ \text{V}) = 42.624\ \text{mW}$

$P_4 = (1.44\ \text{mA})(27\ \text{V}) = 38.88\ \text{mW}$

26. circuit (b)

a. $E_T = 13.5\ \text{V} - 6.2\ \text{V} = 7.3\ \text{V}$

$$R_2 = \frac{2\ \text{V}}{2\text{mA}} = 1.0\ \text{k}\Omega$$

$R_3 = 1.5\ (1.0\ \text{k}\Omega) = 1.5\ \text{k}\Omega$

$$R_T = \frac{7.3\ \text{V}}{2\ \text{mA}} = 3.65\ \text{k}\Omega$$

$R_1 = 3.65\ \text{k}\Omega - 1.0\ \text{k}\Omega - 1.5\ \text{k}\Omega = 1.15\ \text{k}\Omega$

b. $V_1 = (1.15\ \text{k}\Omega)(2.0\ \text{mA}) = 2.3\ \text{V}$

$V_3 = (1.5\ \text{k}\Omega)(2.0\ \text{mA}) = 3.0\ \text{V}$

c. $P_1 = (2\ \text{mA})^2\ (1.15\ \text{k}\Omega) = 4.6\ \text{mW}$

$P_2 = (2\ \text{mA})^2\ (1.0\ \text{k}\Omega) = 4.0\ \text{mW}$

$P_3 = (2\ \text{mA})^2\ (1.5\ \text{k}\Omega) - 6.0\ \text{mW}$

28. a. $$I = \frac{120\ \text{V}}{(36)(25\ \Omega)} = 0.133\ \text{A}$$

b. $$V = \left(\frac{1}{36}\right) 120\ \text{V} = 3.33\ \text{V}$$

c. $P = (3.33\ \text{V})(0.133\ \text{A}) = 0.444\ \text{W}$

d. $$I = \frac{120\ \text{V}}{(34)(25\ \Omega)} = 0.141\ \text{A}$$

$$V = \frac{120\ \text{V}}{34} = 3.53\ \text{V}$$

$P = (3.53\ \text{V})(0.141\ \text{A}) - 0.498\ \text{W}$

e. Since each bulb dissipates more power, life expectancy will decrease.

5.8 Voltage Subscripts

30. circuit (a)

From Problem 5-26, $V_3 = 29.6\ \text{V}$

$V_{ab} = 36\ \text{V} + 29.6\ \text{V} = 65.6\ \text{V}$

$V_{bc} = 29.6\ \text{V}$

circuit (b)

From Problem 5-26, $V_3 = 3.0\ \text{V}$ and

$V_1 = 2.3\ \text{V}$

$V_{ab} = 6.2\ \text{V} + 2\ \text{V} + 2.3\ \text{V} = 10.5\ \text{V}$

$V_{bc} = -2.30\ \text{V}$

32. circuit (a)

a. $$V_{220\ \text{k}\Omega} = \left(\frac{220\ \text{k}\Omega}{180\ \text{k}\Omega + 220\ \text{k}\Omega}\right)$$

$(6\ \text{V} + 2\ \text{V} + 10\ \text{V}) = 9.9\ \text{V}$

$$V_{180\ \text{k}\Omega} = \left(\frac{180\ \text{k}\Omega}{400\ \text{k}\Omega}\right)(18\ \text{V}) = 8.1\ \text{V}$$

b. $$I = \frac{8.1\ \text{V}}{180\ \text{k}\Omega} = 45\ \mu\text{A (left)}$$

c. $V_a = -9.9\ \text{V} + 6\ \text{V} = -3.9\ \text{V}$

circuit (b)

a. $V_{330\ \text{k}\Omega} = 0$ (since there is no current)

$V_{180\ \text{k}\Omega} = 6\ \text{V} - 2\ \text{V} = 4\ \text{V}$

b. $$I = \frac{4\ \text{V}}{180\ \text{k}\Omega} = 2.22\ \mu\text{A (left)}$$

c. $V_a = 2\ \text{V}$

5.9 Internal Resistance of Voltage Sources

34. a. $$I = \frac{22.8\ \text{V}}{10\ \Omega} = 2.28\text{A}$$

$$R_{int} = \frac{24.0\ \text{V} - 22.8\ \text{V}}{2.28\ \text{A}} = 0.526\ \Omega$$

b. Let $$R_{int} = \frac{0.526\ \Omega}{2} = 0.263\ \Omega$$

$$V_L = \left(\frac{10\ \Omega}{10.263\ \Omega}\right)(24\ \text{V}) = 23.4\ \text{V}$$

5.10 Ammeter Loading Effects

36. circuit (a)

$$I_{(NL)} = \frac{15\text{ V}}{10\text{ k}\Omega + 12\text{ k}\Omega + 18\text{ k}\Omega} = 375\ \mu\text{A}$$

$$I_{(L)} = \frac{15\text{ V}}{10\text{ k}\Omega + 12\text{ k}\Omega + 18\text{ k}\Omega + 10\ \Omega}$$

$$= 374.906\ \mu\text{A}$$

$$\text{Loading error} = \frac{375\ \mu\text{A} - 374.906\ \mu\text{A}}{375\ \mu\text{A}} \times 100\%$$

$$= 0.242\%$$

circuit (b)

$$I_{(NL)} = \frac{0.15\text{ V}}{400\ \Omega} = 375\ \mu\text{A}$$

$$I_{(L)} = \frac{0.15\text{ V}}{410\ \Omega} = 365.853\ \mu\text{A}$$

$$\text{Loading error} = \frac{375\ \mu\text{A} - 365.853\ \mu\text{A}}{375\ \mu\text{A}} \times 100\%$$

$$= 2.44\%$$

5.11 Circuit Analysis Using Computers

38.

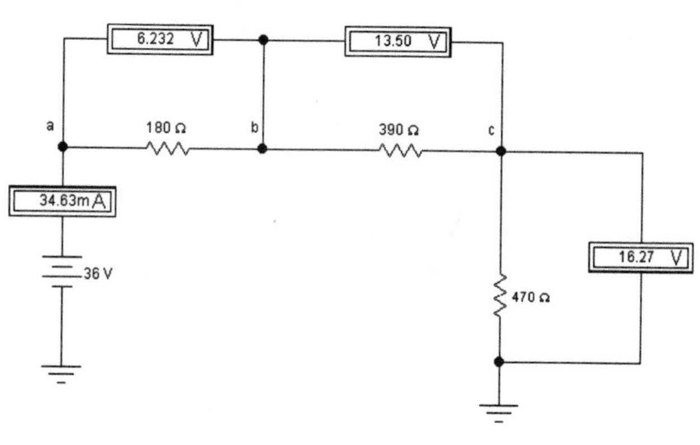

40.

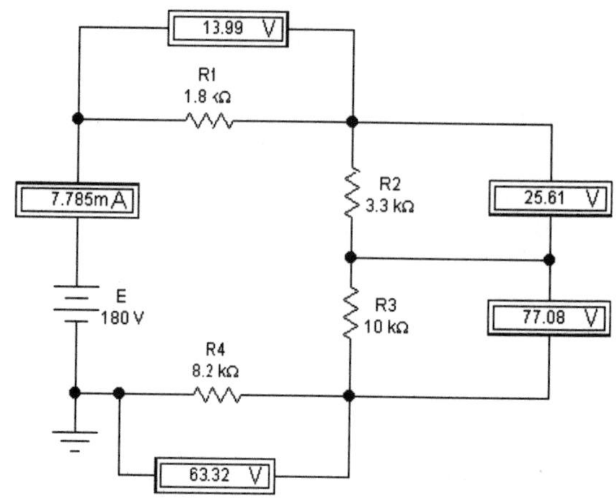

CHAPTER

6

Parallel Circuits

6.1 Parallel Circuits

2. a. R_2 and R_3 are in parallel
R_1 and R_4 are in series
b. R_1 and R_7 are in series
R_2 and R_5 are in series
R_4 and R_6 are in parallel
c. All resistors are in parallel

4.

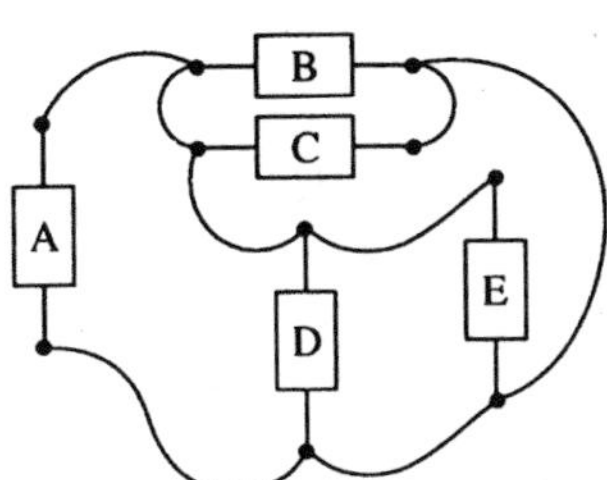

6.2 Kirchhoff's Current Law

6. $I_1 = \dfrac{5\text{ V}}{2.5\text{ k}\Omega} = 2\text{ mA (downward)}$

$I_3 = 4\text{ mA} - 2\text{ mA} = 2\text{ mA (left)}$

8. circuit (a)

$I_1 = 10\text{ mA} - 2\text{ mA} = 8\text{ mA}$

$I_2 = 2\text{ mA} + 1\text{ mA} = 3\text{ mA}$

$I_3 = 8\text{ mA} - 1\text{ mA} = 7\text{ mA}$

$I_4 = 3\text{ mA} + 7\text{ mA} = 10\text{ mA}$

circuit (b)

$I_2 = -(2\text{ A} - 1\text{ A}) = -1\text{ A}$

$I_1 = 6\text{ A} + 1\text{ A} = 7\text{ A}$

$I_3 = 1\text{ A} + 7\text{ A} = 8\text{ A}$

10. a. $I_1 = 3\text{ A}$

$I_2 = 3\text{ A} + 1\text{ A} = 4\text{ A}$

$I_3 = 6\text{ A} - 1\text{ A} = 5\text{ A}$

$I_5 = 2\text{ A} + 5\text{ A} = 7\text{ A}$

$I_4 = 4\text{ A} + 7\text{ A} = 11\text{ A}$

b. $V = (2\ \Omega)(3\text{ A}) + (3\ \Omega)(4\text{ A}) = 18\text{ V}$

c. $E = -(3\ \Omega)(4\text{ A}) - (6\ \Omega)(1\text{ A}) + (5\ \Omega)(5\text{ A}) = 7\text{ V}$

6.3 Resistors in Parallel

12. circuit (a)

$$\frac{1}{R} = 25\text{ mS} - \frac{1}{60\ \Omega} = 8.33\text{ mS}$$

$$R = \frac{1}{8.33\text{ mS}} = 120\ \Omega$$

circuit (b)

$$\frac{1}{R_1} + \frac{2}{R_1} = 500\ \mu\text{S} - \frac{1}{4\text{ k}\Omega}$$

$$\frac{1}{R_1} = \frac{250\ \mu\text{S}}{3} = 83.3\ \mu\text{S}$$

$R_1 = 12\text{ k}\Omega$ $R_2 = 6\text{ k}\Omega$

14.

$$\frac{1}{100\text{ k}\Omega} = \frac{1}{R_1} + \frac{1}{2R_1} + \frac{1}{3R_1} + \frac{1}{4R_1}$$

$$\frac{1}{100\text{ k}\Omega} = \frac{12+6+4+3}{12R_1}$$

$$R_1 = \frac{(25)(100\text{ k}\Omega)}{12} = 208.3\text{ k}\Omega$$

$R_2 = (2)(208.3\text{ k}\Omega) = 416.7\text{ k}\Omega$

$R_3 = (3)(208.3\text{ k}\Omega) = 625\text{ k}\Omega$

$R_4 = (4)(208.3\text{ k}\Omega) = 833.3\text{ k}\Omega$

16. a.

$$\frac{1}{100\text{ k}\Omega} = \frac{1}{R_1} + \frac{1}{2R_1} + \frac{1}{3R_1} + \frac{1}{(2)(3)R_1}$$

$$\frac{1}{100\text{ k}\Omega} = \frac{6+3+2+1}{6R_1}$$

$$R_1 = \frac{(12)(100\text{ k}\Omega}{6} = 200\text{ k}\Omega$$

$R_2 = 400\text{ k}\Omega$

$R_3 = 600\text{ k}\Omega$

$R_4 = 1200\text{ k}\Omega$

b.

$$I_3 = \left(\frac{1200\text{ k}\Omega}{600\text{ k}\Omega}\right)(2\text{ mA}) = 4\text{ mA}$$

$$I_2 = \left(\frac{1200\text{ k}\Omega}{400\text{ k}\Omega}\right)(2\text{ mA}) = 6\text{ mA}$$

$$I_1 = \left(\frac{1200\text{ k}\Omega}{200\text{ k}\Omega}\right)(2\text{ mA}) = 12\text{ mA}$$

c. $I = 2\text{ mA} + 4\text{ mA} + 6\text{ mA} + 12\text{ mA} = 24\text{ mA}$

18. a. $V = (2\text{ A})(10\ \Omega) = 20\text{ V}$

b. $I_2 = \dfrac{20\text{ V}}{40\ \Omega} = 0.5\text{ A}$

c. $I_3 = \dfrac{20\text{ V}}{100\ \Omega} = 0.2\text{ A}$

20. network (a)

$$R_T = \frac{(1.2\text{ M}\Omega)(4.7\text{ M}\Omega)}{1.2\text{ M}\Omega + 4.7\text{ M}\Omega} = 0.956\text{ M}\Omega$$

network (b)

$$\frac{1}{R_T} = \frac{1}{120\ \Omega} + \frac{1}{240\ \Omega} + \frac{1}{360\ \Omega} + \frac{1}{150\ \Omega} = 0.02194\text{ S}$$

$$R_T = \frac{1}{0.02194\text{ S}} = 45.6\ \Omega$$

network (c)

$R_T = 0\ \Omega$ (short circuit)

22. $R_3 = \dfrac{54\text{ V}}{0.5\text{ A}} = 108\ \Omega$

$$\frac{1}{R_1} + \frac{1}{4R_1} = \frac{1}{36\ \Omega} - \frac{1}{108\ \Omega}$$

$$\frac{5}{4R_1} = 0.01852\text{ S}$$

$$R_1 = \frac{5}{4(0.01852\text{ S})} = 67.5\ \Omega$$

$R_2 = 270\ \Omega$

$$I_1 = \frac{54\text{ V}}{67.5\ \Omega} = 0.8\text{ A}$$

$$I_2 = \frac{54\text{ V}}{270\ \Omega} = 0.2\text{ A}$$

24. $R_T \cong 1\text{ k}\Omega$

26. $\dfrac{1}{R_T} = \dfrac{1}{R_1} + \dfrac{1}{R_2} + \dfrac{1}{R_3} = \dfrac{R_2R_3 + R_1R_3 + R_1R_2}{R_1R_2R_3}$

$$R_T = \frac{R_1R_2R_3}{R_1R_2 + R_1R_3 + R_2R_3}$$

6.4 Voltage Sources in Parallel

28. $I = \dfrac{14.2\text{ V} - 9\text{ V}}{0.01\ \Omega)2} = 260\text{ A}$

The rated current of 150 A is exceeded. These batteries should not be connected in parallel to start a car.

6.5 Current Divider Rule

30. network (a)

$$I_1\left(\frac{1\text{ M}\Omega}{1\text{ k}\Omega + 1\text{ M}\Omega}\right)2\text{ mA} = 1.998\text{ mA}$$

$$I_2 = \left(\frac{1\text{ M}\Omega}{1\text{ k}\Omega + 1\text{ M}\Omega}\right)2\text{ mA} = 0.002\text{ mA}$$

network (b)

$$4\text{ mA} = \left(\frac{80\ \Omega}{80\ \Omega + 16\ \Omega}\right)I_1$$

$I_1 = 4.8\text{ mA}$

$$I_2 = \left(\frac{16\ \Omega}{80\ \Omega + 16\ \Omega}\right)4.8\text{ mA} = 0.8\text{ mA}$$

32. network (a)

$$\frac{1}{R_T} = \frac{1}{24\text{ k}\Omega} + \frac{1}{72\text{ k}\Omega} + \frac{1}{36\text{ k}\Omega} + \frac{1}{24\text{ k}\Omega}$$

$R_T = 8\text{ k}\Omega$

$$I_1 = \left(\frac{8\text{ k}\Omega}{24\text{ k}\Omega}\right)24\text{ mA} = 8\text{ mA}$$

$$I_2 = \left(\frac{8\text{ k}\Omega}{72\text{ k}\Omega}\right)24\text{ mA} = 2.67\text{ mA}$$

$I_6 = 8\text{ mA} + 2.67\text{ mA} = 10.67\text{ mA}$

$$I_3 = \left(\frac{8\text{ k}\Omega}{36\text{ k}\Omega}\right)24\text{ mA} = 5.33\text{ mA}$$

$I_4 = I_1 = 8\text{ mA}$

$I_5 = 5.33\text{ mA} + 8\text{ mA} = 13.33\text{ mA}$

network (b)

$$\frac{1}{R_T} = \frac{1}{144\ \Omega} + \frac{1}{120\ \Omega} + \frac{1}{480\ \Omega}$$

$R_T = 57.6\ \Omega$

$$I_1 = \left(\frac{57.6\ \Omega}{144\ \Omega}\right)(18\text{ A}) = 7.2\text{ A}$$

$$I_2 = \left(\frac{57.6\ \Omega}{120\ \Omega}\right)(18\text{ A}) = 8.64\text{ A}$$

$$I_3 = \left(\frac{57.6\ \Omega}{480\ \Omega}\right)(18\text{ A}) = 2.16\text{ A}$$

34. $36\ \mu\text{A} = \left(\dfrac{R_T}{300\text{ k}\Omega}\right)(48\ \mu\text{A})$

$$R_T = (300\text{ k}\Omega)\left(\frac{36\ \mu\text{A}}{48\ \mu\text{A}}\right) = 225\text{ k}\Omega$$

$$(48\ \mu\text{A} - 36\ \mu\text{A}) = \left(\frac{225\text{ k}\Omega}{R}\right)(48\ \mu\text{A})$$

$$R = \frac{(225\text{ k}\Omega)(48\ \mu\text{A})}{12\ \mu\text{R}} = 900\text{ k}\Omega$$

36. a. $R_T = \dfrac{1}{\dfrac{1}{2\text{ k}\Omega} + \dfrac{1}{8\text{ k}\Omega} + \dfrac{1}{4\text{ k}\Omega} + \dfrac{1}{6\text{ k}\Omega}} = 0.96\text{ k}\Omega$

b. $I = \dfrac{48\text{ V}}{0.96\text{ k}\Omega} = 50\text{ mA}$

c. $I_1 = \left(\dfrac{0.96\text{ k}\Omega}{2\text{ k}\Omega}\right)(50\text{ mA}) = 24\text{ mA}$

$$I_2 = \left(\frac{0.96\text{ k}\Omega}{8\text{ k}\Omega}\right)(50\text{ mA}) = 6\text{ mA}$$

$$I_3 = \left(\frac{0.96\text{ k}\Omega}{4\text{ k}\Omega}\right)(50\text{ mA}) = 12\text{ mA}$$

$$I_4 = \left(\frac{0.96\text{ k}\Omega}{6\text{ k}\Omega}\right)(50\text{ mA}) = 8\text{ mA}$$

d. 24 mA + 6 mA + 12 mA + 8 mA = 50 mA

6.6 Analysis of Parallel Circuits

38. a. $$R_T = \frac{1}{\frac{1}{5.6\text{ k}\Omega} + \frac{1}{3.9\text{ k}\Omega} + \frac{1}{4.3\text{ k}\Omega} + \frac{1}{2.7\text{ k}\Omega}} = 0.9635\text{ k}\Omega$$

$$I = \frac{270\text{ V}}{0.9635\text{ k}\Omega} = 280.2\text{ mA}$$

b. $$I_1 = \frac{270\text{ V}}{5.6\text{ k}\Omega} = 48.2\text{ mA}$$

$$I_2 = \frac{270\text{ V}}{3.9\text{ k}\Omega} = 69.2\text{ mA}$$

$$I_3 = \frac{270\text{ V}}{4.3\text{ k}\Omega} = 62.8\text{ mA}$$

$$I_4 = \frac{270\text{ V}}{2.7\text{ k}\Omega} = 100\text{ mA}$$

$I_6 = 62.8\text{ mA} + 100\text{ mA} = 162.8\text{ mA}$

$I_5 = 69.2\text{ mA} + 162.8\text{ mA} = 232.0\text{ mA}$

c. 48.2 mA + 69.2 mA + 62.8 mA + 100 mA = 280.2 mA

d. $P_T = (270\text{ V})(280.2\text{ mA}) = 75.65\text{ W}$

$P_1 = (48.2\text{ mA})^2(5.6\text{ k}\Omega) = 13.01\text{ W}$

$P_2 = (69.2\text{ mA})^2(3.9\text{ k}\Omega) = 18.68\text{ W}$

$P_3 = (62.8\text{ mA})^2(4.3\text{ k}\Omega) = 16.96\text{ W}$

$P_4 = (100\text{ mA})^2(2.7\text{ k}\Omega) = 27.00\text{ W}$

13.01 W + 18.68 W + 16.96 W + 27.00 W = 75.65 W

40. a. $$R_T = \frac{1}{\frac{1}{1.8\text{ k}\Omega} + \frac{1}{2\text{ k}\Omega} + \frac{1}{3\text{ k}\Omega}}$$

$$I_5 = \frac{30\text{ V}}{0.72\text{ k}\Omega} = 41.67\text{ mA}$$

$$I_3 = \frac{30\text{ V}}{1.8\text{ k}\Omega} = 16.67\text{ mA}$$

$$I_1 = \frac{30\text{ V}}{2\text{ k}\Omega} = 15\text{ mA}$$

$$I_2 = \frac{30\text{ V}}{3\text{ k}\Omega} = 10\text{ mA}$$

$I_4 = 10.0\text{ mA} + 15\text{ mA} = 25.0\text{ mA}$

b. $P_1 = (15\text{ mA})^2(2\text{ k}\Omega) = 450\text{ mW}$

$P_2 = (10\text{ mA})^2(3\text{ k}\Omega) = 300\text{ mW}$

$P_3 = (16.67\text{ mA})^2(1.8\text{ k}\Omega) = 500\text{ mW}$

c. $P_T = (30\text{ V})(41.67\text{ mA}) = 1250\text{ mW}$

450 mW + 300 mW + 500 mW = 1250 mW

42. $R_1 = 2700\ \Omega$

$R_2 = 3900\ \Omega$

$R_3 = 200\ \Omega$

$R_4 = 330\ \Omega$

$$P_1 = \frac{(20\text{ V})^2}{2700\ \Omega} = 0.148\text{ W (use }\tfrac{1}{4}\text{ W)}$$

$$P_2 = \frac{(20\text{ V})^2}{3900\ \Omega} = 0.103\text{ W (use }\tfrac{1}{8}\text{ W)}$$

$$P_3 = \frac{(20\text{ V})^2}{200\ \Omega} = 2.00\text{ W (use 2 W)}$$

$$P_4 = \frac{(20\text{ V})^2}{330\ \Omega} = 1.21\text{ W (use 2 W)}$$

44. a. $$R_1 = \frac{(120\text{ V})^2}{1000\text{ W}} = 14.4\ \Omega$$

$$R_T = \frac{120\text{ V}}{15\text{ A}} = 8\ \Omega$$

$$\frac{1}{R_3} = \frac{1}{8\ \Omega} - \frac{1}{14.4\ \Omega} - \frac{1}{24\ \Omega} \quad \rightarrow R_3 = 72\ \Omega$$

b. If R_3 is increased, R_T will increase and current will decrease.

6.7 Voltmeter Loading Effects

46. a. $$V_{ab}\text{ (loaded)} = \left(\frac{1\text{ M}\Omega}{1\text{ M}\Omega + 2\text{ M}\Omega}\right)30\text{ V} = 10\text{ V}$$

V_{ab} (no load) = 30 V

$$\text{load effect} = \frac{30\text{ V} - 10\text{ V}}{30\text{ V}} \times 100\% = 66.7\%$$

48. $$V_{ab} = \left(\frac{10\text{ M}\Omega}{10\text{ M}\Omega + 1\text{ M}\Omega}\right)(25.2\text{ V}) = 22.9\text{ V}$$

6.8 Computer Analysis

50. 

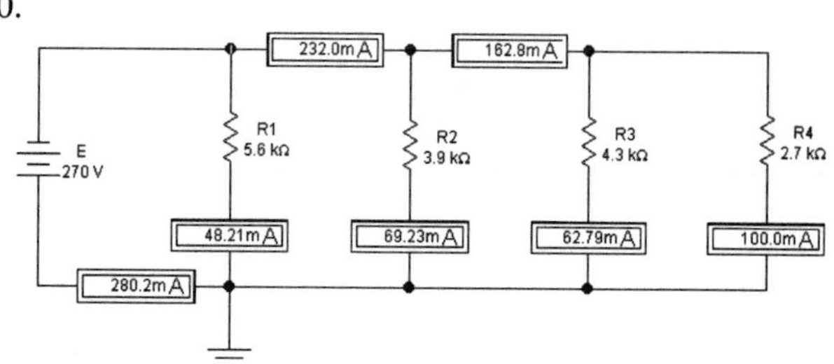

54.

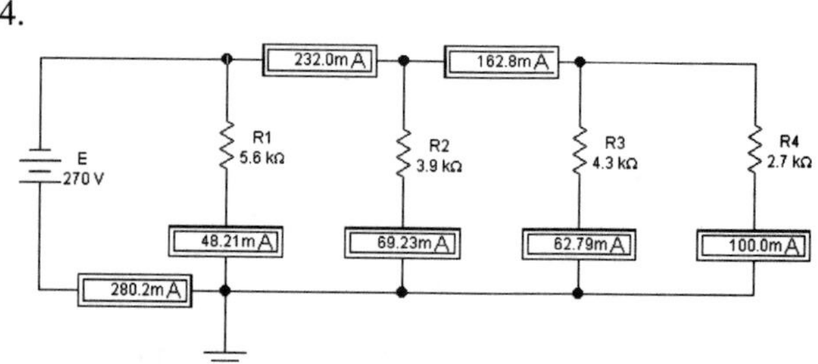

52.

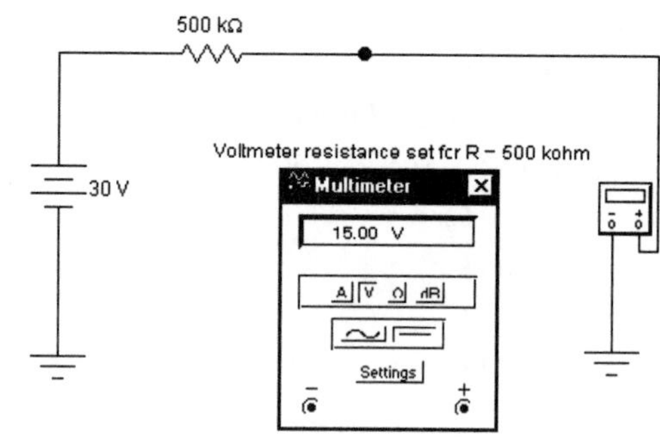

CHAPTER

7

Series-Parallel Circuits

7.1 The Series-Parallel Network

2. network (a)

$R_T = (R_1 \| R_2) + (R_3 \| R_4) + (R_5 \| R_6)$

network (b)

$R_T = R_1 \| (R_2 + R_3) \| (R_4 + R_5 + R_6)$

4. network (a)

$R_{T_1} = R_1 \| (R_2 + R_3)$

$R_{T_2} = R_4 + R_3 \| (R_1 + R_2)$

network (b)

$R_{T_1} = R_1 \| (R_2 + R_3 \| [R_4 + R_5])$

$R_{T_2} = R_5 \| (R_4 + [R_1 + R_2] \| R_3)$

6. a.

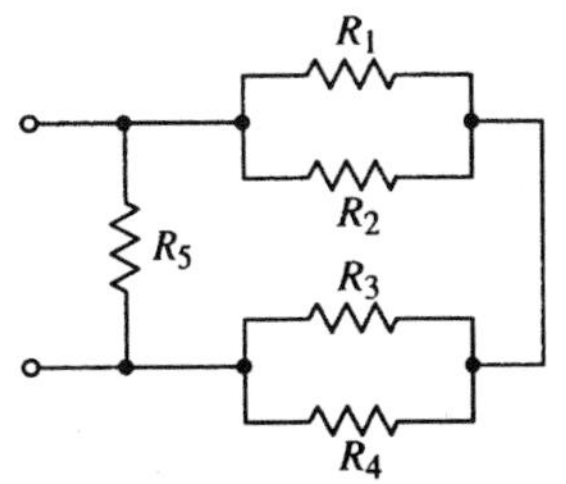

b.

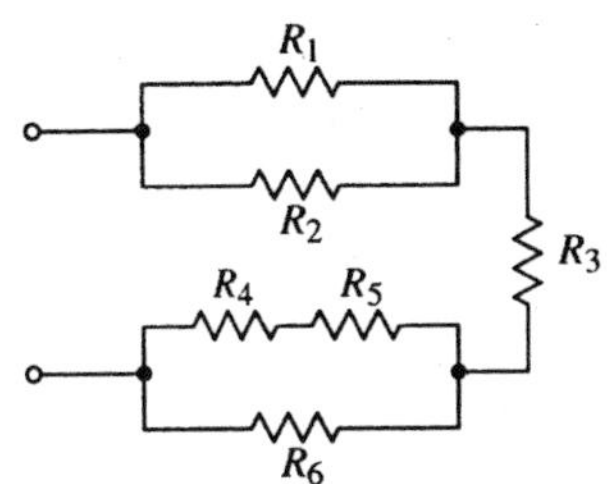

7.2 Analysis of Series-Parallel Circuits

8. network (a):

$R_T = (1\text{ k}\Omega + 1\text{ k}\Omega) \| (1\text{ k}\Omega + [1\text{ k}\Omega + 1\text{ k}\Omega] \| 1\text{ k}\Omega)$
$= 0.909\text{ k}\Omega$

network (b):

$R_T = (1\text{ k}\Omega) \| (1\text{ k}\Omega + 1\text{ k}\Omega + 1\Omega) \| (1\text{ k}\Omega + 1\text{ k}\Omega \| [1\text{ k}\Omega + 1\text{ k}\Omega]) = 0.517\text{ k}\Omega$

10. $R_{ab} = 30\ \Omega + 20\ \Omega + [(160\ \Omega + 40\ \Omega) \| 50\ \Omega + 50\ \Omega] \| 100\ \Omega = 97.37\ \Omega$

$R_{bc} = 20\ \Omega + [50\ \Omega \| (100\ \Omega + 50\ \Omega) + 40\ \Omega] \| 160\ \Omega = 72.21\ \Omega$

12. a. $R_T = 2\text{ k}\Omega + 4\text{ k}\Omega \| [5\text{ k}\Omega + 9\text{ k }\Omega \| (3\text{ k }\Omega + 8\text{ k}\Omega)] = 4.853\text{ k}\Omega$

b. $I_T = \dfrac{36\text{ V}}{4.853\text{ k}\Omega} = 7.418\text{ mA}$

$I_4 = \left(\dfrac{9.95\text{ k}\Omega}{4\text{ k}\Omega + 9.95\text{ k}\Omega}\right)(7.418\text{ mA}) = 5.291\text{ mA}$

$I_3 = \left(\dfrac{4\text{ k}\Omega}{4\text{ k}\Omega + 9.95\text{ k}\Omega}\right)(7.418\text{ mA}) = 2.127\text{ mA}$

$I_1 = \left(\dfrac{3\text{ k}\Omega + 8\text{ k}\Omega}{9\text{ k}\Omega + 3\text{ k}\Omega + 8\text{ k}\Omega}\right)(2.127\text{ mA}) = 1.170\text{ mA}$

$I_2 = \left(\dfrac{9\text{ k}\Omega}{9\text{ k}\Omega + 3\text{ k}\Omega + 8\text{ k}\Omega}\right)(2.127\text{ mA}) = 0.957\text{ mA}$

c. $V_{ab} = (9\text{ k}\Omega)(1.170\text{ mA}) = 10.53\text{ V}$

$V_{bc} = (5\text{ k}\Omega)(2.127\text{ mA}) + (2\text{ k}\Omega)(7.418\text{ V}) = 25.47\text{ V}$

$V_{cd} = -36\text{ V} + (8\text{ k}\Omega)(0.957\text{ mA}) = -28.34\text{ V}$

14. a. $R_T = 60\ \Omega \| 40\ \Omega \| (12\ \Omega + 10\ \Omega \| 40\ \Omega) = 10.91\ \Omega$

$I_T = 11\text{ A}$

$I_5 = \dfrac{120\text{ V}}{60\ \Omega} = 2\text{ A}$

$I_1 = \dfrac{120\text{ V}}{40\ \Omega} = 3\text{ A}$

$I_2 = \dfrac{120\text{ V}}{20\ \Omega} = 6\text{ A}$

$I_3 = \left(\dfrac{40\ \Omega}{40\ \Omega + 10\ \Omega}\right)6\text{ A} = 4.8\text{ A}$

$I_4 = \left(\dfrac{10\ \Omega}{40\ \Omega + 10\ \Omega}\right)6\text{ A} = 1.2\text{ A}$

b. $V_{ab} = -(10\ \Omega)(2\text{ A}) + (12\ \Omega)(6\text{ A}) + (15\ \Omega)(1.2\text{ A}) = 10\text{ V}$

$V_{bc} = -(15\ \Omega)(1.2\text{ A}) - (12\ \Omega)(6\text{ A}) = -90\text{ V}$

c. $P_T = (120\text{ V})(11\text{ A}) = 1320\text{ W}$

$P_1 = (3\text{ A})^2(40\ \Omega) = 360\text{ W}$

$P_2 = (6\text{ A})^2(12\ \Omega) = 432\text{ W}$

$P_3 = (4.8\text{ A})^2(10\ \Omega) = 230.4\text{ W}$

$P_4 = (1.2\text{ A})^2(5\ \Omega) = 7.2\text{ W}$

$P_5 = (2\text{ A})^2(30\ \Omega) = 120\text{ W}$

$P_6 = (1.2\text{ A})^2(15\ \Omega) = 21.6\text{ W}$

$P_7 = (1.2\text{ A})^2(20\ \Omega) = 28.8\text{ W}$

$P_8 = (2\text{ A})^2(10\ \Omega) = 40\text{ W}$

$P_9 = (2\text{ A})^2(20\ \Omega) = 80\text{ W}$

$\sum_{n=1}^{9} P_n = 1320\text{ W}$ (as required)

16. a. When $R_x = 0\ \Omega$:

$R_T = 50\ \Omega + 500\ \Omega \| 1000\ \Omega = 383.3\ \Omega$

$I_1 = \dfrac{10\text{ V}}{383.3\ \Omega} = 26.09\text{ mA}$

$I_2 = \left(\dfrac{1000\ \Omega}{1000\ \Omega + 500\ \Omega}\right)26.09\text{ mA} = 17.39\text{ mA}$

$I_3 = \left(\dfrac{500\ \Omega}{1500\ \Omega}\right)26.09\text{ mA} = 8.70\text{ mA}$

When $R_x = 5\text{ k}\Omega$:

$R_T = 50\ \Omega + 500\ \Omega \| 6000\ \Omega = 511.5\ \Omega$

$I_1 = \dfrac{10\text{ V}}{511.5\ \Omega} = 19.55\text{ mA}$

$I_2 = \left(\dfrac{6000\ \Omega}{6000\ \Omega + 500\ \Omega}\right)19.55\text{ mA} = 18.05\text{ mA}$

$I_3 = \left(\dfrac{500\ \Omega}{6500\ \Omega}\right)19.55\text{ mA} = 1.50\text{ mA}$

b. When $R_x = 0\ \Omega$: $V_{ab} = (0.4\text{ k}\Omega)(17.39\text{ mA}) = 6.96\text{ V}$

When $R_x = 5\text{ k}\Omega$:

$V_{ab} = (0.4\text{ k}\Omega)(18.05\text{ mA}) - (5\text{ k}\Omega)(1.50\text{ mA})$

$= -0.28\text{ V}$

7.3 Applications of Series-Parallel Circuits

18. a. Voltage across R_2 without zener diode connected.

$V_2 = \left(\dfrac{80\ \Omega}{80\ \Omega + 140\ \Omega}\right)30\text{ V} = 16.2\text{ V}$

Since V_2 is greater than $V_z = 6.2$ V, the zener diode will operate.

$I_1 = \dfrac{30\text{ V} - 6.2\text{ V}}{140\ \Omega} = 170\text{ mA}$

$I_2 = \dfrac{6.2\text{ V}}{80\ \Omega} = 77.5\text{ mA}$

$I_z = 170\text{ mA} - 77.5\text{ mA} = 92.5\text{ mA}$

$P_z = (92.5\text{ mA})(6.2\text{ V}) = 573.5\text{ mW}$

The zener diode is likely to be destroyed since $P_z > 250$ mW.

b. $I_1 = \dfrac{30\text{ V} - 6.2\text{ V}}{280\ \Omega} = 85\text{ mA}$

$I_z = 85\text{ mA} - 77.5\text{ mA} = 7.5\text{ mA}$

$P_z = (7.5\text{ mA})(6.2\text{ V}) = 46.5\text{ mW}$

The zener diode will not be destroyed since $P_z < 250$ mW.

20. $R_{\max} = \left(\dfrac{20\text{ V} - 5.6\text{ V}}{5.6\text{ V}}\right)(80\ \Omega) = 205.7\ \Omega$

Maximum zener diode current

$I_z\,(\max) = \dfrac{1000\text{ mW}}{5.6\text{ V}} = 178.6\text{ mA}$

$I_1 = \dfrac{5.6\text{ V}}{80\ \Omega} = 70\text{ mA}$

$R_{\min} = \dfrac{20\text{ V} - 5.6\text{ V}}{178.6\text{ mA} + 70\text{ mA}} = 57.9\ \Omega$

22. $2.0\text{ V} - (10\text{ k}\Omega)I_B - 0.6\text{ V} - (750\ \Omega)I_E = 0.\text{V}$

$I_E \cong 100 I_B$

$I_B = \dfrac{2.0\text{ V} - 0.6\text{ V}}{10\text{ k}\Omega + 75\text{ k}\Omega} = 16.47\ \mu\text{A}$

$I_C = (100)(16.47\ \mu\text{A}) = 1.647\text{ mA} \cong I_E$

$V_B = -0.6\text{ V} - (750\ \Omega)(1.647\text{ mA}) = 1.84\text{ V}$

$V_{CE} = -16\text{ V} + (3.9\text{ k}\Omega + 0.75\text{ k}\Omega)(1.65\text{ mA})$

$= -8.33\text{ V}$

24. a. $I_D = 10\text{ mA}\left[\dfrac{-2.5\text{ V}}{-5.0\text{ V}}\right]^2 = 7.071\text{ mA}$

$V_G = 0\text{ V}$ (since $I_G = 0$)

b. $V_S = +2.5\text{ V}$

$R_S = \dfrac{2.5\text{ V}}{7.071\text{ mA}} = 354\ \Omega$

$R_D = \dfrac{15\text{ V} - 6.0\text{ V} - 2.5\text{ V}}{7.071\text{ mA}} = 919\ \Omega$

26. $V_B = \left(\dfrac{20\text{ k}\Omega}{20\text{ k}\Omega + 20\text{ k}\Omega}\right)16\text{ V} = 8.0\text{ V}$

$V_E = 8.0\text{ V} - 0.7\text{ V} = 7.3\text{ V}$

$I_E = \dfrac{7.3\text{ V}}{2\text{ k}\Omega} = 3.65\text{ mA} \cong I_C$

$V_{CE} = 16\text{ V} - 7.3\text{ V} = 8.7\text{ V}$

7.4 Potentiometers

28. a. When $R_2 = 0\ \Omega$: $V_L = 0$ V

When $R_2 = 10\text{ k}\Omega$:

$R_T = 20\text{ k}\Omega + 10\text{ k}\Omega \| 30\text{ k}\Omega = 27.5\text{ k}\Omega$

$V_L = V_{ac} = \left(\dfrac{7.5\text{ k}\Omega}{27.5\text{ k}\Omega}\right)(36\text{ V}) = 9.82\text{ V}$

$V_L = 0\text{ V} \rightarrow 9.82V$

b. When $R_2 = 2.5\text{ k}\Omega$:

$R_T = 20\text{ k}\Omega + 7.5\text{ k}\Omega + 2.5\text{ k}\Omega \| 30\text{ k}\Omega = 29.8\text{ k}\Omega$

$V_L = V_{bc} = \left(\dfrac{2.31\text{ k}\Omega}{29.8\text{ k}\Omega}\right)(36\text{ V}) = 2.79\text{ V}$

When the load is removed:

$$V_L = \left(\frac{2.5\text{ k}\Omega}{30\text{ k}\Omega}\right)36\text{ V} = 3.0\text{ V}$$

30. $$V_L = \left(\frac{50\ \Omega \| R_2}{50\ \Omega \| R_2 + 100\ \Omega \| R_1}\right)24\text{ V}$$

But $R_1 = 1000\ \Omega - R_2$

$$\frac{6\text{ V}}{24\text{ V}} = \frac{\dfrac{(R_2)(50\ \Omega)}{R_2 + 50\ \Omega}}{\dfrac{(R_2)(50\ \Omega)}{R_2 + 50\ \Omega} + \dfrac{(1000\ \Omega - R_2)(100\ \Omega)}{1100\ \Omega - R_2}}$$

$12.5\ R_22 - 17\ 500\ R_2 + 1\ 250\ 000 = 0$

$R_2 = 75.5\ \Omega$

$R_1 = 924.5\ \Omega$

32. $$V_{\text{out}} = \left(\frac{10\text{ k}\Omega \| R_2}{10\text{ k}\Omega \| R_2) + (10\text{ k}\Omega \| R_1) + 10\text{ k}\Omega}\right)120\text{ V}$$

But $R_1 = 10\text{ k}\Omega - R_2$

$$\frac{40\text{ V}}{120\text{ V}} = \frac{\dfrac{(10\text{ k}\Omega)R_2}{10\text{ k}\Omega + R_2}}{\dfrac{(10\text{ k}\Omega)R_2}{10\ \Omega + R_2} + \dfrac{10\text{ k}\Omega(10\text{ k}\Omega - R_2)}{20\text{ k}\Omega - R_2} + 10\text{ k}\Omega}$$

$300\ R_2 = 3000\text{ k}\Omega$

$R_2 = 10\text{ k}\Omega$

$R_1 = 0$

34. When $R_L = 0\ \Omega$:

$V_{\text{out}} = 0\text{ V}$

When $R_L = 500\ \Omega$:

$R_T = 2\text{ k}\Omega + 1\text{ k}\Omega \| 0.5\text{ k}\Omega = 2.33\text{ k}\Omega$

$$V_{\text{out}} = \left(\frac{0.333\text{ k}\Omega}{2.333\text{ k}\Omega}\right)72\text{ V} = 10.29\text{ V}$$

When $R_L = 1000\ \Omega$:

$R_T = 2\text{ k}\Omega + 1\text{ k}\Omega \| 1\text{ k}\Omega = 2.5\text{ k}\Omega$

$$V_{\text{out}} = \left(\frac{0.5\text{ k}\Omega}{2.5\text{ k}\Omega}\right)72\text{ V} = 14.4\text{ V}$$

7.5 Loading Effects of Instruments

36. a.

$$V_{1.2\text{ M}\Omega}\text{ (unloaded)} = \left(\frac{1.2\text{ M}\Omega}{1.2\text{ M}\Omega + 0.3\text{ M}\Omega}\right)60\text{ V} = 48.0\text{ V}$$

$$V_{1.2\text{ M}\Omega}\text{ (loaded)} = \left(\frac{1.2\text{ M}\Omega \| 0.1\text{ M}\Omega}{1.2\text{ M}\Omega \| 0.1\text{ M}\Omega + 0.3\text{ M}\Omega}\right)60\text{ V} = 14.1\text{ V}$$

$$\text{Loading error} = \frac{48.0\text{ V} - 14.1\text{ V}}{48.0\text{ V}} \times 100\% = 70.6\%$$

b.

$$V_{1.2\text{ M}\Omega}\text{ (loaded)} = \left(\frac{1.2\text{ M}\Omega \| 0.1\text{ m}\Omega}{1.2\text{ M}\Omega \| 0.04\text{ M}\Omega + 0.3\text{ M}\Omega}\right)60\text{ V} = 6.86\text{ V}$$

$$\text{Loading error} = \frac{48.0\text{ V} - 6.86\text{ V}}{48.0\text{ V}} \times 100\% = 85.7\%$$

The meter will not be damaged on the 20 V range. However, loading error is increased.

38. The unloaded currents in the circuit are:

$$I_1 = \frac{0.2\text{ V}}{5.6\ \Omega + 6.8\ \Omega \| 3.9\ \Omega} = 24.75\text{ mA}$$

$$I_2 = \left(\frac{3.9\ \Omega}{3.9\ \Omega + 6.8\ \Omega}\right)24.75\text{ mA} = 9.02\text{ mA}$$

$$I_3 = \left(\frac{6.8\ \Omega}{3.9\ \Omega + 6.8\ \Omega}\right)24.75\text{ mA} = 15.73\text{ mA}$$

a. Loaded currents:

$$I_1 = \frac{0.2\text{ V}}{5.6\ \Omega + 0.5\ \Omega + 6.8\ \Omega \| 3.9\ \Omega} = 23.31\text{ mA}$$

when the ammeter is placed in the I_2 branch.

$R_T = 5.6\ \Omega + (6.8\ \Omega + 0.5\ \Omega) \| 3.9\ \Omega = 8.14\ \Omega$

$$I_T = \frac{0.2\text{ V}}{8.14\ \Omega} = 24.56\text{ mA}$$

$$I_2 = \left(\frac{3.9\ \Omega}{3.9\ \Omega + 6.8\ \Omega + 0.5\ \Omega}\right)24.56\text{ mA} = 8.55\text{ mA}$$

when the ammeter is placed in the I_3 branch.

$R_T = 5.6\ \Omega + 6.8\ \Omega \| (3.9\ \Omega + 0.5\ \Omega) = 8.27\ \Omega$

$$I_T = \frac{0.2\text{ V}}{8.27\ \Omega} = 24.18\text{ mA}$$

$$I_3 = \left(\frac{68\ \Omega}{6.8\ \Omega + 3.9\ \Omega + 0.5\ \Omega}\right)24.18\text{ mA} = 14.68\text{ mA}$$

b. For I_1: loading effect $= \dfrac{24.8\text{ mA} - 23.3\text{ mA}}{24.8\text{ mA}} 100\%$

$= 6.05\%$

For I_2: loading effect $= \dfrac{9.04\text{ mA} - 8.55\text{ mA}}{9.02\text{ mA}} \times 100\%$

$= 5.21\%$

For I_3: loading effect $= \dfrac{15.73\text{ mA} - 14.68\text{ mA}}{15.73\text{ mA}} \times 100\%$

$= 6.68\%$

7.6 Circuit Analysis Using Computers

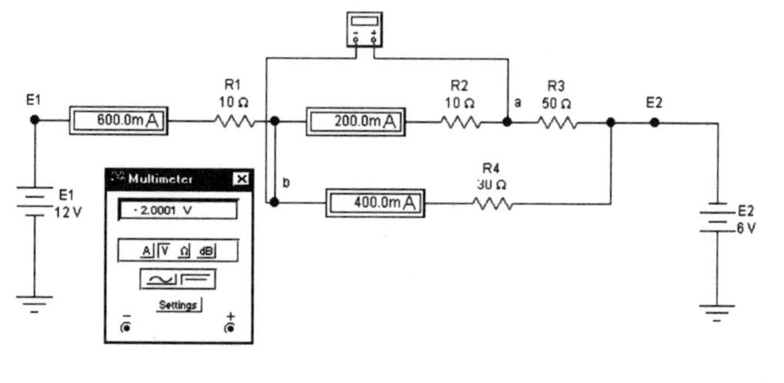

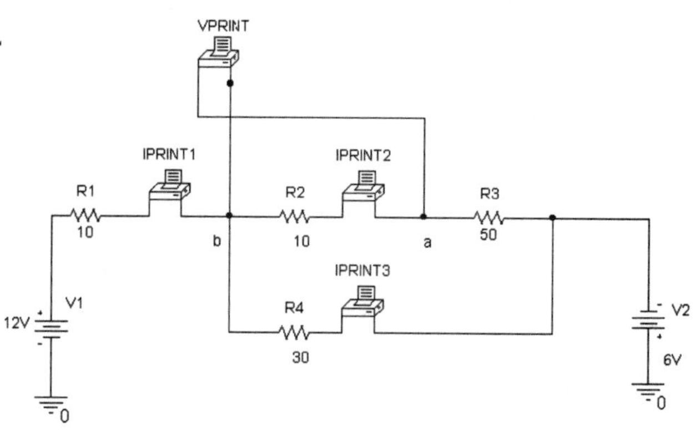

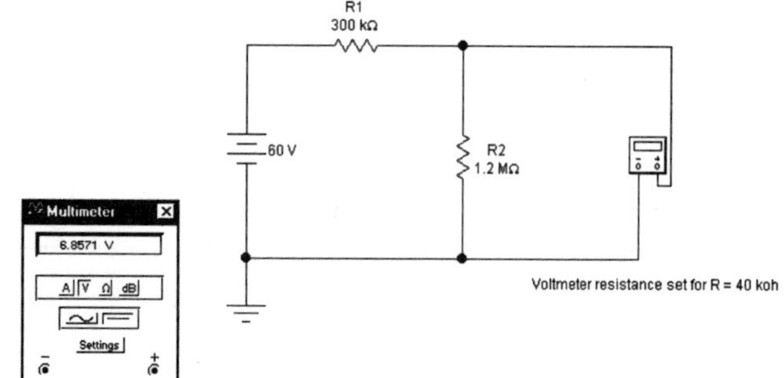

$V_{ab} = -2.00$ V

$I_1 = 0.60$ A

$I_2 = 0.20$ A

$I_3 = 0.40$ A

CHAPTER

8

Methods of Analysis

8.1 Constant Current Sources

2. $V_{4\,k\Omega} = 30\text{ V}$

$V_{2\,k\Omega} = (2\text{ k}\Omega)(5\text{ mA}) = +10\text{ V}$

$V_S = 10\text{ V} + 30\text{ V} = 40\text{ V}$

4. a. $V_2 = \left(\dfrac{5\text{ k}\Omega}{3\text{ k}\Omega + 5\text{ k}\Omega}\right)5\text{V} = 3.125\text{ V}$

$V_S = 5\text{ V}$

b. $I_3 = \dfrac{5\text{ V}}{2\text{ k}\Omega} = 2.5\text{ mA}$

$I = 3.0\text{ mA} + 2.5\text{ mA} = 5.5\text{ mA}$

6. a. $R_T = 20\ \Omega + 30\ \Omega \| (20\ \Omega + 40\ \Omega) = 40\ \Omega$

$V_S = (0.4\text{ A})(40\ \Omega) = 16\text{ V}$

$V_1 = (20\ \Omega)(0.4\text{ A}) = 8\text{ V}$

$V_2 = -16\text{ V} + 8\text{ V} = -8\text{ V}$

b. $I_4 = \left(\dfrac{30\ \Omega}{30\ \Omega + 20\ \Omega + 40\ \Omega}\right)400\text{ mA}$

$= 133.3\text{ mA}$

8. $P_T = (16\text{ V})(0.4\text{ A}) = 6.4\text{ W}$

$P_1 = (0.4\text{ A})^2(20\ \Omega) = 3.2\text{ W}$

$P_2 = \dfrac{(8\text{ V})^2}{30\ \Omega} = 2.13\text{ W}$

$P_3 = (0.1333\text{ A})^2(20\ \Omega) = 0.36\text{ W}$

$P_4 = (0.1333\text{ A})^2(40\ \Omega) = 0.71\text{ W}$

$P_1 + P_2 + P_3 + P_4 = 6.4\text{ W} = P_T$

8.2 Source Conversions

10. 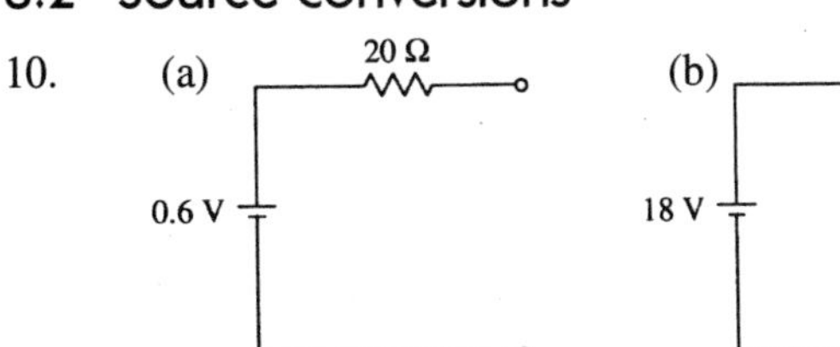

12. Perform a source conversion.

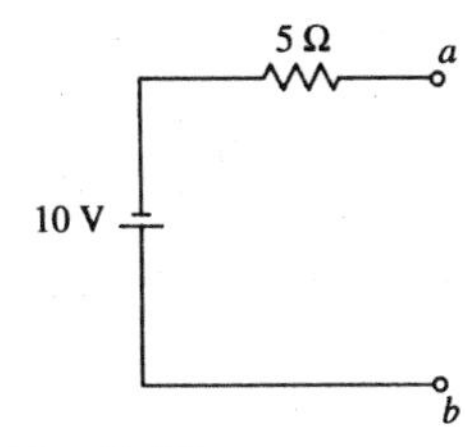

$I_2 = \dfrac{10\text{ V} + 30\text{ V}}{5\ \Omega + 3\ \Omega + 7\ \Omega} = 2.667\text{ A}$

$V_{ab} = (2.667\text{ A})(5\ \Omega) - 10\text{ V} = 3.333\text{ V}$

14. a. 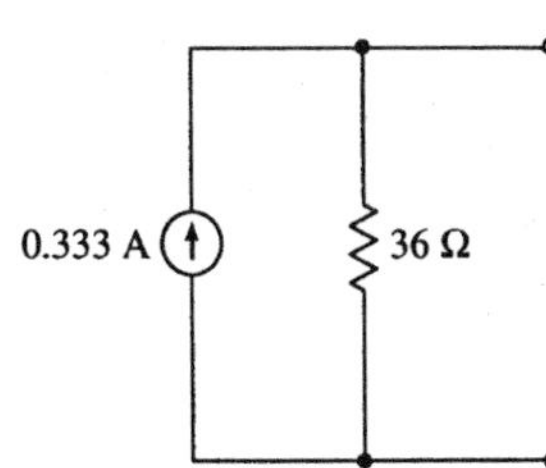

b. $R_T = 36\ \Omega \| 40\ \Omega \| 60\ \Omega = 14.4\ \Omega$

$I = \left(\dfrac{14.4\ \Omega}{60\ \Omega}\right)(0.333\text{ A} - 2\text{ A}) = -0.40\text{ A}$

c. $V_{ab} = (-0.40\text{ A})(60\ \Omega) = -24.0\text{ V}$

8.3 Current Sources in Parallel and Series

16. 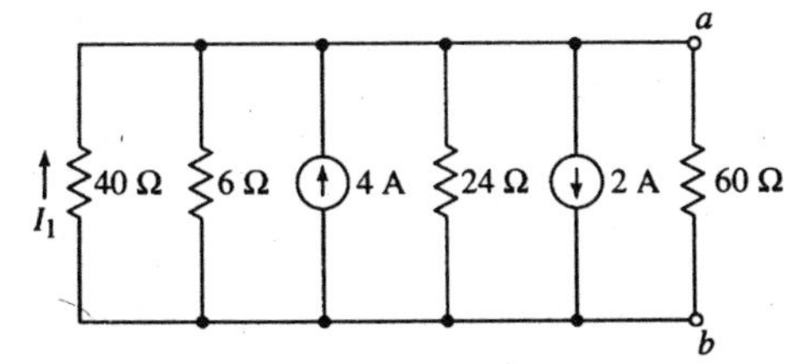

$R_T = 40\ \Omega \| 6\ \Omega \| 24\ \Omega \| 60\ \Omega = 4\ \Omega$

$I_1 = \left(\dfrac{4\ \Omega}{40\ \Omega}\right)(2\text{ A} - 4\text{ A}) = -0.2\text{ A}$

$V_{ab} = (4\text{ A} - 2\text{ A})(4\ \Omega) = 8.0\text{ V}$

18. a.

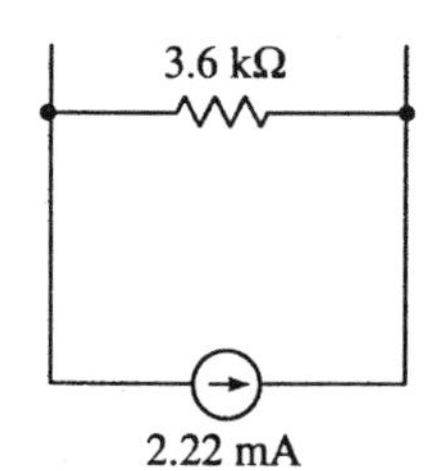

$$I_2 = \left(\frac{3.6\ \Omega}{3.6\ \Omega + 2.4\ \Omega}\right)(3.0\text{ mA} + 2.22\text{ mA}) = 3.13\text{ mA}$$

b. $V_{ab} = -(2.4\text{ k}\Omega)(3.13\text{ mA}) = -7.52\text{ V}$

8.4 Branch Current Analysis

20. a.
$8\text{ V} - (20\ \Omega)I_1 - (10\ \Omega)I_4 = 0$
$(10\ \Omega)I_4 - 2\text{ V} - (10\ \Omega)I_2 + 6\text{ V} = 0$ } KVL
$I_1 = 0.4\text{ A} + I_4 + I_2$ KCL
$20\,I_1 + 0\,I_2 + 10\,I_4 = 8\text{ A}$
$0\,I_1 - 10\,I_2 + 10\,I_4 = -4\text{ A}$
$I_1 - I_2 - I_4 = 0.4\text{ A}$

$$I_1 = \frac{\begin{vmatrix} 8 & 0 & 10 \\ -4 & -10 & 10 \\ 0.4 & -1 & -1 \end{vmatrix}}{\begin{vmatrix} 20 & 0 & 10 \\ 0 & -10 & 10 \\ 1 & -1 & -1 \end{vmatrix}} = 0.48\text{ A}$$

b. $V_{ab} = -2\text{ V} - (4\ \Omega + 16\ \Omega)(0.48\text{ A}) + 8\text{ V} = -3.6\text{ V}$

22. a.
$(6.7\ \Omega)I_1 + 3.3\ \Omega)I_4 = 8\text{ V}$
$(1.0\ \Omega)I_3 = 3\text{ V}$ } KVL
$2\text{ A} + I_1 = I_4$
$I_2 = I_3 + I_1$ } KCL

Note: $I_3 = \dfrac{3\text{ V}}{1\ \Omega} = 3\text{ A}$

$6.7I_1 + 0I_2 + 3.3I_4 = 8\text{A}$
$I_1 + 0I_2 - I_4 = -2\text{ A}$
$-I_1 + I_2 + 0I_4 = 3\text{ A}$

b.

$$I_1 = \frac{\begin{vmatrix} 8 & 0 & 3.3 \\ -2 & 0 & -1 \\ 3 & 1 & 0 \end{vmatrix}}{\begin{vmatrix} 6.7 & 0 & 3.3 \\ 1 & 0 & -1 \\ -1 & 1 & 0 \end{vmatrix}} = \frac{1.4}{10} = 0.14\text{ A}$$

$$I_2 = \frac{\begin{vmatrix} 6.7 & 8 & 3.3 \\ 1 & -2 & -1 \\ -1 & 3 & 0 \end{vmatrix}}{10} = \frac{31.4}{10} = 3.14\text{A}$$

c. $V_{ab} = -(6.7\ \Omega)(0.14\text{ A}) + 8\text{ V} = 7.062\text{ V}$

24. Redraw the circuit.

a.

KVL Equations:
$2\text{ V} - (40\ \Omega)\,I - (60\ \Omega)\,I_3 - 12\text{ V} = 0$
$12\text{ V} + (60\ \Omega)\,I_3 - (80\ \Omega)\,I_2 + 8\text{ V} = 0$
KCL Equation:
$I - I_2 - I_3 = 0$
Linear equations:
$40\,I + 0\,I_2 + 60\,I_3 = -10\text{ A}$
$0\,I - 80\,I_2 + 60\,I_3 = -20\text{ A}$
$I - I_2 - I_3 = 0$

b.

$$I = \frac{\begin{vmatrix} -10 & 0 & 60 \\ -20 & -80 & 60 \\ 0 & -1 & -1 \end{vmatrix}}{\begin{vmatrix} 40 & 0 & 60 \\ 0 & -80 & 60 \\ 1 & -1 & -1 \end{vmatrix}} = \frac{-200}{10\,400} = -19.23\text{ mA}$$

c. $V_{ab} = -(40\ \Omega)(-0.01923\text{ A}) + 2\text{ V} = 2.77\text{ V}$

8.5 Mesh (Loop) Analysis

26. Convert current source to a voltage source.

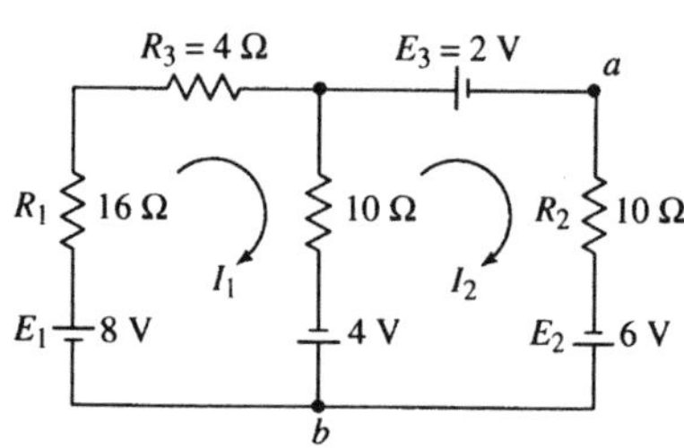

$30I_1 - 10I_2 = 12\text{ A}$
$-10I_1 + 20I_2 = 0$

$$I_1 = \frac{\begin{vmatrix} 12 & -10 \\ 0 & 20 \end{vmatrix}}{\begin{vmatrix} 30 & -10 \\ -10 & 20 \end{vmatrix}} = \frac{240}{500} = 0.48\text{ A}$$

28. Convert the current source to an equivalent voltage source.

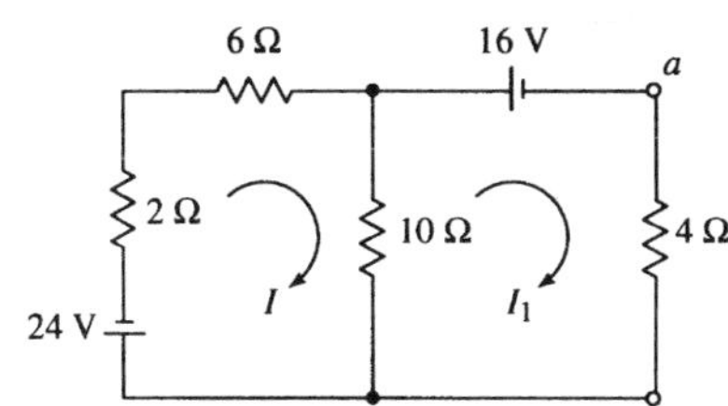

$18\,I - 10I_1 = -24$ A

$-10\,I + 14\,I_1 = -16$ A

$$I = \frac{\begin{vmatrix} -24 & -10 \\ -16 & 14 \end{vmatrix}}{\begin{vmatrix} 18 & -10 \\ -10 & 14 \end{vmatrix}} = \frac{-496}{152} = -3.26 \text{ A}$$

$$I_1 = \frac{\begin{vmatrix} 18 & -24 \\ -10 & -16 \end{vmatrix}}{152} = \frac{-528}{152} = -3.47 \text{ A}$$

$I_2 = -I = 3.26$ A

$V_{ab} = (-3.47 \text{ A})(4\ \Omega) = -13.89$ V

30. Convert current sources into equivalent voltage sources.

Mesh analysis is *not* necessary.

$$I_1 = \frac{18 \text{ V} - 8 \text{ V} - 8 \text{ V}}{12\ \Omega} = 0.167 \text{ A}$$

$V_{ab} = -(0.167 \text{ A})(6\ \Omega) + 18 \text{ V} = 17$ V

Current through the 6 Ω resistor (in the original circuit) is

$$I_{6\,\Omega} = \frac{17 \text{ V}}{6\ \Omega} = 2.83 \text{ A (downward)}$$

32. Loop equations: $5I_1 - 3I_2 + 0I_3 = 9$ mA

$-3I_1 + 7I_2 + 0I_3 = -6$ mA

$0I_1 + 0I_2 + 4I_3 = -3$ mA

$$I_1 = \frac{\begin{vmatrix} 9 & -3 & 0 \\ -6 & 7 & 0 \\ -3 & 0 & 4 \end{vmatrix}}{\begin{vmatrix} 5 & -3 & 0 \\ -3 & 7 & 0 \\ 0 & 0 & 4 \end{vmatrix}} = \frac{180}{104} = 1.731 \text{ mA}$$

$$I_2 = \frac{\begin{vmatrix} 5 & 9 & 0 \\ -3 & -6 & 0 \\ 0 & -3 & 4 \end{vmatrix}}{104} = \frac{-12}{104} = -0.115 \text{ mA}$$

$$I_3 = \frac{-3 \text{ mA}}{4} = -0.75 \text{ mA}$$

8.6 Nodal Analysis

34.
$$\left(\frac{1}{20\ \Omega} + \frac{1}{30\ \Omega}\right)V_a - \left(\frac{1}{30\ \Omega}\right)V_b = 40 \text{ mA} + 60 \text{ mA}$$

$$-\left(\frac{1}{30\ \Omega}\right)V_a + \left(\frac{1}{30\ \Omega} + \frac{1}{50\ \Omega}\right)V_b = -25 \text{ mA} - 60 \text{ mA}$$

$(0.08\overline{3}\text{ S})V_a - (0.0\overline{3}\text{ S})V_b = 100$ mA

$-(0.0\overline{3}\text{ S})V_a + (0.05\overline{3}\text{ S})\,V_b = -85$ mA

$$V_a = \frac{\begin{vmatrix} 0.1 & -0.0\overline{3} \\ -0.085 & 0.05\overline{3} \end{vmatrix}}{\begin{vmatrix} 0.08\overline{3} & -0.0\overline{3} \\ -0.0\overline{3} & 0.05\overline{3} \end{vmatrix}} = \frac{0.0025}{0.00\overline{3}}$$

$$V_b = \frac{\begin{vmatrix} 0.08\overline{3} & 0.1 \\ -0.0\overline{3} & -0.085 \end{vmatrix}}{0.00\overline{3}} = \frac{-0.00375}{0.00\overline{3}} = -1.125 \text{ V}$$

$V_{ab} = 0.75 \text{ V} - (-1.125 \text{ V}) = 1.875$ V

36. Convert the voltage source into a current source (R_3 is shorted).

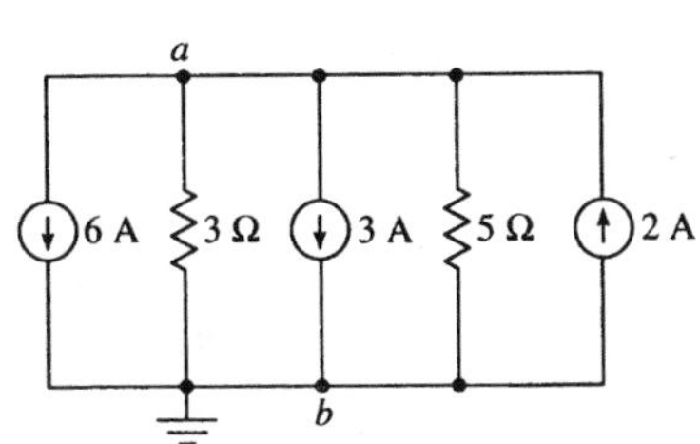

$$\left(\frac{1}{3\ \Omega} + \frac{1}{5\ \Omega}\right)V_a = (-6 \text{ A} - 3 \text{ A} + 2 \text{ A})$$

$$V_{ab} = V_a = \frac{-7 \text{ A}}{0.5\overline{3}\text{ S}} = -13.125 \text{ V}$$

38. Source conversions.

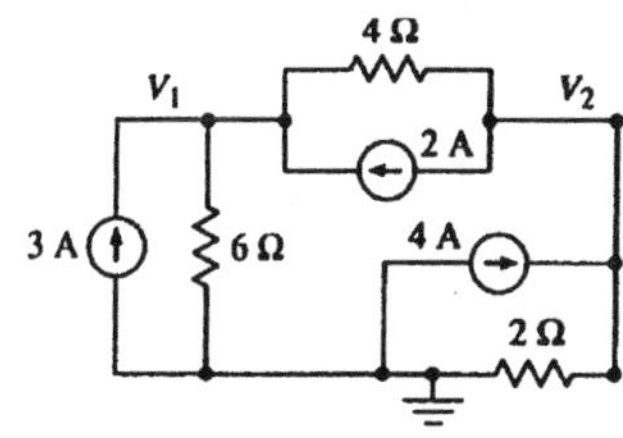

$$+\left(\frac{1}{6\ \Omega} + \frac{1}{4\ \Omega}\right)V_1 - \left(\frac{1}{4\Omega}\right)V_2 = 3 \text{ A} + 2 \text{ A}$$

$$-\left(\frac{1}{4\ \Omega}\right)V_1 + \left(\frac{1}{4\ \Omega} + \frac{1}{2\ \Omega}\right)V_2 = 4 \text{ A} - 2 \text{ A}$$

$+(0.41\overline{6}\text{ S})V_1 - (0.250\text{ S})V_2 = 5$ A

$-(0.250\text{ S})V_1 + (0.750\text{ S})V_2 = +2$ A

$V_1 = 17.00 \text{ V} = V_{6\Omega}$ **D** $= 0.250$

$V_2 = 8.3$ V

8.7 Delta-Wye (Pi-Tee) Conversion

40. circuit (a)

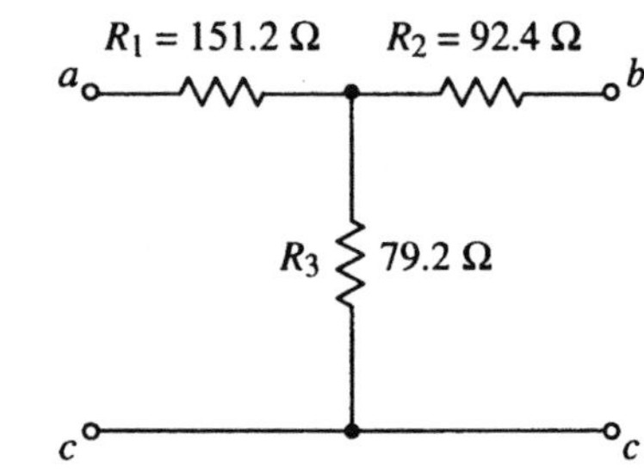

$$R_1 = \frac{(360\ \Omega)(420\ \Omega)}{360\ \Omega + 420\ \Omega + 220\ \Omega} = 151.2\ \Omega$$

$$R_2 = \frac{420\ \Omega)(220\ \Omega)}{1000\ \Omega} = 92.4\ \Omega$$

$$R_3 = \frac{(360\ \Omega)(220\ \Omega)}{1000\ \Omega} = 79.2\ \Omega$$

circuit (b)

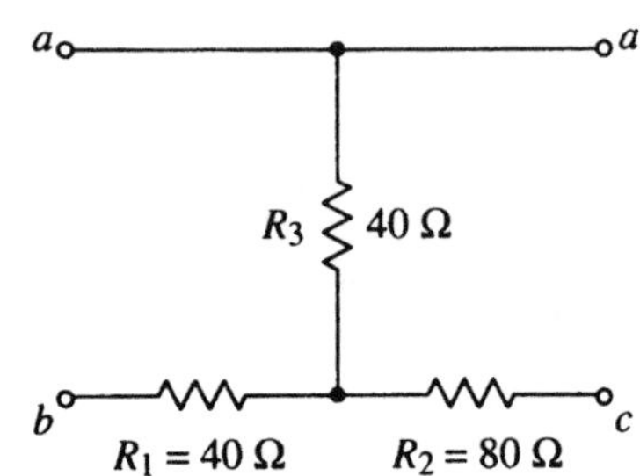

$$R_1 = \frac{100\ \Omega)(200\ \Omega)}{100\ \Omega + 200\ \Omega + 200\ \Omega} = 40\ \Omega = R_3$$

$$R_2 = \frac{(200\ \Omega)(200\ \Omega)}{500\ \Omega} = 80\ \Omega$$

42.

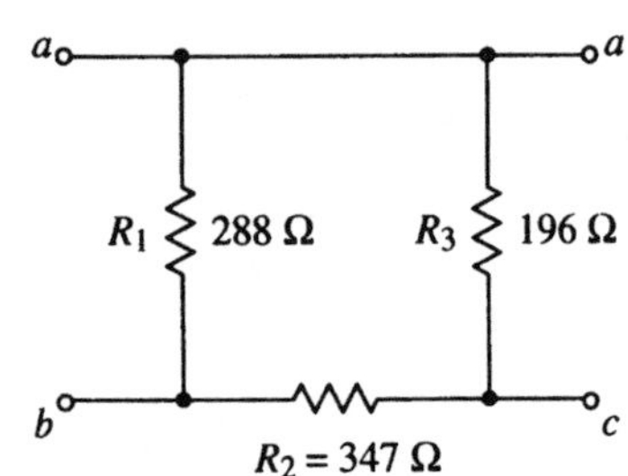

$$R_1 = \frac{(68\ \Omega)(120\ \Omega) + (68\ \Omega)(82\ \Omega)(+ (120\ \Omega)(82\ \Omega)}{82\ \Omega}$$

$= 288\ \Omega$

$$R_2 = \frac{(68\ \Omega)(120\ \Omega) + (68\ \Omega)(82\ \Omega)(+ (120\ \Omega)(82\ \Omega)}{68\ \Omega}$$

$= 347\ \Omega$

$$R_3 = \frac{(68\ \Omega)(120\ \Omega) + (68\ \Omega)(82\ \Omega)(+ (120\ \Omega)(82\ \Omega)}{120\ \Omega}$$

$= 196\ \Omega$

circuit (b)

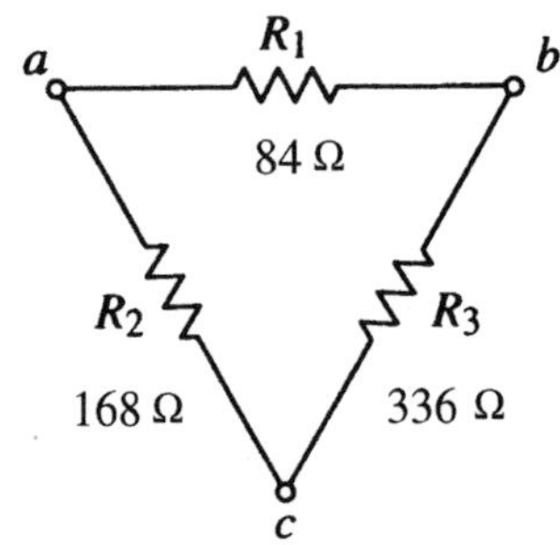

$$R_1 = \frac{(24\ \Omega)(96\ \Omega) + (24\ \Omega)(48\ \Omega)(+ (48\ \Omega)(96\ \Omega)}{96\ \Omega}$$

$= 84\ \Omega$

$$R_2 = \frac{(24\ \Omega)(96\ \Omega) + (24\ \Omega)(48\ \Omega)(+ (48\ \Omega)(96\ \Omega)}{48\ \Omega}$$

$= 168\ \Omega$

$$R_3 = \frac{(24\ \Omega)(96\ \Omega) + (24\ \Omega)(48\ \Omega)(+ (48\ \Omega)(96\ \Omega)}{24\ \Omega}$$

$= 336\ \Omega$

44. Equivalent circuit:

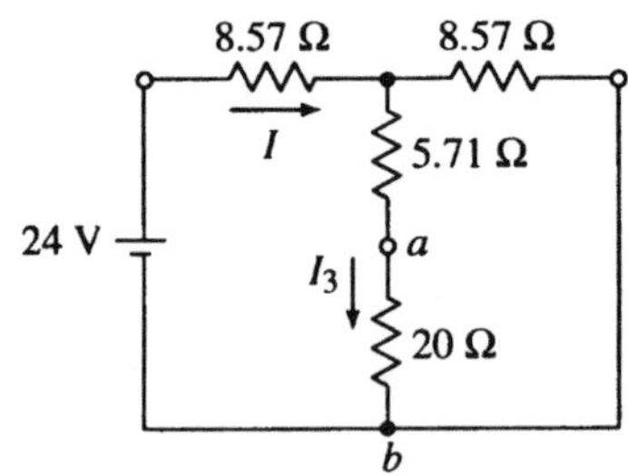

$$R_T = 8.57\ \Omega + \frac{25.71\ \Omega)(8.57\ \Omega)}{25.71\ \Omega + 8.57\ \Omega}$$

$= 15.0\ \Omega$

$$I = \frac{24\ \text{V}}{15\ \Omega} = 1.60\ \text{A}$$

$$I_3 = \left(\frac{8.57\ \Omega}{25.71\ \Omega + 8.57\ \Omega}\right)1.60\ \text{A} = 0.400\ \text{A}$$

$V_{ab} = (0.40\ \text{A})(20\ \Omega) = 8.00\ \text{V}$

46. Equivalent circuit:

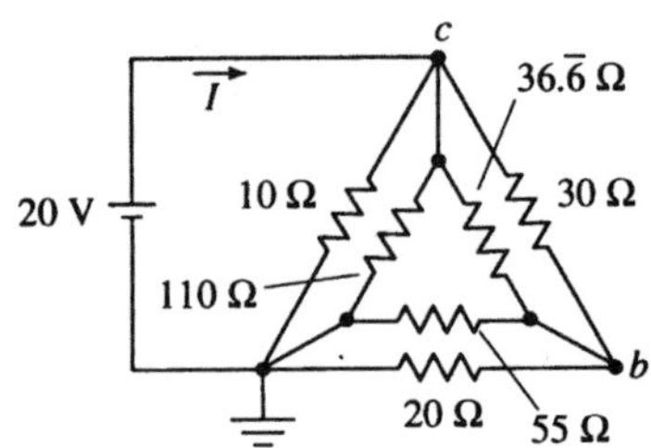

$R_T = (110\ \Omega \| 10\ \Omega) \| (36.\bar{6}\ \Omega \| 30\ \Omega + 55\ \Omega \| 20\ \Omega)$

$= 9.1\bar{6}\ \Omega \| (16.5\ \Omega + 14.\bar{6}\ \Omega)$

$= 9.1\bar{6}\ \Omega \| 31.1\bar{6}\ \Omega = 7.08\bar{3}\ \Omega$

$$I = \frac{20\text{ V}}{7083\ \Omega} = 2.82\text{ A}$$

$$V_{cb} = \left(\frac{16.5\ \Omega}{31.1\bar{6}\ \Omega}\right)20\text{ V} = 10.59\text{ V}$$

$$V_b = 20\text{ V} - 10.59\text{ V} = 9.41\text{ V}$$

Using Kirchhoff's current law

$$I_{R_4} = I_{R_5} - I_{R_3} = \frac{10.59\text{ V}}{30\ \Omega} - \frac{9.41\text{ V}}{20\ \Omega} = -0.1176\text{ A}$$

$$V_{ab} = -(0.1176\text{ A})(10\ \Omega) = -1.176\text{ V}$$

8.8 Bridge Networks

48. a. The bridge is *not* balanced since $\frac{30\ \Omega}{80\ \Omega} \neq \frac{40\ \Omega}{80\ \Omega}$

b. $(110\ \Omega)\,I - (30\ \Omega)\,I_2 - (80\ \Omega)\,I_3 = +90\text{ V}$
$-(30\ \Omega)\,I + (110\ \Omega)\,I_2 - (40\ \Omega)\,I_3 = 0$
$-(80\ \Omega)\,I - (40\ \Omega)\,I_2 + (200\ \Omega)\,I_3 = 0$

c.

$$I_2 = \frac{\begin{vmatrix} 110 & 90 & -80 \\ -30 & 0 & -40 \\ -80 & 0 & 200 \end{vmatrix}}{\begin{vmatrix} 110 & -30 & -80 \\ -30 & 110 & -40 \\ -80 & -40 & 200 \end{vmatrix}} = \frac{828\ 000}{1\ 168\ 000} = 0.7089\text{ A}$$

$$I_3 = \frac{900\ 000}{1\ 168\ 000} = 0.7705\text{ A}$$

$$I_{R_5} = 0.7705\text{ A} - 0.7089\text{ A} = 0.0616\text{ A} = 61.6\text{ mA (right)}$$

d. $V_{R_5} = (0.0616\text{ A})(40\ \Omega) = 2.47\text{ V}$

50. a. For a balanced bridge, $\frac{2\text{ k}\Omega}{4\text{ k}\Omega} = \frac{3\text{ k}\Omega}{R_x}$

$$R_x = \frac{(3\text{ k}\Omega)(4\text{ k}\Omega)}{2\ \Omega} = 6\text{ k}\Omega$$

b. When $R_x = 0\ \Omega$, the equivalent circuit is as follows:

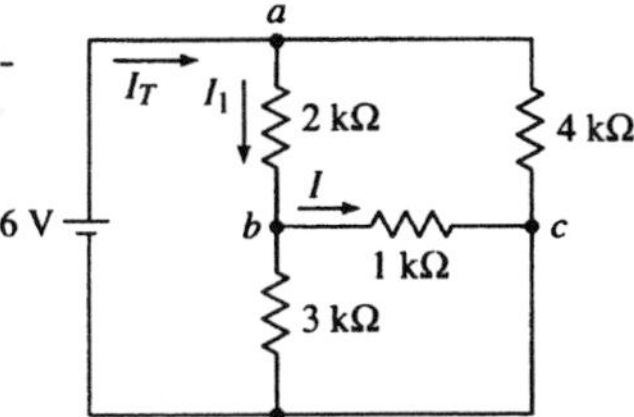

$$R_T = [2\text{ k}\Omega + 3\text{ k}\Omega \| 1\text{ k}\Omega] \| 4\text{ k}\Omega = 2.75\text{ k}\Omega \| 4\text{ k}\Omega = 1.630\text{ k}\Omega$$

$$I_T = \frac{6\text{ V}}{1.630\ \Omega} = 3.68\text{ mA}$$

$$I_1 = \left(\frac{4\ \Omega}{4\text{ k}\Omega + 2.75\text{ k}\Omega}\right)3.68\text{ mA} = 2.18\text{ mA}$$

$$I = \left(\frac{3\ \Omega}{1\ \Omega + 3\text{ k}\Omega}\right)2.18\text{ mA} = 1.636\text{ mA}$$

When $R_x = 10\text{ k}\Omega$ the equivalent circuit is as follows:

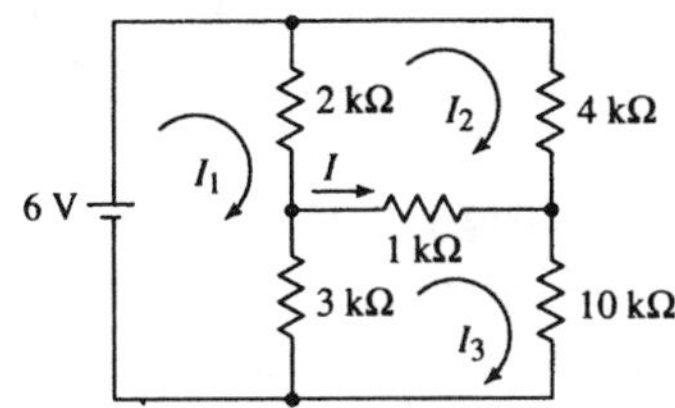

$(5\text{ k}\Omega)\,I_1 - (2\text{ k}\Omega)\,I_2 - (3\text{ k}\Omega)\,I_3 = 6\text{ V}$
$-(2\text{ k}\Omega)\,I_1 + (7\text{ k}\Omega)\,I_2 - (1\text{ k}\Omega)\,I_3 = 0$
$-(3\text{ k}\Omega)\,I_1 - (1\text{ k}\Omega)\,I_2 + (14\text{ k}\Omega)\,I_3 = 0$

$$I_2 = \frac{186}{354}\text{ mA} = 0.525\text{ mA}$$

$$I_3 = \frac{138}{354}\text{ mA} = 0.390\text{ mA}$$

$$I = 0.390\text{ mA} - 0.525\text{ mA} = -0.135\text{ mA}$$

8.9 Circuit Analysis Using Computers

52.

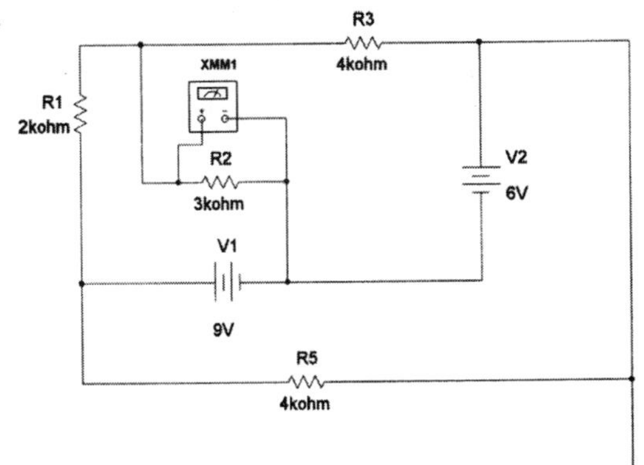

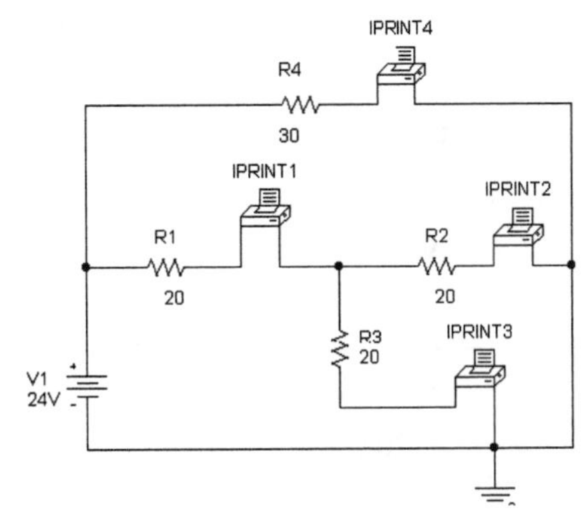

$I_1 = 0.80\text{ A}$
$I_2 = 0.40\text{ A}$
$I_3 = 0.40\text{ A}$
$I_4 = 0.80\text{ A}$

CHAPTER

9

Network Theorems

9.1 Superposition Theorem

2. *current source:* Equivalent circuit

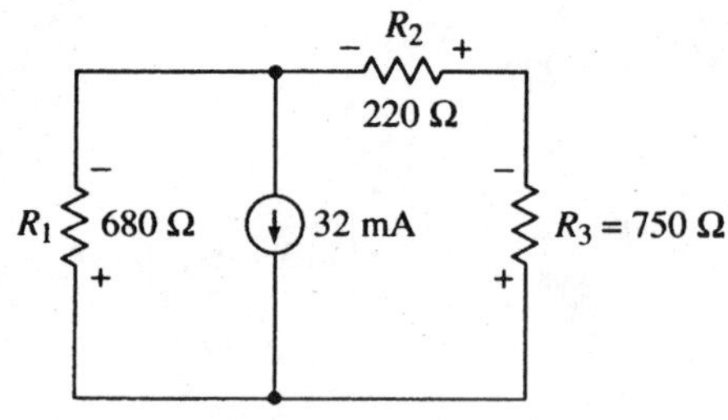

$R_T = 680\ \Omega \| (220\ \Omega + 750\ \Omega = 400\ \Omega$

$V_{R_1(1)} = (400\ \Omega)(32\ \text{mA}) = 12.80\ \text{V}$

$V_{R_2(1)} = \left(\dfrac{220\ \Omega}{220\ \Omega + 750\ \Omega}\right) 12.80\ \text{V} = 2.90\ \text{V}$

$V_{R_3(1)} = 12.80\ \text{V} - 2.90\ \text{V} = 9.90\ \text{V}$

voltage source: Equivalent circuit

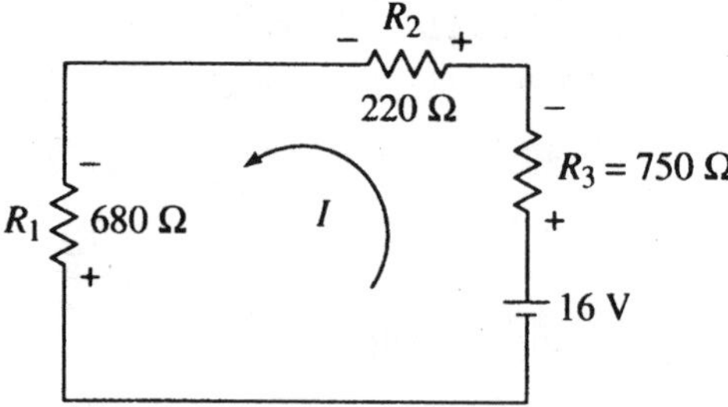

$R_T = 680\ \Omega + 220\ \Omega + 750\ \Omega = 1650\ \Omega$

$V_{R_1(2)} = -\left(\dfrac{680\ \Omega}{1650\ \Omega}\right) 16\ \text{V} = -6.59\ \text{V}$

$V_{R_2(2)} = \left(\dfrac{220\ \Omega}{1650\ \Omega}\right) 16\ \text{V} = 2.13\ \text{V}$

$V_{R_3(2)} = \left(\dfrac{750\ \Omega}{1650\ \Omega}\right) 16\ \text{V} = 7.27\ \text{V}$

$V_{R_1} = 12.80\ \text{V} - 6.59\ \text{V} = 6.21\ \text{V}$

$V_{R_2} = 2.90\ \text{V} + 2.13\ \text{V} = 5.03\ \text{V}$

$V_{R_3} = 9.90\ \text{V} + 7.27\ \text{V} = 17.17\ \text{V}$

4. $I_{(1)} = \left(\dfrac{120\ \Omega}{120\ \Omega + 480\ \Omega}\right) 200\ \text{mA} = 40\ \text{mA}$

$I_{(2)} = \dfrac{200\ \text{V}}{120\ \Omega + 480\ \Omega} = 333\ \text{mA}$

$I_{(3)} = \dfrac{60\ \text{V}}{120\ \Omega + 480\ \Omega} = 100\ \text{mA}$

$I = 40\ \text{mA} + 333\ \text{mA} + 100\ \text{mA} = 473\ \text{mA}$

6. (assume downward current)

$I_L = \sqrt{\dfrac{120\ \text{W}}{60\ \Omega}} = 1.414\ \text{A}$

$V_{40\ \Omega} = (1.414\ \text{A})(16\ \Omega + 60\ \Omega) = 107.48\ \text{V}$

$I_{40\ \Omega} = \dfrac{107.48\ \text{V}}{40\ \Omega} = 2.687\ \text{A (downward)}$

current through the voltage source

$I = 4\ \text{A} + 1.414\ \text{A} + 2.687\ \text{A} = 8.101\ \text{A (upward)}$

Therefore $E = 107.48\ \text{V} + (8.101\ \text{A})(60\ \Omega)$
$= 593.6\ \text{V}$

Considering only the voltage source:

$R_T = 60\ \Omega + 40\ \Omega \| (16\ \Omega + 60\ \Omega) = 86.21\ \Omega$

$I_{(1)} = \dfrac{593.6\ \text{V}}{86.21\ \Omega} = 6.885\ A$

$I_{L(1)} = \left(\dfrac{40\ \Omega}{40\ \Omega + 76\ \Omega}\right) 6.885\ \text{A} = 2.374\ \text{A (down)}$

Considering only the current source:

$R_T = 60\ \Omega \| 40\ \Omega \| (16\ \Omega + 60\ \Omega) = 18.24\ \Omega$

$I_{L(2)} = \left(\dfrac{18.24\ \Omega}{76\ \Omega}\right) 4\ \text{A} = 0.96\ \text{A (up)}$

Therefore $I_L = 2.374\ \text{A} - 0.96\ \text{A} = 1.414\ \text{A}$ (as required)

9.2 Thévenin's Theorem

8. $R_{Th} = 30\ \Omega + 90\ \Omega = 120\ \Omega$

$E_{Th} = (40\ \text{mA})(90\ \Omega) = 3.6\ \text{V}$

$V_{ab} = \left(\dfrac{60\ \Omega}{60\ \Omega + 120\ \Omega}\right) 3.6\ \text{V} = 1.2\ \text{V}$

10. $R_{Th} = 20\ \text{k}\Omega + 50\ \text{k}\Omega = 70\ \text{k}\Omega$

$E_{Th} = (50\ \text{k}\Omega)(100\ \mu\text{A}) = 5.0\ \text{V}$

$V_{ab} = -\left(\dfrac{180\ \Omega}{70\ \Omega + 180\ \Omega}\right) 5.0\ \text{V} = -3.6\ \text{V}$

12. a. $R_{Th} = 5\ \text{k}\Omega \| 15\ \text{k}\Omega = 3.75\ \text{k}\Omega$

Open circuit voltage due to E_1:

$V_{ab(1)} = 10\ \text{V}$

Open circuit voltage due to E_2:

$$V_{ab(2)} = \left(\frac{15\ \Omega}{5\ \Omega + 15\ \Omega}\right)6\ \text{V} = 4.5\ \text{V}$$

Open circuit voltage due to E_3:

$$V_{ab(3)} = -\left(\frac{5\ \text{P}}{5\ \Omega + 15\ \Omega}\right)12\ \text{V} = -3.0\ \text{V}$$

$$E_{\text{Th}} = 10\ \text{V} + 4.5\ \text{V} - 3.0\ \text{V} = 11.5\ \text{V}$$

$R_{\text{Th}} = 3.75\ \text{k}\Omega$ a

$E_{\text{Th}} = 11.5\ \text{V}$ $R_L = 10\ \text{k}\Omega \rightarrow 20\ \text{k}\Omega$

b

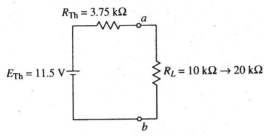

b. When $R_L = 10\ \text{k}\Omega$:

$$V_{ab} = \left(\frac{10\ \Omega}{10\ \text{k}\Omega + 3.75\ \text{k}\Omega}\right)(11.5\ \text{V}) = 8.36\ \text{V}$$

When $R_L = 20\ \text{k}\Omega$:

$$V_{ab} = \left(\frac{20\ \text{k}\Omega}{20\ \text{k}\Omega + 3.75\ \Omega}\right)(11.5\ \text{V}) = 9.68\ \text{V}$$

14. a. $R_{\text{Th}} = 3.3\ \text{k}\Omega \| 3.3\ \text{k}\Omega \| (3.3\ \text{k}\Omega + 3.3\ \text{k}\Omega \| 3.3\ \text{k}\Omega)$
$= 1.2375\ \text{k}\Omega$

Open-circuit voltages:

due to 7 mA current source:

$R_T = 3.3\ \text{k}\Omega \| 3.3\ \text{k}\Omega \| (3.3\ \text{k}\Omega + 3.3\ \text{k}\Omega \| 3.3\ \text{k}\Omega)$
$= 1.2375\ \text{k}\Omega$

$V_T = (1.2375\ \text{k}\Omega)(7\ \text{mA}) = 8.6625\ \text{V}$

$$V_{ab(1)} = -(8.6625\ \text{V})\left(\frac{3.3\ \text{k}\Omega \| 3.3\ \text{k}\Omega}{3.3\ \text{k}\Omega + 3.3\ \text{k}\Omega \| 3.3\ \text{k}\Omega}\right)$$
$= -2.8875\ \text{V}$

due to 50 V voltage source:

$R_T = 3.3\ \text{k}\Omega + (3.3\ \text{k}\Omega \| 3.3\ \text{k}\Omega + (3.3\ \text{k}\Omega \| 3.3\ \text{k}\Omega)$
$= 6.6\ \text{k}\Omega$

$$V_{ab(2)} = -\left(\frac{3.3\ \Omega \| 3.3\ \Omega}{6.6\ \text{k}\Omega}\right)50\ \text{V} = -12.5\ \text{V}$$

due to 20 V source:

$V_{ab(3)} = +20\ \text{V}$

$E_{\text{Th}} = -2.8875\ \text{V} - 12.5\ \text{V} + 20\ \text{V} = 4.6125\ \text{V}$

b. $$V_L = \left(\frac{3.3\ \Omega}{3.3\ \Omega + 1.2375\ \Omega}\right)4.6125\ \text{V} = 3.35\ \text{V}$$

16. a. Redraw the circuit:

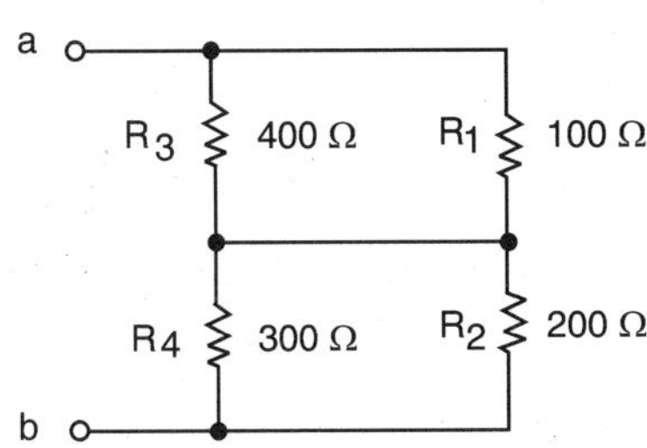

$R_{\text{Th}} = (400\ \Omega \| 100\ \Omega) + (300\ \Omega \| 200\ \Omega)$
$= 80\ \Omega + 120\ \Omega = 200\ \Omega$

$$V_a = \left(\frac{400\ \Omega}{100\Omega + 400\ \Omega}\right)32\ \text{V} = 25.6\ \text{V}$$

$$V_b = \left(\frac{300\ \Omega}{200\Omega + 300\ \Omega}\right)32\ \text{V} = 19.2\ \text{V}$$

$E_{\text{Th}} = V_{ab} = 25.6\ \text{V} - 19.2\ \text{V} = 6.4\ \text{V}$

b.

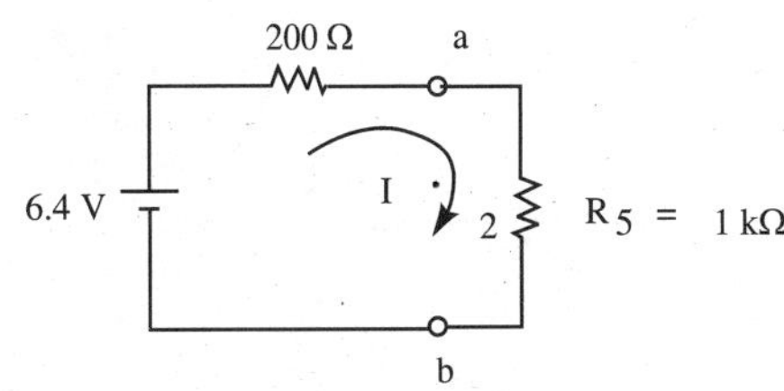

$$\text{I} = \frac{6.4\ \text{V}}{1\ \Omega + 0.2\ \text{k}\Omega} = 5.33\ \text{mA}$$

$V_{\text{ab}} = (1\ \text{k}\Omega)(5.33\ \text{mA}) = 5.33\ \text{V}$

18. a. $\Delta \rightarrow y$ conversion is required.

The equivalent circuit is shown below:

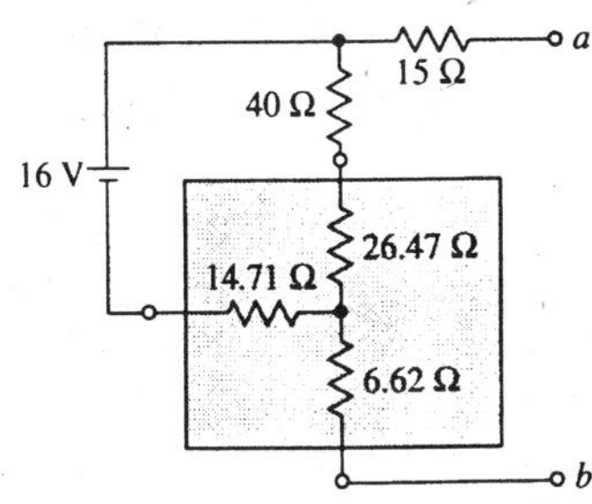

$R_{\text{Th}} = 15\ \Omega + 6.62\ \Omega + 14.71\ \Omega \| (40\ \Omega + 26.47\ \Omega)$
$= 33.66\ \Omega$

$$E_{\text{Th}} = \left(\frac{40\ \Omega + 26.47\ \Omega}{40\ \Omega + 26.47\ \Omega + 14.71\ \Omega}\right)16\ \text{V} = 13.10\ \text{V}$$

b. $$I_L = \frac{13.10\ \text{V}}{25\ \Omega + 33.66\ \Omega} = 0.2233\ \text{A}$$

$P_L = (0.2233\ \text{A})^2(25\ \Omega) = 1.247\ \text{W}$

20. a. $R_{\text{Th}} = 47\ \text{k}\Omega \| 33\ \text{k}\Omega \| 56\ \text{k}\Omega = 14.4\ \text{k}\Omega$

b. $$E_{\text{OC}(1)} = \left(\frac{33\ \text{k}\Omega \| 47\ \text{k}\Omega}{(33\ \text{k}\Omega \| 47\ \text{k}\Omega + 56\ \text{k}\Omega}\right)(6\ \text{V}) = -1.54\ \text{V}$$

$$E_{\text{OC}(2)} = \left(\frac{56\ \text{k}\Omega \| 47\ \text{k}\Omega}{56\ \text{k}\Omega \| 47\ \text{k}\Omega + 33\ \text{k}\Omega}\right)(+8\ \text{V}) = +3.49\ \text{V}$$

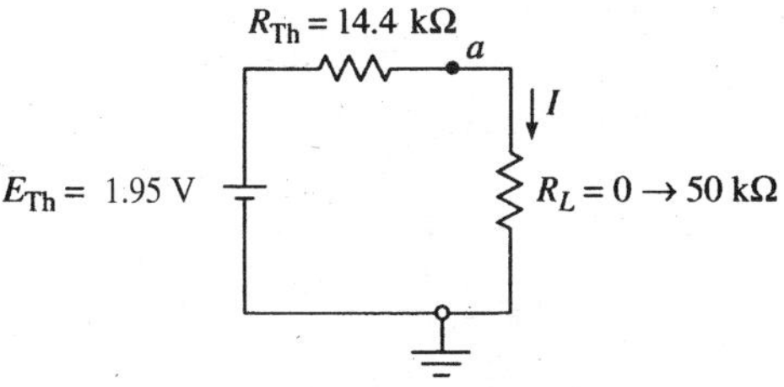

$E_{\text{Th}} = 3.49\ \text{V} - 1.543\ \text{V} = 1.95\ \text{V}$

$R_L = 0 : I = 0.135\ \text{mA}$

$R_L = 10\ \text{k}\Omega : I = 0.0798\ \text{mA}$

$R_L = 50\ \text{k}\Omega : I = 0.0302\ \text{mA}$

22. a. $R_{\text{Th}} = 10\ \Omega + 30\ \Omega = 40\ \Omega$

$V_{ab(1)} = -60\ \text{V}$

$V_{ab(2)} = -(2\text{ A})(10\ \Omega + 30\ \Omega) = -80\text{ V}$

$V_{ab(3)} = -(1\text{ A})(30\ \Omega) = -30\text{ V}$

$E_{Th} = 60\text{ V} + 80\text{ V} + 30\text{ V} = 170\text{ V}$

b. $I_L = \dfrac{170\text{ V}}{40\ \Omega + 20\ \Omega} = 2.83\text{ A (left)}$

24. a. $R_{Th} = 6\text{ k}\Omega$

$V_{ab(1)} = +4\text{ V}$

$V_{ab(2)} = 0\text{ V}$

$V_{ab(3)} = +(3\text{ ma})(6\text{ k}\Omega) = +18\text{ V}$

$E_{Th} = 18\text{ V} + 4\text{ V} = 22\text{ V}$

b. $I_L = \dfrac{22\text{ V}}{6\text{ k}\Omega + 3\text{ k}\Omega} = 2.44\text{ mA (right)}$

9.3 Norton's Theorem

26. $R_N = 30\ \Omega + 90\ \Omega = 120\ \Omega$

$I_N = \left(\dfrac{90\ \Omega}{90\ \Omega + 30\ \Omega}\right)40\text{ mA} = 30\text{ mA}$

$I_L = \left(\dfrac{120\ \Omega}{120\ \Omega + 60\ \Omega}\right)30\text{ mA} = 20\text{ mA}$

28. $R_N = 20\text{ k}\Omega + 50\text{ k}\Omega = 70\text{ k}\Omega$

$I_N = \left(\dfrac{50\text{ k}\Omega}{50\text{ k}\Omega + 20\text{ k}\Omega}\right)100\ \mu\text{A} = 71.43\ \mu\text{A}$

$I_L = \left(\dfrac{70\text{ k}\Omega}{70\text{ k}\Omega + 180\text{ k}\Omega}\right)71.43\ \mu\text{A} = 20\ \mu\text{A}$

30. $R_N = 5\text{ k}\Omega \| 15\text{ k}\Omega = 3.75\text{ k}\Omega$

Short-circuit current:

1. Due to 10 V voltage source:

$R_T = 6\text{ k}\Omega \| 5\text{ k}\Omega \| 15\text{ k}\Omega = 2.308\text{ k}\Omega$

$I_T = \dfrac{10\text{ V}}{2.308\text{ k}\Omega} = 4.33\text{ mA}$

$I_{ab(1)} = \left(\dfrac{2.308\ \Omega}{3.75\ \Omega}\right)4.33\text{ mA} = 2.667\text{ mA}$

2. Due to 6 V source:

$I_{ab(2)} = \dfrac{6\text{ V}}{5\ \Omega} = 1.20\text{ mA}$

3. Due to 12 V source:

$I_{ab(3)} = -\dfrac{12\text{ V}}{15\text{ k}\Omega} = -0.80\text{ mA}$

$I_N = 2.667\text{ mA} + 1.20\text{ mA} - 0.80\text{ mA} = 3.067\text{ mA}$

When $R_L = 10\text{ k}\Omega$:

$I_L = \left(\dfrac{3.75\text{ k}\Omega}{3.75\text{ k}\Omega + 10\text{ k}\Omega}\right)3.067\text{ mA} = 0.836\text{ mA}$

When $R_L = 20\text{ k}\Omega$:

$I_L = \left(\dfrac{3.75\text{ k}\Omega}{3.75\text{ k}\Omega + 20\text{ k}\Omega}\right)3.067\text{ mA} = 0.484\text{ mA}$

32. a. $R_N = 3.3\text{ k}\Omega \| 3.3\text{ k}\Omega \| (3.3\text{ k}\Omega + 3.3\text{ k}\Omega \| 3.3\text{ k}\Omega)$

$= 1.2375\text{ k}\Omega$

Short-circuit current:

1. Due to 7 mA current source:

$I_{ab(1)} = -\dfrac{7\text{ mA}}{3} = -2.33\text{ mA}$

2. Due to 50 V voltage source:

$I_{ab(2)} = -\dfrac{50\text{ V}}{3.3\text{ k}\Omega + (3.3\text{ k}\Omega \| 3.3\text{ k}\Omega)} = -10.10\text{ mA}$

3. Due to 20 V voltage source:

$I_{ab(3)} = \dfrac{20\text{ V}}{3.3\ \Omega \| 3.3\text{ k}\Omega \| (3.3\ \Omega + 3.3\text{ k}\Omega \| 3.3\text{ k}\Omega)}$

$= 16.16\text{ mA}$

$I_N = -2.33\text{ mA} - 10.10\text{ mA} + 16.16\text{ mA} = 3.727\text{ mA}$

b. $R_N = R_{Th} = 1.2375\text{ k}\Omega$

$I_N = \dfrac{4.6125\text{ V}}{1.2375\ \Omega} = 3.727\text{ mA (as required)}$

34. a. Using $\Delta \rightarrow y$ conversion, we have the following equivalent circuit:

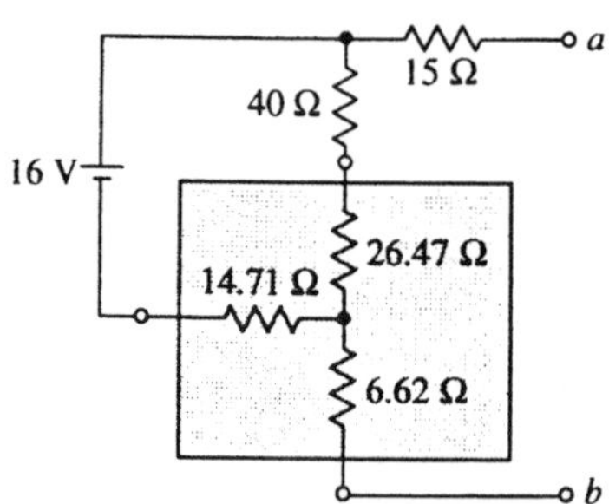

$R_N = 15\ \Omega + 6.62\ \Omega + 14.71\ \Omega \| (40\ \Omega + 26.47\ \Omega)$

$= 33.66\ \Omega$

$R_T = 14.71\ \Omega + (40\ \Omega + 26.47\ \Omega) \| (15\ \Omega + 6.62\ \Omega)$

$= 31.02\ \Omega$

$I_T = \dfrac{16\text{ V}}{31.02\ \Omega} = 0.516\text{ A}$

$I_N = \left(\dfrac{66.47\ \Omega}{66.47\ \Omega + 21.62\ \Omega}\right)0.516\text{ A} = 0.389\text{ A}$

b. $R_N = R_{Th} = 33.66\ \Omega$

$I_N = \dfrac{13.10\ \Omega}{33.66} = 0.389\text{ A (as required)}$

36. a. $R_N = 10\ \Omega + 30\ \Omega = 40\ \Omega$

Short-circuit currents:

1. Due to 2 A current source:

$I_{ab(1)} = -2\text{ A}$

2. Due to 60 V voltage source:

$I_{ab(2)} = -\dfrac{60\text{ V}}{30\ \Omega + 10\ \Omega} = -1.5\text{ A}$

3. Due to 1 A current source:

$I_{ab(3)} = -\left(\dfrac{30\ \Omega}{30\ \Omega + 10\ \Omega}\right)1\text{ A} = -0.75\text{ A}$

$I_N = 2\text{ A} + 1.5\text{ A} + 0.75\text{ A} = 4.25\text{ A}$

b. $I_N = \frac{E_{Th}}{R_{Th}} = \frac{170 \text{ V}}{40\ \Omega} = 4.25 \text{ A (as required)}$

9.4 Maximum Power Transfer Theorem

38. a. For maximum power $R_L = R_{Th} = 14.40\ \text{k}\Omega$

b. $P_{max} = \frac{(1.95 \text{ V})^2}{4(14.40\ \Omega} = 65.9\ \mu\text{W}$

c. $P_L = \left(\frac{E_{Th}}{R_{Th} + R_L}\right)^2 R_L$

R_L(kΩ)	P_L(μW)
0	0
5	50.4
10	63.7
15	65.8
20	64.1
25	61.1
30	57.7
35	54.4
40	51.3
45	48.4
50	45.7

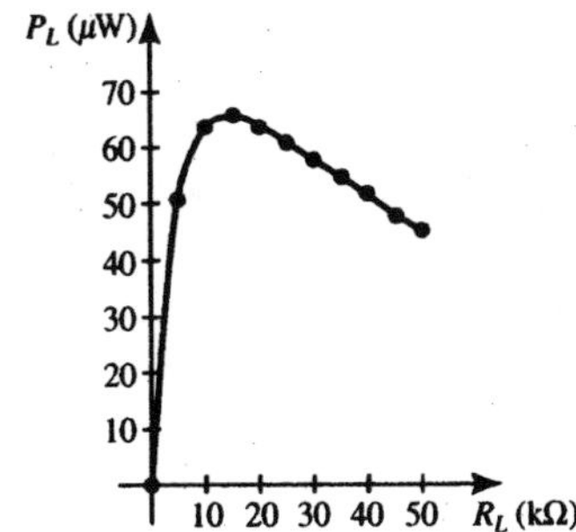

40. a. $R_{Th} = 2\ \text{k}\Omega = 0.5\ \text{k}\Omega + 3\ \text{k}\Omega \| \text{R}$

$\frac{3\ \text{k}\Omega)\ R}{3\ \text{k}\Omega + R} = 2.0\ \text{k}\Omega - 0.5\ \text{k}\Omega = 1.5\ \text{k}\Omega$

$\text{R} = 3.0\ \text{k}\Omega$

b. $E_{Th} = \left(\frac{3\ \text{k}\Omega}{3\ \text{k}\Omega + 3\ \text{k}\Omega}\right) 100 \text{ mV} = 50 \text{ mV}$

$V_L = 25 \text{ mV}$

$P_L = \frac{(25 \text{ mV})^2}{2\ \text{k}\Omega} = 312.5 \text{ nW}$

42. a. $R_{Th} = 25\ \text{k}\Omega = R_1 \| R_2$

$\frac{(200\ \Omega - R_2)(R_2)}{200\ \Omega} = 25\ \text{k}\Omega$

$-R_2^2 + 200\ R_2 - 5000 = 0$

$R_2 = 29.3\ \text{k}\Omega$ or $170.7\ \text{k}\Omega$

$R_1 = 170.7\ \text{k}\Omega$ or $29.3\ \text{k}\Omega$

b. Maximum power delivered to the load when $R_2 = 170.7\ \text{k}\Omega$ ($R_1 = 29.3\ \text{k}\Omega$)

$E_{Th} = \left(\frac{170.7\ \text{k}\Omega}{200 \text{ k}}\right) 25 \text{ V} = 21.3 \text{ V}$

$V_L = \frac{21.3 \text{ V}}{2} = 10.7 \text{ V}$

$P_L = \frac{10.7 \text{ V})2}{25\ \text{k}\Omega} = 4.55 \text{ mW}$

9.5 Substitution Theorem

44. $V_{ab(1)} = \left(\frac{125\ \Omega}{125\ \Omega + 75\ \Omega + 100\ \Omega}\right)(50 \text{ mA})(75\ \Omega)$

$= 1.5625 \text{ V}$

$V_{ab(2)} = -\left(\frac{125\ \Omega}{125\ \Omega + 75\ \Omega + 100\ \Omega}\right) 10 \text{ V} = -4.167 \text{ V}$

$V_{ab} = -2.604 \text{ V}\ I_{ab} = -20.83 \text{ mA}$

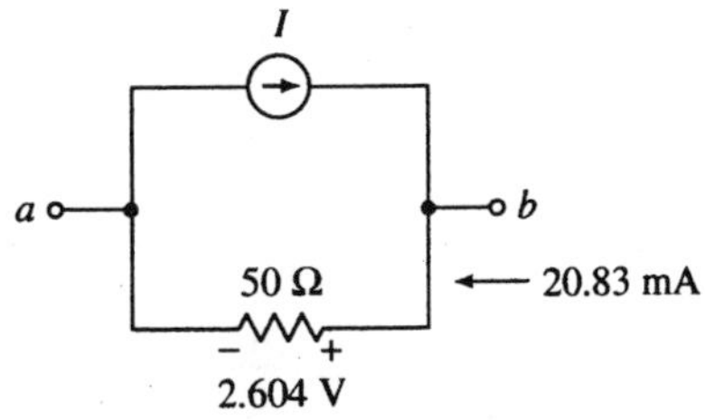

$I_{50\Omega} = \frac{2.604 \text{ V}}{50\ \Omega} = 52.08 \text{ mA}$

$I = 52.08 \text{ mA} - 20.83 \text{ mA}$

$= 31.25 \text{ mA (right)}$

9.6 Millman's Theorem

46. $R_{eq} \frac{1}{\frac{1}{100\ \Omega} + \frac{1}{330\ \Omega} + \frac{1}{390\ \Omega}} = 64.1\ \Omega$

$E_{eq} = \left(\frac{36 \text{ V}}{100\ \Omega} - \frac{24 \text{ V}}{330\ \Omega} + \frac{40 \text{ V}}{390\ \Omega}\right) 64.1\ \Omega = 25.0 \text{ V}$

$I_L = \frac{25.0 \text{ V}}{64.1\ \Omega + 220\ \Omega} = 0.0880 \text{ A}$

$P_L = (0.0880 \text{ A})^2(220\ \Omega) + 1.703 \text{ W}$

48. $$R_{eq} = \frac{1}{\frac{1}{500\ \Omega} + \frac{1}{1500\ \Omega}} = 375\ \Omega$$

$$E_{eq} = \left(30\text{ mA} - \frac{10\text{ V}}{500\ \Omega}\right)375\ \Omega = 3.75\text{ V}$$

$$P_L = (7.5\text{ mA})^2(125\ \Omega) = 7.03\text{ mW}$$

9.7 Reciprocity Theorem

50. a. $R_T = 10\ \Omega + 30\ \Omega \| [22.5\ \Omega + 30\ \Omega \| 60\ \Omega]$
$= 10\ \Omega + 30\ \Omega \| 42.5\ \Omega$
$= 27.6\ \Omega$

$$I_T = \frac{24\text{ V}}{27.6\ \Omega} = 0.870\text{ A}$$

$$I_1 = \left(\frac{30\ \Omega}{30\ \Omega + 42.5\ \Omega}\right)0.870\text{ A} = 0.36\text{ A}$$

$$I = \left(\frac{60\ \Omega}{60\ \Omega + 30\ \Omega}\right)0.36\text{ A} = 0.24\text{ A}$$

b. $R_T = 30\ \Omega + 60\ \Omega \| [22.5\ \Omega + 30\ \Omega \| 10\ \Omega]$
$= 30\ \Omega + 60\ \Omega \| 30\ \Omega$
$= 50\ \Omega$

$$I_T = \frac{24\text{ V}}{50\ \Omega} = 0.48\text{ A}$$

$$I_1\left(\frac{60\ \Omega}{60\ \Omega + 30\ \Omega}\right)(0.48\text{ A}) = 0.32\text{ A}$$

$$I = \left(\frac{30\ \Omega}{30\ \Omega + 10\ \Omega}\right)0.32\text{ A} = 0.24\text{ A}$$

Reciprocity applies.

52. a. $R_T = 50\ \Omega \| 150\ \Omega \| (12.5\ \Omega + 29\ \Omega + 30\ \Omega)$
$= 23.4375\ \Omega$
$V_1 = (3\text{ A})(23.4375\ \Omega) = 70.3125\text{ V}$

$$V = \left(\frac{20\ \Omega}{20\ \Omega + 12.5\ \Omega + 30\ \Omega}\right)(70.3125\text{ V})$$

b. $R_T = 20\ \Omega \| (30\ \Omega + 12.5\ \Omega + 50\ \Omega \| 150\ \Omega$
$= 16\ \Omega$
$V_1 = (3\text{ A})(16\ \Omega) = 48\text{ V}$

$$V = \left(\frac{37.5\ \Omega}{80\ \Omega}\right)48\text{ V} = 22.5\text{ V}$$

Reciprocity applies.

9.8 Circuit Analysis Using Computers

54.

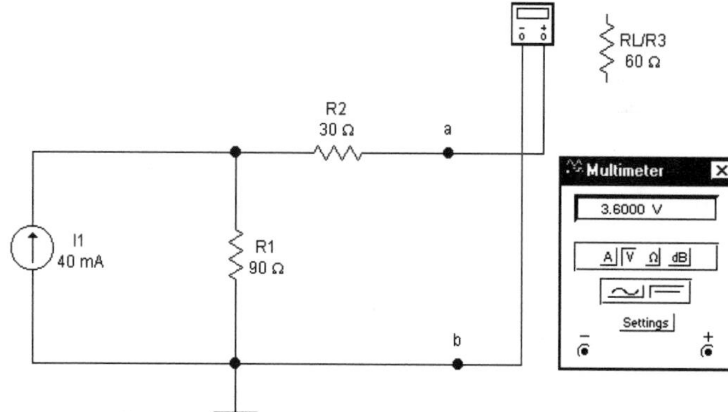

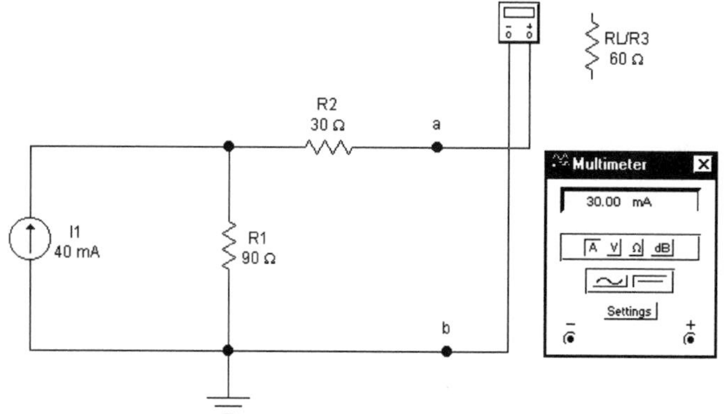

$E_{Th} = 3.6\text{ V}$
$I_N = 30\text{ mA}$
$R_{Th} = R_N = 0.120\text{ k}\Omega = 120\ \Omega$

56.

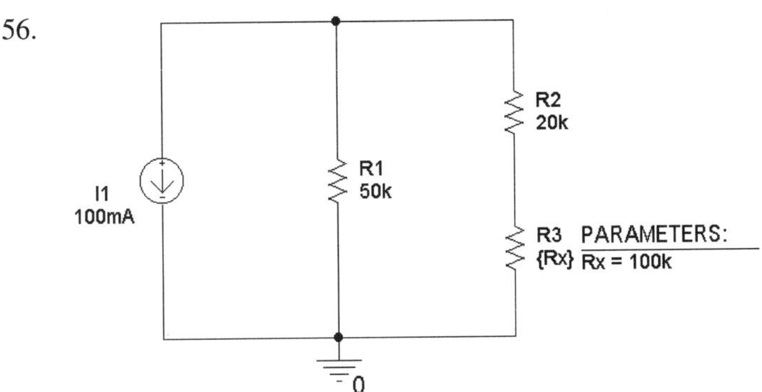
I1
100mA
R1
50k
R2
20k
R3
{Rx}
PARAMETERS:
Rx = 100k
0

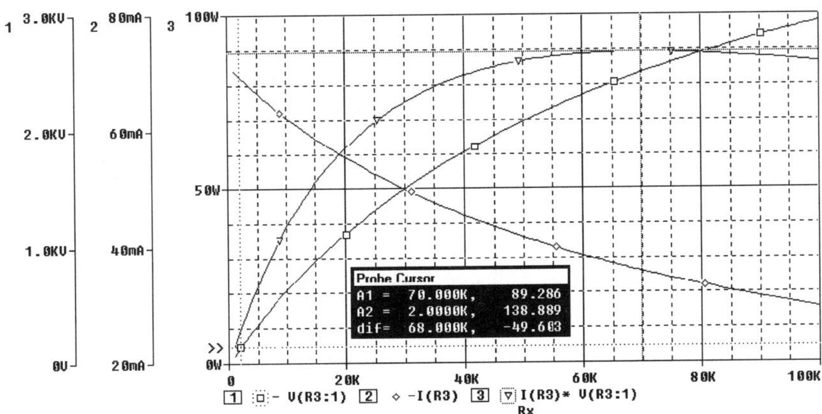
1 3.0KV
2.0KV
1.0KV
0V
2 80mA
60mA
40mA
20mA
3 100W
50W
0W
Probe Cursor
A1 = 70.000K, 89.286
A2 = 2.0000K, 138.889
dif= 68.000K, -49.603
0
20K
40K
60K
80K
100K
1 V(R3:1) 2 -I(R3) 3 I(R3)* V(R3:1)
Rx

CHAPTER

10

Capacitors and Capacitance

10.1 Capacitance

2. a. $C = \frac{Q}{V} = \frac{375 \times 10^{-6}\ C}{2.5 \times 10^{3}\ V} = 150 \times 10^{-9}\ F = 150\ nF$

b. $Q = C\,V = (0.04 \times 10^{-4}\ F)(1.5\ kV) = 6\ mC$

c. $C = \frac{Q}{V} = \frac{6 \times 10^{-5}\ C}{150\ V} = 0.4\ \mu F$

d. $V = \frac{Q}{C} = \frac{10 \times 10^{-6}\ C}{400 \times 10^{-9}\ F} = 25\ V$

e. $Q = C\,V = (40 \times 10^{-5}\ F)(150\ V) = 60\ mC$

f. $V = \frac{Q}{C} = \frac{6 \times 10^{-9}\ C}{800 \times 10^{-12}\ F} = 7.5\ V$

10.2 Factors Affecting Capacitance

4. $C = \frac{Q}{V} = \frac{10\ \mu C}{25\ V} = 0.4\ \mu F$

6. $A = \frac{\pi d^2}{4} = \frac{\pi}{4}(0.1\ m)^2 = 0.7854 \times 10^{-2}\ m^2$

$$C = \epsilon_o \frac{A}{d} = 8.854 \times 10^{-12}\left(\frac{0.7854 \times 10^{-2}\ m^2}{0.1 \times 10^{-3}\ m}\right) = 0.695\ nF$$

8. $C = \epsilon_r C_o \therefore C_o = \frac{C}{\epsilon_r} = \frac{73\ pF}{5.5} = 13.3\ pF$

10. $C = (0.01\ \mu F)\left(\frac{1}{7500} \times \frac{1}{2} \times 4\right) = 2.67\ pF$

12. $A = 4.5\ in.^2 = (4.5\ \cancel{in.^2}) \times \left(6.452 \times 10^{-4} \frac{m^2}{\cancel{in.^2}}\right) = 29.0 \times 10^{-4}\ m^2$

$$d = 5 \times 10^{-3}\ in. = (5 \times 10^{-3}\ \cancel{in.})\left(2.54 \times 10^{-3}\ \frac{m}{\cancel{in.}}\right) = 0.127 \times 10^{-3}\ m$$

$$C = \epsilon_r \epsilon_o \frac{A}{d} = \frac{(80)(8.854 \times 10^{-12}\ F/m)(29.0 \times 10^{-4}\ m^2)}{0.127 \times 10^{-3}\ m} = 16.2\ nF$$

10.3 Electric Fields

14. $\mathscr{E} = \frac{V}{d} = \frac{150\ V}{1 \times 10^{-3}\ m} = 150\ kV/m$. (Does not depend on C.)

10.4 Dielectrics

16. $d = 2 \times 10^{-3}\ in = (2 \times 10^{-3})(25.4) = 0.0508\ mm$

Breakdown occurs at 40 kV/m $\therefore V = (0.0508\ \cancel{mm})\left(\frac{40\ kV}{\cancel{mm}}\right) = 2.03\ kV$

18. $C = \epsilon \frac{A}{d} \therefore d = \frac{\epsilon A}{C} = \frac{(3)(8.854 \times 10^{-12}\ F/m)(0.625\ m^2)}{200 \times 10^{-9}\ F} = 0.083\ mm$

Breakdown occurs at 16 kV/mm $\therefore V = \left(\frac{16\ kV}{\cancel{mm}}\right)(0.083\ \cancel{mm}) = 1328\ V$

20. No. When the gap with the lowest rating breaks down, it arcs over. The voltage across the arc will always be lower than the voltage needed to break down the second gap.

10.5 Nonideal Effects

22. $\Delta C = 0.1\ \mu\text{F}$. Thus, $\dfrac{\Delta C}{\Delta T} = \dfrac{0.1\ \mu\text{F}}{40°\text{C}} = 2.5\ \text{nF/°C}$

Thus, $\dfrac{2.5\ \text{nF/°C}}{4.7\ \mu\text{F}} = \dfrac{532\ \text{F}}{10^6\ \text{F}}$ per degree C.

Coefficient = 532 ppm/°C (positive)

24. $C_T = C_1 + C_2 + C_3$. Convert all capacitors to a common prefix, then add.

$C_T = 0.1\ \mu\text{F} + 0.22\ \mu\text{F} + 0.47\ \mu\text{F} = 0.79\ \mu\text{F}$

26. Convert all capacitors to a common prefix. Then, $\dfrac{1}{C_{eq}} = \dfrac{1}{0.1\ \mu\text{F}} + \dfrac{1}{0.22\ \mu\text{F}} + \dfrac{1}{0.47\ \mu\text{F}}\ \therefore C_{eq} = 0.06\ \mu\text{F}$

28. a. Redraw the circuit as in (i). Note that the 47 μF capacitor is shorted out, leaving the circuit of (ii). The 0.15 μF and 0.22 μF capacitors are in parallel, yielding an equivalent of 0.37 μF. This is in series with the 0.47 μF capacitor as in (iii). Thus, $\dfrac{1}{C_{eq}} = \dfrac{1}{0.47\ \mu\text{F}} + \dfrac{1}{0.37\ \mu\text{F}}\ \therefore C_{eq} = 0.207\ \mu\text{F}$

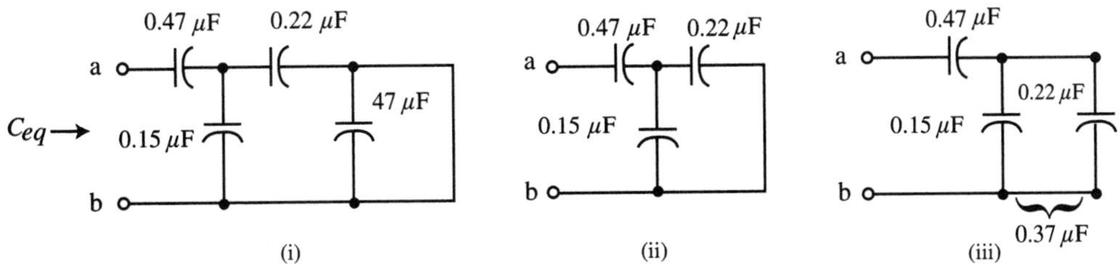

b. Convert capacitances to a common prefix (e.g., nF). Redraw the circuit as in (i), then successively combine capacitances. Finally, from (iii), $C_T = 0.333\ \text{nF} + 0.143\ \text{nF} = 0.476\ \text{nF}$

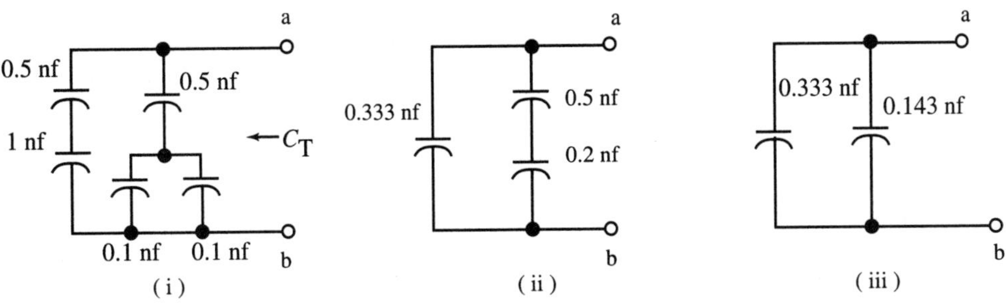

c. Convert all capacitances to μF. Redraw the circuit as in (i), then successively combine capacitances to yield circuit (ii). From (ii), $C_T = 0.165\ \mu\text{F}$.

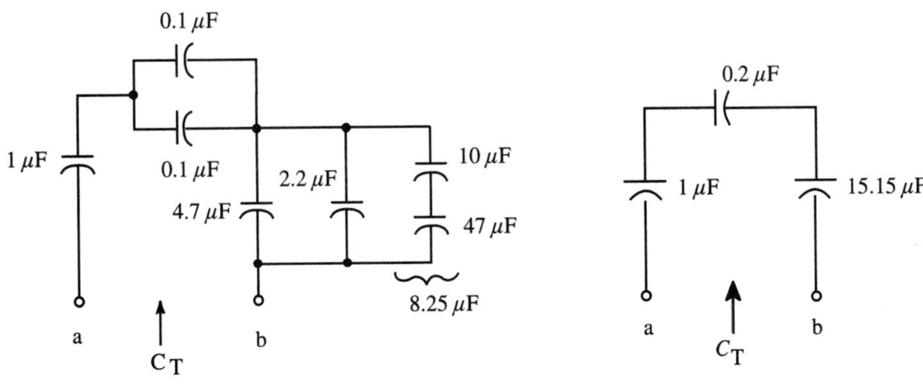

d. Using step by step reduction, capacitances are combined as shown below. From (c), $\frac{1}{C_T} = \frac{1}{16\,\mu\text{F}} + \frac{1}{18.6\,\mu\text{F}} + \frac{1}{10\,\mu\text{F}} + \frac{1}{14\,\mu\text{F}}$. Thus, $C_T = 3.48\,\mu\text{F}$.

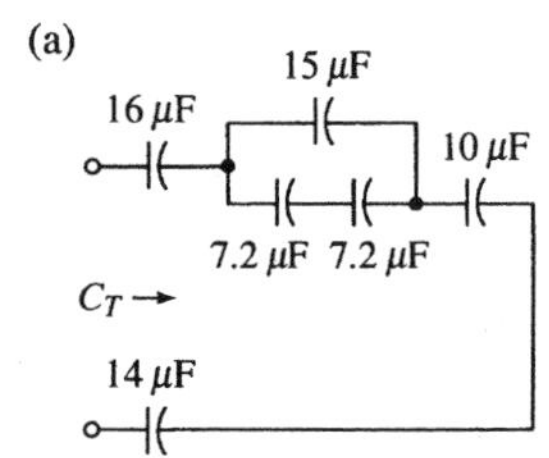

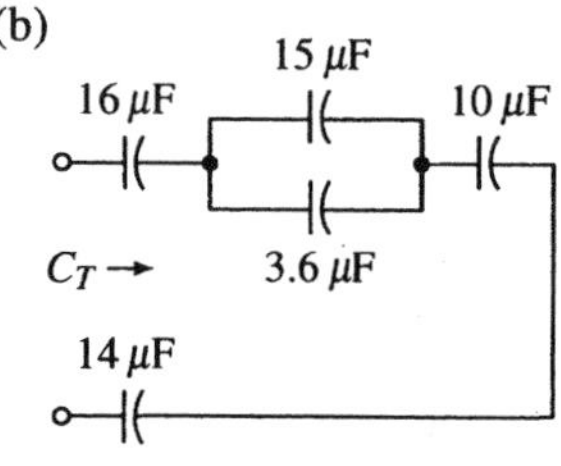

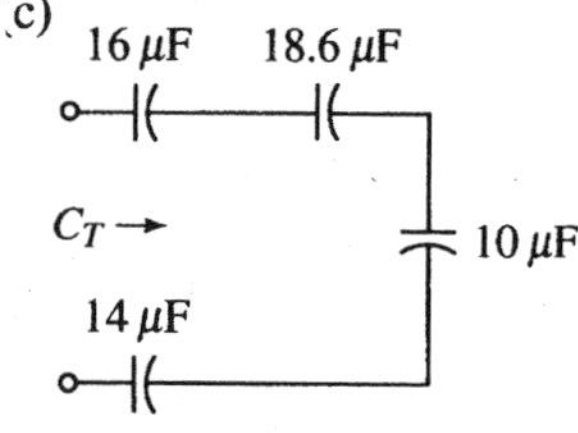

30. $10\,\mu\text{F}$ in series $40\,\mu\text{F}$ yields $\frac{(10\,\mu\text{F})(40\,\mu\text{F})}{10\,\mu\text{F} + 40\,\mu\text{F}} = 8\,\mu\text{F}$.

The reduced circuit is shown in (b). Thus, $C_X + 8\,\mu\text{F} = 20\,\mu\text{F}$ and $C_X = 12\,\mu\text{F}$.

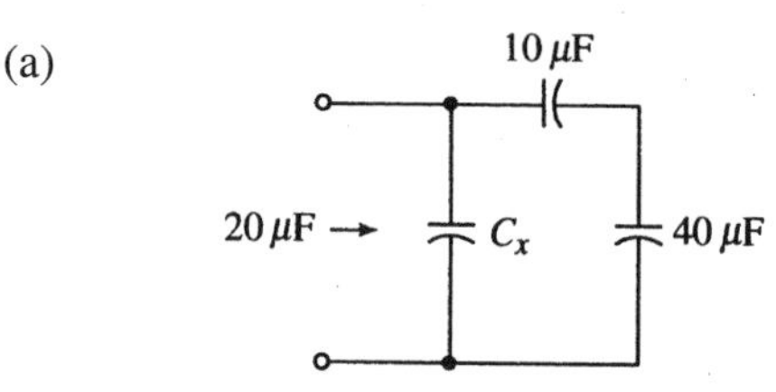

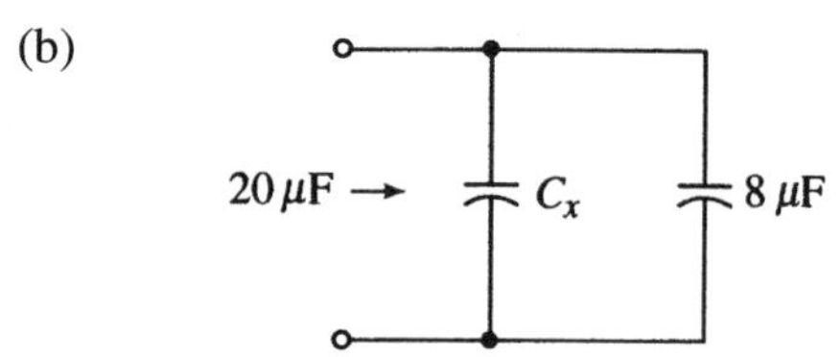

32. $C_1 = \frac{Q_1}{V} = \frac{100 \times 10^{-6}\,\text{C}}{10\,\text{V}} = 10\,\mu\text{F}$

The circuit may be reduced step-by-step as shown below. Thus, $C_T = 10\,\mu\text{F} + 30\,\mu\text{F} = 40\,\mu\text{F}$.

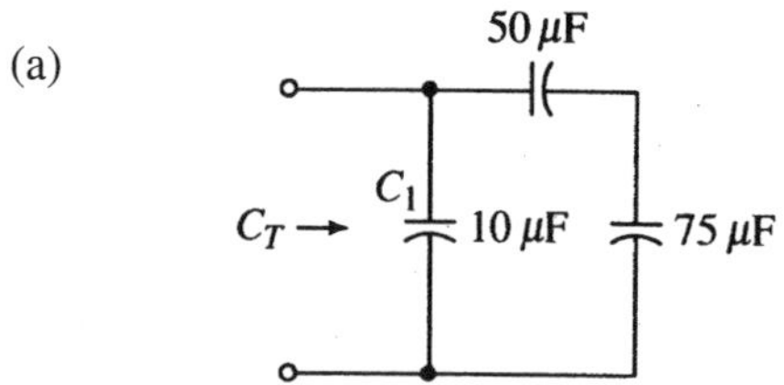

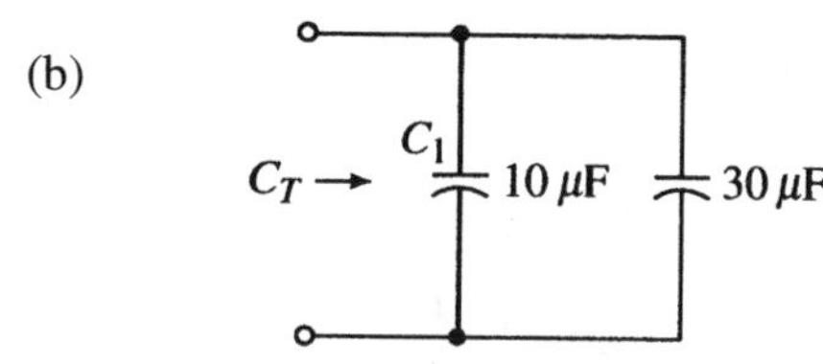

34. Since $10\,\mu\text{F} \| 4.7\,\mu\text{F} = 14.7\,\mu\text{F}$, the third capacitor must be connected in series as below. Thus, $\frac{1}{2.695\,\mu\text{F}} = \frac{1}{C_x} + \frac{1}{14.7\,\mu\text{F}}$ $\therefore C_X = 3.3\,\mu\text{F}$.

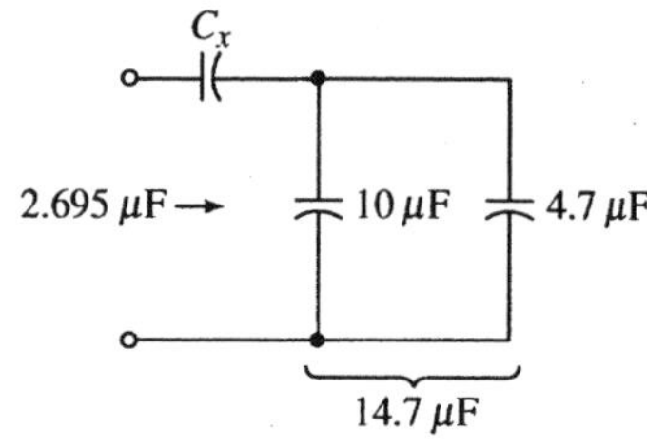

36. To yield a value smaller than $10\,\mu\text{F}$, the $10\,\mu\text{F}$ capacitor must be in series with at least one of the other capacitors. Only the connection shown below works.

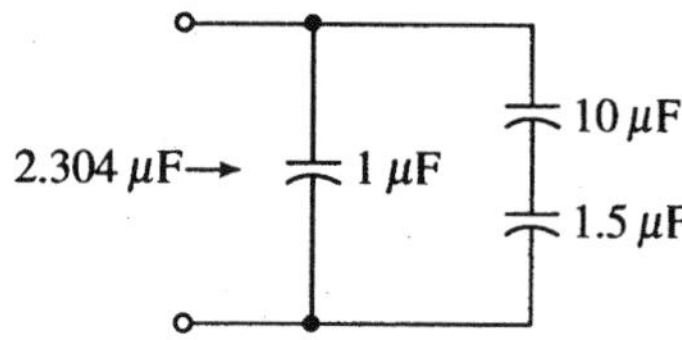

38. For the circuit of Figure 10-37. $\frac{1}{C_T} = \frac{1}{60\ \mu\text{F}} + \frac{1}{30\ \mu\text{F}} + \frac{1}{20\ \mu\text{F}}$. Thus, $C_T = 10\ \mu\text{F}$.

$V_1 = \left(\frac{C_T}{C_1}\right)E = \left(\frac{10\ \mu\text{F}}{60\ \mu\text{F}}\right)(120\ \text{V}) = 20\ \text{V}$.

Similarly, $V_2 = 40$ V and $V_3 = 60$ V.

40. 50 μF in series with 75 μF reduces to 30 μF as shown below Since half the source voltage appears across each capacitance of (b), both must be equal. Therefore, $C_x = 30\ \mu\text{F}$.

(a)

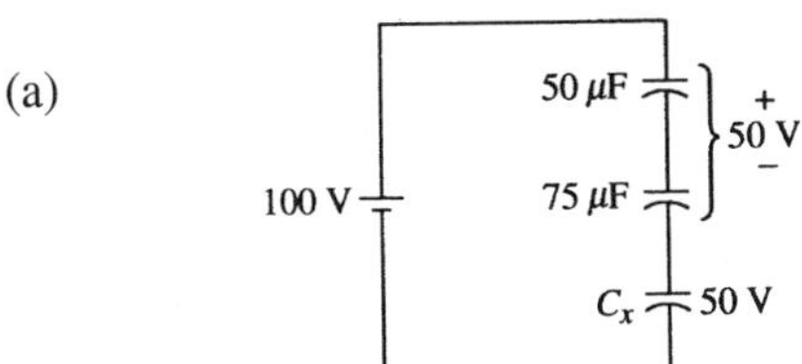

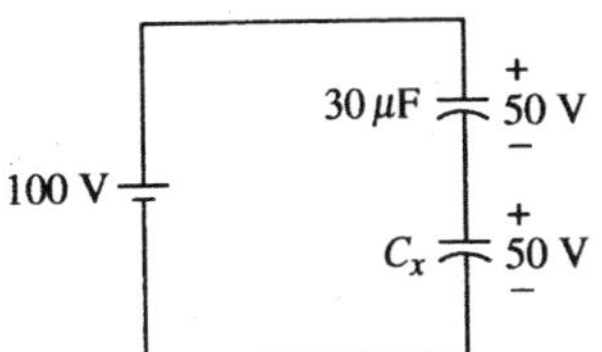

42. a. Redraw the circuit as below. Apply the capacitive voltage divider rule. Thus,

$V_2 = \left(\frac{40\ \mu\text{F}}{10\ \mu\text{F}}\right)(80\ \text{V}) = 320\ \text{V}$

$E = V_2 + 80\ \text{V} = 320\ \text{V} + 80\ \text{V} = 400\ \text{V}$

b. $C_T = 12\ \mu\text{F} + 8\ \mu\text{F} = 20\ \mu\text{F}$

$Q_T = C_T E = (20\ \mu\text{F})\ (400\ \text{V}) = 8\ \text{mC}$

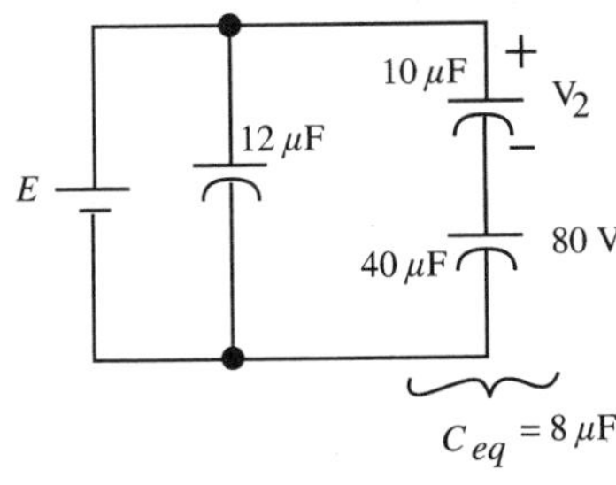

10.8 Capacitor Current and Voltage

44. $i = C\frac{\Delta v_C}{\Delta t}$

0 ms – 1 ms :

$20\ \text{mA} = (1\ \mu\text{F})\left(\frac{\Delta v_C}{1\ \text{ms}}\right) \therefore \Delta v_C = 20\ \text{V}$

Since $v_C = 0$ V at $t = 0$, it will rise to 20 V at $t = 1$ ms as shown (next page).

1 ms – 2 ms :

$40\ \text{mA} = (1\ \mu\text{F})\left(\frac{\Delta v_C}{1\ \text{ms}}\right) \therefore \Delta v_C = 40\ \text{V}$

Therefore, voltage rises from 20 V to 60 V at $t = 2$ ms.

2 ms – 3 ms :

$-10\ \text{mA} = (1\ \mu\text{F})\left(\frac{\Delta v_C}{1\ \text{ms}}\right) \therefore \Delta v_C = -10\ \text{V}$ and v_C drops to 50 V at $t = 3$ ms.

3 ms – 4 ms :

$0\ \text{mA} = (1\ \mu\text{F})\left(\frac{\Delta v_C}{1\ \text{ms}}\right) \therefore \Delta v_C = 0\ \text{V}$ and v_C remains constant at 50 V from 3 to 4 ms.

4 ms – 5 ms :

Here you find $\Delta v_C = 10$ V and v_C rises to 60 V at $t = 6$ ms.

$t > 5$ ms :

$i_C = 0 \therefore \Delta v_C = 0$ and v_C remains constant at 60 V for $t \geq 5$ ms as indicated.

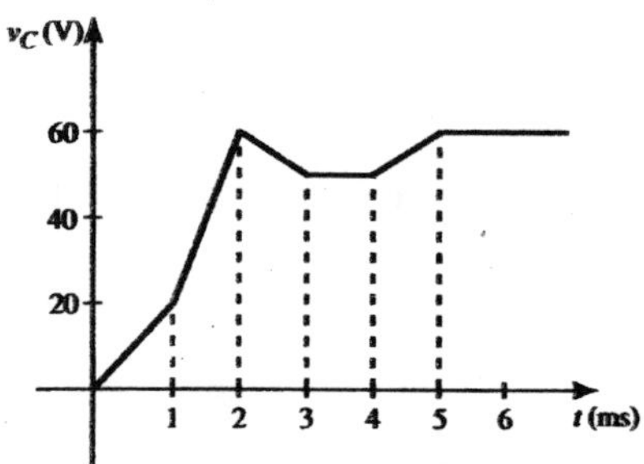

10.9 Energy Stored by a Capacitor

46. $W = \frac{1}{2} CV^2$

$W_1 = \frac{1}{2}(60 \times 10^{-6}\text{ F})(20\text{ V})^2 = 12\text{ mJ}$

$W_2 = \frac{1}{2}(30 \times 10^{-6}\text{ F})(40\text{ V})^2 = 24\text{ mJ}$

$W_3 = \frac{1}{2}(20 \times 10^{-6}\text{ F})(60\text{ V})^2 = 36\text{ mJ}$

10.10 Capacitor Failures and Troubleshooting

48. a. C_3 shorted.
    b. C_2 open.
    c. C_2 shorted.

CHAPTER 11

Capacitor Charging, Discharging and Simple Waveshaping Circuits

11.1 Introduction

2. a. $v_C(0^+) = 0\text{ V}; i_C(0^+) = \frac{E}{R} = \frac{-60\text{ V}}{4\ \Omega} = -15\text{ A}$

   b. $v_C = E = -60\text{ V}; i_C = 0\text{ A}$

4. $i(0^+) = \frac{E}{R} = \frac{25\text{ V}}{2.2\text{ k}\Omega} = 11.4\text{ mA}$

11.2 Capacitor Charging Equations

6. $RC = (4\ \Omega)(10 \times 10^{-6}\text{ F}) = 40\ \mu\text{s}; \frac{1}{RC} = 25\ 000$

   a. $v_C = E(1 - e^{-t/RC}) = 20(1 - e^{-25\ 000t})\text{ V}$

   b. $i_C = \frac{E}{R}e^{-t/RC} = \frac{20\text{ V}}{4\ \Omega}e^{-25\ 000t} = 5e^{-25\ 000t}\text{ A}$

   c.

t (μs)	v_C (V)	i_C (A)
0	0	5
40	12.6	1.84
80	17.3	0.677
120	19.0	0.249
160	19.6	0.092
200	19.9	0.034

   Example:

   At $t = 40\ \mu$s,

   $v_C = 20(1 - e^{-25\ 000 \times 40 \times 10^{-6}})$

   $= 20(1 - e^{-1}) = 20(0.632) = 12.6\text{ V}$

   d.

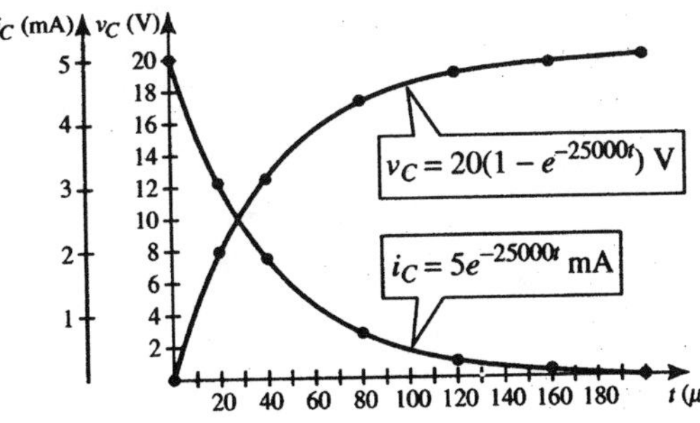

8. Because of the polarity of the source, capacitor voltage and current are negative.

   Thus, $v_C = -20(1 - e^{-t/RC})\text{ V}$

   $= -20(1 - e^{-10t})\text{ V}$

   $i_C = -\frac{20\text{ V}}{10\text{ k}\Omega}e^{-10t} = -2e^{-10t}\text{ mA}$

   At $t = 50$ ms, $v_C = -20(1 - e^{-0.5}) = -7.87\text{ V}$

   $i_C = -2e^{-0.5} = -1.21\text{ mA}$

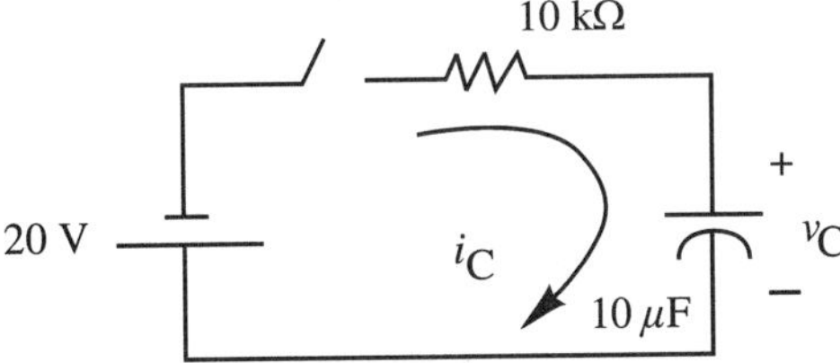

10. $i(0^+) = \frac{E}{R} = \frac{80\text{ V}}{R} = 20\text{ mA} \therefore R = 4\text{ k}\Omega$

    $RC = (4 \times 10^3\ \Omega)(10 \times 10^{-6}\text{ F})$

    $= 40\text{ ms and } \frac{1}{RC} = 25$

    $v_C = E(1 - e^{-t/RC}) = 80(1 - e^{-25t})\text{ V}$

    $i_C = \frac{E}{R}e^{-t/RC} = 20e^{-25t}\text{ mA}$

12. $5\tau = 200\text{ ms} \qquad \tau = 40\text{ ms}$

    $\tau = RC \therefore C = \frac{\tau}{R} = \frac{40 \times 10^{-3}}{5 \times 10^3} = 8\ \mu\text{F}$

14. $e^{-t/\tau} = e^{-40t} \therefore \tau = \frac{1}{40} = 25\text{ ms and } 5\tau = 125\text{ ms.}$

16. Since $v_C = E(1 - e^{-t/RC})$, $E = 100$ V.

    $R = \frac{E}{I_0} = \frac{100\text{ V}}{25\text{ mA}} = 4\text{ k}\Omega; \quad \tau = \frac{1}{50} = 0.02\text{ s};$

    $C = \frac{0.02}{R} = \frac{0.02\text{ s}}{4\text{ k}\Omega} = 5\ \mu\text{F}$

18. At $t = \tau$, $v_C = 0.632E$ (Figure 11-15)

    $\therefore 0.632E = 41.08\text{ V} \therefore E = 65\text{ V}$

At $t = 2\tau$, $i_C = 0.135i(0^+)$ (Figure 11-15)

$\therefore 0.135i(0^+) = 219.4$ mA $\therefore i(0^+) = 1.625$ A

But $i(0^+) = \frac{E}{R} \therefore R = \frac{E}{i(0+)} = \frac{65 \text{ V}}{1.625 \text{ A}} = 40\ \Omega$

11.3 Capacitor with an Initial Voltage

20. $i(0^+) = \frac{20 - (-10)}{4\ \Omega} = \frac{30 \text{ V}}{4\ \Omega} = 7.5$ A

22. a. $v_C = E + (V_0 - E)e^{-t/RC}$ $\tau = RC = 40\ \mu$s

$= 20 - 25e^{-25\,000t}$ V

b. $i = \left(\frac{E - V_0}{R}\right)e^{-t/RC} = \left[\frac{20 \text{ V} - (-5 \text{ V})}{4\ \Omega}\right]e^{-25\,000t}$

$= 6.25e^{-25\,000t}$ A

c.

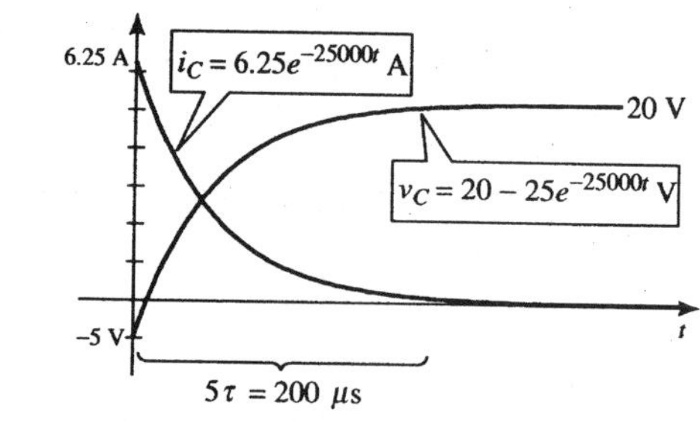

11.4 Capacitor Discharging Equations

24. $\tau = RC = (25\text{ k}\Omega)(20\ \mu\text{F}) = 0.5$ s. Therefore, the times indicated are multiples of τ and we can use the Universal Curves, Fig 11.15.

E.g., at τ, $v_C = 0.368\ V_0 = 0.368\ (55 \text{ V}) = 20.2$ V

$i_C = -0.368\left(\frac{V_0}{R}\right) = -0.368\left(\frac{55 \text{ V}}{25 \text{ k}\Omega}\right) = -0.810$ mA

Continuing in this manner, you get

t	τ	v_C (V)	i_C (mA)
0^+	0	55	–2.2
0.5	1	20.2	–0.810
1.0	2	7.43	–0.297
1.5	3	2.74	–0.110
2.0	4	1.01	–0.0403
2.5	5	0.371	–0.0148

26. From $t = 0$ to $t = 1$s, v_C decays exponentially. After $t = 1$s, the voltage remains constant—see diagram. Note: $v_C = 55e^{-2t}$ V. At $t = 1$s, $v_C = 7.43$ V. At $t = 3.25$s, it will still be 7.43 V

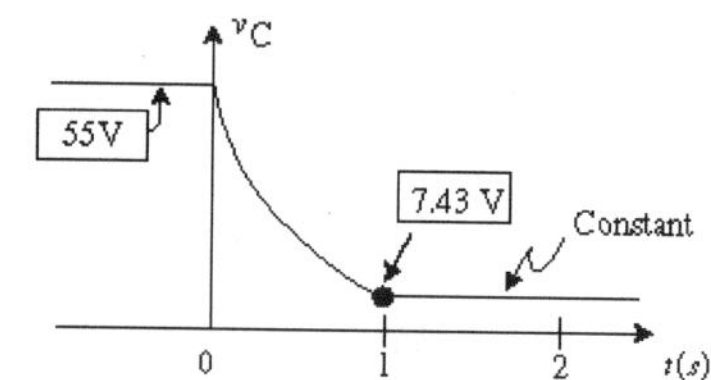

28. $i(0^+) = \frac{-V_0}{15\text{ k}\Omega + R_2} = -\frac{80 \text{ V}}{15\text{ k}\Omega + R_2} = -4$ mA $\therefore R_2 = 5$ kΩ

$\tau_d = \frac{20 \text{ ms}}{5} = 4$ ms $\qquad C = \frac{\tau_d}{R_d} = \frac{4 \times 10^{-3} \text{ s}}{15\text{ k}\Omega + 5\text{ k}\Omega} = 0.2\ \mu$F

11.5 More Complex Circuits

30. $R_{Th} = 30\ \Omega \| 60\ \Omega = 20\ \Omega$

$E_{Th} = \left(\frac{60\ \Omega}{90\ \Omega}\right)(225 \text{ V}) = 150$ V

$\tau_{Th} = R_{Th}C = (20\ \Omega)(100\ \mu\text{F}) = 2$ ms and $\frac{1}{\tau_{Th}} = 500$

(a)

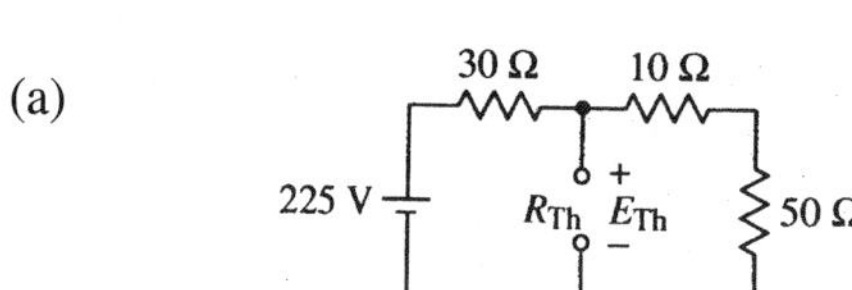

(b)

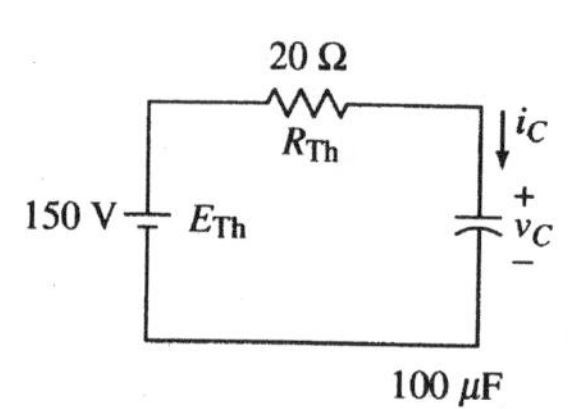

a. $v_C = E_{Th}(1 - e^{-t/\tau_{Th}}) = 150(1 - e^{-500t})$ V

$i_C = \frac{E_{Th}}{R_{Th}}e^{-t/\tau_{Th}} = \frac{150 \text{ V}}{20\ \Omega}e^{-500t} = 7.5e^{-500t}$ A

b. At $t = 2$ ms,

$v_C = 150(1 - e^{-500 \times 2 \times 10^{-3}}) = 150(1 - e^{-1}) = 94.8$ V

c. At $t = 2$ ms, $i_C = 7.5e^{-500 \times 2 \times 10^{-3}} = 7.5e^{-1} = 2.76$ A

Continuing in this manner, you get

t (ms)	v_C (V)	i_C (A)
0	0	7.5
2	94.8	2.76
4	129.7	1.02
6	142.5	0.374
8	147.3	0.137
10	149.0	0.051
12	149.6	0.019

d. Capacitor is a short at $t = 0^+$

$\therefore i(0^+) = \dfrac{225\text{ V}}{30\ \Omega} = 7.5$ A

32. a. $\tau_C = (R_1 + R_3)C = (25\text{ k}\Omega)(0.5\ \mu\text{F}) = 12.5$ ms

b. $\tau_d = (R_2 + R_3)C = (40\text{ k}\Omega)(0.5\ \mu\text{F}) = 20$ ms

c. $v_C = E(1 - e^{-t/\tau_C}) = 80(1 - e^{-80t})$ V

$i_C = \dfrac{E}{R_1 + R_3}e^{-t/\tau_C} = \dfrac{80}{25\text{ k}\Omega}e^{-80t} = 3.2e^{-80t}$ mA

d. $5\tau_d = 100$ ms

e. Charging time is $5\tau_c = 62.5$ ms. Therefore, capacitor is fully charged before SW is moved to discharge.

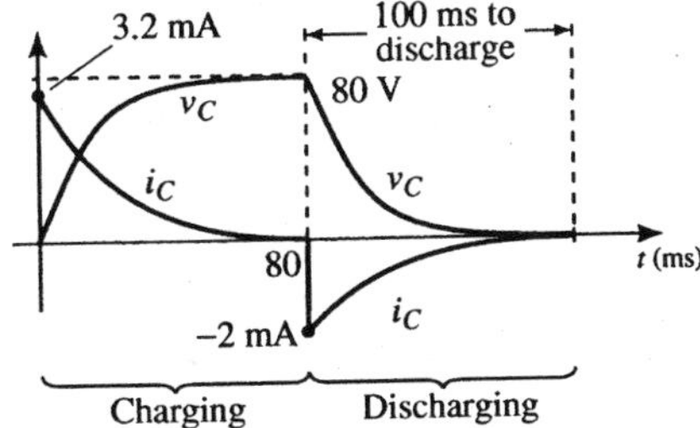

34. Convert the current source to a voltage source.

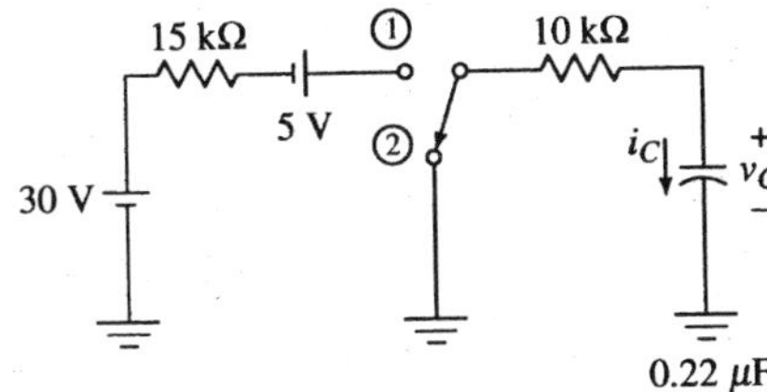

a. $\tau_C = (15\text{ k}\Omega + 10\text{ k}\Omega)(0.22\ \mu\text{F}) = 5.5$ ms

b. $\tau_d = (10\text{ k}\Omega)(0.22\ \mu\text{F}) = 2.2$ ms

c. $v_C = E(1 - e^{-t/\tau_c}) = 35(1 - e^{-t/5.5\text{ ms}})$ V

$i_C = \dfrac{E}{R_c}e^{-t/\tau_c} = \dfrac{35\text{ V}}{25\text{ k}\Omega}e^{-t/\tau_c} = 1.4e^{-t/5.5\text{ ms}}$ mA

d. At $t = 2\tau_C$: $v_C = 35(1 - e^{-2}) = 30.3$ V.

Now redefine $t = 0$ to the instant that the switch is moved to discharge. At this instant, $V_0 = 30.3$ V. Thus,

$v_C = V_0e^{-t/\tau_d} = 30.3e^{-t/2.2\text{ ms}}$ V

$i_C = -\dfrac{V_0}{R_d}e^{-t/\tau_d} = -\dfrac{30.3\text{ V}}{10\ \Omega}e^{-t/\tau_d}$

$= -3.03e^{-t/2.2\text{ ms}}$ mA.

e.

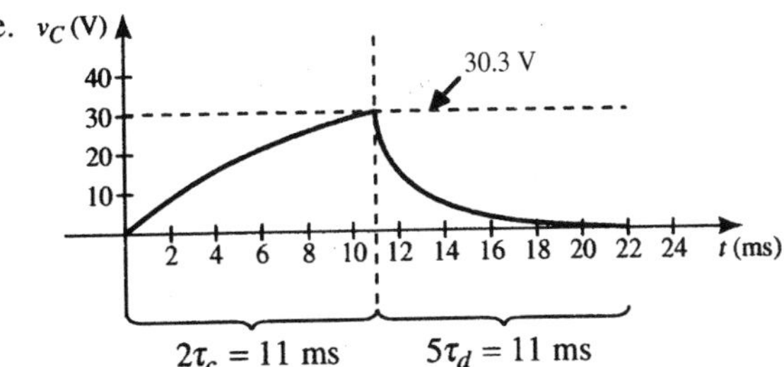

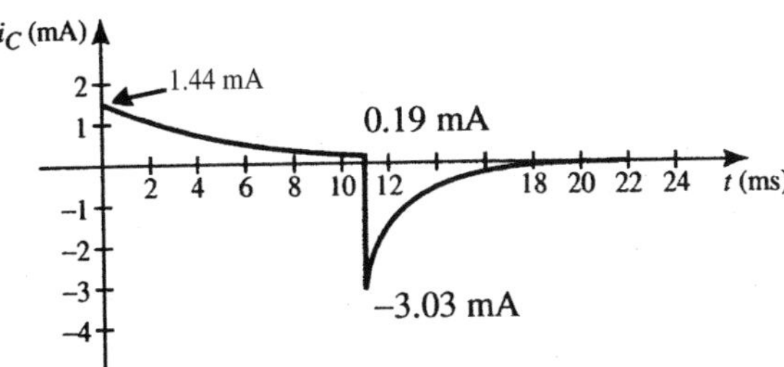

36. As indicated in (a), $E_{Th} = V_{OC} = 45$ V. If a short is placed across a-b,

$I_{SC} = \dfrac{E_{Th}}{R_{Th}}\ \therefore\ R_{Th} = \dfrac{E_{Th}}{I_{SC}} = \dfrac{45\text{ V}}{1.5\text{ mA}} = 30\text{ k}\Omega.$

Now consider (b).

$\tau = R_{Th}C = (30\text{ k}\Omega)(500\ \mu\text{F}) = 15$ s

$v_C = E_{Th}(1 - e^{-t/\tau}) = 45(1 - e^{-t/15\text{ s}})$V

$i_C = \dfrac{E_{Th}}{R_{Th}}e^{-t/\tau} = 1.5e^{-t/15\text{ s}}$mA

At $t = 25$ s, $v_C = 45(1 - e^{-25/15}) = 36.5$ V

$i_C = 1.5e^{-25/15} = 0.283$ mA

(a)

(b)

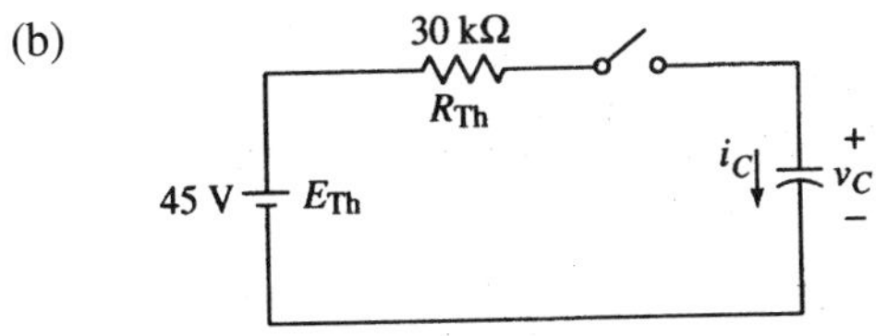

11.6 An RC Timing Application

38. $v_C = E(1 - e^{-t/RC})$

$4.2 = 5(1 - e^{-t/RC})$

$e^{-t/RC} = \frac{5 - 4.2}{5} = 0.16$

$\ln(e^{-t/RC}) = \ln(0.16)$

$-\frac{t}{RC} = -1.8326$

$\therefore R = \frac{t}{1.8326C} = \frac{37 \text{ s}}{1.8326(47 \times 10^{-6})} = 429.6 \text{ k}\Omega$

Choose nearest higher value: $R = 430 \text{ k}\Omega$.

11.7 Pulse Response of RC Circuits

40. a. $T = 4$ ms

b. Duty cycle $= \frac{t_p}{T} \times 100\% = \frac{3 \text{ ms}}{4 \text{ ms}} \times 100\% = 75\%$

c. $\text{PRR} = \frac{1}{T} = \frac{1}{4 \times 10^{-3} \text{ s}} = 250$ pulses/s

42. a. $\tau = RC = (2 \text{ k}\Omega)(1\ \mu\text{F}) = 2$ ms.

$\therefore 5\tau = 10$ ms

Since this is equal to the pulse width, the capacitor fully charges and you get the waveform of (a).

(a)

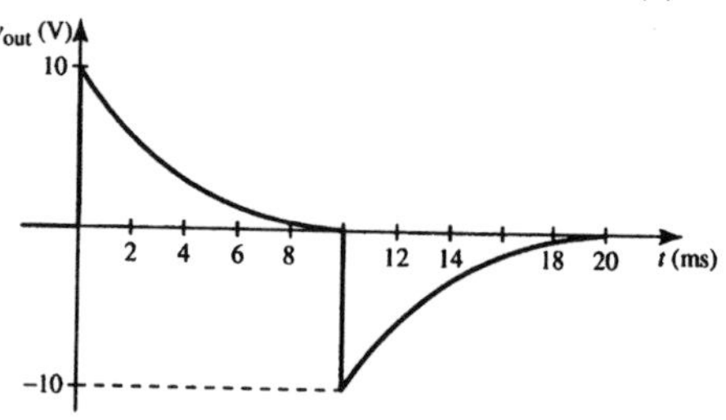

b. $\tau = RC = (2 \text{ k}\Omega)(0.1\ \mu\text{F}) = 0.2 \text{ ms} \therefore 5\tau = 1$ ms.

The waveform is shown in (b).

(b)

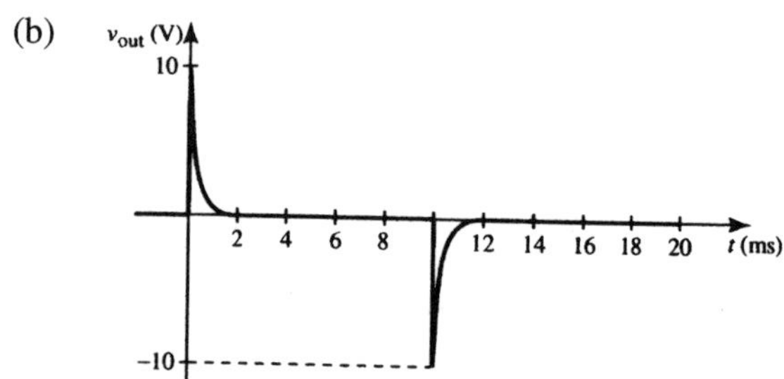

44. a. $\tau = RC = (2 \text{ k}\Omega)(0.1\ \mu\text{F}) = 0.2$ ms

$\therefore 5\tau = 1$ ms

Since the pulse lasts 10 ms, the capacitor fully charges and discharges in the first 1 ms as shown in (a).

b. $\tau = RC = (20 \text{ k}\Omega)(1.0\ \mu\text{F}) = 20$ ms

$\therefore 5\tau = 100$ ms

Since the pulse width is 10 ms, rise and fall occurs on the linear portion of the exponential as shown in (b).

(a)

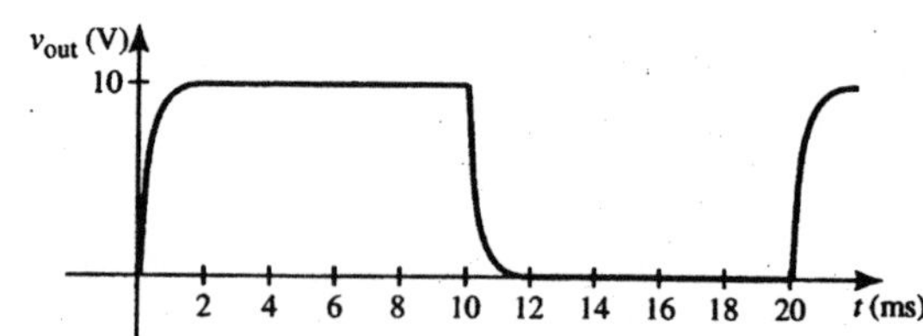

(b)

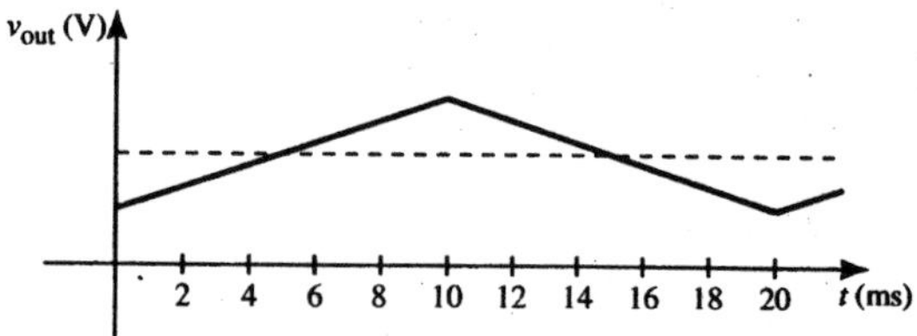

11.8 Transient Analysis Using Computers

To identify nodes for MSM problems, build the circuit, then click Options, Preference, Show Node Names, OK. You may also want to use more than the minimum number of time points to get a smoother curve.

46. Case 1: Initially Uncharged Capacitor: Create the circuit. Click Simulate, Analysis, Transient, Initial Conditions set to zero, set TSTOP to 0.25, select the appropriate node for display, then run the simulation. At 50 ms, the voltage should be $40\ e^{-1} = 14.72$ V. Thus, $i_C = 14.72\ V/1\ k\Omega = 14.72$ mA. Check: $i_C = 40\ e^{-1}$ mA = 14.72 mA.

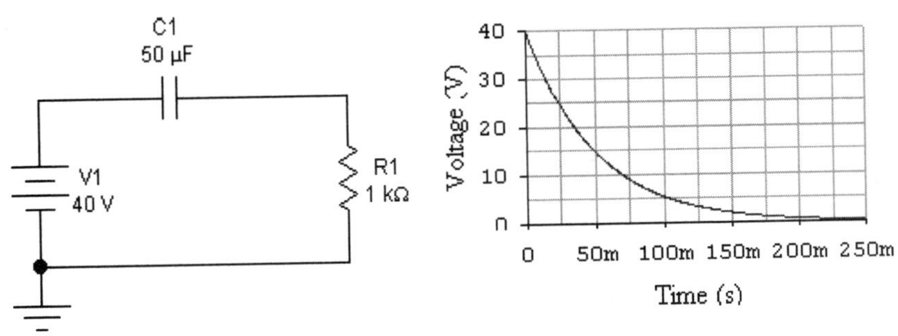

Case 2: Initial Voltage = 100 V: Double click the capacitor, select Initial Condition, key in 100, select V, then click OK. Click the Analysis icon, select Transient Analysis, select "User-defined" for Initial Conditions, then run the simulation. With the cursor, you find voltage at 50 ms is –22.1 V. Thus, current is –22.1 V/1 kΩ = –22.1 mA. Check: At $t = 50$ ms, $i_C = -60\ e^{-1} = -22.1$ mA.

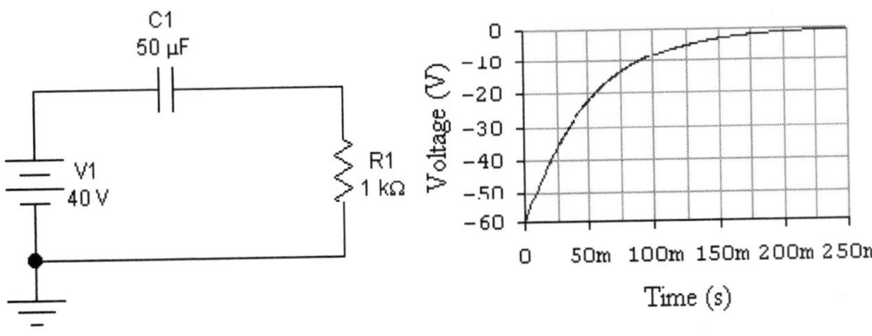

48. Create the circuit shown; then, referring to Problem 46 for guidance, perform a transient analysis. With the cursor, measure the capacitor voltage at $t = 1$ s. You should get approximately 8.6 V. Check: $\tau = RC = (10\ k\Omega)\ (50\ \mu F) = 0.5$ s. The charging equation is

$v_C = E(1 - e^{-t/\tau}) = 10(1 - e^{-2t})$ V.

At $t = 1$ s, this yields $10(1 - e^{-2}) = 8.65$ V.

The solution is unavailable for MultiSIM 2001. See the website if you have a later version of MultiSIM.

50. Capacitor initially uncharged: Create the circuit as shown. Double click the capacitor symbol and set its initial condition (IC) to 0V. Use differential markers to plot capacitor voltage. Set up the simulation profile for transient analysis, then click the run icon. Following simulation, add the second axis, then use Add Trace to create the capacitor current plot. Scale values with the cursor. At 50 ms, the current should be 40 mA e^{-1} = 14.72 mA.

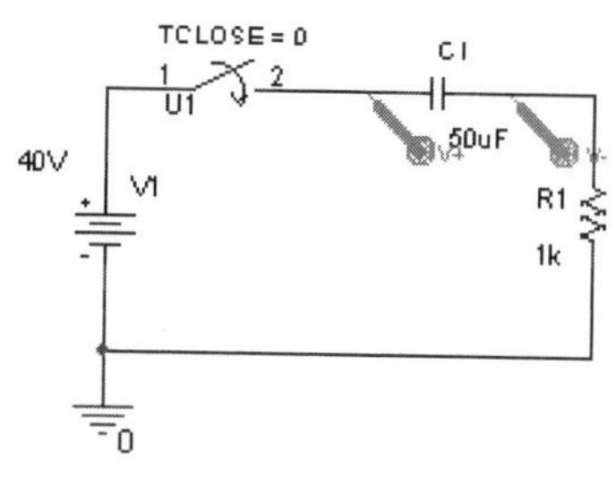

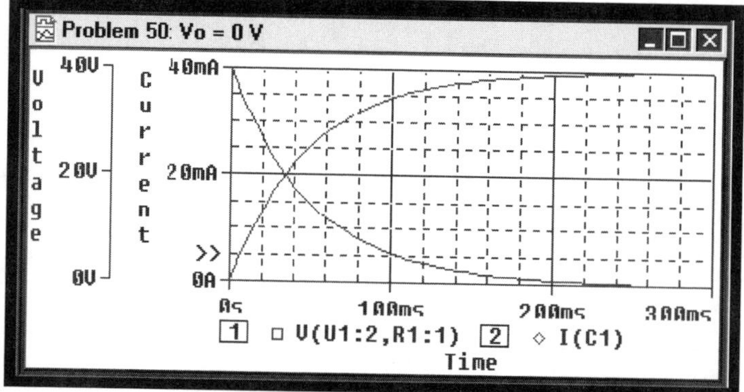

Initial voltage = 100 V: Double click the capacitor and set its initial voltage (IC) to 100V, then run the simulation. At 50 ms, the current should be –60 mA e^{-1} = –22.1 mA.

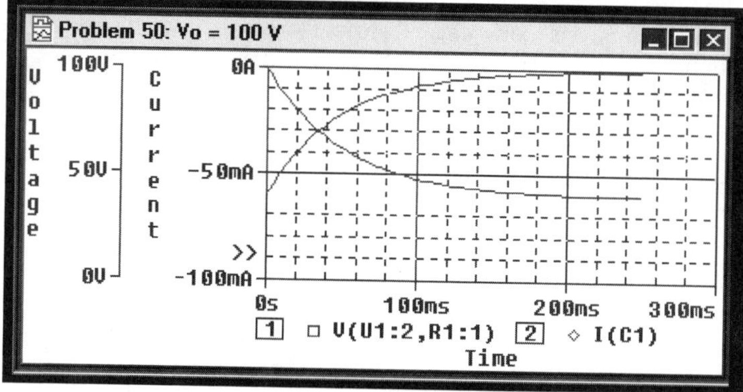

52. See Example 11-7. Change the source pulse width to 0.5s, but leave everything else the same. Here are the voltage and current plots. Analytic answers are 17.54 V and 0.493 mA at $0.5s^{-}$ and –3.5 mA at $0.5s^{+}$. Use the cursor to compare answers. Agreement is good.

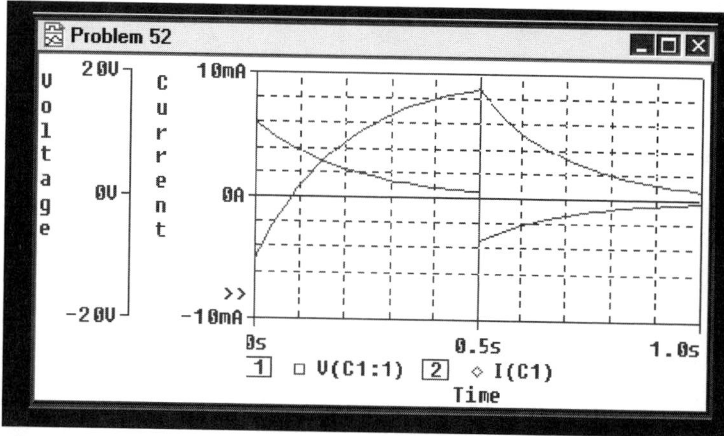

CHAPTER

12

Magnetism and Magnetic Circuits

12.3 Flux and Flux Density

2. $\Phi = 250 \times 10^{-6}\text{ Wb} = 250 \times 10^{-6} \times \dfrac{10^8\text{ lines}}{\text{Wb}} = 25 \times 10^3\text{ lines}$

$$B = \frac{\Phi}{A_1} = \frac{25 \times 10^3\text{ lines}}{1.25\text{ in.}^2} = 20\text{ kilolines/in.}^2$$

4. $d = r_2 - r_1 = 4.5 - 3.5 = 1\text{ in.}$

$$A = \frac{\pi d^2}{4} = \frac{\pi}{4}(1)^2 = 0.7854\text{ in.}^2$$

$$\Phi = 628 \times 10^{-6}\text{ Wb} = 628 \times 10^{-6}\ \cancel{\text{Wb}} \times \frac{10^8\text{ lines}}{\cancel{\text{Wb}}} = 62.8\text{ kilolines}$$

$$B = \frac{\Phi}{A} = \frac{62.8\text{ kilolines}}{0.7854\text{ in.}^2} = 80\text{ kilolines/in.}^2$$

12.6 Series Elements and Parallel Elements

6. $\Phi = B_2A_2 = (0.6\text{ T})(0.015\text{ m}^2) = 9 \times 10^{-3}\text{ Wb}$

$$B_1 = \frac{\Phi}{A_1} = \frac{9 \times 10^{-3}\text{ Wb}}{0.02\text{ m}^2} = 0.45\text{ T}$$

$$B_3 = \frac{\Phi}{A_3} = \frac{9 \times 10^{-3}\text{ Wb}}{0.01\text{ m}^2} = 0.9\text{ T}$$

8. $\Phi_1 = B_1A_1 = (0.8\text{ T})(0.02\text{ m2}) = 16\text{ mWb}$

$\Phi_2 = B_2A_2 = (0.6\text{ T})(0.01\text{ m2}) = 6\text{ mWb}$

$\Phi_3 = \Phi_1 - \Phi_2 = 10\text{ mWb}$

$$B_3 = \frac{\Phi_3}{A_3} = \frac{10 \times 10^{-3}\text{ Wb}}{0.016\text{ m}^2} = 0.625\text{ T}$$

12.8 Magnetic Field Intensity and Magnetization Curves

10. $$B = \frac{\Phi}{A} = \frac{\mathscr{F}/\mathscr{R}}{A} = \frac{\mathscr{F}}{\mathscr{R}A} = \frac{NI}{\left(\dfrac{\ell}{\mu A}\right)A} = \mu\left(\frac{NI}{\ell}\right) = \mu H$$

12.9 Ampere's Circuital Law

12. $N_1I_1 = H_1\ell_1 + H_2\ell_2$

$0 = H_2\ell_2 - H_3\ell_3$

14. $N_1I_1 = H_1\ell_1 + H_2\ell_2$

$N_2I_2 = H_2\ell_2 + H_3\ell_3$

12.10 Series Magnetic Circuits: Given Φ find NI

16. $$B_{steel} = \frac{0.16 \times 10^{-3}\text{ Wb}}{(0.85)(3.2 \times 10^{-4}\text{ m}^2)} = 0.59\text{ T}$$

$\therefore H_{steel} = 125\text{ At/m}$

From Problem 15, $H_{iron} = 1550\text{ At/m}$

$\therefore NI = (125\text{ At/m})(0.14\text{ m}) + (1550\text{ At/m})(0.06\text{ m})$
$= 110.5\text{ At}$

$$I = \frac{110.5\text{ At}}{300\text{ t}} = 0.37\text{ A}$$

18.

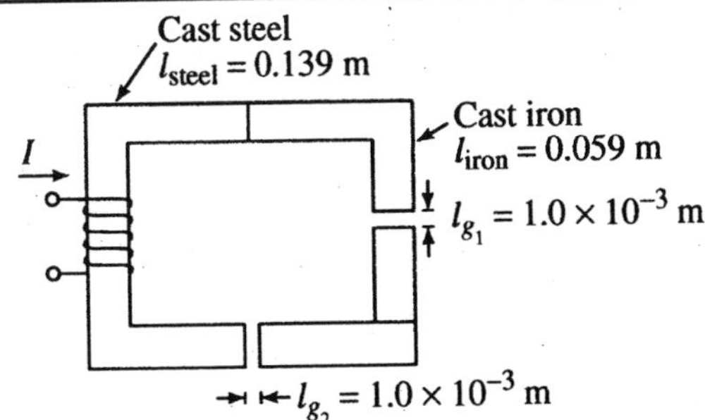

$$B = \frac{0.128 \times 10^{-3}\text{ Wb}}{3.2 \times 10^{-4}\text{ m}^2} = 0.4\text{ T (All sections)}$$

$$\left.\begin{array}{l} H_{steel} = 300 \text{ At/m} \\ H_{iron} = 1050 \text{ At/m} \end{array}\right\} \text{From Fig. 12–19}$$

$$H_{g1} = H_{g2} = \frac{B_g}{\mu_0} = \frac{0.4 \text{ T}}{4\pi \times 10^{-7}} = 318.3 \times 10^3 \text{ At/m}$$

$NI = H_{steel}\ell_{steel} + H_{iron}\ell_{iron} + 2\, H_g\ell_g$
$= (300)(0.139) + (1050)(0.059) + 2(318.3 \times 10^3)(1 \times 10^{-3})$
$= 740.3$ At

$$I = \frac{740.3 \text{ At}}{300 \text{ t}} = 2.47 \text{ A}$$

20. Cast Steel: $B_{cast} = \dfrac{\Phi}{A_{cast}} = \dfrac{141 \times 10^{-6} \text{ Wb}}{1 \times 10^{-4} \text{ m}^2} = 1.41 \text{ T}$

From B-H curve: $H_{cast} = 2050$ At/m

Sheet Steel: $B_{sheet} = \dfrac{\Phi}{A_{eff}} = \dfrac{141 \times 10^{-6} \text{ Wb}}{(0.94)(1 \times 10^{-4} \text{ m}^{2})} = 1.5 \text{ T} \therefore H_{sheet} = 2150$ At/m

$NI = (2050 \text{ At/m})(0.16 \text{ m}) + (2150 \text{ At/m})(0.1 \text{ m}) = 543$ At

$$I = \frac{543 \text{ At}}{400 \text{ t}} = 1.36 \text{ A}$$

22. Convert to SI units

$$\Phi = 25\,000 \text{ lines} = 25\,000 \text{ lines} \times \frac{1 \text{ Wb}}{10^8 \text{ lines}} = 25 \times 10^{-5} \text{ Wb}$$

$A_1 = 1 \text{ in.}^2 = 6.452 \times 10^{-4} \text{ m}^2;\ A_2 = 12.904 \times 10^{-4} \text{ m}^2$

$$B_1 = \frac{\Phi}{A_1} = \frac{25 \times 10^{-5} \text{ Wb}}{6.452 \times 10^{-4}} = 0.39 \text{ T};\ B_2 = \frac{\Phi}{A_2} = 0.194 \text{ T}$$

Section 1: Cast iron: $B_1 = 0.39 \text{ T} \therefore H_1 = 1025$ At/m
$\ell_1 = 2 \text{ in.} = 0.0508$ m

Section 2: Cast iron: $B_2 = 0.194 \text{ T} \therefore H_2 = 500$ At/m
$\ell_2 = 3\frac{1}{2} \text{ in.} = 0.0889$ m

Section 3: Cast steel: $B_3 = 0.194 \text{ T} \therefore H_3 = 200$ At/m
$\ell_3 = 5.8 \text{ in.} = 0.1473$ m

Section 4: Sheet steel: $B_4 = 0.194 \text{ T} \therefore H_4 = 75$ At/m
$\ell_4 = 7\frac{1}{2} \text{ in.} = 0.1905$ m

Air Gap: $B_g = 0.194$ T $\qquad H_g = \dfrac{B_g}{\mu_0} = 154.4 \times 10^3$ At/m
$\ell_g = 0.2 \text{ in.} = 5.08 \times 10^{-3}$ m

$NI = H_1\ell_1 + H_2\ell_2 + H_3\ell_3 + H_4\ell_4 + H_g\ell_g$
$= (1025)(0.0508) + (500)(0.0889) + (200)(0.1473) + (75)(0.1905) + (154.4 \times 10^3)(5.08 \times 10^{-3})$
$NI = 925$ At

$$I = \frac{NI}{N} = \frac{925 \text{ At}}{600 \text{ t}} = 1.54 \text{ A}$$

12.11 Series-Parallel Magnetic Circuits

24. To simplify notation, let $\ell_1 = \ell_{cda}$ and $\ell_3 = \ell_{abc}$.

$$B_g = \frac{\Phi_g}{A_g} = \frac{80 \times 10^{-6} \text{ Wb}}{4 \times 10^{-4} \text{ m}^2} = 0.2 \text{ T}$$

$H_g = 7.96 \times 10^5\ B_g = (7.96 \times 10^5)(0.2\text{ T}) = 159.2 \times 10^3$ At/m

Center Leg: $B_2 = B_g = 0.2$ T

From Fig. 12–19, $H_2 = 200$ At/m

Loop 2: $H_3\ell_3 - H_2\ell_{cy} - H_g\ell_g - H_2\ell_{xa} = 0$

$H_3\ell_3 = H_2\ell_{cy} + H_g\ell_g + H_2\ell_{xa} = (200)(0.039) + (159.2 \times 10^3)(1 \times 10^{-3}) + (200)(0.039)$

$$\therefore H_3 = \frac{174.8\text{ At}}{\ell_3} = \frac{174.8\text{ At}}{0.14\text{ m}} = 1250\text{ At/m}$$

From Fig. 12–19, $B_3 = 1.24$ T

$\Phi_3\ B_3A = (1.24\text{ T})(4 \times 10^{-4}\text{ m}^2) = 496\ \mu\text{Wb}$

$\Phi_1 = \Phi_2 + \Phi_3 = 80\ \mu\text{Wb} + 496\ \mu\text{Wb} = 576\ \mu\text{Wb}$

$$B_1 = \frac{\Phi_1}{A} = \frac{576 \times 10^{-6}\text{ Wb}}{4 \times 10^{-4}\text{ m}^2} = 1.44\text{ T} \therefore H_1 = 2250$$

Loop 1: $NI = H_1\ell_1 + H_3\ell_3 = (2250\text{ At/m})(0.16\text{ m}) + (1250\text{ At/m})(0.14\text{ m}) = 535$ At

$$\therefore I = \frac{NI}{N} = \frac{535\text{ At}}{100\text{ T}} = 5.35\text{A}$$

12.12 Series Magnetic Circuits: Given NI, Find Φ

26. $NI = H_{iron}\ell_{iron} + H_g\ell_g$

$H_g\ell_g \approx 0.9\ NI = (0.9)(2500\ t)(0.2\text{ A}) = 450\ \text{A}t$

$$H_g = \frac{450\text{ At}}{\ell_g} = \frac{450\text{ At}}{2.54 \times 10^{-3}\text{ m}} = 177.2 \times 10^3\text{ At/m}$$

$B_g = \mu_0 H_g = 4\pi \times 10^{-7} \times 177.2 \times 10^3 = 0.223$ T

$\Phi_g = B_g A_g = (0.223\text{ T})(0.02\text{ m}^2) = 4.5$ mWb

28. $\ell_g = 4 \times 10^{-3}\text{ m} \therefore \ell_{steel} = 0.314\text{ m} - 0.004\text{ m} = 0.310\text{ m}.$

Assume 90% of the mmf appears across the gap. Thus,

$H_g\ell_g \approx (0.09)(644\text{ At}) = 579.6$ At

$$H_g = \frac{579.6\text{ At}}{\ell_g} = \frac{579.6\text{ At}}{4 \times 10^{-3}\text{ m}} = 144.9 \times 10^3\text{ At/m}$$

$B_g = \mu_0 H_g = 4\pi \times 10^{-7} \times 144.9 \times 10^3 = 0.182$ T.

Since $B_{steel} = B_g$, $B_{steel} = 0.182$ T.

From Fig. 12–19, $H_{steel} = 200$ At/m

Trial 1

$NI = H_{steel}\ell_{steel} + H_g\ell_g$

$= (200\text{ At/m})(0.310\text{ m}) + (144.9 \times 10^3\text{ At/m})(4 \times 10^{-3}\text{ m})$

$= 641.6$ At (Excellent agreement)

Since this is within 5%, no further trials are needed.

$$\therefore \Phi = BA = (0.182\text{ T})\underbrace{(3.14 \times 10^{-4}\text{ m}^2)}_{\text{From Problem 25}}$$

$= 57\ \mu Wb$

12.13 Force Due to an Electromagnet

30. $B_g = \frac{\Phi_g}{A_g} = \frac{4 \times 10^{-4}\ \text{Wb}}{(0.025\ \text{m})^2} = 0.64\ \text{T}$

At each gap: $F = \frac{0.5B_g{}^2A}{\mu_0} = \frac{(0.5)(0.64)^2(0.025)^2}{4\pi \times 10^{-7}} = 101.9\ \text{N}$

Total force = 2(101.9) = 203.8 N = 45.8 lb

CHAPTER

13

Inductance and Inductors

13.2 Induced Voltage and Inductance

2. $e = N\dfrac{\Delta\Phi}{\Delta t}$ $\quad \dfrac{\Delta\Phi}{\Delta t} = \dfrac{1 \times 10^{-3}\text{ Wb}}{0.5 \times 10^{-3}\text{ s}} = 2\text{ Wb/s}$

$80\text{ V} = N(2\text{ Wb/s})$

$N = \dfrac{80\text{ V}}{2\text{ Wb/}s} = 40\text{ turns}$

13.3 Self-Inductance

4. $v_L = L\dfrac{\Delta i}{\Delta t} = (0.4\text{ H})(200\text{ A/s}) = 80\text{ V}$

6. $v_L = L\dfrac{\Delta i}{\Delta t}\ \therefore\ L = \dfrac{v_L}{\Delta i/\Delta t} = \dfrac{25\text{ V}}{5\text{ A/}s} = 5\text{ H}$

8. Current is changing at a rate ten times as fast. Therefore, induced voltage is ten times as great. Thus,
$e_2 = 10(45\text{ V}) = 450\text{ V}$.

10. $A = \left(1.5\text{ in.} \times 0.0254\dfrac{\text{m}}{\text{in.}}\right)\left(1.2\text{ in.} \times 0.0254\dfrac{\text{m}}{\text{in.}}\right)$

$= 1.161 \times 10^{-3}\text{ m}^2$

$\ell = 0.2\text{ in.} = 5.08 \times 10^{-3}\text{ m}$

$L = \dfrac{\mu_0 N^2 A_g}{\ell_g}$

$= \dfrac{(4\pi \times 10^{-7})(2000t)^2(1.161 \times 10^{-3}\text{ m}^2)}{5.08 \times 10^{-3}\text{ m}}$

$= 1.15\text{ H}$

13.4 Computing Induced Voltage

12. $v_L = L\dfrac{\Delta i}{\Delta t}$ $\quad L = 0.75\text{ H}$

Time Interval (ms)	$\dfrac{\Delta i}{\Delta t}$ (A/s)	v_L (V)
0–1	0	0
1–3	5	3.75
3–4	20	15
4–6	0	0
6–9	–15	–11.25
> 9	0	0

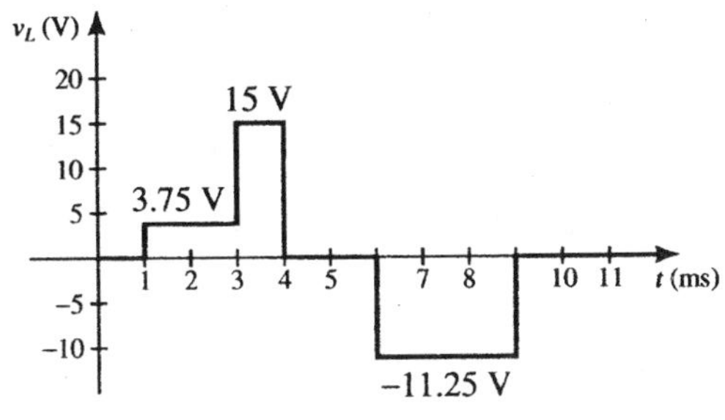

14. At $t = 10$ ms, current changes abruptly. Therefore, its rate of change is infinite, and $v_L = -\infty$ as shown below. This is not possible, therefore this is not a valid inductor current.

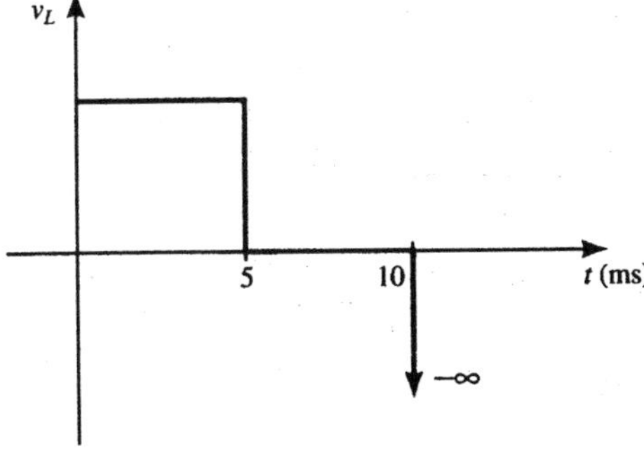

16. $v_L = L\dfrac{di}{dt} = 25\text{ H}\dfrac{d}{dt}(20e^{-12t} \times 10^{-3}\text{ A})$

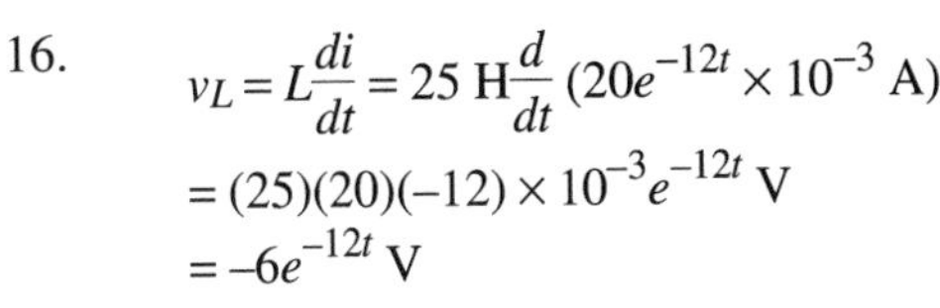

$= (25)(20)(-12) \times 10^{-3}e^{-12t}\text{ V}$

$= -6e^{-12t}\text{ V}$

13.5 Inductances in Series and Parallel

18. $L_T = L_1 + L_2 + L_3 + L_4$. Convert all to a common prefix.
$L_T = 10\text{ mH} + 22\text{ mH} + 86\text{ mH} + 12\text{ mH} = 130\text{ mH}$

20. $\frac{1}{L_T} = \frac{1}{10\text{ mH}} + \frac{1}{22\text{ mH}} + \frac{1}{86\text{ mH}} + \frac{1}{12\text{ mH}}$
$\therefore L_T = 4.16\text{ mH}$

22. Through successive reduction, for the circuit of (a). $L_T = 36.2$ H, while for (b), $L_T = 30$ H.

(a)

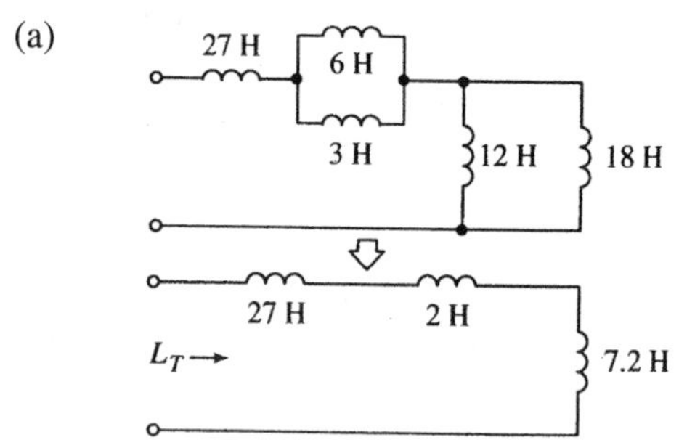

(b)

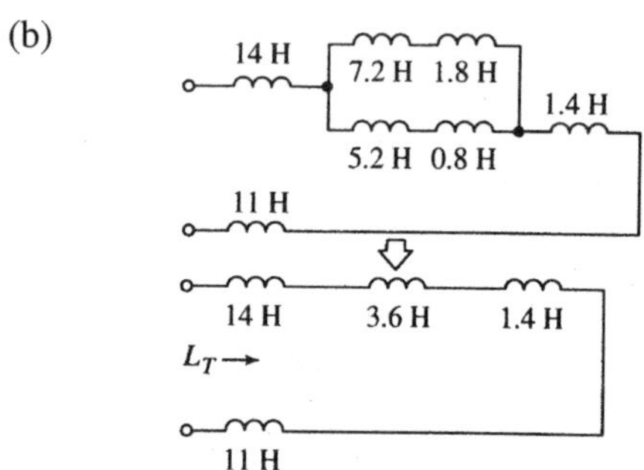

24. Consider (a). $6\text{ H} = 18\text{ H} \| L_{eq} \therefore L_{eq} = 9\text{ H}$
Consider (b). $9\text{ H} = 2\text{ H} + L'_{eq} + 5\text{ H} \therefore L'_{eq} = 2\text{ H}$
But $L'_{eq} = 6\text{ H} \| L_x \therefore 2\text{ H} = \frac{(6\text{ H})L_x}{6\text{ H} + L_x}$ and $L_x = 3$ H

(a)

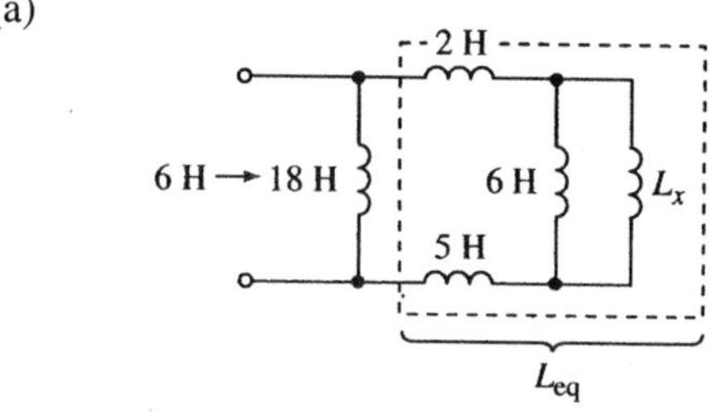

(b)

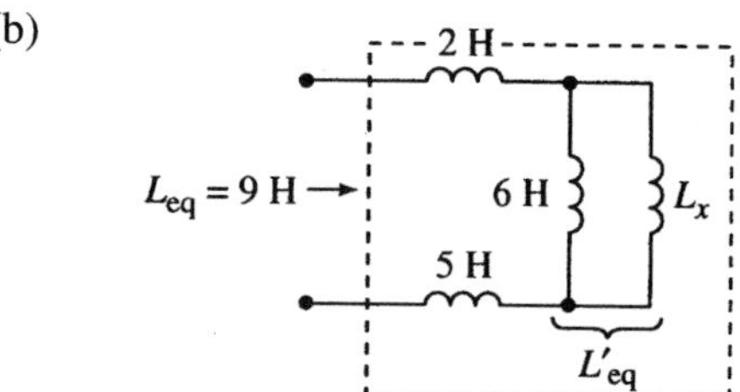

26. Largest when in series; smallest when in parallel.
$L_{largest} = 24\text{ mH} + 36\text{ mH} + 22\text{ mH} + 10\text{ mH} = 92\text{ mH}$

$\frac{1}{L_{smallest}} = \frac{1}{24\text{ mH}} + \frac{1}{36\text{ mH}} + \frac{1}{22\text{ mH}} + \frac{1}{10\text{ mH}}$
$\therefore L_{smallest} = 4.65\text{ mH}$

28. Only the circuit below yields $L_T = 3.6$ H.

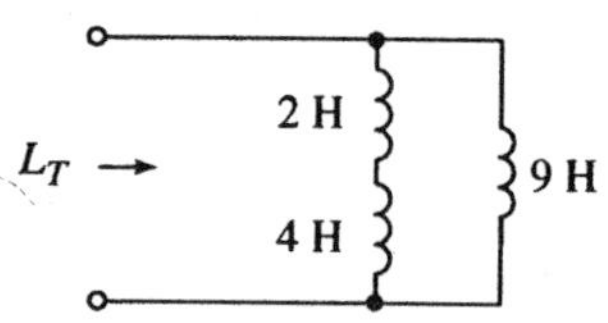

30. By KCL, $i = i_1 + i_2 + \ldots + i_N$
Differentiate both sides.

$\frac{di}{dt} = \frac{di_1}{dt} + \frac{di_2}{d_t} + \ldots + \frac{di_N}{dt}$

But $v = L_T\frac{di}{dt} \therefore \frac{di}{dt} = \frac{v}{L_T}$

Similarly $\frac{di_1}{dt} = \frac{v}{L_1}, \frac{di_2}{dt} = \frac{v}{L_2}$, etc.

Thus, $\frac{v}{L_T} = \frac{v}{L_1} + \frac{v}{L_2} + \ldots + \frac{v}{L_N}$.

Cancelling v yields

$\frac{1}{L_T} = \frac{1}{L_1} + \frac{1}{L_2} + \ldots + \frac{1}{L_N}$

13.7 Inductance and Steady State DC

32. a. Replace all inductances by short circuits. Thus,
$E = (4\text{ A})(15\Omega) = 60$ V.

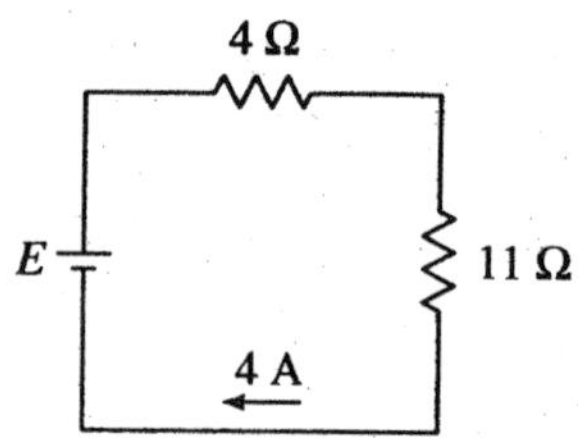

b. Replace inductances by shorts and capacitances by opens.

$$I = \frac{18\text{ V} - 13.5\text{ V}}{4.5\ \Omega} = 1\text{ A}$$

Thus, $V_X = 13.5\text{ V} - (9\ \Omega)(1\text{ A}) = 4.5\text{ V}$

$$I_6 = \frac{4.5\text{ V}}{6\ \Omega} = 0.75\text{ A and } I_X = 1\text{ A} - 0.75\text{ A} = 0.25\text{ A}$$

$$R_X = \frac{V_X}{I_X} = \frac{4.5\text{ V}}{0.25\text{ A}} = 18\ \Omega$$

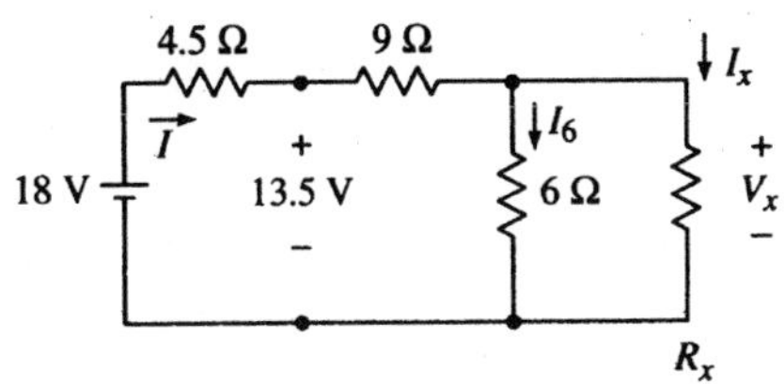

13.8 Energy Storage by an Inductance

34. Replace each inductance by a short yields.

$$I = \frac{100\text{ V}}{20\ \Omega} = 5\text{A}$$

$$W_T = \frac{1}{2}L_T I^2 \therefore L_T = \frac{W_T}{\frac{1}{2}I^2} = \frac{75\text{ J}}{\frac{1}{2}(5\text{ A})^2} = 6\text{ H}$$

But $L_T = L_1 + L_2 = 2L_2 + L_2 = 3L_2$

$\therefore 3L_2 = 6\text{ H}$ and $L_2 = 2\text{ H}$

$L_1 = 2L_2 = 4\text{ H}$

13.9 Inductor Troubleshooting Hints

36. By inspection, either L_2 or L_3 is shorted.

CHAPTER

14

Inductive Transients

14.1 Introduction

2. Replace inductors with open circuits. The result is a simple dc circuit that can be solved using standard dc analysis techniques. Answers are as indicated.

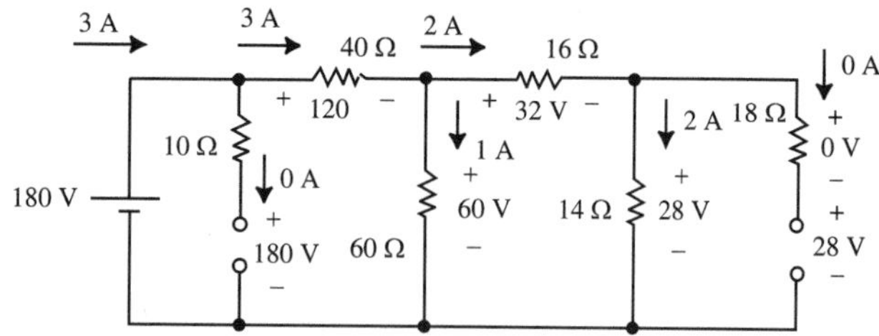

14.2 Current Buildup Transients

4. a. $i_L = 8(1 - e^{-500t})$ A. At $t = 0.006$ s, $i_L = 8(1 - e^{-500(0.006)}) = 8(1 - e^{-3}) = 7.60$ A.

   b. $v_L = 125e^{-500t}$ V. At $t = 0.005$ s, $v_L = 125e^{-500(0.005)} = 125e^{-2.5} = 10.3$ V.

6. $$i_L = \frac{E}{R}(1 - e^{-Rt/L}) = \frac{18\text{ V}}{390\ \Omega}(1 - e^{-390t/0.6}) = 46.2(1 - e^{-650t})\text{ mA}$$

   $v_L = Ee^{-Rt/L} = 18\ e^{650t}$ V

   At $t = 1.8$ ms: $i_L = 46.2(1 - e^{-1.17})$ mA $= 31.9$ mA

   $v_L = 18\ e^{-1.17}$ V $= 5.59$ V

8. $$\tau = \frac{L}{R} = \frac{3\text{ H}}{60\ \Omega} = 50\text{ ms}$$

   ∴ You can use the curve.

   At $t = T = 50$ ms, $v_L = 0.368\ E = 0.368\ (180\text{ V}) = 66.2$ V

   $$i_L = 0.632\ I_f = 0.632\left(\frac{E}{R}\right) = 0.632\left(\frac{180\text{ V}}{60\ \Omega}\right) = 1.90\text{ A}$$

10. Note that v_L is negative. Thus, $v_L = 0.368\ (-40\text{ V}) = -14.7$ V

12. $v_L = Ee^{-Rt/L}\ \therefore\ E = 40$ V

    $$i_L = \frac{E}{R}(1 - e^{-Rt/L})\ \therefore\ \frac{E}{R} = 20\text{ mA and } R = \frac{40\text{ V}}{20\text{ mA}} = 2\text{ k}\Omega$$

    $5\tau = 0.625$ ms $\therefore\ \tau = 0.125$ ms

    $$\tau = \frac{L}{R}\ \therefore\ L = R\tau = (2\text{ k}\Omega)(0.125\text{ ms}) = 0.25\text{ H}$$

14.4 De-Energizing Transients

14. a. $$\tau = \frac{L}{R_1} = \frac{0.5\text{ H}}{200\ \Omega} = 2.5\text{ms} \therefore 5\tau = 12.5\text{ms}$$

    $$i_{L_{ss}} = \frac{E}{R_1} = 0.4\text{ A}$$

    b. $$\tau' = \frac{L}{R_1 + R_2} = \frac{0.5\text{ H}}{500\ \Omega}$$

$= 1$ ms

$\therefore 5\tau' = 5$ ms $\quad i_{L_{ss}} = 0$

c. $I_0 = \dfrac{E}{R_1} = \dfrac{80\text{ V}}{200\ \Omega} = 400$ mA

$i_L = I_0 e^{-t/\tau'} = 400\text{ mA}e^{-1000t}$

$v_L = V_0 e^{-t/\tau'}$ where $V_0 = -I_0(R_1 + R_2) = -200$ V

Thus,

$v_L = -200\text{ V}e^{-1000t}$

16. As shown in the solution to Problem 15, v_L starts at -1250 V and decays to 0. Thus, at 3 time constants (Figure 14–10),

$v_L = 0.0498\ (-1250\text{ V}) = -62.3$ V

Similarly, $i_L = (0.0498)(5\text{ A}) = 0.249$ A

18. At the instant the switch is closed, full source voltage appears across L. Therefore, $E = 150$ V. Steady state current is $\dfrac{E}{R_1}$. This is I_0, the inductor current at the instant the switch is opened. Thus,

$I_0 = \dfrac{E}{R_1} \ \therefore\ 3\text{ A} = \dfrac{150\text{ V}}{R_1} \ \therefore\ R_1 = 50\ \Omega$

The circuit as it looks just after the switch is opened is shown below.

$v_L = -I_0(R_1 + R_2)$

$-750\text{ V} = -3\text{ A}(50\ \Omega + R_2) \ \therefore\ R_2 = 200\ \Omega$

$5\tau' = 5\text{ ms} \ \therefore\ \tau' = 1$ ms

$\tau' = \dfrac{L}{R_1 + R_2} \ \therefore\ 1 \times 10^{-3}\text{ s} = \dfrac{L}{250\ \Omega}$

$\therefore L = 0.25$ H

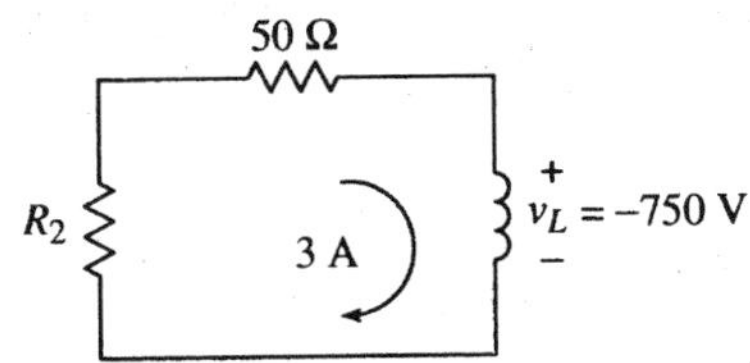

20. R_2 has no effect on i_L and v_L during energization. Thus,

$i_L = \dfrac{E}{R_1}(1 - e^{-R_1 t/L}) = 2(1 - e^{-10t})$ A

$\therefore \dfrac{E}{R_1} = 2$ A and $\dfrac{R_1}{L} = 10 \ \therefore\ L = 0.1R_1$.

The decay circuit is shown in (b). $I_0 = 2$ A.

$v_L = -400e^{-25t}$ V

$= -I_0(R_1 + R_2)e^{-(R_1 + R_2)t/L}$ V.

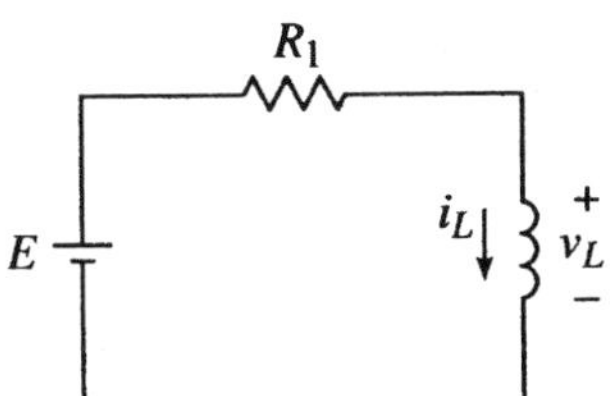

(a) Energization

Therefore,

$25 = \dfrac{R_1 + R_2}{L} = \dfrac{R_1}{L} + \dfrac{R_2}{L} = 10 + \dfrac{R_2}{L}$

$\therefore R_2 = 15L = 15(0.1R_1) = 1.5R_1$.

In addition, $400 = I_0(R_1 + R_2) = 2(R_1 + 1.5R_1) = 5\ R_1$.

$\therefore R_1 = 80\ \Omega$

$L = 0.1R_1 = 8$ H

$R_2 = 1.5R_1 = 120\ \Omega$

$E = (2\text{ A})R_1 = 160$ V.

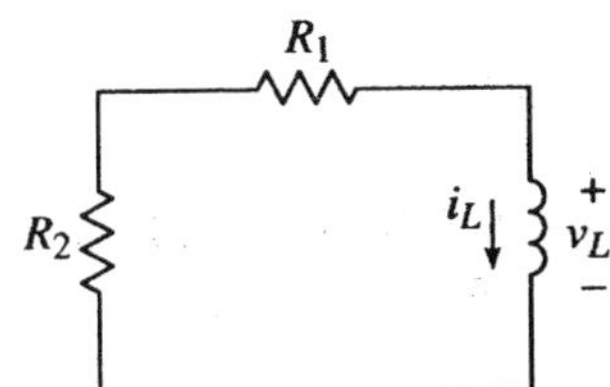

(b) De-energization

14.5 More Complex Circuits

22. a. $R_{Th} = 10\text{ k}\Omega \| 30\text{ k}\Omega = 7.5\text{ k}\Omega$; $E_{Th} = \left(\dfrac{30\text{ k}\Omega}{30\text{ k}\Omega + 10\text{ k}\Omega}\right)(120\text{ V}) = 90$ V

$\tau = \dfrac{L}{R_T} = \dfrac{0.36\text{ H}}{18\text{ k}\Omega} = 20\ \mu$s

b. $i_L = \dfrac{E_{Th}}{R_T}(1 - e^{-t/\tau}) = \dfrac{90\text{ V}}{18\text{ k}\Omega}(1 - e^{-t/20\ \mu s}) = 5(1 - e^{-50\,000t})$ mA

$v_L = E_{Th}\, e^{-t/\tau} = 90e^{-t/20\ \mu s}\text{ V} = 90e^{-50\,000t}$ V

c. At $t = 20\ \mu s, v_L = 90e^{-1} = 33.1$ V

$i_L = 5(1 - e^{-1}) = 3.16$ mA

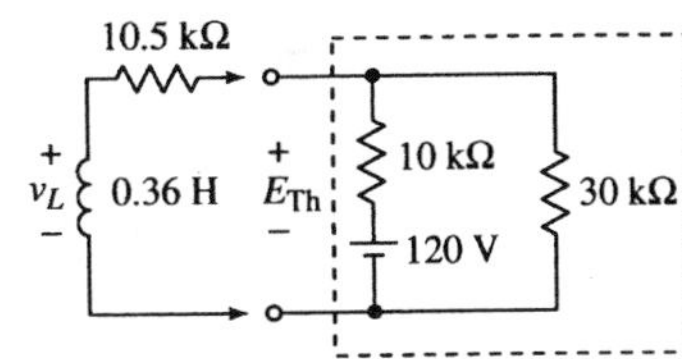

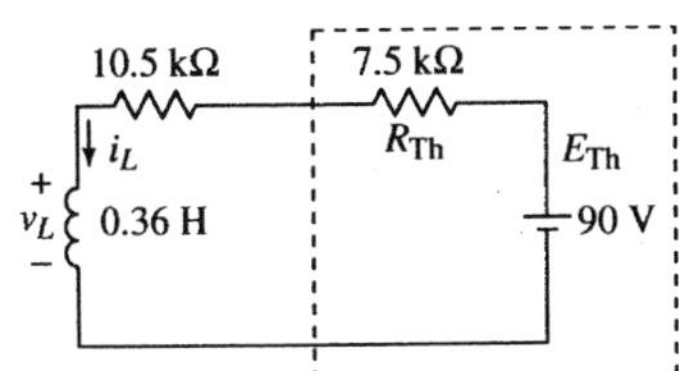

24. $\tau = \frac{L}{R} = \frac{0.36\text{ H}}{40.5\text{ k}\Omega} = 8.89\ \mu\text{s}$. Thus, 17.8 μs represents 2 time constants. From Problem 23, v_L starts at –202.5 V and decays to 0 V. From Figure 14-10, at $t = 2\tau$, v_L drops to 13.5% of its initial value. Thus, at 17.8 μs, $v_L = (0.135)(-202.5\text{ V}) = -27.3$ V. Similarly, $i_L = (0.135)(5\text{ mA}) = 0.675$ mA.

26. a. $\tau = \frac{L}{R_T} = \frac{4\text{ H}}{580\ \Omega} = 6.90$ ms

b. From Problem 25, $I_0 = 90$ mA

$i_L = I_0 e^{-t/\tau} = 90e^{-t/6.9\text{ ms}}$ mA

$v_L = -i_L R_T = -(90\text{ mA})(580\ \Omega)e^{-t/6.9\text{ ms}} = -52.2e^{-t/6.9\text{ ms}}$ V

c. At $t = 13.8$ ms, $v_L = -52.2e^{-13.8\text{ ms}/6.9\text{ ms}} = -52.2e^{-2} = -7.06$ V

$i_L = 90e^{-2} = 12.2$ mA

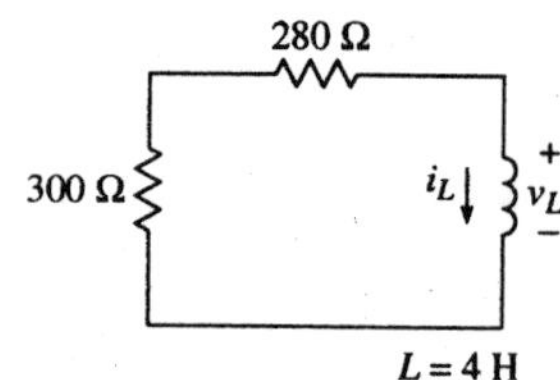

28. Position 1: The circuit is in steady state here with inductor voltage and current equal to zero.

Position 2: This is the current build-up position, shown in (a) below. Note that v_L and i_L are both negative because of the references used and that the 30 Ω resistor has no effect. The time constant here is 5 H/50 Ω = 0.1 s. The build-up equations are

$$i_L = -\frac{25\text{ V}}{50\ \Omega}\left(1 - e^{-t/0.1\text{s}}\right) = -0.5\left(1 - e^{-10t}\right)\text{A}$$

$$v_L = -25e^{-10t}\text{ V}$$

Position 3: The switch remains in Position 2 long enough for the circuit to reach steady state. Thus, the inductor current is –0.5 A at the instant the switch is moved to Position 3. (Call this current I_0.) It then decays to zero. The decay circuit is shown below as (b). Note that the resistance of the decay circuit is $R_d = 50\ \Omega + 15\ \Omega \| 30\ \Omega = 60\ \Omega$. Note also that the voltage across L at the instant the switch is moved to Position 3 is $-I_0 R_d = -(-0.5\text{ A})(60\ \Omega) = 30$ V. It then decays exponentially to 0 V. Thus, the decay equations are:

$$i_L = I_0 e^{-R_d t/L} = -0.5e^{-12t}\text{ A}$$

$$v_L = 30e^{-12t}\text{ V}$$

where $t = 0$ has been redefined as the instant the switch is moved to Position 3. Curves are shown below. At $t = 0.1$ s,

$$i_L = -0.5(1 - e^{-1}) = -0.316\text{ A}$$

$$v_L = -25e^{-1} = -9.2\text{ V}$$

Now consider $t = 1.1$ s. This is 0.1 s into decay. Thus, inductor voltage and current are:

$$i_L = -0.5e^{-12(0.1)} = -0.5e^{-1.2} = -0.151\text{ A}$$

$$v_L = 30e^{-1.2} = 9.04\text{ V}$$

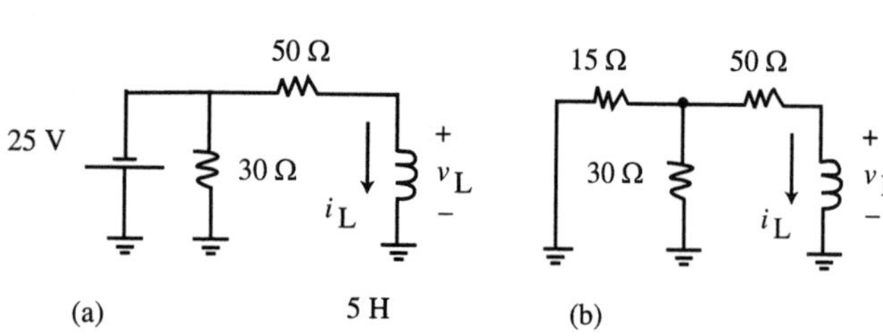

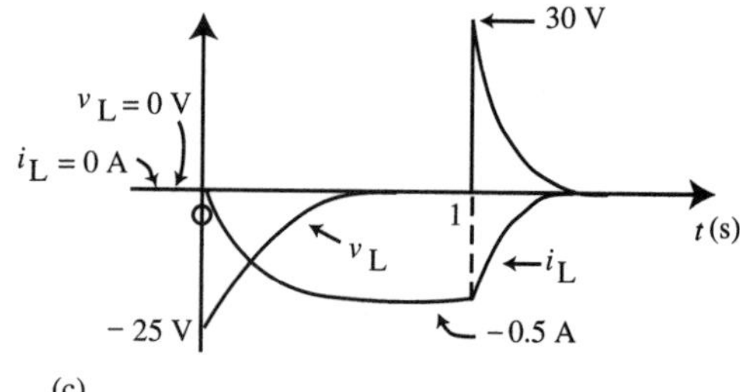

14.6 RL Transients Using Computers (MSM)

Create each circuit on your screen as indicated. Click Options, Preferences, then Show node names (to identify the nodes of interest). Click the Analysis icon, select Transient, select Initial Conditions Set to Zero, set TSTOP as applicable, select the nodes that you wish to display, then click Simulate. (If you get a choppy waveform, set the Minimum number of time points to 1000 or more.)

30. Using the curvor, $v_L = 13.2$ V at $t = 10$ ms. Check: Determine the Thévenin equivalent of the circuit. (You get $R_{Th} = 400\ \Omega$ and $E_{Th} = 36$ V.) This yields $v_L = 36e^{-100t}$ V, and at $t = 10$ ms, $v_L = 13.2$ V, the same as MSM.

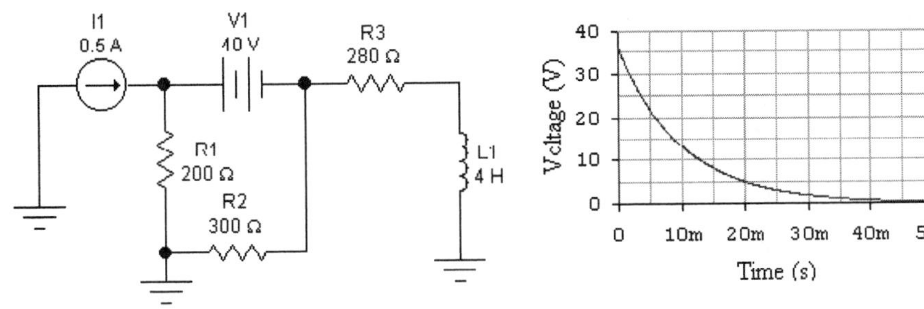

32. From the graph, $v_L = 7.36$ V at $t = 200$ ms and 1.64 V at 500 ms. Check: Analytically, $v_L = 20e^{-5t}$ V. Substituting $t =$ 200 ms and 500 ms yields the same values as determined by MSM.

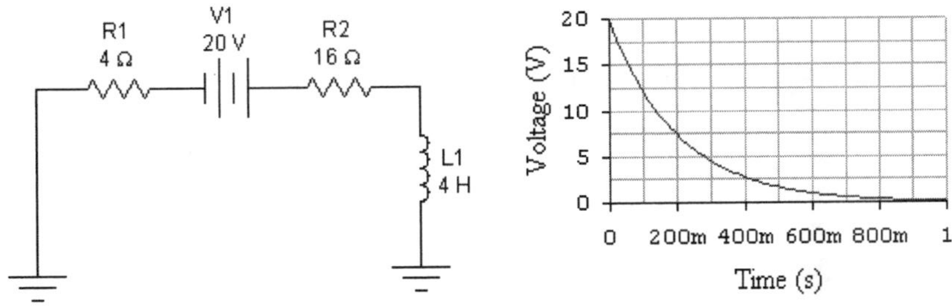

14.6 RL Transients Using Computers (PSpice)

Following the procedures set out in this chapter, build the circuits on your screen as indicated, then perform a transient analysis.

30. Using the cursor, you get 13.2 V at $t = 10$ ms. (This agrees very well with the analytic solution—see MSM Problem 30 above.)

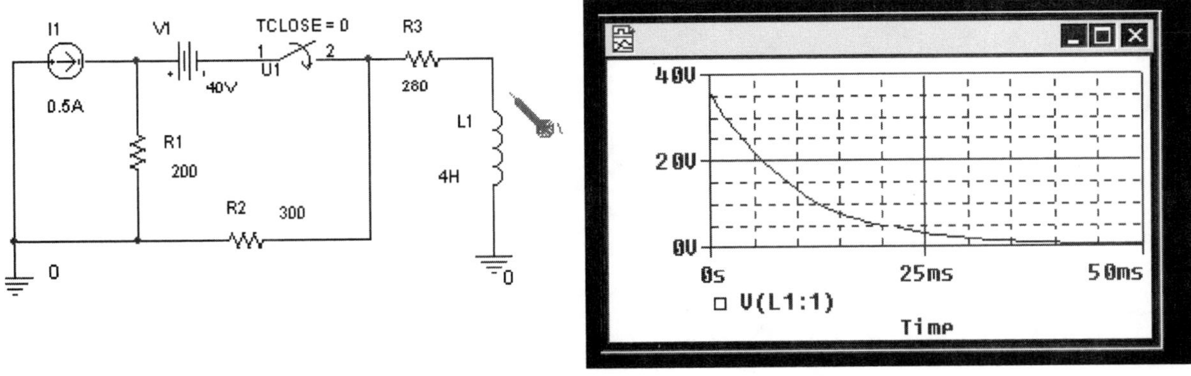

32. From the graph, $v_L = 7.36$ V at $t = 200$ ms and 1.64 V at 500 ms, while $i_L = 0.632$ A and 0.918 A. (For an analytic check on voltages, see the MSM solution. For currents, $i_L = (1 - e^{-5t})$ A. At 200 ms, this yields 0.632 A and at 500 ms, 0.918 A. Thus, results agree.

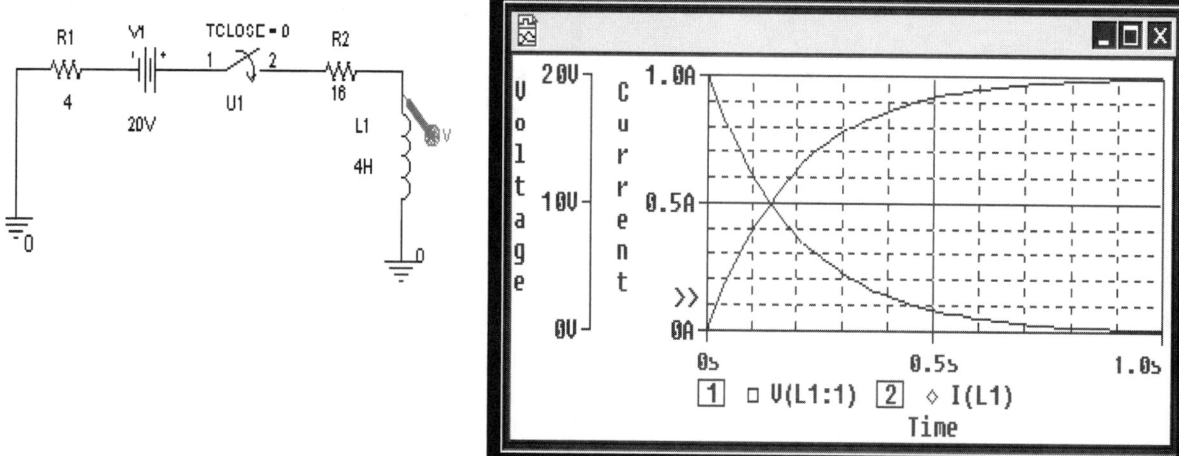

34. The switching action specified cannot be obtained with a single switch. Thus, use two switches as shown below. Analytic answers (obtained by substitution into the equations of Problems 22 and 23) are 4.48 V and 4.75 mA at $t = 60\ \mu$s and –37.5 V and 0.925 mA at $t = 165\ \mu$s. (Remember however, 165 μs is 15 μs into the decay time scale.) You will probably find that the accuracy at 165 μs is not as good as desired.

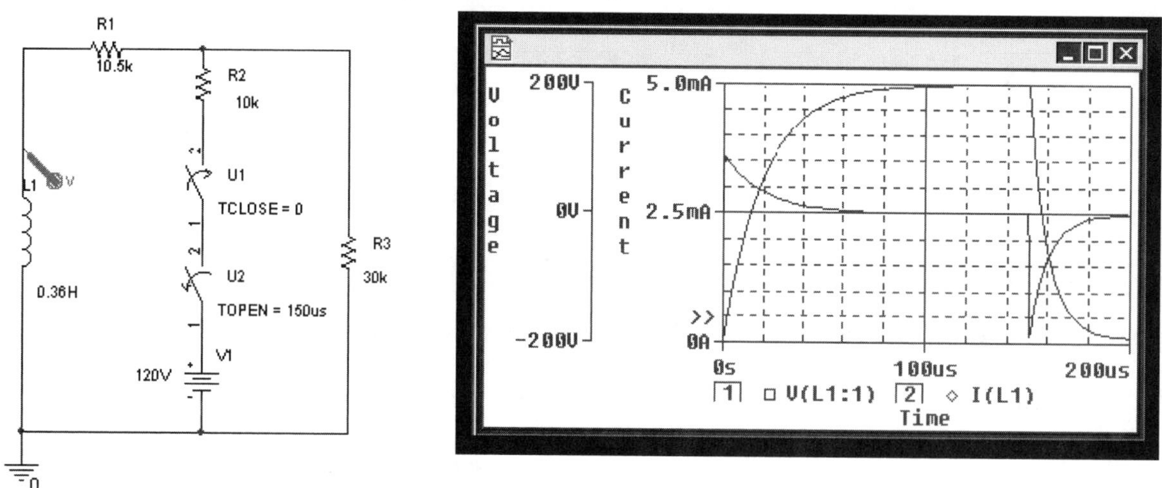

CHAPTER

15

AC Fundamentals

15.2 Generating ac Voltages

2. The speed must double to 1200 rpm.

15.3 Voltage and Current Conventions for ac

4. Pos. $I = \dfrac{40\text{ V}}{25\ \Omega} = 1.6\text{ A}$; Pos. 2: $I = \dfrac{-70\text{ V}}{25\ \Omega} = -2.8\text{ A}$

15.4 Frequency, Period, Amplitude, and Peak Value

6. a. $T = \dfrac{1}{f} = \dfrac{1}{100}\text{ Hz} = 10\text{ ms}$ b. $25\mu s$ c. 5ns

8. $T = \dfrac{1}{f} = \dfrac{1}{1.25 \times 10^6} = 0.8\ \mu s$

$$t = \frac{8 \times 10^7\text{ cycles}}{1.25 \times 10^6\text{ cycles/s}} = 64\text{ s}$$

10. $T = 8\ \mu s\ \therefore f = \dfrac{1}{8\ \mu s} = 125\text{ kHz}$

2 cycles are shown.

12. $625T = 12.5\text{ ms}$; $T = \dfrac{12.5\text{ ms}}{625} = 20\ \mu s$;

$$f = \frac{1}{20\ \mu s} = 50\text{ kHz}$$

14. a. $5\frac{1}{4}$ cycles in 525 μs $\therefore$ Thus, $5.25\ T = 525\ \mu s$ and $T = 100\ \mu s$

b. $f = \dfrac{1}{T} = \dfrac{1}{100\ \mu s} = 10\text{ kHz}$

c. Peak-to-peak = 2(75 V) = 150 V

16. $T_1 = 7$ ms (Fig. 15–79)

$$T_2 = \frac{T_1}{4} = 1.75\text{ ms}\ \therefore f_2 = \frac{1}{1.75\text{ ms}} = 571.4\text{ Hz}$$

15.5 Angular and Graphic Relationships for Sine Waves

18. a. $i = 50 \sin \alpha$ A

b. At $\alpha = 40°$, $i = 50 \sin 40° = 32.1$ A
At $\alpha = 120°$, $i = 50 \sin 120° = 43.3$ A
At $\alpha = 200°$, $i = 50 \sin 200° = -17.1$ A
At $\alpha = 310°$, $i = 50 \sin 310° = -38.3$ A

20. $\alpha_{degrees} = \dfrac{180}{\pi} = \alpha_{rad}$. Thus,

a. 15° b. 120° c. 270°
d. 81.9° e. 974° f. 5760°.

22.

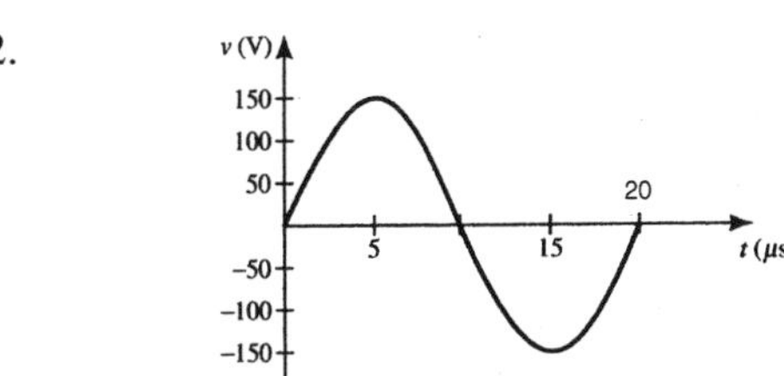

24. $4\ \mu s \Rightarrow \left(\dfrac{4\ \mu s}{60\ \mu s}\right)(360°) = 24°$ and $v = 80\sin 24° = 32.5$ V

26. $v_1 = V_m \sin \alpha_1$ $v_2 = V_m \sin \alpha_2$

$$\therefore \frac{V_2}{V_1} = \frac{\sin \alpha_2}{\sin \alpha_1}$$

$$\therefore V_2 = \left(\frac{\sin 330°}{\sin 60°}\right)(57\text{ V}) = -32.9\text{ V}$$

15.6 Voltages and Currents as Functions of Time

28. $f = \dfrac{\omega}{2\pi} = \dfrac{100 \text{ rad/s}}{2\pi} = 15.9 \text{ Hz}$

$T = \dfrac{1}{f} = 62.8 \text{ ms}$

b. $\omega = \dfrac{40 \text{ rad}}{20 \text{ ms}} = 2000 \text{ rad/s}$

$f = \dfrac{\omega}{2\pi} = 318 \text{ Hz}$

$T = \dfrac{1}{f} = 3.14 \text{ ms}$

c. $\omega = 34 \times 10^3 \text{ rad/s}$

$f = \dfrac{\omega}{2\pi} = 5411 \text{ Hz}$

$T = \dfrac{1}{f} = 185\ \mu\text{s}$

30. a. $\omega = 200\pi \text{ rad/s} \therefore f = \dfrac{\omega}{2\pi} = 100 \text{ Hz};$

$T = \dfrac{1}{f} = 10 \text{ ms}$; Amplitude = 75 V

b. $\omega = 300 \text{ rad/s} \therefore f = 47.75 \text{ Hz}; T = 20.9 \text{ ms}$

Amplitude = 8 A

32. a. $\omega = 200\pi \therefore T = \dfrac{2\pi}{\omega} = 10 \text{ ms}$

b. $T = 80\ \mu\text{s}$

Thus,

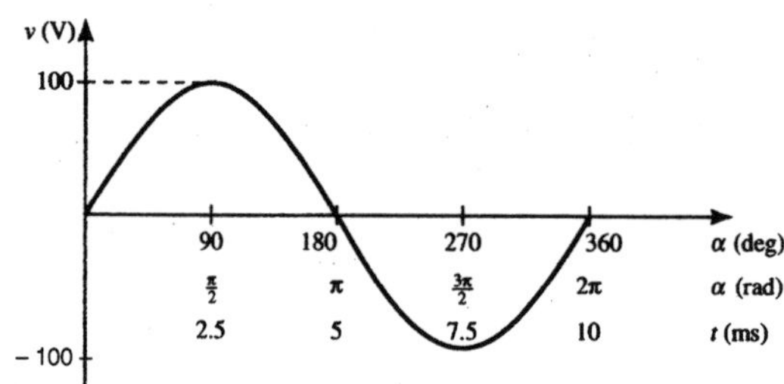

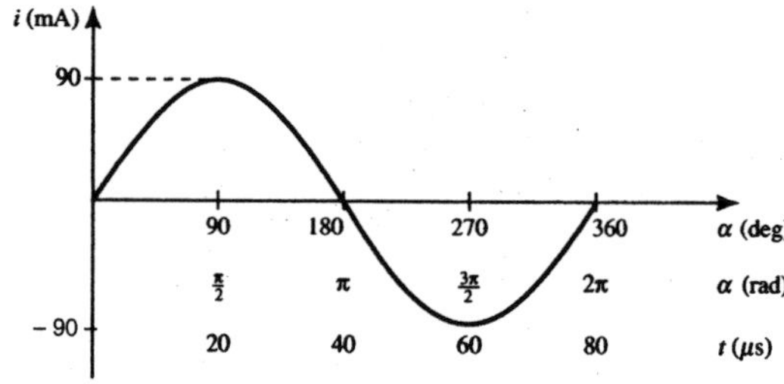

34. a. $v = 100 \sin \alpha$ V

$86.6 = 100 \sin \alpha_1 \therefore \sin \alpha_1 = 0.866$

$\alpha_1 = \sin^{-1}(0.866) = 60^\circ = \dfrac{\pi}{3} \text{ rad}$

$\alpha_2 = 180^\circ - 60^\circ = 120^\circ = \dfrac{2\pi}{3} \text{ rad}$

Check: $100 \sin 60^\circ = 86.6$; $100 \sin 120^\circ = 86.6$

b. $\alpha = \omega t \therefore t = \dfrac{\alpha}{\omega}$

$t_1 = \dfrac{\alpha_1}{\omega} = \dfrac{\dfrac{\pi}{3} \text{ rad}}{\left(\dfrac{100\,\pi}{60}\right) \text{rad/s}} = 200 \text{ ms}$

$t_2 = \dfrac{\alpha_2}{\omega} = \dfrac{\dfrac{2\,\pi}{3} \text{ rad}}{\left(\dfrac{100\,\pi}{60}\right) \text{rad/s}} = 400 \text{ ms}$

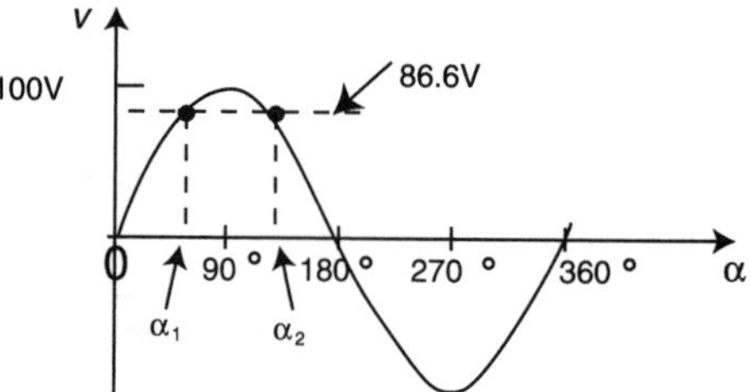

36. a. $T = \dfrac{2\pi}{\omega} = \dfrac{2\pi}{232.7 \text{ rad/s}} = 27 \text{ ms}$

$40^\circ \Rightarrow \left(\dfrac{40^\circ}{360^\circ}\right)(27 \text{ ms}) = 3 \text{ ms}$

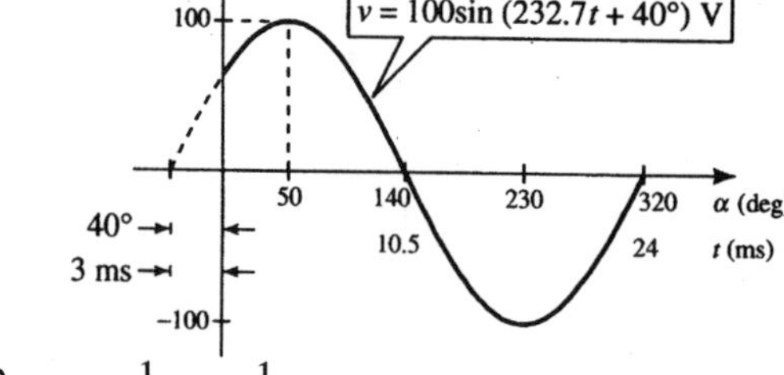

b. $T = \dfrac{1}{f} = \dfrac{1}{200 \text{ Hz}} = 5 \text{ ms}$

$60^\circ \Rightarrow \left(\dfrac{60^\circ}{360^\circ}\right)(5 \text{ ms}) = 0.833 \text{ s}$

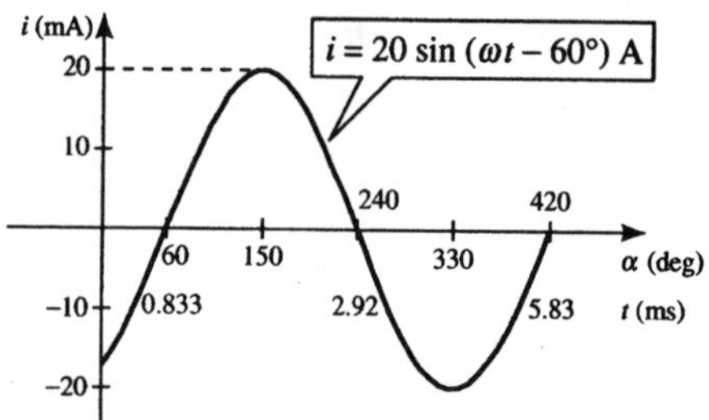

38. a. $T = 10\ \mu\text{s} \therefore \omega = \dfrac{2\pi}{T} = 200\pi \times 10^3 \text{ rad/s}$

As indicated below, this matches Fig. 15–31(b) with $\theta = 180^\circ - 40^\circ = 140^\circ$. Thus,

$v = 80 \sin(200\,\pi \times 10^3\, t - 140^\circ)$ V

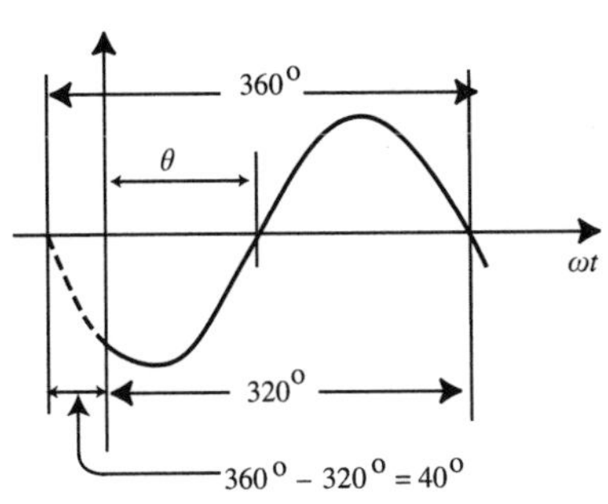

40. $i = I_m\sin(\omega t - 60°)$

$i_1 = I_m\sin(180° - 60°) = I_m\sin 120°$

$i_2 = I_m\sin(350° - 60°) = I_m\sin 290°$

$\frac{i_2}{i_1} = \frac{\sin 290°}{\sin 120°}$

$i_2 = \left(\frac{\sin 290°}{\sin 120°}\right)(15.6\text{ A}) = -16.9\text{ A}$

b. This matches Fig. 15–31(a). $T = \frac{1}{f} = 1200\ \mu\text{s}$

$\theta = \left(\frac{160\ \mu s}{1200\ \mu s}\right)(360°) = 48°$; $\omega = 2\pi f = 5236$ rad/s

Thus, $v = 100 \sin(5236t + 48°)$ V

15.7 Introduction to Phasors

42. a. $v = V_m\sin(\omega t + \theta) = 100\sin(\omega t + 70°)$ V
b. $i = 20 \sin(\omega t + 140°)\ A$
c. $i = 10 \sin(\omega t - 35°)\ mA$

(a)

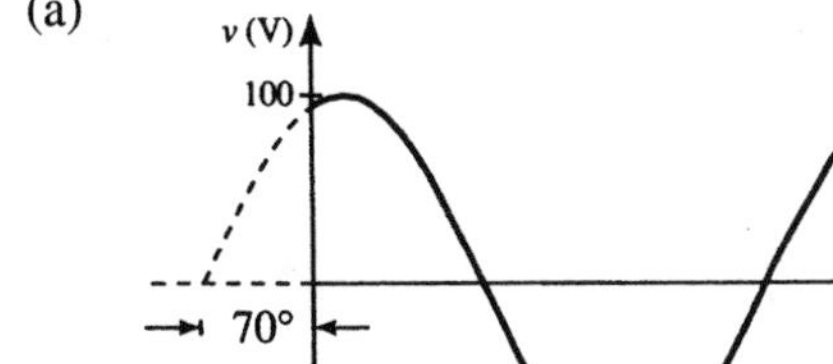

(b)

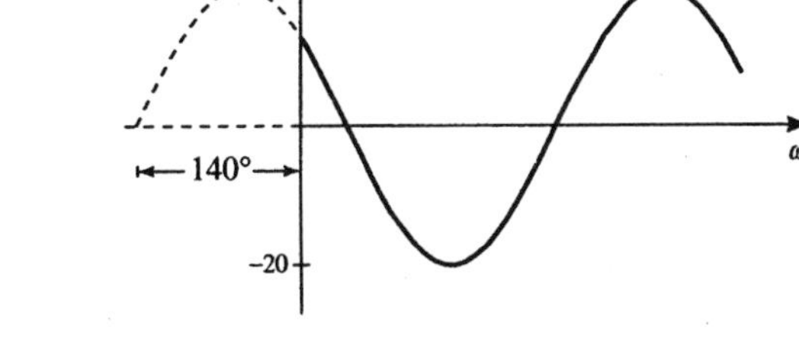

(c)

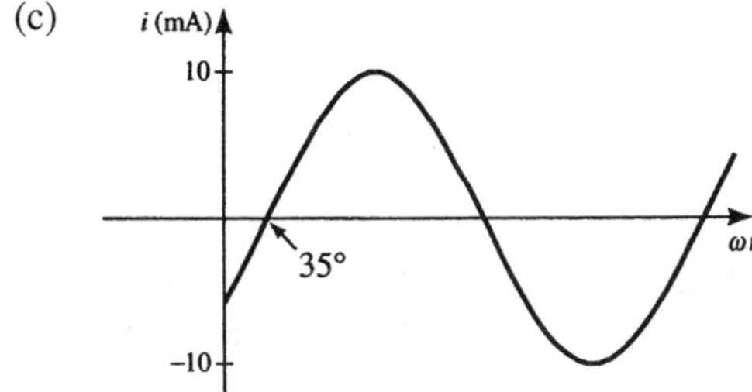

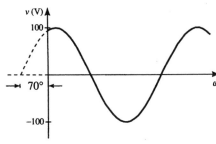

44. a. Voltage leads by 30°.

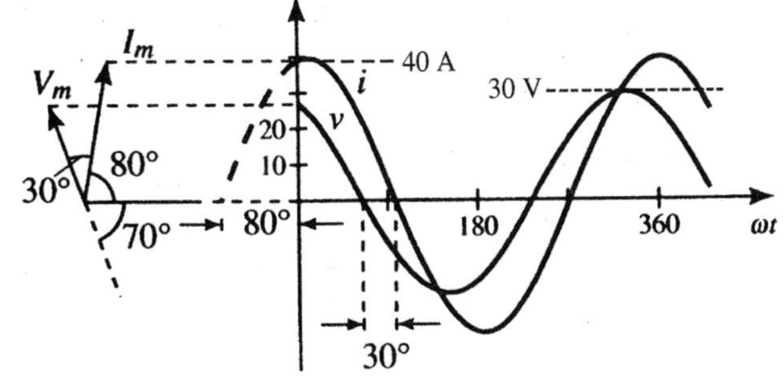

b. Voltage leads by 110°.

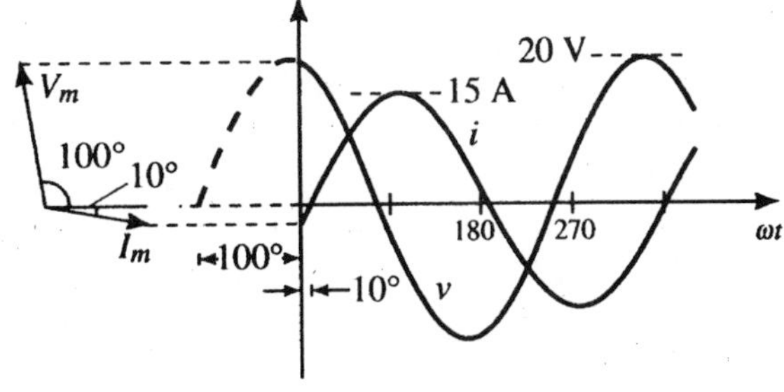

$v = 20\cos(\omega t + 10°) = 20\sin(\omega t + 100°)$

c. Current leads by 20°.

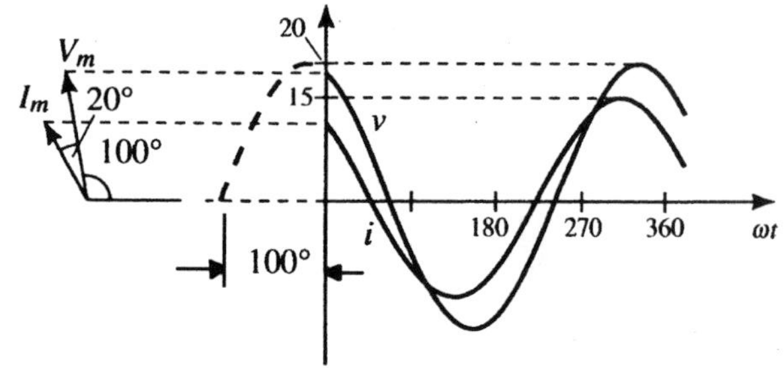

$v = 20\cos(\omega t + 10°) = 20\sin(\omega t + 100°)$

d.

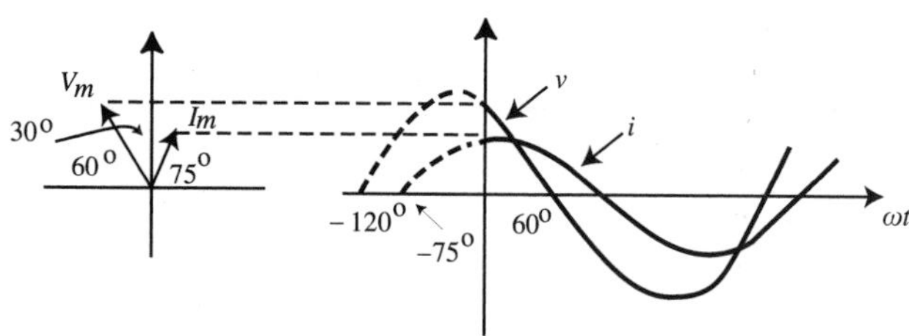

46. Extend the waveforms to the $t = 0$ s axis. The phasors are now apparent.

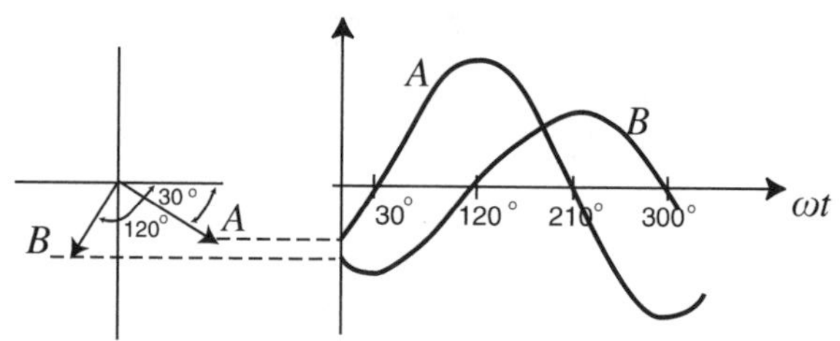

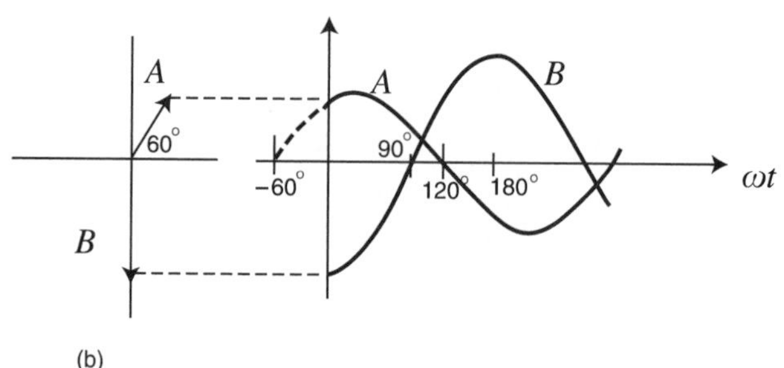

(b)

15.8 AC Waveforms and Average Value

48. $\Delta x = \dfrac{\pi}{12}$ rad. $y = \sin x$. Compute y at $\dfrac{\pi}{12}$ (i.e., 15°) intervals and substitute. Thus,

$y_0 = \sin 0° = 0$

$y_1 = \sin 15° = 0.2588.$

x (deg)	y
0	0
15	0.2588
30	0.5
45	0.7071
60	0.866
75	0.9659
90	1.0
105	0.9659
120	0.866
135	0.7071
150	0.50
165	0.2588
180	0

Sum = 7.5958

$$A = \left(\frac{y_0}{2} + y_1 + y_2 + \ldots + \frac{y_{12}}{2}\right)\Delta x$$

$$= \left(\frac{0}{2} + 7.5958 + \frac{0}{2}\right)\left(\frac{\pi}{12}\right) = 1.9886 \approx 2.0$$

50. $\text{Avg} = \dfrac{(I_m \times 4) - (I_m \times 2)}{6} = 10 \text{ A} \therefore I_m = 30 \text{ A}$

52. Consider the curve below. Values at various points are calculated, tabulated and plotted as shown.

t (s)	v (V)
0	0
0.25	0.1875
0.5	0.75
0.75	1.6875
1.0	3.0
1.25	4.6875
1.50	6.75
1.75	9.1875
2.0	12.0

$$A_1 = \left(\frac{v_0}{2} + v_1 + v_2 + \ldots + \frac{v_9}{2}\right)\Delta t$$

$$= \left(\frac{0}{2} + 0.1875 + 0.75 + \ldots + 9.1875 + \frac{12}{2}\right)(0.25 \text{ s})$$

$= 8.0625$

Total area $A = 8.0625 + (12 \times 1) - (6 \times 1) = 14.0625$

$$V_{aug} = \frac{\text{Area}}{\text{base}} = \frac{14.0625 \text{ V–s}}{5 \text{ s}} = 2.81 \text{ V}$$

(Exact Answer: $V_{aug} = 2.80$ V)

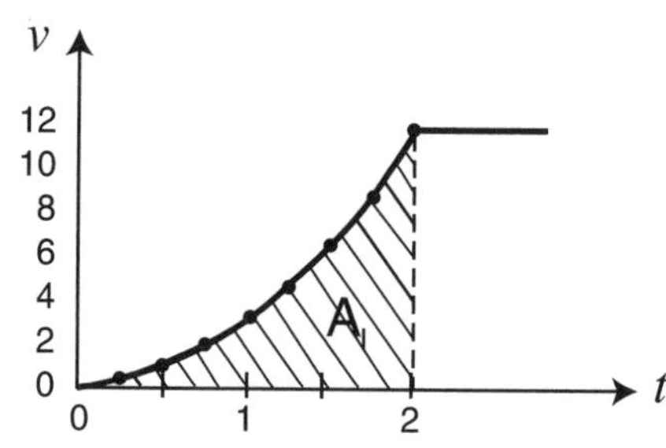

15.9 Effective Values

54. Since they are all sine waves, multiply each magnitude by 0.707. Thus,

a. 70.7 V

b. 5.66 A

c. 28.3 V

d. 84.8 mA

56. $V_m = \dfrac{V_{\text{eff}}}{0.707} = \dfrac{9\text{ V}}{0.707} = 12.7\text{ V}$

58. a.

$$I_{\text{eff}} = \sqrt{\frac{\text{Area under squared curve}}{\text{Base}}} = \sqrt{\frac{(2^2 \times 3) + 0 + (2^2 \times 1) + ((-3)^2 \times 1) + (3^2 \times 2) + 0}{10}} = 2.07\text{ A}$$

b.

$$I_{\text{eff}} = \sqrt{\frac{(30^2 \times 4) + ((-30)^2 \times 2)}{6}} = 30\text{ A}$$

60. $V_{\text{dc}} = -4$ V, thus $v = 6 \sin \omega t - 4$ V

$V_{\text{eff}} = \sqrt{V_{dc}^2 + V_{ac}^2}$ where V_{ac} is rms.

Thus: $V_{\text{eff}} = \sqrt{(4)^2 + \left(\dfrac{6}{\sqrt{2}}\right)^2} = 5.83\text{ V}$

62. The squared curve is shown below.

$A_2 = (400)(2) = 800$ and $A_3 = (1600)(2) = 3200$.

To find A_1, use numerical techniques.

$$A_1 = \left(\frac{y_0}{2} + y_1 + y_2 + \frac{y_3}{2}\right)\Delta t = \left(0 + 178 + 711 + \frac{1600}{2}\right)(1) = 1689.$$

Thus, $I_{\text{eff}} = \sqrt{\dfrac{1689 + 800 + 3200}{8}} = 26.7\text{ mA}.$

(The exact answer is 26.5 mA.)

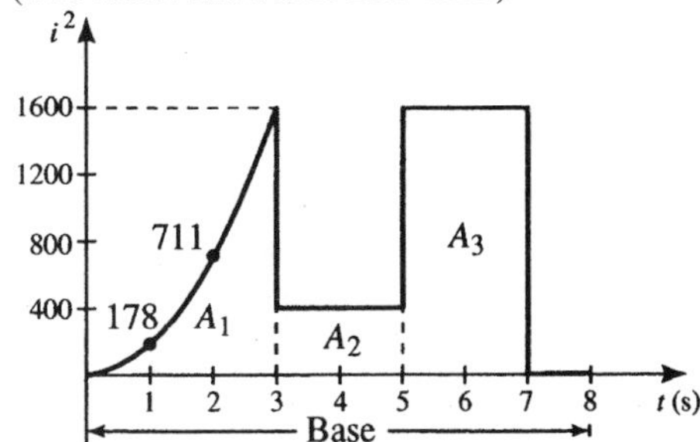

15.11 AC Voltage and Current Measurement

64. a. 0.707(153 V) = 108 V

b. 120 V

c. Meaningless

d. 0.707(597 V) = 422 V

15.12 Circuit Analysis Using Computers (MSM)

Notes

1. Review Notes 1 and 2 on page 525 regarding phase angles for MultiSIM. If you are using MultiSIM 2001 for example, you will likely have to enter 315 degrees instead of 45 degrees as shown, etc.
2. In Figure 15-71, we used resistors to create node points to use in graphing source voltages. An alternate technique is shown below. Here, we use a junction dot to create the needed node. Either technique works well.
3. To achieve the best accuracy in reading values when using the cursor, expand the display to full screen.

66. Using a frequency of $f = \omega/2\pi = 10$ Hz, set up the circuit below. To get the node dot, position the cursor at an empty spot on the screen, click the right mouse button, select *Place Junction*, then drag and place the dot. Wire the circuit, then perform a transient analysis using the procedure associated with Figure 15-71 as a guide. Scale values from the graph and compare to the answers of Problem 37.

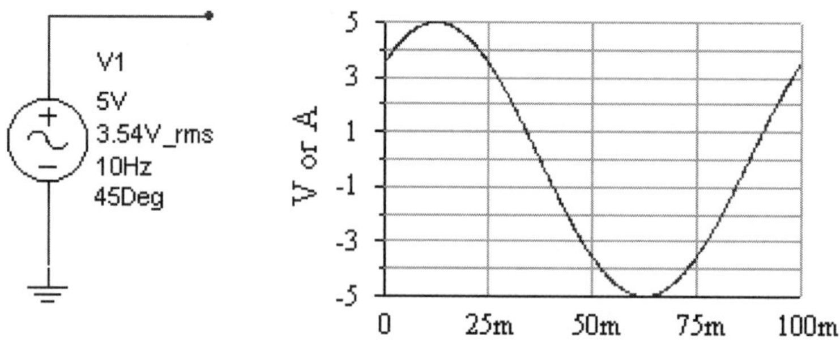

68. Since phase difference is independent of frequency, you can choose any convenient frequency you want. For example, if you choose a period of T of 360 ms, the result is a time scale where 1 ms represents 1°. Thus, choose a frequency of $f = 1/T = 2.778$ Hz. Select Transient analysis. Following simulation, position the cursors at 0 V crossover points for each waveform, then interpret the time difference as a phase shift directly in degrees.

Case a: This is shown below. Set the TSTOP value to 0.36 s to get a full cycle on the screen as indicated in (b). If you want better accuracy, expand the trace as in (c). To do this, set TSTART to a time value before the first crossover and TSTOP to a time value after the second crossover. (Alternatively, drag the mouse pointer to enclose the times of interest.) The 20-degree phase shift is now clearly evident. Repeat for all other waveform pairs.

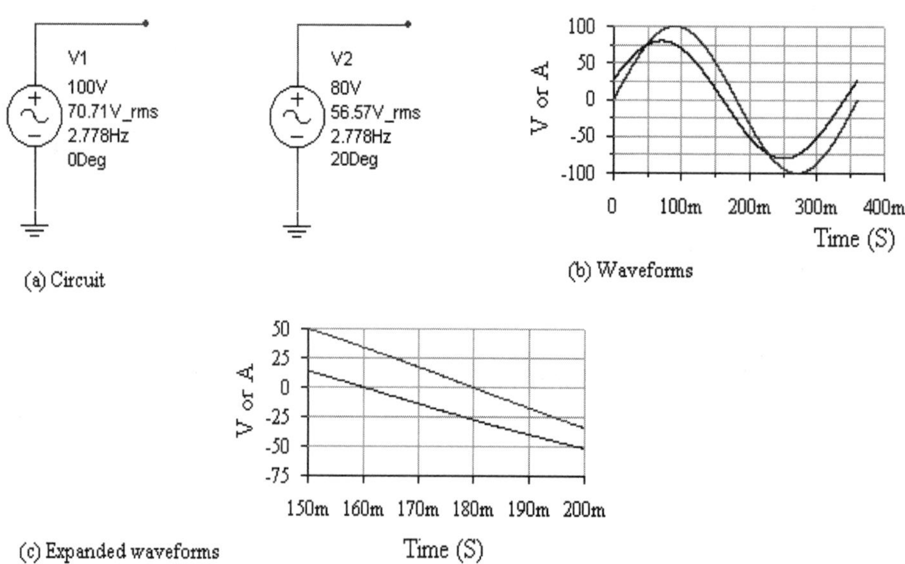

(a) Circuit

(b) Waveforms

(c) Expanded waveforms

15.12 Circuit Analysis Using Computers (PSpice)

Notes

1. In Figure 15-74, we used resistors to create node points to use in graphing source voltages. An alternate technique is shown below. Either technique works well.
2. To achieve the best accuracy in reading values when using the cursor, expand the display to full screen.

66. Using a frequency of $f = \omega/2\pi = 10$ Hz, set up the circuit below. (You can add the junction dot by clicking the *Place Junction* icon on the toolbar and dragging it into place.) Double click the source, and in the dialogue box cell labeled PHASE, type 45deg. Set other parameters as indicated, then perform a transient analysis using the procedure associated with Figure 15-74 as a guide. Scale values from the graph and compare to the answers of Problem 37.

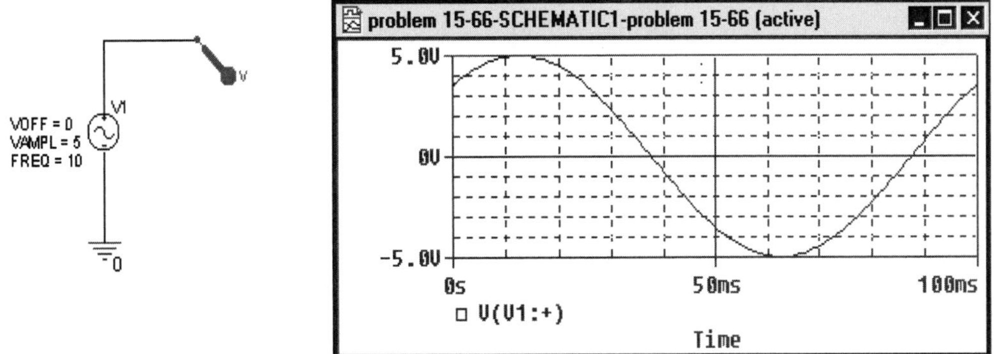

68. See MSM Problem 68 for background then using source VSIN, build the circuit and set parameter values as shown. Select transient analysis and run the solution to 360ms to get a full cycle on the screen as in (b). Expand the plot by selecting Plot from the menu, click Axis Settings, User Defined, enter 140ms and 200ms and click OK. From the expanded waveforms of (c), the 20° phase shift is clearly evident. Repeat for other waveform pairs.

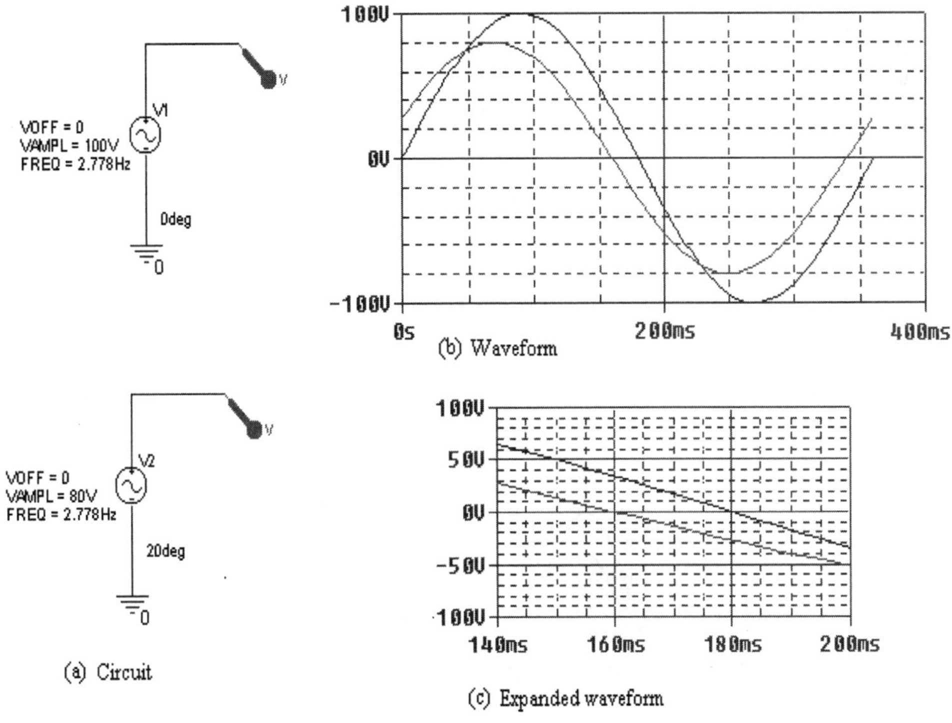

(a) Circuit

(b) Waveform

(c) Expanded waveform

CHAPTER

16

R, L, and C Elements and the Impedance Concept

16.1 Complex Number Review

2. a. $5.2 + j3.0$ b. $0 + j14$ c. $16 + j0$ d. $-5.2 + j3.0$
   e. $-15.3 - j12.9$ f. $-10.4 - j6.0$ g. $13.0 + j\,7.50$

4. a. $j(1 - j) = j - j^2 = 1 + j$
   b. $(-j)(2 + j5) = -j2 - j^2 5 = 5 - j2$
   c. $j(j(1 + j6)) = j^2(1 + j6) = -(1 + j6)$
   d. $(j4)(-j2 + 4) = -j^2 8 + j16 = 8 + j16$
   e. $(2 + j3)(3 - j4) = 6 - j8 + j9 - j^2 12 = 18 + j1$

6. a. $(37 + j9.8)(3.6 - j12.3) = (38.28\angle 14.84^\circ)(12.82\angle -73.69^\circ) = 491\angle -58.9^\circ$
   b. $(41.9\angle -80^\circ)(16.12\angle 7.13^\circ) = 676\angle -72.9^\circ$
   c. $\dfrac{42 + j18.6}{19.1 - j4.8} = \dfrac{45.93\angle 23.9^\circ}{19.69\angle -14.1^\circ} = 2.33\angle 38.0^\circ$
   d. $\dfrac{42.6 + j187.5}{11.2\angle 38^\circ} = \dfrac{192.3\angle 77.2^\circ}{11.2\angle 38^\circ} = 17.2\angle 39.2^\circ$

16.2 Complex Numbers in ac Analysis

8. a.

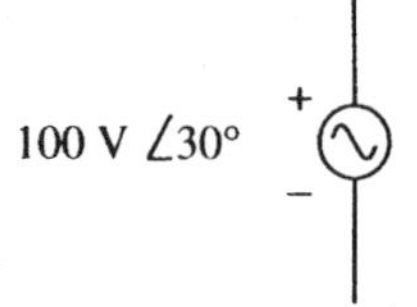

b.

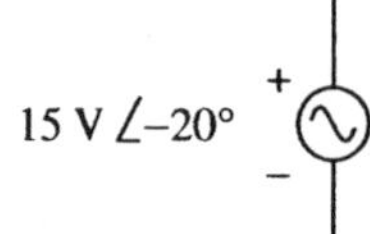

c. 50 V ∠90°

d. 50 V ∠90°

e.

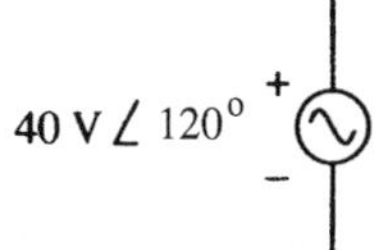

f.

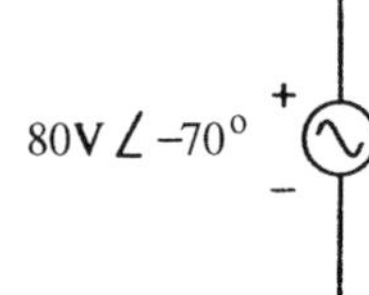

10. a. $\mathbf{E}_1 = 10\text{ V}\angle 30^\circ$ $\mathbf{E}_2 = 15\text{ V}\angle -20^\circ$
    b. $\mathbf{V} = 10\text{ V}\angle 30^\circ + 15\text{ V}\angle -20^\circ = 22.8\text{ V}\angle -0.328^\circ$
    c. $v = 22.8 \sin(\omega t - 0.328^\circ)\text{ V}$
    d.

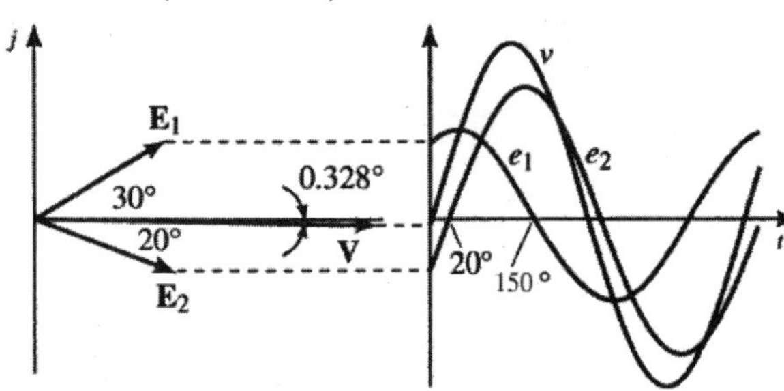

12. a. $v = 70.7 \sin \omega t$ V $\quad \mathbf{V} = 50\ \text{V}\angle 0^\circ$
b. $v = 90 \sin(\omega t + 30^\circ)$ V $\quad \mathbf{V} = 63.6\ \text{V}\angle 30^\circ$
c. $i = -100 \sin \omega t$ mA $\quad \mathbf{I} = 70.7\ \text{mA}\angle 180^\circ$
d. $v = 10 \sin(\omega t + 160^\circ)$ V $\quad \mathbf{V} = 7.07\ \text{V}\angle 160^\circ$

14. a. $\mathbf{I}_T = 35.35\ \text{A}\angle 60^\circ$; $\quad \mathbf{I}_2 = 14.14\ \text{A}\angle -30^\circ$
b. $\mathbf{I}_1 = \mathbf{I}_T - \mathbf{I}_2 = 35.35\angle 60^\circ - 14.14\angle -30^\circ = 38.07\ \text{A}\angle 81.8^\circ$
c. $i_1 = \sqrt{2}(38.07)\sin(\omega t + 81.8^\circ) \therefore i_1 = 53.8 \sin(\omega t + 81.8^\circ)$ A

16. $\mathbf{I}_2 = \mathbf{I}_T - \mathbf{I}_1 - \mathbf{I}_3 = 26.92\angle -21.8^\circ - 25\angle 0^\circ - 20\angle -90\angle = 10\ \text{A}\angle 90^\circ$
$\therefore i_2 = 14.1 \sin(\omega t + 90^\circ)$ A

16.4 to 16.6

18. $R = \dfrac{V_m}{I_m} = \dfrac{120\ \text{V}}{15\ \text{mA}} = 8\ \text{k}\Omega$

20. Consider voltage: Its phasor is $\mathbf{V} = 84.9\ \text{V}\angle 55^\circ$. Consider current: $\cos(\omega t + 145^\circ)$ can be represented by a phasor at $90^\circ + 145^\circ = 235^\circ$. Consider $-\cos(\omega t + 145^\circ)$. The minus sign represents a 180° phase shift. Thus, $-\cos(\omega t + 145^\circ)$ is represented by a phasor at $235^\circ - 180^\circ = 55^\circ$ as illustrated below. Thus, voltage and current are in phase and the component is a resistor. Its value is

$R = \dfrac{V_m}{I_m} = \dfrac{120\ \text{V}}{18\ \text{mA}} = 6.67\ \text{k}\Omega$

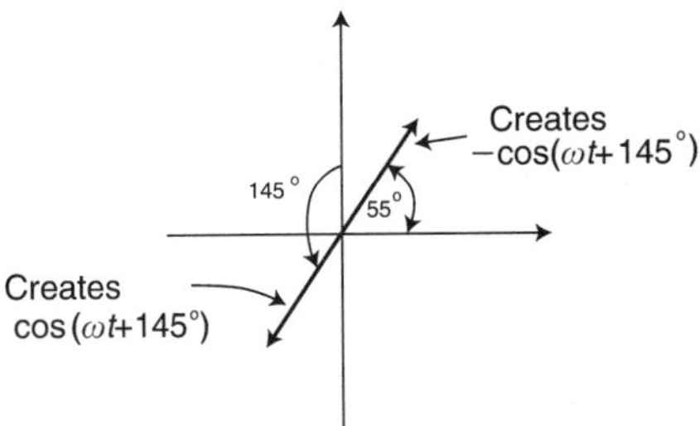

22. a. $X_L = \omega L = (2\pi)(60\ \text{Hz})(0.5\ \text{H}) = 188.5\ \Omega$
b. $X_L = (2\pi)(1000\ \text{Hz})(0.5\ \text{H}) = 3142\ \Omega$
c. $X_L = (500\ \text{rad/s})(0.5\ \text{H}) = 250\ \Omega$

24. a. $X_L = \omega L = (377\ \text{rad/s})(0.2\ \text{H}) = 75.4\ \Omega$

$I_m = \dfrac{V_m}{X_L} = \dfrac{100\ \text{V}}{75.4\ \Omega} = 1.33$ A

Current lags voltage by 90°.

$\therefore i_L = 1.33 \sin(377t - 90^\circ)$ A

b. $X_L = \omega L = (2\pi \times 400)(0.2\text{H}) = 502.7\ \Omega$
$V_m = I_m X_L = (10\ \text{mA})(502.7\ \Omega) = 5.03$ V
Voltage leads current by 90°.
$\therefore v_L = 5.03 \sin(2\pi \times 400t + 30^\circ)$ V

26. a. $i_C = 5 \sin(\omega t + 150^\circ)$ A
b. $i_C = 5 \sin(\omega t + 75^\circ)$ A
c. $v_C = 10 \sin(\omega t - 60^\circ)$ V
d. $v_C = 10 \sin(\omega t - 80^\circ)$ V

28. a. $I_m = \dfrac{E_m}{X_C} = \dfrac{100\ \text{V}}{530.5\ \Omega} = 0.189$ A

$i_C = I_m \sin(\omega t + 90^\circ) = 0.189 \sin(377t + 90^\circ)$ A

b. $I_m = \dfrac{100\ \text{V}}{31.83\ \Omega} = 3.14$ A; $\omega = 6283$ rad/s

$\therefore i_C = 3.14 \sin(6283t + 90^\circ)$ A

c. $I_m = \dfrac{100\ \text{V}}{400\ \Omega} = 0.25$ A; $\omega = 500$ rad/s

$\therefore i_C = 0.25 \sin(500t + 90^\circ)$ A

30. a. $X_C = \dfrac{V_m}{I_m} = \dfrac{362\ \text{V}}{94\ \text{mA}} = 3851\ \Omega$

$X_C = \dfrac{1}{2\pi f C} \therefore f = \dfrac{1}{2\pi X_C C} = \dfrac{1}{2\pi(3851)(2.2\ \mu F)}$
$= 18.8$ Hz

b. $X_C = \dfrac{3.6\ \text{V}}{0.35\ \text{A}} = 10.29\ \Omega$

$C = \dfrac{1}{2\pi f X_C} = \dfrac{1}{2\pi(12\ \text{kHz})(10.29)} = 1.29\ \mu\text{F}$

$\theta = 40^\circ - 90^\circ = -50^\circ$

16.7 The Impedance Concept

32. a. $\mathbf{I}_R = \dfrac{\mathbf{E}}{\mathbf{Z}_R} = \dfrac{100\text{V}\angle 0^\circ}{50\ \Omega} = 2\ \text{A}\angle 0^\circ$

$\mathbf{I}_L = \dfrac{\mathbf{E}}{\mathbf{Z}_L} = \dfrac{100\text{V}\angle 0^\circ}{j25\ \Omega} = 4\ \text{A}\angle -90^\circ$

$\mathbf{I}_C = \dfrac{\mathbf{E}}{\mathbf{Z}_C} = \dfrac{100\text{V}\angle 0^\circ}{-j10\ \Omega} = 10\ \text{A}\angle 90^\circ$

b. $i_R = \sqrt{2} I_R \sin(\omega t + \theta_R) = \sqrt{2}(2\ \text{A})\sin(\omega t + 0^\circ)$
$= 2.83 \sin \omega t$ A

$i_L = \sqrt{2}(4\ \text{A}) \sin(\omega t - 90^\circ) = 5.66 \sin(\omega t - 90^\circ)$ A

$i_C = \sqrt{2}(10\ \text{A}) \sin(\omega t + 90^\circ) = 14.1 \sin(\omega t + 90^\circ)$ A

34. a. $\mathbf{Z} = \dfrac{240\ \text{V}\angle -30^\circ}{4\ \text{A}\angle -30^\circ} = 60\angle 0^\circ$ (Resistive)

b. $\mathbf{Z} = \dfrac{40\ \text{V}\angle 30^\circ}{4\ \text{A}\angle -60^\circ} = 10\ \Omega\angle 90^\circ$ (Inductive)

c. $\mathbf{Z} = \dfrac{60\ \text{V}\angle -30^\circ}{4\ \text{A}\angle 60^\circ} = 15\Omega\angle -90^\circ$ (Capacitive)

d. $\mathbf{Z} = \dfrac{140 \text{ V}\angle{-30°}}{14 \text{ mA}\angle{-120°}} = 10 \text{ k}\Omega\angle 90°$ (Inductive)

36. a. $X_L = 2\pi fL = (2\pi)(10 \text{ kHz})(600\ \mu\text{H}) = 37.7\ \Omega$

$\mathbf{I}_L = \dfrac{\mathbf{V}_L}{\mathbf{Z}_L} = \dfrac{120 \text{ V } 67°}{j37.7\ \Omega} = 3.18 \text{ A}\angle{-23°}$

b. $X_L = 2\pi(700 \text{ Hz})(0.55 \text{ H}) = 2149\ \Omega$

$\mathbf{V}_L = \mathbf{I}_L\mathbf{Z}_L = (48 \text{ mA}\angle{-43°})(2149\ \Omega\angle 90°)$
$= 116 \text{ V}\angle 47°$

c. $X_C = \dfrac{1}{2\pi fC} = \dfrac{1}{(2\pi)(470 \text{ kHz})(390 \text{ pF})} = 868\ \Omega$

$\mathbf{Z}_C = -j868\ \Omega = 868\ \Omega\angle{-90°}$

$\mathbf{I}_C = \dfrac{\mathbf{V}_C}{\mathbf{Z}_C} = \dfrac{50 \text{ V}\angle{-36°}}{868\ \Omega\angle{-90°}} = 57.6 \text{ mA}\angle 54°$

d. $X_C = \dfrac{1}{(2\pi)(1.2 \text{ MHz})(6.5 \text{ nF})} = 20.4\ \Omega$

$\mathbf{V}_C = I_C\mathbf{Z}_C = (95 \text{ mA}\angle 87°)(20.4\angle{-90°})$
$= 1.94 \text{ V}\angle{-3°}$

16.8 Computer Analysis of AC Circuits

38. Analytical Solution: $X_L = 2\pi fL = (2\pi)(60 \text{ Hz})(0.2 \text{ H}) = 75.4\ \Omega$

$I = \dfrac{120 \text{ V}}{75.4\ \Omega} = 1.59 \text{ A}.$

40. The PSpice solution is shown below. Use source VAC. (Be sure to include the low value resistance shown to avoid a source-inductor loop.) Use AC Sweep to sweep the frequency from 1 Hz to 500 Hz. (Use about 100 points to get a smooth curve.) To get reactance, use Add Trace to plot the ratio of inductor voltage to current—see the graph legend below. The x-axis will default to a logarithmic frequency scale yielding a curved plot instead of the straight line shown. Click Plot, Axis Settings, x-axis and for the scale, select Linear. This straightens the plot as shown. Using the cursor, measure reactance at various frequencies and compare to the L_1 curve of Figure 16–28.

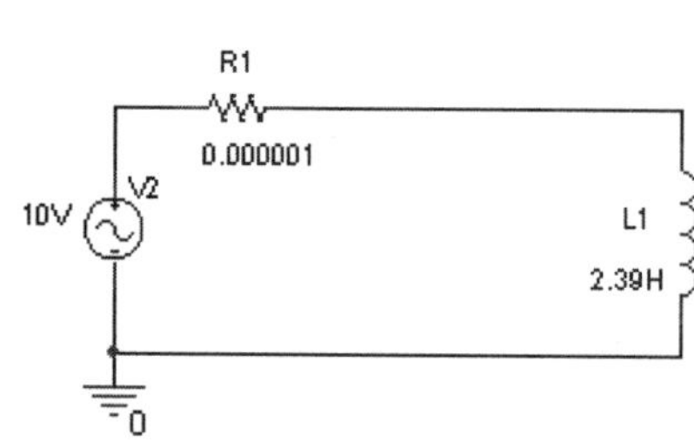

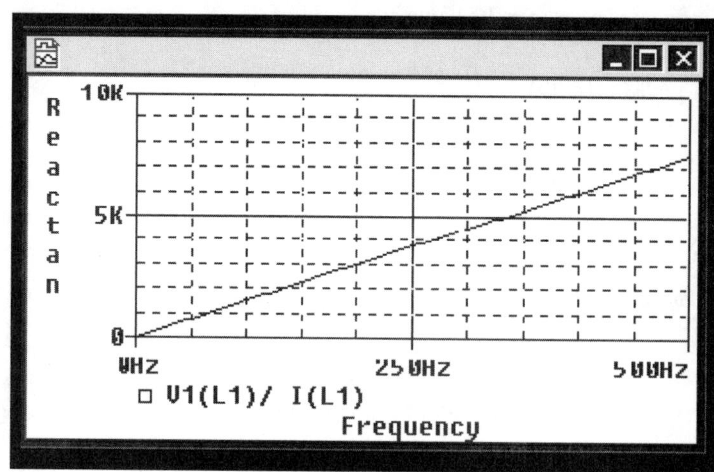

CHAPTER

17

Power in AC Circuits

17.1 to 17.4 Power to Loads

2. Real power is power that does work. It is also referred to as active power.

   Reactive power represents energy that flows back and forth between the source and the load.

   Reactive power has an average value of zero.

4. $Q_L = \dfrac{V^2}{X_L} = \dfrac{(100\text{ V})^2}{8}\ \Omega = 1250\text{ VAR}$

   $P_L = 0\text{ W}$

6. $P = I^2R \therefore R = \dfrac{P}{I^2} = \dfrac{625\text{ W}}{(12.5\text{ A})^2} = 4\ \Omega$

   $X_L = \dfrac{Q_L}{I^2} = \dfrac{(2500\text{ VAR})}{(12.5\text{ A})^2} = 16\ \Omega$

8. a. $P = \dfrac{V^2}{R} = \dfrac{(60\text{ V})^2}{8\ \Omega} = 450\text{ W}$

   b. $Q_L = \dfrac{V^2}{X_L} \therefore X_L = \dfrac{V^2}{Q_L} = \dfrac{(60\text{ V})^2}{40\text{ VAR}} = 90\ \Omega$

   c. $X_L = \omega L \therefore L = \dfrac{X_L}{\omega} = \dfrac{90\ \Omega}{(2\pi)(10\text{ Hz})} = 1.43\text{ H}$

10. $Q_C = \dfrac{V^2}{X_C} = \dfrac{(85\text{ V})^2}{42.5\ \Omega} = 170\text{ VAR}$

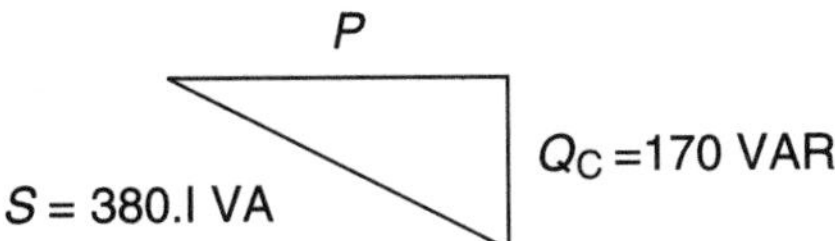

$P = \sqrt{S^2 - Q_C^2} = \sqrt{(380.1)^2 - (170)^2} = 340\text{ W}$

$R = \dfrac{V^2}{P} = \dfrac{(85\text{ V})^2}{340\text{ W}} = 21.25\ \Omega$

12. Exactly the same as in Problem 11. Power is independent of current direction.

14. $V_{R22} = (2.5\text{ A}\angle 0°)(22\ \Omega) = 55\text{ V}\angle 0°.$

    $V_C = V_{R22} = 55\text{ V}\angle 0°$

    $I_C = \dfrac{V_C}{-jX_C} = \dfrac{55\text{ V}\angle 0°}{-j6\ \Omega} = 9.17\text{ A}\angle 90°$

    $I_T = I_{R22} + I_C = 2.5\angle 0° + 9.17\angle 90° = 9.50\text{ A}\angle 74.7°$

    $P_T = (9.50\text{ A})^2 (10\ \Omega) + (2.5\text{ A})^2 (22\ \Omega) = 1040\text{ W}$

    $Q_T = \dfrac{V_C^2}{X_C} = \dfrac{(55\text{ V})^2}{6\ \Omega} = 504\text{ VAR (cap.)}$

16. $P_1 = \dfrac{V^2}{R_1} = \dfrac{(600\text{ V})^2}{20\ \Omega} = 18\text{ kW}$

    $P_2 = I_2^2 R_2 = (2.4\text{ A})^2(40\ \Omega) = 230.4\text{ W}$

    $P_T = 18\text{ kW} + 1152\text{ W} + 230.4\text{ W} = 19\ 382\text{ W}$

    $Q_1 = \dfrac{V^2}{X_C} = \dfrac{(600\text{ V})^2}{50\ \Omega} = 7.2\text{ kVAR (cap.)}$

    $Q_2 = (2.4\text{ A})^2(40\ \Omega) = 230.4\text{ VAR (ind.)}$

    $Q_T = -7200 - 633.6 + 230.4$

    $= -7603 = 7603\text{ VAR (Cap.)}$

18. $\mathbf{S} = 80 - j20 = 82.5\angle -14.0°\text{ VA}$

    $\therefore S = 82.5\text{ VA or } S = \sqrt{P^2 + Q^2} = 82.5\text{ VA}$

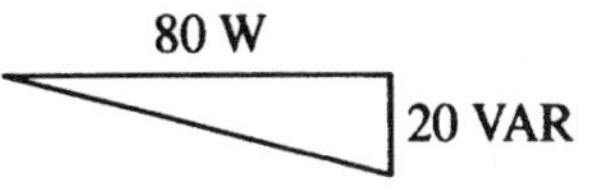

17.7 The Relationship Between P, Q, and S

20. $P_T = 1200\text{ W} + 200\text{ W} = 1400\text{ W}$

    $Q_T = -800\text{ VAR} + 200\text{ VAR} = -600\text{ VAR}$

    $S_T = \sqrt{P_T^2 + Q_T^2} = 1523\text{ VA}$

    $\therefore I = \dfrac{S_T}{V} = \dfrac{1523\text{ VA}}{120\text{ V}} = 12.7\text{ A}$

22. a. $\theta = 60° - 40° = 20°$

    b. $P = VI\cos\theta = (100\text{ V})(10\text{ A})\cos 20° = 940\text{ W}$

    c. $Q = VI\sin\theta = (100\text{ V})(10\text{ A})\sin 20° = 342\text{ VAR}$

    d. From the triangle, $\mathbf{S} = 940 + j342 = 1000\text{ VA}\angle 20°$

    e. $\mathbf{VI^*} = (100\text{ V}\angle 60°)(10\text{ A}\angle -40°) = 1000\text{ VA}\angle 20°$

24. a. $S_1 = \sqrt{P_1^2 + Q_1^2} = 1476\text{ VA}; S_2 = 100\text{ VA};$

    $S_3 = 1000\text{ VA}; S_4 = 80\text{ VA}; S_5 = 1206\text{ VA}$

    $S_1 + S_2 + S_3 + S_4 + S_5 = 3862\text{ VA}$

    Actual $S_T = 1803$ VA (from Example 17-5)

    $\therefore S_T \neq S_1 + S_2 + S_3 + S_4 + S_5$

17.8 Power Factor

26. a. $P_O = (10 \text{ hp})(746 \text{ W/hp}) = 7460 \text{ W}$

$$P_{in} = \frac{P_O}{\eta} = \frac{7460 \text{ W}}{0.87} = 8575 \text{ W} = P_m$$

b. $\theta_m = \cos^{-1}(0.65) = 49.5°$

$Q_m = P_{in.} \times \tan\theta_m = (8575 \text{ W}) \tan 49.5°$

$= 10\,026 \text{ VAR}$

c. $S_m = \sqrt{P_m^2 + Q_m^2} = 13\,193 \text{ VA}$

28. The new circuit is shown at right.

a. $P_T = 12 \text{ kW} + 54 \text{ kW} + 120 \text{ kW} = 186 \text{ kW}$

b. $Q_T = 72 \text{ kVAR} + 35 \text{ kVAR} = 107 \text{ kVAR (ind.)}$

c. $S_T = \sqrt{P_T^2 + Q_T^2} = 215 \text{ kVA}$

d. Place the capacitor across the load from a to b.

e. $Q_c = 107 \text{ kVAR}$

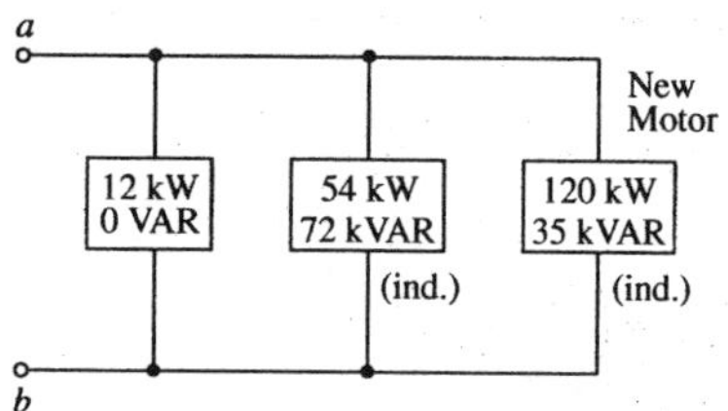

17.9 AC Power Measurement

30. a. A wattmeter measures only the real power on its load side.

b. See diagram below.

c. W = 700 W + 300 W + 1200 W = 2200 W

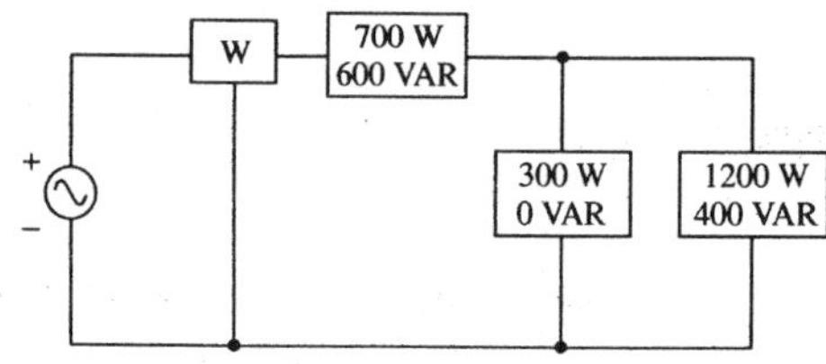

32. Wattmeter reads only real power. Thus, it indicates $\frac{(120 \text{ V})^2}{40\ \Omega} = 360 \text{ W}$.

17.12 Circuit Analysis Using Computers

34. Use current source ISIN. Note that we want current $i = 4 \sin \omega t$ A out of the source. However, PSpice works on the basis of current into nodes, not out of them. Thus, to get $4 \sin \omega t$ A out of the source, you must specify $-4 \sin \omega t$ A into it. To do this, double click each source parameter box and type in values as shown. Select Transient Analysis and set TSTOP to 1ms (to get a full cycle on the screen). Run the simulation and a sine wave of current as in Figure 17-4 of the text should appear. Click Plot, add a new Y-axis, then use Add Trace to add the inductor voltage waveform. Note that it is a cosine wave as Figure 17-4 indicates that it should be. Click Plot and add a third Y-axis. Now click Add Trace and in the dialog box, enter the product of voltage times current, i.e., V1(L1)*I(L1) and click OK. You should now get the power waveform. Click Plot, Axis Settings, Y Axis, select Y Axis 3 (to correspond to the power curve), User defined, then change to –50W to 50W, then click OK. Note how well it compares to Figure 17-4. Note from Figure 17-4 that the peak power should be VI where V and I are the rms values of voltage and current. Compute V and I and from them, determine peak power. Verify by measuring peak power with the cursor.

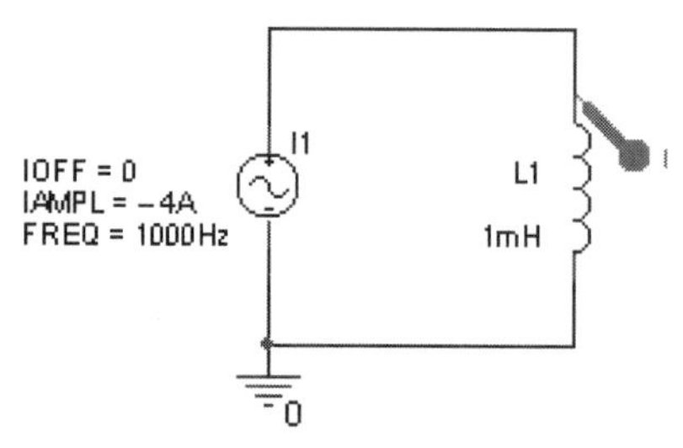

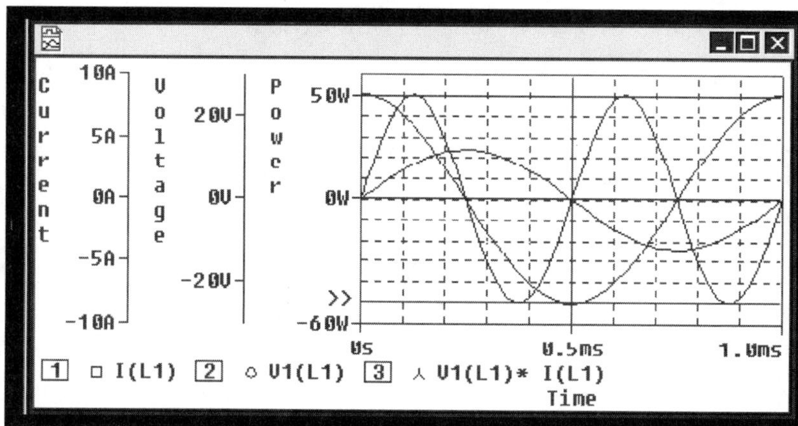

36. a. Review Example 10-9 (Chapter 10). Over each time interval, current is given by $i_C = C\frac{\Delta v}{\Delta t}$. (For example, from $t = 0$ to $t = 1$ ms, $i_C = (200 \times 10^{-6})\left[\frac{10\text{ V}}{1 \times 10^{-3}}\right] = 2$ A.) Results are plotted below. Multiply v_C times i_C point by point. You get the sawtooth power waveform indicated.

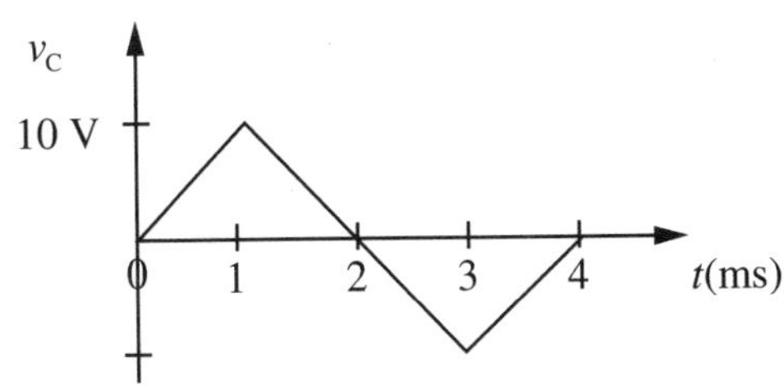

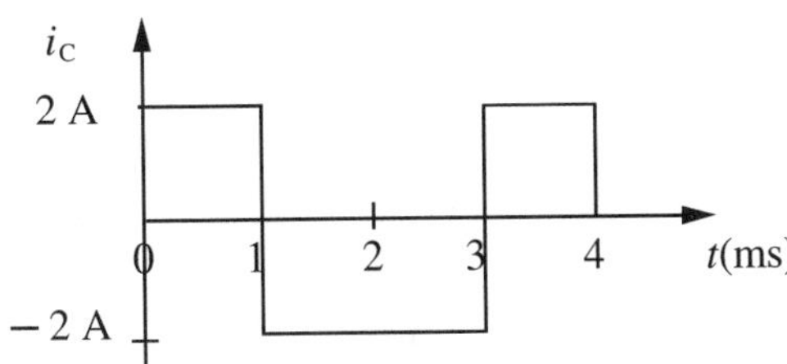

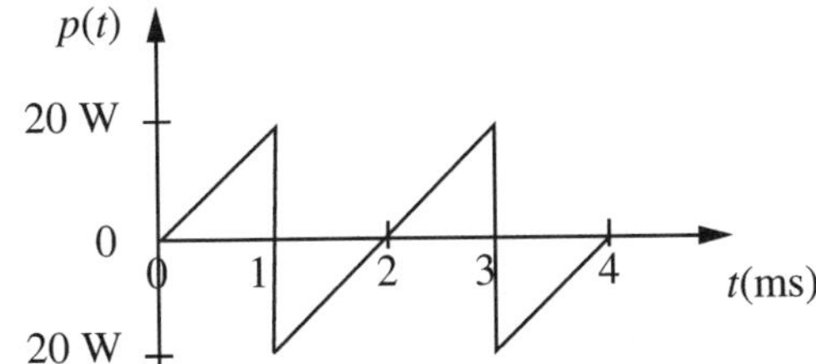

b. The PSpice solution is below. Select Transient analysis. Following simulation, the voltage/current plot appears. To create a new window for the power plot, click Windows, New Window, then use Add Trace to plot the product of voltage times current, i.e., V1(C1)*I(C1) as indicated. Use the cursor to measure power at various points and compare to the analytical solution. Note that results agree exactly.

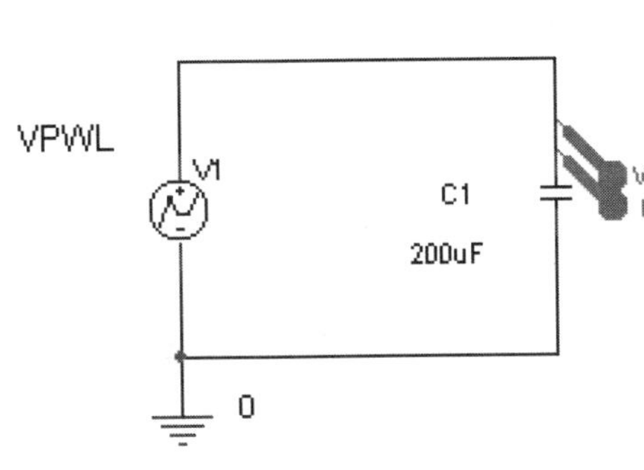

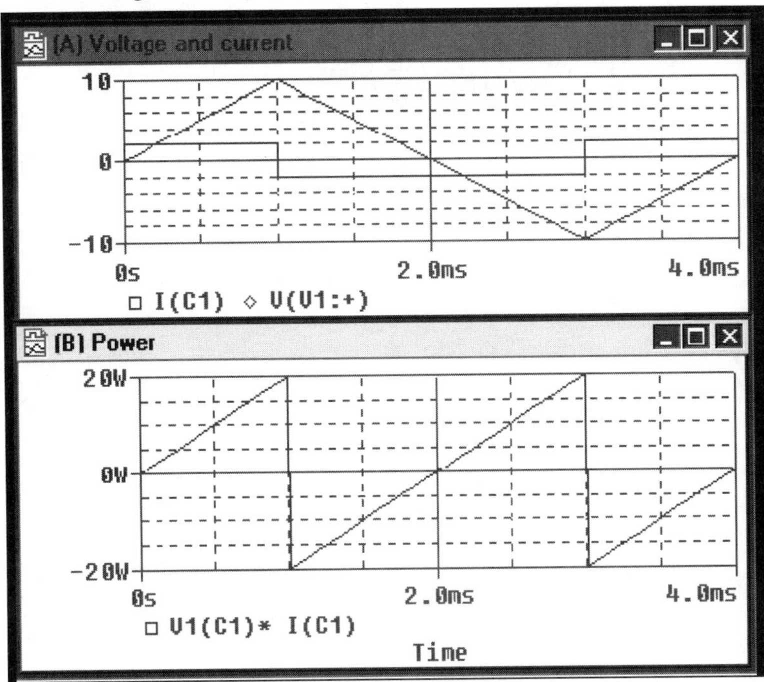

CHAPTER

18

AC Series-Parallel Circuits

18.1 Ohm's Law for ac Circuits

2. a. $\mathbf{V} = (6\text{ k}\Omega)(30\text{ mA}\angle -40^\circ) = 180\text{ V}\angle -40^\circ$

   $v = 255\sin(\omega t - 40^\circ)$

   b.

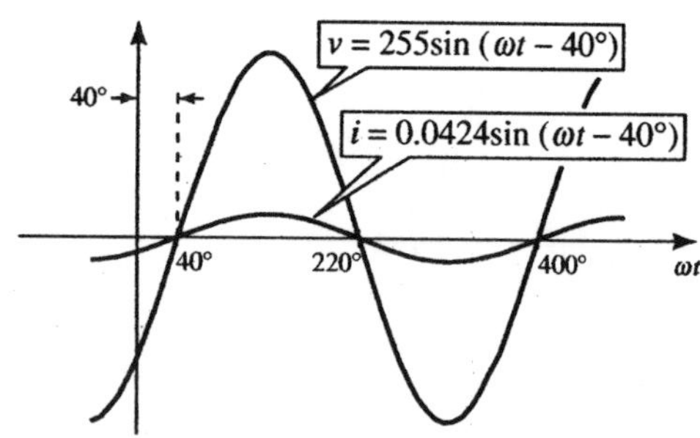

   c.

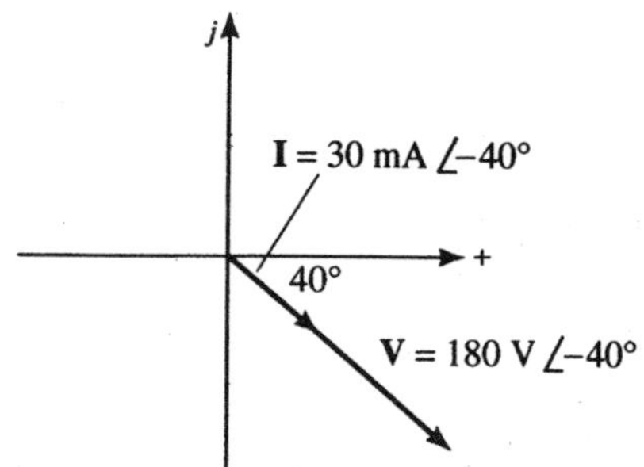

4. a. $\mathbf{I} = 7.07\text{ A}\angle 60^\circ$

   $\mathbf{V} = (33\ \Omega)(7.07\text{ A}\angle 60^\circ) = 233\text{ V}\angle 60^\circ$

   b.

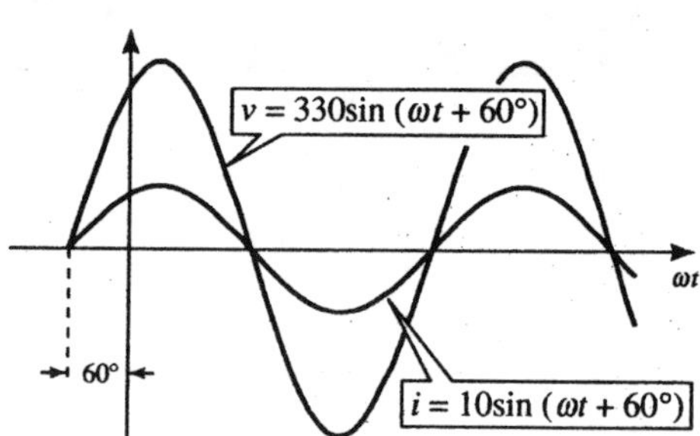

   c.

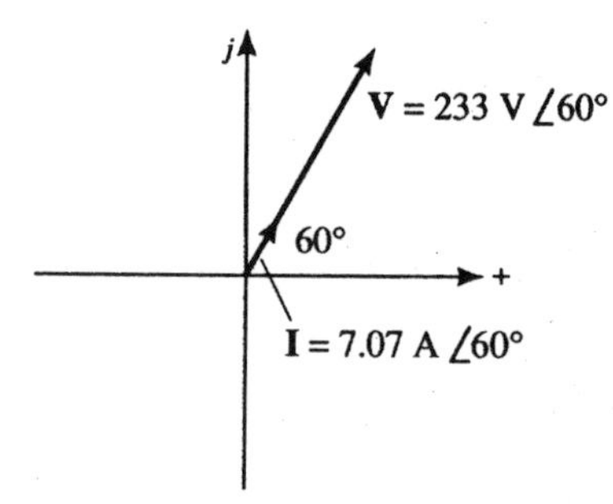

6. a. $\mathbf{V} = 1.626\text{ V}\angle -120^\circ$

   $\mathrm{I} = \dfrac{1.626\text{ V}\angle -120^\circ}{5\text{ k}\Omega\angle 90^\circ} = 325\ \mu\text{A}\angle 150^\circ$

   $i = 460\times 10^{-6}\sin(\omega t + 150^\circ)$

   b.

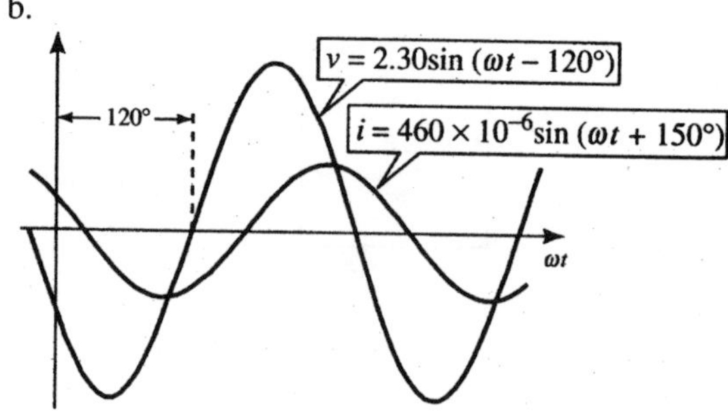

   c.

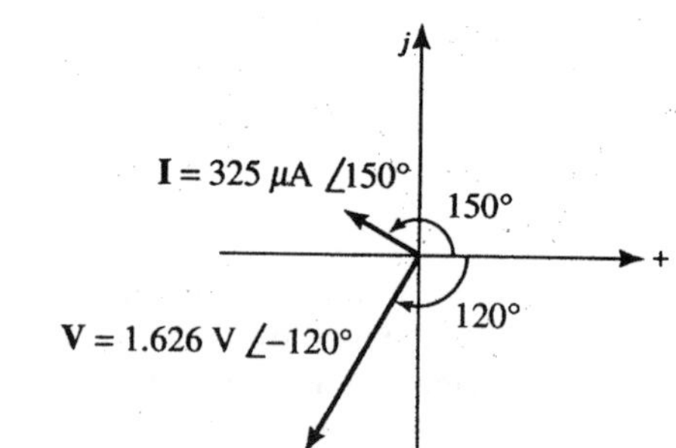

8. a. $X_C = \dfrac{1}{2\pi(1\text{ kHz})(0.47\ \mu\text{F})} = 339\ \Omega$

   $\mathbf{I} = \dfrac{200\text{ mV}\angle 90^\circ}{339\ \Omega\angle -90^\circ} = 591\ \mu\text{A}\angle 180^\circ$

   $i = 835\times 10^{-6}\sin(2000\pi t + 180^\circ)$

   b.

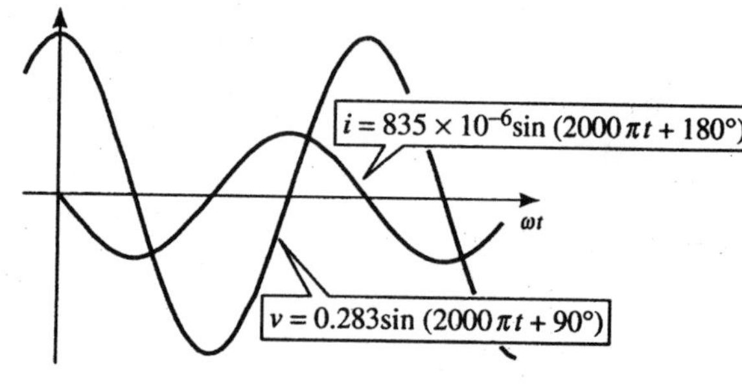

c.

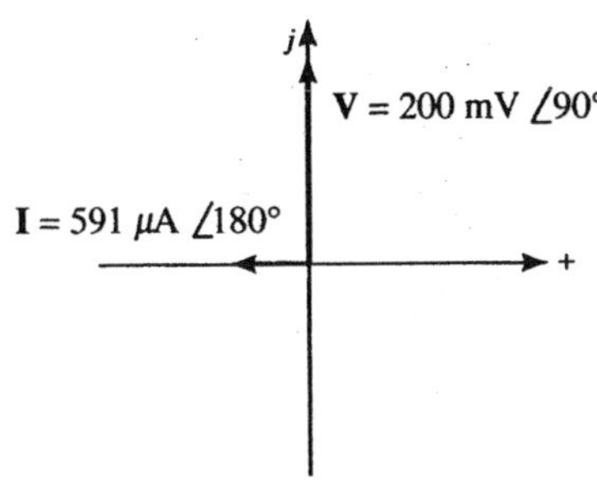

10. a. $X_L\,(200)(240\,\mu\text{H}) = 48\text{ m}\Omega$

$V = 5.66\text{ V}\angle 60^\circ$

$I = \dfrac{5.66\text{ V}\angle 60^\circ}{0.048\ \Omega\angle 90^\circ} = 117.9\text{ A}\angle -30^\circ$

$i = 166.7\sin(200t - 30^\circ)$

b.

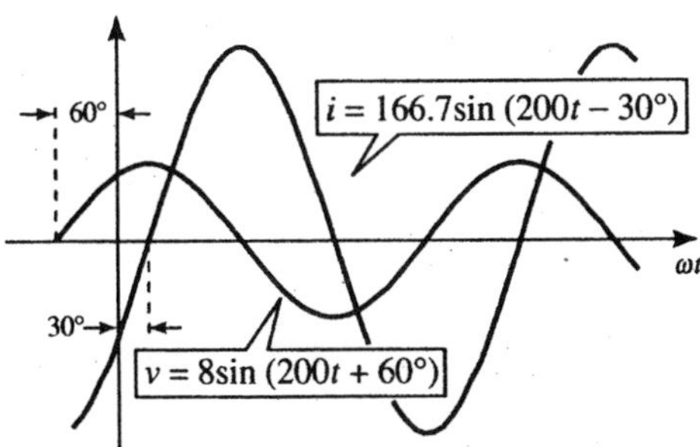

c.

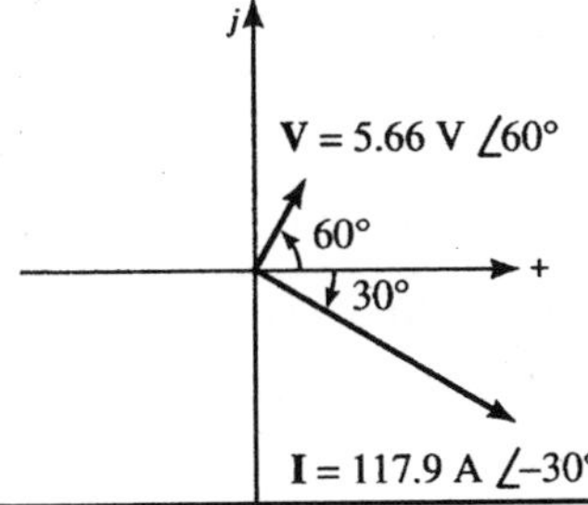

12. a. $X_C = \dfrac{1}{(377)(0.0033\,\mu\text{F})} = 804\text{ k}\Omega$

$\mathbf{V} = 120.2\text{ V}\angle 40^\circ$

$\mathbf{I} = \dfrac{120.2V\angle 40^\circ}{804\text{ k}\Omega\angle -90^\circ} = 149.6\,\mu\text{A}\angle 130^\circ$

$i = 211\times 10^{-6}\sin(377t + 130^\circ)$

b.

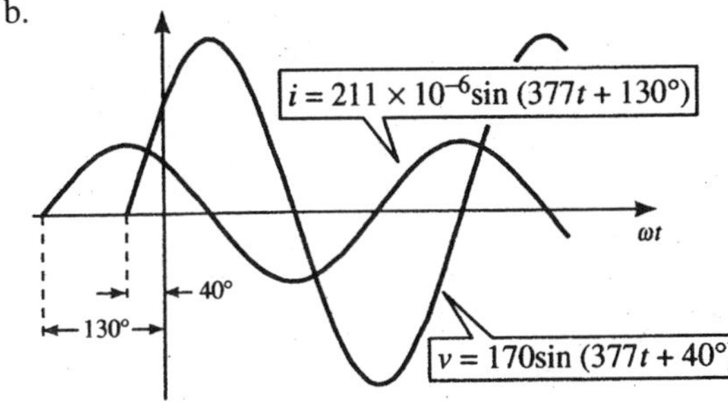

c.

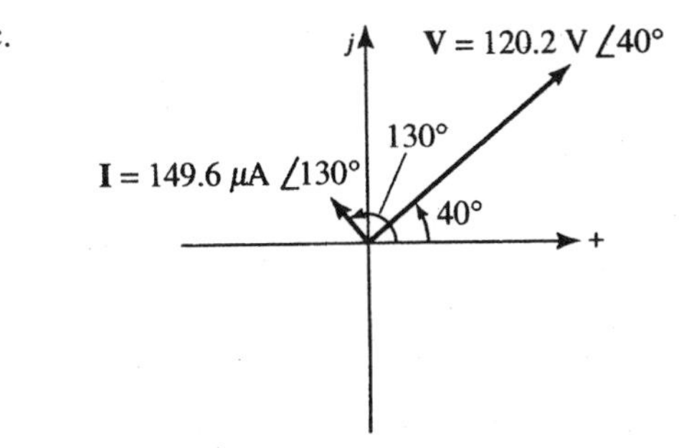

18.2 AC Series Circuits

14. network (a)

$\mathbf{Z}_T = (30\ \Omega - j40\ \Omega) + (80\ \Omega\angle 60^\circ)$

$= 70\ \Omega + j29.3\ \Omega = 75.9\ \Omega\angle 22.70^\circ$

network (b)

$\mathbf{Z}_T = (30\ \Omega\angle 20^\circ) + (55\ \Omega\angle -30^\circ) + (20\ \Omega\angle -90^\circ)$

$= 84.5\ \Omega\angle -26.16^\circ = 75.8\ \Omega - j37.2\ \Omega$

16. $\mathbf{Z} = 90\ \Omega\angle 25^\circ - 16\ \Omega\angle -30^\circ - 25\ \Omega$

$= 62.8\ \Omega\angle 47.15^\circ$

18. $\mathbf{Z}_T = 24.0\text{ k}\Omega\angle -30^\circ = 20.8\text{ k}\Omega - j12.0\text{ k}\Omega$

$X_C = 12.0\text{ k}\Omega$

$C = \dfrac{1}{2\pi(2\text{ kHz})(12.0\text{ k}\Omega)} = 6.63\text{ nF}$

$R = 20.8\text{ k}\Omega$

20. at 2 kHz: $X_L = 2\pi(2\text{ kHz})(20\text{ mH}) = 251\ \Omega$

$\mathbf{Z} = (50\ \Omega\angle 60^\circ) - 10\ \Omega - j251\ \Omega = 15\ \Omega - j208\ \Omega$

$X_C = 208\ \Omega$

$C = \dfrac{1}{2\pi(2\text{ kHz})(208\ \Omega)} = 0.382\,\mu\text{F}$

$R = 15\ \Omega$ in series with $C = 0.382\,\mu\text{F}$

22. a. $\mathbf{Z}_T = 4\text{ k}\Omega + j6\text{ k}\Omega - j3\text{ k}\Omega = 4\text{ k}\Omega + j3\text{ k}\Omega$

$= 5\text{ k}\Omega\angle 36.87^\circ$

b. $\mathbf{I} = \dfrac{10\text{ V}\angle 0^\circ}{5\text{ k}\Omega\angle 36.87^\circ} = 2\text{ mA}\angle -36.87^\circ$

$\mathbf{V}_R = (2\text{ mA}\angle -36.87^\circ)(4\text{ k}\Omega\angle 0^\circ) = 8\text{ V}\angle -36.87^\circ$

$\mathbf{V}_L = (2\text{ mA}\angle -36.87^\circ)(6\text{ k}\Omega\angle 90^\circ) = 12\text{ V}\angle 53.13^\circ$

$\mathbf{V}_C = (2\text{ mA}\angle -36.87^\circ)(3\text{ k}\Omega\angle -90^\circ)$

$= 6\text{ V}\angle -126.87^\circ$

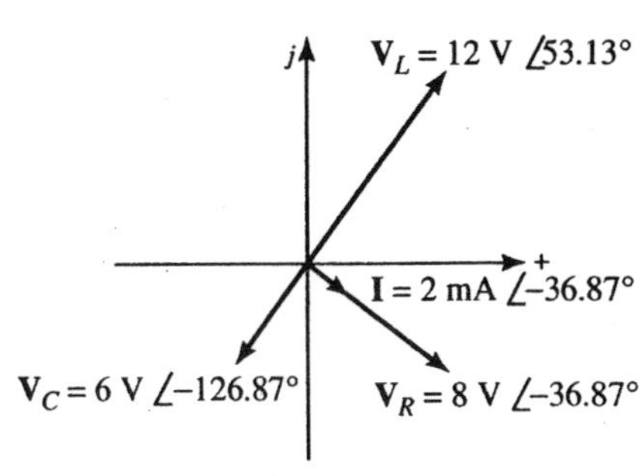

c. $i = 2.83 \times 10^{-3} \sin(\omega t - 36.87°)$
$e = 14.14 \sin \omega t$ $v_R = 11.31 \sin(\omega t - 36.87°)$
$v_L = 16.97 \sin(\omega t + 53.13°)$
$v_C = 8.49 \sin(\omega t - 126.87°)$

d.

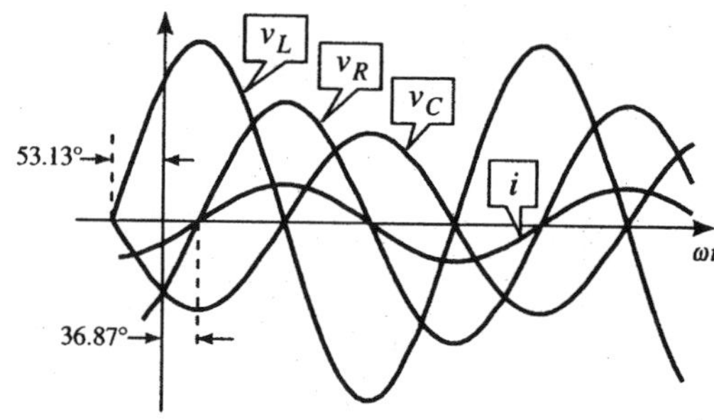

e. $P_R = \dfrac{(8\text{ V})^2}{4\text{ k}\Omega} = 16\text{mW}$

f. $F_p = \cos 36.87° = 0.8$
$P_T = (10\text{ V})(2\text{ mA})(0.8) = 16\text{ mW}$ (same as e.)

24. $\mathbf{E} = 7.07\text{ V} \angle 0°$

$I = \sqrt{\dfrac{200\text{ mW}}{100\ \Omega}} = 44.7\text{ mA}_{\text{rms}}$

$Z = \dfrac{7.07\text{ V}}{44.7\text{ mA}} = 158.1\ \Omega$

a. $X = \sqrt{(158.1\ \Omega)^2 - (100\ \Omega)^2} = 122.5\ \Omega$
$X_C = 122.5\ \Omega + 50\ \Omega = 172.5\ \Omega$

b. $\mathbf{Z}_T = 100\ \Omega - j172.5\ \Omega + j50\ \Omega$
$= 100\ \Omega - j122.5\ \Omega = 158.1\Omega\angle{-50.77°}$

$\mathbf{I} = \dfrac{7.07\text{ V}\angle 0°}{158.1\Omega\angle{-50.77°}} = 44.7\text{ mA}\ \angle 50.77°$

$i = 0.0632 \sin(\omega t + 50.77°)$

18.3 Kirchhoff's Voltage Law and the Voltage Divider Rule

26. $\mathbf{V}_1 = \left(\dfrac{30\ \Omega - j40\ \Omega}{(30\ \Omega - j40\ \Omega) + 80\ \Omega\angle 60°}\right) 240\text{ V} \angle 30° = 158.1\text{ V} \angle -45.83°$

$\mathbf{V}_2 = \left(\dfrac{80\ \Omega\angle 60°}{(30\ \Omega - j40\ \Omega) + 80\ \Omega\angle 60°}\right) 240\text{ V} \angle 30° = 253.0\text{ V} \angle 67.30°$

b. $158.1\text{ V} \angle -45.83° + 253.0\text{ V} \angle 67.30° = 240\text{ V} \angle 30°$ (as required)

28. a. $\mathbf{V}_R = \left(\dfrac{50\ \Omega}{50\ \Omega + j20\ \Omega}\right)(120V\angle 0° - 118.8V\angle{-45°})$
$= 84.9\text{ V} \angle 45°$

$\mathbf{V}_L = \left(\dfrac{j20\ \Omega}{50\ \Omega + j20\ \Omega}\right)(120V\angle 0° - 118.8V\angle{-45°}).$
$= 33.9\text{ V} \angle 135°$

b. $\mathbf{I} = \dfrac{84.9\text{ V}\angle 45°}{50\ \Omega} = 1.698\text{ A} \angle 45°$

$X_C = \dfrac{118.8\text{ V}}{1.698\text{ V}} = 70\ \Omega$

30. $R_T = \dfrac{P_T}{I^2} = \dfrac{500\text{ W}}{(2\text{ A})^2} = 125\ \Omega$

$\mathbf{Z} = 25\ \Omega \pm jX$

$\mathbf{Z}_T = 100\ \Omega + 25\ \Omega \pm jX + j200\ \Omega$
$= 125\ \Omega + j(200\ \Omega + X)$

But $Z_T = \dfrac{600\text{ V}}{2\text{ A}} = 300\ \Omega$

and $Z_T = \sqrt{(125\ \Omega)^2 + (200\ \Omega + X)^2}$

$(200 + X) = \pm\sqrt{(300\ \Omega)^2 - (125\ \Omega)^2}$

$X = \pm 272.72\ \Omega - 200\ \Omega$

$X = 72.72\ \Omega$ or $X = 472.72\ \Omega$

$\mathbf{Z} = 25\ \Omega + j72.72\ \Omega$

or $\mathbf{Z} = 25\ \Omega - j472.72\ \Omega$

b. $\mathbf{I} = \dfrac{600\text{ V}\angle 30°}{100\ \Omega + 25\ \Omega + j72.72 + j200\ \Omega}$
$= 2.00\text{ A} \angle{-35.38°}$

c. $\mathbf{V}_R = 200\text{ V} \angle{-35.38°}$
$\mathbf{V}_L = 400\text{ V} \angle 54.62°$
$\mathbf{V}_Z = 153.8\text{ V} \angle 35.65°$

18.4 AC Parallel Circuits

32. network (a)

$\mathbf{Y}_T = \dfrac{1}{-j600\ \Omega} + \dfrac{1}{j900\Omega} + \dfrac{1}{-j1800\Omega}$
$= 1.11\text{ mS} \angle 90°$

$\mathbf{Z}_T = \dfrac{1}{1.11\text{ mS}\angle 90°} = 900\ \Omega \angle -90°$

network (b)

$\mathbf{Y}_t = \dfrac{1}{50\text{ k}\Omega} + \dfrac{1}{j3\text{ k}\Omega} + \dfrac{1}{j6\text{ k}\Omega}$
$= 500.4\ \mu\text{S} \angle -87.71°$

$\mathbf{Z}_T = \dfrac{1}{500.4\ \mu\text{S}\angle{-87.71°}} = 1998\ \Omega \angle 87.71°$

34. $X_C = \dfrac{1}{(10\,000\text{ rad/s})(1\ \mu\text{F})} = 100\ \Omega$

$X_L = (10\,000\text{ rad/s})(20\text{ mH}) = 200\ \Omega$

a. $\mathbf{Z}_T = \dfrac{1}{\dfrac{1}{25\text{ k}\Omega} + j\dfrac{1}{100\ \Omega} - j\dfrac{1}{200\ \Omega}} = 200\ \Omega \angle -89.54°$

$\mathbf{E} = \dfrac{50\text{ V}}{\sqrt{2}} \angle 0° = 35.36\text{ V} \angle 0°$

$\mathbf{I}_T = \dfrac{35.36\text{ V}\angle 0^\circ}{200\ \Omega\angle -89.54^\circ} = 176.8\text{ mA}\angle 89.54^\circ$

$\mathbf{I}_1 = \dfrac{35.36\text{ V}\angle 0^\circ}{25\text{ k}\Omega} = 1.414\text{ mA}\angle 0^\circ$

$\mathbf{I}_2 = \dfrac{35.36\text{ V}\angle 0^\circ}{100\ \Omega\angle -90^\circ} = 353.6\text{ mA}\angle 90^\circ$

$\mathbf{I}_3 = \dfrac{35.36\text{ V}\angle 0^\circ}{200\ \Omega\angle 90^\circ} = 176.8\text{ mA}\angle -90^\circ$

b.

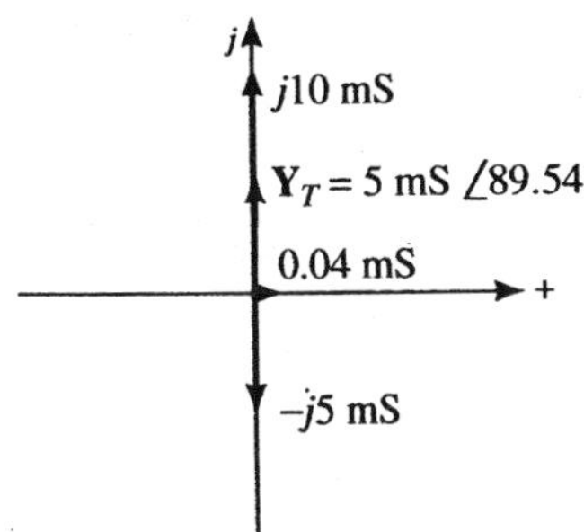

c.

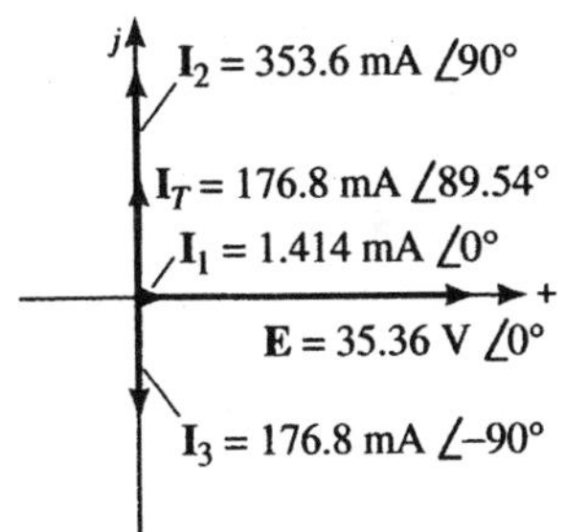

d. $i_T = 250 \times 10^{-3}\sin(10\,000t + 89.54^\circ)$
$i_1 = 2 \times 10^{-3}\sin(10\,000t)$
$i_2 = 500 \times 10^{-3}\sin(10\,000t + 90^\circ)$
$i_3 = 250 \times 10^{-3}\sin(10\,000t - 90^\circ)$

e.

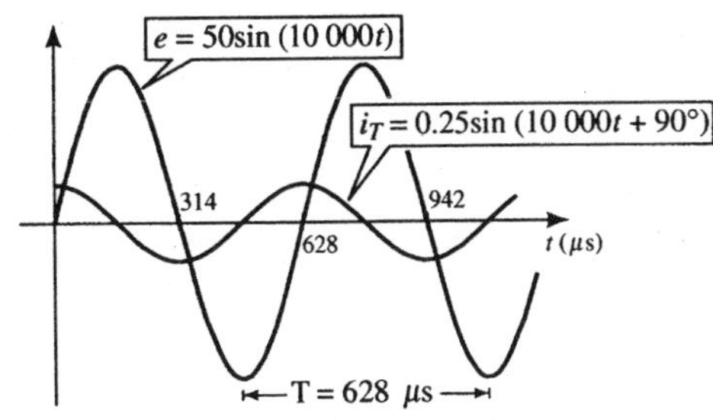

f. $P_R = (1.414\text{ mA})^2(25\text{ k}\Omega) = 50\text{ mW}$

g. $P_T = (35.36\text{ V})(176.8\text{ mA})\cos 89.54^\circ$
$= 50\text{ mW}$ (as required)

36. a. $\mathbf{Z}_T = \dfrac{1}{\dfrac{1}{30\ \Omega - j60\ \Omega} + \dfrac{1}{10\ \Omega + j40\ \Omega}}$
$= 61.85\ \Omega\angle 39.09^\circ$

b. $\mathbf{V} = (100\text{ mA}\angle 30^\circ)(30\ \Omega - j60\ \Omega)$
$= 6.708\text{ V}\angle -33.43^\circ$

c. $\mathbf{I}_2 = \dfrac{6.708\text{ V}\angle -33.43^\circ}{10\ \Omega + j40\ \Omega} = 162.7\text{ mA}\angle -109.40^\circ$

$\mathbf{I} = \dfrac{6.708\text{ V}\angle -33.43^\circ}{61.85\ \Omega\angle 39.09^\circ} = 108.5\text{ mA}\angle -72.52^\circ$

38. $\dfrac{1}{\mathbf{Z}_2} = \dfrac{1}{1.2\text{ k}\Omega\angle 0^\circ} - \dfrac{1}{3\text{ k}\Omega - j1\text{ k}\Omega}$
$= 0.5426\text{ mS}\angle -10.62^\circ$

$\mathbf{Z}_2 = \dfrac{1}{0.5426\text{ mS}\angle -10.62^\circ} = 1.843\text{ k}\Omega\angle 10.62^\circ$

18.5 Kirchhoff's Current Law and the Current Divider Rule

40. network (a)

$\mathbf{Z}_T = 900\ \Omega\angle -90^\circ$

$\mathbf{I}_1 = \left(\dfrac{900\ \Omega\angle -90^\circ}{600\ \Omega\angle -90^\circ}\right)(10\text{ mA}\angle -30^\circ)$
$= 15\text{ mA}\angle -30^\circ$

$\mathbf{I}_2 = \left(\dfrac{900\ \Omega\angle -90^\circ}{900\ \Omega\angle 90^\circ}\right)(10\text{ mA}\angle -30^\circ)$
$= 10\text{ mA}\angle 150^\circ$

$\mathbf{I}_3 = \left(\dfrac{900\ \Omega\angle -90^\circ}{1800\ \Omega\angle -90^\circ}\right)(10\text{ mA}\angle -30^\circ)$
$= 5\text{ mA}\angle -30^\circ$

network (b)

$\mathbf{Z}_T = 1.9984\text{ k}\Omega\angle 87.71^\circ$

$\mathbf{I}_1$ mark $= \left(\dfrac{1.9984\text{ k}\Omega\angle 87.71^\circ}{50\text{ k}\Omega\angle 0^\circ}\right)(10\text{ mA}\angle -30^\circ)$
$= 0.4\text{ mA}\angle 57.71^\circ$

$\mathbf{I}_2 = \left(\dfrac{1.9984\text{ k}\Omega\angle 87.71^\circ}{3\text{ k}\Omega\angle 90^\circ}\right)(10\text{ mA}\angle -30^\circ)$
$= 6.66\text{ mA}\angle -32.29^\circ$

$\mathbf{I}_3 = \left(\dfrac{1.9984\text{ k}\Omega\angle 87.71^\circ}{6\text{ k}\Omega\angle 90^\circ}\right)(10\text{ mA}\angle -30^\circ)$
$= 3.33\text{ mA}\angle -32.29^\circ$

42. $\mathbf{V} = (20\ \Omega\angle 90^\circ)(4\text{ A}\angle 30^\circ) = 80\text{ V}\angle 120^\circ$

$\mathbf{I}_C = \dfrac{80\text{ V}\angle 120^\circ}{10\ \Omega\angle -90^\circ} = 8\text{ A}\angle 210^\circ$

$\mathbf{I}_R = \dfrac{80\text{ V}\angle 120^\circ}{20\ \Omega\angle -90^\circ} = 4\text{ A}\angle 120^\circ$

$\mathbf{Z} = \dfrac{1}{\dfrac{1}{10\ \Omega\angle -90^\circ} + \dfrac{1}{20\ \Omega} + \dfrac{1}{20\ \Omega\angle 90^\circ}}$
$= 14.14\ \Omega\angle -45^\circ$

$\mathbf{I} = \dfrac{80\text{ V}\angle 120^\circ}{14.14\ \Omega\angle -45^\circ} = 5.66\text{ A}\angle 165^\circ$

$4\text{A}\angle 30^\circ + 8\text{ A}\angle 210^\circ + 4\text{ A}\angle 120^\circ = 5.66\text{ A}\angle 165^\circ$
(as required)

44. $\mathbf{I}_C$ leads $\mathbf{I}_R$ by 90°

a. $I_R = \sqrt{(3\text{ A})^2 - (2\text{ A})^2} = 2.236\text{ A}$

$\mathbf{I}_R = 2.236\text{ A}\angle -90^\circ$

b. $\mathbf{V} = (2.236 \text{ A} \angle -90^\circ)(10\ \Omega)$
$= 22.36 \text{ V} \angle -90^\circ$
$X_C = \dfrac{22.36 \text{ V}}{2 \text{ A}} = 11.18\ \Omega$

c. $\mathbf{I} = 2.236 \text{ A} \angle -90^\circ + 2 \text{ A} \angle 0^\circ$
$= 3.0 \text{ A} \angle -48.19^\circ$

18.6 Series-Parallel Circuits

46. a. $\mathbf{Z}_T = 8\text{ k}\Omega - j4\text{ k}\Omega + \dfrac{1}{\dfrac{1}{3\text{ k}\Omega + j9\text{ k}\Omega} + \dfrac{1}{30\text{ k}\Omega}}$
$= 8\text{ k}\Omega - j4\text{ k}\Omega + 8.32\text{ k}\Omega \angle 56.31^\circ$
$= 12.95\text{ k}\Omega \angle 13.05^\circ$
$\mathbf{I}_1 = \dfrac{20\text{ V}\angle 0^\circ}{12.95\text{ k}\Omega\angle 13.05^\circ} = 1.544\text{ mA} \angle -13.05^\circ$
$\mathbf{I}_2 = \left(\dfrac{8.32\text{ k}\Omega\angle 56.31^\circ)}{3\text{ k}\Omega + j9\text{ k}\Omega}\right)1.544\text{ mA} \angle -13.05^\circ$
$= 1.355\text{ mA} \angle -28.30^\circ$
$\mathbf{I}_3 = \left(\dfrac{8.32\text{ k}\Omega\angle 56.31^\circ)}{30\text{ k}\Omega\angle 0^\circ}\right)1.544\text{ mA} \angle -13.05^\circ$
$= 0.428\text{ mA} \angle 43.26^\circ$

b.

j
$\mathbf{I}_3 = 0.428$ mA $\angle 43.26^\circ$
$\mathbf{E} = 20$ V $\angle 0^\circ$
+
$\mathbf{I}_1 = 1.544$ mA $\angle -13.05^\circ$
$\mathbf{I}_2 = 1.355$ mA $\angle -28.30^\circ$

c. $P_1 = (1.544\text{ mA})^2(8\text{ k}\Omega) = 19.08\text{ mW}$
$P_2 = (1.355\text{ mA})^2(3\text{ k}\Omega) = 5.51\text{ mW}$
$P_3 = (0.428\text{ mA})^2(30\text{ k}\Omega) = 5.50\text{ mW}$

d. $P_T = (20\text{ V})(1.544\text{ mA}) \cos 13.05^\circ = 30.08\text{ mW}$
$P_1 + P_2 + P_3 = 19.08\text{ mW} + 5.51\text{ mW} + 5.50\text{ mW}$
$= 30.09\text{ mW}$ (as required)

48. a. $\mathbf{Z}_T = -j1\ \Omega + \dfrac{1}{\dfrac{1}{20\ \Omega} + \dfrac{1}{-j30\ \Omega + j40\ \Omega + 10\ \Omega}}$
$= -j1\ \Omega + 8.944\ \Omega \angle 26.57^\circ = 8.544\ \Omega \angle 20.56^\circ$
$\mathbf{I}_T = \dfrac{5\text{ V}\angle 0^\circ}{8.544\ \Omega\angle 20.56^\circ} = 0.5852\text{ A} \angle -20.56^\circ$
$\mathbf{I}_1 = \left(\dfrac{8.944\ \Omega\angle 26.57^\circ}{20\ \Omega}\right)(0.5852\text{ A} \angle -20.56^\circ)$
$= 0.2617\text{ A} \angle 6.01^\circ$
$\mathbf{I}_2 = \left(\dfrac{8.944\ \Omega\angle 26.57^\circ}{10\ \Omega + j10\ \Omega}\right)(0.5852\text{ A} \angle -20.56^\circ$
$= 0.3701\text{ A} \angle -38.99^\circ$

b. $\mathbf{V} = (40\ \Omega \angle 90^\circ)(0.3701\text{ A} \angle -38.99^\circ)$
$= 14.80\text{ V} \angle 51.01^\circ$

50. a. $\mathbf{Z}_T = \dfrac{1}{\dfrac{1}{400\text{ k}\Omega} + \dfrac{1}{-j50\text{ k}\Omega} + \dfrac{1}{20\text{ k}\Omega + j40\text{ k}\Omega}}$
$= 80\text{ k}\Omega \angle 0^\circ$
$\mathbf{I}_1 = \left(\dfrac{80\text{ k}\Omega\angle 0^\circ}{400\text{ k}\Omega\angle 0^\circ}\right)(1\ \mu\text{A} \angle 0^\circ) = 0.2\ \mu\text{A} \angle 0^\circ$
$\mathbf{I}_2 = \left(\dfrac{80\text{ k}\Omega\angle 0^\circ}{50\text{ k}\Omega\angle -90^\circ}\right)(1\ \mu\text{A} \angle 0^\circ) = 1.6\ \mu\text{A} \angle 90^\circ$
$\mathbf{I}_3 = \left(\dfrac{80\text{ k}\Omega\angle 0^\circ}{20\text{ k}\Omega + j40\text{ k}\Omega}\right)(1\ \mu\text{A} \angle 0^\circ)$
$= 1.789\ \mu\text{A} \angle -63.43^\circ$

b. $\mathbf{V} = (40\text{ k}\Omega \angle 90^\circ)(1.789\ \mu\text{A} \angle -63.43^\circ)$
$= 71.6\text{ mV} \angle 26.57^\circ$

18.7 Frequency Effects

52. $\omega_C = \dfrac{2\text{ k}\Omega}{2\text{ mH}} = 1\ M\ rad/s$

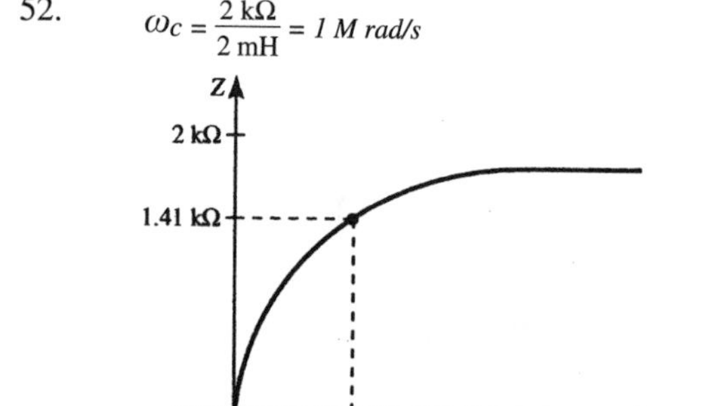

54. $f_C = \dfrac{2.7\text{ k}\Omega}{2\pi(20\ mH)} = 21.49\text{ kHz}$

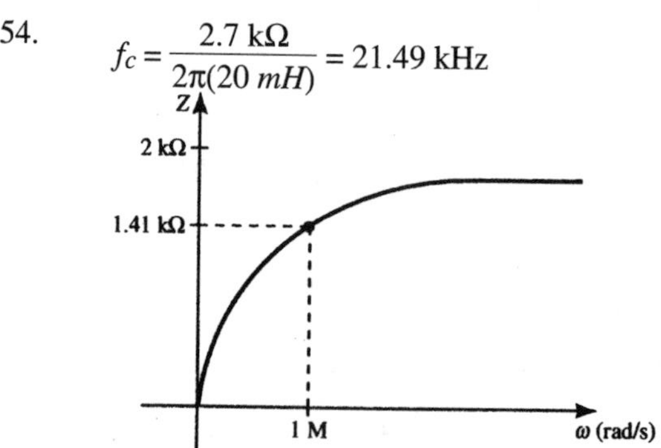

18.8 Applications

56. network (a)

$$\mathbf{Z}_T = 2.5\text{ k}\Omega + \frac{1}{\dfrac{1}{30\text{ k}\Omega} + \dfrac{1}{j10\text{ k}\Omega}}$$

$$= 10.55\text{ k}\Omega \angle 58.57^\circ$$

$$\mathbf{Y}_T = 0.0948\text{ mS} \angle -58.57^\circ$$

$$= 0.0494\text{ mS} - j0.0809\text{ mS}$$

$R = 20.2\ \Omega$ $X_L = 12.36\ \Omega$

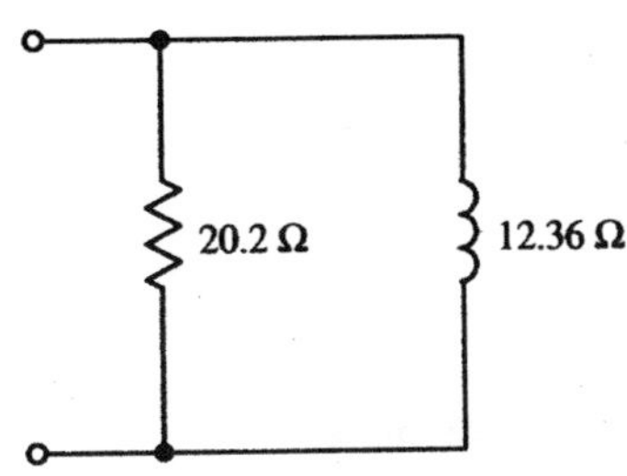

network (b)

$$\mathbf{Z}_T = \frac{1}{\dfrac{1}{j300\ \Omega} + \dfrac{1}{270\ \Omega - j90\ \Omega}} = 249.6\ \Omega \angle 33.69^\circ$$

$$\mathbf{Y}_T = 0.00\overline{3}\text{ S} - j0.00\overline{2}\text{ S}$$

$$R = \frac{1}{0.00\overline{3}} = 300\ \Omega$$

$$X_L = \frac{1}{0.00\overline{2}} = 450\ \Omega$$

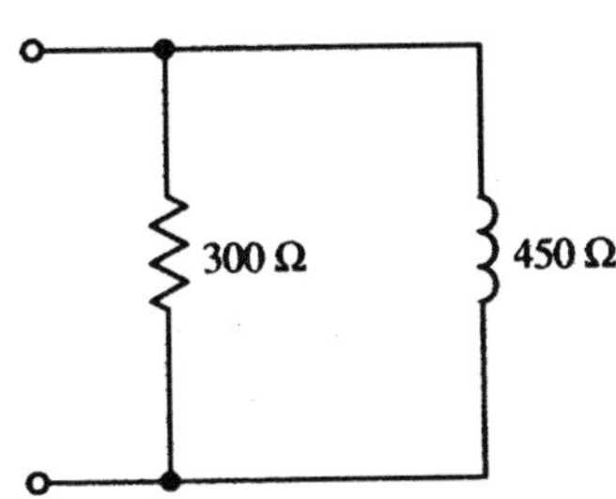

58. *at 5 rad/s:*

$X_{L1} = (5\text{ rad/s})(100\text{ H}) = 500\ \Omega$

$X_{L2} = (5\text{ rad/s})(25\text{ H}) = 125\ \Omega$

network (a)

$$\mathbf{Z}_T = 100\ \Omega + \frac{1}{\dfrac{1}{100\ \Omega} + \dfrac{1}{100\ \Omega + j500\ \Omega}}$$

$$= 193.1\ \Omega + j17.2\ \Omega = 193.9\ \Omega \angle 5.10^\circ$$

network (b)

$$\mathbf{Z}_T = 150\ \Omega + \frac{1}{\dfrac{1}{j125\ \Omega} + \dfrac{1}{50\ \Omega}}$$

$$= 193.1\ \Omega + j17.2\ \Omega \text{ (as required)}$$

at 10 rad/s:

$X_{L1} = 1000\ \Omega$

$X_{L2} = 250\ \Omega$

network (a)

$$\mathbf{Z}_T = 100\ \Omega + \frac{1}{\dfrac{1}{j100\ \Omega} + \dfrac{1}{100\ \Omega + j1000\ \Omega}}$$

$$= 198.1\ \Omega + j9.62\ \Omega = 198.3\ \Omega \angle 2.78^\circ$$

network (b)

$$\mathbf{Z}_T = 150\ \Omega + \frac{1}{\dfrac{1}{j250\ \Omega} + \dfrac{1}{50\ \Omega}}$$

$$= 198.1\ \Omega + j9.62\ \Omega \text{ (as required)}$$

18.9 Circuit Analysis Using Computers

60.

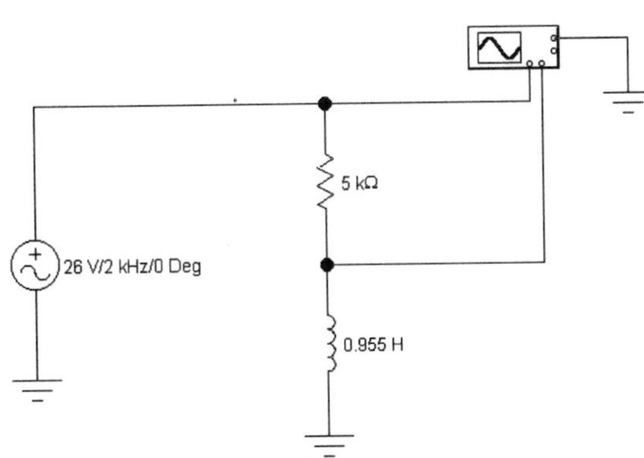

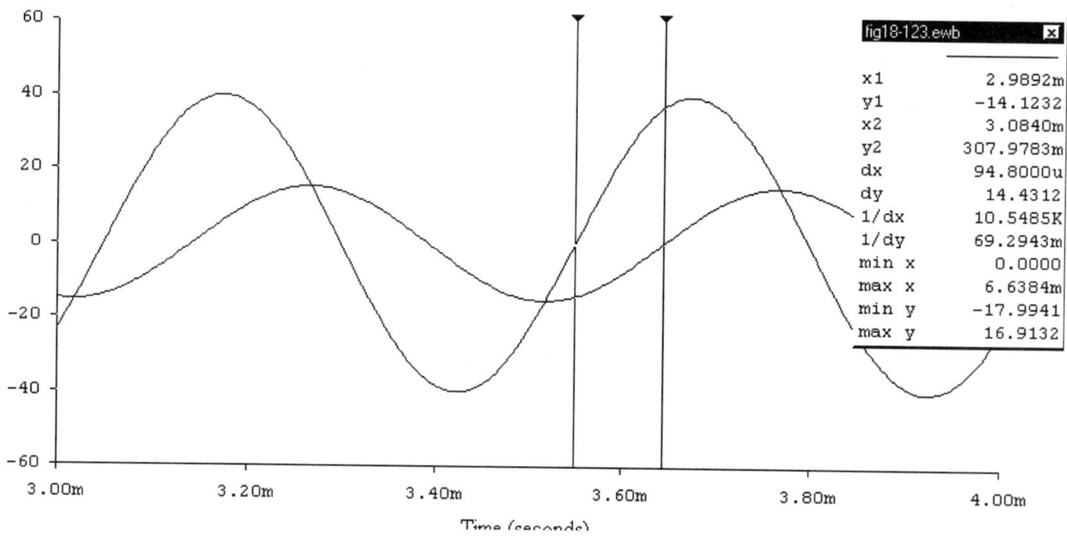

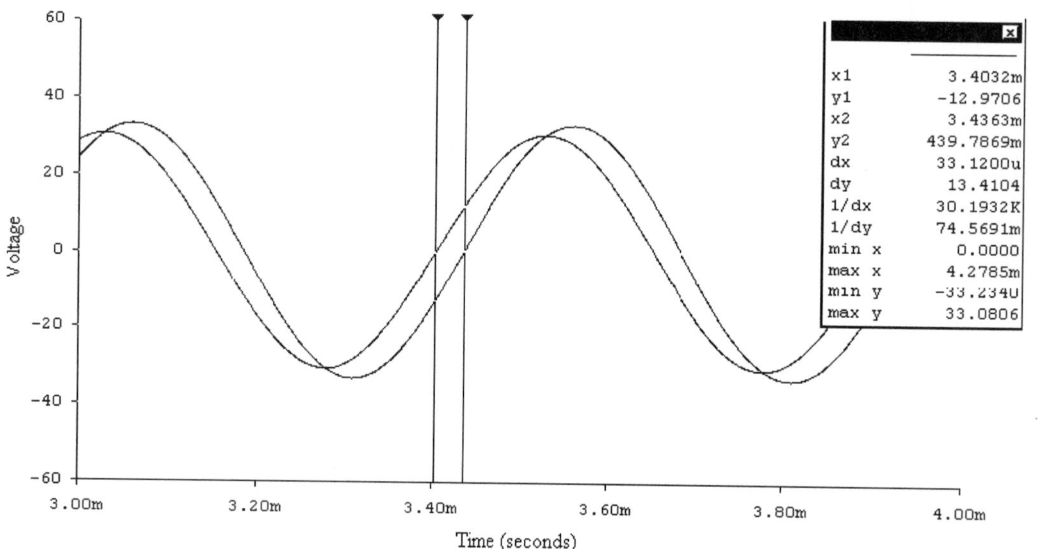

$$\theta_R = -\frac{94.3\ \mu s}{500\ \mu s} \times 360° = -67.90°$$

$$\theta_L = \frac{33.12\ \mu s}{500\ \mu s} \times 360° = 23.85°$$

$$\mathbf{V}_R = \frac{12.72\text{ V}}{\sqrt{2}} \angle -67.90° = 8.99\text{ V} \angle -67.90°$$

$$\mathbf{V}_L = \frac{30.54\text{ V}}{\sqrt{2}} \angle 23.85° = 21.6\text{ V} \angle 23.85°$$

The results compare well to those of Example 18-9.

62.

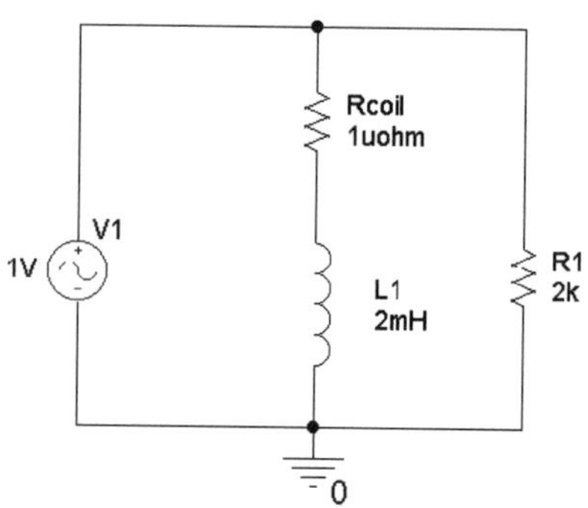

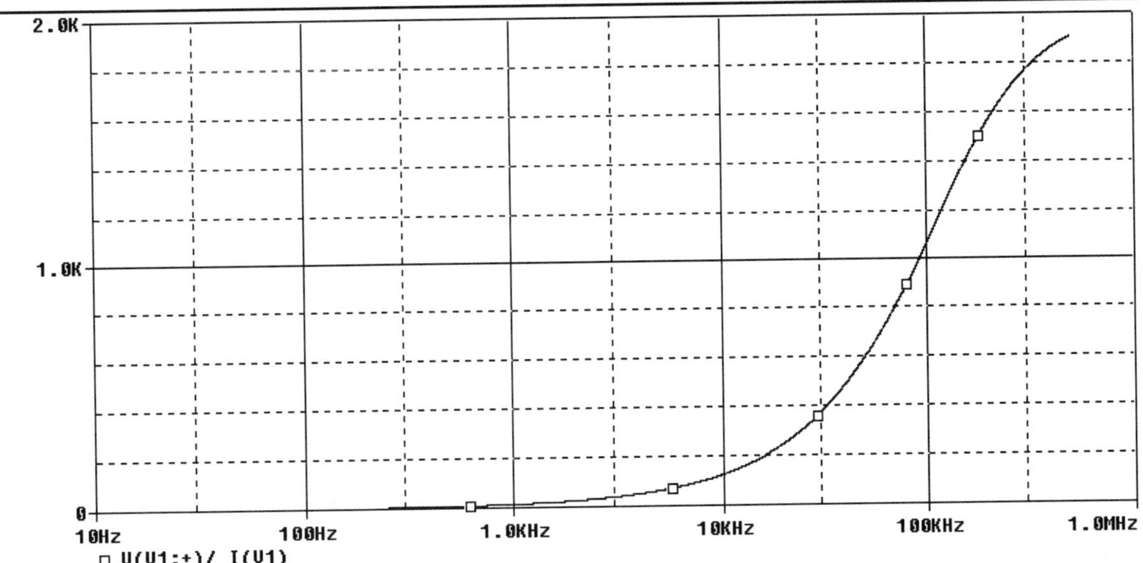
2.0K
1.0K
0
10Hz
100Hz
1.0KHz
10KHz
100KHz
1.0MHz
V(V1:+)/ I(V1)
Frequency

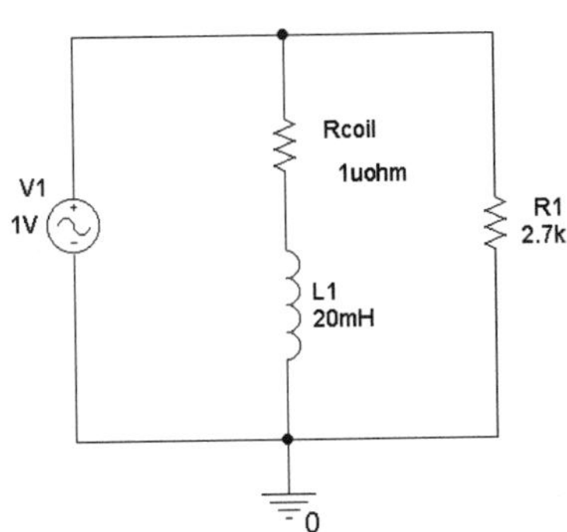
V1
1V
Rcoil
1uohm
L1
20mH
R1
2.7k
0

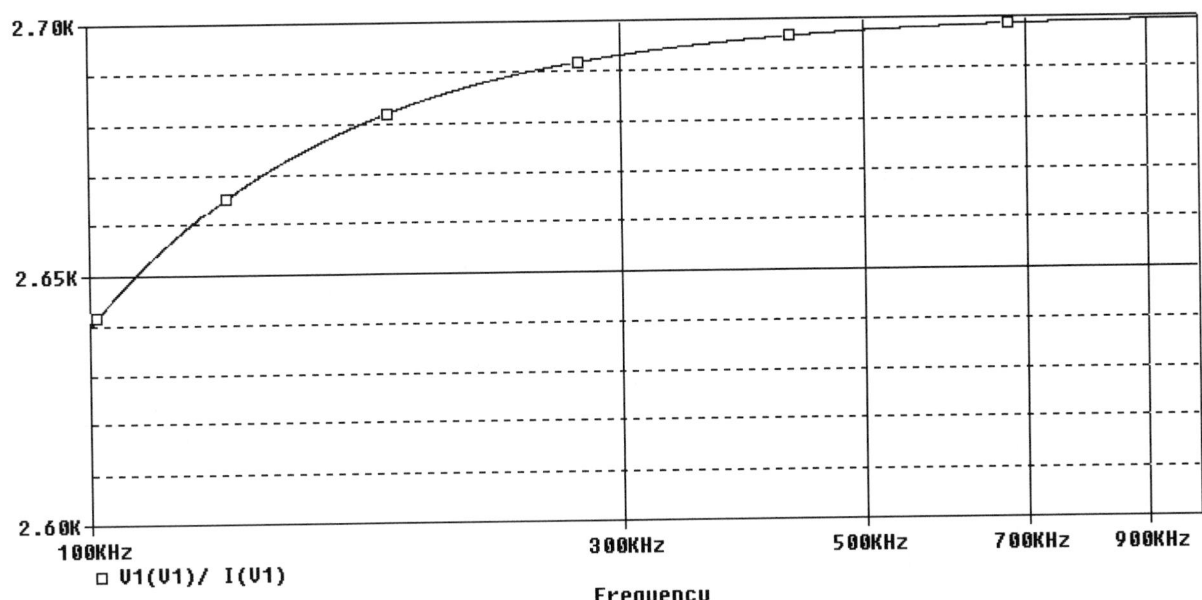
2.70K
2.65K
2.60K
100KHz
300KHz
500KHz
700KHz
900KHz
V1(V1)/ I(V1)
Frequency

CHAPTER

19

Methods of AC Analysis

19.1 Dependent Sources

2. a. $\mathbf{I} = \frac{-200\ \mathbf{V}}{120\ \text{k}\Omega} = \frac{-(200)(30\ \text{mV}\angle 0°)}{120\ \text{k}\Omega}$

$= 50\ \mu\text{A} \angle 180°$

b. $\mathbf{I} = \frac{-(200)(60\ \text{mV}\angle -180°)}{120\ \text{k}\Omega} = 100\ \mu\text{A} \angle 0°$

c. $\mathbf{I} = \frac{-(200)(100\ \text{mV}\angle -30°)}{120\ \text{k}\Omega} = 166.7\ \mu\text{A} \angle 150°$

4. a. $\mathbf{I} = \left(\frac{60\ \text{k}\Omega}{60\ \text{k}\Omega + 30\ \text{k}\Omega}\right)(6.0\ \text{mS})(\mathbf{V}) = (4.0\ \text{mS})\mathbf{V}$

$= (4.0\ \text{mS})(30\ \text{mV} \angle 0°) = 120\ \mu\text{A} \angle 0°$

b. $\mathbf{I} = (4.0\ \text{mS})(60\ \text{mV} \angle -180°) = 240\ \mu\text{A} \angle -180°$

c. $\mathbf{I} = (4.0\ \text{mS})(100\ \text{mV} \angle -30°) = 400\ \mu\text{A} \angle -30°$

6. $\mathbf{V}_1 = \left(\frac{1.5\ \text{k}\Omega}{1.5\ \text{k}\Omega - j2\ \text{k}\Omega}\right)(20\ \text{mV} \angle 0°)$

$= 12\ \text{mV} \angle 53.13°$

$\mathbf{V}_{out} = -(5\ \text{mS})(12\ \text{mV} \angle 53.13°)\left(\frac{(20\ \text{k}\Omega)(5\ \text{k}\Omega)}{25\ \text{k}\Omega}\right)$

$= 240\ \text{mV} \angle -126.87°$

19.2 Source Conversion

8. network (a):

$\mathbf{I} = \frac{5\ \text{V}\angle -25°}{40\ \Omega\angle 90°} = 125\ \text{mA} \angle -115°$

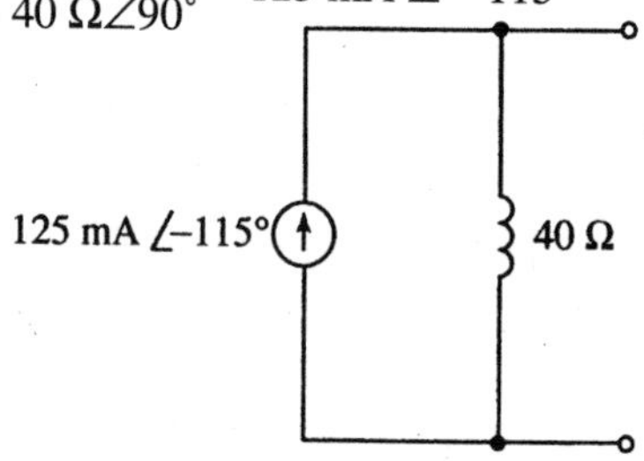

125 mA ∠–115°   40 Ω

network (b):

$\mathbf{I} = \frac{82\ \text{V}\angle 70°}{9\ \Omega - j40\ \Omega} = 2\ \text{A} \angle 147.32°$

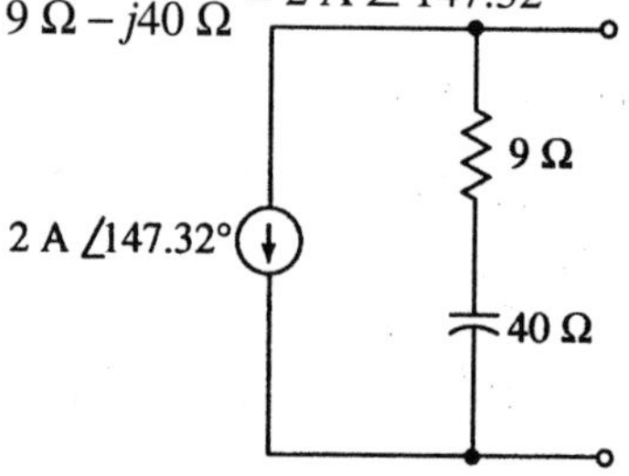

2 A ∠147.32°   9 Ω   40 Ω

10. a. $\mathbf{V} = (3\ \mu\text{A} \angle 0°)(10\ \text{k}\Omega) = 30\ \text{mV} \angle 0°$

$\mathbf{V}_L = -(5\ \text{mS})(30\ \text{mV} \angle 0°)\left(\frac{120\ \text{k}\Omega)(40\ \text{k}\Omega}{160\ \text{k}\Omega}\right)$

$= 4.5\ \text{V} \angle 180°$

b. Converting the current source into an equivalent voltage source:

$\mathbf{E} = (5\ \text{mS})(30\ \text{mV} \angle 0°)(120\ \text{k}\ \Omega)$

$= 18\ \text{V} \angle 0°$

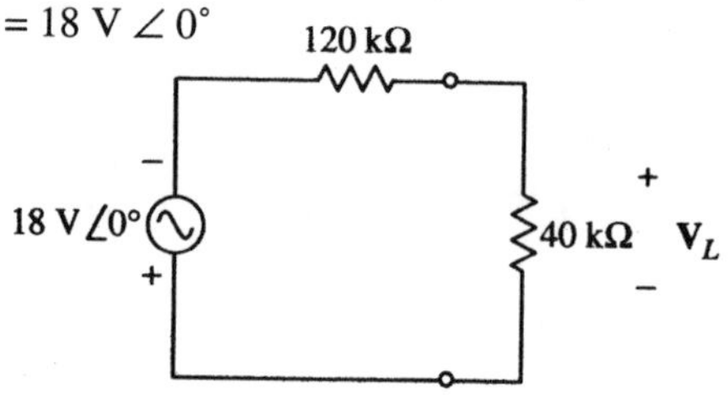

120 kΩ   18 V ∠0°   40 kΩ $\mathbf{V}_L$

$\mathbf{V}_L = -\left(\frac{40\ \text{k}\Omega}{40\ \text{k}\Omega + 120\ \text{k}\Omega}\right)(18\ \text{V} \angle 0°)$

$= 4.5\ \text{V} \angle 180°$

c. $\mathbf{V} = (5\ \mu\text{A} \angle 0°)(10\ \text{k}\Omega) = 50\ \text{mV} \angle 0°$

$\mathbf{V}_L = -(5\ \text{mS})(50\ \text{mV} \angle 0°)\left(\frac{(120\ \text{k}\Omega)(40\ \text{k}\Omega}{160\ \text{k}\Omega}\right)$

$= 7.5\ \text{V} \angle 180°$

19.3 Mesh (Loop) Analysis

12. a. $(5\ \Omega - j5\ \Omega)\mathbf{I}_1 - (j25\ \Omega)\mathbf{I}_2 = 4\ \text{V} \angle 20° - 2\ \text{V} \angle -40° = 3.46\ \text{V} \angle 50°$

$-(j25\ \Omega)\mathbf{I}_1 + (12\ \Omega + j9\ \Omega)\mathbf{I}_2 = 2\ \text{V} \angle -40°$

b.
$$\mathbf{I}_1 = \frac{\begin{vmatrix} 3.46\ \text{A}\angle 50° & -j25 \\ 2\ \text{A}\angle -40° & 12 + j9 \end{vmatrix}}{\begin{vmatrix} 5-j5 & -j25 \\ -j25 & 12+9 \end{vmatrix}} = \frac{96.73\ \text{A}\angle 68.80°}{730.2\angle -1.18°} = 0.1325\ \text{A} \angle 69.98°$$

$$\mathbf{I}_2 = \frac{\begin{vmatrix} 5-j5 & 3.46\ \text{A}\angle 50° \\ -j25 & 2\text{A}\angle -40° \end{vmatrix}}{730.2\angle -1.18°} = 0.1058\ \text{A} \angle 148.62°$$

c. $\mathbf{I} = \mathbf{I}_1 - \mathbf{I}_2 = 0.1325\ \text{A} \angle 69.98° - 0.1058\ \text{A} \angle 148.62° = 0.1524\ \text{A} \angle 27.09°$

14. Convert current sources into voltage sources.

$\mathbf{E}_1 = (4\ \text{A} \angle 0°)(2\ \Omega \angle 90°) = 8\ \text{V} \angle 90°$

$\mathbf{E}_2 = (2\ \text{A} \angle 45°)(4\ \Omega = 8\ \text{V} \angle 45°$

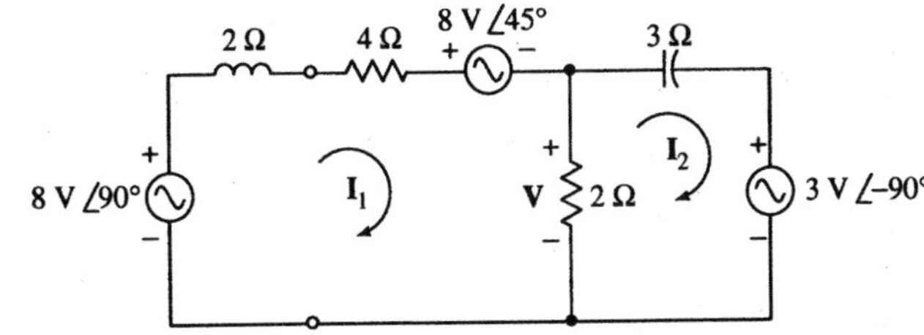

a. $(6\ \Omega + j\,2\ \Omega)\ \mathbf{I}_1 - (2\ \Omega)\ \mathbf{I}_2 = 8\ \text{V} \angle 90° - 8\ \text{V} \angle 45° = 6.12\ \text{V} \angle 157.5°$

$-(2\ \Omega)\ \mathbf{I}_1 + (2\ \Omega - j3\ \Omega)\ \mathbf{I}_2 = -3\ \text{V} \angle 90°$

b.

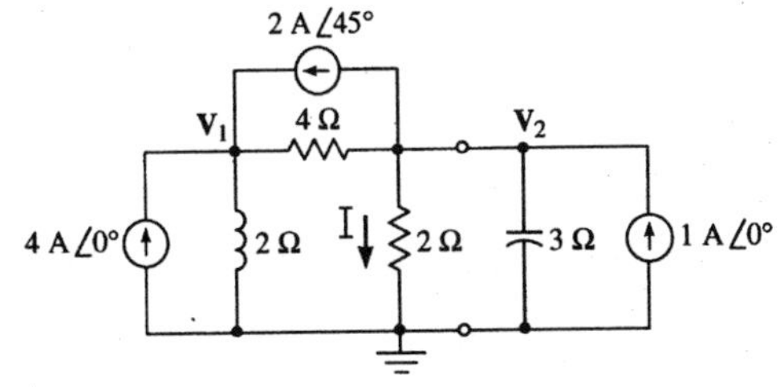

$$\mathbf{I}_1 = \frac{\begin{vmatrix} 6.12A\angle 157.5° & -2 \\ 3\ \text{A}\angle 90° & 2-j3 \end{vmatrix}}{\begin{vmatrix} 6+j2 & -2 \\ -2 & 2-j3 \end{vmatrix}} = \frac{27.987\ \text{A}\angle 98.81°}{19.799\angle -45°}$$

$= 1.414\ \text{A} \angle 143.81°$

$$\mathbf{I}_2 = \frac{\begin{vmatrix} 6+j2 & 6.12\ \text{A}\angle 157.5° \\ -2 & 3\ \text{A}\angle 90° \end{vmatrix}}{19.799\angle -45°} = \frac{28.538\ \text{A}\angle 127.35°}{19.799\angle -45°} = 1.441\ \text{A}\angle 172.35°$$

$\mathbf{I} = \mathbf{I}_1 - \mathbf{I}_2 = 1.414\ \text{A} \angle 143.81° - 1.441\ \text{A} \angle 172.35° = 0.704\ \text{A} \angle 65.88°$

c. $\mathbf{V} = (0.704\ \text{A} \angle 65.88°)(2\ \Omega) = 1.409\ \text{V} \angle 65.88°$

16. Convert the current source into an equivalent voltage source.

$\mathbf{E} = (1\ \text{mA} \angle 0°)(12\ \text{k}\Omega - j16\ \Omega) = 20\ \text{V} \angle -53.13°$

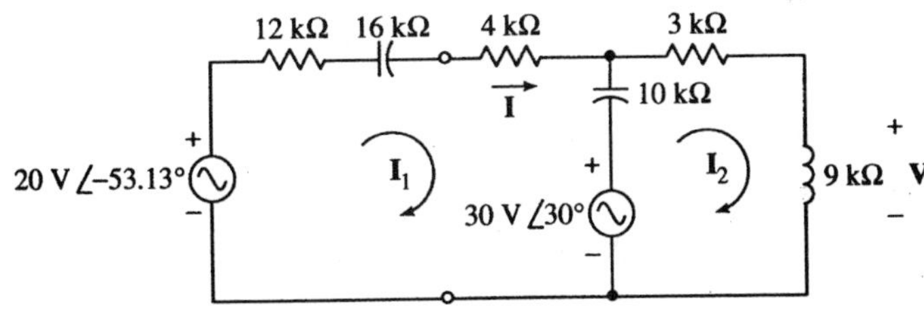

$(16\ \text{k}\Omega - j26\ \text{k}\Omega)\mathbf{I}_1 - (-j10\ \text{k}\Omega)\ \mathbf{I}_2 = 20\ \text{V} \angle -53.13° - 30\ \text{V} \angle 30° = 34.007\ \text{V} \angle -114.27°$

$-(-j10\ \text{k}\Omega)\ \mathbf{I}_1 + (3\ \text{k}\Omega - j1\ \text{k}\Omega)\ \mathbf{I}_2 = 30\ \text{V} \angle 30°$

$$\mathbf{I}_1 = \frac{\begin{vmatrix} 34.007 \text{ mA}\angle -114.27^\circ & j10 \\ 30 \text{ mA}\angle 30^\circ & 3-j1 \end{vmatrix}}{\begin{vmatrix} 16-j26 & j10 \\ j10 & 3-j1 \end{vmatrix}} = \frac{347.5 \text{ mA}\angle -30.82^\circ}{122-j94} = 2.256 \text{ mA}\angle -39.57^\circ$$

$$\mathbf{I}_2 = \frac{\begin{vmatrix} 16-j26 & 34.007 \text{ mA}\angle -114.27^\circ \\ j10 & 30 \text{ mA}\angle 30^\circ \end{vmatrix}}{122-j94} = \frac{577.2 \text{ mA}\angle -30.82^\circ}{122-j94} = 3.748 \text{ mA}\angle 6.80^\circ$$

$\mathbf{I} = \mathbf{I}_1 = 2.256 \text{ mA} \angle -39.57^\circ$

$\mathbf{V} = (3.748 \text{ mA} \angle 6.80^\circ)(9 \text{ k}\Omega \angle 90^\circ) = 33.73 \text{ V} \angle 96.80^\circ$

19.4 Nodal Analysis

18. a. $\left(\frac{1}{j6}\Omega + \frac{1}{-j3}\Omega\right)\mathbf{V}_1 - \left(\frac{1}{-j3}\Omega\right)\mathbf{V}_2 = 2 \text{ A} \angle 0^\circ - 2 \text{ A} \angle 90^\circ = 2.828 \text{ A} \angle -45^\circ$

$-\left(\frac{1}{-j3\,\Omega}\right)\mathbf{V}_1 + \left(\frac{1}{2\,\Omega} + \frac{1}{-j3\,\Omega}\right)\mathbf{V}_2 = 3 \text{ A} \angle -90^\circ + 2 \text{ A} \angle 90^\circ = 1 \text{ A} \angle -90^\circ$

b.

$$\mathbf{V}_1 = \frac{\begin{vmatrix} 2.828 \text{ V}\angle -45^\circ & \frac{1}{j3} \\ 1 \text{ V}\angle -90^\circ & \frac{1}{2} - \frac{1}{j3} \end{vmatrix}}{\begin{vmatrix} \frac{1}{j6} - \frac{1}{j3} & \frac{1}{j3} \\ \frac{1}{j3} & \frac{1}{2} - \frac{1}{j3} \end{vmatrix}} = \frac{2.0276 \text{ V}\angle -9.46^\circ}{0.0\overline{5} + j0.08\overline{3}} = 20.24 \text{ V}\angle -65.77^\circ$$

$$\mathbf{V}_2 = \frac{\begin{vmatrix} \frac{1}{j6} - \frac{1}{j3} & 2.828 \text{ V}\angle -45^\circ \\ \frac{1}{j3} & 1 \text{ V}\angle -90^\circ \end{vmatrix}}{0.0\overline{5} + j0.08\overline{3}} = \frac{1.067 \text{ V}\angle 38.66^\circ}{0.0\overline{5} + j0.08\overline{3}} = 10.65 \text{ A}\angle -17.65^\circ$$

c. $\mathbf{V} = \mathbf{V}_1 - \mathbf{V}_2 = 20.24 \text{ V} \angle -65.75^\circ - 10.654 \text{ V} \angle -17.65^\circ = 15.33 \text{ V} \angle -96.89^\circ$

20. Convert the voltage source into an equivalent current source.

$\mathbf{I} = \frac{3 \text{ V}\angle -90^\circ}{3\,\Omega\angle -90^\circ} = 1 \text{ A}\angle 0^\circ$

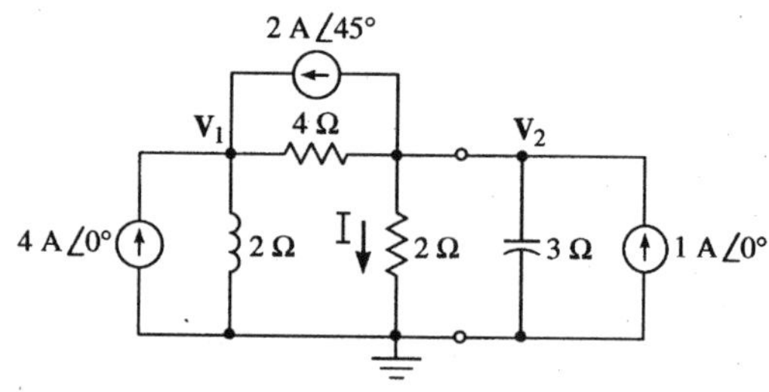

a. $\left(\frac{1}{4\,\Omega} + \frac{1}{j2\,\Omega}\right)\mathbf{V}_1 - \left(\frac{1}{4\,\Omega}\right)\mathbf{V}_2 = 4 \text{ A} \angle 0^\circ + 2 \text{ A} \angle 45^\circ = 5.596 \text{ A}\angle 14.64^\circ$

$-\left(\frac{1}{4\,\Omega}\right)\mathbf{V}_1 + \left(\frac{1}{2\,\Omega} + \frac{1}{4\,\Omega} + \frac{1}{-j3\,\Omega}\right)\mathbf{V}_2 = 2 \text{ A} \angle 45^\circ + 1 \text{ A} \angle 0^\circ = 1.4736 \text{ A} \angle -106.32^\circ$

b.

$$\mathbf{V}_1 = \frac{\begin{vmatrix} 5.596\text{ V}\angle 14.64^\circ & -\frac{1}{4} \\ 1.4736\text{ V}\angle -106.32^\circ & \frac{3}{4}-\frac{1}{j3} \end{vmatrix}}{\begin{vmatrix} \frac{1}{4}+\frac{1}{j2} & -\frac{1}{4} \\ -\frac{1}{4} & \frac{3}{4}-\frac{1}{j3} \end{vmatrix}} = \frac{4.297\text{ V}\angle 35.78^\circ}{0.291\bar{6} - j0.291\bar{6}} = 10.416\text{ V}\angle 80.79^\circ$$

$$\mathbf{V}_2 = \frac{\begin{vmatrix} \frac{1}{4}+\frac{1}{j2} & 5.596\text{ V}\angle 14.64^\circ \\ -\frac{1}{4} & 1.4736\text{ V}\angle -106.32^\circ \end{vmatrix}}{0.291\bar{6} - j0.291\bar{6}} = \frac{0.5811\text{ V}\angle 20.88^\circ}{0.291\bar{6} - j0.291\bar{6}} = 1.409\text{ V}\angle 65.88^\circ$$

c. $\mathbf{I} = \dfrac{1.409\text{ V}\angle 65.88^\circ}{2\ \Omega} = 0.7045\text{ A}\angle 65.88^\circ$

22. Convert the voltage to an equivalent current source.

$$\mathbf{I}_S = \frac{30\text{ V}\angle 30^\circ}{10\text{ k}\Omega\angle -90^\circ} = 3\text{ mA}\angle 120^\circ$$

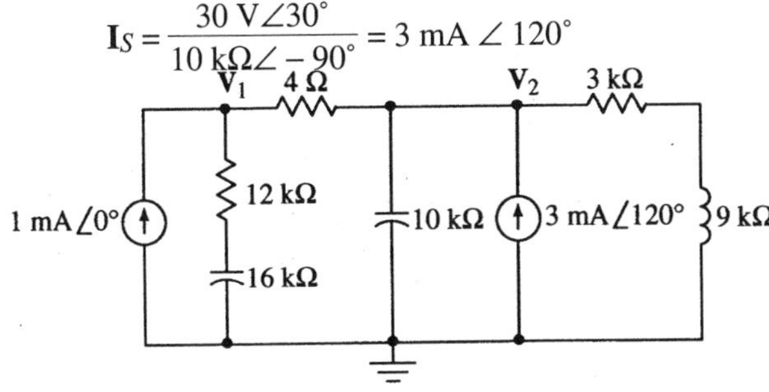

$$\left(\frac{1}{12\text{ k}\Omega - j16\text{ k}\Omega} + \frac{1}{4\text{ k}\Omega}\right)\mathbf{V}_1 - \left(\frac{1}{4\text{ k}\Omega}\right)\mathbf{V}_2 = 1\text{ mA}\angle 0^\circ$$

$$-\left(\frac{1}{4\text{ k}\Omega}\right)\mathbf{V}_1 + \left(\frac{1}{4\text{ k}\Omega} + \frac{1}{-j10\text{ k}\Omega} + \frac{1}{3\text{ k}\Omega + j9\text{ k}\Omega}\right)\mathbf{V}_2 = 3\text{ mA}\angle 120^\circ$$

$$\mathbf{V}_1 = \frac{\begin{vmatrix} 1\text{ V}\angle 0^\circ & -0.25 \\ 3\text{ V}\angle 120^\circ & 0.28\bar{3} \end{vmatrix}}{\begin{vmatrix} 0.28 + j0.04 & -0.25 \\ -0.25 & 0.28\bar{3} \end{vmatrix}} = \frac{0.65596\angle 98.03^\circ}{0.0168\bar{3} + j0.011\bar{3}} = 32.324\text{ V}\angle 64.08^\circ$$

$$\mathbf{V}_2 = \frac{\begin{vmatrix} 0.28 + j0.04 & 1\text{ V}\angle 0^\circ \\ -0.25 & 3\text{ V}\angle 120^\circ \end{vmatrix}}{0.0168\bar{3} + j0.01\bar{3}} = \frac{0.72148\text{ V}\angle 112.31^\circ}{0.0168\bar{3} + j0.01\bar{3}} = 35.553\text{ V}\angle 78.36^\circ$$

$$\mathbf{I} = \frac{32.324\text{ V}\angle 64.08^\circ - 35.553\text{ V}\angle 78.36^\circ}{4\text{ k}\Omega} = 2.256\text{ mA}\angle -39.57^\circ$$

$$\mathbf{V} = \left(\frac{j9\text{ k}\Omega}{3\text{ k}\Omega + j9\text{ k}\Omega}\right)(35.553\text{ V}\angle 78.36^\circ) = 33.73\text{ V}\angle 96.79^\circ$$

19.5 Delta-to-Wye and Wye-to-Delta Conversions

24. network (a)

$$\mathbf{Z}_1 = \frac{(25\ \Omega)(-j50\ \Omega) + (25\ \Omega)(j75\ \Omega) + (-j50\ \Omega)(j75\ \Omega}{25\ \Omega}$$

$$= \frac{3750\ \Omega + j625\ \Omega}{25} = 150\ \Omega + j25\ \Omega$$

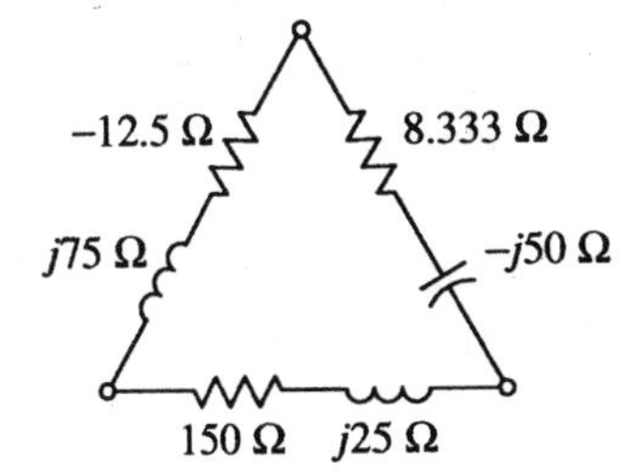

$$\mathbf{Z}_2 = \frac{3750\ \Omega + j625\ \Omega}{-j50} = -12.5\ \Omega + j75\ \Omega$$

$$\mathbf{Z}_3 = \frac{3750\ \Omega + j625\ \Omega}{j75} = 8.333\ \Omega - j50\ \Omega$$

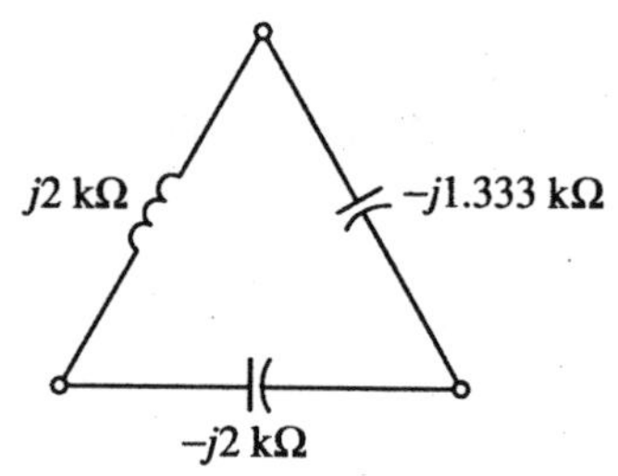

network (b)

$$\mathbf{Z}_1 = \frac{(j2\ \text{k}\Omega)(j3\ \text{k}\Omega) + (j2\ \text{k}\Omega)(-12\ \text{k}\Omega) + (j3\ \text{k}\Omega)(-j2\ \text{k}\Omega)}{j2\ \text{k}\Omega}$$

$$= \frac{4\ \text{k}\Omega}{j2} = -j2\ \text{k}\Omega$$

$$\mathbf{Z}_2 = \frac{4\ \text{k}\Omega}{-j2} = j2\ \text{k}\Omega$$

$$\mathbf{Z}_3 = \frac{4\ \text{k}\Omega}{j3} = -j1.333\ \text{k}\Omega$$

26. Convert the Y to an equivalent Δ

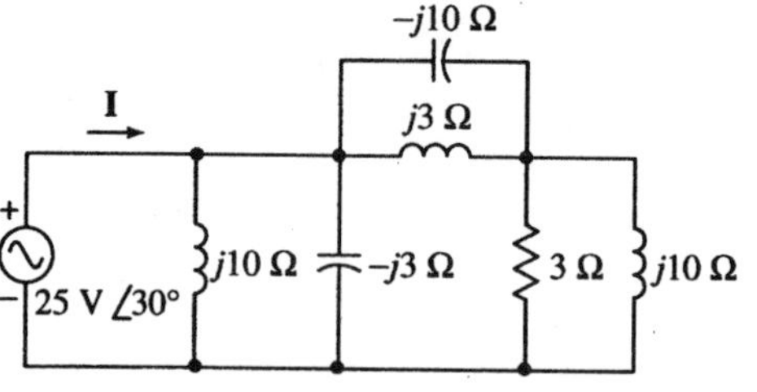

$$\mathbf{Z}_1 = \frac{(3\ \Omega)(j3\ \Omega) + (3\ \Omega)(-j3\ \Omega) + (j3\ \Omega)(-j3\ \Omega)}{-j3\ \Omega}$$

$$= \frac{9\ \Omega}{-j3} = j3\ \Omega$$

$$\mathbf{Z}_2 = \frac{9\ \Omega}{j3} = -j3\ \Omega$$

$$\mathbf{Z}_3 = \frac{9\ \Omega}{3} = 3\ \Omega$$

$$\mathbf{Z}_T = (j10\ \Omega)\|(-j3\ \Omega)\|[(-j10\ \Omega)\|(j3\ \Omega) + (3\ \Omega)\|(j10\ \Omega)] = (j10\ \Omega)\|(-j3\ \Omega)\|(5.8053\ \Omega\ \angle\ 61.70^\circ)$$

$$= 8.66\ \Omega\ \angle -45^\circ$$

$$\mathbf{I} = \frac{25\ \text{V}\angle 30^\circ}{8.66\ \Omega\angle -45^\circ} = 2.887\ \text{A}\ \angle\ 75^\circ$$

28. $X_L = (1000\ \text{rad/s})(5\ \text{H}) = 5\ \text{k}\Omega$

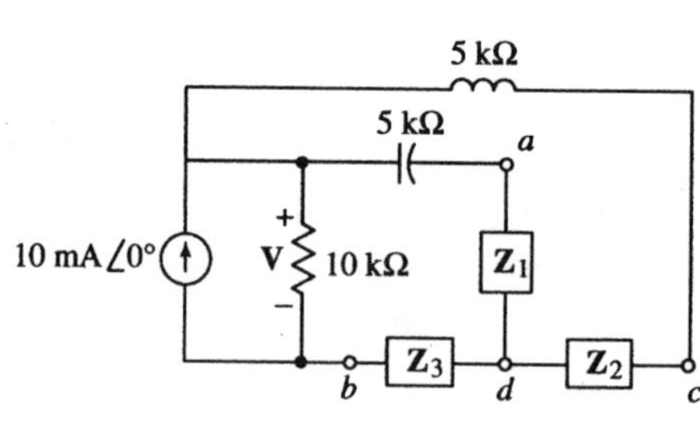

$$X_{C1} = \frac{1}{(1000\ \text{rad/s})(0.2\ \mu\text{F}} = 5\ \text{k}\Omega$$

$$X_{C2} = \frac{1}{(1000\ \text{rad/s})(0.1\ \mu\text{F}} = 10\ \text{k}\Omega$$

Convert the Δ to an equivalent Y.

$$\mathbf{Z}_1 = \frac{(8\ \text{k}\Omega)(2\ \text{k}\Omega)}{2\ \text{k}\Omega + 8\ \text{k}\Omega - j10\ \text{k}\Omega} = \frac{16\ \text{k}\Omega}{10 - j10}$$

$$= 1.1314\ \ \text{k}\Omega\ \angle\ 45^\circ$$

$$\mathbf{Z}_2 = \frac{(8\ \text{k}\Omega)(-j10)}{10 - j10} = 5.6569\ \text{k}\Omega\ \angle -45^\circ$$

$$\mathbf{Z}_3 = \frac{2\ \text{k}\Omega)(-j10)}{10 - j10} = 1.4142\ \text{k}\Omega\ \angle -45^\circ$$

$$\mathbf{Z}_T = 10\ \text{k}\Omega\|[(-j5\ \text{k}\Omega + \mathbf{Z}_1)\|(+j5\ \text{k}\Omega + \mathbf{Z}_2) + \mathbf{Z}_3]$$

$$= 10\ \text{k}\Omega\|[(4.28\ \text{k}\Omega\ \angle -79.22^\circ)\ \|(4.12\ \text{k}\Omega\ \angle\ 14.04^\circ) + \mathbf{Z}_3$$

$$= 10\ \text{k}\Omega\|[3.06\ \text{k}\Omega\ \angle -31.49^\circ + 1.41\ \text{k}\Omega\ \angle -45^\circ$$

$$= 10\ \text{k}\Omega\|4.443\ \text{k}\Omega\ \angle -35.76^\circ\ 3.208\ \text{k}\Omega\ \angle -24.95^\circ$$

$$\mathbf{V} = (10\ \text{mA}\ \angle\ 0^\circ)(3.208\ \text{k}\Omega\ \angle -24.95^\circ) = 32.08\ \text{V}\ \angle -24.95^\circ$$

$$\mathbf{V}_{db} = \left(\frac{1.414\ \text{k}\Omega\angle -45^\circ}{4.443\ \text{k}\Omega\angle -35.75^\circ}\right)(32.08\ \text{V}\ \angle -24.95^\circ = 10.21\ \text{V}\ \angle -34.20^\circ$$

$$\mathbf{V}_{ad} = \left(\frac{1.1314\ \text{k}\Omega - 45^\circ}{4.2755\ \text{k}\Omega\angle -79.21^\circ}\right)(32.08\ \text{V}\ \angle -24.95^\circ - 10.21\ \text{V}\ \angle -34.20^\circ) = 5.839\ \text{V}\ \angle\ 103.53^\circ$$

$$\mathbf{V}_1 = 10.21\ \text{V}\ \angle -34.20 + 5.839\ \text{V}\ \angle\ 103.53^\circ = 7.08\ \text{V}\ \angle -0.50^\circ$$

19.6 Bridge Networks

30. a. $\mathbf{Z}_4 = (50\ \text{k}\Omega)\|(-j25\ \text{k}\Omega) = 22.3607\ \text{k}\Omega \angle -63.43^\circ$

$= 10\ \text{k}\Omega - j20\ \text{k}\Omega$

$$\mathbf{Z}_1 = \frac{(5\ \text{k}\Omega)(200\ \Omega)}{22.3607\ \text{k}\Omega \angle -63.43^\circ} = 44.72\ \Omega \angle 63.43^\circ$$

$= 20\ \Omega + j40\ \Omega$

b. $\mathbf{Z}_T = (20\ \Omega + j40\ \Omega + 200\ \Omega)\|(5\ \text{k}\Omega + 10\ \text{k}\Omega - j20\ \text{k}\ \Omega)$

$= (220\ \Omega + j40\ \Omega)\|(15\ \text{k}\Omega - j20\ \text{k}\Omega)$

$= 222.71\ \Omega \angle 9.85^\circ$

$$\mathbf{I} = \frac{20\ \text{V}\angle 0^\circ}{222.71\ \Omega\angle 9.85^\circ} = 89.80\ \text{mA} \angle -9.85^\circ$$

32.

$$X_{C1} = \frac{1}{(2000\pi\ \text{rad/s})(0.05\ \mu\text{F})} = 3183\ \Omega$$

$$X_{C3} = \frac{1}{(2000\pi\ \text{rad/s})(0.2\ \mu\text{F})} = 795.8\ \Omega$$

$$X_{C4} = \frac{1}{2000\pi\ \text{rad/s})(0.08\ \mu\text{F})} = 1989\ \Omega$$

$\mathbf{Z}_1 = (-j3183\ \Omega)\|(800\ \Omega) = 775.9\ \Omega \angle -14.11^\circ$

$$\frac{775.9\ \Omega\angle -14.11^\circ}{2000\ \Omega} \stackrel{?}{=} \frac{795.8\angle -90^\circ}{500\ \Omega - j1989\ \Omega}$$

$0.388 \angle -14.11^\circ = 0.388 \angle -14.11$

(as required)

34.

$$\frac{R_1 + \dfrac{1}{j\omega C}}{R_2} = \frac{R_3}{R_x + j\omega L_x}$$

$$\frac{1 + j\omega R_1 C}{j\omega R_2 C} = \frac{R_3}{R_x + j\omega L_x}$$

$(1 + j\omega R_1 C)(R_x + j\omega L_x) = j\omega R_2 R_3 C$

$R_x + j\omega R_1 R_x C + j\omega L_x - \omega^2 R_1 C L_x = j\omega R_2 R_3 C$

$R_x - \omega^2 R_1 C L_x + j\omega(R_1 R_x C + L_x) = j\omega R_2 R_3 C$

$R_1 R_x C + L_x = R_2 R_3 C$ (1)

and $R_x = \omega^2 R_1 C L_x$ (2)

substitute eqn (2) into eqn (1):

$R_1(\omega^2 R_1 C L_x)C + L_x = R_2 R_3 C$

$$L_x = \frac{R_2 R_3 C}{1 + (\omega R_1 C)^2} \quad (3)$$

substitute eqn (3) into eqn (2):

$$R_x = \frac{\omega^2 R_1 R_2 R_3 C^2}{1 + (\omega R_1 C)^2} \quad (4)$$

36. Schering Bridge

$$C_3 = \frac{R_2 C_x}{R_1} = \frac{(5\ \text{k}\Omega)(0.1\ \mu\text{F}}{1\ \text{M}\Omega} = 500\ \text{pF}$$

$$C_1 = \frac{R_x C_3}{R_2} = \frac{(1\ \text{k}\Omega)(500\ \text{pF})}{5\ \text{k}\Omega)} = 100\ \text{pF}$$

19.7 Computer Analysis

38.

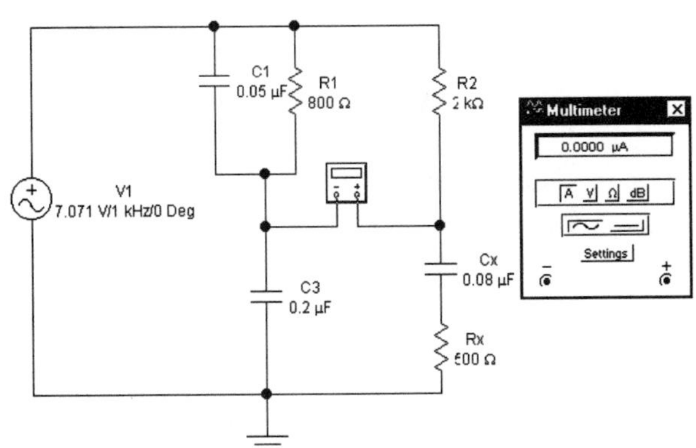

40.

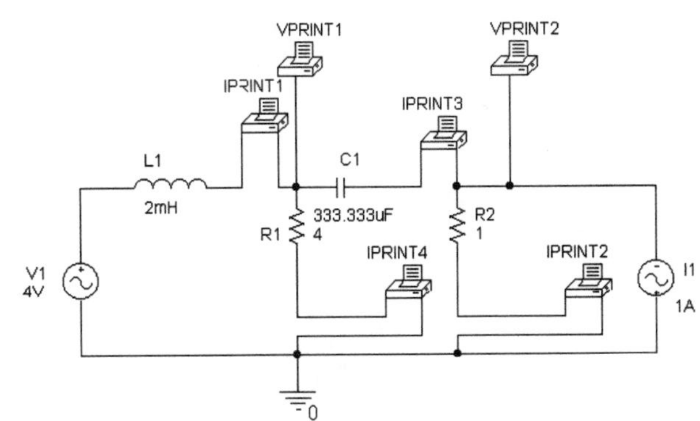

$\mathbf{I}_1 = 1.961\ \text{A} \angle -25.56^\circ$

$\mathbf{I}_1 = 2.193\ \text{A} \angle 1.01^\circ$

$\mathbf{I}_3 = 1.193\ \text{A} \angle 1.85^\circ$

$\mathbf{I}_4 = 1.056\ \text{A} \angle -56.89^\circ$

$\mathbf{V}_1 = 4.225\ \text{V} \angle -56.89^\circ$

$\mathbf{V}_2 = 2.193\ \text{V} \angle 1.01^\circ$

42.

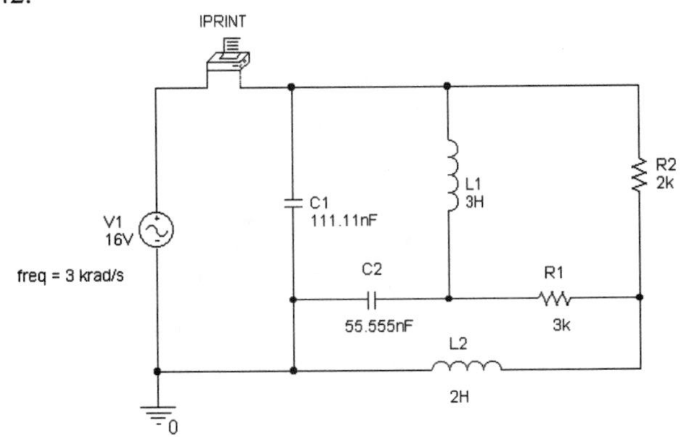

CHAPTER

20

AC Network Theorems

20.1 Superposition Theorem—Independent Sources

2. Consider the voltage source:

$\mathbf{Z}_T = 2\text{ k}\Omega + j1.5\text{ k}\Omega + (-j1.5\text{ k}\Omega)\|(2\text{ k}\Omega)$
$= 2\text{ k}\Omega - j1.5\text{ k}\Omega + (0.72\text{ k}\Omega - j0.96\text{ k}\Omega)$
$= 2.773\text{ k}\Omega \angle 11.23°$

$\mathbf{I}_{(1)} = -\dfrac{20\text{ V}\angle 0°}{2.773\text{ k}\Omega\angle 11.23°} = 7.212\text{ mA} \angle 168.77°$

Consider the current source:

$\mathbf{Z}_T = (2\text{ k}\Omega + j1.5\text{ k}\Omega)\|(-j1.5\text{ k}\Omega)\|(2\text{ k}\Omega)$
$= 1.0817\text{ k}\Omega \angle -27.49°$

$\mathbf{I}_{(2)} = \left(\dfrac{1.0818\text{ k}\Omega\angle -27.49°}{2\text{ k}\Omega + j1.5\text{ k}\Omega}\right)(10\text{ mA} \angle 0°$
$= 4.327\text{ mA} \angle -64.36°$

$\mathbf{I} = 7.212\text{ mA} \angle 168.77° + 4.327\text{ mA} \angle -64.36°$
$= 5.76\text{ mA} \angle -154.36°$

4. Consider the voltage source:

$\mathbf{Z}_T = 2.773\text{ k}\Omega \angle 11.23°$

$\mathbf{V}_{ab(1)} = -\left(\dfrac{2\text{ k}\Omega\| - j1.5\text{ k}\Omega}{2.773\text{ k}\Omega\angle 11.23°}\right)(20\text{ V} \angle 0°)$
$= 8.655\text{ V} \angle 115.64°$

Consider the current source:

$\mathbf{Z}_T = 1.0818\text{ k}\Omega \angle -27.49°$
$\mathbf{V}_{ab(2)} = -(1.08\text{ k}\Omega \angle -27.49°)(10\text{ mA} \angle 0°)$
$= 10.82\text{ V} \angle 152.51°$
$\mathbf{V}_{ab} = 8.655\text{ V} \angle 115.64 + 10.82\text{ V} \angle 152.51°$
$= 18.5\text{ V} \angle 136.20°$

6. a. Convert the current source into an equivalent voltage source

$\mathbf{E} = (250\text{ mA} \angle 30°)(20\ \Omega \angle -90°) = 5\text{ V} \angle -60°$

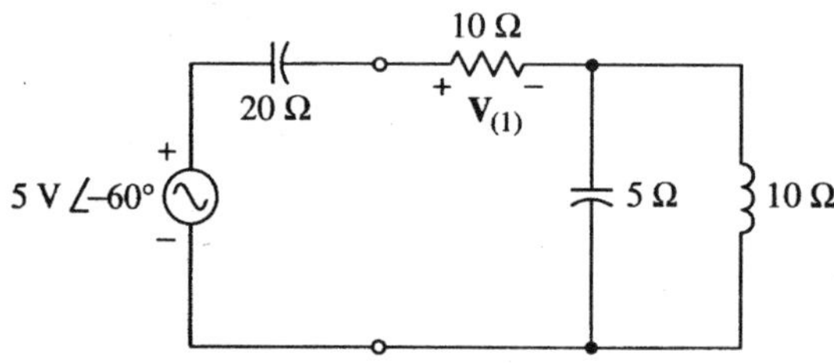

$\mathbf{Z}_T = -j20\ \Omega + 10\ \Omega\ (-j5\ \Omega)\|(j\ 10\ \Omega)$
$= 31.62\ \Omega \angle -71.57°$

$\mathbf{V}_{(1)} = \left(\dfrac{10\ \Omega}{31.62\ \Omega\angle -71.57°}\right)(5\text{ V} \angle -60°)$
$= 1.5811\text{ V} \angle 11.57°$

Consider the voltage source:

$\mathbf{V}_{(2)} = \left(\dfrac{10\ \Omega}{31.62\ \Omega\angle -72.57°}\right)(3.6\text{ V} \angle -60°)$
$= 1.1385\text{ V} \angle 11.57°$

$\mathbf{V} = 1.5811\text{ V} \angle 11.57° + 1.1385\text{ V} \angle 11.57°$
$= 2.72\text{ V} \angle 11.57°$

b. Power dissipated by the 10-Ω resistor:

$P = \dfrac{(2.72\text{ V})^2}{10\ \Omega} = 740\text{ mW}$

Assuming superposition applies for power;

$P_{(1)} = \dfrac{1.581\text{ V})^2}{10\ \Omega} = 250\text{ mW}$

$P_{(2)} = \dfrac{1.139\text{ V})^2}{10\ \Omega} = 130\text{ mW}$

Clearly $P \neq P_{(1)} + P_{(2)}$. Therefore, superposition does not apply for power.

8. Current source #1:

$\mathbf{I}_{(1)} = \left[\dfrac{2\text{ k}\Omega - j3\text{ k}\Omega}{(2\text{ k}\Omega - j3\text{ k}\Omega) + (5\text{ k}\Omega + j4\text{ k}\Omega)}\right]$
$(3\text{ mA} \angle 0°) = 1.530\text{ mA} \angle -64.44°$

Current source #2:

$\mathbf{I}_{(2)} = \left(\dfrac{5\text{ k}\Omega}{2\text{ k}\Omega - j3\text{ k}\Omega + 5\text{ k}\Omega + j4\text{ k}\Omega}\right)(4\text{ mA} \angle 0°)$
$= 2.828\text{ mA} \angle -8.13°$

$\mathbf{I} = \mathbf{I}_{(1)} + \mathbf{I}_{(2)} = 3.89\text{ mA} \angle -27.22°$

10. Current source #1:

$\mathbf{Z}_T = (2\text{ k}\Omega - j3\text{ k}\Omega)\|(5\text{ k}\Omega + j4\text{ k}\ \Omega)$
$= 3.26\text{ k}\Omega \angle -25.78°$
$\mathbf{V}_{(1)} = (3\text{ mA} \angle 0°)(3.26\text{ k}\Omega \angle -25.78°)$
$= 9.79\text{ V} \angle -25.78°$

$\mathbf{V}_{R1(1)} = \left(\dfrac{2\text{ k}\Omega}{2\text{ k}\Omega - j3\text{ k}\Omega}\right)(9.79\text{ V} \angle -25.78°)$
$= 5.43\text{ V} \angle 30.53°$

Current source #2:

$\mathbf{Z}_T = 5\text{ k}\Omega\|(2\text{ k}\Omega + j44\text{ k}\Omega + j3\text{ k}\Omega) = 1.58\text{ k}\Omega \angle 18.43°$
$\mathbf{V}_{(2)} = -(1.58\text{ k}\Omega \angle 18.43°)(4\text{ mA} \angle 0°)$
$= 6.32\text{ V} \angle -161.57°$

$\mathbf{V}_{R1(2)} = \left(\dfrac{2\text{ k}\Omega}{2\text{ k}\Omega + j4\text{ k}\Omega - j3\text{ k}\Omega}\right)$
$(6.32\text{ V} \angle -161.57°) = 5.66\text{ V} \angle 171.87°$
$\mathbf{V}_{R1} = \mathbf{V}_{R1(1)} + \mathbf{V}_{R1(2)} = 3.68\text{ V} \angle 104.49°$
$v_{R1} = 5.20 \sin(\omega t + 104.49°)$

20.2 Superposition Theorem—Dependent Sources

12. a. Consider the dependent voltage source:

$r\mathbf{I} = (2\ \text{k}\Omega)(3\ \text{mA} \angle 0°) = 6.0\ \text{V} \angle 0°$

Convert to an equivalent current source.

$\mathbf{I}_S = \dfrac{60\ \text{V}\angle 0°}{3\ \text{k}\Omega\angle 0°} = 2.0\ \text{mA} \angle 0°$

$\mathbf{Z}_T = 3\ \text{k}\Omega \| (j4\ \text{k}\Omega) \| 12\ \text{k}\Omega = 2.058\ \text{k}\Omega \angle 30.96°$

$\mathbf{V}_{L(1)} = (2.0\ \text{mA} \angle 0°)(2.058\ \text{k}\Omega \angle 30.96°)$
$= 4.116\ \text{V} \angle 30.96°$

Consider the current source:

$\mathbf{V}_{L(2)} = (4.0\ \text{mA} \angle 0°)(2.058\ \text{K}\Omega \angle 30.96°)$
$= 8.232\ \text{V} \angle 30.96°$

$\mathbf{V}_L = 4.116\ \text{V} \angle 30.96° + 8.232\ \text{V} \angle 30.96°$
$= 12.35\ \text{V} \angle 30.96°$

b. $\mathbf{V}_{L(1)} = \dfrac{2}{3}(4.116\ \text{V} \angle 30.96°) = 2.744\ \text{V} \angle 30.96°$

$\mathbf{V}_L = 2.744\ \text{V} \angle 30.96° + 8.232\ \text{V} \angle 30.96°$
$= 10.98\ \text{V} \angle 30.96°$

14. Consider the dependent voltage source:

$r\mathbf{I} = 6.0\ \text{V} \angle 0°$

$\mathbf{I}_T = \dfrac{6.0\ \text{V}\angle 0}{3\ \text{k}\Omega + 12\ \text{k}\Omega \| j4\ \text{k}\Omega} = 1.085\ \text{mA} \angle -40.60°$

$\mathbf{I}_{1(1)} = \left(\dfrac{12\ \text{k}\Omega}{12\ \text{k}\Omega + j4\ \text{k}\Omega}\right) 1.085\ \text{mA} \angle -40.60°$
$= 1.03\ \text{mA} \angle -59.04°$

Consider the independent current source:

$\mathbf{Z}_T = 3\ \text{k}\Omega \| j4\ \text{k}\ \Omega \| 12\ \text{k}\Omega = 2.058\ \text{k}\Omega \angle 30.96°$

$\mathbf{I}_{1(2)} = \left(\dfrac{2.058\ \text{k}\Omega\angle 30.96°}{4\ \text{k}\Omega\angle 90°}\right)(4\ \text{mA} \angle 0°)$
$= 2.06\ \text{mA} \angle -59.04°$

$\mathbf{I}_1 = \mathbf{I}_{1(1)} + \mathbf{I}_{1(2)} = 3.09\ \text{mA} \angle -59.04°$

16.

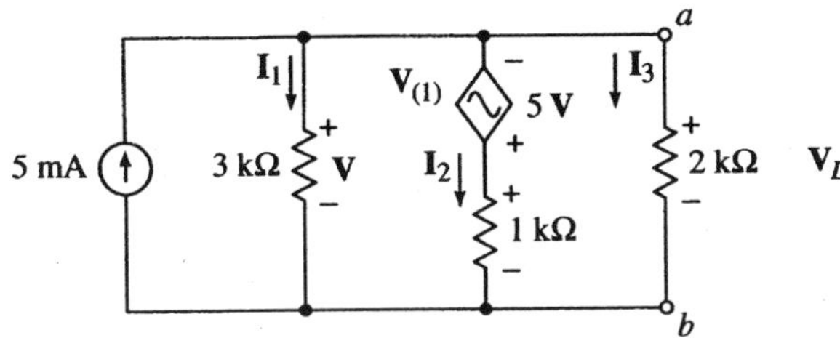

18. Current source #1:

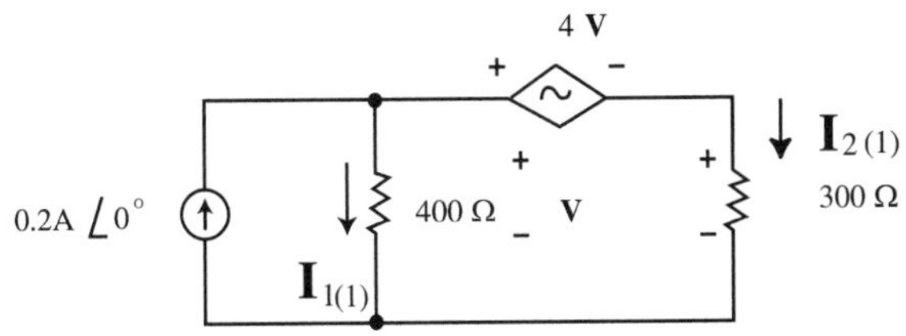

$\mathbf{I}_{1(2)} + \mathbf{I}_{2(1)} = 0.2\ \text{A}$

$\dfrac{\mathbf{V}}{400\ \Omega} - \dfrac{3\mathbf{V}}{300\ \Omega} = 0.2\ \text{A} \angle 0°$

$\mathbf{V} = \dfrac{0.2\ \text{A}\angle 0°}{-0.0075\ \text{S}} = -26.67\ \text{V} \angle 0°$

$\mathbf{I}_{2(1)} = \dfrac{-3(-26.67\ \text{V}\angle 0°)}{300\ \Omega} = 0.2667\ \text{A} \angle 0°$

Current source #2:

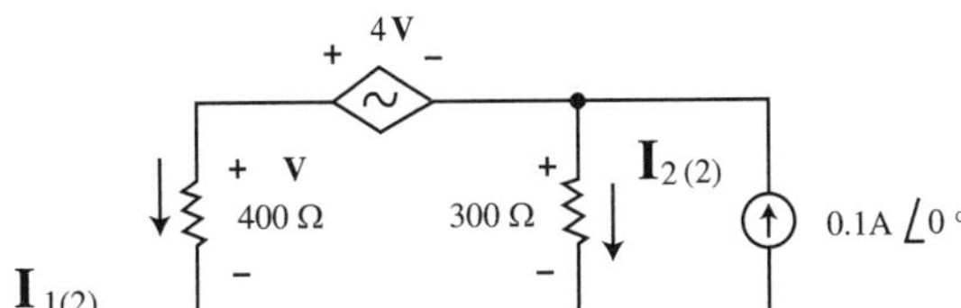

$\mathbf{I}_{1(2)} + \mathbf{I}_{2(2)} = 0.1\text{A} \angle 0°$

$\dfrac{\mathbf{V}}{400\ \Omega} - \dfrac{3\mathbf{V}}{300\ \Omega} = 0.1\ \text{A} \angle 0°$

$\mathbf{V} = \dfrac{0.1\ \text{A}\angle 0°}{-0.0075\ \text{S}} = -13.33\ \text{V} \angle 0°$

$\mathbf{I}_{2(2)} = \dfrac{-3(-13.33\ \text{V}\angle 0°)}{300\ \Omega} = 0.1333\ \text{A} \angle 0°$

$\mathbf{I} = \mathbf{I}_{2(1)} + \mathbf{I}_{2(2)} = 0.400\ \text{A} \angle 0°$

20.3 Thévenin's Theorem—Independent Sources

20. Remove the local impedance

a. $\mathbf{Z}_{\text{Th}} = (-j10\ \Omega) + (-j16\ \Omega) \| (12\ \Omega + j24\ \Omega)$
$= -j10\ \Omega + 29.77\ \Omega \angle -60.26°$
$= 38.77\ \Omega \angle -67.61°$

Voltage source:

$\mathbf{V}_{ab(1)} = \left(\dfrac{-j16\ \Omega}{12\ \Omega + j24\ \Omega - j16\ \Omega}\right)(5\ \text{V} \angle 0°)$
$= 5.547\ \text{V} \angle -123.69°$

Current source:

$\mathbf{Z}_T = \mathbf{Z}_{\text{Th}} = 38.77\ \Omega \angle -67.61°$

$\mathbf{V}_{ab(2)} = -(500\ \text{mA} \angle 0°)(38.77\ \Omega \angle -67.61°)$
$= 19.385\ \text{V} \angle 112.39°$

$\mathbf{E}_{\text{Th}} = \mathbf{V}_{ab} = 5.547\ \text{V} \angle -123.69° + 19.385\ \text{V} \angle 112.39°$
$= 16.9\ \text{V} \angle 128.17°$

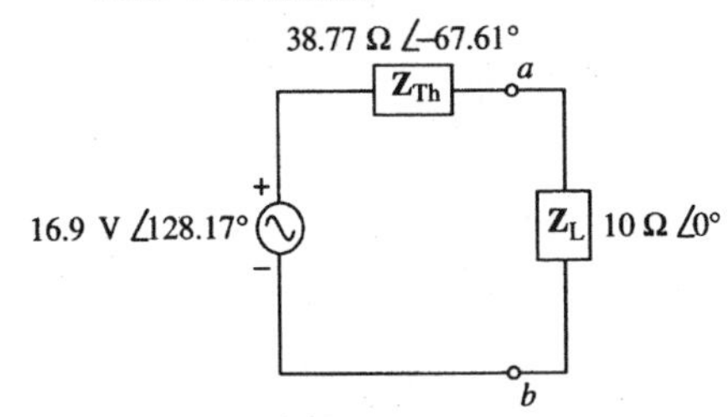

b. $\mathbf{V}_L = \left(\dfrac{10\ \Omega\angle 0°}{10\ \Omega + 38.77\ \Omega\angle -67.61°}\right)(16.9\ \text{V} \angle 128.17°) = 3.89\ \text{V} \angle -176.47°$

$P_L = \dfrac{(3.89\ \text{V})^2}{10\ \Omega} = 1.51\ \text{W}$

22. $X_C = \dfrac{1}{2\pi(1\ \text{kHz})(1\ \mu\text{F})} = 159.15\ \Omega$

$X_L = 2\pi(1\ \text{kHz})(1\ \text{mH}) = 6.2832\ \Omega$

a. Remove the load impedance

$\mathbf{Z}_{Th} = (j6.2832\ \Omega) \| (50\ \Omega - j159.15\ \Omega)$
$= 6.62\ \Omega \angle 89.33°$

Voltage source:

$\mathbf{V}_{ab(1)} = \left(\dfrac{j6.2832\ \Omega}{50\ \Omega - j159.15\ \Omega + j6.28\ \Omega}\right)(10\ \text{V} \angle 0°)$
$= 0.3907\ \text{V} \angle 161.89°$

Current source:

$\mathbf{V}_{ab(2)} = (100\ \text{mA} \angle 0°)(6.617\ \Omega \angle 89.33°)$
$= 0.6617\ \text{V} \angle 89.33°$

$\mathbf{E}_{Th} = 0.3907\ \text{V} \angle 161.89° + 0.6617\ \text{V} \angle 89.33°$
$= 0.863\ \text{V} \angle 114.90°$

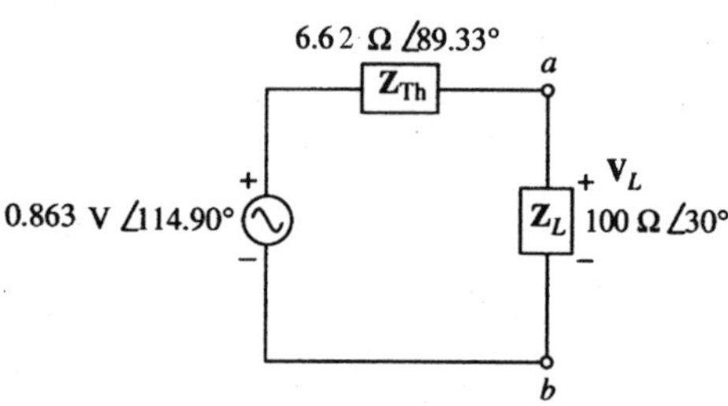

b. $\mathbf{V}_L = \left(\dfrac{100\ \Omega\angle 30°}{6.62\ \Omega\angle 89.33° + 100\ \Omega\angle 30°}\right)(0.863\ \text{V} \angle 114.90°) = 0.834\ \text{V} \angle 111.75°$

$P_L = \dfrac{(0.834\ \text{V})^2}{100\ \Omega} \cos 30° = 6.02\ \text{mW}$

24. $\mathbf{Z}_{Th} = -j1.5\ \text{k}\Omega \| (2\ \text{k}\Omega + j1.5\ \text{k}\Omega)$
$= 1.875\ \text{k}\Omega \angle -53.13°$

Consider the voltage source:

$\mathbf{V}_{ab(1)} = -\left(\dfrac{(-j1.5\ \text{k}\Omega)}{2\ \text{k}\Omega + j1.5\ \text{k}\Omega - j1.5\ \text{k}\Omega}\right)(20\ \text{V} \angle 0°)$
$= 15\ \text{V} \angle 90°$

Consider the current source:

$\mathbf{V}_{ab(2)} = -(10\ \text{mA} \angle 0°)(1.875\ \text{k}\Omega \angle -53.13°)$
$= 18.75\ \text{V} \angle 126.87°$

$\mathbf{E}_{Th} = \mathbf{V}_{ab} = \mathbf{V}_{ab(1)} + \mathbf{V}_{ab(2)} = 32.04\ \text{V} \angle 110.56°$

26. $\mathbf{Z}_{Th} = -j5\ \Omega \| (10\ \Omega - j20\ \Omega) = 4.152\ \Omega \angle -85.24°$

Consider the current source:

$\mathbf{Z}_T = -j20\ \Omega \| (10\ \Omega - j5\ \Omega) = 8.305\ \Omega \angle -48.37°$

$\mathbf{V} = (0.250\ \text{A} \angle 30°)(8.305\ \Omega \angle -48.37°)$
$= 2.08\ \text{V} \angle -18.37°$

$\mathbf{V}_{ab(1)} = \left(\dfrac{-j5\ \Omega}{10\ \Omega - j5\ \Omega}\right)(2.08\ \text{V} \angle -18.37°)$
$= 0.928\ \text{V} \angle -81.80°$

Consider the voltage source:

$\mathbf{V}_{ab(2)} = \left(\dfrac{-j5\ \Omega}{10\ \Omega - j5\ \Omega - j20\ \Omega}\right)(3.6\ \text{V} \angle -60°)$
$= 0.669\ \text{V} \angle -81.80°$

$\mathbf{E}_{Th} = \mathbf{V}_{ab} = \mathbf{V}_{ab(1)} + \mathbf{V}_{ab(2)} = 1.60\ \text{V} \angle -81.80°$

28. a. Redraw the circuit:

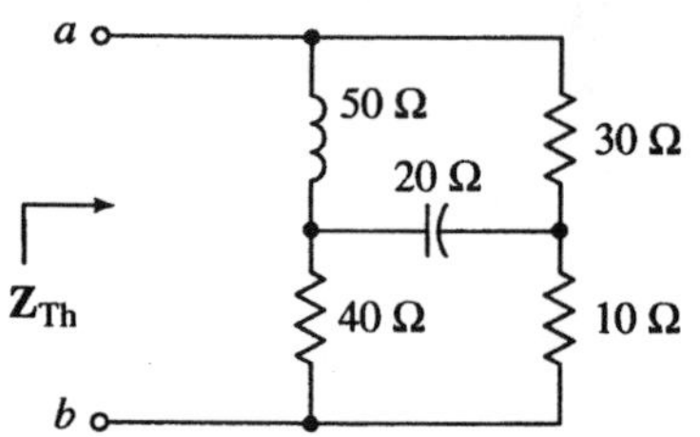

Use Δ to Y conversion to simplify the network.

$\mathbf{Z}_1 = \dfrac{(-j20\ \Omega)(40\ \Omega)}{40\ \Omega + 10\ \Omega - j20\ \Omega} = \dfrac{-j800\ \Omega}{50 - j20}$
$= 14.856\ \Omega \angle -68.20°$

$\mathbf{Z}_2 = \dfrac{(-j20\ \Omega)(10\ \Omega)}{50\ \Omega - j20\ \Omega} = 3.714\ \Omega \angle -68.20°$

$\mathbf{Z}_3 = \dfrac{(40\ \Omega)(10\ \Omega)}{50\ \Omega - j20\ \Omega} = 7.428\ \Omega \angle 21.80°$

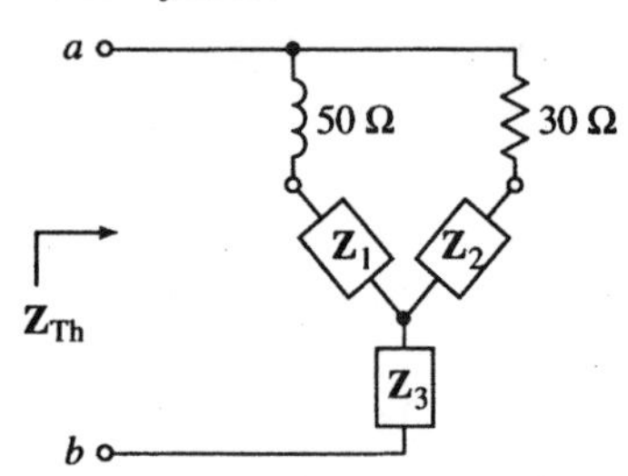

$\mathbf{Z}_{Th} = (j50\ \Omega + \mathbf{Z}_1) \| (30\ \Omega + \mathbf{Z}_2) + \mathbf{Z}_3$
$= 23.433\ \Omega \angle 33.46° + 7.428\ \Omega \angle 21.80°$
$= 30.74\ \Omega \angle 30.66°$

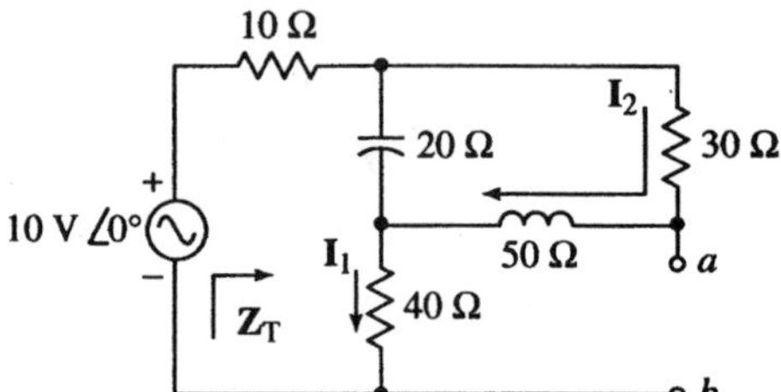

$\mathbf{Z}_T = 10\ \Omega + (-j20\ \Omega) \| (30\ \Omega + j50\ \Omega) + 40\ \Omega$
$= 50\ \Omega + 27.49\ \Omega \angle -75.97°$
$= 62.63\ \Omega \angle -25.20°$

$\mathbf{I}_1 = \dfrac{10\ \text{V}\angle 0°}{62.63\ \Omega\angle -25.20°} = 0.15967\ \text{A} \angle 25.20°$

$$\mathbf{I}_2 = \left(\frac{-j20\ \Omega}{30\ \Omega + j50\ \Omega - j20\ \Omega}\right)(0.15967\ \text{A} \angle 25.20^\circ) = 0.07527\ \text{A} \angle -109.80^\circ$$

$$\mathbf{E}_{Th} = \mathbf{V}_{ab} = (0.15967\ \text{A} \angle 25.20^\circ)(40\ \Omega) + (0.07527\ \text{A} \angle -109.80^\circ)(j50\ \Omega)$$
$$= 9.431\ \text{V} \angle 8.81^\circ$$

b.

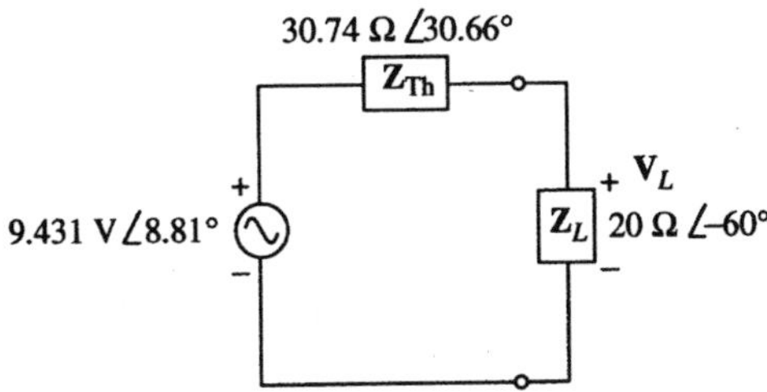

$$\mathbf{V}_L = \left(\frac{20\ \Omega\angle -60^\circ}{20\ \Omega\angle -60^\circ + 30.74\ \Omega\angle 30.66^\circ}\right)(9.431\ \text{V} \angle 8.81^\circ) = 5.17\ \text{V} \angle -48.61^\circ$$

$$P_L = \frac{(5.17\ \text{V})^2}{20\ \Omega}\cos 60^\circ = 0.668\ \text{W}$$

20.4 Norton's Theorem—Independent Sources

30. $\mathbf{Z}_N = (-j1.5\ \text{k}\Omega) \| (2\ \text{k}\Omega + j1.5\ \text{k}\Omega) = 1.875\ \text{k}\Omega \angle -53.13^\circ$

Consider the voltage source:

$$\mathbf{I}_{ab(1)} - \frac{20\ \text{V}\angle 0^\circ}{2\ \text{k}\Omega + j1.5\ \text{k}\Omega} = 8.00\ \text{mA} \angle 143.13^\circ$$

Consider the current source:

$\mathbf{I}_{ab(2)} = -10\ \text{mA} \angle 0^\circ = 10\ \text{mA} \angle 180^\circ$

$\mathbf{I}_N = \mathbf{I}_{ab} = 17.09\ \text{mA} \angle 163.69^\circ$

32. a. $\mathbf{Z}_N = 7\ \text{k}\Omega - j3\ \text{k}\Omega = 7.616\ \text{k}\Omega \angle -23.20^\circ$

Consider current source #1:

$$\mathbf{I}_{ab(1)} = \left(\frac{2\ \text{k}\Omega - j3\ \text{k}\Omega}{7\ \text{k}\Omega - j3\ \text{k}\Omega}\right)(3\ \text{mA} \angle 0^\circ) = 1.42\ \text{A} \angle -33.11^\circ$$

Consider current source #2:

$$\mathbf{I}_{ab(2)} = \left(\frac{5\ \text{k}\Omega}{7\ \text{k}\Omega - j3\ \text{k}\Omega}\right)(4\ \text{mA} \angle 0^\circ) = 2.63\ \text{A} \angle 23.20^\circ$$

$\mathbf{I}_N = \mathbf{I}_{ab} = \mathbf{I}_{ab(1)} + \mathbf{I}_{ab(2)} = 3.61\ \text{mA} \angle 4.11^\circ$

b. $$\mathbf{I} = \left(\frac{7\ \text{k}\Omega - j3\ \text{k}\Omega}{7\ \text{k}\Omega - j3\ \text{k}\Omega + j4\ \text{k}\Omega}\right)(3.61\ \text{mA} \angle 4.11^\circ) = 3.89\ \text{mA} \angle -27.22^\circ$$

c. Since the load is an inductor, $P_L = 0$

34. a. Remove the load impedance.

$\mathbf{Z}_N = -j5\ \Omega \| (10\ \Omega\ -j20\ \Omega)$
$= 4.152\ \Omega \angle -85.24^\circ$

Consider the voltage source:

$$\mathbf{I}_{ab(1)} = \frac{3.6\ \text{V}\angle -60^\circ}{10\ \Omega - j20\ \Omega} = 0.16100\ \text{A} \angle 3.43^\circ$$

Consider the current source:

$$\mathbf{I}_{ab(2)} = \left(\frac{-j20\ \Omega}{10\ \Omega - j20\ \Omega}\right)(250\ \text{mA} \angle 30^\circ)$$
$$= 0.2236\ \text{A} \angle 3.43^\circ$$

$\mathbf{I}_N = 0.3846\ \text{A} \angle 3.43^\circ$

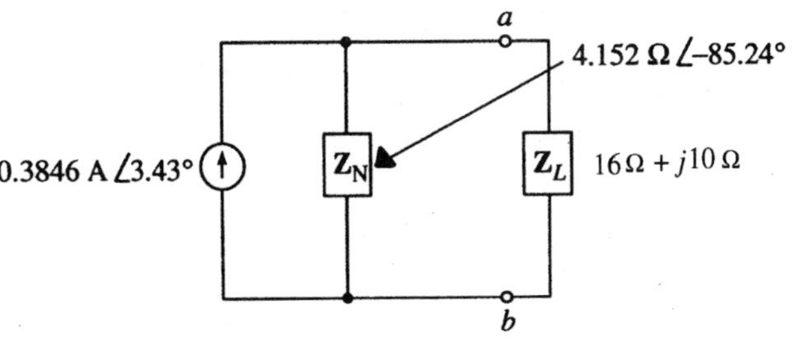

b. $\mathbf{I}_L = \left(\dfrac{4.152\ \Omega\angle -85.24^\circ}{4.152\ \Omega\angle -85.24^\circ + 16\ \Omega + j10\ \Omega}\right)$
$(0.3846\ \text{A} \angle 3.43^\circ) = 0.0920\ \text{A} \angle -101.59^\circ$

c. $P = (0.0920\ \text{A})^2\,(16\ \Omega) = 0.135\ \text{W}$

36. $X_L = 2\pi(8\ \text{kHz})(1\ \text{mH}) = 50.265\ \Omega$

$X_C = \dfrac{1}{2\pi(8\ \text{kHz})(1\ \mu\text{F})} = 19.894\ \Omega$

a. $\mathbf{Z}_N = j50.27\ \Omega \| (50\ \Omega - j19.89\ \Omega$
$= 46.24\ \Omega + 37.03^\circ$

Consider the voltage source:

$\mathbf{I}_{ab(1)} = \dfrac{10\ \text{V}\angle 0^\circ}{50\ \Omega - j19.89\ \Omega} = 0.1858\ \text{A} \angle 21.70^\circ$

Consider the current source:
$\mathbf{I}_{ab(2)} = 0.100\ \text{A} \angle 0^\circ$

$\mathbf{I}_N = 0.1858\ \text{A} \angle 21.70^\circ + 0.100\ \text{A} \angle 0^\circ$
$= 0.2812\ \text{A} \angle 14.14^\circ$

b. $\mathbf{I}_L = \left(\dfrac{46.24\ \Omega\angle 37.03^\circ}{46.24\ \Omega\angle 37.03^\circ + 30\ \Omega}\right)(0.2812\ \text{A} \angle 14.14^\circ)$
$= 0.1794\ \text{A} \angle 28.57^\circ$

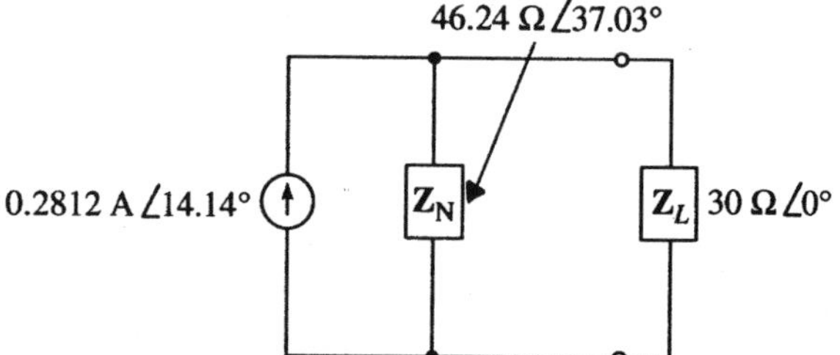

20.5 Thévenin's and Norton's Theorems for Dependent Sources

38. a. Since the controlling element is not in the same circuit, $\mathbf{Z}_N$ is easily determined as
$\mathbf{Z}_N = (3\ \text{k}\Omega) \| (j4\ \text{k}\Omega) = 2.4\ \text{k}\Omega \angle 36.87^\circ$
Consider the dependent voltage source:

$\mathbf{I}_{ab(1)} = \dfrac{(2\ \text{k}\Omega)(3\ \text{mA}\angle 0^\circ)}{3\ \text{k}\Omega} = 2\ \text{mA} \angle 0^\circ$

Consider the current source:
$\mathbf{I}_{ab(2)} = 4\ \text{mA} \angle 0^\circ$
$\mathbf{I}_N = 2\ \text{mA} \angle 0^\circ + 4\ \text{mA} \angle 0^\circ = 6\ \text{mA} \angle 0^\circ$

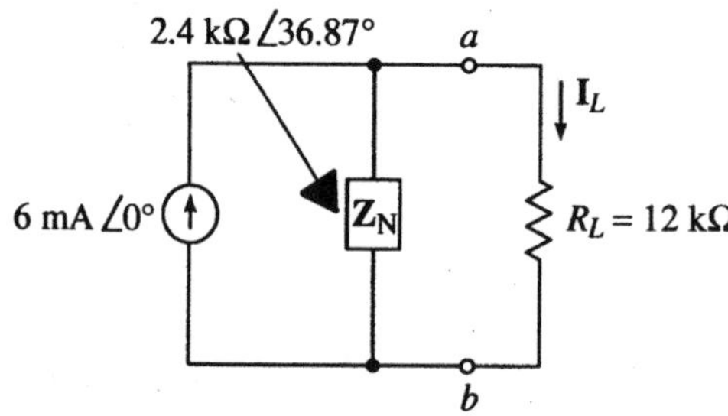

b. $\mathbf{I}_L = \left(\dfrac{2.4\ \text{k}\Omega\angle 36.87^\circ}{2.4\ \text{k}\Omega\angle 36.87^\circ + 12\ \text{k}\Omega}\right)(6\ \text{mA} \angle 0^\circ)$
$= 1.0290\ \text{mA} \angle 30.96^\circ$

c. $P_L = (1.0290\ \text{mA})^2(12\ \text{k}\Omega) = 12.71\ \text{mW}$

40. Thévenin voltage:

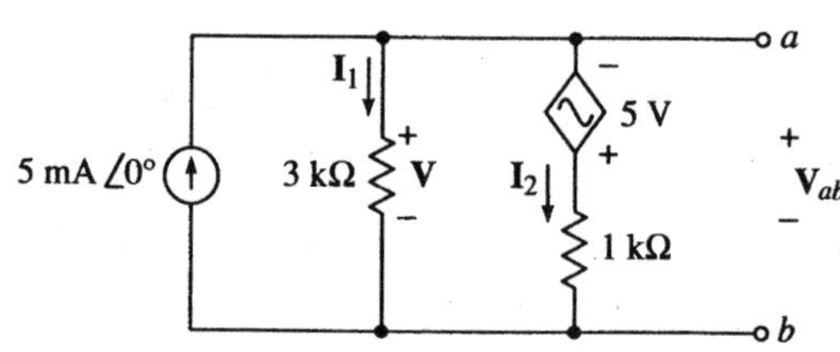

$\mathbf{I}_1 + \mathbf{I}_2 = 5\ \text{mA} \angle 0^\circ$

$\dfrac{\mathbf{V}}{3\ \text{k}\Omega} + \dfrac{6\mathbf{V}}{1\ \text{k}\Omega} = 5\ \text{mA} \angle 0^\circ$

$\mathbf{V}\ (0.1579\ \text{k}\Omega)(5\ \text{mA}) = 0.7895\ \text{V} \angle 0^\circ$

$\mathbf{E}_{Th} = \mathbf{V}_{ab} = \mathbf{V} = 0.7895\ \text{V} \angle 0^\circ$

Norton Current:

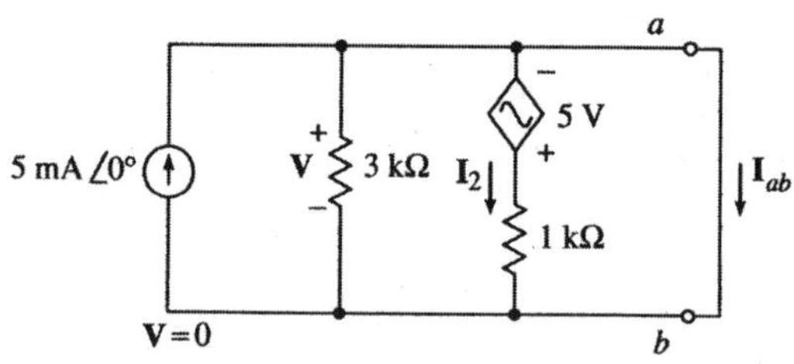

$\mathbf{I}_N = 5\ \text{mA} \angle 0^\circ$

$\mathbf{Z}_{Th} = \mathbf{Z}_N = \dfrac{0.7895\ \text{V}\angle 0^\circ}{5\ \text{mA}\angle 0^\circ} = 0.1579\ \text{k}\Omega \angle 0^\circ$

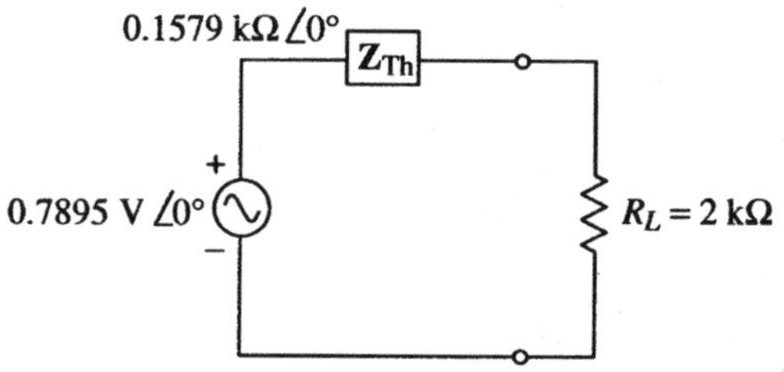

0.1579 kΩ∠0° $\mathbf{Z}_{Th}$

0.7895 V ∠0° $R_L = 2\ \text{k}\Omega$

20.6 Maximum Power Transfer Theorem

42. $\mathbf{Z}_{Th} = -j4\text{ k}\Omega + (j1\text{ k}\Omega)\|(100\ \Omega + 200\ \Omega - j900\ \Omega) = 3\text{ k}\Omega - j4\text{ k}\Omega$

Consider the current source:

Convert the current source into an equivalent voltage source

$\mathbf{E} = (100\ \Omega)(0.5\text{ A} \angle 90°) = 50\text{ V} \angle 90°$

$$\mathbf{V}_{ab(1)} = \frac{j1\text{ k}\Omega)(50\text{ V}\angle 90°}{100\ \Omega + 200\ \Omega - j900\ \Omega + j1000\ \Omega} = 158.11\text{ V} \angle 161.57°$$

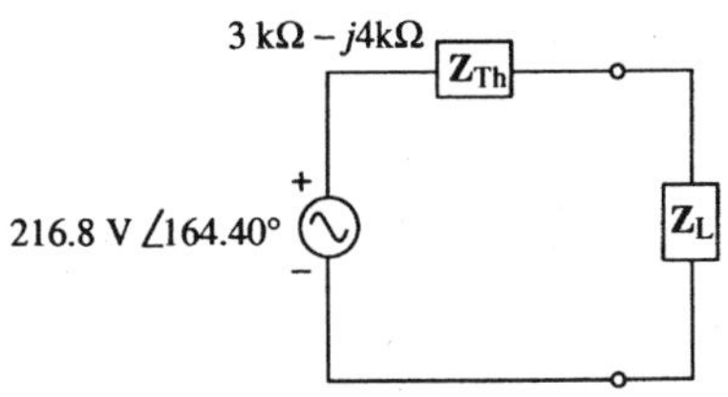

Consider the voltage source:

$$\mathbf{V}_{ab(2)} = 40\text{ V} \angle -60° - \left(\frac{j1\text{ k}\Omega}{300\ \Omega + j100\ \Omega}\right)(40\text{ V} \angle -60°) = 39.96\text{ V} \angle -60.17°$$

$\mathbf{E}_{Th} = \mathbf{V}_{ab} = 158.11\text{ V} \angle 161.57° + 131.0\text{ V} \angle 173.29°$

a. For maximum power transfer,

$\mathbf{Z}_L = 3\text{ k}\Omega + j4\text{ k}\Omega = 5\text{ k}\Omega \angle 53.13°$

b. $$\mathbf{V}_L = \left(\frac{3\text{ k}\Omega + j4\text{ k}\Omega}{3\text{ k}\Omega + j4\text{ k}\Omega + 3\text{ k}\Omega - j4\text{ k}\Omega}\right)131.0\text{ V} \angle 173.29° = 109.2\text{ V} \angle -133.58°$$

$$P_L = \frac{109.2\text{ V})^2}{5\text{ k}\Omega}\cos 53.13° = 2.384\text{ W}$$

44. $\mathbf{Z}_{Th} = j20\ \Omega + (j30\ \Omega)\|(30\ \Omega - j40\ \Omega) = 64.88\ \Omega \angle 65.41°$

Consider the voltage source:

$$\mathbf{V}_{ab(1)} = 10\text{ V} \angle -40° - \left(\frac{j30\ \Omega}{30\ \Omega - j40\ \Omega + j30\ \Omega}\right)(10\text{ V} \angle -40°) = 15.811\text{ V} \angle -74.70°$$

Consider the current source:

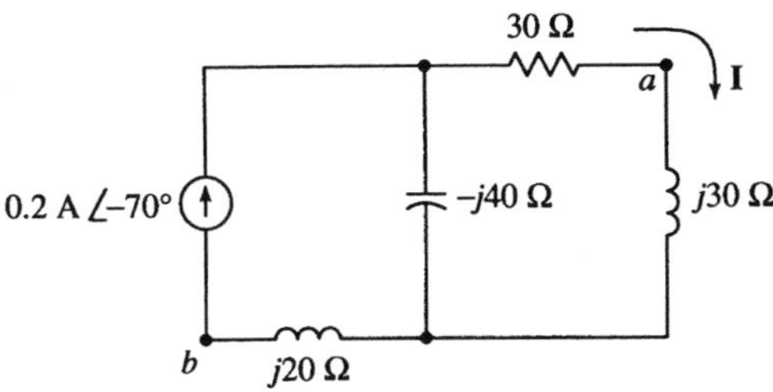

$$\mathbf{I} = \left(\frac{-j40\ \Omega}{30\ \Omega + j30\ \Omega - j40\ \Omega}\right)(0.2\text{ A} \angle -70°)$$

$= 0.2530\text{ A} \angle -141.57°$

$\mathbf{V}_{ab(2)} = (j30\ \Omega)(0.2530\text{ A} \angle -141.57°) + (j20\ \Omega)(0.2\text{ A} \angle -70°) = 9.634\text{ V} \angle -28.37°$

$\mathbf{E}_{Th} = \mathbf{V}_{ab} = 15.811\text{ V} \angle -74.70° + 9.634\text{ V} \angle -28.37° = 23.52\text{ V} \angle -57.47°$

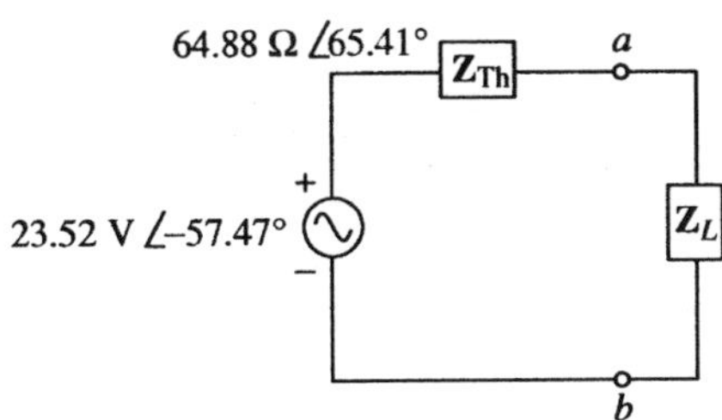

a. For maximum power transfer,

$\mathbf{Z}_L = 64.88\ \Omega \angle -65.41^\circ$

$= 27.00\ \Omega - j59.00\ \Omega$

b. $\mathbf{I} = \dfrac{23.52\ \text{V}\angle -57.47^\circ}{2(27\ \Omega)} = 0.4356\ \text{A} \angle -57.47^\circ$

$P_L = (0.4356\ \text{A})^2(27\ \Omega) = 5.12\ \text{W}$

46. From Problem 27, the Thévenin equivalent circuit is as follows:

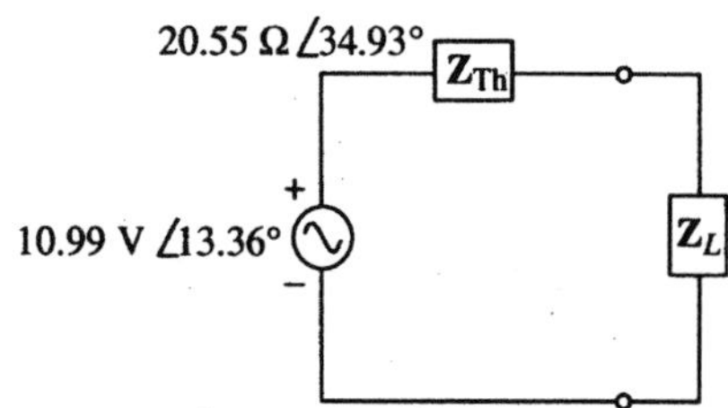

For maximum power

$\mathbf{Z}_L = 20.55\ \Omega \angle -34.93^\circ = 16.85\ \Omega - j11.77\Omega$

$\mathbf{I} = \dfrac{10.99\ \text{V}\angle 13.36^\circ}{2(16.85\ \Omega)} = 0.3261\ \text{A} \angle 13.36^\circ$

$P_L = (0.3261\ \text{A})^2(16.85\ \Omega) = 1.792\ \text{W}$

48. From Problem 22, the Thévenin equivalent circuit at 1 kHz is as follows:

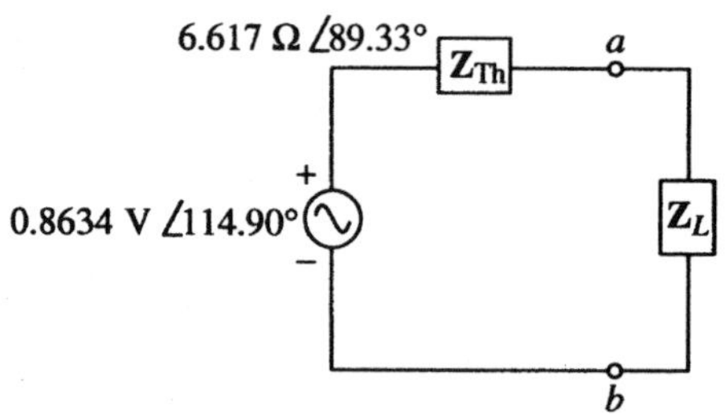

a. For maximum power transfer,

$\mathbf{Z}_L = 6.617\ \Omega \angle -89.33^\circ = 0.0774\ \Omega - j6.617\ \Omega$

$\mathbf{I}_L = \dfrac{0.8634\ \text{V}\angle 114.90^\circ}{2(0.0774\ \Omega)} = 5.578\ \text{A} \angle 114.90^\circ$

$P_L = (5.578\ \text{A})^2(0.0774\ \Omega) = 2.41\ \text{W}$

b. $X_C = \dfrac{1}{2\pi(1000\ \text{Hz})(1\ \mu\text{F})} = 159.15\ \Omega$

$X = 159.15\ \Omega - 6.62\ \Omega = 152.53\ \Omega$

$R_L = \sqrt{(0.0774\ \Omega)^2 + (152.53\ \Omega)^2} = 152.5\ \Omega$

c. $\mathbf{I}_L = \dfrac{0.8634\ \text{V}\angle 114.90^\circ}{6.617\ \Omega\angle 89.33^\circ + 152.5\ \Omega - j159.15\ \Omega}$

$= 4.00\ \text{mA} \angle 159.89^\circ$

$P_L = (4.00\ \text{mA})^2(152.5\ \Omega) = 2.44\ \text{mW}$

20.7 Circuit Analysis Using Computers

50.

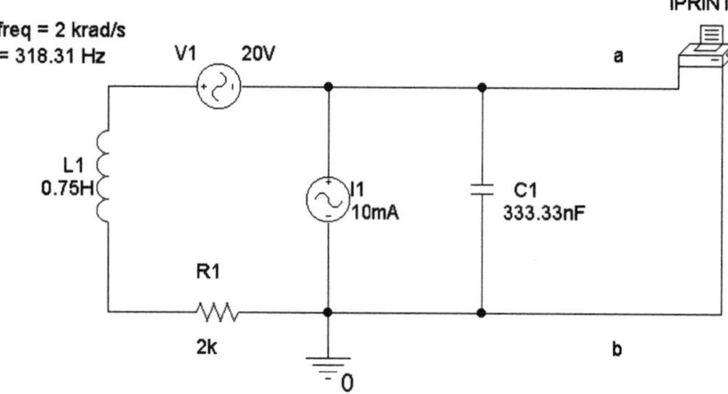

$\mathbf{E}_{Th} = \mathbf{V}_{ab} = 32.04\ \text{V} \angle 110.6^\circ$

$\mathbf{I}_N = \mathbf{I}_{ab} = 17.09\ \text{mA} \angle 163.7^\circ$

$\mathbf{Z}_{Th} = \mathbf{Z}_N = \dfrac{32.04\ \text{V}\angle 110.6^\circ}{17.09\ \text{mA}\angle 163.7^\circ} = 1.875\ \text{k}\Omega \angle -53.1^\circ$

52.

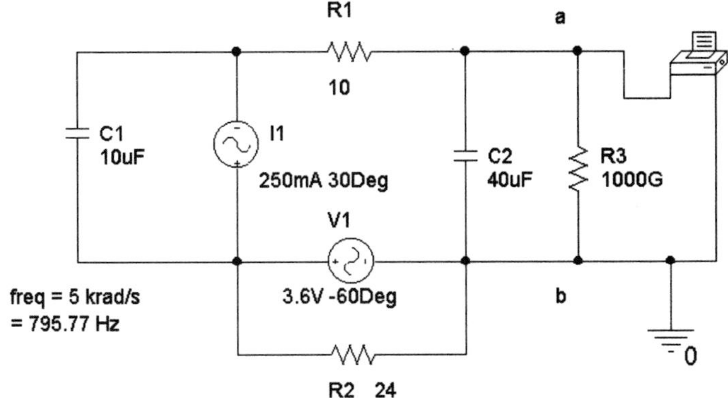

$\mathbf{E}_{Th} = 1.597 \text{ V} \angle -81.80°$

$\mathbf{I}_N = 0.3846 \text{ A} \angle 3.435°$

$$\mathbf{Z}_{Th} = \frac{1.597 \text{ V}\angle -81.80}{0.3846 \text{ A}\angle 3.44°} = 4.152\ \Omega \angle -85.24°$$

54.

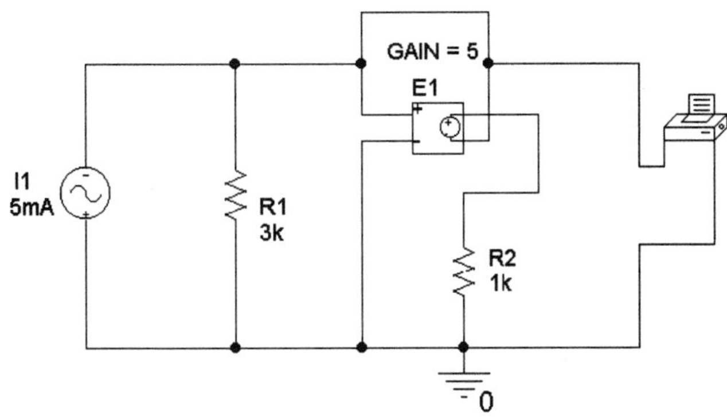

$\mathbf{E}_{Th} = 0.7895 \text{ V} \angle 0°$

$\mathbf{I}_N = 5.0 \text{ mA} \angle 0°$

$\mathbf{Z}_{Th} = \mathbf{Z}_N = 0.1579 \text{ k}\Omega \angle 0°$

56.

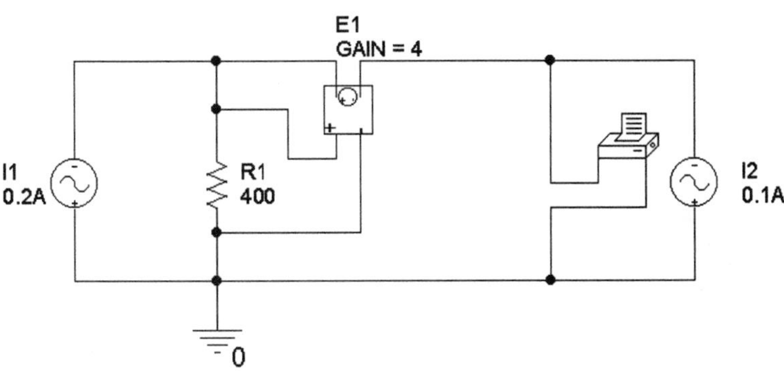

$\mathbf{E}_{Th} = \mathbf{V}_{ab} = 360 \text{ V} \angle 180°$

$\mathbf{I}_N = \mathbf{I}_{ab} = 0.300 \text{ A} \angle 0°$

$\mathbf{Z}_{Th} = \mathbf{Z}_N = 1200\ \Omega \angle -180° = -1200\ \Omega$

Note: Negative resistance is only possible when using "active" devices such as transistors.

58. 

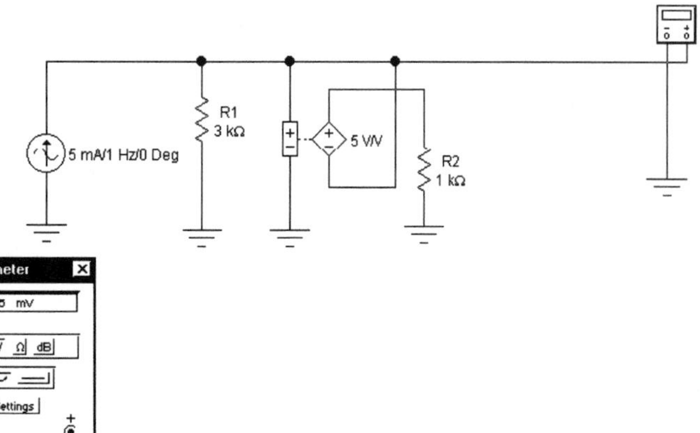

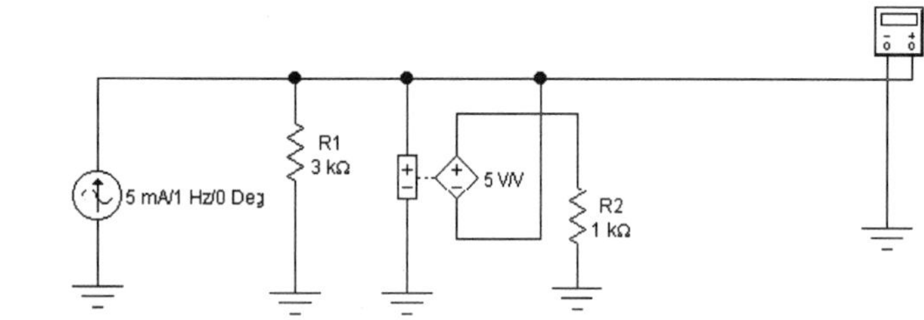

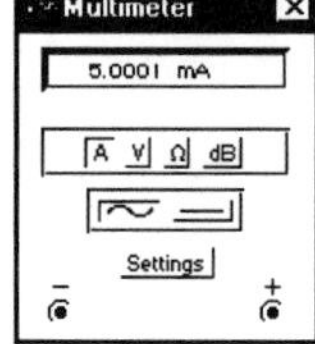

$\mathbf{E}_{\mathrm{Th}} = 0.7895\ \mathrm{V}$

$\mathbf{I}_{\mathrm{N}} = 5.00\ \mathrm{mA}$

$$\mathbf{Z}_{\mathrm{Th}} = \frac{0.7895\ \mathrm{V}}{5.00\ \mathrm{mA}} = 157.9\Omega$$

60.

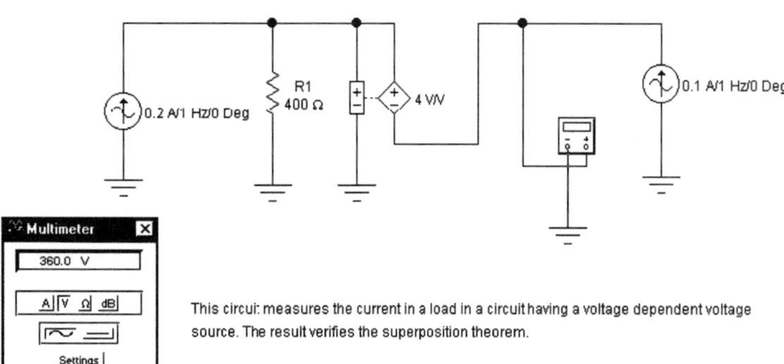

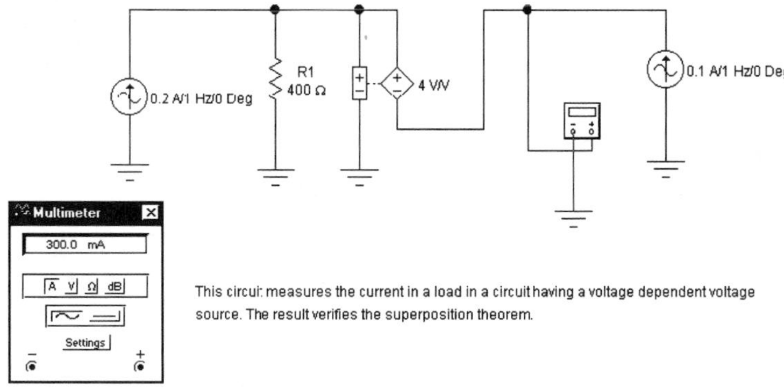

$\mathbf{E}_{Th} = 360$ V

$\mathbf{I}_N = 300$ mA

$\mathbf{Z}_{Th} = \mathbf{Z}_N = 1200\ \Omega$

Note: EWB does not show phase angles, so we are unable to determine the phase angle for $\mathbf{Z}_{Th}$ ($\mathbf{Z}_N$).

CHAPTER

21

Resonance

21.1 Series Resonance

2. a. $\omega = \dfrac{1}{\sqrt{(180\text{ mH})(0.033\ \mu\text{F})}} = 12.975$ krad/s

$f = \dfrac{12.975\text{ krad/s}}{2\pi} = 2.065$ kHz

b. $E = \dfrac{0.20\text{ V}}{\sqrt{2}} = 0.1414$ V

$\mathbf{I} = \dfrac{0.1414\text{ V}\angle 0°}{60\ \Omega} = 2.357\text{ mA}\angle 0°$

c. $P = (2.357\text{ mA})^2(60\ \Omega) = 333.3\ \mu\text{W}$

d. $X_C = X_L = \omega L = 2335\ \Omega$

$\mathbf{V}_L = (2335\ \Omega \angle 90°)(2.357\text{ mA} \angle 0°)$

$= 5.505\text{ V} \angle 90°$

$\mathbf{V}_R = (60\ \Omega)(2.357\text{ mA} \angle 0°) = 0.1414\text{ V} \angle 0°$

e. $v_L = 7.78 \sin(12\,975t + 90°)$

$v_R = 0.20 \sin(12\,975t)$

4. a. $C = \dfrac{1}{4\pi^2(100\text{ kHz})^2(220\ \mu\text{H})} = 0.0115\ \mu\text{F}$

b. $E = \dfrac{0.075\text{ V}}{\sqrt{2}} = 53.03$ mV

$\mathbf{I} = \dfrac{53.03\text{ mV}\angle 0°}{5\ \Omega + 2.5\ \Omega} = 7.071\text{ mA} \angle 0°$

$X_L = 2\pi(100\text{ k}\Omega)(200\ \mu\text{H}) = 138.23\ \Omega$

$\mathbf{V}_L = (2.5\ \Omega + j\,138.23\ \Omega)(7.071\text{ mA} \angle 0°)$

$= 0.9776\text{ V} \angle 88.96°$

$\mathbf{V}_R = E = 53.03\text{ mV} \angle 0°$

c. $i = 0.010 \sin(200 \times 10^3\pi t)$

$v_L = 1.383 \sin(200 \times 10^3\pi t + 88.96°)$

$v_R = 0.075 \sin(200 \times 10^3\pi t)$

d. $P_C = 0$ W

$P_L = (2.5\ \Omega)(7.071\text{ mA})^2 = 125\ \mu\text{W}$

$P_R = (5\ \Omega)(7.07\text{ mA})^2 = 250\ \mu\text{W}$

Note: The internal resistance of the coil will dissipate some power.

21.2 Quality Factor, Q

6. a. $X_L = 2\pi(2.5\text{ kHz})(250\text{ mH}) = 3927\ \Omega$

$R_T = \dfrac{3927\ \Omega}{10} = 392.7\ \Omega$

$R = 372.7\ \Omega$

$C = \dfrac{1}{4\pi^2(2.5\text{ kHz})^2(250\text{ mH})} = 16.21$ nF

b. $Q_{\text{coil}} = \dfrac{3927\ \Omega}{20\ \Omega} = 196$

c. $\mathbf{Z}_T = R_T = 392.7\ \Omega \angle 0°$

$E = \dfrac{0.300\text{ V}}{\sqrt{2}} = 0.2121$ V

$\mathbf{I} = \dfrac{0.2121\text{ V}\angle 0°}{392.7\ \Omega\angle 0°} = 540.2\ \mu\text{A} \angle 0°$

$\mathbf{V}_C = (3.927\text{ k}\Omega \angle -90°)(540.2\ \mu\text{A} \angle 0°)$

$= 2.121\text{ V} \angle -90°$

$\mathbf{V}_R = \mathbf{E} = 0.2121\text{ V} \angle 0°$

d. $i = 764 \times 10^{-6} \sin(50\,000\pi t)$

e. $v_C = 3 \sin(50000\pi t - 90°)$

$v_R = 0.3 \sin(50000\pi t)$

f. $P_T = (540.2\ \mu\text{A})^2(392.7\ \Omega) = 114.6\ \mu\text{W}$

$Q_C = Q_L = (540.2\ \mu\text{A})^2(3927\ \Omega)$

$= 1.146$ mVAR

8. a. $L = \dfrac{1}{(400\text{ krad/s})^2(0.01\ \mu\text{F})} = 625\ \mu\text{H}$

$X_C = X_L = (400\text{ krad/s})(625\ \mu\text{H}) = 250\ \Omega$

$R_T = \dfrac{250\ \Omega}{10} = 25\ \Omega$

$R = 25\ \Omega - 7.8\ \Omega = 17.2\ \Omega$

b. $\mathbf{I} = \dfrac{250\ \mu\text{V}\angle 0°}{25\ \Omega} = 10\ \mu\text{A} \angle 0°$

$P = (10\ \mu\text{A})^2(25\ \Omega) = 2.5$ nW

c. $\mathbf{V}_L = (7.8\ \Omega + j250\ \Omega)(10\ \mu\text{A} \angle 0°)$

$= 2.501\text{ mV} \angle 88.21°$

21.3 Impedance of a Series Resonant Circuit

10. a. $\omega_T = \dfrac{1}{\sqrt{(12.5\text{ mH})(1.25\ \mu\text{F})}} = 8000\text{ rad/s}$

b.

ω (rad/s)	$\mathbf{Z}_T$
800	$50\ \Omega - j990\ \Omega = 991\ \Omega\angle-87.11°$
1 600	$50\ \Omega - j480\ \Omega = 483\ \Omega\angle-84.05°$
4 000	$50\ \Omega - j150\ \Omega = 158\ \Omega\angle-71.57°$
8 000	$50\ \Omega\angle 0°$
16 000	$50\ \Omega + j150\ \Omega = 158\ \Omega\angle-71.57°$
40 000	$50\ \Omega + j480\ \Omega = 483\ \Omega\angle-84.05°$
80 000	$50\ \Omega + j990\ \Omega = 991\ \Omega\angle-87.11°$

c.

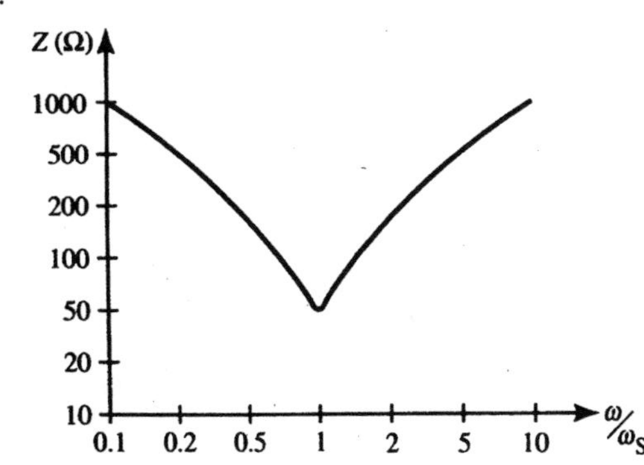

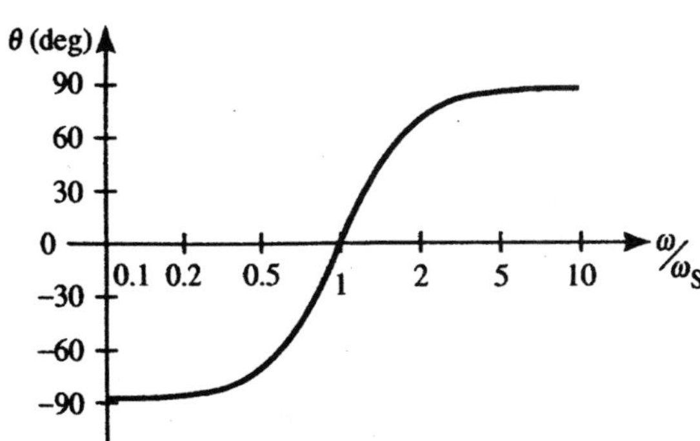

d.

ω (rad/s)	I
800	20.2 mA
1 600	41.4 mA
4 000	126.8 mA
8 000	400 mA
16 000	126.8 mA
40 000	41.4 mA
80 000	20.2 mA

e.

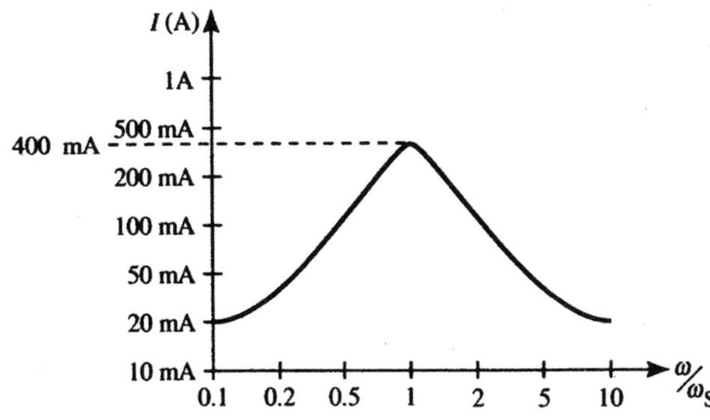

21.4 Power, Bandwidth, and Selectivity of a Series Resonant Circuit

12. a. $\omega = \dfrac{1}{\sqrt{(40\text{ mH})(1\ \mu\text{F})}} = 5000\text{ rad/s}$

$X_C = X_L = \omega L = (5000\text{ rad/s})(40\text{ mH}) = 200\ \Omega$

$Q = \dfrac{200\ \Omega}{100\ \Omega} = 2.0$

$BW = \dfrac{5000\text{ rad/s}}{2} = 2500\text{ rad/s}$

b. $E = \dfrac{70.7\text{ V}}{\sqrt{2}} = 50\text{ V}$

$P_{\max} = \dfrac{(50\text{ V})^2}{100\ \Omega} = 25.0\text{ W}$

c. The approximate half-power frequencies occur at

$\omega_1 \cong 5000\text{ rad/s} - \dfrac{2500\text{ rad/s}}{2} = 3750\text{ rad/s}$

$\omega_2 \cong 5000\text{ rad/s} + \dfrac{2500\text{ rad/s}}{2} = 6250\text{ rad/s}$

d. Actual half-power frequencies:

$\omega_1 = -\dfrac{100\ \Omega}{2(40\text{ mH})} + \sqrt{\dfrac{(100\ \Omega)^2}{4(40\text{ mH})^2} + \dfrac{1}{(40\text{ mH})(1\ \mu\text{F})}}$

$= -1250\text{ rad/s} + 5153.88\text{ rad/s}$

$= 3903.88\text{ rad/s}$

$\omega_2 = 1250\text{ rad/s} + 5153.88\text{ rad/s}$

$= 6403.88\text{ rad/s}$

e. There is a significant discrepancy between the approximations and the actual half-power frequencies. This is because Q is very small.

f. at $\omega_1 = 3903.88$ rad/s,

$X_L = (3903.88\text{ rad/s})(40\text{ mH})$

$= 156.16\ \Omega$

$$X_C = \frac{1}{(3903.88 \text{ rad/s})(1\ \mu\text{F})} = 256.16\ \Omega$$

$$\mathbf{Z}_T = 100\ \Omega + j156.16\ \Omega - j256.16\ \Omega$$
$$= 100\ \Omega - j\,100\ \Omega = 141.4\ \Omega \angle -45^\circ$$

$$\mathbf{I} = \frac{50\text{ V}\angle 0^\circ}{141.4\ \Omega\angle -45^\circ} = 0.3536\text{ A} \angle 45^\circ$$

$$P = (0.3536\text{ A})^2(100\ \Omega) = 12.50\text{ W}$$

14. a. $$C = \frac{1}{4\pi^2(580\text{ kHz})^2(10\text{ mH})} = 7.530\text{ pF}$$

$$X_C = X_L = 2\pi(580\text{ kHz})(10\text{ mH}) = 36.442\text{ k}\Omega$$

$$Q = \frac{580\text{ kHz}}{10\text{ kHz}} = 58$$

$$R = \frac{36.442\text{ k}\Omega}{58} = 628.3\ \Omega$$

b. $$E = \frac{35.4\text{ V}}{\sqrt{2}} = 25.0\text{ V}$$

$$P = \frac{(25.0\text{ V})^2}{628.3\ \Omega} = 0.995\text{ W}$$

c. $$\mathbf{V}_{\text{out}} = \left(\frac{36.442\text{ k}\Omega\angle 90^\circ}{628.3\ \Omega}\right)(25.0\text{ V}) = 1450\text{ V} \angle 90^\circ$$

$$v_{\text{out}} = 2051 \sin(1160 \times 10^3\pi t + 90^\circ)$$

21.5 Series-to-Parallel RL and RC Conversion

16. network (a)

$$X_L = (20\text{ krad/s})(22\text{ mH}) = 440\ \Omega$$

a. $$Q = \frac{440\ \Omega}{1.8\ \Omega} = 244.4$$

b. $$R_P \cong (244.4)^2(1.8\ \Omega) = 107.56\text{ k}\Omega$$

$$X_{LP} = \frac{107.56\text{ k}\Omega}{244.4} = 440\ \Omega\ (L_P = 22\text{ mH})$$

c. $$X_L = (100\text{ krad/s})(22\text{ mH}) = 2200\ \Omega$$

$$Q = \frac{2200\ \Omega}{1.8\ \Omega} = 1222.2$$

$$R_P \cong (1222.2)^2(1.8\ \Omega) = 2.689\text{ M}\Omega$$

$$X_{LP} = \frac{2.689\text{ M}\Omega}{1222.2} = 2200\ \Omega \quad (L_P = 22\text{ mH})$$

network (b)

a. $$X_L = (20\text{ krad/s})(10\text{ mH}) = 200\ \Omega$$

$$Q = \frac{200\ \Omega}{100\ \Omega} = 2$$

b. $$R_P = (2^2 + 1)(100\ \Omega) = 500\ \Omega$$

$$X_{LP} = \frac{500\ \Omega}{2} = 250\ \Omega \quad (L_P = 12.5\text{ mH})$$

c. $$X_L = (100\text{ krad/s})(10\text{ mH}) = 1000\ \Omega$$

$$Q = \frac{1000\ \Omega}{100\ \Omega} = 10$$

$$R_P = (10^2 + 1)(100\ \Omega) = 10.1\text{ k}\Omega$$

$$X_{LP} = \frac{10.1\text{ k}\Omega}{10} = 1.01\text{ k}\Omega \quad (L_P = 10.1\text{ mH})$$

network (c)

a. $$X_L = (20\text{ krad/s})(40\ \mu\text{H}) = 0.80\ \Omega$$

$$Q = \frac{0.80}{1\ \Omega} = 0.8$$

b. $$R_P = (0.8^2 + 1)(1\ \Omega) = 1.64\ \Omega$$

$$X_{LP} = 1.64\frac{\Omega}{0.8} = 2.05\ \Omega \quad (L_P = 102.5\ \mu\text{H})$$

c. $$X_L = (100\text{ krad/s})(40\ \mu\text{H}) = 4.0\ \Omega$$

$$Q = \frac{4.0\ \Omega}{1\ \Omega} = 4.0$$

$$R_P = (4.0^2 + 1)(1\ \Omega) = 17\ \Omega$$

$$X_{LP} = \frac{17\ \Omega}{4} = 4.25\ \Omega \quad (L_P = 42.5\ \mu\text{H})$$

18. $$\mathbf{Y}_T = \frac{1}{R_P} - j\frac{1}{X_{LP}} = \frac{X_{LP} - jR_P}{R_P X_{LP}}$$

$$\mathbf{Z}_T = \frac{R_P X_{LP}(X_{LP} + jR_P)}{(X_{LP} - jR_P)(X_{LP} + jR_P)} = \frac{R_P X_{LP}^2 + jX_{LP}R_P^2}{X_{LP}^2 + R_P^2}$$

But $\mathbf{Z}_T = R_S + jX_{LS}$

Therefore

$$R_S = \frac{R_P X_{LP}^2}{X_{LP}^2 + R_P^2} \text{ and } X_{LS} = \frac{X_{LP}R_P^2}{X_{LP}^2 + R_P^2}$$

20. network (a)

$$Q = \frac{9\text{ k}\Omega}{3\text{ k}\Omega} = 3$$

$$R_S = \frac{9\text{ k}\Omega}{3^2 + 1} = 0.9\text{ k}\Omega$$

$$X_S = (0.9\text{ k}\Omega)(3) = 2.7\text{ k}\Omega$$

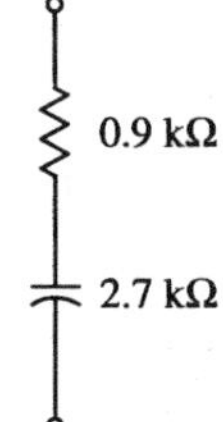

network (b)

$$Q = \frac{10\text{ k}\Omega}{25\text{ k}\Omega} = 0.4$$

$$R_S = \frac{10\text{ k}\Omega}{(0.4)^2 + 1} = 8.621\text{ k}\Omega$$

$$X_S = (8.621\text{ k}\Omega)(0.4) = 3.448\text{ k}\Omega$$

8.62 kΩ

3.45 kΩ

network (c)

$$X_C = \frac{10\text{ k}\Omega}{3} = 3.333\text{ k}\Omega$$

$$R_S = \frac{10\text{ k}\Omega}{3^2+1} = 1\text{ k}\Omega$$

$$X_S = (3)(1\text{ k}\Omega) = 3\text{ k}\Omega$$

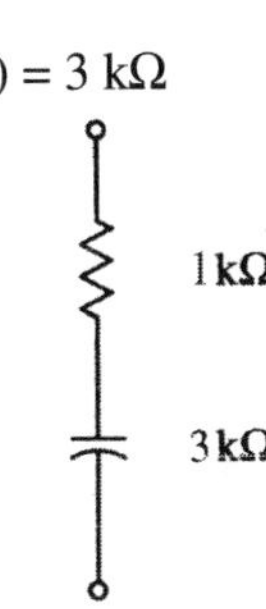

22.

$$10\text{ k}\Omega = (Q^2+1)1\text{ k}\Omega$$

$$Q = \sqrt{\frac{10\text{ k}\Omega}{1\text{ k}\Omega} - 1} = 3.0$$

$$X_{CP} = \frac{10\text{ k}\Omega}{3.0} = 3.333\text{ k}\Omega$$

$$C_P = \frac{1}{(48\text{ krad/s})(3.333\text{ k}\Omega)} = 6250\ \mu\text{F}$$

$$X_{CS} = (3)(1\text{ k}\Omega) = 3.0\text{ k}\Omega$$

$$C_S = \frac{1}{(48\text{ krad/s})(3\text{ k}\Omega)} = 6944\ \mu\text{F}$$

21.6 Parallel Resonance

24.

$$\omega_p = \frac{1}{\sqrt{(12.5\text{ nF})(200\text{ mH})}} = 20\text{ krad/s}$$

b.

ω	$\mathbf{Z}_T$
2 krad/s	0.404 kΩ ∠ 89.42°
4 krad/s	0.833 kΩ ∠ 88.81°
10 krad/s	2.661 kΩ ∠ 86.19°
20 krad/s	40 kΩ ∠ 0°
40 krad/s	2.661 kΩ ∠ – 86.19°
100 krad/s	0.833 kΩ ∠ – 88.81°
200 krad/s	0.404 kΩ ∠ – 89.42°

c.

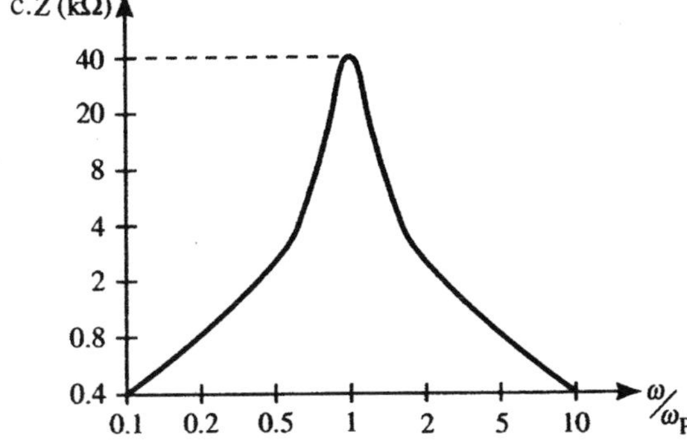

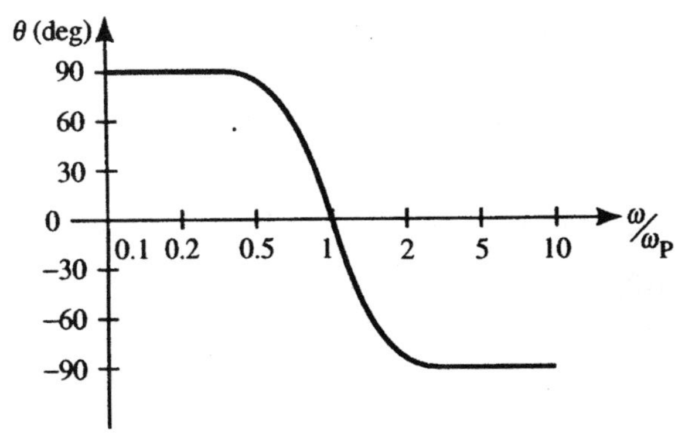

d.

ω	**V**
2 krad/s	0.808 V ∠ 89.42°
4 krad/s	1.667 V ∠ 88.81°
10 krad/s	5.322 V ∠ 86.19°
20 krad/s	80 V ∠ 0°
40 krad/s	5.322 V ∠ – 86.19°
100 krad/s	1.667 V ∠ – 88.81°
200 krad/s	0.808 V ∠ – 89.42°

e.

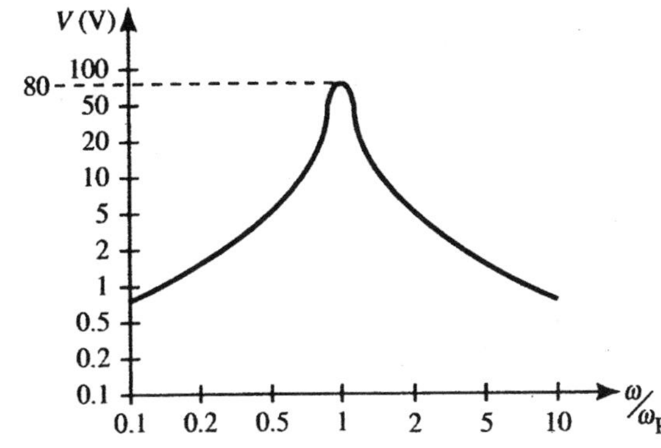

26. a.

$$\omega_P = \frac{1}{\sqrt{(40\text{ mH})(10\text{ nF})}} = 50\text{ krad/s}$$

$$f_P = \frac{50\text{ krad/s}}{2\pi} = 7958\text{ Hz}$$

b. $X_C = X_L = (50\text{ krad/s})(40\text{ mH}) = 2\text{ k}\Omega$

$$Q_{\text{coil}} = \frac{2\text{ k}\Omega}{200\ \Omega} = 10$$

$$R_P \cong (10^2)(200\ \Omega) = 20\text{ k}\Omega$$

$$R_{eq} = 20\text{ k}\Omega \| 100\text{ k}\Omega = 16.67\text{ k}\Omega$$

$$Q = \frac{16.67\text{ k}\Omega}{2\text{ k}\Omega} = 8.33$$

c. $\mathbf{V} = (10\ \mu\text{A}\ \angle\ 0°)(16.67\text{ k}\Omega) = 0.1667\text{ V}\ \angle\ 0°$

$$\mathbf{I}_R = \frac{0.1667\text{ V}\angle 0°}{100\text{ k}\Omega} = 1.667\ \mu\text{A}\ \angle\ 0°$$

$$\mathbf{I}_C = \frac{0.1667\text{ V}\angle 0^\circ}{2\text{ k}\Omega\angle -90^\circ} = 83.3\ \mu\text{A}\ \angle\ 90^\circ$$

$$\mathbf{I}_L = \frac{0.1667\text{ V}\angle 0^\circ}{200\ \Omega + j2\text{ k}\Omega} = 82.9\ \mu\text{A}\ \angle -84.29^\circ$$

d. $P = (10\ \mu\text{A})^2(16.67\text{ k}\Omega) = 1.67\ \mu\text{W}$

e. $\text{BW} = \dfrac{50\text{ krad/s}}{8.33} = 6\text{ krad/s}$

$\text{BW} = \dfrac{7958\text{ Hz}}{8.33} = 955\text{ HZ}$

f.

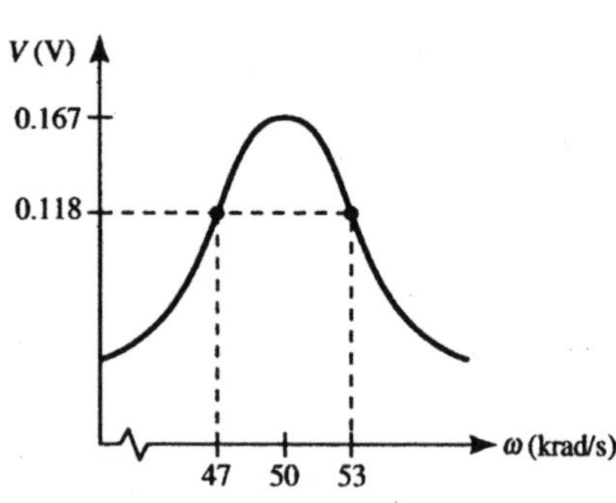

(Note: x-axis is not to scale.)

28. $C = \dfrac{1}{(100\text{ krad/s})^2(50\text{ mH})} = 2\text{ nF}$

$X_C = X_L = (100\text{ krad/s})(50\text{ mH}) = 5000\ \Omega$

$Q_{\text{coil}} = \dfrac{5000\ \Omega}{50\ \Omega} = 100$

$R_P = 100^2\ 50\ \Omega = 500\text{ k}\Omega$

$Q = \dfrac{100\text{ krad/s}}{10\text{ krad/s}} = 10$

$R_{eq} = (10)(5\text{ k}\Omega) = 50\text{ k}\Omega$

$R = \dfrac{1}{\dfrac{1}{50\text{ k}\Omega} - \dfrac{1}{500\text{ k}\Omega}} = 55.56\text{ k}\Omega$

30. a. $X_{LP} = 2\text{ k}\Omega$ for resonance

But $X_{LP} = \dfrac{X_{LS}^2 + R_s^2}{X_{LS}}$

$2000\ \Omega = \dfrac{X_{LS}^2 + (100\ \Omega)^2}{X_{LS}}$

$X_{LS}^2 - 2000\ X_{LS} + 10{,}000 = 0$

Solving the quadratic equation gives:

$X_{LS} = 1995\ \Omega$, ~~$5\ \Omega$~~

b. $Q_{\text{coil}} = \dfrac{1995\ \Omega}{100\ \Omega} = 19.95$

$R_P = (2\text{ k}\Omega)(19.95) = 39.9\text{ k}\Omega$

$R_{eq} = 39.9\text{ k}\Omega \| 400\text{ k}\Omega = 36.28\text{ k}\Omega$

$Q = \dfrac{36.28\text{ k}\Omega}{2\text{ k}\Omega} = 18.14$

c. $\text{BW} = \dfrac{2000\text{ rad/s}}{18.14} = 110.3\text{ rad/s}$

d. $C = \dfrac{1}{(2000\text{ rad/s})(2\text{ k}\Omega)} = 250\text{ nF}$

$L = \dfrac{1995\ \Omega}{2\text{ krad/s}} = 997.5\text{ mH} \cong 1.0\text{ H}$

e. $\mathbf{V}_C = (50\text{ mA}\ \angle\ 0^\circ)(36.28\text{ k}\Omega) = 1814\text{ V}\ \angle\ 0^\circ$

21.7 Circuit Analysis Using Computers

32.

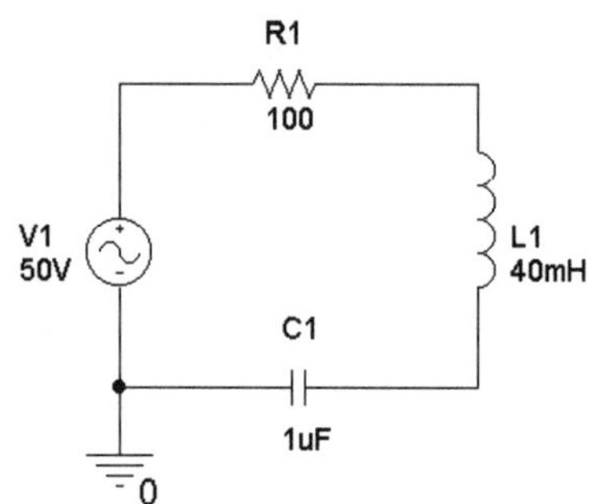

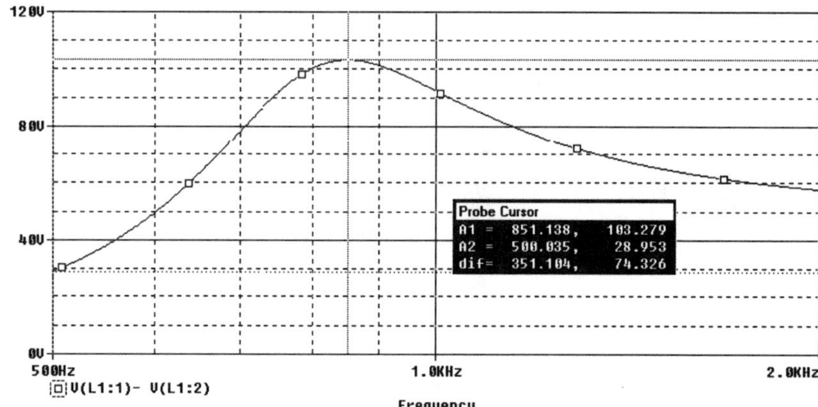

34.

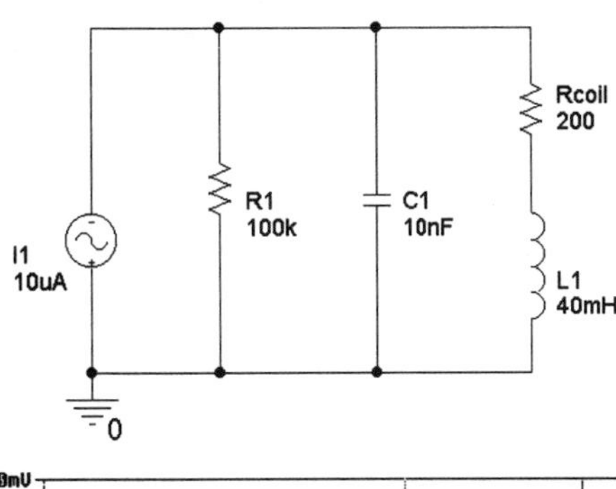
Rcoil
200
R1
100k
C1
10nF
I1
10uA
L1
40mH
0

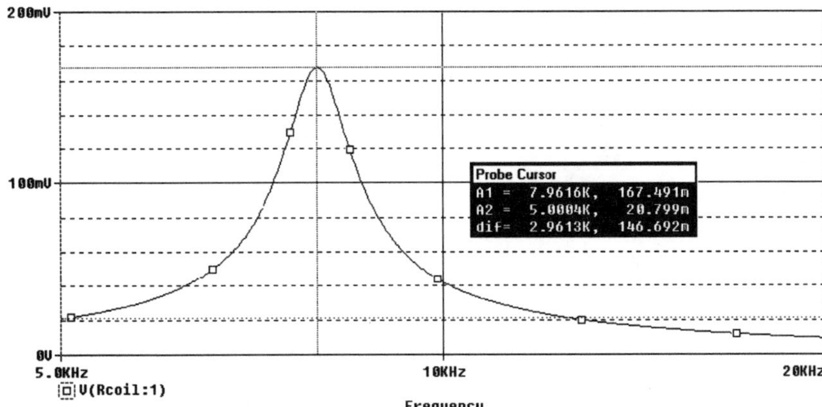
200mV
100mV
0V
5.0KHz
10KHz
20KHz
V(Rcoil:1)
Frequency
Probe Cursor
A1 = 7.9616K, 167.491m
A2 = 5.0004K, 20.799m
dif= 2.9613K, 146.692m

36.

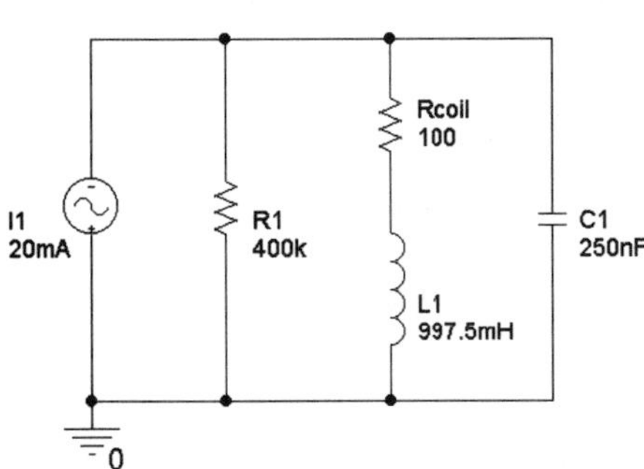
Rcoil
100
I1
20mA
R1
400k
C1
250nF
L1
997.5mH
0

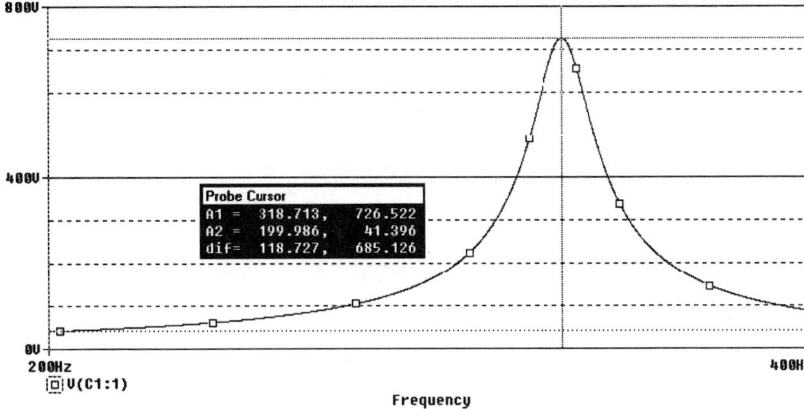
800V
400V
0V
200Hz
400Hz
V(C1:1)
Frequency
Probe Cursor
A1 = 318.713, 726.522
A2 = 199.986, 41.396
dif= 118.727, 685.126

CHAPTER

22

Filters and the Bode Plot

22.1 The Decibel

2. a. $P_{in} = \dfrac{(20\text{ mV})^2}{600\ \Omega} = 0.6667\ \mu\text{W}$

$P_{out} = \dfrac{(100\text{ mV})^2}{2\text{ k}\Omega} = 5\ \mu\text{W}$

$A_{P(\text{dB})} = 10\log\left(\dfrac{5\ \mu\text{W}}{0.6667\ \mu\text{W}}\right) = 8.75\text{ dB}$

b. $P_{in} = \dfrac{(100\ \mu\text{V})^2}{600\ \Omega} = 16.67\text{ pW}$

$P_{out} = \dfrac{(400\ \mu\text{V})^2}{2\text{ k}\Omega} = 80\text{ pW}$

$A_{P(\text{dB})} = 10\log\left(\dfrac{80\text{ pW}}{16.67\text{ pW}}\right) = 6.81\text{ dB}$

c. $P_{in} = \dfrac{(320\text{ mV})^2}{600\ \Omega} = 170.7\ \mu\text{W}$

$P_{out} = \dfrac{(600\text{ mV})^2}{2\text{ k}\Omega} = 180\ \mu\text{W}$

$A_{P(\text{dB})} = 10\log\left(\dfrac{180\ \mu\text{W}}{170.7\ \mu\text{W}}\right) = 0.231\text{ dB}$

d. $P_{in} = \dfrac{(2\ \mu\text{V})^2}{600\ \Omega} = 6.667\text{ nW}$

$P_{out} = \dfrac{(8\text{ V})^2}{2\text{ k}\Omega} = 32\text{ mW}$

$A_{P(\text{dB})} = 10\log\left(\dfrac{32\text{ mW}}{6.667\text{ nW}}\right) = 66.81\text{ dB}$

4. a. $P_{in} = \dfrac{(2\text{ mV})^2}{5\text{ k}\Omega} = 800\text{ pW}$

$V_{out} = \sqrt{(2\text{ k}\Omega)(200\text{ mW})} = 20\text{ V}$

$A_V = \dfrac{20\text{ V}}{2\text{ mV}} = 10\ 000$

$A_{V(\text{dB})} = 20\log 10\ 000 = 80\text{ dB}$

$A_P = \dfrac{200\text{ mW}}{800\text{ pW}} = 2.5 \times 10^8$

$A_{P(\text{dB})} = 10\log(2.5 \times 10^8) = 83.98\text{ dB}$

b. $P_{in} = \dfrac{(2\text{ mV}}{2\text{ k}\Omega} = 2\text{ nW}$

$V_{out} = \sqrt{(10\text{ k}\Omega)(200\text{ mW})} = 44.72\text{ V}$

$A_V = \dfrac{44.72\text{ V}}{2\text{ mV}} = 22\ 361$

$A_{v(\text{dB})} = 20\log 22\ 361 = 86.99$

$A_P = \dfrac{200\text{ mW}}{2\text{ mW}} = 100$

$A_{P(\text{dB})} = 10\log 100 = 20\text{ dB}$

c. $P_{in} = \dfrac{(2\text{ mV})^2}{300\text{ k}\Omega} = 13.33\text{ pW}$

$V_{out} = \sqrt{(1\text{ k}\Omega)(200\text{ mW})} = 14.14\text{ V}$

$A_V = \dfrac{14.14\text{ V}}{2\text{ mV}} = 7071$

$A_{V(\text{dB})} = 20\log 7071 = 76.99\text{ dB}$

$A_P = \dfrac{200\text{ mW}}{13.33\text{ pW}} = 15 \times 10^9$

$A_{p(\text{dB})} = 10\log(15 \times 10^9) = 101.76\text{ dB}$

d. $P_{in} = \dfrac{(2\text{ mV})^2}{1\text{ k}\Omega} = 4\text{ nW}$

$V_{out} = \sqrt{(1\text{ k}\Omega)(200\text{ mW})} = 14.14\text{ V}$

$A_V = \dfrac{14.14\text{ V}}{2\text{ mV}} = 7071$

$A_{V(\text{dB})} = 20\log 7071 = 76.99\text{ dB}$

$A_P = \left(\dfrac{(200\text{ mW}}{4\text{ nW}}\right) = 50 \times 10^9$

$A_P = 10\log(50 \times 10^9) = 106.99\text{ dB}$

6. $A_P = \dfrac{P_{out}}{P_{in}} = 10^{35/10} = 3162$

$P_{in} = \dfrac{(250\text{ mV})^2}{10\text{ k}\Omega} = 6.25\ \mu\text{W}$

$P_{out} = (3162)(6.25\ \mu\text{W}) = 19.76\text{ mW}$

$V_{out} = \sqrt{(19.76\text{ mW})(250\ \Omega)} = 2.22\text{ V}$

$A_V = \dfrac{2.22\text{ V}}{250\text{ mV}} = 8.89$

$A_{V(\text{dB})} = 20\log 8.89 = 18.98$

8. a. $P = 10\log\left(\dfrac{250\text{ W}}{1\text{ mW}}\right) = 53.98\text{ dBm}$

$\equiv 23.98\text{ dBW}$

b. $P = 10\log\left(\dfrac{250\text{ kW}}{1\text{ mW}}\right) = 83.98\text{ dBm}$

$\equiv 53.98\text{ dBW}$

c. $P = 10\log\left(\dfrac{540\text{ nW}}{1\text{ mW}}\right) = -32.68\text{ dBm}$

$\equiv -62.68\text{ dBW}$

d. $P = 10 \log\left(\dfrac{27\text{ mW}}{1\text{ mW}}\right) = 14.31\text{ dBm}$

$\equiv -15.69\text{ dBW}$

10\. a. $P = (1\text{ mW})(10^{16/10}) = 39.8\text{ mW}$

b. $P = (1\text{ W})(10^{-43/10}) = 50.1\ \mu\text{W}$

c. $P = (1\text{ mW})(10^{-47.3/10}) = 18.62\text{ nW}$

d. $P = (1\text{ W})(10^{29/10}) = 794\text{ W}$

12\. a. $20 \log \dfrac{25\ \mu\text{V}}{1\text{ V}} = -92.04\text{ dBV}$

b. $20 \log \dfrac{90\text{ V}}{1\text{ V}} = 39.08\text{ dBV}$

c. $20 \log \dfrac{72.5\text{ mV}}{1\text{ V}} = -22.79\text{ dBV}$

d. $20 \log \dfrac{0.84\text{ V}}{1\text{ V}} = 1.51\text{ dBV}$

14\. a. $10^{20/20} = 10\text{ V}$

b. $10^{-42/20} = 0.00794\text{ V}$

c. $10^{-6/20} = 0.501\text{ V}$

d. $10^{3/20} = 1.413\text{ V}$

16\. $9.20\text{ dBV} \equiv 10^{9.2/20} = 2.88\ \text{V}_{\text{rms}}$

$\equiv (2.88)(2\sqrt{2})$

$= 8.16\ \text{V}_{\text{p-p}}$

22.2 Multistage Systems

18\. $[A_{P2}]_{\text{dB}} = 10 \log 25 = 14.0\text{ dB}$

$[A_{P3}]_{\text{dB}} = 10 \log 0.25 = -6.0\text{ dB}$

$[P_{\text{in}}]_{\text{dBm}} = 15\text{ dBm} - 17\text{ dB} = -2.0\text{ dBm}$

$[P_2]_{\text{dBm}} = 15\text{ dBm} + 14.0\text{ dB} = 29.0\text{ dBm}$

$[P_{\text{out}}]_{\text{dBm}} = 29.0\text{ dBm} - 6.0\text{ dB} = 23.0\text{ dBm}$

20\. a. $P_{\text{out}} = \dfrac{(2\text{ V})^2}{3.6\text{ k}\Omega} = 1.111\text{ mW } (0.458\text{ dBm})$

$P_1 = 0.458\text{ dBm} - 10.8\text{ dB} = -10.34\text{ dBm}$

$P_1 = (1\text{ mW})10^{-10.34/10} = 92.4\ \mu\text{W}$

$P_{\text{in}} = -10.34\text{ dBm} - 30\text{ dB} = 40.34\text{ dBm}$

$P_{\text{in}} = (1\text{ mW})10^{-40.34/10} = 92.5\text{ nW}$

b. $V_{\text{in}} = \sqrt{(92.5\text{ nW})(1.5\text{ k}\Omega)} = 11.78\text{ mV}$

c. $V_{\text{in}} = 20 \log \dfrac{11.787\text{ mV}}{1\text{ V}} = -38.6\text{ dBV}$

$V_L = 20 \log \dfrac{2\text{ V}}{1\text{ V}} = 6.02\text{ dBV}$

d. $A_{V(\text{dB})} = 6.02\text{ dBV} + 38.6\text{ dBV} = 44.62\text{ dB}$

22\. $[A_P]_{\text{dB}} = 10 \log 400 = 26.0\text{ dB}$

a. $[P_{\text{out}}]_{\text{dBm}} = 10 \log \dfrac{200\text{ W}}{1\text{ mW}} = 53.0\text{ dBm}$

$[P_{\text{in}}]_{\text{dBm}} = 53.0\text{ dBm} - 26\text{ dB} = 27.0\text{ dBm}$

b. $V_{\text{out}} = \sqrt{(200\text{ W})(8\ \Omega)} = 40\ \text{V}_{\text{rms}}$

$P_{\text{in}} = (10^{27/10})(1\text{ mW}) = 0.50\text{ W}$

$V_{\text{in}} = \sqrt{(0.50\text{ W})(1000\ \Omega)} = 22.4\ \text{V}_{\text{rms}}$

c. $[V_{\text{out}}]_{\text{dBV}} = 20 \log 40 = 32.0\text{ dBV}$

$[V_{\text{in}}]_{\text{dBV}} = 20 \log 22.4 = 27.0\text{ dBV}$

d. $[A_V]_{\text{db}} = 32.0\text{ dBV} - 27.0\text{ dBV} = 5.0\text{ dB}$

22.3 Simple RC and RL Transfer Functions

24\. a. $\omega_C = \dfrac{1}{0.001\text{ s}} = 1000\text{ rad/s}$

$f_C = \dfrac{1000\text{ rad/s}}{2\pi} = 159.15\text{ Hz}$

b.

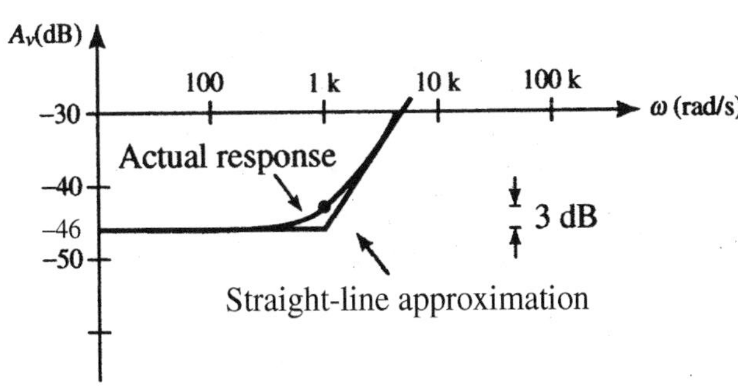

c.

A_v(dB)
100
1 k
10 k
100 k
ω (rad/s)
−30
−40
−46
−50
Actual response
3 dB
Straight-line approximation

26\. a. $\omega_1 = \dfrac{1}{0.04\text{ s}} = 25\text{ rad/s } (3.98\text{ Hz})$

$\omega_2 = \dfrac{1}{0.004\text{ s}} = 250\text{ rad/s } (39.8\text{ Hz})$

$\omega_3 = \dfrac{1}{0.001\text{ s}} = 1000\text{ rad/s } (159.2\text{ Hz})$

b.

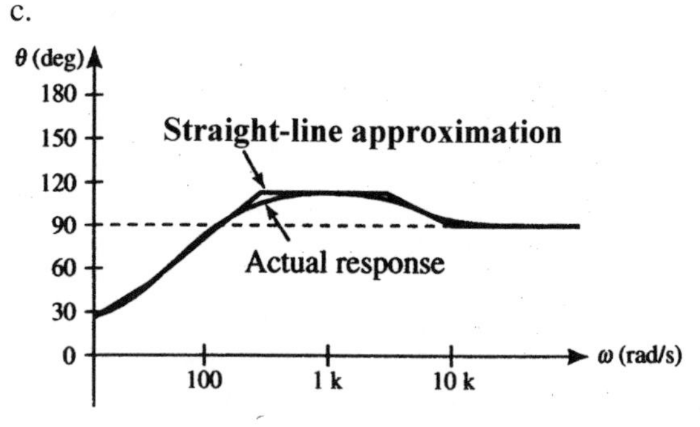

c.

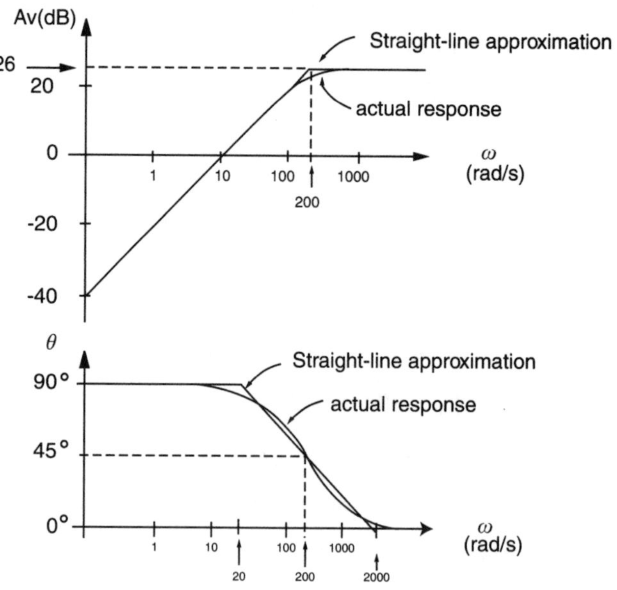

28.

$$\omega_1 = \frac{1}{0.01\text{ s}} = 10\text{ rad/s (1.592 Hz)}$$

$$\omega_2 = \frac{1}{0.005\text{ s}} = 200\text{ rad/s (31.83 Hz)}$$

22.4 The Low-Pass Filter Circuit

30.

$$\tau_C = \frac{1}{2\pi(2500\text{ Hz})} = 64.66\ \mu\text{s}$$

$$R = \frac{63.66\ \mu\text{s}}{1.0\ \mu\text{F}} = 63.66\ \Omega$$

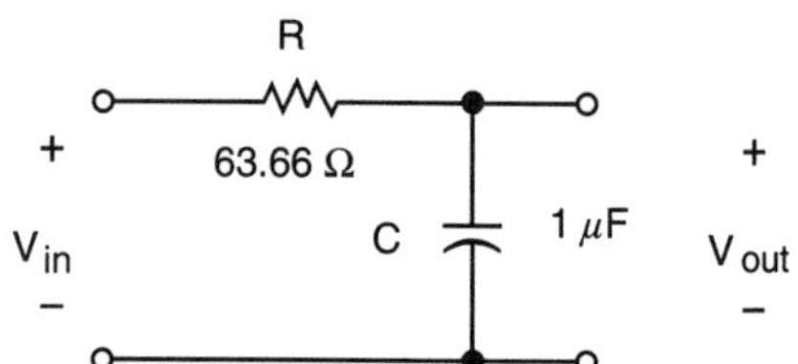

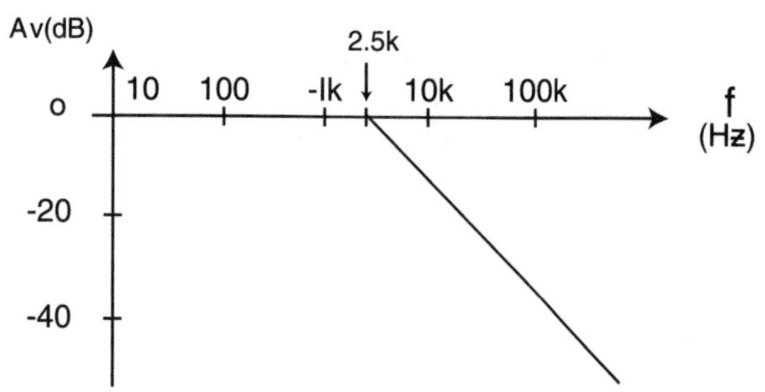

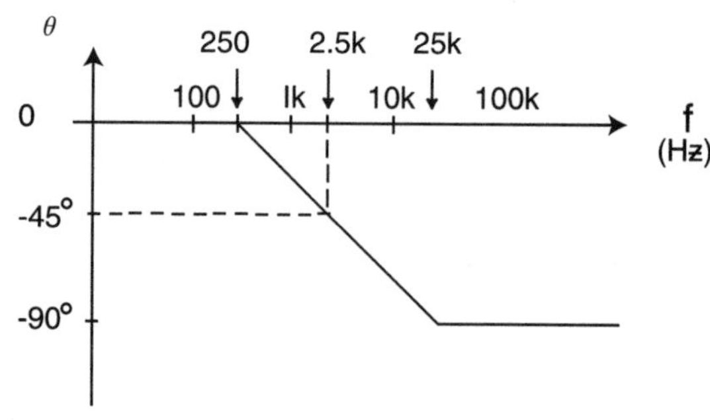

32.

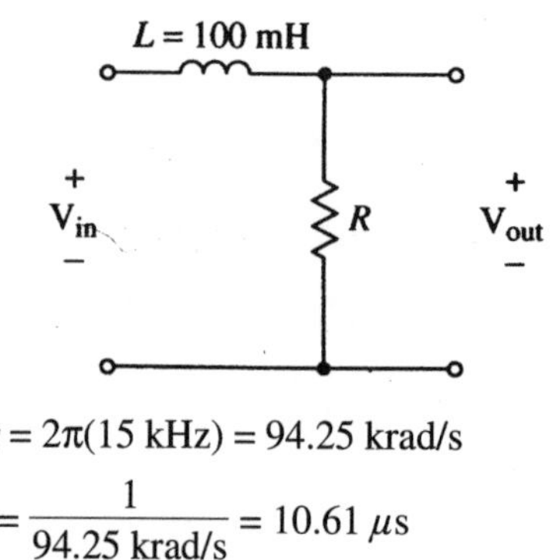

$$\omega_C = 2\pi(15\text{ kHz}) = 94.25\text{ krad/s}$$

$$\tau_C = \frac{1}{94.25\text{ krad/s}} = 10.61\ \mu\text{s}$$

$$R = \frac{100\text{ mH}}{10.61\ \mu\text{s}} = 9.42\text{ k}\Omega$$

34.

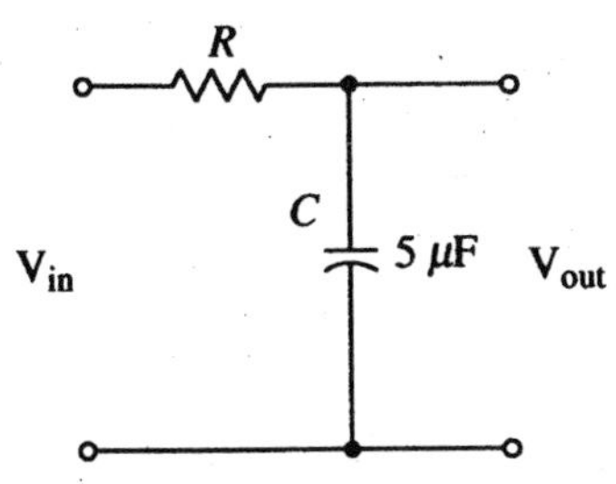

$\omega_C = 100$ krad/s

$\tau_C = 10\ 1\ \mu$s

$R = \dfrac{10\ \mu\text{s}}{5\ \mu\text{F}} = 2.0\ \Omega$

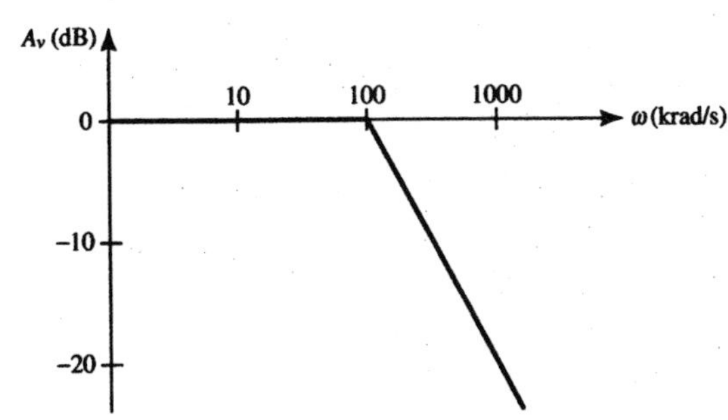

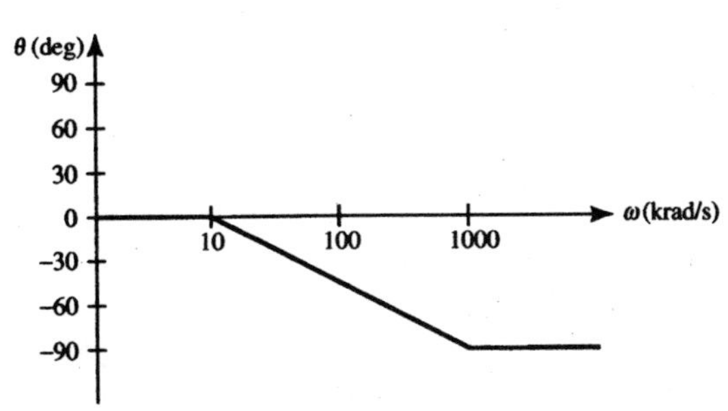

36.

$$TF = \frac{R_2}{R_1 + R_2 + j\omega L}$$

$$= \left(\frac{R_2}{R_1 + R_2}\right)\frac{1}{\left(1 + \dfrac{j\omega L}{R_1 + R_2}\right)}$$

$$= \frac{0.25}{1 + j0.000050\omega}$$

$$\omega_C = \frac{1}{50\ \mu\text{s}} = 20 \text{ krad/s}$$

Low frequency gain:

$A_{V\,(\text{dB})} = 20\log(0.25) = -12$ dB

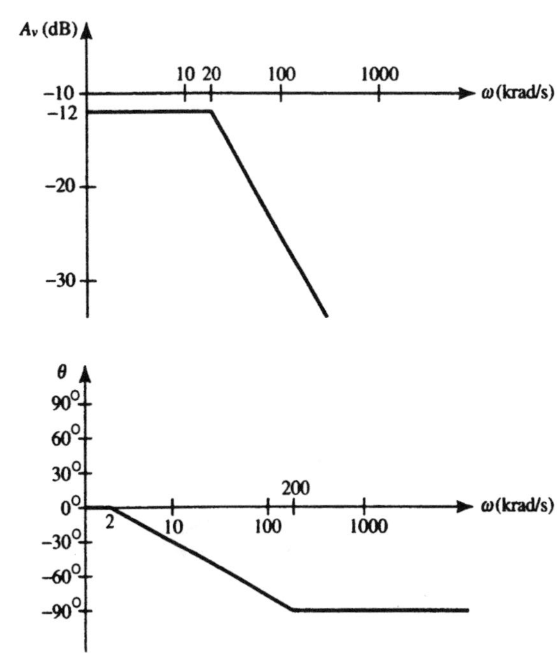

22.5 The High-Pass Filter

38.

$$\tau_C = \frac{1}{2\pi(5\text{ kHz})} = 31.83\ \mu\text{s}$$

$$R = \frac{31.83\ \mu\text{s}}{2.2\text{ nF}} = 14.5\text{ k}\Omega$$

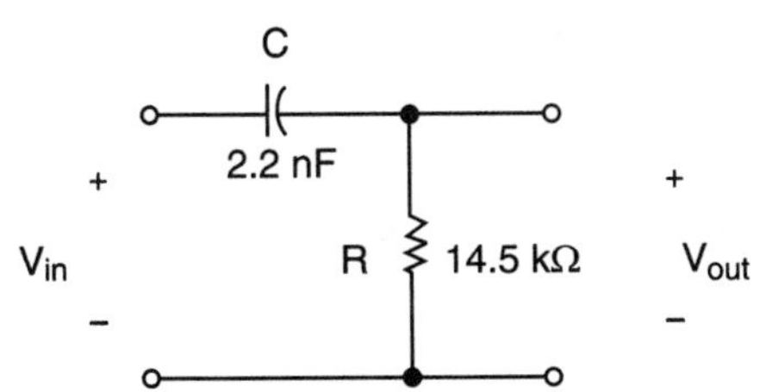

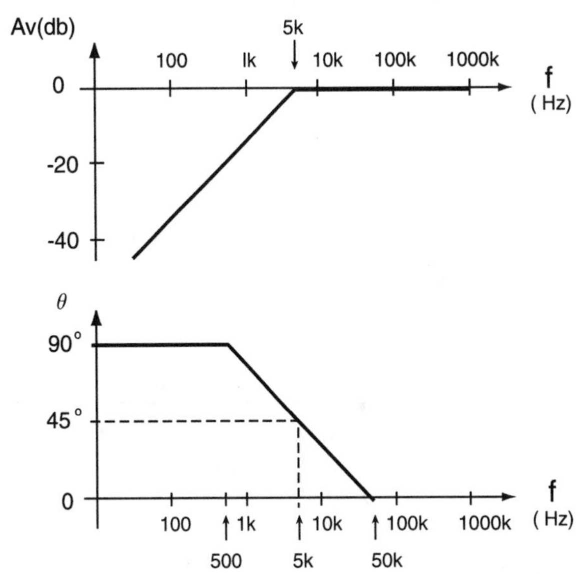

40.

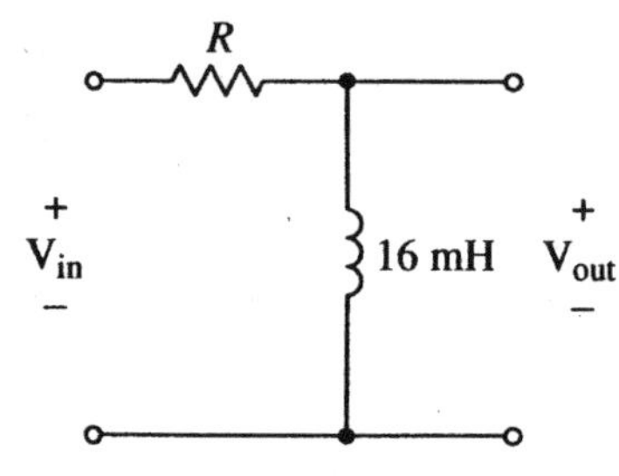

$\omega_c = 2\pi(250 \text{ kHz}) = 1.5708 \text{ Mrad/s}$

$\tau_c = 0.6366\ \mu\text{s}$

$R = \dfrac{16 \text{ mH}}{0.6366\ \mu\text{s}} = 25.13 \text{ k}\Omega$

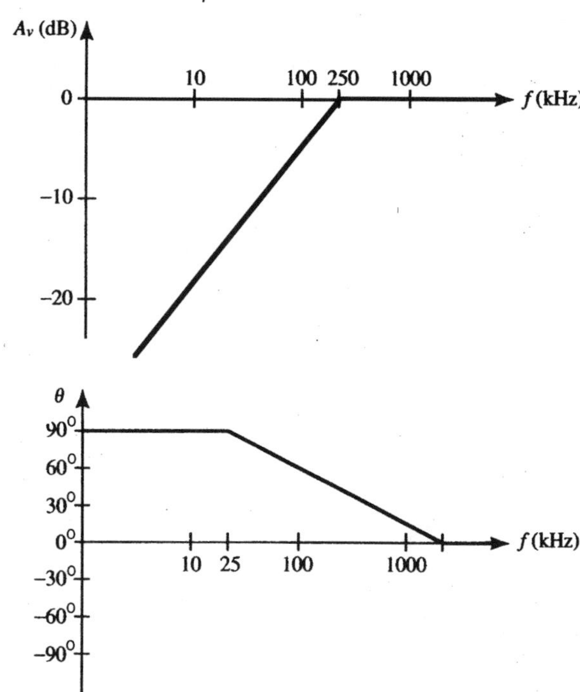

42.

$$\text{T.F.} = \frac{\mathbf{Z}_L \| R_2}{R_1 + \mathbf{Z}_L \| R_2} = \frac{\dfrac{j\omega R_2 L}{R_2 + j\omega L}}{R_1 + \dfrac{j\omega R_2 L}{R_2 + j\omega L}}$$

$$= \frac{j\omega R_2 L}{R_1 R_2 + j\omega R_1 L + j\omega R_2 L}$$

$$= \frac{j\omega R_2 L}{R_1 R_2 \left(1 + \dfrac{j\omega(R_1 + R_2)L}{R_1 R_2}\right)}$$

$$\text{T.F.} = \frac{j\omega\, L/R_1}{1 + j\omega\left(\dfrac{R_1 + R_2}{R_1 R_2}\right)L}$$

$$\omega_1 = \frac{R_1 R_2}{(R_1 + R_2)L} = 577 \text{ krad/s}$$

$$\omega_2 = \frac{R_1}{L} = 2500 \text{ krad/s}$$

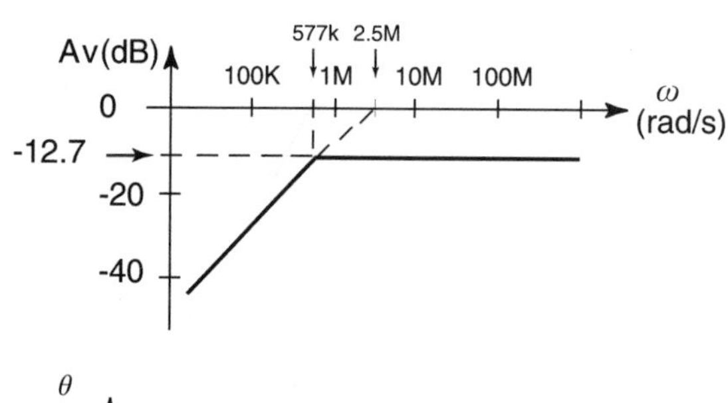

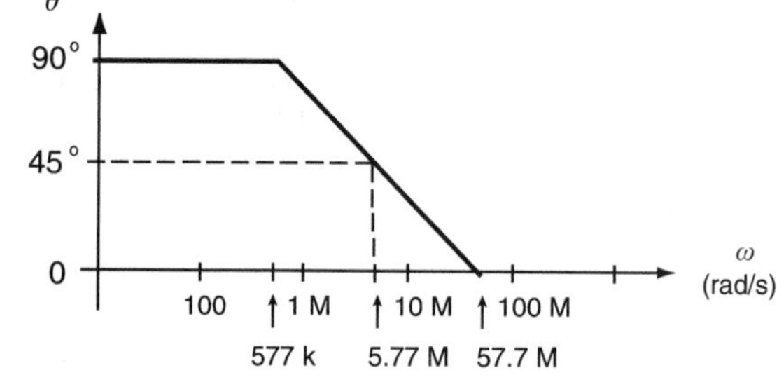

22.6 The Band-Pass Filter

44. a.

$\tau_1 = \dfrac{60 \text{ mH}}{3 \text{ k}\Omega} = 20\ \mu\text{s}$, $\omega_1 = \dfrac{1}{20\ \mu\text{s}} = 50 \text{ krad/s}$ } Low-pass filter

$\tau_2 = \dfrac{20 \text{ mH}}{400\ \Omega} = 50\ \mu\text{s}$, $\omega_1 = \dfrac{1}{50\ \mu\text{s}} = 20 \text{ krad/s}$ } High-pass filter

b.

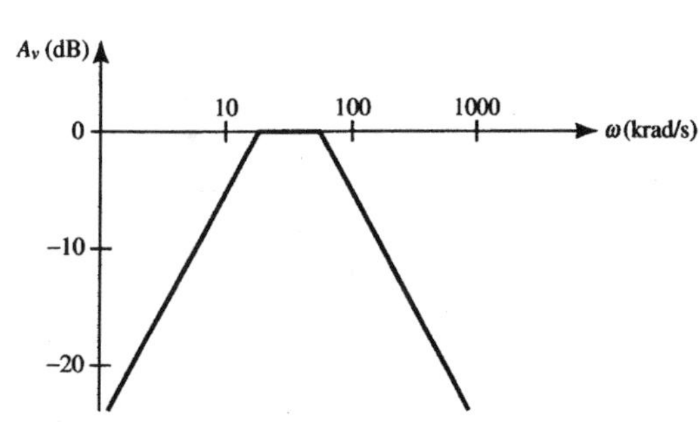

c.

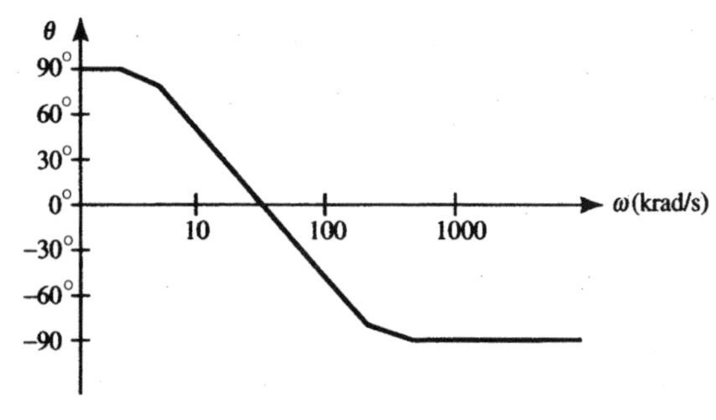

46. a.

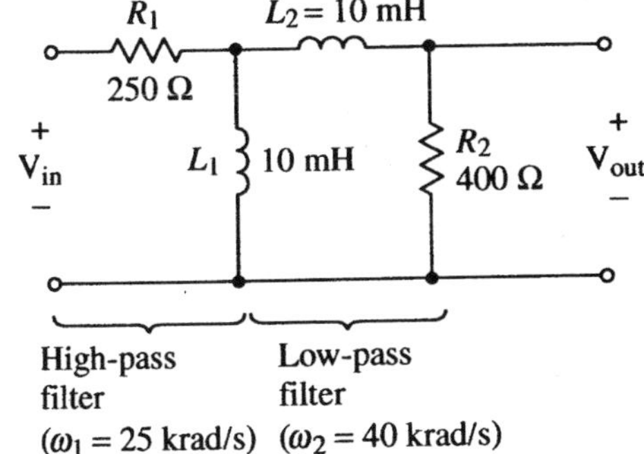

$$\tau_1 = \frac{1}{25 \text{ krad/s}} = 40\ \mu\text{s}$$

$$R_1 = \frac{10 \text{ mH}}{40\ \mu s} = 250\ \Omega$$

$$\tau_2 = \frac{1}{40 \text{ krad/s}} = 25\ \mu s$$

$$R_2 = \frac{10 \text{ mH}}{25\ \mu s} = 400\ \Omega$$

b.

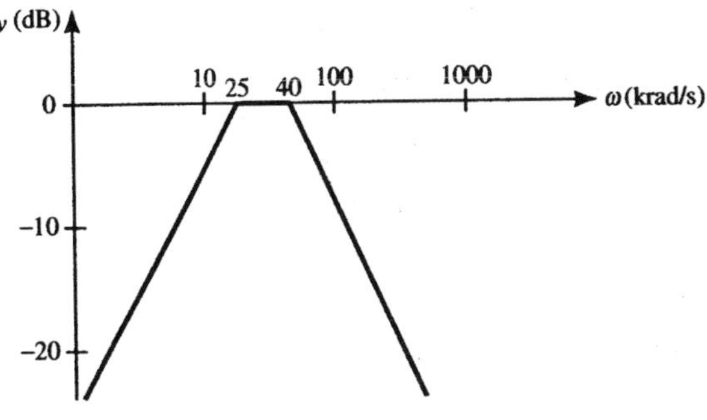

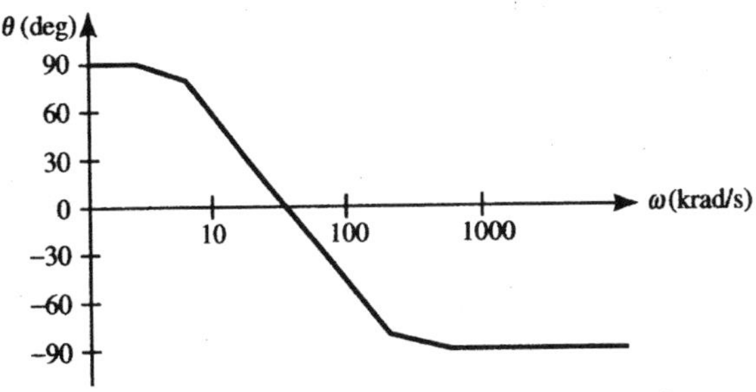

c. The cutoff frequencies will not likely occur at the design values, since the break frequencies are separated by less than a decade.

22.7 The Band-Reject Filter

48. a. $$\omega = \frac{1}{\sqrt{(100\ \mu\text{H})(0.01\ \mu\text{F})}} = 1.00 \text{ Mrad/s} \quad (159 \text{ kHz})$$

b. $X_L = (1 \text{ Mrad/s})(100\ \mu\text{H}) = 100\ \Omega$

$$Q = \frac{100\ \Omega}{8\ \Omega} = 12.5$$

c. $$\text{BW} = \frac{1 \text{ Mrad/s}}{12.5} = 0.080 \text{ Mrad/s} \quad (12.7 \text{ kHz})$$

$\omega_1 = 1000 \text{ krad/s} - 40 \text{ krad/s} = 960 \text{ krad/s}$

$\omega_2 = 1000 \text{ krad/s} + 40 \text{ krad/s} = 1040 \text{ krad/s}$

d. At the resonant frequency of the filter:

$$\text{Av} = \frac{\text{V}_{\text{out}}}{\text{V}_{\text{in}}} = \frac{8\Omega}{800\Omega + 8\Omega} = 0.00990$$

$[\text{Av}]_{\text{dB}} = 20 \log 0.0099 = -40.1 \text{ dB}$

50. a $$\omega_0 \cong \frac{1}{\sqrt{LC}} = 31.623 \text{ krad/s} \equiv 5033 \text{ Hz}$$

b. $$Q_{\text{coil}} = \frac{\omega L}{R_1} = 395$$

c. At the resonant frequency, the impedance of the "tank circuit" is

$R_P = Q^2 R_S = 1.25 \text{ M}\Omega$

$$\left[A_V\right]_{\text{dB}} = 20 \log\left(\frac{32\ \Omega}{1.25\ \text{M}\Omega}\right) = -91.8 \text{ dB}$$

d. $$\text{At } \omega = 0,\ A_V = \frac{32\ \Omega}{40\ \Omega} = 0.8 \equiv -1.94 \text{ dB}$$

and

as $\omega \to \infty$, $A_V = 1 \equiv 0$ dB

e. $$\text{BW} = \frac{31.623 \text{ krad/s}}{395} = 80 \text{ rad/s} (\equiv 12.7 \text{ Hz})$$

$\omega_1 = 31.583$ krad/s (5027 Hz)

$\omega_2 = 31.663$ krad/s (5039 Hz)

22.8 Circuit Analysis Using Computers

52.

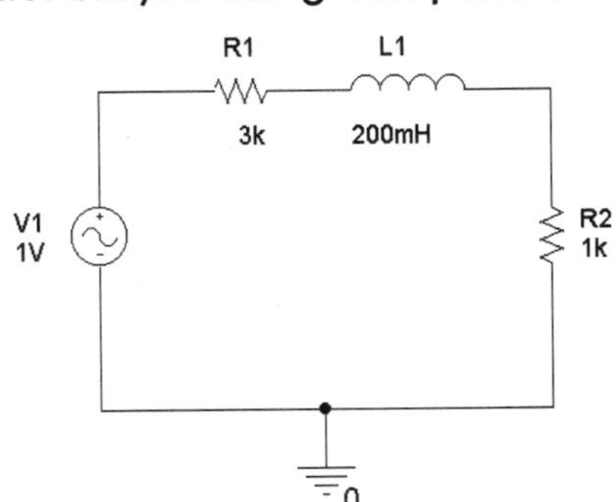

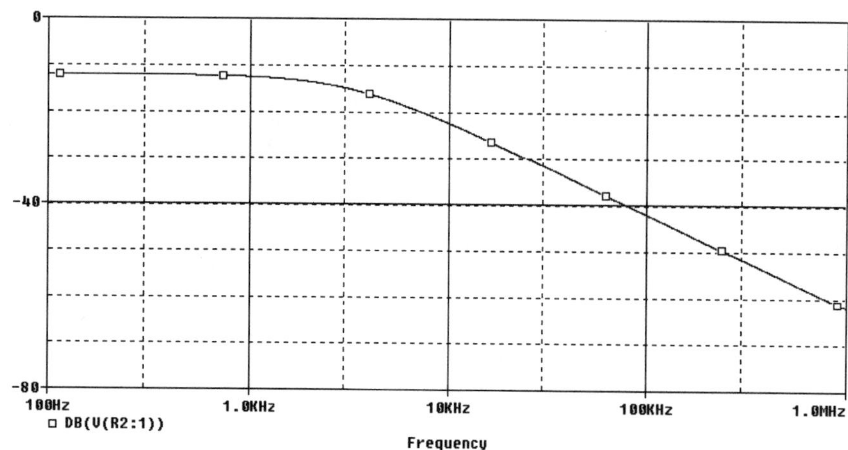
0
-40
-80
100Hz
1.0KHz
10KHz
100KHz
1.0MHz
DB(V(R2:1))
Frequency

54.

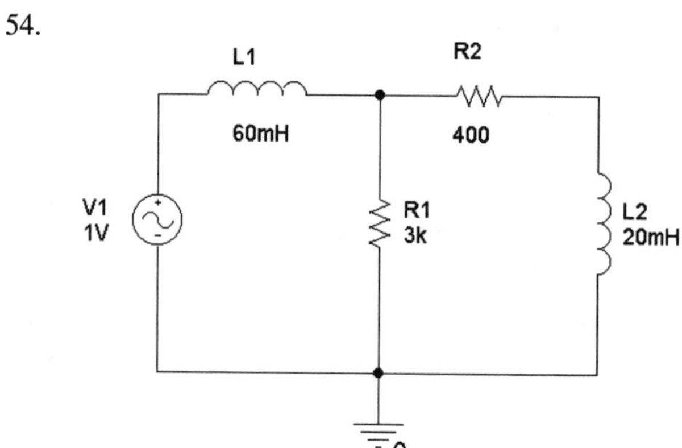
L1
60mH
R2
400
V1
1V
R1
3k
L2
20mH
0

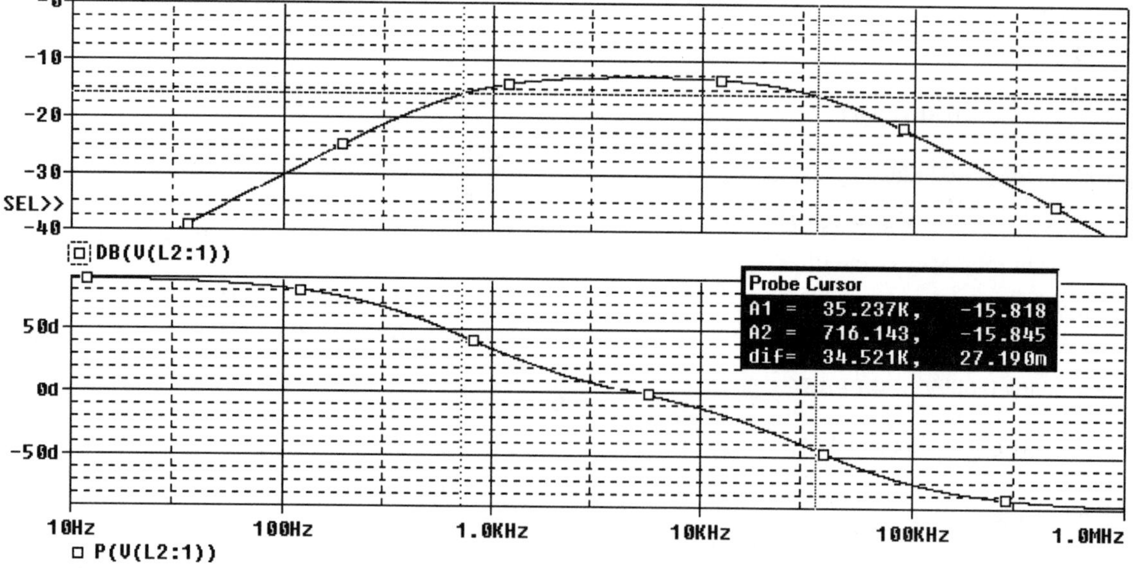
-0
-10
-20
-30
SEL>>
-40
DB(V(L2:1))
50d
0d
-50d
Probe Cursor
A1 = 35.237K, -15.818
A2 = 716.143, -15.845
dif= 34.521K, 27.190m
10Hz
100Hz
1.0KHz
10KHz
100KHz
1.0MHz
P(V(L2:1))

56.

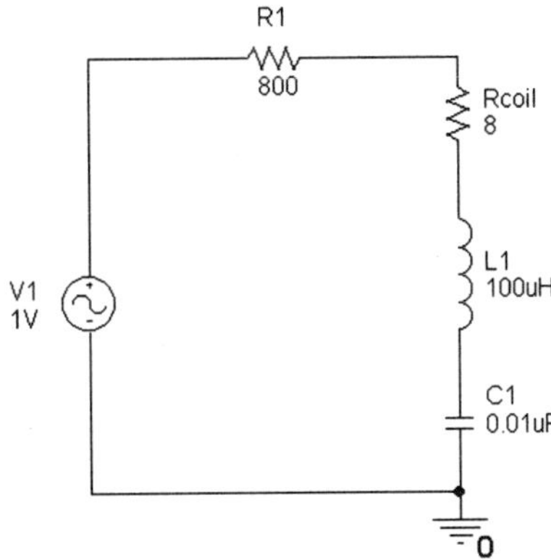
R1
800
Rcoil
8
L1
100uH
V1
1V
C1
0.01uF
0

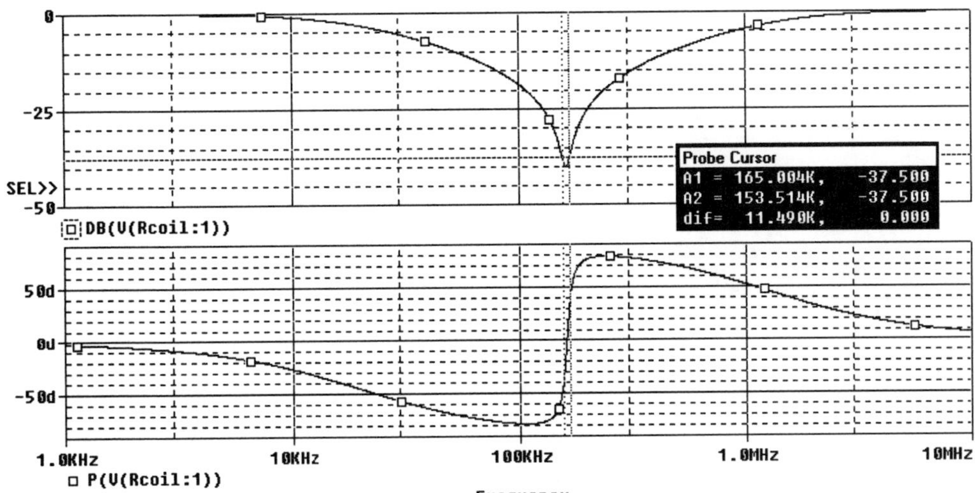
0
-25
SEL>>
-50
DB(V(Rcoil:1))
Probe Cursor
A1 = 165.004K, -37.500
A2 = 153.514K, -37.500
dif= 11.490K, 0.000
50d
0d
-50d
1.0KHz
10KHz
100KHz
1.0MHz
10MHz
P(V(Rcoil:1))
Frequency

58.

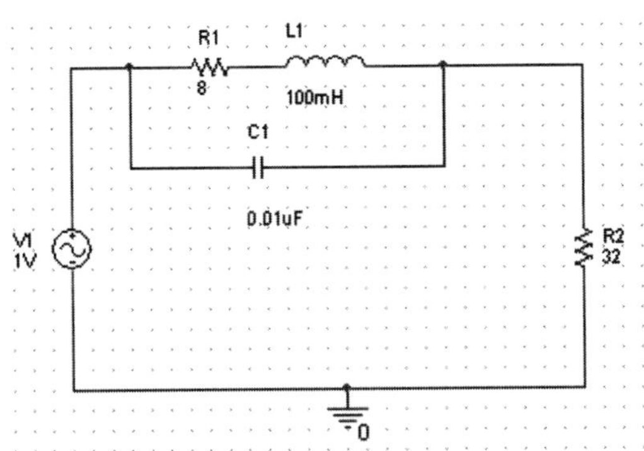
R1
8
L1
100mH
C1
0.01uF
V1
1V
R2
32
0

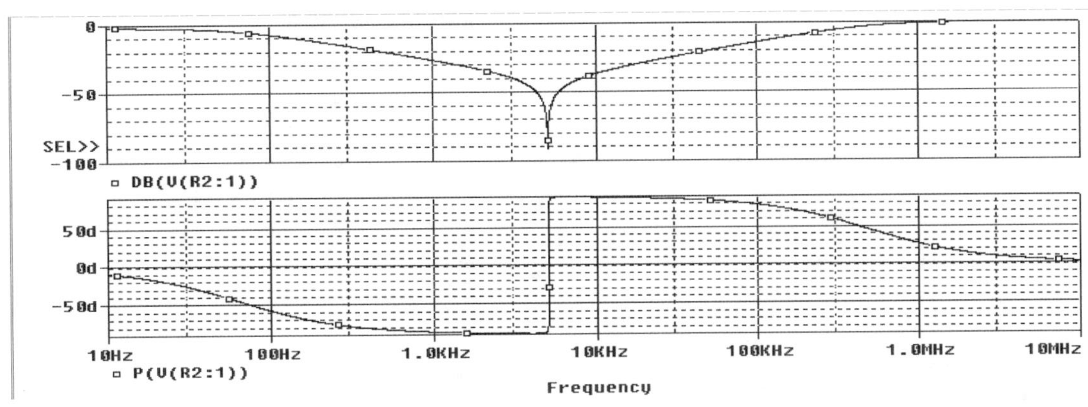
0
-50
SEL>>
-100
DB(V(R2:1))
50d
0d
-50d
10Hz
100Hz
1.0KHz
10KHz
100KHz
1.0MHz
10MHz
P(V(R2:1))
Frequency

60.

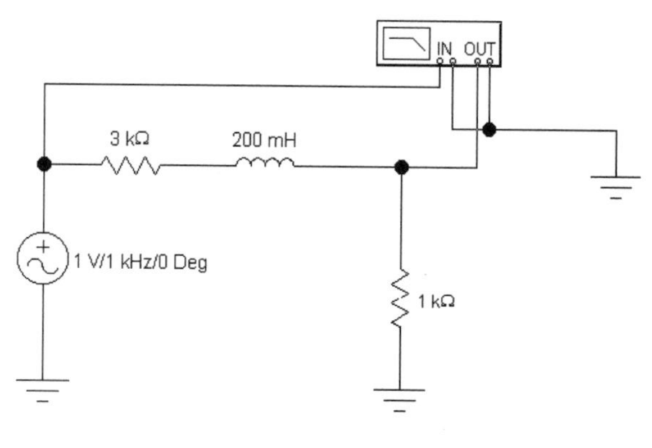
IN OUT
3 kΩ
200 mH
1 V/1 kHz/0 Deg
1 kΩ

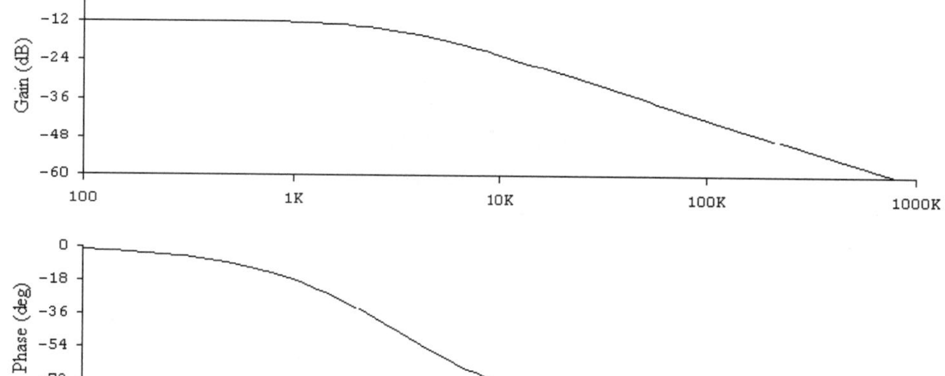
Gain (dB)
0
-12
-24
-36
-48
-60
100
1K
10K
100K
1000K
Phase (deg)
0
-18
-36
-54
-72
-90
100
1K
10K
100K
1000K
Frequency (Hz)

62.

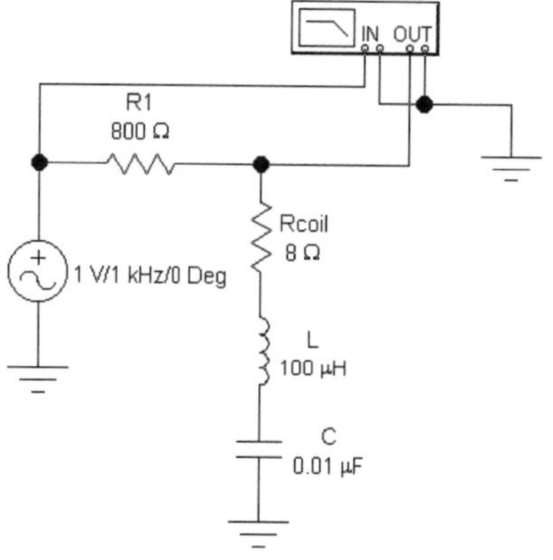
IN OUT
R1
800 Ω
Rcoil
8 Ω
1 V/1 kHz/0 Deg
L
100 μH
C
0.01 μF

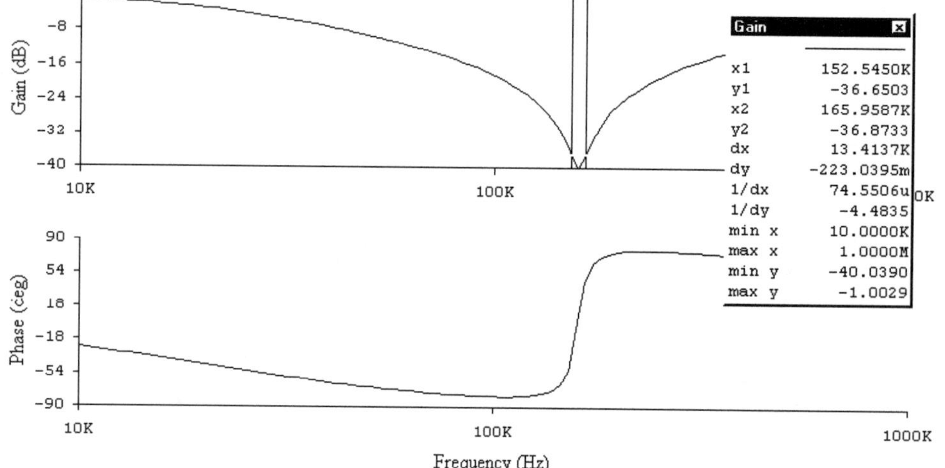
Gain (dB)
0
-8
-16
-24
-32
-40
10K
100K
Gain
x1 152.5450K
y1 -36.6503
x2 165.9587K
y2 -36.8733
dx 13.4137K
dy -223.0395m
1/dx 74.5506u
1/dy -4.4835
min x 10.0000K
max x 1.0000M
min y -40.0390
max y -1.0029
Phase (deg)
90
54
18
-18
-54
-90
10K
100K
1000K
Frequency (Hz)

64.

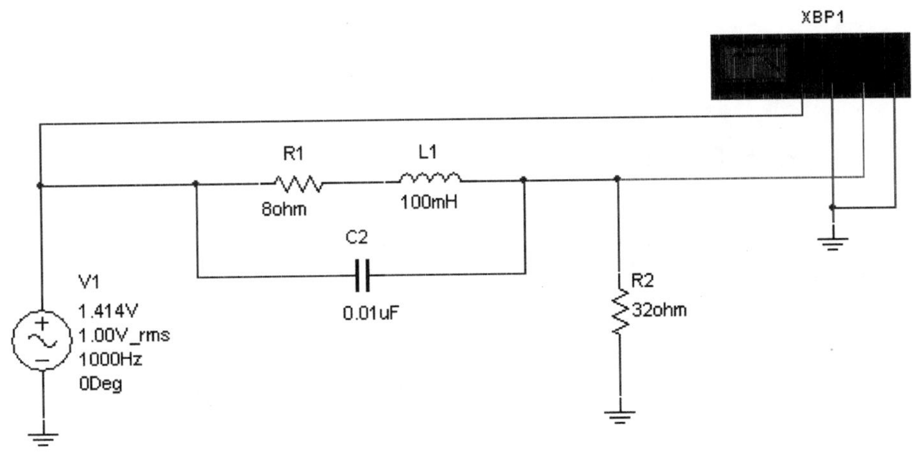
XBP1
R1
8ohm
L1
100mH
C2
0.01uF
V1
1.414V
1.00V_rms
1000Hz
0Deg
R2
32ohm

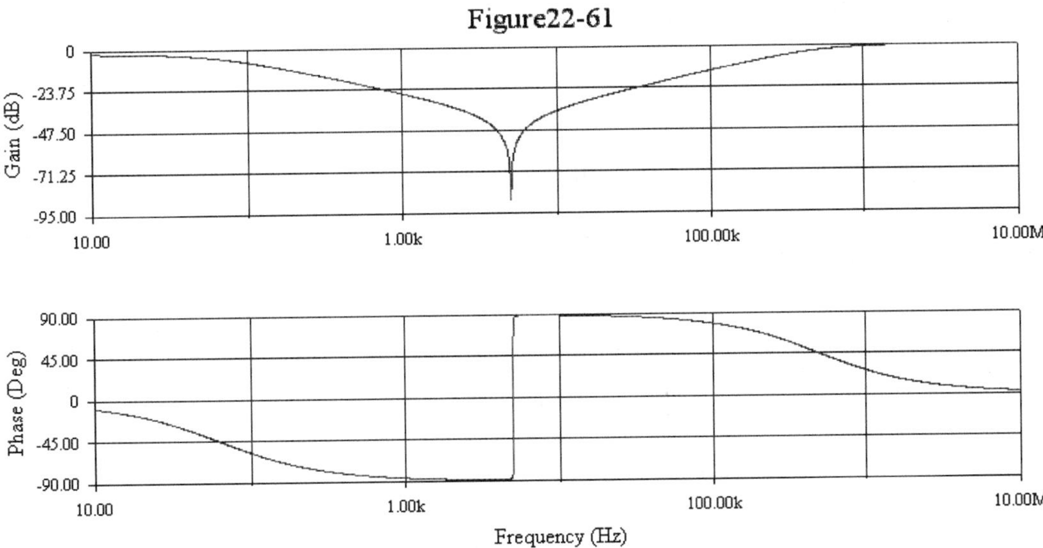
Figure22-61
Gain (dB)
0
-23.75
-47.50
-71.25
-95.00
10.00
1.00k
100.00k
10.00M
Phase (Deg)
90.00
45.00
0
-45.00
-90.00
10.00
1.00k
100.00k
10.00M
Frequency (Hz)

CHAPTER

23

Transformers and Coupled Circuits

23.2 Iron-Core Transformer: The Ideal Model

2. Winding resistance, leakage flux, core loss, and magnetizing current

4. $$I_p = \frac{I_s}{a} = \frac{6\text{ A}}{3} = 2\text{ A}$$

6. a. $$\mathbf{V}_L = \frac{\mathbf{E}_p}{a} = \frac{\mathbf{E}_g}{a} = \frac{240\text{ V}\angle 0^\circ}{2} = 120\text{ V}\angle 0^\circ$$

b. $$\mathbf{I}_L = \frac{\mathbf{V}_L}{\mathbf{Z}_L} = \frac{120\text{ V}\angle 0^\circ}{8\ \Omega - j6\ \Omega} = 12\text{ A}\angle 36.9^\circ$$

c. $$\mathbf{I}_g = \frac{\mathbf{I}_L}{a} = 6\text{ A}\angle 36.9^\circ$$

8. $\mathbf{I}_L = \text{a}\,\mathbf{I}_p = \text{a}\,\mathbf{I}_g = (2)(0.5\text{ A}\angle 10^\circ) = 1\text{ A}\angle 10^\circ$

$$\mathbf{Z}_L = \frac{\mathbf{V}_L}{\mathbf{I}_L} = \frac{40\text{ V}\angle 0^\circ}{1\text{ A}\angle 10^\circ} = 40\ \Omega\angle -10^\circ$$

10. a. $\mathbf{V}_L = \mathbf{I}_L\,\mathbf{Z}_L = (4\text{ A}\angle 25^\circ)(10\ \Omega\angle -5^\circ)$
$= 40\text{ V}\angle 20^\circ$
$\mathbf{E}_g = a\mathbf{E}_s = (3)(40\text{ V}\angle 20^\circ)$
$= 120\text{ V}\angle 20^\circ$
$$\mathbf{I}_g = \frac{\mathbf{I}_s}{a} = \frac{4\text{ A}\angle 25^\circ}{3}$$
$= 1.33\text{ A}\angle 25^\circ$

b. $P_L = V_L I_L \cos\theta_L = (40\text{ V})(4\text{ A})\cos 5^\circ = 159\text{ W}$

c. $P_g = V_g I_g \cos\theta_g = (120\text{ V})(1.33\text{ A})\cos 5^\circ = 159\text{ W}$

d. Yes

23.3 Reflected Impedance

12. circuit (a)

a. $$\mathbf{I}_g = \frac{\mathbf{E}_g}{\mathbf{Z}_P} = \frac{120\text{ V}\angle 40^\circ}{40\ \Omega - j80\ \Omega} = 1.34\text{ A}\angle 103.4^\circ$$

b. $\mathbf{I}_L = a\mathbf{I}_g = (2)(1.34\text{ A}\angle 103.4^\circ) = 2.68\text{ A}\angle 103.4^\circ$

c. $$\mathbf{V}_L = \frac{\mathbf{E}_g}{a} = \frac{120\text{ V}\angle 40^\circ}{2} = 60\text{ V}\angle 40^\circ$$

circuit (b)

a. $$\mathbf{I}_g = \frac{120\text{ V}\angle 40^\circ}{1.25\ \Omega + j2\ \Omega} = 50.9\text{ A}\angle -18^\circ$$

b. $\mathbf{I}_L = a\mathbf{I}_g = (0.5)(50.9\text{ A}\angle -18^\circ) = 25.4\text{ A}\angle -18^\circ$

c. $\mathbf{V}_L = \mathbf{I}_L\,\mathbf{Z}_L = 205\text{ V}\angle 64.9^\circ$

14. $\mathbf{Z}\text{p} = \text{a}^2\mathbf{Z}_L \quad \therefore a^2 = \dfrac{\mathbf{Z}_P}{\mathbf{Z}_L}$

$$a^2 = \frac{84.9\angle 58^\circ}{5 + j8} = \frac{84.9\angle 58^\circ}{9.43\angle 58^\circ} = 9$$
$\therefore a = 3$

16. circuit (a)

a. $$\mathbf{I}_g = \frac{\mathbf{E}_g}{\mathbf{Z}_T} = \frac{120\text{ V}\angle -40^\circ}{22\ \Omega + j6\ \Omega} = 5.26\text{ A}\angle -55.3^\circ$$

b. $\mathbf{I}_L = a\mathbf{I}_g = (3)(5.26\text{ A}\angle -55.3^\circ) = 15.8\text{ A}\angle -55.3^\circ$

c. $\mathbf{V}_L = \mathbf{I}_L\mathbf{Z}_L = (15.8\text{ A}\angle -55.3^\circ)(2\ \Omega) = 31.6\text{ V}\angle -55.3^\circ$

circuit (b)

a. $$\mathbf{I}_g = \frac{\mathbf{E}_g}{\mathbf{Z}_T} = \frac{120\text{ V}\angle -40^\circ}{26\ \Omega + j3\ \Omega} = 4.585\text{ A}\angle -46.6^\circ$$

b. $\mathbf{I}_L = a_1 a_2\,\mathbf{I}_g = (4)(0.5)(4.585\text{ A}\angle -46.6^\circ)$
$= 9.17\text{ A}\angle -46.6^\circ$

c. $\mathbf{V}_L = \mathbf{I}_L\,\mathbf{Z}_L = (9.17\text{ A}\angle -46.6^\circ)(6\ \Omega)$
$= 55.0\text{ V}\angle -46.6^\circ$

23.4 Transformer Power Ratings

18. a. 48 kVA

b. $P = F_p S = (0.75)(48\text{ kVA}) = 36\text{ kW}$

c. $S = \dfrac{P}{F_p} = \dfrac{45\text{ KW}}{0.6} = 75\text{ kVA}$ Yes

23.5 Transformer Applications

20. Let R_L' be the reflected load. Thus, $R_L' = a^2 R_L = (4)^2(8\ \Omega) = 128\ \Omega$. Since R_L' is equal to R_{Th}, the load is matched.

Voltages are as indicated. Since the transformer is considered lossless, $P_{\text{speaker}} = P_{R'_L} = \frac{(5\text{ V})^2}{128\ \Omega} = 0.195\text{ W}$

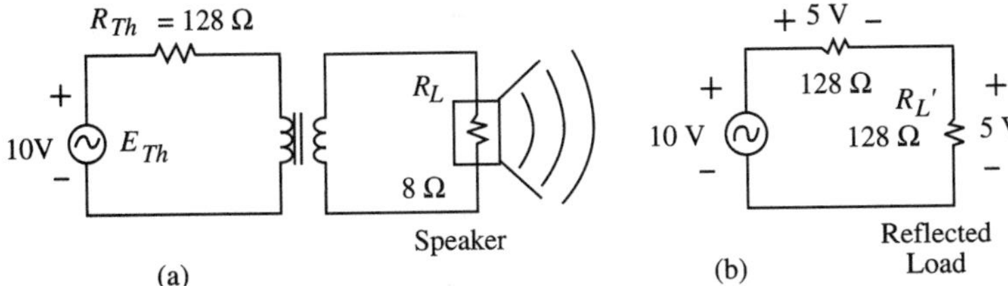

22. From Tap 2 to common, the turns ratio is 10. Since $N_S = 200$ turns, there are 2000 turns from Tap 2 to common. Thus, there are 2100 from Tap 1 to common and 1880 from Tap 3 to common. For Tap 1, we need $120\text{ V} \times \frac{2100\text{ turns}}{200\text{ turns}} = 1260\text{ V}$. Similarly, for Tap 3, we need 1128 V.

24. a.

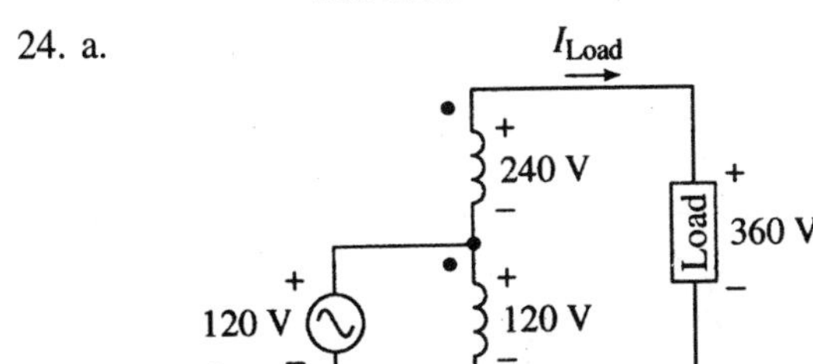

b. Rating of 240 V winding $= \frac{5000\text{ VA}}{240\text{ V}} = 20.83\text{ A}$

$\therefore$ Load can draw $I_{\text{Load}} = 20.83\text{ A}$

c. Load kVA = (360 V)(20.83 A) = 7.5 kVA

d. $S_{\text{in}} = S_{\text{out}}\ \therefore\ 120\, I_g = 7500\text{ VA}$ and $I_g = 62.5\text{ A}$

23.6 Practical Iron-Core Transformers

See Problem 25 (in Answers to Odd-Numbered Questions, page 102) for equivalent circuit.

26. a. $\mathbf{I}_L = \frac{\mathbf{V}_L}{\mathbf{Z}_L} = \frac{118\text{ V}\angle 0^\circ}{4\ \Omega + j4\ \Omega} = 20.86\text{ A}\angle -45^\circ$

b. $\mathbf{I}_g = \frac{\mathbf{I}_L}{a} = \frac{20.86\text{ A}\angle -45^\circ}{10} = 2.086\text{ A}\angle -45^\circ$

c. $\mathbf{E}_g = \mathbf{I}_g\mathbf{Z}_{eq} + a\mathbf{V}_L = (2.068\text{ A}\angle -45^\circ)(6\ \Omega + j6\ \Omega) + (10)(118\text{ V}\angle 0^\circ) = 1198\text{ V}\angle 0^\circ$

d. $V_{NL} = \frac{E_g}{a} = \frac{1198\text{ V}}{10} = 119.8\text{ V}$

e. $\text{Reg} = \left(\frac{V_{NL} - V_{FL}}{V_{FL}}\right) \times 100 = \left(\frac{119.8 - 118}{118}\right) \times 100 = 1.53\%$

23.7 Transformer Tests

28. a. Since the transformer is operating at rated kVA, $P_{\text{copper}} = 96\text{ W}$,

$\therefore P_{\text{loss}} = P_{\text{copper}} + P_{\text{core}} = 96\text{ W} + 24\text{ W} = 120\text{ W}$

$P_{\text{in}} = P_{\text{out}} + P_{\text{loss}} = 5000\text{ W} + 120\text{ W} = 5120\text{ W}$

$\eta = \frac{P_{\text{out}}}{P_{\text{in}}} \times 100\% = \left(\frac{5000\text{ W}}{5120\text{ W}}\right) \times 100 = 97.7\%$

b. At $\frac{1}{4}$ kVA, copper losses are $\left(\frac{1}{4}\right)^2$ of their value at rated kVA. Therefore,

$P_{\text{copper}} = \left(\frac{1}{4}\right)^2 (96\text{ W}) = 6\text{ W}.$

Thus, $P_{\text{loss}} = P_{\text{copper}} + P_{\text{core}} = 6\text{ W} + 24\text{ W} = 30\text{ W}.$

$P_{out} = \left(\frac{1}{4}\right)(5000 \text{ VA})(0.8) = 1000 \text{ W}$

$\therefore P_{in} = P_{out} + P_{loss} = 1000 \text{ W} + 30 \text{ W} = 1030 \text{ W}$

$\eta = \frac{P_{out}}{P_{in}} \times 100\% = \left(\frac{1000 \text{ W}}{1030 \text{ W}}\right) \times 100 = 97.1\%.$

23.9 Loosely Coupled Circuits

30. $M = k\sqrt{L_1L_2} = (0.85)\sqrt{(0.25 \text{ H})(0.4 \text{ H})} = 0.269 \text{ H}$

32. $v_{11} = L_1\frac{di_1}{dt}$ where $\frac{di_1}{dt} = 1200 \text{ A/S}$

$v_{11} = (25 \times 10^{-3})(1200 \text{ A/S}) = 30 \text{ V}$

$v_{21} = M\frac{di_1}{dt} = (0.8 \times 10^{-3})(1200 \text{ A/S}) = 0.96 \text{ V}$

34. a. $L_T = L_1 + L_2 - 2M = 8 \text{ H} + 0.5 \text{ H} - 2(1 \text{ H}) = 6.5 \text{ H}$

b. $M = k\sqrt{L_1L_2} \therefore 4 \text{ mH} = 0.4\sqrt{50 \times 10^{-3}L_1} \therefore L_1 = 2$ mH

$L_T = L_1 + L_2 - 2M = 2 \text{ mH} + 50 \text{ mH} - 2(4 \text{ mH}) =$ 44 mH

36. $M = k\sqrt{L_1L_2} = 0.8\sqrt{(1 \text{ H})(4 \text{ H})} = 1.6 \text{ H}$

$L_T = L_1 + L_2 + 2M = 1 \text{ H} + 4 \text{ H} + 3.2 \text{ H} = 8.2 \text{ H}$

$X_T = \omega L_T = (2\pi)(60 \text{ Hz})(8.2 \text{ H}) = 3091 \ \Omega$

$\mathbf{I} = \frac{\mathbf{E}}{\mathbf{Z}} = \frac{100 \text{ V}\angle 0°}{400 \ \Omega + j3091 \ \Omega} = 32.1 \text{ mA} \angle -82.6°$

23.10 Magnetically Coupled Circuits with AC Excitation

38. Loop 1: $\mathbf{E}_1 - R_1\mathbf{I}_1 - j\omega L_1\mathbf{I}_1 + j\omega M\mathbf{I}_2 = 0$

Loop 2: $\mathbf{E}_2 - j\omega L_2\mathbf{I}_2 + j\omega M\mathbf{I}_1 - R_2\mathbf{I}_2 = 0$

Rearranging and substituting values yields

$(10 + j20)\mathbf{I}_1 - j5\mathbf{I}_2 = 100 \angle 0°$

$-j5\mathbf{I}_1 + (30 + j40)\mathbf{I}_2 = 150 \angle 30°.$

40. $(35 - j40)\mathbf{I}_1 - 25\mathbf{I}_2 = 100 \angle 0°$

$-25\mathbf{I}_1 + (30 + j40)\mathbf{I}_2 - j15\mathbf{I}_3 = 0$

$-j15\mathbf{I}_2 + (80 + j30)\mathbf{I}_3 = -150 \angle 30°$

23.11 Coupled Impedance

42. a. $\mathbf{Z}_{in} = \mathbf{Z}_p + \frac{(\omega M)^2}{\mathbf{Z}_s + \mathbf{Z}_L}$

$= (15 \ \Omega + j\omega L_1) + \frac{(\omega M)^2}{(20 \ \Omega + j\omega L_2) - jX_C}$

$= (15 \ \Omega + j37.7 \ \Omega) + \frac{(30.16)^2}{(20 \ \Omega + j75.4) - j265.25}$

$= 45.2 \ \Omega \angle 69.9°$

b. $\mathbf{I}_g = \frac{\mathbf{E}}{\mathbf{Z}_{in}} = \frac{100 \text{ V} \angle 0}{45.2 \ \Omega \angle 69.9°} = 2.21\text{A}\angle{-69.9°}$

23.12 Circuit Analysis Using Computers (MSM)

44. Use the virtual transformer with its turns ratio set to 10 and other parameters set as noted in the text. Set all meters for AC and $f = 60$ Hz. Energize the circuit using MSM's power ON/OFF switch. Verification: See PSpice Problem 44 below.

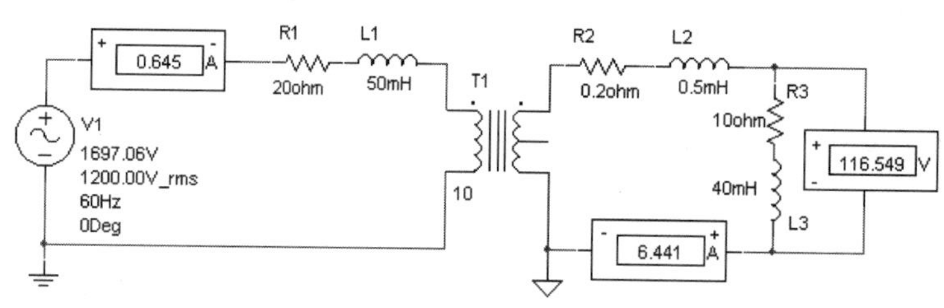

23.12 Circuit Analysis Using Computers (PSpice)

44. Use source VAC and XFRM_LINEAR. Set a = 10 as described on page 862 of the text. Set all meters for *AC*, *MAG* and *PHASE*. Simulate using *AC Sweep* with *Start* and *End* frequencies set to 60 Hz. Following simulation, scroll the output. Verification: $\omega = 2\pi f = 377$ rad/s and $a = 10$. Reflecting the secondary impedance into the primary yields an input impedance of $\mathbf{Z}_{in} = 20 + j(377)(50 \text{ mH}) + (10)^2[0.2 + j(377)(0.5 \text{ mH}) + 10 + j(377)(40 \text{ mH})] = 1040 + j1545.7 = 1863\ \Omega \angle 56.07°$. This yields $\mathbf{I}_g = 1200 \text{ V} \angle 0° / 1863\ \Omega \angle 56.07° = 0.644 \text{ A} \angle -56.07°$. Thus, $\mathbf{I}_{Load} = (10)\mathbf{I}_g = 6.441 \text{ A} \angle -56.07°$ and $\mathbf{V}_{Load} = (6.441 \text{ A} \angle -56.07°)(10 + j15.08) = 116.6 \text{ V} \angle 0.385°$. PSpice values agree very well with these.

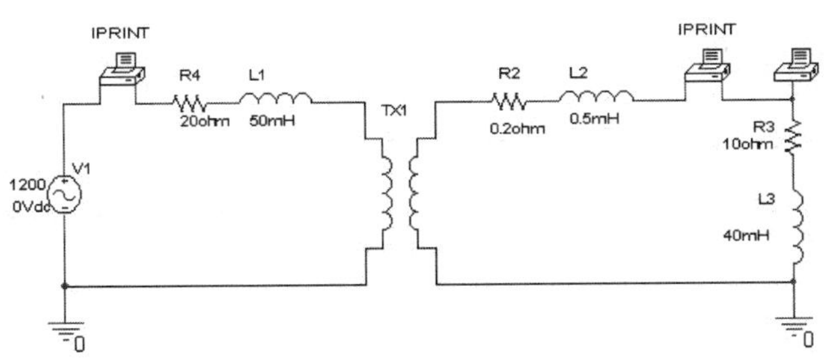

46. Use source VAC. Set all meters for *AC*, *MAG* and *PHASE*. Simulate using *AC Sweep* with *Start* and *End* frequencies set to $f = \omega/2\pi = 15.9155$ Hz. Following simulation, scroll the output. Answers agree extremely well with Example 23-15.

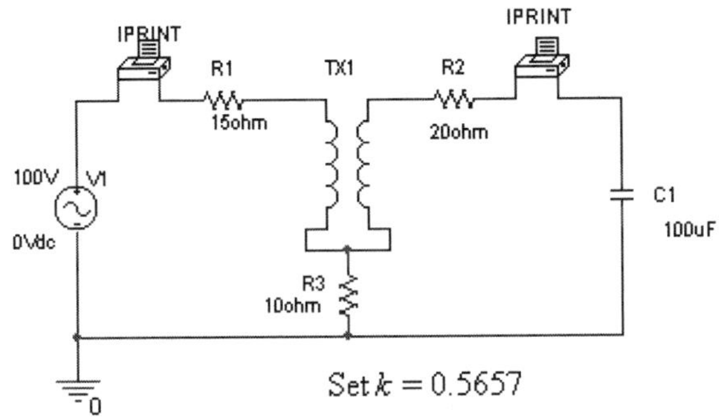

48. Several reactances are given. These must be converted to inductance and capacitance values. For example, there is a capacitor in the circuit with a reactance of 5 Ω at 1000 rad/s. Its equivalent capacitance is thus

$C = \dfrac{1}{\omega X_C} = \dfrac{1}{(1000)(5\ \Omega)} = 200\ \mu\text{F}$ as indicated on the diagram. Use source VAC. Set all meters for *AC*, *MAG*, and *PHASE*. Simulate using *AC Sweep* with *Start* and *End* Frequencies set to $f = \omega/2\pi = 159.155$ Hz. Following simulation, scroll the output file for input current. The answer agrees with that of Example 23-16.

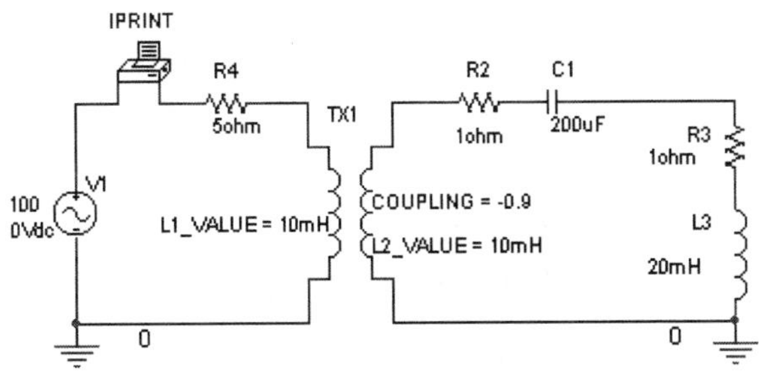

CHAPTER

24

Three-Phase Systems

24.2 Basic Three-Phase Circuit Connections

2. a. $\mathbf{E}_{BN} = 277\text{ V} \angle -135°$

$\mathbf{E}_{CN} = 277\text{ V} \angle 105°$

b. $\mathbf{I}_A = \dfrac{\mathbf{E}_{AN}}{R} = \dfrac{277\text{ V}\angle{-15°}}{5.54\ \Omega} = 50\text{ A} \angle -15°$

$\mathbf{I}_B = \dfrac{\mathbf{E}_{BN}}{R} = \dfrac{277\text{V}\angle -135°}{5.54\Omega} = 50\text{ A}\angle -135°$

$\mathbf{I}_C = \dfrac{\mathbf{E}_{CN}}{R} = \dfrac{277\text{ V}\angle 105°}{5.54\ \Omega} = 50\text{ A} \angle 105°$

c. $\mathbf{I}_A + \mathbf{I}_B + \mathbf{I}_C = 50 \angle -15° + 50 \angle -135° + 50 \angle 105°$

$= (48.3 - j12.9) + (-35.4 - j35.4) + (-12.9 + j48.3)$

$= 0$

4. a. $\mathbf{E}_{BN} = 7620\text{ V} \angle -138°$

$\mathbf{E}_{CN} = 7620\text{ V} \angle 102°$

b. $\mathbf{E}_{AB} = \sqrt{3}\,\mathbf{E}_{AN} \angle 30° = \sqrt{3}(7620\text{ V})\ \underline{\angle -18° + 30°}$

$= 13\,200\text{ V} \angle 12°$

$\mathbf{E}_{BC} = 13\,200\text{ V} \angle -108°$

$\mathbf{E}_{CA} = 13\,200\text{ V} \angle 132°$

$\mathbf{E}_{CA} = 13200\text{ V} \angle 132°$

$\mathbf{E}_{CN} = 7620\text{ V} \angle 102°$

$\mathbf{E}_{AB} = 13200\text{ V} \angle 12°$

$\mathbf{E}_{AN} = 7620\text{ V} \angle -18°$

$\mathbf{E}_{BN} = 7620\text{ V} \angle -138°$

$\mathbf{E}_{BC} = 13200\text{ V} \angle -108°$

24.3 Basic Three-Phase Relationships

6. a. $\mathbf{V}_{ab} = 208\text{ V} \angle -30°$

$\mathbf{V}_{bc} = 208\text{ V} \angle -150°$

b. $\mathbf{V}_{an} = \dfrac{\mathbf{V}_{ab}}{\sqrt{3}\angle 30°} = \dfrac{208\text{ V}\angle -30°}{\sqrt{3}\angle 30°} = 120\text{ V} \angle -60°$

$\mathbf{V}_{bn} = 120\text{ V} \angle -180°$

$\mathbf{V}_{cn} = 120\text{ V} \angle 60°$

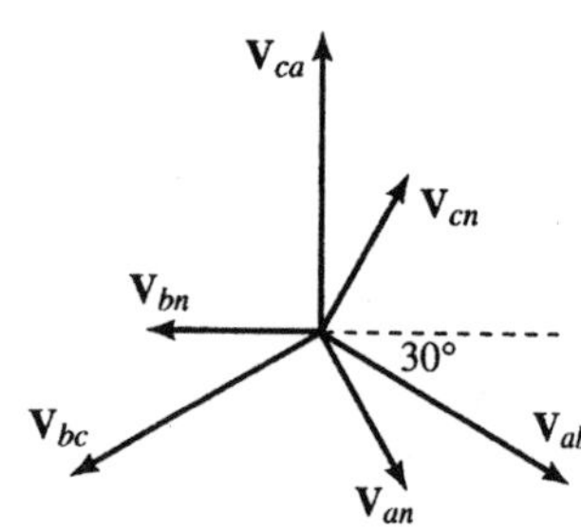

8. $\mathbf{V}_{an} = \mathbf{I}_a\mathbf{Z}_{an}$

$= (7.8\text{ A} \angle -10°)(12\ \Omega + j9\ \Omega) = 117\text{ V} \angle 26.9°$

$\therefore\ \mathbf{V}_{bn} = 117\text{ V} \angle -93.1°$

$\mathbf{V}_{cn} = 117\text{ V} \angle 146.9°$

$\mathbf{V}_{ab} = \sqrt{3}\,\mathbf{V}_{an} \angle 30°$

$= \sqrt{3}(117\text{ V})\ \underline{\angle 26.9° + 30°} = 203\text{ V} \angle 56.9°$

$\therefore\ \mathbf{V}_{bc} = 203\text{ V} \angle -63.1°$

$\mathbf{V}_{ca} = 203\text{ V} \angle 176.9°$

10. $\mathbf{I}_a = \sqrt{3}\,\mathbf{I}_{ab} \angle -30° = (\sqrt{3} \angle -30°)\ (29.3 \angle 43°) =$
$50.7\text{ A} \angle 13°$

12. $\mathbf{I}_a = \sqrt{3}\,\mathbf{I}_{ab}\angle -30°$

$\therefore\ \mathbf{I}_{ab} = \dfrac{\mathbf{I}_a}{\sqrt{3}\angle -30°} = \dfrac{41.0\text{ A}\angle -46.7°}{\sqrt{3}\angle -30°}$

$= 23.7\text{ A} \angle -16.7°$

$\therefore\ \mathbf{I}_{bc} = 23.7\text{ A} \angle -136.7°$

$\mathbf{I}_{ca} = 23.7\text{ A} \angle 103.3°$

14. $\mathbf{I}_{ab} = \dfrac{\mathbf{I}_a}{\sqrt{3}\angle -30°} = \dfrac{11.0\text{ A}\angle 30°}{\sqrt{3}\angle -30°} = 6.35\text{ A} \angle 60°$

$\mathbf{V}_{ab} = \mathbf{I}_{ab}\mathbf{Z}_{ab}$

$= (6.35\text{ A}\angle 60°)(20\ \Omega - j15\ \Omega)$

$= 159\text{ V} \angle 23.1°$

$\therefore\ \mathbf{V}_{bc} = 159\text{ V} \angle -96.9°$

$\mathbf{V}_{ca} = 159\text{ V} \angle 143.1°$

16. a. $\mathbf{I}_{ab} = \dfrac{\mathbf{V}_{ab}}{\mathbf{Z}_{ab}} = \dfrac{208\text{ V}\angle 0°}{27\Omega\angle -57°} = 7.70\text{ A} \angle 57°$

$\therefore\ \mathbf{I}_{bc} = 7.70\text{ A} \angle -63°$ and $\mathbf{I}_{ca} = 7.70\text{ A} \angle 177°$

b. $\mathbf{I}_a = \sqrt{3}\,\mathbf{I}_{ab} \angle -30° = 13.3\text{ A} \angle 27°$

$\therefore\ \mathbf{I}_b = 13.3\text{ A} \angle -93°$ and $\mathbf{I}_c = 13.3\text{ A} \angle 147°$

18. Assume $\mathbf{I}_{ab} = I \angle 0°$. Then $\mathbf{I}_{ca} = I \angle +120°$

$\mathbf{I}_a = \mathbf{I}_{ab} - \mathbf{I}_{ca} = I \angle 0° - I \angle 120°$

$= I(1 \angle 0° - 1 \angle 120°)$

$= 1.732I \angle -30°$

$= \sqrt{3}I \angle -30°$

$\therefore \mathbf{I}_a = \sqrt{3}I \angle -30° = (\sqrt{3} \angle -30°)(I \angle 0°)$.

But $I \angle 0° = \mathbf{I}_{ab} \therefore \mathbf{I}_a = \sqrt{3}\,\mathbf{I}_{ab} \angle -30°$.

20. $\mathbf{V}_{ab} = \sqrt{3}\mathbf{V}_{an} \angle 30° = \sqrt{3}(120 \text{ V}) \angle 30°$

$= 208 \text{ V} \angle 30°$

$$\mathbf{I}_{ab} = \frac{\mathbf{I}_a}{\sqrt{3}\angle -30°} = \frac{43.6 \text{ A}\angle -37.5}{\sqrt{3}\angle -30°}$$

$= 25.2 \text{ A} \angle -7.5°$

$$\mathbf{Z}_{ab} = \frac{\mathbf{V}_{ab}}{\mathbf{I}_{ab}} = \frac{208 \text{ V}\angle 30°}{25.2 \text{ A}\angle -7.5°} = 8.25\ \Omega \angle 37.5°$$

24.4 Examples

22. Convert to a single phase equivalent. Then,

a. $$\mathbf{I}_a = \frac{\mathbf{E}_{AN}}{\mathbf{Z}_T} = \frac{120 \text{ V}\angle 20°}{(0.1 + j0.3) + (12 + j9)}$$

$= 7.863 \text{ A} \angle -17.55°$

$\mathbf{V}_{an} = \mathbf{I}_a\mathbf{Z}_{an} = (7.863 \text{ A} \angle -17.55°)(12\ \Omega + j9\ \Omega)$

$\mathbf{V}_{an} = 118 \text{ A} \angle 19.3°$.

b. $\mathbf{V}_{ab} = \sqrt{3}\mathbf{V}_{an} \angle 30° = \sqrt{3}(118 \text{ V}) \angle (19.3° + 30°)$

$= 204 \text{ V} \angle 49.32°$

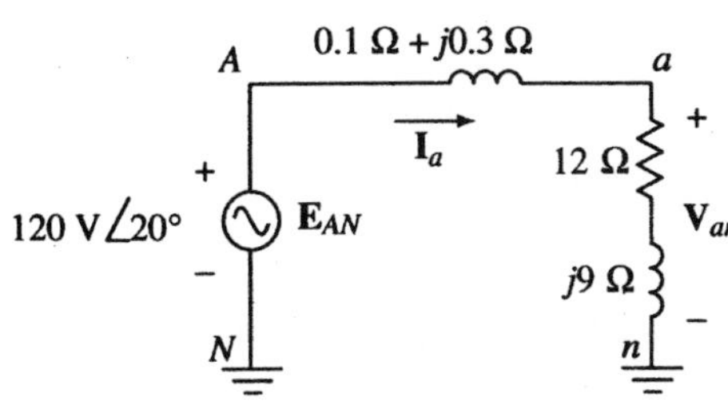

24. $\mathbf{E}_{AN} = 120 \text{ V} \angle 20°$ and $\mathbf{Z}_{an} = 8.33\ \Omega \angle -36.9°$

$$\mathbf{I}_a = \frac{\mathbf{E}_{AN}}{\mathbf{Z}_{an}} = \frac{120 \text{ V}\angle 20°}{8.33\angle -36.9°} = 14.4\angle 56.9°$$

$\therefore \mathbf{I}_b = 14.4 \text{ A} \angle -63.1°$ and $\mathbf{I}_c = 14.4 \text{ A} \angle 176.9°$

26. $$\mathbf{I}_{ab} = \frac{\mathbf{I}_a}{\sqrt{3}\angle -30°} = \frac{14.4 \text{ A}\angle 34.9°}{\sqrt{3}\angle -30°}$$

$= 8.31 \text{ A} \angle 64.9°$

$\therefore \mathbf{I}_{bc} = 8.31 \text{ A} \angle -55.1°$

$\mathbf{I}_{ca} = 8.31 \text{ A} \angle -175.1°$

28. a. Convert the Δ load to an equivalent Y.

$$\mathbf{Z}_Y' = \frac{\mathbf{Z}_\Delta}{3} = \frac{27\ \Omega + j36\ \Omega}{3} = 9\ \Omega + j12\ \Omega$$

b. $$\mathbf{I}_a = \frac{\mathbf{V}_{an}}{\mathbf{Z}_Y} = \frac{120 \text{ V}\angle 0°}{12\ \Omega + j9\ \Omega} = 8 \text{ A} \angle -36.87°$$

$$\mathbf{I}_a' = \frac{\mathbf{V}_{an}}{\mathbf{Z}_Y'} = \frac{120 \text{ V}\angle 0°}{9\ \Omega + j12\ \Omega} = 8 \text{ A} \angle -53.13°$$

$\mathbf{I}_A = \mathbf{I}_a + \mathbf{I}_a' = 8 \text{ A} \angle -36.87° + 8 \text{ A} \angle -53.13°$

$= 15.84 \angle -45°$

$\mathbf{E}_{AN} = \mathbf{I}_A\mathbf{Z}_{\text{line}} + \mathbf{V}_{an}$

$= (15.84 \text{ A} \angle -45°)(0.1\ \Omega + j0.1\ \Omega) + 120 \text{ V} \angle 0°$

$= 122 \text{ V} \angle 0°$

30. Convert the Δ to a Y. The single phase equivalent of the loads is shown below. Since both loads are identical, $\mathbf{I}_a = \mathbf{I}_a' = I_A/2$. For the Y load, phase currents are

$$\mathbf{I}_a = \frac{46.2 \text{ A}\angle -36.9°}{2} = 23.1 \text{ A} \angle -36.9° \text{ and}$$

$\mathbf{I}_b = 23.1 \text{ A} \angle -156.9°$ and $\mathbf{I}_c = 23.1 \text{ A} \angle 83.1°$.

For the Δ load, phase currents are

$$\mathbf{I}_{a'b'} = \frac{\mathbf{I}_a'}{\sqrt{3}\angle -30°} = \frac{23.1 \text{ A}\angle -36.9°}{\sqrt{3}\angle -30°}$$

$= 13.3 \text{ A} \angle -6.9°$

$\therefore \mathbf{I}_{b'c'} = 13.3 \text{ A} \angle -126.9°$ and

$\mathbf{I}_{c'a'} = 13.3 \text{ A} \angle 113.1°$.

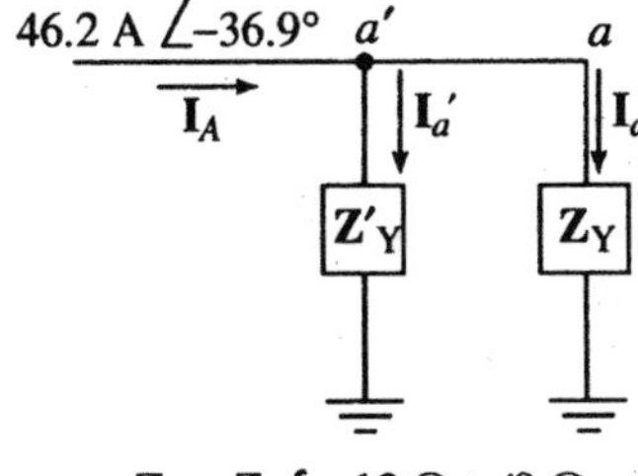

$\mathbf{Z}_Y = \mathbf{Z}_Y' = 12\ \Omega + j9\ \Omega$

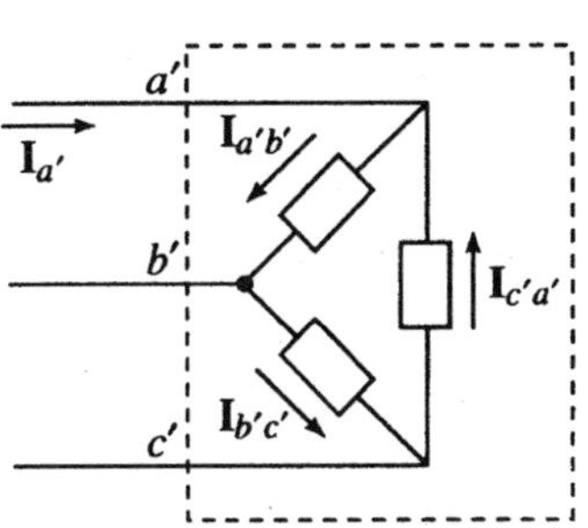

24.5 Power in a Balanced System

32. $$V_\phi = \frac{600 \text{ V}}{\sqrt{3}} = 346.4 \text{ V}$$

$$P_\phi = \frac{V_\phi^2}{R} = \frac{(346.4 \text{ V})^2}{40\ \Omega} = 3 \text{ kW} \therefore P_T = 9 \text{ kW}$$

$Q_\phi = 0$ VAR (since load is resistive)

$\therefore Q_T = 0$ VAR

$S_\phi = 3$ kVA; $S_T = 9$ kVA

34. a. $\mathbf{Z}_\phi = 12\ \Omega + j9\ \Omega = 15\ \Omega \angle 36.87°$

$$\mathbf{I}_\phi = \frac{\mathbf{V}_\phi}{\mathbf{Z}_\phi} = \frac{120 \text{ V}}{15\ \Omega} = 8 \text{ A}$$

$P_\phi = V_\phi I_\phi \cos\theta_\phi = (120\text{ V})(8\text{ A})\cos 36.87°$

$= 768\text{ W}$

$Q_\phi = V_\phi I_\phi \sin\theta_\phi = (120\text{ V})(8\text{ A})\sin 36.87°$

$= 576\text{ VAR}$

$S_\phi = V_\phi I_\phi = (120\text{ V})(8\text{ A}) = 960\text{ VA}$

b. $P_T = 3P_\phi = 2304\text{ W}$

$Q_T = 3Q_\phi = 1728\text{ VAR (ind.)}$

$S_T = 3S_\phi = 2880\text{ VA}$

36. a. $Z_\phi = 20\ \Omega - j15\ \Omega = 25\ \Omega \angle -36.87°$

$I_\phi = \dfrac{V_\phi}{Z_\phi} = \dfrac{208\text{ V}}{25\ \Omega} = 8.32\text{ A}$

$P_\phi = V_\phi I_\phi \cos\theta_\phi = (208\text{ V})(8.32\text{ A})\cos 36.87°$

$= 1384\text{ W}$

$Q_\phi = V_\phi I_\phi \sin\theta_\phi = (208\text{ V})(8.32\text{ A})\sin 36.87°$

$= 1038\text{ VAR}$

$S_\phi = V_\phi I_\phi = (208\text{ V})(8.32\text{ A}) = 1731\text{ VA}$

b. $P_T = 3P_\phi = 4152\text{ W}$

$Q_T = 3Q_\phi = 3114\text{ VAR}$

$S_T = 3S_\phi = 5193\text{ VA}$

38. $Z_\phi = 16 - j3 = 16.28 \angle -10.62°$

$I_\phi = \dfrac{V_\phi}{Z_\phi} = \dfrac{277\text{ V}}{16.28\ \Omega} = 17.0\text{ A}$

$P_T = 3I^2_\phi R_\phi = 3[(17.0\text{ A})2(16\ \Omega)] = 13.9\text{ k}\Omega$

$QT = 3I2_\phi X_\phi = 3[(17.0\text{ A})2(3\ \Omega)] = 2.6\text{ kVAR}$ (cap.)

$ST = 3V_\phi I_\phi = 3[(277\text{ V})(17.0\text{ A})] = 14.1\text{ kVA}$

$\text{Fp} = \cos 10.62° = 0.983$

40. $I = \dfrac{V_\phi}{Z_\phi} = \dfrac{120\text{ V}}{5\ \Omega} = 24\text{ A}$

a. $P_{T(\text{load})} = 3P_{\phi(\text{load})} = 3I^2R_\phi$

$= 3(24\text{ A})2(4\ \Omega) = 6912\text{ W}$

$Q_{T(\text{load})} = 3Q_{\phi(\text{load})} = 3I^2X_\phi$

$= 3(24\text{ A})^2(3\ \Omega) = 5184\text{ VAR (cap.)}$

$S_{T(\text{load})} = 3S_{\phi(\text{load})} = 3I^2Z_\phi = 3(24\text{ A})^2(5\ \Omega)$

$= 8640\text{ VA}$

b. For a balanced system, neutral current is zero. Therefore, total power is that supplied to the load plus the losses in the phase conductors.

$P_T = 3I^2R_{\text{line}} + 3P_{\phi(\text{load})}$

$= 3(24\text{ A})^2(0.2\ \Omega) + 6912\text{ W} = 7258\text{ W}$

$Q_T = 3I^2X_{\text{line}} - 3Q_{\phi(\text{load})}$

$= 3(24\text{ A})^2(0.2\ \Omega) - 5184\text{ VAR}$

$= -4838\text{ VAR} = 4838\text{ VAR (cap.)}$

$S_T = \sqrt{P_T^2 + Q_T^2} = 8723\text{ VA}$

42. a. $I_\phi = \dfrac{V_\phi}{Z_\phi} = \dfrac{120\text{ V}}{20\ \Omega} = 6\text{ A} \qquad \theta_\phi = 0°$

$P_{T_Y} = 3V_\phi I_\phi \cos\theta_\phi = 3(120\text{ V})(6\text{ A})\cos 0° = 2160\text{ W}$

$Q_{T_Y} = 0$ VAR (purely resistive) $\therefore S_{T_Y} = 2160\text{ VA}$

b. $I_\phi = \dfrac{V_\phi}{Z_\phi} = \dfrac{208\text{ V}}{30\ \Omega} = 6.93\text{ A}$

$P_{T_\Delta} = 3V_\phi I_\phi \cos\theta_\phi = 3(208\text{ V})(6.93\text{ A})\cos 10°$

$= 4259\text{ W}$

$Q_{T_\Delta} = 3(208\text{ V})(6.93\text{ A})\sin 10° = 751\text{ VAR (ind.)}$

$S_{T_\Delta} = 3(208\text{ V})(6.93\text{ A}) = 4324\text{ VA}$

c. $P_T = 2160 + 4259 = 6419\text{ W}$

$Q_T = 0 + 751 = 751\text{ VAR (ind.)}$

$S_T = \sqrt{P_T^2 + Q_T^2} = 6463\text{ VA}$

44. Motor:

$P_{\text{out}} = 100\text{ hp} = 74.6\text{ kW}$

$P_{\text{in}} = \dfrac{P_{\text{out}}}{\eta} = \dfrac{74.6}{0.8} = 93.25\text{ kW}$ (total 3 phase)

Single phase equivalent:

$P_m = P_{\text{in}}/3 = 93.25/3 = 31.08\text{ kW}$

$\theta_m = \cos^{-1}(0.85) = 31.79°$

$\therefore Q_m = P_m \tan\theta_m = 31.08 \tan 31.79° = 19.26\text{ kVAR}$

$Q_c = 45\text{ kVAR}/3 = 15\text{ kVAR}$

See diagram below.

$P_\phi = 31.08\text{ kW}$

$Q_\phi = 19.26\text{ kVAR} - 15\text{ kVAR} = 4.26\text{ kVAR}$

$\theta = \tan^{-1}\left(\dfrac{Q_T}{P_T}\right) = \tan^{-1}\left(\dfrac{4.26}{31.08}\right) = 7.80°$

$F_P = \cos 7.80° = 0.991$

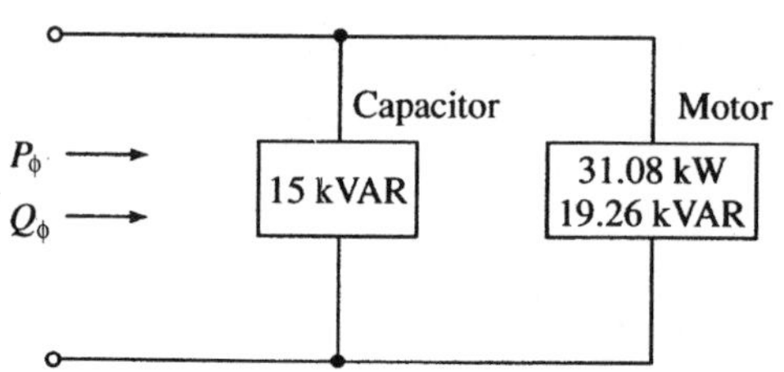

24.6 Measuring Power in Three-Phase Circuits

46. a. The wattmeter reads the power to Phase *an*. Thus,

$W = P_{an} = I_a^2 R_{an} = (4\text{ A})^2(40\ \Omega) = 640\text{ W}$

b. If the lead is balanced, $P_T = 3P_{an} = 3(640\text{ W})$

$= 1920\text{ W}$

48. Place the CC of W_1 in line *b* and the CC of W_2 in line *c*. Connect both voltage terminals to line *a*.

50. $\tan\theta_\phi = \sqrt{3}\left(\dfrac{P_h - P_\ell}{P_h - P_\ell}\right)$

$= \sqrt{3}\left(\dfrac{1000 + 400}{1000 - 400}\right)$

$= 4.0415$

$\theta_\phi = 76.1°$

$\therefore F_P = \cos 76.1° = 0.240$

$\dfrac{P_\ell}{P_h} = -0.4$ From Fig. 24-34, $F_P \approx .24$

52. a. $\mathbf{I}_{ab} = \dfrac{\mathbf{V}_{ab}}{\mathbf{Z}_{ab}} = \dfrac{208\text{ V}\angle 0°}{16 + j12} = 10.4\text{ A}\angle -36.87°$

$\mathbf{I}_a = \sqrt{3}\mathbf{I}_{ab}\angle -30° = 18.0\text{ A}\angle -66.87°$

$\therefore \mathbf{I}_b = 18.0\text{ A}\angle -186.87°$

b. $P_\phi = I_\phi^2 R_\phi = (10.4\text{ A})^2(16\ \Omega) = 1730.6\text{ W}$

$\therefore P_T = 3(1730.6) = 5192\text{ W}$

c. Wattmeter 1: $W_1 = V_{ac}I_a\cos\theta_1$ where θ_1 is the angle between $\mathbf{V}_{ac}$ and $\mathbf{I}_a$

The angle of $\mathbf{V}_{ca}$ is 120° ∴ the angle of $\mathbf{V}_{ac}$ is –60°. The angle of $\mathbf{I}_a$ is –66.87°. Therefore, $\theta_1 = 6.87°$

Thus, $W_1 = (208\text{ V})(18.0\text{ A})\cos 6.87° = 3717\text{ W}$

Wattmeter 2: $W_2 = V_{bc}I_b\cos\theta_2$ where θ_2 is the angle between $\mathbf{V}_{bc}$ and $\mathbf{I}_b$

The angle of $\mathbf{V}_{bc}$ is –120° and the angle of $\mathbf{I}_b$ is –186.87°. Thus, $\theta_2 = 66.87°$ and W_2

$= (208\text{ V})(18.0\text{ A})\cos 66.87° = 1472\text{ W}$

$W_1 + W_2 = 5189\text{ W}$ (Compare to 5192 W. Small difference is due to round-off and truncation errors.)

24.7 Unbalanced Systems

54. $R_{ab} = \dfrac{V_{ab}^2}{P_{ab}} = \dfrac{(240\text{ V})^2}{2400\text{ W}} = 24\ \Omega$

$\mathbf{Z}_{bc} = 50\ \Omega\angle 40° = 38.3\ \Omega + j32.1\ \Omega$

a. $\mathbf{I}_{ab} = \dfrac{\mathbf{V}_{ab}}{\mathbf{Z}_{ab}} = \dfrac{240\text{ V}\angle 0°}{24\ \Omega} = 10\text{ A}\angle 0°$

$\mathbf{I}_{bc} = \dfrac{\mathbf{V}_{bc}}{\mathbf{Z}_{bc}} = \dfrac{240\text{ V}\angle -120°}{50\ \Omega\angle 40°} = 4.8\text{ A}\angle -160°$

$\mathbf{I}_{ca} = \dfrac{\mathbf{V}_{ca}}{\mathbf{Z}_{ca}} = \dfrac{240\text{ V}\angle 120°}{50\ \Omega - j60\ \Omega} = 3.07\text{ A}\angle 170.2°$

$\mathbf{I}_a = \mathbf{I}_{ab} - \mathbf{I}_{ca} = 10\text{ A}\angle 0° - 3.07\text{ A}\angle 170.2°$

$= 13.0\text{ A}\angle -2.30°$

$\mathbf{I}_b = \mathbf{I}_{bc} - \mathbf{I}_{ab} = 4.8\angle -160° - 10\angle 0°$

$= 14.6\text{ A}\angle -173.5°$

$\mathbf{I}_c = \mathbf{I}_{ca} - \mathbf{I}_{bc} = 3.07\text{ A}\angle 170.2° - 4.8\angle -160°$

$= 2.62\text{ A}\angle 55.5°$

b. $P_{ab} = I_{ab}^2 R_{ab} = (10\text{ A})^2(24\ \Omega) = 2400\text{ W}$

$P_{bc} = I_{bc}^2 R_{bc} = (4.8\text{ A})^2(38.3\ \Omega) = 882\text{ W}$

$P_{ca} = I_{ca}^2 R_{ca} = (3.07\text{ A})^2(50\ \Omega) = 471\text{ W}$

$P_T = 2400\text{ W} + 882\text{ W} + 471\text{ W} = 3753\text{ W}$

56. Redraw the circuit as we did for Figure 24–36.

$(58 - j20)\mathbf{I}_1 - (40 - j20)\mathbf{I}_2 = 208\text{ V}\angle 30°$

$-(40 - j20)\mathbf{I}_1 + (70 + j20)\mathbf{I}_2 = 208\text{ V}\angle -90°$

$\mathbf{I}_1 = 1.943\text{ A}\angle -0.7372°$

$\mathbf{I}_2 = 3.566\text{ A}\angle -88.63°$

$\mathbf{I}_a = \mathbf{I}_1 = 1.94\text{ A}\angle -0.737°$

$\mathbf{I}_b = \mathbf{I}_2 - \mathbf{I}_1 = 4.0\text{ A}\angle -117.7°$

$\mathbf{I}_c = -\mathbf{I}_2 = 3.57\text{ A}\angle 91.4°$

24.9 Circuit Analysis Using Computers

Analytic solutions yield the following answers:

Problem 58: $\mathbf{I}_a = 23.13\text{ A}\angle -21.87°$

Problem 60: $\mathbf{I}_{ab} = 19.19\text{ A}\angle -36.87°$; $\mathbf{I}_a = 33.24\text{ A}\angle -66.87°$

MultiSIM

58. Build the circuit as shown. (When assigning angles for sources, remember that MultiSIM does not accept angles with a minus sign. In addition, for MultiSIM 2001 users, recall Note 2, page 525, Chapter 15. Thus, MultiSIM 2001 users, enter angles of 345°, 105°, and 225° respectively.) Set all meters for AC. Energize the circuit using the power ON/OFF switch. Compare to the analytic results.

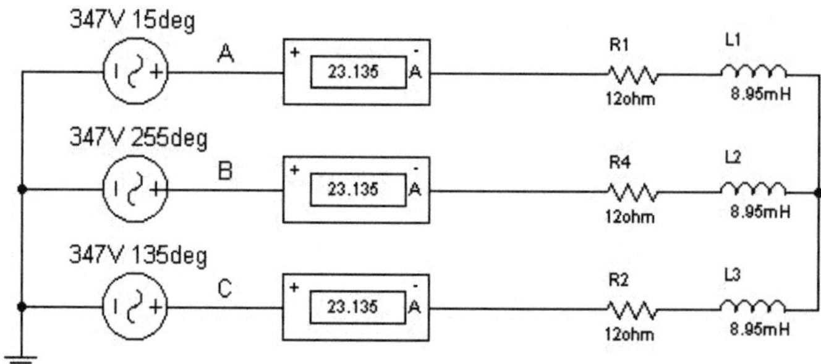

60. Same instructions as Problem 58.

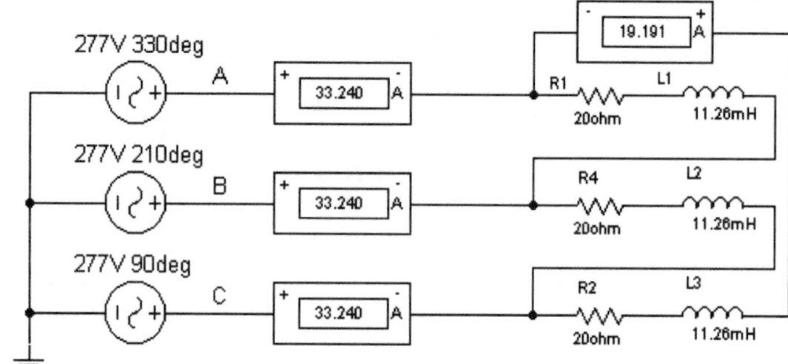

PSpice Solutions

58. Build the circuit as shown. Use source VAC and set source voltage angles to 15°, –105° and 135° respectively. Set all meters to AC, MAG and PHASE. Use AC Sweep with the start and end frequencies set to 212Hz. Following simulation, scroll the output. Compare to the analytic results above.

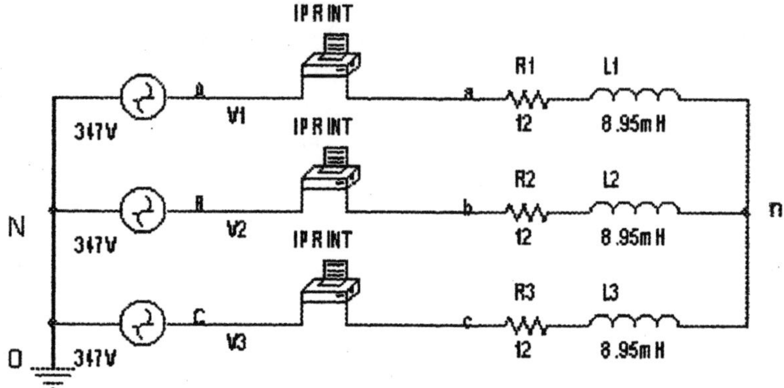

60. Same instructions as for PSpice Problem 58, except use voltage source angles as shown.

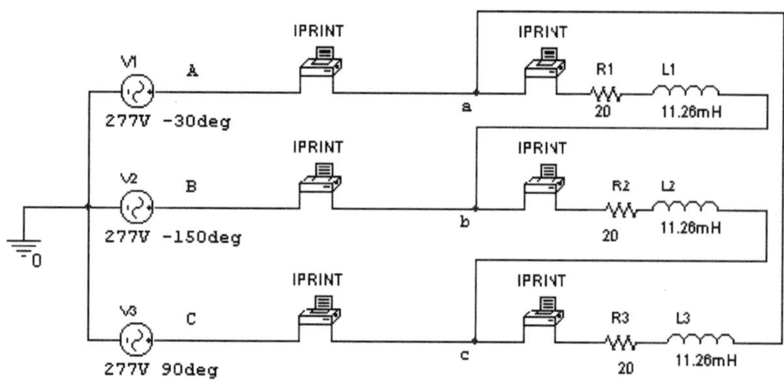

CHAPTER

25

Nonsinusoidal Waveforms

25.1 Composite Waveforms

2. a. $V_{avg} = V_{dc} = \dfrac{-10\text{ V} + (-50\text{ V})}{2} = -30\text{ V}$

$V_{ac} = \dfrac{-10\text{ V} - (-30\text{ V})}{\sqrt{2}} = 14.14\text{ V}$

$V_{rms} = \sqrt{(-30\text{ V})^2 + (14.14\text{ V})^2} = 33.2\text{ V}$

b. $P = \dfrac{(33.2\text{ V})^2}{250\ \Omega} = 4.40\text{ W}$

4. a. $V_{avg} = V_{dc} = \dfrac{+20\text{ V} + (-40\text{ V})}{2} = -10\text{ V}$

$V_{ac} = \dfrac{+20 - (-10\text{ V})}{\sqrt{2}} = 21.21\text{ V}$

$V_{rms} = \sqrt{(-10\text{ V})^2 + (21.21\text{ V})^2} = 23.5\text{ V}$

b. $P = \dfrac{(23.5\text{ V})^2}{10\text{ k}\Omega} = 55.0\text{ mW}$

25.2 Fourier Series

6. $v(t) = 4t \qquad -1\text{ s} < t < 1\text{ s}$

$$a_0 = \frac{1}{2}\int_{t=-1}^{1} 4t\,dt$$

$$= \frac{1}{2}\left(\frac{4t^2}{2}\right)\Big|_{-1}^{1} = 1 - 1 = 0$$

$$a_n = \frac{2}{2}\int_{t=-1}^{1}(4t)\cos(n\omega t)dt$$

$$\omega = \frac{2\pi}{T} = \pi$$

$$= \int_{t=-1}^{1}(4t)\cos(n\pi t)dt$$

$$= 4\left[\frac{\cos(n\omega t)}{n^2\pi^2} + \frac{t\sin(n\omega t)}{n\pi}\right]_{-1}^{1}$$

$$= 4\left[\left(\frac{\cos(n\pi)}{n^2\pi^2} + \frac{(1)\sin(n\pi)}{\pi}\right) - \left(\frac{\cos(-n\pi)}{n^2\pi^2} - \frac{\sin(-n\pi)}{n\pi}\right)\right] = 0$$

$$b_n = \frac{2}{2}\int_{t=-1}^{1}(4t)\sin(n\omega t)dt$$

$$\omega = \frac{2\pi}{T} = \pi$$

$$= 4\int_{t=-1}^{1} t\sin(n\pi t)dt$$

$$= 4\left[\frac{\sin(n\pi t)}{n^2\pi^2} - \frac{t\cos(n\pi t)}{n\pi}\right]_{-1}^{1}$$

$$= 4\left[\left(\frac{\sin(n\pi)}{n^2\pi^2} - \frac{(1)\cos(n\pi)}{n\pi}\right) - \left(\frac{\sin(-n\pi)}{n^2\pi^2} + \frac{\cos(-n\pi)}{n\pi}\right)\right]$$

$$= \frac{4}{n\pi}[-\cos(n\pi) - \cos(-n\pi)]$$

for

$n = 1 \qquad b_1 = \dfrac{4}{(1)(\pi)}(+2) = \dfrac{8}{\pi}$

$n = 2 \qquad b_2 = \dfrac{4}{(2)(\pi)}(-2) = \dfrac{-8}{2\pi}$

$n = 3 \qquad b_3 = \dfrac{4}{(3)(\pi)}(+2) = \dfrac{8}{3\pi}$

$$v(t) = \frac{8}{\pi}\sin\pi t - \frac{8}{2\pi}\sin 2\pi t + \frac{8}{3\pi}\sin 3\pi t - \ldots$$

25.3 Series of Common Waveforms

8. $\omega = \dfrac{2\pi}{5\ \mu s} = 4 \times 10^5\ \pi$ rad/s

From Figure 25–17

$$v(t) = \frac{250\text{ mV}}{2} - \frac{250\text{ mV}}{\pi}\left[\frac{\sin\omega t}{1} + \frac{\sin 2\omega t}{2} + \frac{\sin 3\omega t}{3} + \ldots\right]$$

$$v(t) = 0.125 - \frac{250}{\pi}\sin\omega t - \frac{250}{2\pi}\sin 2\omega t - \ldots$$

10. $T = 20$ ms $\quad \omega = \dfrac{2\pi}{20\text{ ms}} = 100\pi$ rad/s

From Figure 25–18

$$v(t) = \frac{2(10\text{ V})}{\pi} - \frac{4(10\text{ V})}{\pi}\left[\frac{\cos 2\omega t}{1 \cdot 3} + \frac{\cos 4\omega t}{3 \cdot 5} + \frac{\cos 6\omega t}{5 \cdot 7} + \ldots\right]$$

$$v(t) = 6.366 - 4.244\cos 2\omega t - 0.849\cos 4\omega t$$
$$-0.364\cos 6\omega t - 0.202\cos 8\omega t - \ldots$$

12. $T = 1.2\text{ s} - 0.2\text{ s} = 1.0\text{ s}$

$$\omega = \frac{2\pi}{1\text{ s}} = 2\pi\text{ rad/s}$$

$$\theta = -\left(\frac{0.2\text{ s}}{1.0\text{ s}}\right)(360^\circ) = -72^\circ$$

Refer to Figure 25–15

$$v(t) = \frac{30}{2} - \frac{4(30)}{\pi^2}\left[\frac{\cos(\omega t + \theta)}{(1)^2} + \frac{\cos[3(\omega t + \theta)]}{(3)^2} + \frac{\cos[5(\omega t + \theta)]}{(5)^2} + \ldots\right]$$

$$v(t) = 15 - 12.159\cos(2\pi t - 72^\circ) - 1.351\cos(6\pi t - 216^\circ)$$
$$- 0.486\cos(10\pi t - 360^\circ) - 0.248\cos(14\pi t - 504^\circ)$$

14. a.

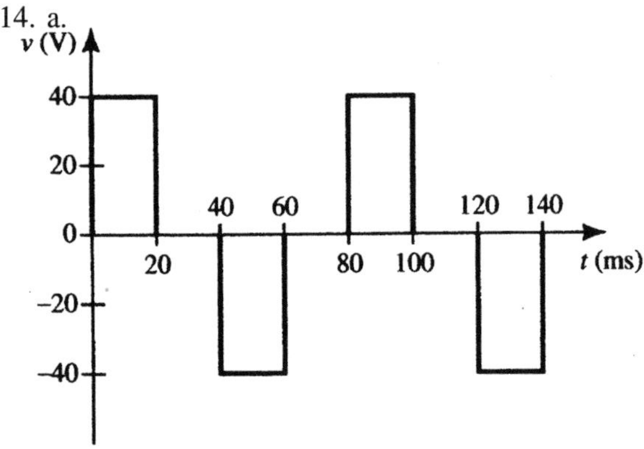

b. $T = 80$ ms $\qquad \omega = 2\dfrac{\pi}{80}$ ms $= 25\pi$ rad/s

$$\theta = +\left(\frac{20\text{ ms}}{80\text{ ms}}\right)(360^\circ) = 90^\circ$$

$$v_1(t) = \frac{4(20)}{\pi}\left[\frac{\sin(\omega t + \theta)}{1} + \frac{\sin[3(\omega t + \theta)]}{3} + \frac{\sin[5(\omega t + \theta)]}{5} + \ldots\right]$$

$$= \frac{80}{\pi}\left[\frac{\sin(\omega t + 90^\circ)}{1} + \frac{\sin(3\omega t + 270^\circ)}{3} + \frac{\sin(5\omega t + 450^\circ)}{5} + \ldots\right]$$

$$= \frac{80}{\pi}\left[\frac{\sin(\omega t + 90^\circ)}{1} + \frac{\sin(3\omega t - 90^\circ)}{3} + \frac{\sin(5\omega t + 90^\circ)}{5} + \ldots\right]$$

$$v_2(t) = \frac{80}{\pi}\left[\frac{\sin\omega t}{1} + \frac{\sin(3\omega t)}{3} + \frac{\sin(5\omega t)}{5} + \ldots\right]$$

Note:

$\sin(\omega t + 90^\circ) = \cos\omega t$
$\sin(\omega t - 90^\circ) = -\cos\omega t$

and

$A\sin\omega t + A\cos\omega t = A\sqrt{2}\sin(\omega t + 45^\circ)$
$A\sin\omega t - A\cos\omega t = A\sqrt{2}\sin(\omega t - 45^\circ)$

$$\begin{aligned} v &= v_1(t) + v_2(t) \\ &= 36.01 \sin(25\pi t + 45°) + 12.00 \sin(75\pi t - 45°) \\ &\quad + 7.20 \sin(125\pi t + 45°) + 5.14 \sin(175\pi t - 45°) \end{aligned}$$

16\. a.

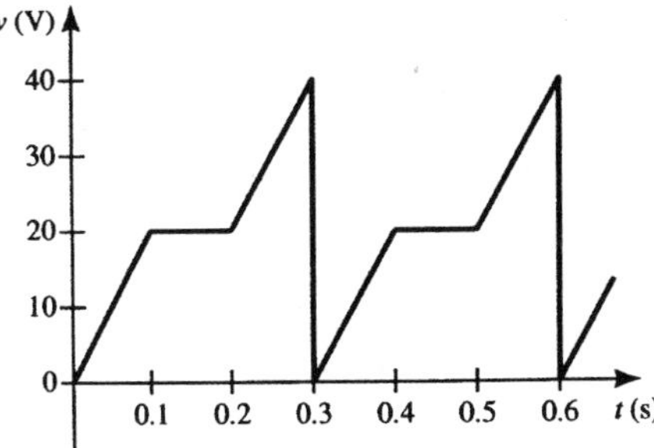

b.

$$V_{dc} = 10\frac{\text{V}}{2} + 30\frac{\text{V}}{2} = 20 \text{ V}$$

c. From Figure 25–15:

$$v_1(t) = \frac{10}{2} - \frac{40}{\pi^2}\left[\frac{\cos\omega_1 t}{1^2} + \frac{\cos 3\omega_1 t}{3^2} + \frac{\cos 5\omega_1 t}{5^2} + \ldots\right]$$

where $T_1 = 0.2$ s $\quad \omega_2 = 10\pi$ rad/s

From Figure 25–17

$$v_2(t) = \frac{30}{2} - \frac{30}{\pi}\left[\frac{\sin\omega_2 t}{1} + \frac{\sin 2\omega_2 t}{2} + \frac{\sin 3\omega_2 t}{3} + \ldots\right]$$

where $T_2 = 0.3$ s $\quad \omega_2 = 6.\overline{6}\pi$ rad/s

d.

$$\begin{aligned} v_1(t) &= 5 - 4.053 \cos 10\pi t - 0.450 \cos 30\pi t \\ &\quad - 0.162 \cos 50\pi t - 0.083 \cos 70\pi t\ldots \\ v_2(t) &= 15 - 9.549 \sin 6.\overline{6}\pi t - 4.775 \sin 13.\overline{3}\pi t \\ &\quad - 3.183 \sin 20\pi t - 2.387 \sin 26.6\pi t \\ v = v_1(t) + v_2(t) &= 20 - 9.549 \sin 6.\overline{6}\pi t - 4.053 \cos 10\pi t \\ &\quad - 4.775 \sin 13.\overline{3}\pi t - 3.183 \sin 20\pi t \\ &\quad - 2.387 \sin 26.\overline{3}\pi t - 0.450 \cos 30\pi t \end{aligned}$$

18\. $v_{dc} = 2$ V

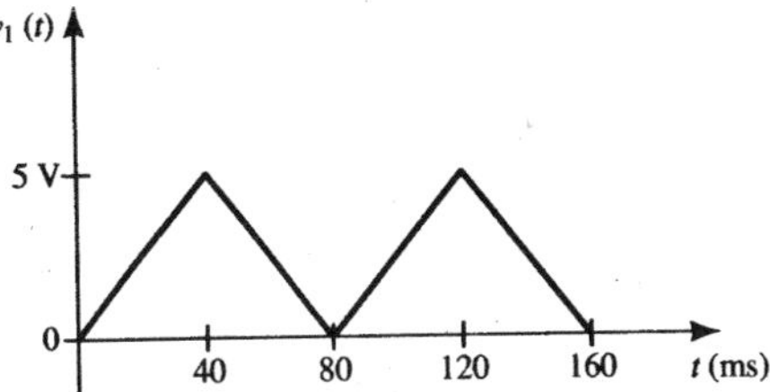

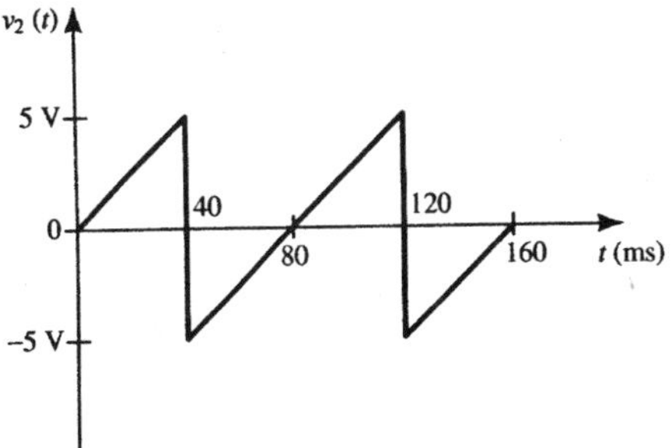

From Figure 25–15:

$T = 80$ ms $\quad \omega = \dfrac{2\pi}{80 \text{ ms}} = 25\pi$ rad/s

$$v_1(t) = \frac{5}{2} - \frac{20}{\pi^2}\cos 25\pi t - \frac{20}{3^2\pi^2}\cos 75\pi t - \ldots$$

From Figure 25–16:

$T = 80$ ms $\quad \omega = \dfrac{2\pi}{80 \text{ ms}} = 25\pi$ rad/s

$$v_2(t) = -\frac{10}{\pi}\sin 25\pi t + \frac{10}{2\pi}\sin 50\pi t - \frac{10}{3\pi}\sin 75\pi t + \ldots$$

$$\begin{aligned} v(t) &= v_{dc} + v_1(t) + v_2(t) \\ v(t) &= 4.5 + 3.773\sin(25\pi t - 147.52°) \\ &\quad + 1.592 \sin(50\pi t) \\ &\quad + 1.085 \sin(75\pi t - 168.02°) \\ &\quad + 0.796 \sin(100\pi t) \end{aligned}$$

25.4 Frequency Spectrum

20\. $V_{dc} = 125$ mV

$$V_1 = \frac{250}{\pi} \text{ mVp} \equiv 56.3 \text{ mV}_{\text{rms}}$$

$$V_2 = \frac{250}{2\pi} \text{ mVp} \equiv 28.1 \text{ mV}_{\text{rms}}$$

$$V_3 = \frac{250}{3\pi} \text{ mVp} \equiv 18.8 \text{ mV}_{\text{rms}}$$

$$V_4 = \frac{250}{4\pi} \text{ mVp} \equiv 14.1 \text{ mV}_{\text{rms}}$$

$$\begin{aligned} V_{\text{rms}} &= \sqrt{(125 \text{ mV})^2 + (56.3 \text{ mV})^2 + (28.1 \text{ mV})^2 + (18.8 \text{ mV})^2 + (14.1 \text{ mV})^2} \\ &= 141.9\ mV_{\text{rms}} \end{aligned}$$

$$P = \frac{(141.9 \text{ mV})^2}{50\ \Omega} = 402.7\ \mu\text{W}$$

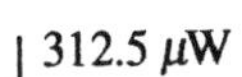

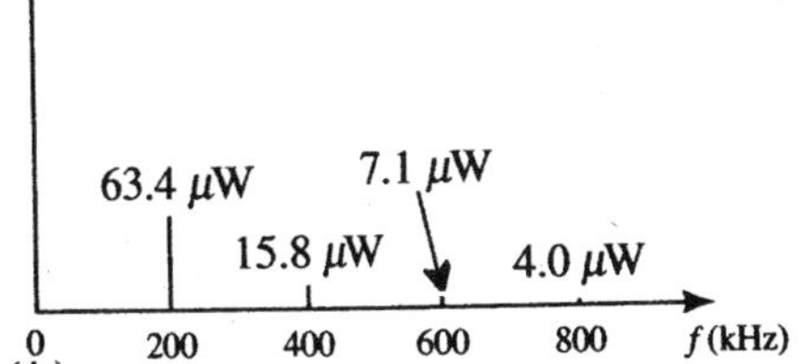

22.

$$V_0 = \frac{20}{\pi} = 6.366V$$

$$V_1 = \frac{40}{\pi(1)(3)} = 4.244\ V_p \equiv 3.001\ V_{rms}$$

$$V_2 = \frac{40}{\pi(3)(5)} = 0.849\ V_p \equiv\ 0.600\ V_{rms}$$

$$V_3 = \frac{40}{\pi(5)(7)} = 0.364\ V_p \equiv\ 0.257\ V_{rms}$$

$$V_4 = \frac{40}{\pi(7)(9)} = 0.202\ V_p \equiv 0.143\ V_{rms}$$

$$P_0 = \frac{(6.366\ V)^2}{50\ \Omega} = 0.811\ W(29.1\ dBm)$$

$$P_1 = \frac{(3.001\ V)^2}{50\ \Omega} = 0.180\ W(22.6\ dBm)$$

$$P_2 = \frac{(0.600\ V)^2}{50\ \Omega} = 72\ mW(18.6\ dBm)$$

$$P_3 = \frac{(0.257\ V)^2}{50\ \Omega} = 1.32\ mW(1.2\ dBm)$$

$$P_4 = \frac{(0.143\ V)^2}{50\ \Omega} = 0.409\ mW(-3.9\ dBm)$$

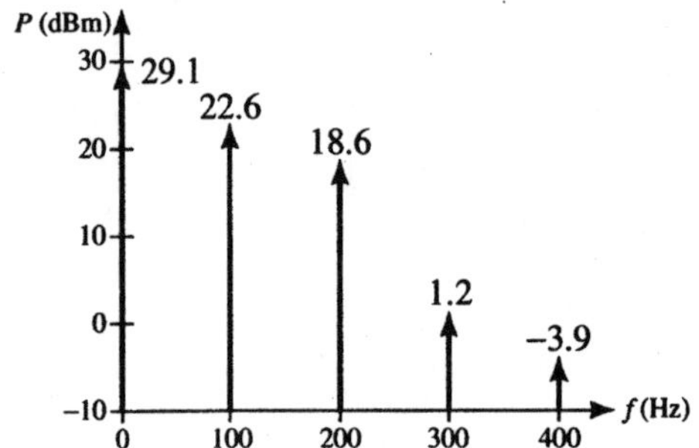

25.5 Circuit Response to a Nonsinusoidal Waveform

24. $T = 1.0$ ms $\quad f = 1$ kHz

$\omega = 2000\pi$ rad/s

From Figure 25–7:

$$v_1 = 0.5 + \frac{4}{\pi}\sin\omega t + \frac{4}{3\pi}\sin 3\omega t + \frac{4}{5\pi}\sin 5\omega t + \ldots$$

a. $V_0(dc) = 0$ V

b. $V_1 = \left(\frac{4}{\pi}\right)10^{-14.5/20} = 0.240\ V_p$

$\theta_1 = +78^\circ$

$V_3 = \left(\frac{4}{3\pi}\right)10^{-6/20} = 0.213\ V_p$

$\theta_3 = +61^\circ$

$V_5 = \left(\frac{4}{5\pi}\right)10^{-3/20} = 0.180\ V_p$

$\theta_5 = +45^\circ$

$V_7 = \left(\frac{4}{7\pi}\right)10^{-1.5/20} = 0.153\ V_p$

$\theta_7 = +36^\circ$

25.6 Circuit Analysis Using Computers

26.

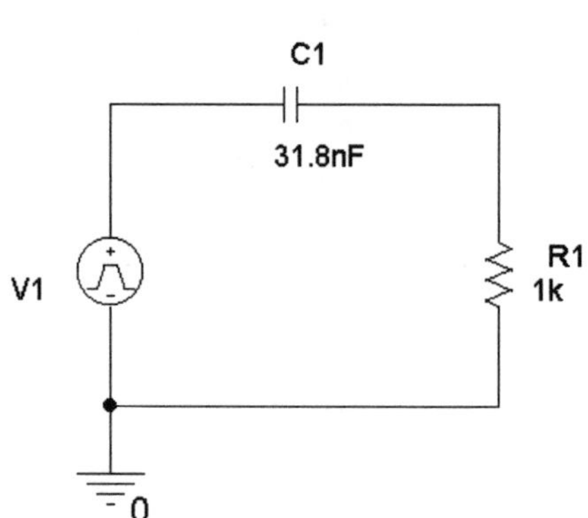

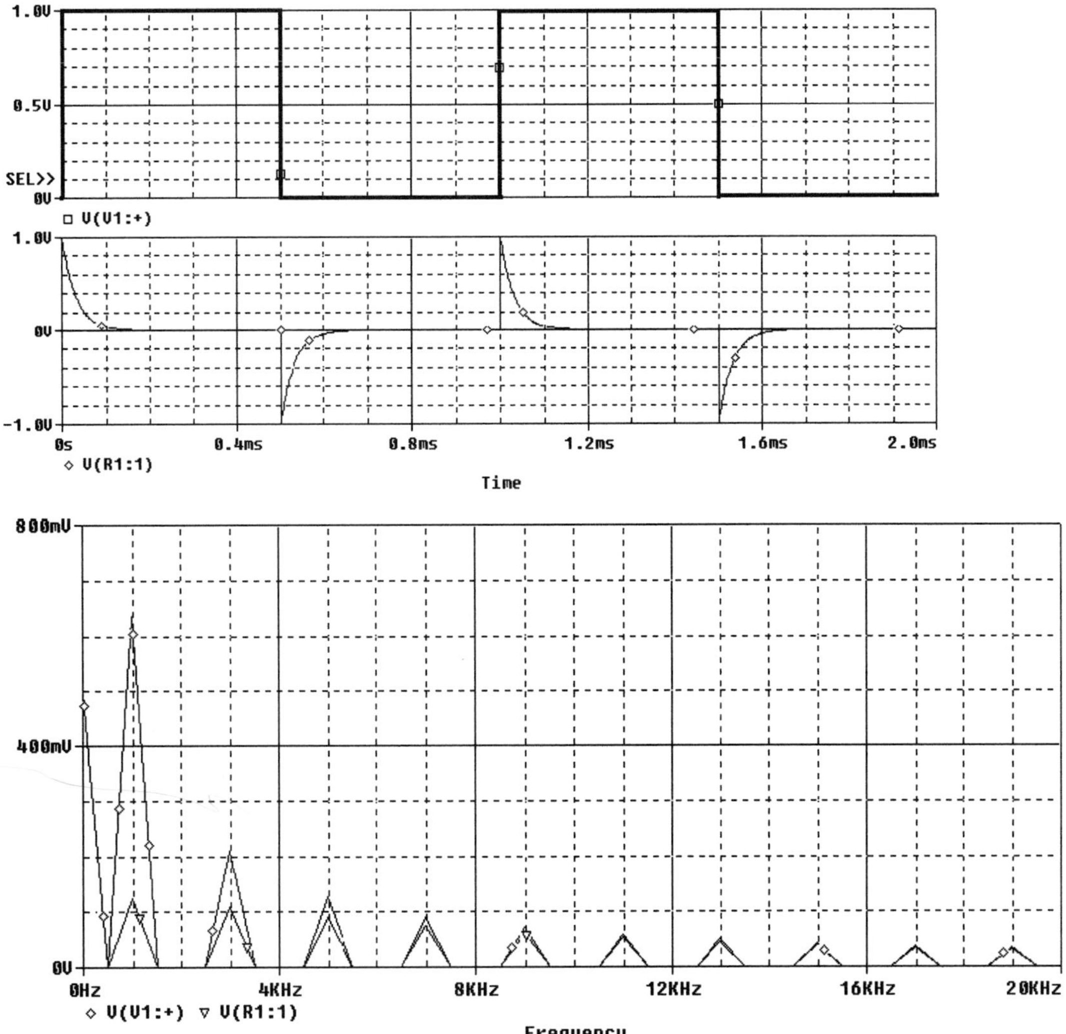
1.0V
0.5V
SEL>>
0V
□ V(V1:+)
1.0V
0V
-1.0V
0s
0.4ms
0.8ms
1.2ms
1.6ms
2.0ms
◇ V(R1:1)
Time
800mV
400mV
0V
0Hz
4KHz
8KHz
12KHz
16KHz
20KHz
◇ V(V1:+) ▽ V(R1:1)
Frequency

Answers to Selected Even-Numbered Questions,

Chapters 24–31

CIRCUIT ANALYSIS WITH DEVICES: THEORY AND PRACTICE

Chapter

24

Introduction to Semiconductors

24.1 Semiconductor Basics

2. The electron in shell N, since electrons in outer orbits have greater energy than those in inner orbits.

4. $$W = 1.762 \times 10^{-19}\ \text{J} \times \frac{1\ \text{eV}}{1.602 \times 10^{-19}\ \text{J}} = 1.1\ \text{eV}$$

6.

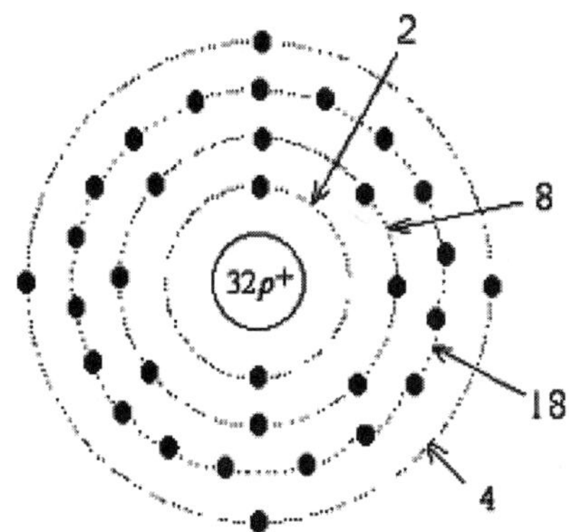

24.2 Conduction in Semiconductors

8. Copper has on the order of 10^{23} free electrons/cm^3 while germanium has on the order of 10^{12}. Thus, copper has on the order of 10^{11} as many free electrons per unit volume and consequently is a much better conductor. Summary: Copper has on the order of 10^{11} times the number that germanium has and 10^{13} times the number that silicon has.

10. Since valence orbits for germanium are larger than those for silicon, valence electrons for germanium have higher energy, and it takes less additional energy to cause them to escape and become free electrons. Thus, at a given temperature, germanium will have more free electrons than silicon and hence, better conductivity.

24.3 Doping

12. Intrinsic means pure, while extrinsic means doped with an appropriate impurity.

14. Vastly increases the conductivity.

16. Holes

18. *p*-type

24.4 The p-n Junction

20. You must maintain a continuous crystalline structure at the junction. If you have two pieces butted together, the continuity of the crystalline structure is broken.

22. Diode

24. Germanium because of the 0.3 V. The *p*-side is on the right.

24.5 The Biased p-n Junction

26. Reverse; small

28. Minority

30. Same except $V_D \approx 0.3$ V

Chapter

25

Diode Theory and Application

25.1 Diode Models

2.

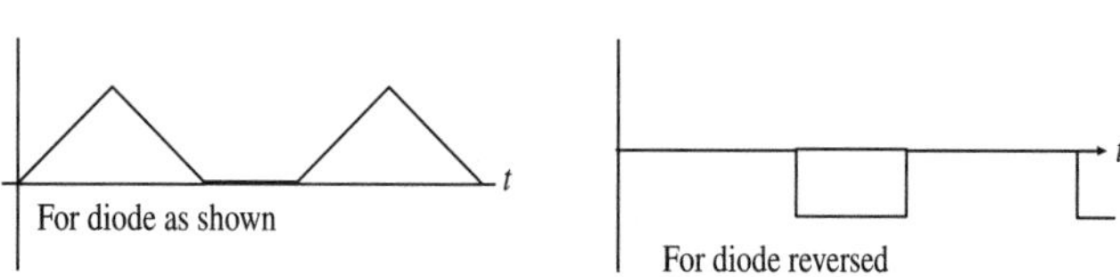

4.

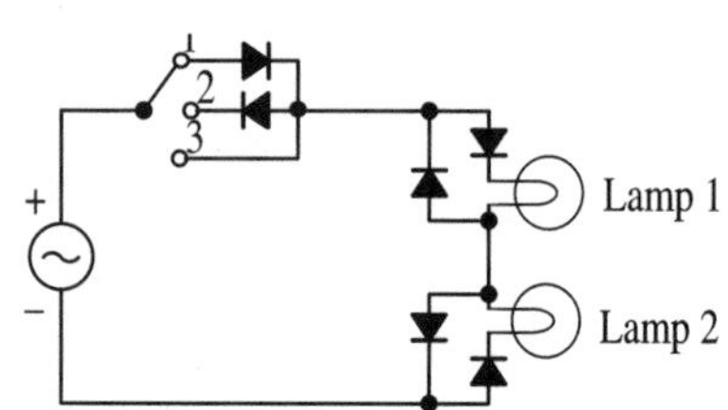

6. $R_T = 2.5 \text{ k}\Omega + 6 \text{ k}\Omega \parallel 3 \text{ k}\Omega = 4.5 \text{ k}\Omega$. Thus,

$$I_D = \frac{E - V_D - V_D}{R_T} = \frac{18 \text{ V} - 0.7 \text{ V} - 0.7 \text{ V}}{4.5 \text{ k}\Omega} = 3.69 \text{ mA}$$

8. Using the Thévenin equivalent values from Problem 7 yields

a. $I_D = \dfrac{E_{Th} - V_D}{R_T} = \dfrac{30 \text{ V} - 0.3 \text{ V}}{120 \ \Omega} = 0.248 \text{ A}$

b. $I_D = \dfrac{28 \text{ V} - 0.3 \text{ V} - 10 \text{ V}}{900 \ \Omega} = 19.7 \text{ mA}$

25.2 to 25.4 Diode Characteristics, Data Sheets, etc.

10. At $I_D = 4$ mA, $V_D = 0.76$ V. Thus, $E = (4 \text{ mA})(1.8 \text{ k}\Omega) + 0.76 \text{ V} = 7.96 \text{ V}$

12. 20 % of 400 V is 80 V. Thus, the peak voltage you can apply is $V_m = 320$ V i.e., 0.707(320 V) = 226 V rms.

14. From the curve of Figure 25-13, we find $T \approx 108°\text{C}$.

16. Working backward as indicated, we find 105 nA at 25°C.

420 nA at 45°C
210 nA at 35°C
105 nA at 25°C

25.5 The Zener Diode

18. For the 1N4744A (Figure 25-19), $I_{ZK} = 0.25$ mA and $I_{ZM} = 61$ mA. This is the range of I_Z over which it regulates. Its maximum power rating at 40°C is 1 W. Above 50°C, derate by 6.67 mW/°C. Thus, at 60°C, $P_{derated} = 1 \text{ W} - (6.67 \text{ mW/°C})(60°\text{C} - 50°\text{C}) = 933 \text{ mW}$.

20. Using the procedure that we used in Problem 19, we find $E_{Th} = 22.86$ V and $R_{Th} = 114.29 \ \Omega$. Reinserting the zener and applying Ohm's law yields $I_Z = \dfrac{22.86 \text{ V} - 18 \text{ V}}{114.29 \ \Omega} = 42.5$ mA. Thus, $P_D = V_Z I_Z = (18 \text{ V})(42.5 \text{ mA}) = 765 \text{ mW}$.

22. The circuit is shown below. $I_R = \dfrac{E - V_Z}{R_1} = \dfrac{20 \text{ V} - 12 \text{ V}}{91 \ \Omega} = 87.9$ mA and $I_L = I_R - I_z$. From the data sheet, knee current is $I_Z = I_{ZK} = 0.25$ mA. Thus, $I_L = 87.91 \text{ mA} - 0.25 \text{ mA} = 87.66$ mA and $R_L = \dfrac{V_L}{I_L} = \dfrac{12 \text{ V}}{87.66 \text{ mA}} = 137 \ \Omega$. At the other extreme, $I_Z = I_{ZM} = 76$ mA, yielding $I_L = 87.91 \text{ mA} - 76 \text{ mA} = 11.91$ mA and $R_L = 1008 \ \Omega$. Thus, R_L ranges from 137 Ω to 1008 Ω.

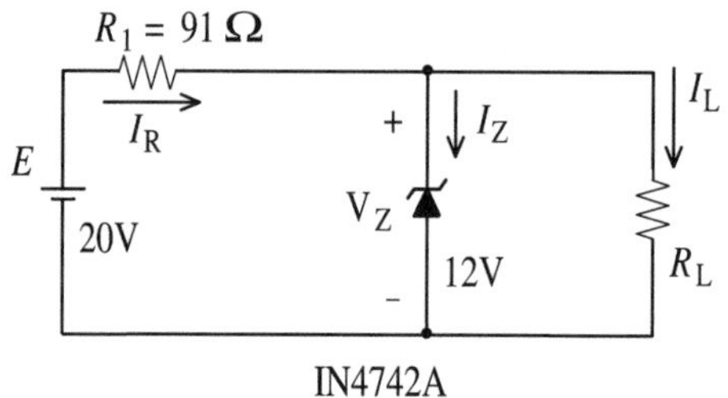

24. $I_{L_{min}} = \frac{10\text{ V}}{800\ \Omega} = 12.5$ mA and $I_{L_{max}} = \frac{10\text{ V}}{150\ \Omega} = 66.7$ mA. As noted in Problem 23, min E corresponds to min I_Z and max I_L. (This case is shown below). KVL yields E_{min} = (0.25 mA + 66.7 mA)(120 Ω) + 10 V = 18.0 V. Max voltage corresponds to max I_Z and min I_L. Thus, E_{max} = (91 mA + 12.5 mA)(120 Ω) + 10 V = 22.4 V.

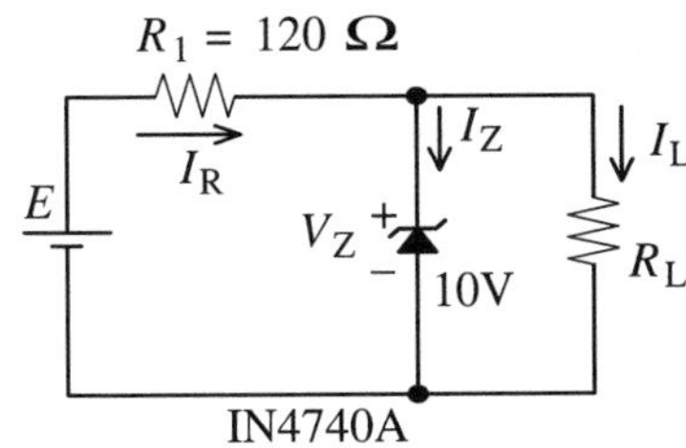

26. $Z_Z = \frac{\Delta V}{\Delta I} = \frac{13.4\text{ V} - 12.8\text{ V}}{80\text{ mA} - 0.2\text{ mA}} = 7.52\ \Omega$. Reworking Equation 25-4 yields $V_{Z_2} = V_{Z_1} + Z_Z \times \Delta I_Z$ = 13.4 V + (7.52 Ω)(22 mA – 80 mA) = 13.0 V. Alternatively, V_{Z_2} = 12.8 V + (7.52 Ω)(22 mA – 0.2 mA) = 13.0 V.

28. From Figure 25-23(c), $I_Z = \frac{E_{Th} - V_Z}{R_{Th}}$. Note from this that you need to know V_Z in order to compute I_Z. However (unless you assume the ideal model), you can't find V_Z until you know I_Z (recall Example 25-3). Thus, neither V_Z nor I_Z can be found without knowing the other one first. To get around this problem, use trial and error. Assuming that V_Z = 12 V at I_{ZT}, we know that to a good first approximation, $V_Z \approx$ 12 V everywhere in the zener region. Thus, $I_Z \approx$ (16 V – 12 V)/80 Ω = 50 mA. Using the procedure of Example 25-3, we can get a better estimate of V_Z. Thus, $V_Z \approx$ 12 V + (9 Ω)(50 mA – 21 mA) = 12.26 V. Now recompute the current as $I_Z \approx$ (16 V – 12.26 V)/80 Ω = 46.75 mA. Using this, we find $V_Z \approx$ 12 V + (9 Ω)(46.75 mA – 21 mA) = 12.23 V. Repeating, a third trial yields 12.24 V. Since V_Z barely changes, we can assume that this is the actual value. Thus, V_L = 12.23 V and I_L = 12.23 V/240 Ω = 51.0 mA. Conclusion: Since the "ideal zener" solution and the "exact" solution differ only by a few percent and since other uncertainties cause even greater errors, it doesn't make much sense to go to all this trouble. Thus, in practice, we generally use the ideal model.

25.7 Half-Wave and Full-Wave Rectifier Circuits

30. For the circuit below, let e be at its maximum value E_m. KVL around the source/D2/D4 loop (assuming ideal diodes) yields E_m – 0 V – V_D = 0. Thus, $V_D = E_m$.

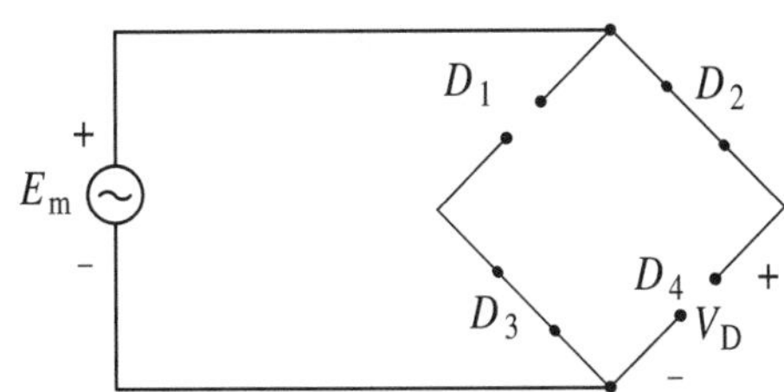

25.8 Power Supply Filtering

32. $V_{dc} = V_m - \frac{V_{r_{pp}}}{2}$. Substituting $V_{r_{pp}} = \frac{2 V_m}{1 + \frac{2 R_L C}{T}}$ yields

$$V_{dc} = V_m - \frac{1}{2}\left(\frac{2 V_m}{1 + \frac{2 R_L C}{T}}\right) = V_m - \frac{V_m}{1 + \frac{2 R_L C}{T}}$$

$$= V_m - \frac{V_m T}{T + 2 R_L C}$$

$$= V_m\left(1 - \frac{T}{T + 2 R_L C}\right) = V_m\left(\frac{2 R_L C}{T + 2 R_L C}\right)$$

$$= \frac{V_m}{1 + \frac{T}{2 R_L C}}$$

34. $$V_{r_{pp}} = \frac{2 V_m}{1 + \frac{2 R_L C}{T}} = \frac{2(20\text{ V})}{1 \frac{2(650\ \Omega)(390\ \mu\text{F})}{16.7\text{ ms}}} = 1.27\text{ V}$$

36. $V_{r_{pp}} = \frac{2 V_m}{1 + \frac{2 R_L C}{T}}$. Thus, $0.6\text{ V} = \frac{2(20\text{ V})}{1 + \frac{2(1000\ \Omega)C}{8.33\text{ ms}}}$

Solving yields C = 274 μF.

Use the next higher standard value.

38. $$r = \frac{T}{2\sqrt{3}\, R_L C} = \frac{8.33\text{ ms}}{2\sqrt{3}(300\ \Omega)(470\ \mu\text{F})} = 0.0171 = 1.71\%$$

40. $V_{r_{pp}} = \frac{V_{dc} T}{R_L C}$. Thus,

$$V_{dc} = \frac{V_{r_{pp}} R_L C}{T} = \frac{(1.22\text{ V})(600\ \Omega)(220\ \mu\text{F})}{8.33\text{ ms}} = 19.3\text{ V}$$

$$V_{r(rms)} = \frac{V_{r_{pp}}}{2\sqrt{3}} = \frac{1.22\text{ V}}{2\sqrt{3}} = 0.352\text{ V}$$

$$r = \frac{\text{rms ripple voltage}}{\text{dc voltage}} = \frac{0.352\text{ V}}{19.3\text{ V}} = 0.0182 = 1.82\%$$

42. The filter portion of the circuit is shown in (a), and the waveform in (b). Capacitor voltage is $v_C(t) = V_m e^{-t/\tau}$ where V_m = 32.54 V and $\tau = R_L C$ = (430 Ω)(330 μF) = 141.9 ms. Discharge time looks

to be about 90% of 8.33 ms ≈ 7.5 ms. Thus, as a first estimate, $v_{C(min)} \approx 32.54\,e^{-7.5\text{ ms}/141.9\text{ ms}} =$ 30.86 V. Now consider the waveform of (c). Here, $v = V_m \sin x$. Substituting values yields 30.86 = 32.54 sin x_1. Thus, x_1 = 71.51°. But 180° corresponds to 8.33 ms. Thus, 71.51° corresponds to 3.31 ms, and the estimated discharge time T_2 shown in (c) is 8.33 ms/2 + 3.31 ms = 7.48 ms. This means that our guess of 7.5 ms is very good and we could probably stop here. However, let's do one more iteration. Using 7.48 ms as our next guess yields $v_{C(min)} \approx 32.54\,e^{-7.48\text{ ms}/141.9\text{ ms}}$ = 30.87 V. (Since there is no significant change between trials, we can stop.) Thus, $V_{r_{pp}}$ = 32.54 V – 30.87 V = 1.67 V and $V_{dc} = V_m - \frac{V_{r_{p\text{-}p}}}{2} = 32.54\text{ V} - \frac{1.67\text{ V}}{2} = 31.7\text{ V}$. (As you can see, these values agree quite well with the approximate solutions, thus confirming that the approximate analyses are quite good.)

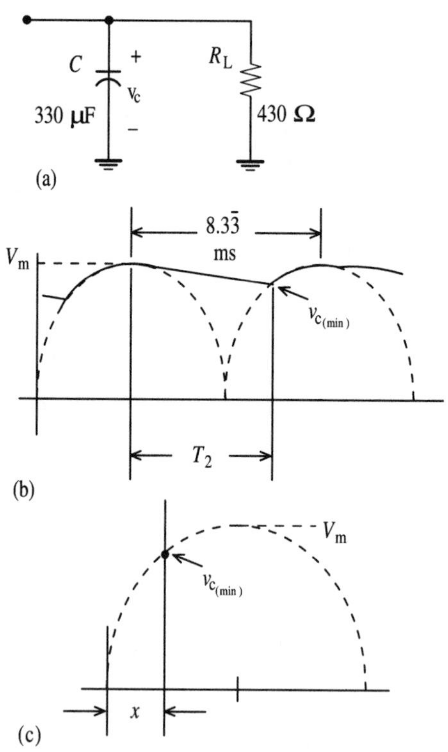

25.9 Computer Analysis (MultiSIM and PSpice)

44(a). MultiSIM: The solution is shown below. Set an initial condition of 7 V on each capacitor as per Note 4, page 919 of the text. Perform a transient analysis, selecting User Defined for the initial conditions. With the cursor, measure ripple. (It is about 2.6 V.) To find the dc voltage, add a dc voltmeter across the load and click the ON/OFF switch to ON to run the simulation. You will find the dc voltage is about 7.9 V.

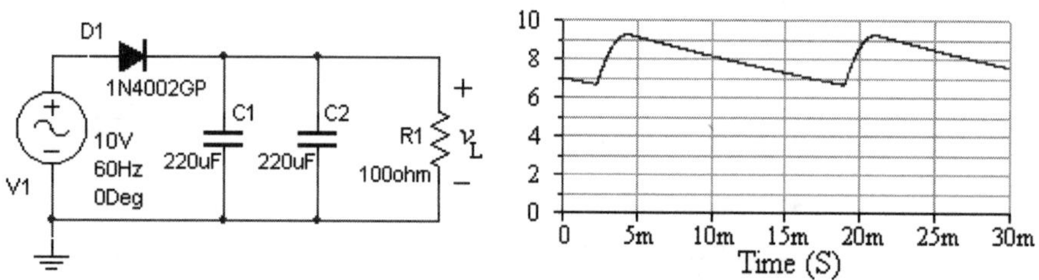

44(a). PSpice: The solution is shown below. Set an initial condition of 7 V on each capacitor as per Note 4, page 919 of the text. With the cursor, measure ripple. (It is about 2.6 V.) To find the average voltage, use *Add Trace* to plot AVG(V(R1)) as in Practice Problem 11, page 921 of the text. After the waveform stabilizes, estimate its average. It is about 7.9 V.

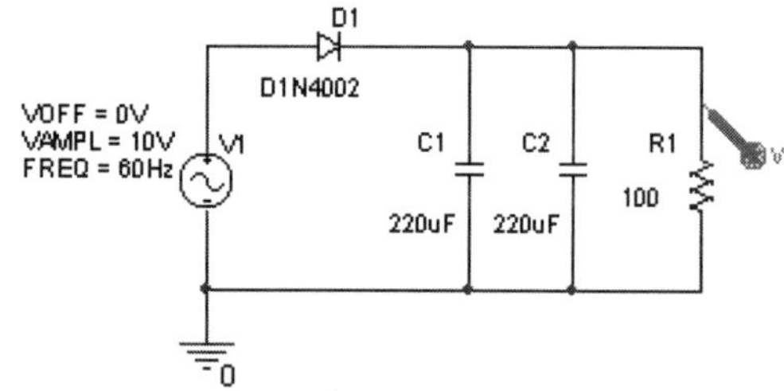

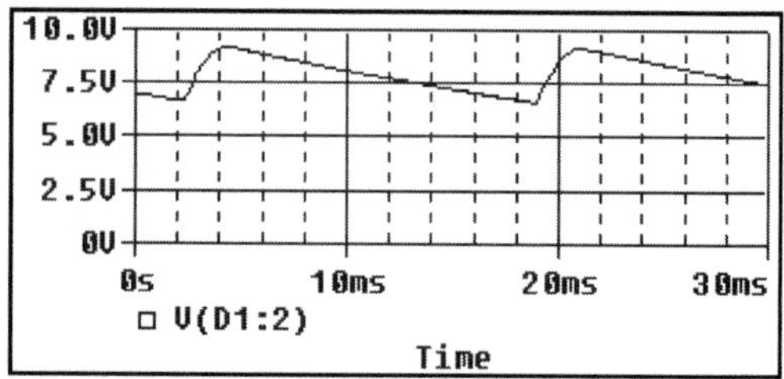

44(b). Analytic Solution: Using a value of V_F = 0.74 V for the diode drop yields V_m = 10 – 0.74 = 9.26 V.

$$V_{r_{pp}} = \frac{2\,V_m}{1 + \frac{2\,R_L C}{T}} = \frac{2(9.26\text{ V})}{1 + \frac{2(100\ \Omega)(440\ \mu\text{F})}{16.67\text{ ms}}} = 2.95\text{ V} \qquad V_{dc} = V_m - \frac{V_{r_{pp}}}{2} = 9.26 - \frac{2.95}{2} = 7.79\text{ V}$$

Note how well the results agree. In particular, note that the approximate answer for the dc voltage differs from the computer answers by less than 0.2 V.

Chapter

26

Basic Transistor Theory

26.2 Transistor Operation

2. $I_B = 25.1 \text{ mA} - 24.5 \text{ mA} = 0.6 \text{ mA}$

$$\alpha = \frac{24.5 \text{ mA}}{25.1 \text{ mA}} = 0.976$$

$$\beta = \frac{24.5 \text{ mA}}{0.6 \text{ mA}} = 40.83$$

4. $I_C = (0.92)(3.50 \text{ mA}) = 3.22 \text{ mA}$

$$\beta = \frac{0.92}{1-0.92} = 11.5$$

$I_B = 3.50 \text{ mA} - 3.22 \text{ mA} = 0.28 \text{ mA}$

6. $$\begin{aligned} I_E &= I_C + I_B \\ &= \beta I_B + I_B \\ &= (\beta + 1) I_B \end{aligned}$$

8. $$\begin{aligned} \beta &= \frac{I_C}{I_B} \\ &= \frac{I_C}{I_E - I_C} \\ &= \frac{\alpha I_E}{I_E - \alpha I_E} \\ &= \frac{\alpha}{1-\alpha} \end{aligned}$$

26.3 Transistor Specifications

10. $V_{(BR)CBO} = 60 \text{ V}$

This is the maximum voltage that can be applied between the collector and the base (emitter is open) before the transistor can be expected to break down.

The test conditions are $I_C = 10\ \mu\text{A}$, $I_E = 0$

26.4 Collector Characteristic Curves

12. $$\beta_{dc} = \frac{10.5 \text{ mA}}{100\ \mu\text{A}} = 105$$

14. $I_B \simeq 36\ \mu\text{A}$

$$\beta_{dc} = \frac{4.0 \text{ mA}}{36\ \mu\text{A}} = 111$$

16. Cutoff

26.5 dc Load Line

18.

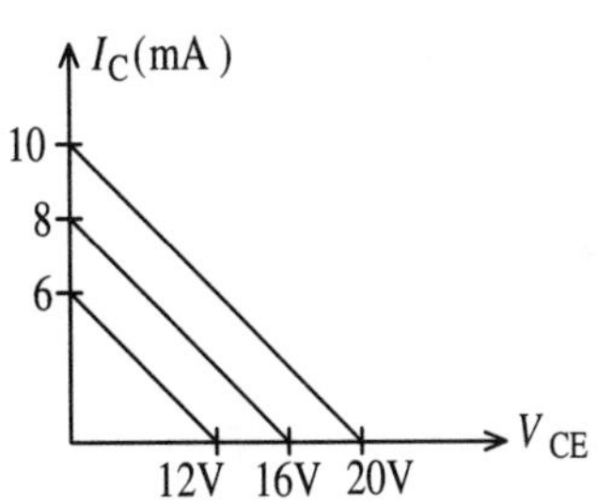

The load line remains parallel with both $V_{CE(OFF)}$ and $I_{C(SAT)}$ increasing.

20. a. $$I_{C(SAT)} = \frac{16 \text{ V}}{2 \text{ k}\Omega} = 8 \text{ mA}$$

at the Q-point $I_{CQ} = 4$ mA, $I_{BQ} = 4$ mA, $I_{BQ} = 36\ \mu\text{A}$

$$R_B = \frac{5 \text{ V} - 0.7 \text{ V}}{36\ \mu\text{A}} = 119 \text{ k}\Omega \ (\textit{use } R_B = 120 \text{ k}\Omega)$$

b. $$\beta = \frac{4 \text{ mA}}{36\ \mu\text{A}} = 111$$

26.6 Transistor Biasing

22. a. $(620\text{ k}\Omega)\,I_B + 0.7\text{ V} = 16\text{ V}$

$$I_B = \frac{15.3\text{ V}}{620\text{ k}\Omega} = 24.7\ \mu\text{A}$$

$I_C = (240)(24.7\mu\text{A}) = 5.92\text{ mA} \cong I_E$

$V_{CE} = 16\text{ V} - (5.92\text{ mA})(2\text{ k}\Omega) = 4.15\text{ V}$

b. The change in I_C is

$$\Delta I_C = \frac{5.92\text{ mA} - 2.96\text{ mA}}{2.96\text{ mA}} \times 100\% = 100\%$$

c. As β increases, the Q-point moves toward saturation.

24. a. $$I_{C(SAT)} = \frac{24\text{ V}}{3.9\text{ k}\Omega} = 6.15\text{ mA}$$

$$I_B = \frac{24\text{ V} - 0.7\text{ V}}{1.2\text{ M}\Omega} = 19.42\ \mu\text{A}$$

$I_C = (240)(19.42\ \mu\text{A}) = 4.66\text{ mA} \cong I_E$

$V_{CE} = 24\text{ V} - (4.66\text{ mA})(3.9\text{ k}\Omega) = 5.83\text{ V}$

b. Increasing beta results in the Q-point moving towards saturation. Therefore, a decrease in β will result in the Q-point moving toward cutoff.

26. a. $I_{C(SAT)} = 4.49\text{ mA}$

$$I_B = \frac{22\text{ V} - 0.7\text{ V}}{1.5\text{ M}\Omega + (301)(1\text{ k}\Omega)} = 11.83\ \mu\text{A}$$

$I_C = (300)(11.83\ \mu\text{A}) = 3.55\text{ mA} \cong I_E$

$V_{CE} = 22\text{ V} - (3.55\text{ mA})(3.9\text{ k}\Omega + 1\text{ k}\Omega) = 4.61\text{ V}$

b. I_C increases by

$$\Delta I_C = \frac{3.55\text{ mA} - 1.94\text{ mA}}{1.94\text{ mA}} \times 100\% = 83.3\%$$

28. a. $I_{C(SAT)} = 10\text{ mA}$

$(2.0\text{ k}\Omega)I + (270\text{ k}\Omega)I_B + 0.7\text{ V} = 20\text{ V}$

$$I_B = \frac{19.3\text{ V}}{270\text{ k}\Omega + (251)(2\text{ k}\Omega)} = 25.0\ \mu\text{A}$$

$I_C = (250)(25.0\ \mu\text{A}) = 6.25\text{ mA}$

$I = 6.28\text{ mA}$

$V_{CE} = 20\text{ V} - (2.0\text{ k}\Omega)(6.28\text{ mA}) = 7.45\text{ V}$

b. I_C increases by

$$\Delta I_C = \frac{6.25\text{ mA} - 4.62\text{ mA}}{4.62\text{ mA}} \times 100\% = 35.3\%$$

30. a. $$I_{C(SAT)} = \frac{24\text{ V}}{4.3\text{ k}\Omega} = 5.58\text{ mA}$$

b. $$I_B = \frac{24\text{ V} - 0.7\text{ V}}{(121)(1\text{ k}\Omega) + 820\text{ k}\Omega} = 24.8\ \mu\text{A}$$

$I_C = (120)(24.8\ \mu\text{A}) = 2.97\text{ mA} \cong I_E$

$V_{CE} = -24\text{ V} + (2.97\text{ mA})(4.3\text{ k}\Omega) = -11.22\text{ V}$

c.

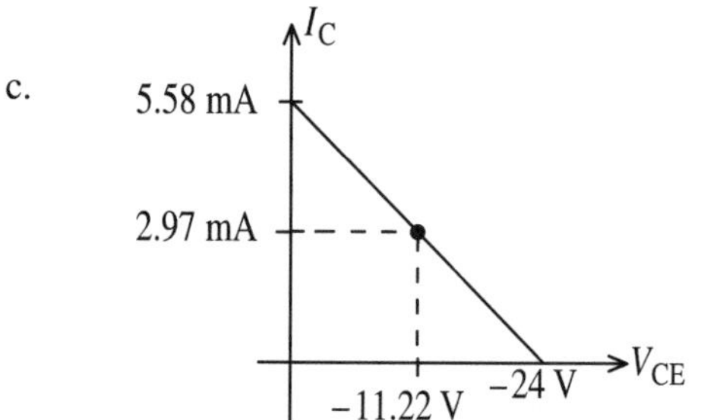

d. $$I_B = \frac{2.0\text{ mA}}{120} = 16.67\ \mu\text{A}$$

$$R_B = \frac{23.3\text{ V}}{16.67\ \mu\text{A}} - (121)(1\text{ k}\Omega) = 1.277\text{ M}\Omega$$

32. a. $R_{BB} = 33\text{ k}\Omega // 5.1\text{ k}\Omega = 4.42\text{ k}\Omega$

$$V_{BB} = \frac{5.1\text{k}\Omega}{33\text{ k}\Omega + 5.1\text{ k}\Omega} \times 16\text{ V} = 2.14\text{ V}$$

$$I_B = \frac{2.14\text{ V} - 0.7\text{ V}}{4.42\text{ k}\Omega + 241\ (0.51\text{ k}\Omega)} + 11.51\ \mu\text{A}$$

$I_C = (240)(11.51\ \mu\text{A}) = 2.76\text{ mA} \cong I_E$

$V_{CE} = 16\text{ V} - (2.76\text{ mA})(1.5\text{ k}\Omega + 0.51\text{ k}\Omega)$
$= 10.45\text{ V}$

b. Change in I_C:

$$\Delta I_C = \frac{2.76\text{ mA} - 2.62\text{ mA}}{2.62\text{ mA}} \times 100\% = 5.64\%$$

34. a. $R_{BB} = 4.42\text{ k}\Omega$

$V_{BB} = 2.14\text{ V}$ (same as Problem 32)

$$I_B = \frac{2.14\text{ V} - 0.7\text{ V}}{44.2\text{ k}\Omega + 241\ (0.51\text{ k}\Omega)} = 8.62\ \mu\text{A}$$

$I_C = (240)(8.62\ \mu\text{A}) = 2.07\text{ mA} \cong I_E$

$V_{CE} = 16\text{ V} - (2.07\text{ mA})(1.5\text{ k}\Omega + 0.51\text{ k}\Omega)$
$= 11.84\text{ V}$

b. Change in I_C:

$$\Delta I_C = \frac{2.07\text{ mA} - 2.62\text{ mA}}{2.62\text{ mA}} \times 100\% = -20.9\%$$

36. a. $$V_B = \frac{51\text{ k}\Omega}{330\text{ k}\Omega + 51\text{ k}\Omega} \times 16\text{ V} = 2.14\text{ V}$$

$V_E \cong 2.14\text{ V} - 0.7\text{ V} = 1.44\text{ V}$

$$I_E = \frac{1.44\text{ V}}{0.51\text{ k}\Omega} = 2.83\text{ mA} \cong I_C$$

$V_{CE} = 16\text{ V} - (2.83\text{ mA})(1.5\text{ k}\Omega + 0.51\text{ k}\Omega)$
$= 10.32\text{ V}$

b. $$\Delta I_C = \frac{2.83\text{ mA} - 1.63\text{ mA}}{1.63\text{ mA}} \times 100\% = 73\%$$

$$\Delta V_{CE} = \frac{10.32\text{ V} - 12.72\text{ V}}{12.71\text{ V}} \times 100\% = 18.9\%$$

38. $V_E \cong -(3.0\text{ mA})(1.0\text{ k}\Omega) = -3.00\text{ V}$

$V_B \cong -3.00\text{ V} - 0.7\text{ V} = -3.70\text{ V}$

Using the approximate method,

$$R_1 = \frac{R_2}{V_B}(V_{CC} - V_B) = \left(\frac{8.2\text{ k}\Omega}{3.70\text{ V}}\right)(30\text{ V} - 3.70\text{ V})$$
$= 58.3\text{ k}\Omega$

40.

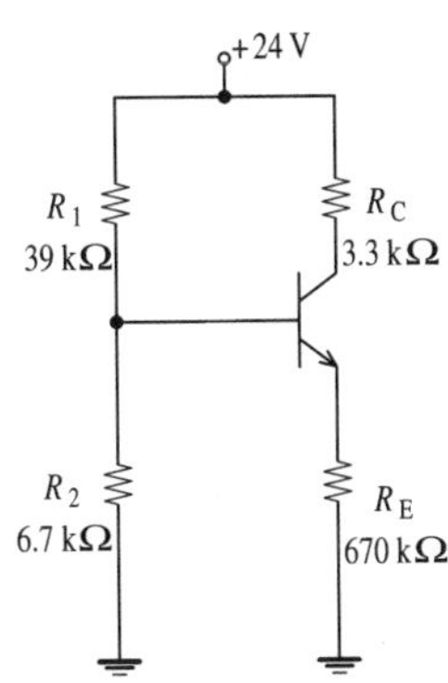

$$R_C + R_E = \frac{24\text{ V}}{6\text{ mA}} = 4.0\text{ k}\Omega$$

$$R_C = \frac{4.0\text{ k}\Omega}{1.20} = 3.33\text{ k}\Omega\text{ (use 3.3 k}\Omega\text{)}$$

$$R_E + \frac{3.33\text{ k}\Omega}{5} = 0.667\text{ k}\Omega\text{ (use 670 }\Omega)$$

"Worst case" $\beta = 100$

Let $R_2 = \frac{1}{10}\beta R_E = 6.7\text{ k}\Omega$

$V_E = (0.667\text{ k}\Omega)(4\text{ mA}) = 2.67\text{ V}$

$V_B = 2.67\text{ V} + 0.7\text{ V} = 3.37\text{ V}$

$$R_1 = \left(\frac{6.67\text{ k}\Omega}{3.37\text{ V}}\right)(24\text{ V} - 3.37\text{ V}) = 40.9\text{ k}\Omega$$

(use39kΩ)

42\. a. $$I_{C(SAT)} = \frac{8\text{ V} + 12\text{ }V}{2.2\text{ k}\Omega + 1.8\text{ k}\Omega} = 5.0\text{ mA}$$

b. $$I_E = \frac{8\text{ V} - 0.7\text{ V}}{2.2\text{ k}\Omega} = 3.32\text{ mA} \cong I_C$$

$$I_B = \frac{3.32\text{ mA}}{180} = 18.43\ \mu\text{A}$$

$$V_{CE} = -20\text{ V} + (3.32\text{ mA})(2.2\text{ k}\Omega + 1.8\text{ k}\Omega) = -6.73\text{ V}$$

c.

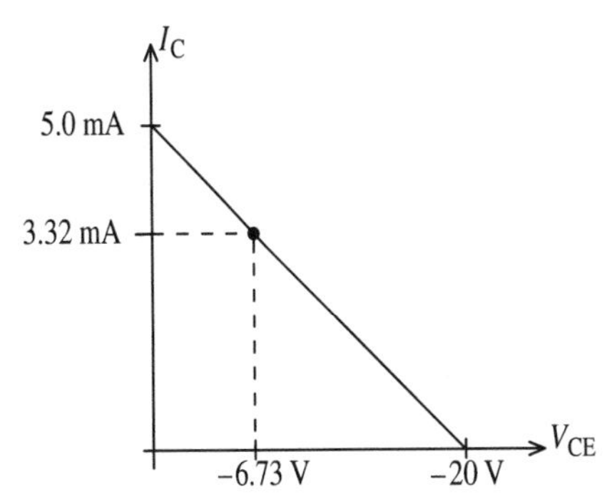

26.7 The Transistor Switch

44\. $$R_C = \frac{8\text{ V} - 1.6\text{ V}}{25\text{ mA}} = 256\ \Omega\text{ (use 270 }\Omega)$$

26.8 Testing a Transistor with a Multimeter

46\. Pin 1 → Base (n- type material)
Pin 3 → Emitter
Pin 2 → Collector
Transistor is pnp

48\. The transistor is faulty, since the B-E gives a low reading in both directions.

26.9 Junction Field Effect Transistor Construction and Operation

50\. a. n-channel

b. $$I_D = 10\text{ mA}\left(1 - \frac{2\text{ V}}{4\text{ V}}\right)^2 = 2.5\text{ mA}$$

c. $$I_D = 10\text{ mA}\left(1 - \frac{3\text{ V}}{4\text{ V}}\right)^2 = 0.625\text{ mA}$$

d. $I_D = 0$ (Since V_{GS} is greater than $V_{GS(OFF)}$)

26-10 JFET Biasing

52\. $V_{GS} = -(1\text{ k}\Omega)\, I_D$ ①

$I_D = (10\text{ mA})\,(1 - \frac{V_{GS}}{-5\text{ V}})^2$ ②

Quadratic equation

$$-V_{GS} = 10\left(1 + \frac{V_{GS}}{5}\right)^2$$

$$-25\ V_{GS} = 10(25 + 10\ V_{GS} + V_{GS}^2)$$

$$V_{GS}^2 + 12.5\ V_{GS} + 25 = 0$$

$$V_{GS} = -12.5 \pm \frac{\sqrt{(12.5)^2 - (4)(1)(25)}}{2} = -2.5\text{ V}, -10\text{ V}$$

(−10 V crossed out)

$I_{DQ} = 2.5\text{ mA}$

$V_{DSQ} = 20\text{ V} - (2.5\text{ mA})(2.4\text{ k}\Omega) + 1.0\text{ k}\Omega) = 11.5\text{ V}$

(refer to graph at top of next page)

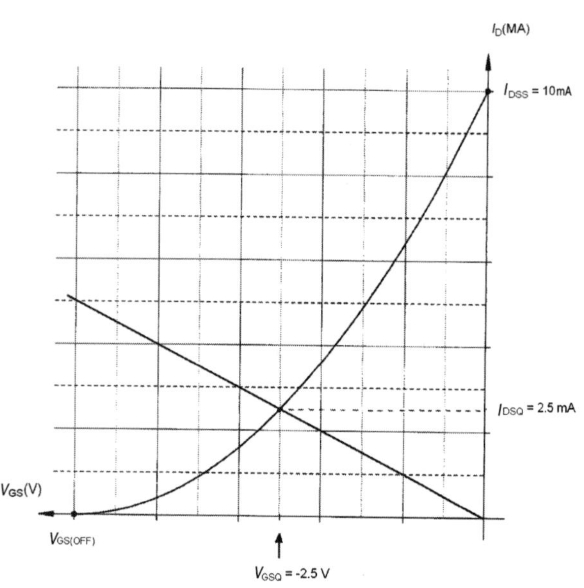

54. $V_G = \dfrac{1\ \text{M}\Omega}{7.7\ \text{M}\Omega} = 20\ \text{V} = 2.60\ \text{V}$

Exact method:

$V_{GS} = 2.60\ \text{V} - I_D(2\ \text{k}\Omega)$ ①

$I_D = 10\ \text{mA}\left(1 + \dfrac{V_{GS}}{5\ \text{V}}\right)^2$ ②

Quadratic Equation:

$$\frac{2.60 - V_{GS}}{2} = 10\left(1 + \frac{V_{GS}}{5}\right)^2$$

$$V_{GS}^2 + 11.25V_{GS} + 21.75 = 0$$

$$V_{GS} = \frac{-11.25 \pm \sqrt{(11.25)^2 - (4)(1)(21.75)}}{2}$$

$$= \cancel{-8.77\ \text{V}}, -2.48\ \text{V}$$

$I_{DQ} = 2.54$ mA

$V_{DSQ} = 20\ \text{V} - (2.54\ \text{mA})(3.9\ \text{k}\Omega + 2.0\ \text{k}\Omega) = 5.02\ \text{V}$

(Refer to graph below)

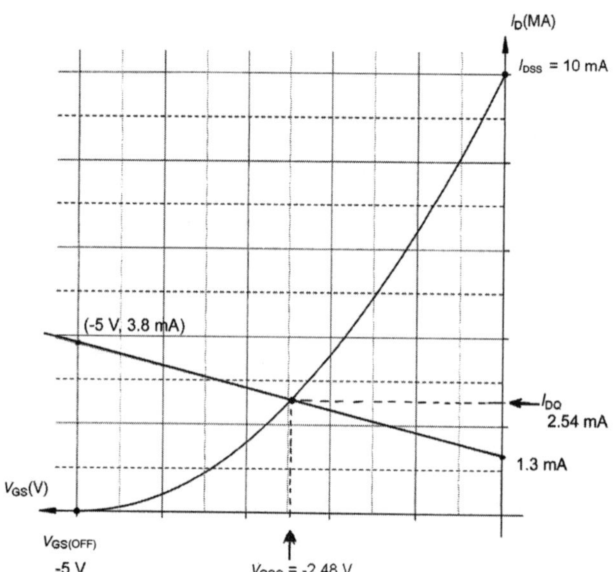

26.11 MOSFET

56. a. $V_G = \dfrac{680\ \text{k}\Omega}{1880\ \text{k}\Omega} \times 20\ \text{V} = 7.23\ \text{V}$

Exact method:

$V_{GS} = 7.23\ \text{V} - 0.62\ \text{k}\Omega\ I_D$ ①

$I_D = 10\ \text{mA}\left(1 + \dfrac{V_{GS}}{5\ \text{V}}\right)^2$ ②

Quadratic equation:

$V_{GS}^2 + 14.03\ V_{GS} - 4.169 = 0$

$V_{GS} = +0.291\ \text{V}, \cancel{-14.32\ \text{V}}$

$I_{DQ} = 11.20$ mA

$V_{DSQ} = 20\ \text{V} - (11.20\ \text{mA})(0.68\ \text{k}\Omega + 0.62\ \text{k}\Omega)$
$= 5.44\ \text{V}$

b. The MOSFET is operating in its enhancement mode.

c. $V_{DSQ} = 20\ \text{V} - (11.20\ \text{mA})(0.68\ \text{k}\Omega + 0.62\ \text{k}\Omega)$
$= 5.44\ \text{V}$

58. $I_D = k\,(V_{GS} - V_{GS(th)})^2$

$$k = \frac{I_D}{(V_{GS} - V_{GS(th)})^2} = \frac{20\ \text{mA}}{(15\ \text{V} - 3\ \text{V})^2}$$

$$I_D = \left(0.139\ \frac{\text{mA}}{V^2}\right)(V_{GS} - 3\ \text{V})^2$$

60. $V_{GS} = V_{DS}$ since $I_G = 0$

$I_D = \left(0.139\ \dfrac{\text{mA}}{V^2}\right)(V_{GS} - 3\ \text{V})^2$ ①

$V_{GS} = 30\ \text{V} - I_D\,(0.68\ \text{k}\Omega)$

$I_D = \dfrac{30\ \text{V} - V_{GS}}{0.68\ \text{k}\Omega}$ ②

Quadratic equation:

$V_{GS}2 + 4.59\ V_{GS} - 308.6 = 0$

$V_{GSQ} = 15.42\ \text{V}, \cancel{-20.01\ \text{V}}$

$I_{DQ} = 21.44$ mA

$V_{DSQ} = 15.42$ V

26.12 Troubleshooting a Transistor Circuit

62. Meter 1 indicates that the base current is normal ($I_B \cong 38$ μA).

The B-E voltage is normal, therefore the transistor is correctly biased.

The low voltage on meter 3 indicates there is very little collector current. Meter 4 also shows that the transistor is "cut off."

The transistor collector and emitter terminals may have been reversed (if this is a new circuit). If the circuit once was operational, the collector-base junction may have been damaged.

26.13 Computer Analysis of Transistor Circuits

64.

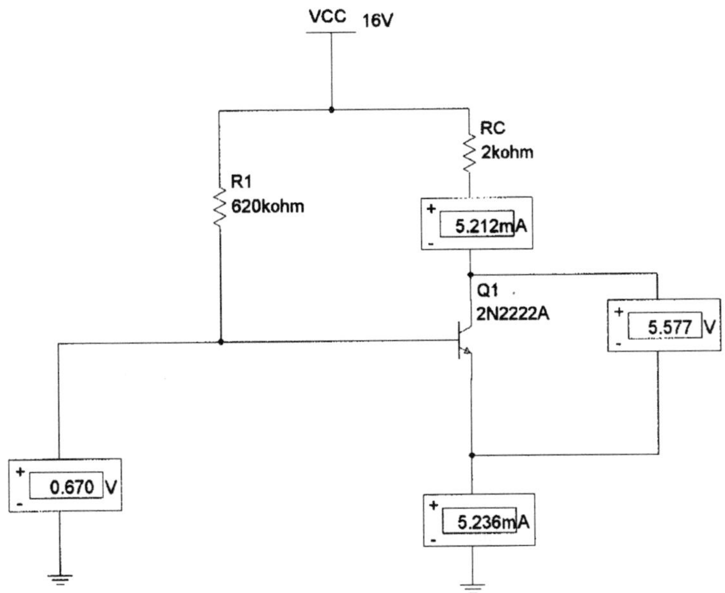

Discrepancies in the bias conditions are due to variations in the transistors' betas.

66.

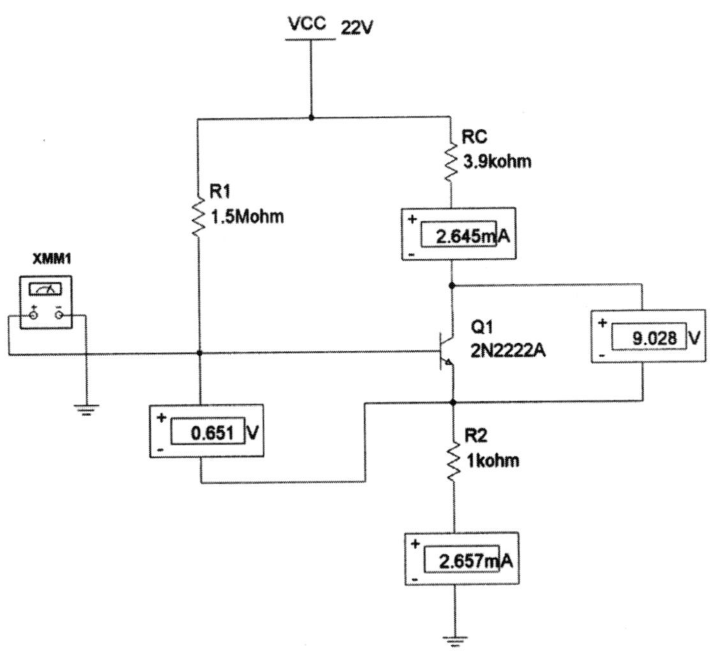

Discrepancies in the bias conditions are due to variations in the transistors' betas.

68.

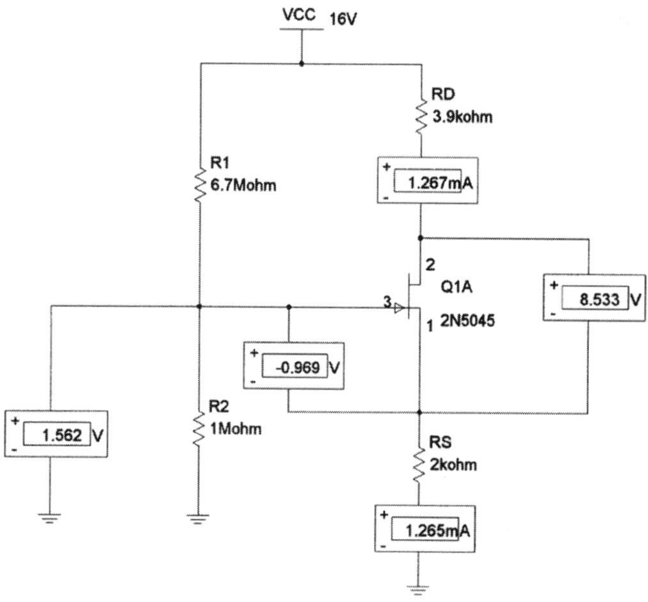

Discrepancies in the bias conditions are due to variations in I_{DSS} and $V_{GS(OFF)}$

70.

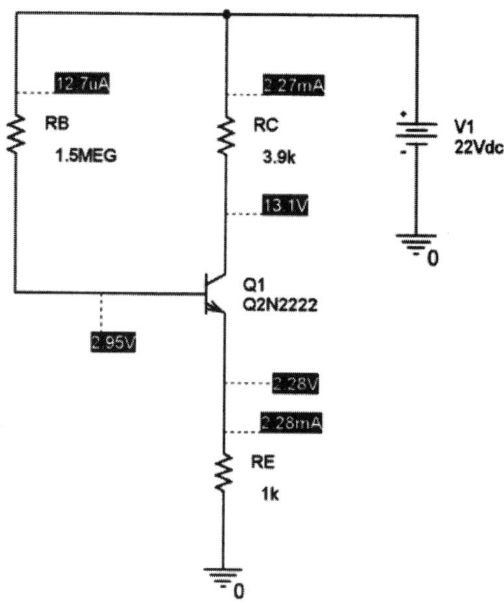

Discrepancies in the bias conditions are due to variations in the transistors' betas.

72.

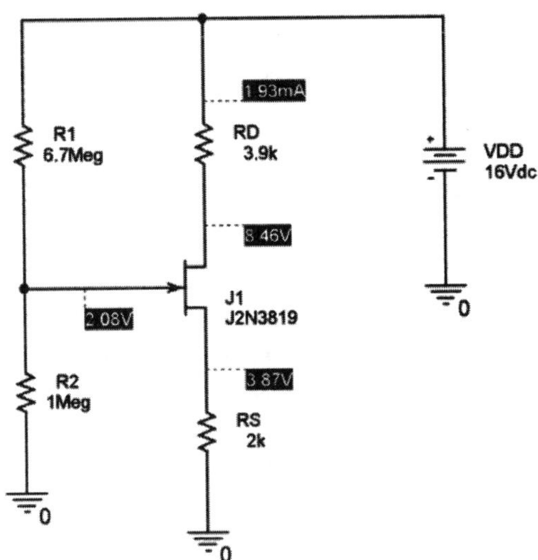

Discrepancies in the bias conditions are due to variations in I_{DSS} and $V_{GS\,(OFF)}$

Chapter

27

Transistor Amplifiers

27.1 The Use of Capacitors in Amplifier Circuits

2. a. $X_C \le \dfrac{600\ \Omega + 20\ \Omega}{10} = 62\ \Omega$

$C_{min} = \dfrac{1}{2\ \pi\ (10\ \text{kHz})(62\ \Omega)} = 257\ \text{nF}$

b. $v_{in} = \left(\dfrac{20\ \Omega}{620\ \Omega + j62\ \Omega}\right) 5\ \text{mV}_p = 0.160\ \text{mV}_p$

at 200 kHz, $X_C = 3.10\ \Omega$

$v_{in} = \left(\dfrac{20\ \Omega}{620\ \Omega + j3.10\ \Omega}\right) 5\ \text{mVp} = 0.161\ \text{mVp}$

4. $X_C \le \dfrac{1.2\ \text{k}\Omega}{10} = 120\ \Omega$

$C_{min} = \dfrac{1}{2\ \pi\ (500\ \text{Hz})(120\ \Omega)} = 2.65\ \mu\text{F}$

27.4 The Common-Emitter Amplifier

6. a. $I_B = \dfrac{12\ \text{V} - 0.7\ \text{V}}{560\ \text{k}\Omega} = 20.2\ \mu\text{A}$

$I_C = (130)(20.2\ \mu\text{A}) = 2.62\ \text{mA} \cong I_E$

$V_{CE} = 12\ \text{V} - (2.62\ \text{mA})(2.2\ \text{k}\Omega) = 6.23\ \text{V}$

b. $r_e = \dfrac{26\ \text{mV}}{2.62\ \text{mA}} = 9.91\ \Omega$

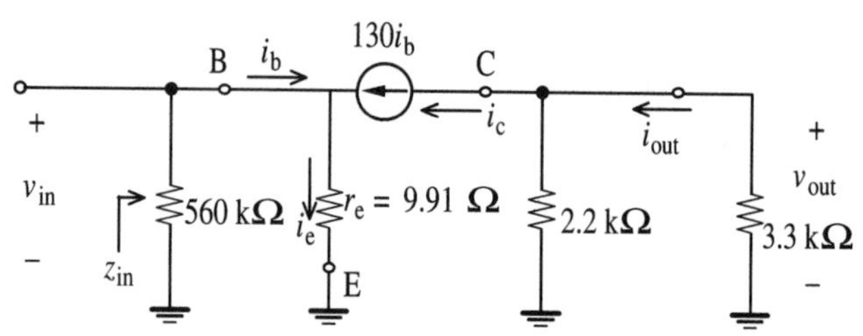

c. $A_v = -\dfrac{130\ i_b\ (3.3\ \text{k}\Omega\ //\ 2.2\ \text{k}\Omega)}{(131\ i_b)(9.91\ \Omega)} = -132$

$z_{in} = 560\ \text{k}\Omega\ //\ [(131)(9.91\ \Omega) = 1295\ \Omega$

$z_{out} = 2.2\ \text{k}\Omega$

$A_i = \dfrac{(132)(1295\ \Omega)}{3300\ \Omega} = 51.8$

$A_p = (51.8)(132) = 6840$

8. a. $r_e = \dfrac{26\ \text{mV}}{2.60\ \text{mA}} = 10\ \Omega$

b. $A_v = -\dfrac{150\ i_b)(3.3\ \text{k}\Omega)}{(151\ i_b)(10\ \Omega)} = -328$

$z_{in} = 910\ \text{k}\Omega\ //\ [(151i_b)(10\ \Omega) = 1510\ \Omega$

$z_{out} = 3.3\ \Omega$

$A_i = \dfrac{(328)(1510\ \Omega)}{3300\ \Omega} = 150$

10. a. $I_B = \dfrac{22\ \text{V} - 0.7\ \text{V}}{750\ \text{k}\Omega} = 28.4\ \mu\text{A}$

$I_C = (160)(28.4\ \mu\text{A}) = 4.54\ \text{mA}$

$V_{CE} = -22\ \text{V} + (4.54\ \text{mA})(2.7\ \text{k}\Omega) = -9.73\ \text{V}$

b. $h_{ie} \cong 1.0\ \text{k}\Omega$

$h_{fe} \cong 150$

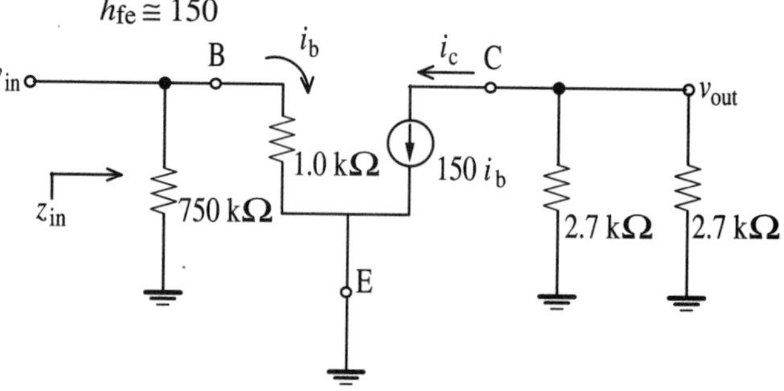

c. $A_v = -\dfrac{150\ i_b\ (2.7\ \text{k}\Omega\ //\ 2.7\ \text{k}\Omega)}{i_b\ (1.0\ \text{k}\Omega)} = -203$

$z_{in} = 750\ \text{k}\Omega\ //\ 1.0\ \text{k}\Omega = 1\ \text{k}\Omega$

$z_{out} = 2.7\ \text{k}\Omega$

$v_{in} = \left(\dfrac{1000\ \Omega}{2200\ \Omega}\right) 10\ \text{mV}_p = 4.55\ \text{mV}_p$

$v_{out} = 0.923\ \text{V}_p$

d.

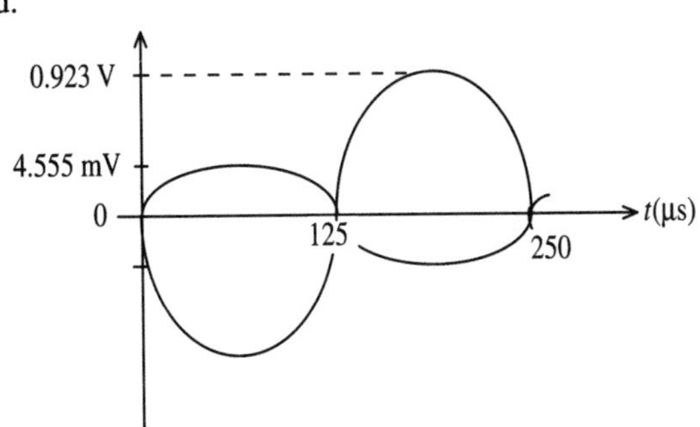

12. a. No. The capacitor is an open-circuit at d.c.

b.

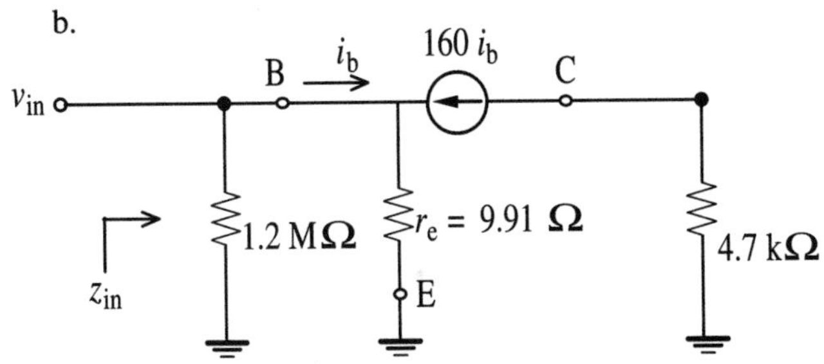

c. $$A_v = \frac{-160(4.7\ \text{k}\Omega)}{(161)(9.91\ \Omega)} - 4 = 71$$

$z_{in} = 1.2\ \text{M}\Omega\ //\ [(161)(9.91\ \Omega)] = 1600\ \Omega$

$z_{out} = 4.7\ \text{k}\Omega$

$$A_i = \frac{(471)(1600\text{k}\Omega)}{4700\ \Omega} = 160$$

d. *i)* No change

ii) z_{in} decreases

iii) A_v increases

14. a. $$I_B = \frac{16\ \text{V} - 0.7\ \text{V}}{680\ \text{k}\Omega + (151)(780\ \Omega)} = 19.2\ \mu\text{A}$$

$I_C = (150)(19.2\ \mu\text{A}) = 2.88\ \text{mA}$

$V_{CE} = -16\ \text{V} + (2.88\ \text{mA})(2.7\ \text{k}\Omega + 0.220\ \text{k}\Omega + 0.56\ \text{k}\Omega)$
$= -5.99\ \text{V}$

b.

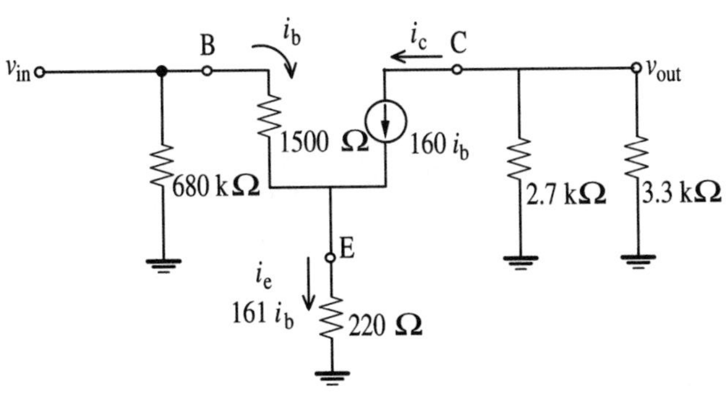

c. $$A_v = \frac{-160\ i_b\ (2.7\ \text{k}\Omega\ //\ 3.3\ \text{k}\Omega)}{i_b\ (1.5\ \text{k}\Omega) + (161\ i_b)(0.22\ \text{k}\Omega)} = -6.43$$

$z_{in} = 680\ \text{k}\Omega\ //\ [1.5\ \text{k}\Omega + 161(0.22\ \text{k}\Omega)] = 35.0\ \text{k}\Omega$

$z_{out} = 2.7\ \text{k}\Omega$

$$A_i = \frac{(6.43)(35.0\ \text{k}\Omega)}{3.3\ \text{k}\Omega} = 68.2$$

d. $$v_{in} = \left(\frac{35.0\ \text{k}\Omega}{35.0\ \text{k}\Omega + 2.5\ \text{k}\Omega}\right) 5\ \text{mV} = 4.67\ \text{mV}_\text{p}$$

$v_{out} = (6.43)(4.67\ \text{mV}) = 21.8\ \text{mV}_\text{p}$

16. a.

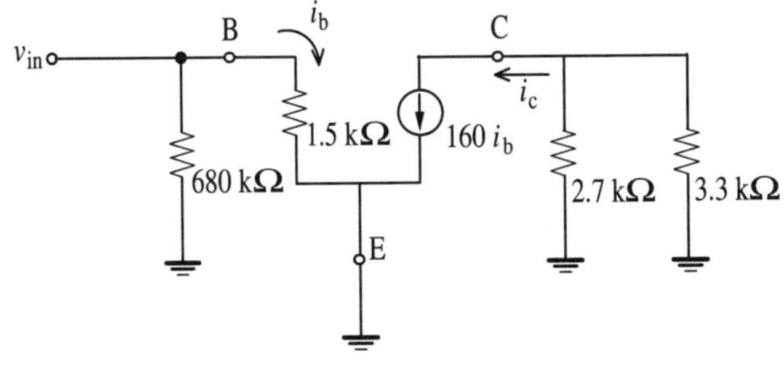

b. $$A_v = \frac{-160\ i_b\ (2.7\ \text{k}\Omega\ //\ 3.3\ \text{k}\Omega)}{i_b\ (1.5\ \text{k}\Omega)} = -158$$

$z_{in} = 680\ \text{k}\Omega\ //\ 1.5\ \text{k}\Omega = 1.5\ \text{k}\Omega$

$z_{out} = 2.7\ \text{k}\Omega$

$$A_i = \frac{(158)(1.5\ \text{k}\Omega)}{3.3\ \text{k}\Omega} = 71.7$$

c. $$v_{in} = \left(\frac{1.5\ \text{k}\Omega}{1.5\ \text{k}\Omega + 2.5\ \text{k}\Omega}\right) 5\ \text{mV} = 1.88\ \text{mV}_\text{p}$$

$v_{out} = (158)(1.88\ \text{mV}) = 296\ \text{mV}$

18. a. $R_{BB} = 91\ \text{k}\Omega\ //\ 10\ \text{k}\Omega = 9.01\ \text{k}\Omega$

$$V_{BB} = \left(\frac{10\ \text{k}\Omega}{101\ \text{k}\Omega}\right) 22\ \text{V} = 2.18\ \text{V}$$

$$I_B = \frac{2.18\ \text{V} - 0.7\ \text{V}}{9.01\ \text{k}\Omega + (161)(0.22\ \text{k}\Omega)} = 33.3\ \mu\text{A}$$

$I_C = (160)(33.3\ \mu\text{A}) = 5.33\ \text{mA} \cong I_E$

$V_{CE} = 22\ \text{V} - 5.33\ \text{mA}\ (2.2\ \text{k}\Omega + 0.22\ \text{k}\Omega)$
$= 9.10\ \text{V}$

b. $$r_e = \frac{26\ \text{mV}}{5.33\ \text{mA}} = 4.88\ \Omega$$

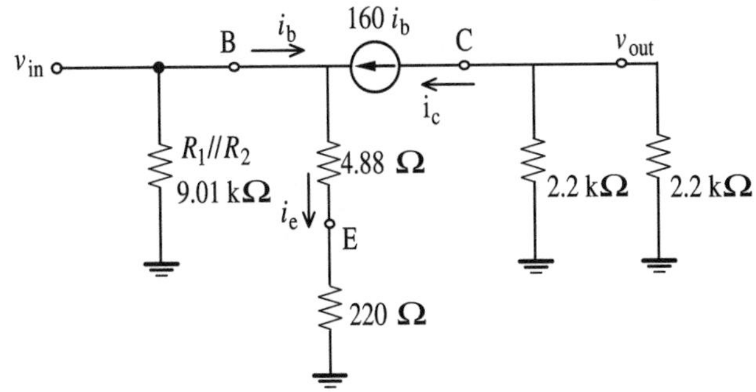

$$A_v = \frac{-(160\ i_b)(2.2\ \text{k}\Omega \mathbin{//} 2.2\ \text{k}\Omega)}{(161\ i_b)(220\ \Omega + 4.88\ \Omega)} = -4.86$$

$$z_{in} = 9.01\ \text{k}\Omega \mathbin{//} [(161)(220\ \Omega + 4.88\ \Omega)]$$
$$= 7.21\ \text{k}\Omega$$

$$z_{out} = 2.2\ \text{k}\Omega$$

$$A_i = \frac{(4.86)(7.21\ \text{k}\Omega)}{2.2\ \text{k}\Omega} = 15.94$$

20. a. $$V_B = \left(\frac{9.1\ \text{k}\Omega}{9.1\ \text{k}\Omega + 67\ \text{k}\Omega}\right)(-20\ \text{V}) = -2.39\ \text{V}$$

$$V_E = -1.69\ \text{V}$$

$$I_E = \frac{1.69\ \text{V}}{470\ \Omega + 470\ \Omega} = 1.80\ \text{mA} \cong \text{I}_C$$

$$V_{CE} = -20\ \text{V} + 1.80\ \text{mA}\ (4.3\ \text{k}\Omega + 940\ \Omega)$$
$$= -10.57\ \text{V}$$

b. From the data sheets:

$h_{ie} \cong 2.2\ \text{k}\Omega$

$h_{fe} \cong 150$

c.

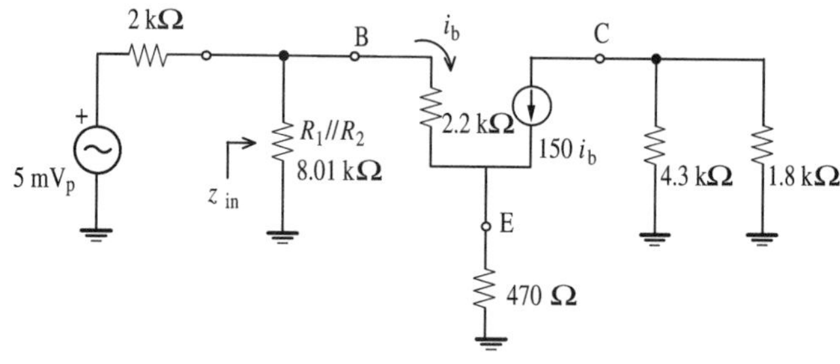

$$A_v = \frac{-(150\ i_b)(4.3\ \text{k}\Omega \mathbin{//} 1.8\ \text{k}\Omega)}{i_b\ (2.2\ \text{k}\Omega) + (151)(0.47\ \text{k}\Omega)} = -2.60$$

$$z_{in} = 8.01\ \text{k}\Omega \mathbin{//} [2.2\ \text{k}\Omega + 151(0.47\ \text{k}\Omega)] = 7.21\ \text{k}\Omega$$

$z_{out} = 4.3\ \text{k}\Omega$ $\quad A_i = \frac{(2.60)(7.21\ \text{k}\Omega)}{1.8\ \text{k}\Omega} = 10.43$

d. $v_{in} = 3.91\ \text{mV}_p$ $\quad v_{out} = 10.18\ \text{mV}_p$

22. a. $$V_B = \left(\frac{43\ \text{k}\Omega}{51.2\ \text{k}\Omega}\right)18\ \text{V} = 15.12\ \text{V}$$

$$I_E = \frac{18\ \text{V} - 15.12\ \text{V} - 0.7\ \text{V}}{0.33\ \text{k}\Omega + 0.47\ \text{k}\Omega} = 2.73\ \text{mA} \cong I_C$$

$$V_{CE} = -18\ \text{V} + 2.73\ \text{mA}(0.33\ \text{k}\Omega + 0.47\ \text{k}\Omega + 4.3\ \text{k}\Omega)$$
$$= -4.10\ \text{V}$$

b. $$r_e = \frac{26\ \text{mV}}{2.73\ \text{mA}} = 9.54\ \Omega$$

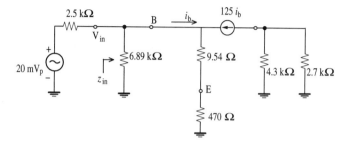

c. $$A_v = \frac{-(125\ i_b)(4.3\ \text{k}\Omega \mathbin{//} 2.7\ \text{k}\Omega)}{(126\ i_b)(9.54\ \Omega + 470\ \Omega)} = -3.43$$

$$z_{in} = 6.89\ \text{k}\Omega \mathbin{//} [(126)(9.54\ \Omega + 470\ \Omega)]$$
$$= 6.18\ \text{k}\Omega$$

$$z_{out} = 4.3\ \text{k}\Omega$$

$$A_i = \frac{(3.43)(6.18\ \text{k}\Omega)}{4.3\ \text{k}\Omega} = 4.93$$

d. $$v_{in} = \left(\frac{6.18\ \text{k}\Omega}{2.5\ \text{k}\Omega + 6.18\ \text{k}\Omega}\right)20\ \text{mV}_p = 14.2\ \text{mV}_p$$

$$v_{out} = (3.43)(14.2\ \text{mV}_p) = 48.8\ \text{mV}$$

27.5 The ac Load Line

24. a. $$I_B = \frac{18.8\ \text{V} - 0.7\ \text{V}}{905\ \text{k}\Omega} = 20\ \mu\text{A}$$

$$I_{CQ} = (100)(20\ \mu\text{A}) = 2.00\ \text{mA}$$

$$V_{CEQ} = 18.8\ \text{V} - (2.00\ \text{mA})(5.4\ \text{k}\Omega) = 8.00\ \text{V}$$

b.

$r_c = 5.4\ \text{k}\Omega // 1.8\ \text{k}\Omega = 1.35\ \text{k}\Omega$

c. $$I_{C(DC-SAT)} = \frac{18.8\ \text{V}}{5.4\ \text{k}\Omega} = 3.48\ \text{mA}$$

$$V_{CE(DC-OFF)} = 18.8\ \text{V}$$

$$I_{C(AC-SAT)} = 2.00\ \text{mA} + \frac{8.00\ \text{V}}{1.35\ \text{k}\Omega} = 7.93\ \text{mA}$$

$$V_{CE(AC-OFF)} = 8.00\ \text{V} + (2.00\ \text{mA})(1.35\ \text{k}\Omega)$$
$$= 10.7\ \text{V}$$

d.

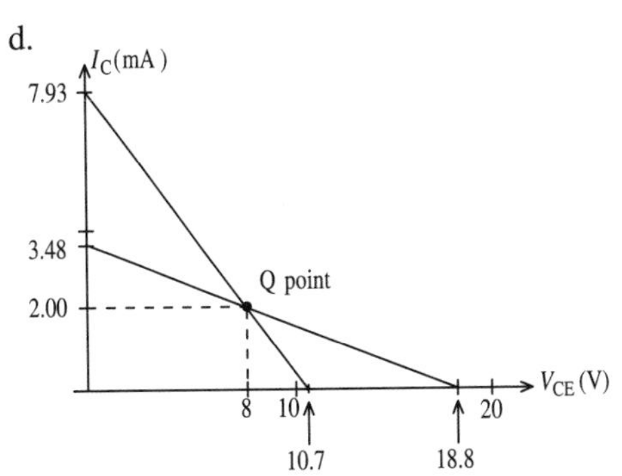

$V_{CE(MAX)} = 2(10.7\text{ V} - 8.00\text{ V}) = 5.4\text{ V}_{p\text{-}p}$

$I_{C(MAX)} = 2(2.00\text{ mA}) = 4.00\text{ mA}_{p\text{-}p}$

26. a. $V_B = 1.76\text{ V}$

$V_E = 1.057\text{ V}$

$I_E = 2.64\text{ mA} \cong I_{CQ}$

$V_{CEQ} = -16\text{ V} + (2.64\text{ mA})(2.6\text{ k}\Omega) = -9.13\text{ V}$

b.

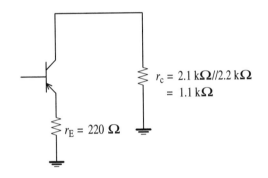

$r_c = 2.1\text{ k}\Omega // 2.2\text{ k}\Omega = 1.1\text{ k}\Omega$

$r_E = 220\ \Omega$

c. $$I_{C(DC-SAT)} = \frac{16\text{ V}}{2.6\text{ k}\Omega} = 6.15\text{ mA}$$

$V_{CE(DC\text{-}OFF)} = -16\text{ V}$

$$I_{C(AC-SAT)} = 2.64\text{ mA} + \frac{9.13\text{ V}}{1.32\text{ k}\Omega} = 9.56\text{ mA}$$

$V_{CE(AC\text{-}OFF)} = -9.13\text{ V} - (2.64\text{ mA})(1.32\text{ k}\Omega)$
$= -12.61\text{ V}$

d.

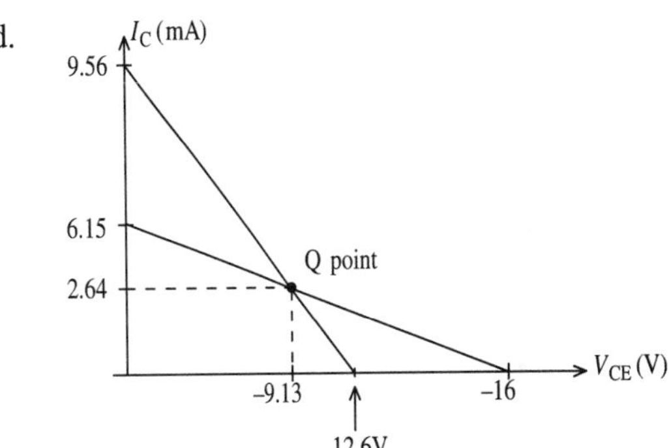

$V_{CE(MAX)} = 2(12.6\text{ V} - 9.13\text{ V}) = 6.94\text{ V}_{p\text{-}p}$

$I_{C(MAX)} = 2(2.64\text{ mA}) = 5.28\text{ mA}$

28. a. $I_{CQ} = 2.88\text{ mA}$ $\quad V_{CEQ} = -5.99\text{ V}$

$$I_{C(DC-SAT)} = \frac{16\text{ V}}{3.49\text{ k}\Omega} = 4.60\text{ mA}$$

$V_{CE(DC\text{-}OFF)} = -16\text{ V}$

$$I_{C(AC-SAT)} = 2.88\text{ mA} + \frac{5.99\text{ V}}{0.22\text{ k}\Omega + 2.7\text{ k}\Omega // 3.3\text{ k}\Omega}$$

$= 6.39\text{ mA}$

$V_{CE(AC\text{-}OFF)} = -5.99\text{ V} - (2.88\text{ mA})(0.22\text{ k}\Omega + 2.7\text{ k}\Omega // 3.3\text{ k}\Omega) = -10.90\text{ V}$

b.

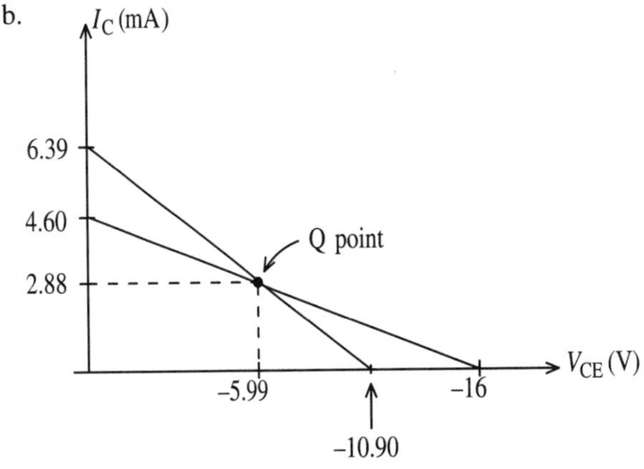

c. $I_{C(MAX)} = 2(2.88\text{mA}) = 5.76\text{ mA}_{p\text{-}p}$

$V_{CE(MAX)} = 2(10.90\text{ V} - 5.99\text{ V}) = 9.82\text{ V}_{p\text{-}p}$

$$v_{out(max)} = \left(\frac{2.7\text{ k}\Omega // 3.3\text{ k}\Omega}{0.22\text{ k}\Omega + 2.7\text{ k}\Omega // 3.3\text{ k}\Omega}\right) 9.82\text{ V}_{p\text{-}p}$$

$= 8.55\text{ V}_{p\text{-}p}$

$$v_{in(max)} = \left|\frac{8.55\text{ V}_{p\text{-}p}}{6.43}\right| = 1.33\text{ V}_{p\text{-}p}$$

27.6 The Common-Collector Amplifier

30. a. $$I_B = \frac{20\text{ V} - 0.7\text{ V}}{150\text{ k}\Omega + 120(1\text{ k}\Omega)} = 71.5\ \mu\text{A}$$

$I_C = (120)(71.5\text{ mA}) = 8.58\text{ mA}$

$V_{CE} = 20\text{ V} - (8.58\text{ mA})(1\text{ k}\Omega) = 11.42\text{ V}$

b. $$r_e = \frac{26\text{ mV}}{8.58\text{ mA}} = 3.03\ \Omega$$

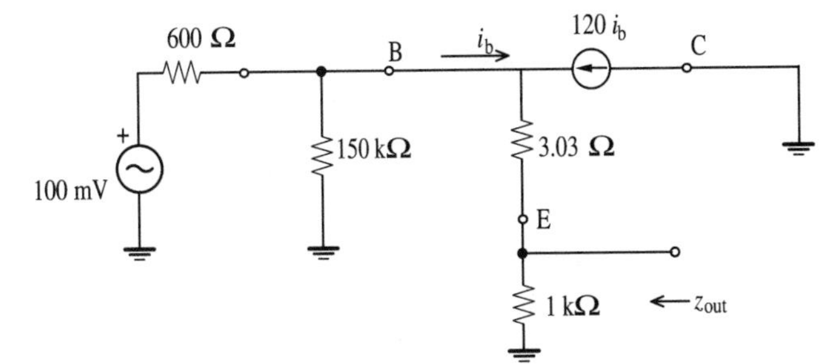

$$A_v = \frac{(121)(1000\ \Omega)}{(121)(1003.03\ \Omega)} = 0.997 \cong 1.0$$

$$z_{in} = 150\ \text{k}\Omega\ //\ [(3.03\ \Omega + 1000\ \Omega)(121)]$$
$$= 67.1\ \text{k}\Omega$$

$$z_{out} = 1\ \text{k}\Omega\ //\left(3.03\ \Omega + \frac{600\ \Omega}{120}\right) = 7.97\ \Omega$$

$$A_i = \frac{(1.0)(67.1\ \text{k}\Omega)}{1\ \text{k}\Omega} = 67.1$$

$$A_p = (1.0)(67.1) = 67.1$$

32. a. $V_B = \left(\frac{20\ \text{k}\Omega}{35\ \text{k}\Omega}\right)24\ \text{V} = 13.71\ \text{V}$

$V_E = 13.71\ \text{V} - 0.7\ \text{V} = 13.01\ \text{V}$

$I_E = \frac{13.01\ \text{V}}{2.0\ \text{k}\Omega} = 6.51\ \text{mA} \cong I_{CQ}$

$V_{CEQ} = 24\ \text{V} - (6.51\ \text{mA})(2.0\ \text{k}\Omega) = 10.99\ \text{V}$

b. $r_e = \frac{26\ \text{mV}}{6.51\ \text{mA}} = 3.99\ \Omega$

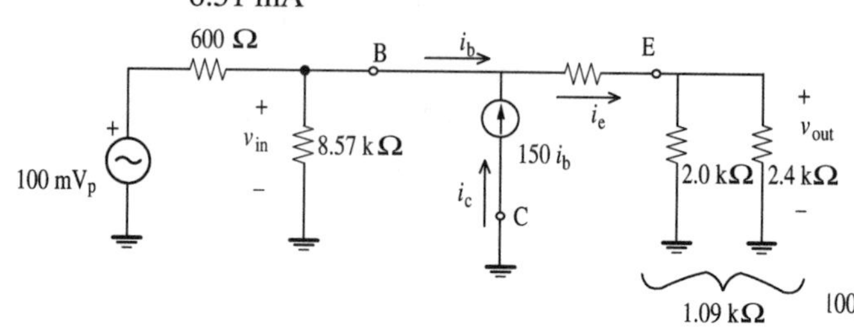

c. $A_v = \frac{(151\ i_b)(2.0\ \text{k}\Omega\ //\ 2.4\ \text{k}\Omega)}{(151\ i_b)(3.99\ \Omega + 2.0\ \text{k}\Omega\ //\ 2.4\ \text{k}\Omega)} = 0.996 \cong 1.0$

$z_{in} = 8.57\ \text{k}\Omega\ //\ [(151\ i_b)(3.99\ \Omega + 2.0\ \text{k}\Omega\ //\ 2.4\ \text{k}\Omega)$
$= 8.15\ \text{k}\Omega$

$z_{out} = 2.0\ \text{k}\Omega\ //\left[3.99\ \Omega + \frac{8.57\ \text{k}\Omega\ //\ 0.6\ \text{k}\Omega}{151}\right] = 7.67\ \Omega$

$A_i = \frac{(0.996)(8.15\ \text{k}\Omega)}{2.4\ \text{k}\Omega} = 3.38$

$A_p = (0.996)(3.38) = 3.37$

34. a. At the operating point ($I_{CQ} = 8.58$ mA and $V_{CE} = 11.42$ V), the h-parameters are:

$h_{fe} \cong 180$, $h_{oe} \cong 60\ \mu\text{s}$, $h_{ie} \cong 600\Omega$

$h_{re} \cong 2.2 \times 10^{-4}$

b.

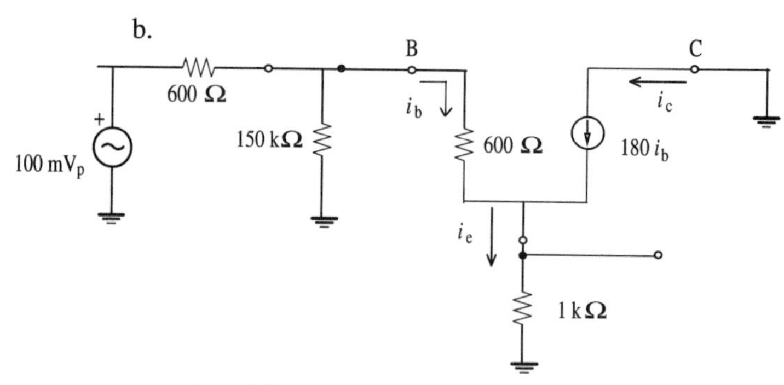

c. $A_v \cong 1.0$

$z_{in} = 150\ \text{k}\Omega\ //\ [600\Omega + (181)(1\text{k}\Omega)] = 82.1\ \text{k}\Omega$

$z_{out} = 1\ \text{k}\Omega\ //\left(\frac{600\Omega + 600\Omega}{181}\right) \cong 6.6\ \Omega$

$A_i = \frac{(1.0)(82.1\ \text{k}\Omega)}{1\ \text{k}\Omega} = 82.1$

$A_p = (1.0)(82.1) = 82.1$

36. a. At the operating point ($I_{CQ} = 6.51$ mA, $V_{CEQ} = 11.0$ V) the h-parameters are:

$h_{fe} \cong 170$, $h_{oe} \cong 45\ \mu\text{s}$, $h_{ie} \cong 700\ \Omega$

$h_{re} \cong 1.8 \times 10^{-4}$

b.

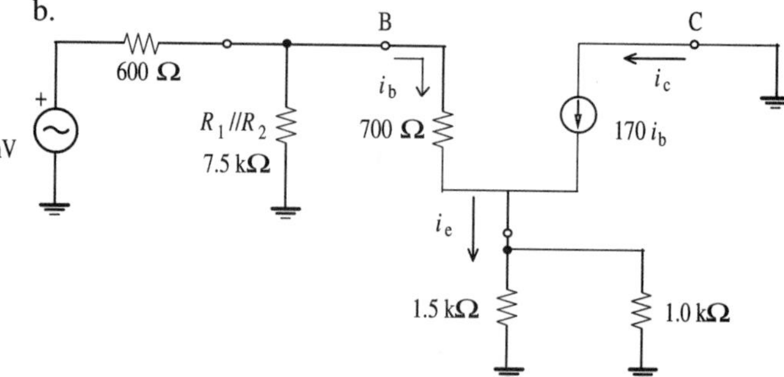

c. $A_v \cong 1.0$

$z_{in} = 7.5\ \text{k}\Omega\ //\ [700\ \Omega + 171\ (1.5\ \text{k}\Omega\ //\ 1.0\ \text{k}\Omega)]$
$= 6.99\ \text{k}\Omega$

$z_{out} = 1.5\ \text{k}\Omega\ //\left[\frac{700\ \Omega + 600\ \Omega//7500\ \Omega}{171}\right] = 7.31\ \Omega$

$A_i = \frac{(1.0)(6.99\ \text{k}\Omega)}{1.0\ \text{k}\Omega} = 6.99$

$A_p = (1.0)(6.99) = 6.99$

27.7 The FET Small-Signal Model

38. a. $g_{mo} = \frac{2(9.0\ \text{mA})}{5.0\ \text{V}} = 3.6\ \text{mS}$

$g_m = 3.6\ \text{mS}\left(1 - \frac{2.0\ \text{V}}{5.0\ \text{V}}\right) = 2.16\ \text{mS}$

b. $g_m = 3.6\ \text{mS}\left(1 - \frac{1.5\ \text{V}}{5.0\ \text{V}}\right) = 2.52\ \text{mS}$

c. $I_D = 9.0\ \text{mA}\left(1 - \frac{V_{GS}}{5.0\ \text{V}}\right)^2$

$V_{GS} = (5.0\ \text{V})\left(1 - \sqrt{\frac{6.0\ \text{mA}}{9.0\ \text{mA}}}\right) = 0.918\ \text{V}$

$g_m = 3.6\ \text{mS}\left(1 - \frac{0.918\ \text{V}}{5.0\ \text{V}}\right) = 2.94\ \text{mS}$

40. a. $50\text{ mA} = k\,(5.0\text{ V} - 3.0\text{ V})^2$

$k = 12.5\,\dfrac{\text{mA}}{\text{V}^2}$

b. $g_m = 2\left(12.5\,\dfrac{\text{mA}}{V^2}\right)(5.0\text{ V} - 3.0\text{ V}) = 50\text{ mS}$

c. $30\text{ mA} = 12.5\,\dfrac{\text{mA}}{V^2}\,(V_{GS} - 3.0\text{ V})^2$

$V_{GS} = 3.0\text{ V} + \sqrt{\dfrac{30\text{ mA}}{12.5\,\dfrac{\text{mA}}{V^2}}} = 4.55\text{ V}$

$g_m = 2\left(12.5\,\dfrac{\text{mA}}{V^2}\right)(4.55\text{ V} - 3.0\text{ V}) = 38.7\text{ mS}$

d. $V_{GS} = 5.19\text{ V}$ $\qquad g_m = 54.8\text{ mS}$

27.8 The Common-Source Amplifier

42. a. $I_D = 10\text{ mA}\left(1 - \dfrac{V_{GS}}{-5\text{ V}}\right)^2$ ①

$V_{GS} = -(1.0\text{ k}\Omega)\,I_D$ ②

Quadratic equation:

$V_{GS}^2 + 12.5\,V_{GS} + 25 = 0$

$V_{GS} = -12.5 \pm \sqrt{\dfrac{(12.5)^2 - 4(25)}{2(1)}} = -2.5\text{ V}, \cancel{-10\text{ V}}$

$I_{DQ} = 2.5\text{ mA},\qquad V_{DSQ} = 3.75\text{ V}$

b. $g_{mo} = \dfrac{2(10\text{ mA})}{5\text{ V}} = 4.0\text{ mS}$

$g_m = 4.0\text{ ms}\left(1 - \dfrac{2.5\text{ V}}{5.0\text{ V}}\right) = 2.0\text{ mS}$

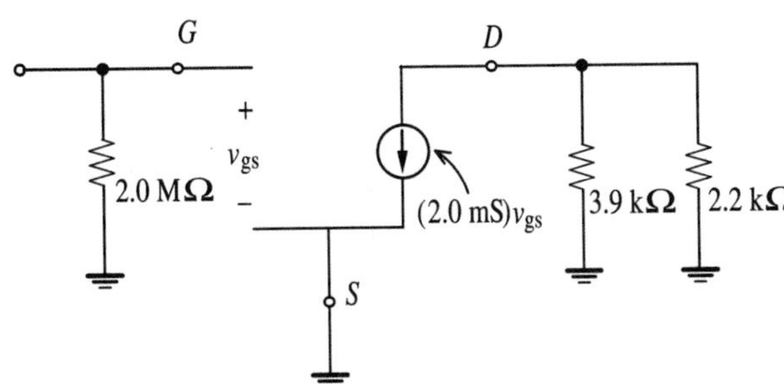

$A_v = -\dfrac{(2.0\text{ mS})\cancel{v_{gs}}(3.9\text{ k}\Omega \,//\, 2.2\text{ k}\Omega)}{\cancel{v_{gs}}} - 2.81$

$z_{in} = 2.0\text{ M}\Omega$

$z_{out} = 3.9\text{ k}\Omega$

44. a. $V_G = \left(\dfrac{220\text{ k}\Omega}{690\text{ k}\Omega}\right)16\text{ V} = 5.10\text{ V}$

$I_D = 8\text{ mA}\left(1 + \dfrac{V_{GS}}{+4\text{ V}}\right)^2$ ①

$5.10\text{ V} = V_{GS} + I_D\,(1.1\text{ k}\Omega)$ ②

Quadratic equation:

$V_{GS}^2 + 9.82\,V_{GS} + 6.72 = 0$

$V_{GS} = \dfrac{-9.82 \pm \sqrt{(9.82)^2 - 4(1)(6.72)}}{2(1)}$

$= -0.741\text{ V}, \cancel{9.08\text{ V}}$

$I_{DQ} = 5.31\text{ mA}\qquad V_{DSQ} = 4.32\text{ V}$

b. $g_{mo} = \dfrac{2(8\text{ mA})}{4\text{ V}} = 4.0\text{ mS}$

$g_m = 4.0\text{ mS}\left(1 - \dfrac{-0.741\text{ V}}{-4\text{ V}}\right) = 3.26\text{ mS}$

$A_v = -\dfrac{(3.26\text{ mS})\cancel{v_{gs}}(1.1\text{ k}\Omega \,//\, 2.2\text{ k}\Omega)}{\cancel{v_{gs}}} = -2.39$

$z_{in} = 150\text{ k}\Omega\qquad z_{out} = 1.1\text{ k}\Omega$

46. a. $V_G = \left(\dfrac{220\text{ k}\Omega}{1220\text{ k}\Omega}\right)(-20\text{ V}) = -3.61\text{ V}$

$I_D = 7.5\text{ mA}\left(1 - \dfrac{V_{GS}}{4.0\text{ V}}\right)^2$ ①

$-3.61\text{ V} = V_{GS} - I_D\,(0.87\text{ k}\Omega)$ ②

Quadratic equation:

$V_{GS}^2 - 10.5\,V_{GS} + 7.16 = 0$

$V_{GS} = 0.737\text{ V}, \cancel{9.72\text{ V}}$

$I_{DSQ} = 4.99\text{ mA}\ ,\ V_{DSQ} = -9.67\text{ V}$

b. $g_{mo} = \dfrac{2(7.5\text{ mA})}{4.0\text{ V}} = 3.75\text{ mS}$

$g_m = 3.75\text{ mS}\left(1 - \dfrac{0.737\text{ V}}{4.0\text{ V}}\right) = 3.06\text{ mS}$

c.

$$A_V = -\frac{(3.06\text{ mS})v_{gs}(1.2\text{ k}\Omega \,//\, 1.5\text{ k}\Omega)}{v_{gs} + (3.06\text{ mS})v_{gs}(0.2\text{ k}\Omega}= -1.26$$

$z_{in} = 180\text{ k}\Omega,$ $z_{out} = 1.2\text{ k}\Omega$

27.9 The Common-Drain (Source Follower) Amplifier

48. a. $$I_D = 10\text{ mA}\left(1 + \frac{V_{GS}}{5\text{ V}}\right)^2$$

$V_{GS} = -0.47\text{ k}\Omega\, I_D$

Quadratic equation:

$V_{GS}^2 + 15.3\, V_{GS} + 25 = 0$

$V_{GS} = -1.86$ V, ~~-6.73 V~~

b. $I_{DQ} = 3.95$ mA, $V_{DSQ} = 14.14$ V

$$g_{mo} = \frac{2(10\text{ mA})}{5\text{ V}} = 4.0\text{ mS}$$

$$g_m = 4.0\text{ mS}\left(1 - \frac{V_{GS}}{-5\text{ V}}\right) = 2.51\text{ mS}$$

c.

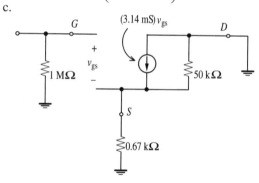

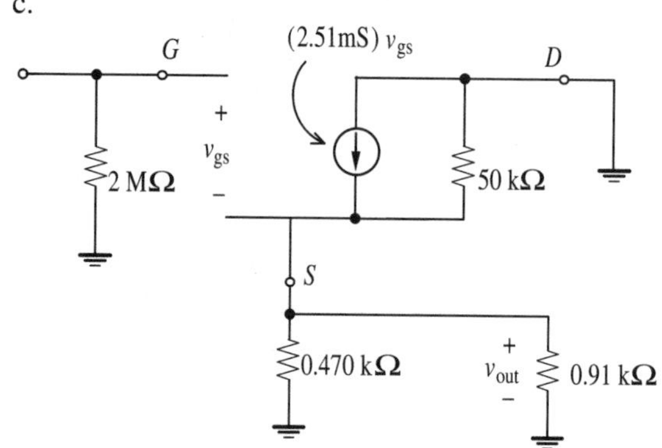

$$A_V = \frac{(2.51\text{ mS})v_{gs}(0.47\text{ k}\Omega \,//\, 0.91\text{ k}\Omega)}{v_{gs} + (2.51\text{ mS})v_{gs}(0.47\text{ k}\Omega \,//\, 0.91\text{ k}\Omega)} = 0.438$$

$z_{in} = 2\text{ M}\Omega$

$$z_{out} = 0.470\text{ k}\Omega \,//\left(\frac{1}{2.51\text{ mS}}\right) = 216\ \Omega$$

50. a. $$V_G = \left(\frac{220\text{ k}\Omega}{1220\text{ k}\Omega}\right)(-16\text{ V}) = -2.89\text{ V}$$

$$I_D = 7.5\text{ mA}\left(1 - \frac{V_{GS}}{4\text{ V}}\right)^2 \qquad ①$$

$$-2.89\text{ V} = V_{GS} - (0.67\text{ k}\Omega)\, I_D \qquad ②$$

Quadratic equation:

$V_{GS}^2 - 11.18\, V_{GS} + 6.81 = 0$

$V_{GS} = 0.647$ V, ~~10.54 V~~

$I_{DQ} = 5.27$ mA $V_{DSQ} = -12.47$ V

b. $$g_{mo} = \frac{2(7.5\text{ mA})}{4\text{ V}} = 3.75\text{ mS}$$

$$g_m = 3.75\text{ mS}\left(1 - \frac{0.647\text{ V}}{4\text{ V}}\right) = 3.14\text{ mS}$$

c.

$$A_V = \frac{(3.14\text{ mS})v_{gs}(0.67\text{ k}\Omega)}{v_{gs} + (3.14\text{ mS})v_{gs}(0.67\text{ k}\Omega)} = 0.678$$

$z_{in} = 1\text{ M}\Omega$

$$z_{out} = \frac{1}{3.14\text{ mS}} = 318\ \Omega$$

27.10 Troubleshooting a Transistor Amplifier Circuit

52. Noise can be the result of:

- An incorrectly placed electrolytic capacitor
- A faulty electrolytic capacitor.

54. a. $$I_B = \frac{20\text{ V} - 0.7\text{ V}}{910\text{ k}\Omega + 150(0.66\text{ k}\Omega)} = 19.13\ \mu\text{A}$$

$I_C = 2.87$ mA, $V_{CE} = -10.36$ V

b. $A_V \approx -13.5$

c. i) R_{E2} would be shorted, resulting in:

$$I_B = \frac{20\text{ V} - 0.7\text{ V}}{910\text{ k}\Omega + 150(0.1\text{ k}\Omega)} = 20.9\ \mu\text{A}$$

$I_C = 3.13$ mA, $V_{CE} = -11.24$ V

ii) $$A_V \approx \frac{2.7\text{ k}\Omega \parallel 2.7\text{ k}\Omega}{0.1\text{ k}\Omega} = -13.5$$

d. i) There is no effect on the operating point.

ii) $A_V \approx -\dfrac{2.7\ \text{k}\Omega \parallel 2.7\ \text{k}\Omega}{0.66\ \text{k}\Omega} = -2.05$

(The voltage gain decreases.)

56. a. If C_E is an open circuit there is no change in the operating point, since the original calculations are based on this assumption.

$I_C \cong 2.24$ mA, $V_{CE} \cong -9.50$ V

b. Voltage will decrease

$$A_V = \frac{-(150\ i_b)(3.3\ \text{k}\Omega\ //\ 2.2\ \text{k}\Omega)}{2.0\ \text{k}\Omega i_b + (151)(0.18\ \text{k}\Omega + 0.67\ \text{k}\Omega)} = -1.52$$

27.11 Computer Analysis of Transistor Amplifier Circuits

58.

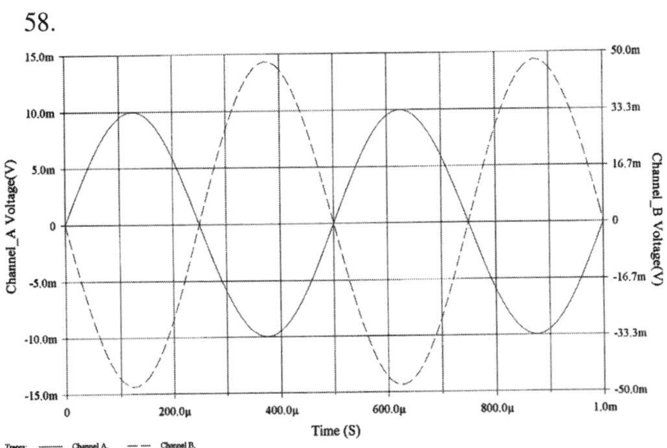

$$A_V = -\frac{47.79\ \text{mV}}{10\ \text{mV}} = -4.78$$

60.

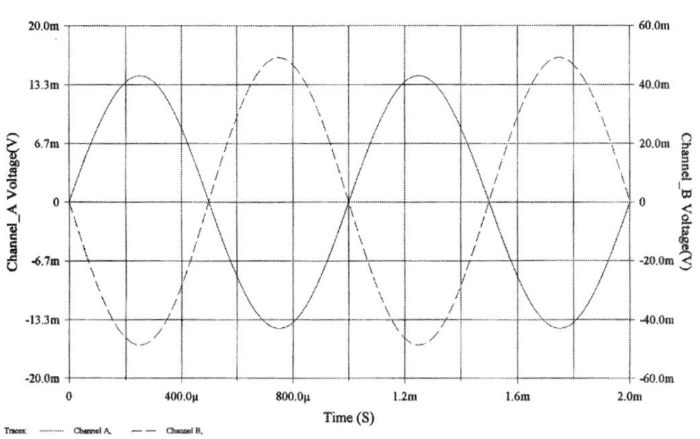

$$A_V = -\frac{49.25\ \text{mV}}{14.36\ \text{mV}} = -3.43$$

62.

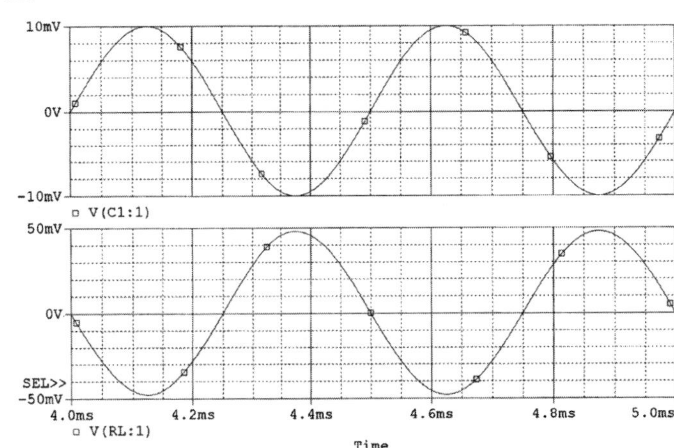

$$A_V = -\frac{48.0\ \text{mV}}{10\ \text{mV}} = -4.80$$

64.

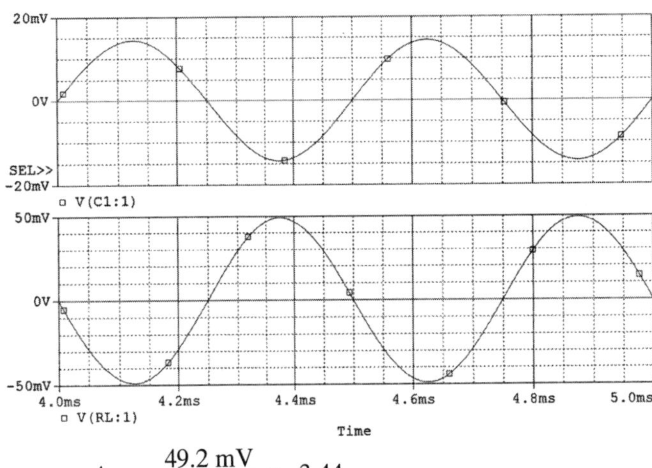

$$A_V = -\frac{49.2\ \text{mV}}{14.31\ \text{mV}} = -3.44$$

Chapter

28

Operational Amplifiers

28.1 Introduction to the Operational Amplifier

2. a. Inverting mode (single-ended)
   b. Differential mode

28.2 The Differential Amplifier and Common-Mode Signals

4. $V_E = -0.7$ V

$$I_E = \frac{-0.7\text{ V} - (-12\text{ V})}{1.8\text{ k}\Omega} = 6.28\text{ mA}$$

$$I_{C1} = I_{C2} = \frac{6.28\text{ mA}}{2} = 3.14\text{ mA}$$

$$V_{C1} = V_{C2} = 12\text{ V} - (3.14\text{ mA})(1.2\text{ k}\Omega) = 8.23\text{ V}$$

6. a. $$[\text{CMRR}]_{\text{dB}} = 20\log\left(\frac{100{,}000}{0.02}\right) = 134\text{ dB}$$

   b. Yes

8. $$\text{CMRR} = 10{,}000 = \frac{A_{vd}}{A_{vc}}$$

$$A_{vc} = \frac{20}{10{,}000} = 0.002$$

$$V_{S(\text{input})} = \frac{10\text{ V}_{\text{p-p}}}{20} = 0.5\text{ V}_{\text{p-p}}$$

$$V_{N(\text{input})} = \frac{10\text{ V}_{\text{p-p}}}{1000} = 10\text{ mV}_{\text{p-p}}$$

$$V_{N(\text{input})} = \frac{10\text{ mV}_{\text{p-p}}}{0.002} = 5.0\text{ V}_{\text{p-p}}$$

28.4 The Inverting Amplifier

10. $$A_v = -\frac{68\text{ k}\Omega}{15\text{ k}\Omega} = -4.53 \quad , z_{in} = 15\text{ k}\Omega$$

$$z_{out} = (1 + 4.53)\left(\frac{75\ \Omega}{200{,}000}\right) = 2.08\text{ m}\Omega$$

$$v_{out} = -2.27\text{ V}$$

12. $R_1 = z_{in} = 7.5\text{ k}\Omega$

$R_2 = 4(7.5\text{ k}\Omega) = 30\text{ k}\Omega$

28.5 Non-inverting Amplifier

14. $$A_v = \left(\frac{68\text{ k}\Omega}{15\text{ k}\Omega} + 1\right) = 5.53$$

$$z_{in} = \left(\frac{1 + 200{,}000}{5.53}\right)(2\text{ M}\Omega) = 72.3\text{ G}\Omega$$

$$z_{out} = \left(\frac{5.53}{200{,}000}\right)75\ \Omega = 2.08\text{ m}\Omega$$

16. Select $R_1 = 10\text{ k}\Omega$

$R_2 = (4 - 1)(10\text{ k}\Omega) = 30\text{ k}\Omega$

18. a. $$v_{out} = \left(\frac{100\ \Omega}{10.1\text{ k}\Omega}\right)100\text{ mV}_p = 0.99\text{ mV}_p$$

   b. $$v_{in} = \left(\frac{400\text{ G}\Omega}{400\text{ G}\Omega + 10\text{ k}\Omega}\right)100\text{ mV}_p = 100\text{ mV}_p$$

$v_{out} = 100\text{ mV}_p$ (as required).

28.6 Op-Amp Specifications

20. $A_v = 1.0$

$V_{out} = (1)(2.0\text{ mV}) = 2.0\text{ mV}$

22. $$I_B = \frac{65\text{ nA} + 45\text{ nA}}{2} = 55\text{ nA}$$

$$I_{OS} = 65\text{ nA} - 45\text{ nA} = 20\text{ nA}$$

24. $$0.7\text{ V} = (1\text{ M}\Omega)I_{B(-)}\left(\frac{20\text{ k}\Omega}{1\text{ k}\Omega} + 1\right) + 20\text{ k}\Omega I_{B(-)}$$

$$= (21\text{ M}\Omega)I_{B(-)} + (20\text{ k}\Omega)I_{B(-)}$$

$$I_{B(-)} = \frac{0.7\text{ V}}{20.02\text{ M}\Omega} = 35.0\text{ nA}$$

26. $$\text{BW} = \frac{1 \times 10^6 \text{ Hz}}{4.53} = 220 \text{ kHz}$$

28. $$\text{BW} = \frac{1 \times 10^6 \text{ Hz}}{4} = 250 \text{ kHz}$$

30. Slew rate for 741 op-amp is 0.5 V/μs

$$A = \frac{\text{slew rate}}{2\,\pi f} = \frac{0.5 \text{ V/μs}}{2\,\pi\,(10 \text{ kHz})} = 7.96 \text{ V}_\text{P}$$

$$V_{in(max)} = \frac{7.96 \text{ V}_\text{P}}{4} = 1.99 \text{ V}_\text{P}$$

32. $R_C = 15 \text{ kΩ} \,//\, 68 \text{ kΩ} = 12.3 \text{ kΩ}$

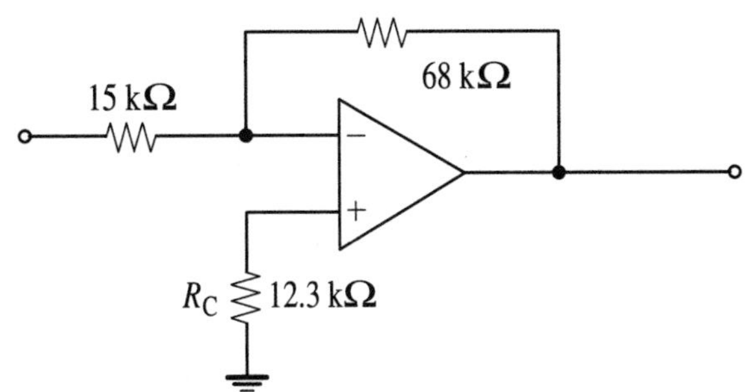

28.7 Troubleshooting an Op-Amp Circuit

34. Feedback resistor becomes an open-circuit.
Input resistor is shorted.

36.

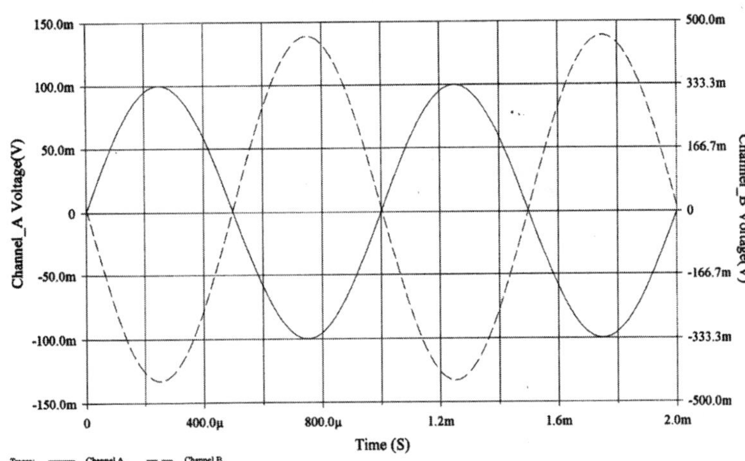

$$A_V = -\frac{463.7 \text{ mV}}{100 \text{ mV}} = -4.64$$

28.8 Computer Analysis of Op-Amp Circuits

38.

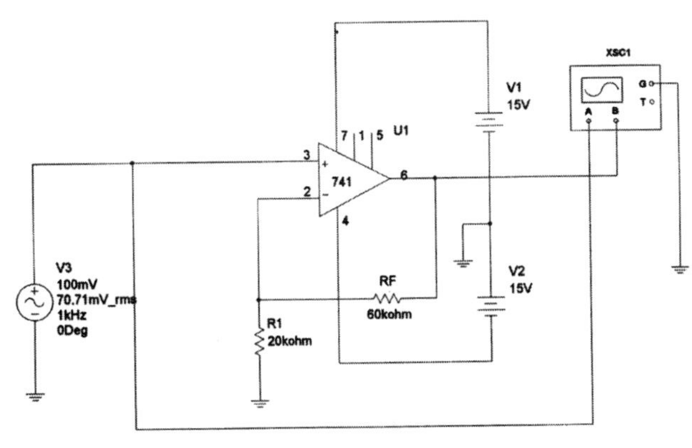

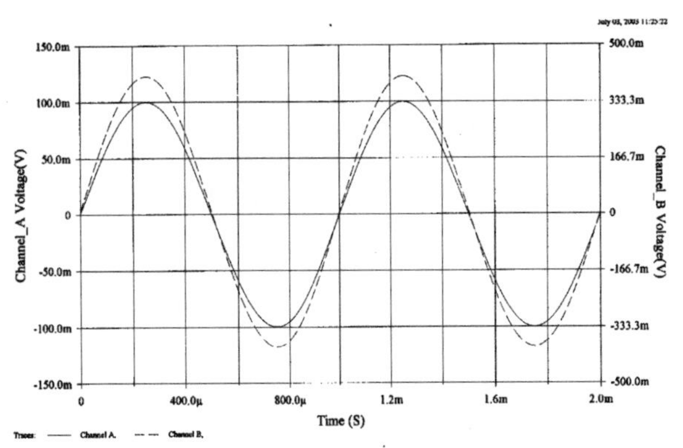

$$A_V = +\frac{408.3 \text{ mV}}{100 \text{ mV}} = +4.08$$

40.

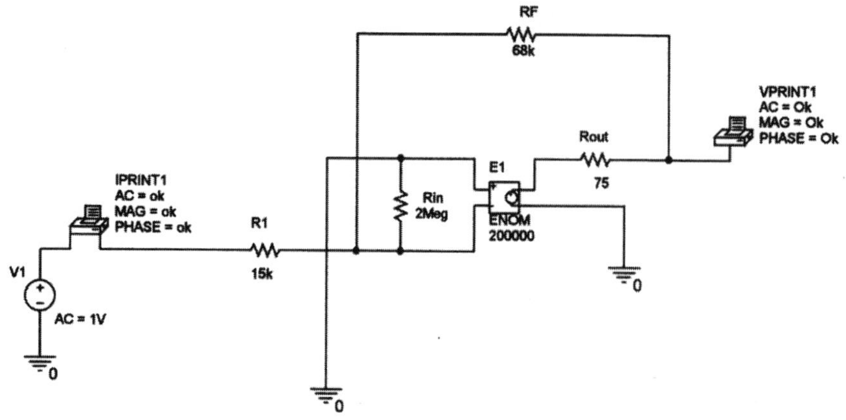

From the output file, we have:

$$z_{in} = \frac{1.00 \text{ V}}{6.667 \times 10^{-5} \text{ A}} = 15 \text{ k}\Omega$$

$$z_{out} = \frac{4.533 \text{ V}}{2.171 \times 10^{3} \text{ A}} = 2.09 \text{ m}\Omega$$

42.

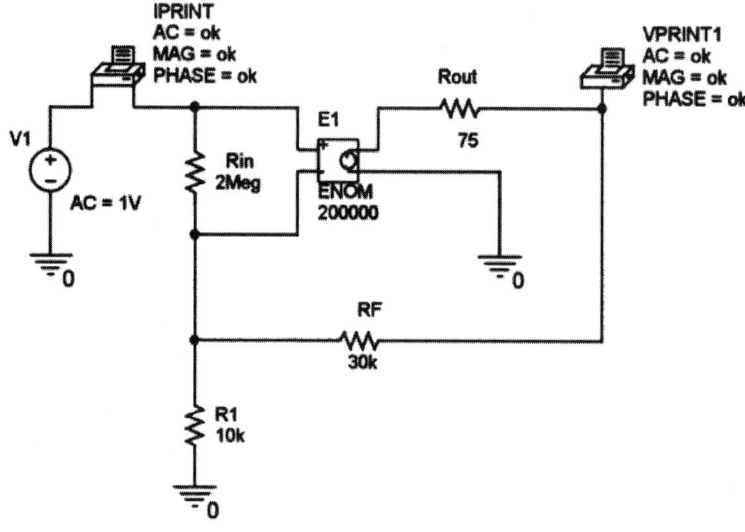

From the output file:

$$z_{in} = \frac{1.00 \text{ V}}{1.002 \times 10^{-11} \text{ A}} = 99.8 \text{ G}\Omega$$

$$z_{out} = \frac{4.00 \text{ V}}{2.657 \times 10^{3} \text{ A}} = 1.505 \text{ m}\Omega$$

Chapter

29

Applications of Op-Amps

29.1 Comparators

2.

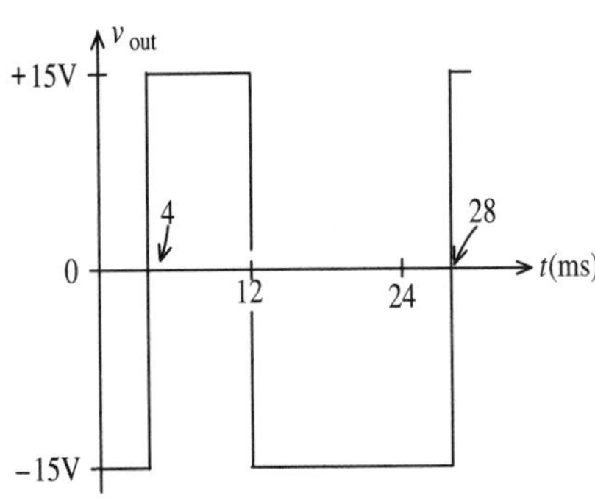

4.

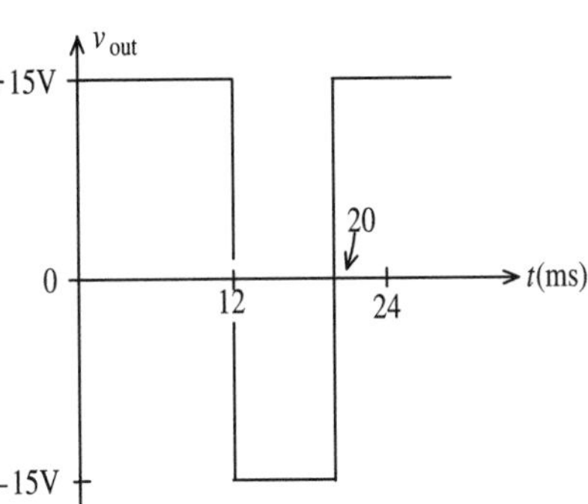

6. $v_{in} = 8$ V at 12.8 μs, 19.2 μs

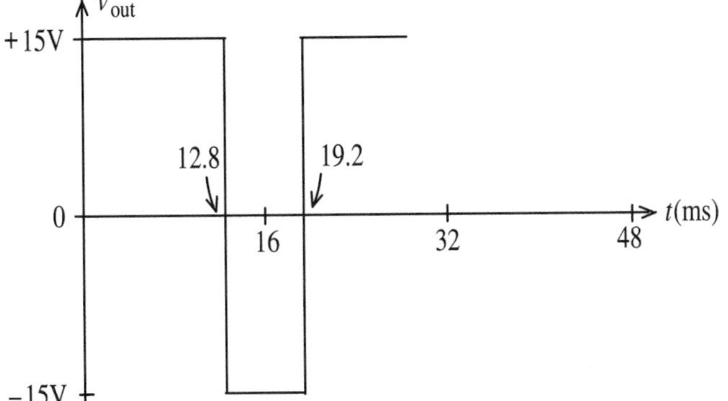

8. $v_{in} = -6$ V at 41.6 μs, 54.4 μs

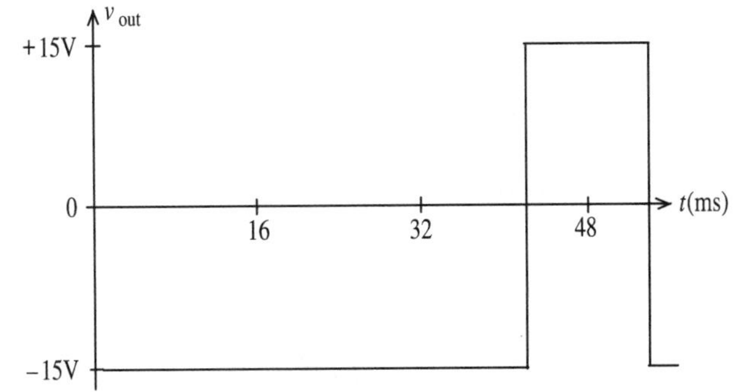

10.
$$V_{REF1} = \left(\frac{20\text{ k}\Omega}{30\text{ k}\Omega}\right)30\text{ V} + (-15\text{ V}) = +5\text{ V}$$
$$V_{REF2} = \left(\frac{10\text{ k}\Omega}{30\text{ k}\Omega}\right)30\text{ V} + (-15\text{ V}) = -5\text{ V}$$

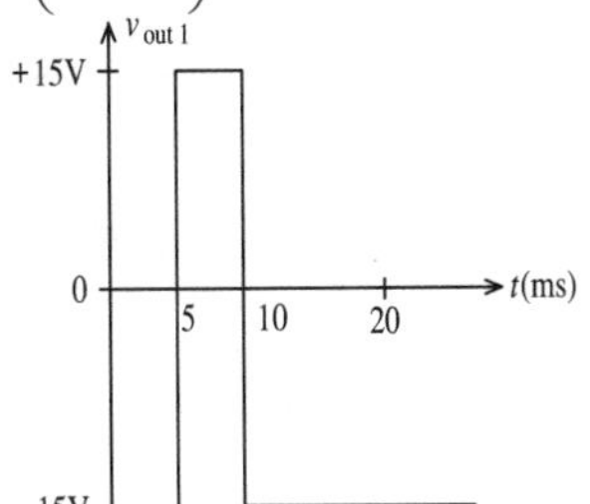

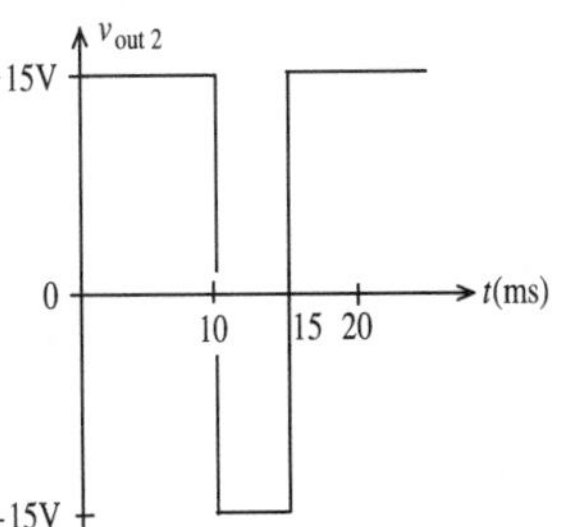

29.2 Voltage Summing Amplifier

12.
$$I_1 = \frac{2\text{ V}}{10\text{ k}\Omega} = 200\ \mu\text{A}$$
$$I_2 = \frac{1.5\text{ V}}{20\text{ k}\Omega} = 75\ \mu\text{A}$$
$$I_3 = -\frac{2.5\text{ V}}{30\text{ k}\Omega} = -83.3\ \mu\text{A}$$

$I_F = 200\ \mu\text{A} + 75\ \mu\text{A} - 83.3\ \mu\text{A} = 191.7\ \mu\text{A}$

$V_{out} = -(191.7\ \mu\text{A})(20\text{ k}\Omega) = -3.83\text{ V}$

14.

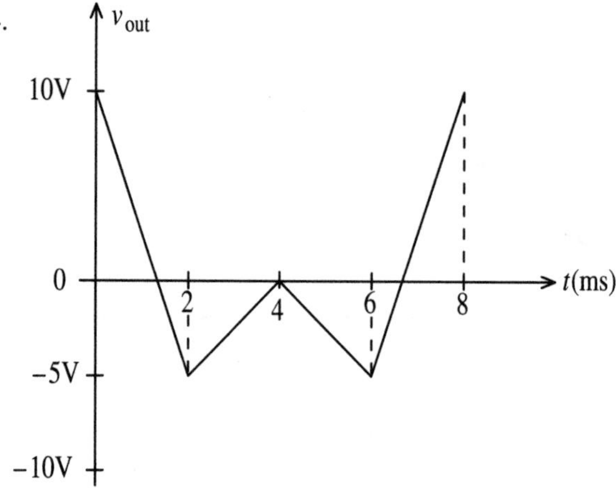

29.3 Integrators and Differentiators

16. $$T = \frac{1}{500\ \text{Hz}} = 2.00\ \text{ms}$$

charging time $= t = \frac{T}{2} = 1.00$ ms

a. $$v_{out} = -\frac{1}{(10\ \text{k}\Omega)(0.05\ \mu\text{F})}(4.0\ \text{V})(1\ \text{ms}) = -8.00\ \text{V}$$

If we assume $V_0 = 0$ V, this results in an output voltage $v_{out} = 8.00\ V_{p\text{-}p}$

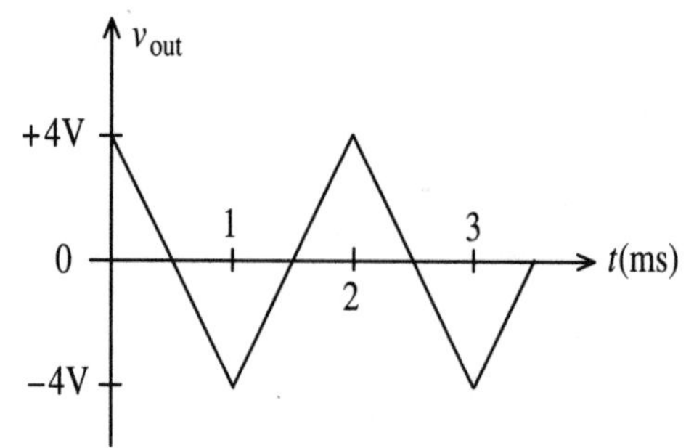

(The feedback resistor removes the dc offset voltage.)

18. $$C_{min} = \frac{(2.0\ \text{V})(1\ \text{ms})}{(10\ \text{k}\Omega)(30\ \text{V})} = 6.67\ \text{nF}$$

20. a. $$v(t) = 2000\frac{\text{V}}{\text{s}}t - 2\ \text{V}$$

$$v_{out} = -(10\ \text{k}\Omega)(100\ \text{nF})(2000\frac{\text{V}}{\text{s}}) = -2.0\ \text{V}$$

b.

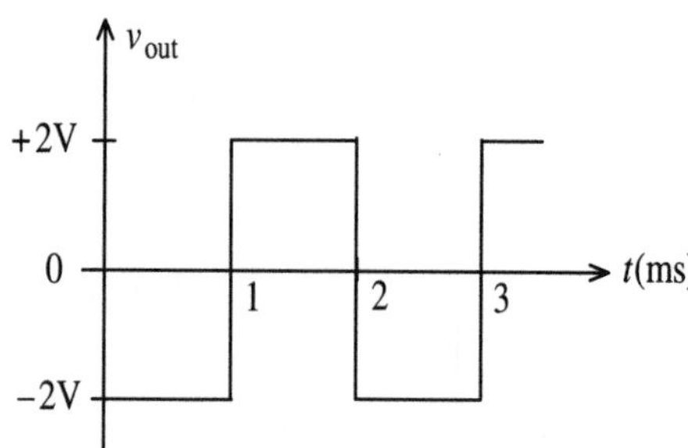

22. ① $(10\ \text{k}\Omega)(100\ \text{nF}) = (10^4)\ R_{in}\ C_F$

② $(10\ \text{k}\Omega)C_F = (R_{in})(100\ \text{nF})$

$$C_F = \frac{0.1 \times 10^{-6}}{R_{in}} \quad ①$$

$$C_F = (1.0 \times 10^{-11})\ R_{in} \quad ②$$

$$R_{in} = \sqrt{\frac{0.1 \times 10^{-6}}{1.0 \times 10^{-11}}} = 100\ \Omega$$

$C_F = 1.0$ nF

29.4 Instrumentation Amplifiers

24. $$I_{10\ \text{k}\Omega} = \frac{0.5\ \text{V}}{10\ \text{k}\Omega} = 50\ \mu\text{A} \quad \text{(downward)}$$

$$v_{out} = (0.050\ \text{mA})(68\ \text{k}\Omega + 10\ \text{k}\Omega + 68\ \text{k}\Omega) = 7.3\ \text{V}$$

26. $$V_{R1} = V_{R3} = \frac{30\ \text{V}}{2} = 15\ \text{V}$$

$$V_{R4} = \left(\frac{100.002\ \Omega}{200.002\ \Omega}\right)30\ \text{V} = 15.000150\ \text{V}$$

$v_{in1} = 15.000150\ \text{V} - 15\ \text{V} = 150\ \mu\text{V}$

$v_{in2} = 0$ V

$$A_v = \frac{680\ \text{k}\Omega}{10\ \text{k}\Omega} = 68$$

$v_{out} = -(68)(0.150\ \text{mV}) = -10.2$ mV

29.5 Active Filters

28. $\omega = (2\pi)(5\text{ kHz}) = 31.416\text{ krad/s}$

$$R_1C = \tau = \frac{1}{\omega} = 31.83\ \mu\text{s}$$

$$R_1 = \frac{31.83\ \mu\text{s}}{0.002\ \mu\text{F}} = 15.92\text{ k}\Omega$$

$$R_F = (20)(15.92\text{ k}\Omega) = 318\text{ k}\Omega$$

$$R_2 = \frac{1}{\frac{1}{R_1} - \frac{1}{R_F}} = 16.8\text{ k}\Omega$$

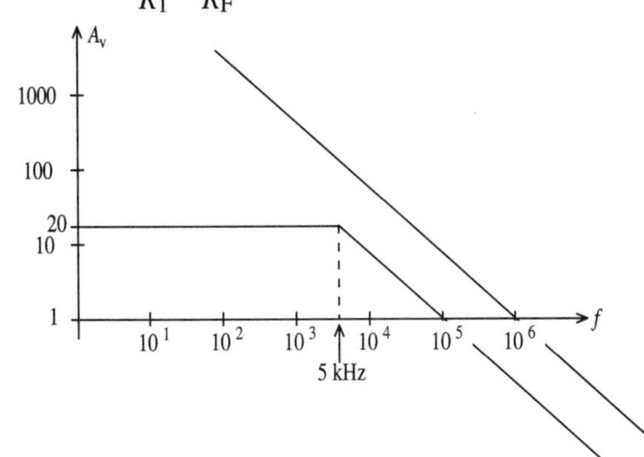

30. $$R_1 = \frac{1}{2\pi(250\text{ Hz})(0.4\ \mu\text{F})} = 1592\ \Omega$$

$$R_F = R_2(10 - 1)$$

$$R_F = 9R_2$$

But $R_1 = R_2 \,//\, R_F$; Therefore $R_2 = \frac{R_1}{0.9} = 1768\ \Omega$

$$R_F = 15.915\text{ k}\Omega$$

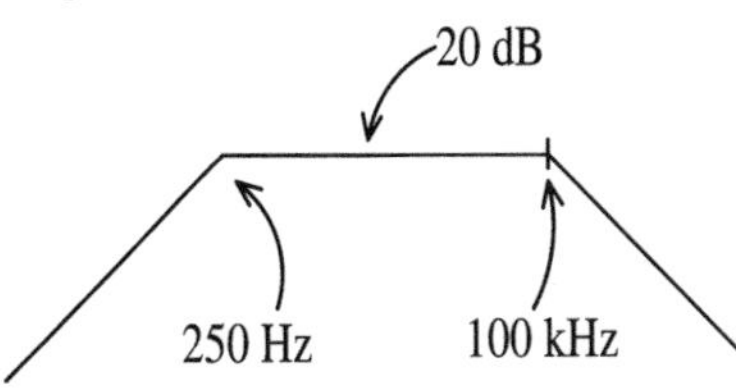

32. $f_0 = 500\text{ Hz}$, BW = 50 Hz

$$R = \frac{0.1591}{(50\text{ Hz})(0.1\ \mu\text{F})} = 31.82\text{ k}\Omega$$

$$500 = \frac{0.1125}{(31.82\text{ k}\Omega)(0.1\ \mu\text{F})}\sqrt{1 + \frac{31.82\text{ k}\Omega}{R_1}}$$

$$1 + \frac{31.82\text{ k}\Omega}{R_1} = 200$$

$$R_1 = 159.9\ \Omega$$

29.6 Voltage Regulation

34. For $E = 40$ V: $R_{Th} = 100\ \Omega \,//\, 100\ \Omega = 50\ \Omega$

$$E_{Th} = \left(\frac{100\ \Omega}{200\ \Omega}\right)40\text{ V} = 20\text{ V}$$

$$V_{out} = 10\text{ V} + 7\ \Omega\left(\frac{20\text{ V}}{50\ \Omega + 7\ \Omega}\right)$$

$$= 12.456\text{ V}$$

For $E = 60$ V: $$E_{Th} = \left(\frac{100\ \Omega}{200\ \Omega}\right)60\text{ V} = 30\text{ V}$$

$$V_{out} = 10\text{ V} + 7\ \Omega\left(\frac{30\text{ V}}{50\ \Omega + 7\ \Omega}\right)$$

$$= 13.684\text{ V}$$

$$\%\text{ line regulation} = \frac{\Delta V_{out}}{\Delta V_{in}} \times 100\ \% = 6.14\ \%$$

36. For $R_L = 50\ \Omega$: $R_{Th} = 50\ \Omega \,//\, 100\ \Omega = 33.33\ \Omega$

$$E_{Th} = \left(\frac{50\ \Omega}{150\ \Omega}\right)40\text{ V} = 13.33\text{ V}$$

$$V_{out} = 10\text{ V} + 7\ \Omega\left(\frac{13.33\text{ V}}{33.33\ \Omega + 7\ \Omega}\right)$$

$$= 12.314\text{ V}$$

For $R_L = 100\ \Omega$: $R_{Th} = 100\ \Omega \,//\, 100\ \Omega = 50\ \Omega$

$$E_{Th} = 20\text{ V}$$

$$V_{out} = 10\text{ V} + 7\ \Omega\left(\frac{20\text{ V}}{50\ \Omega + 7\ \Omega}\right)$$

$$= 12.456\text{ V}$$

Load regulation =
$$\frac{12.456\text{ V} - 12.314\text{ V}}{12.314\text{ V}} \times 100\ \% = 1.15\ \%$$

38. a. For $I_Z \geq 10$ mA,

$$V_{out(min)} = 6.2\text{ V} + (10\text{ mA})(0.33\text{ k}\Omega) = 9.5\text{ V}$$

$$V_{out(max)} = 28\text{ V} - 3\text{ V} = 25\text{ V}$$

$$V_{out} = 9.5\text{ V} \rightarrow 25\text{ V}$$

b. When $V_{out} = 9.5$ V,

$$I_{2k\Omega} = \frac{9.5\text{ V}}{4\text{ k}\Omega} = 2.38\text{ mA}$$

$$I_{330\Omega} = 10\text{ mA}$$

$$I_L = \frac{9.5\text{ V}}{50\ \Omega} = 190\text{ mA}$$

$$I_T = 190\text{ mA} + 10\text{ mA} + 2.38\text{ mA}$$

$$= 202\text{ mA}$$

$$P = (28\text{ V} - 9.5\text{ V})(0.202\text{ mA}) = 3.75\text{ W}$$

When $V_{out} = 25$ V,

$$I_{2k\Omega} = \frac{25\text{ V}}{4\text{ k}\Omega} = 6.25\text{ mA}$$

$$I_{330\Omega} = \frac{25\text{ V} - 6.2\text{ V}}{0.33\text{ k}\Omega} = 56.97\text{ mA}$$

$$I_L = \frac{25\text{ V}}{50\ \Omega} = 500\text{ mA}$$

$$I_T = 500\text{ mA} + 57\text{ mA} + 6\text{mA} = 563\text{ mA}$$

$$P = (3\text{ V})(0.563\text{ mA}) = 1.69\text{ W}$$

40. $$[\text{ripple rejection}]_{dB} = 20 \log \frac{V_{r(in)}}{V_{r(out)}}$$

$$V_{r(max\text{-}out)} = V_{r(in)}\, 10^{-58/20} = (4\ V_{p\text{-}p})\, 10^{-2.9} = 5.0\ mV_{p\text{-}p}$$

42.

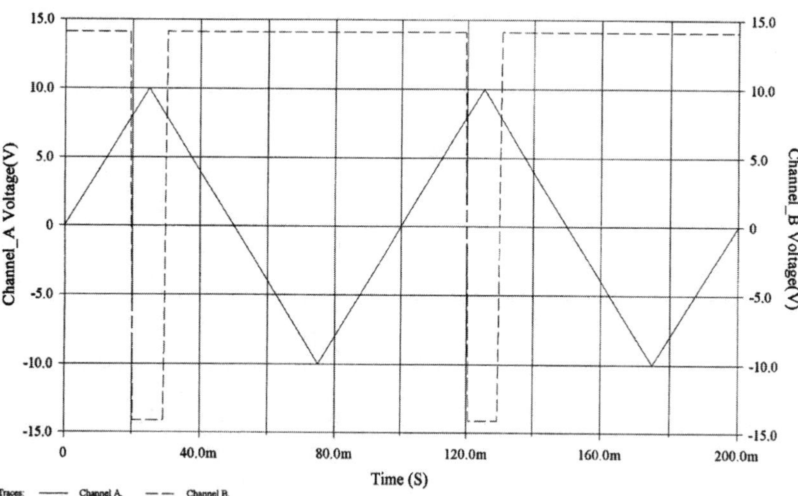

44.

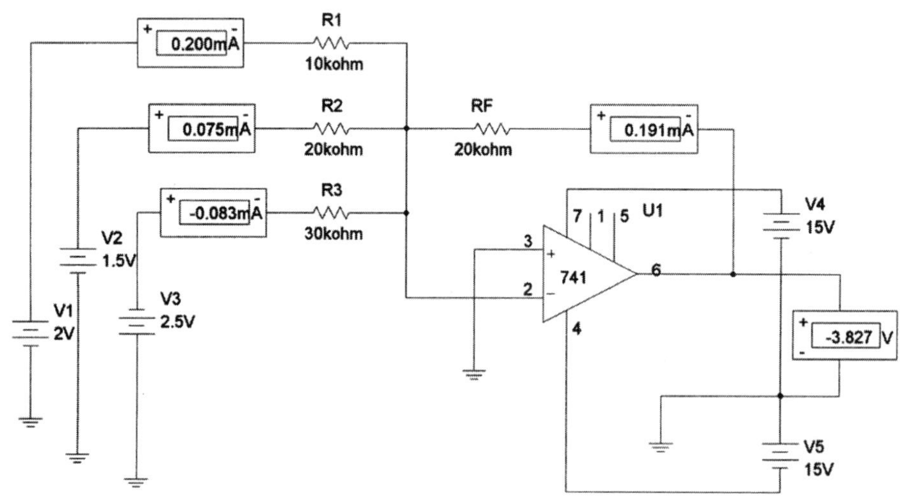

46.

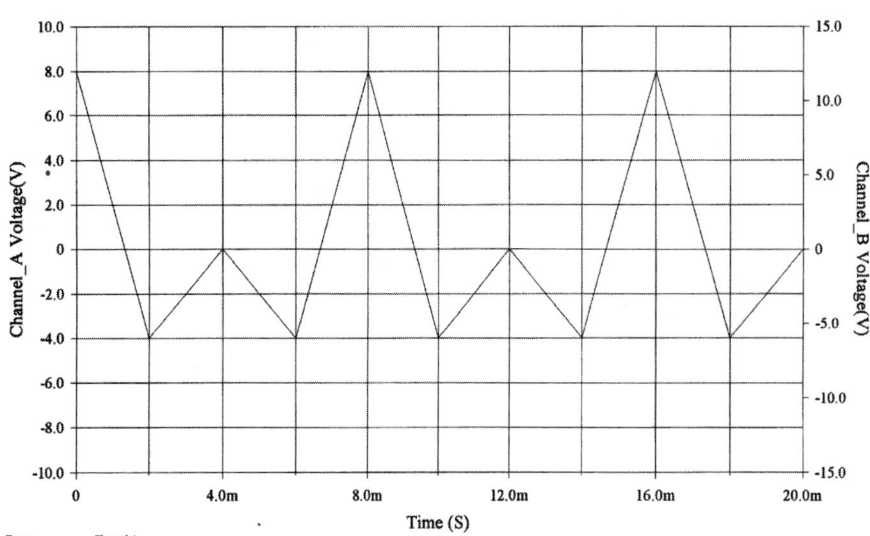

48. 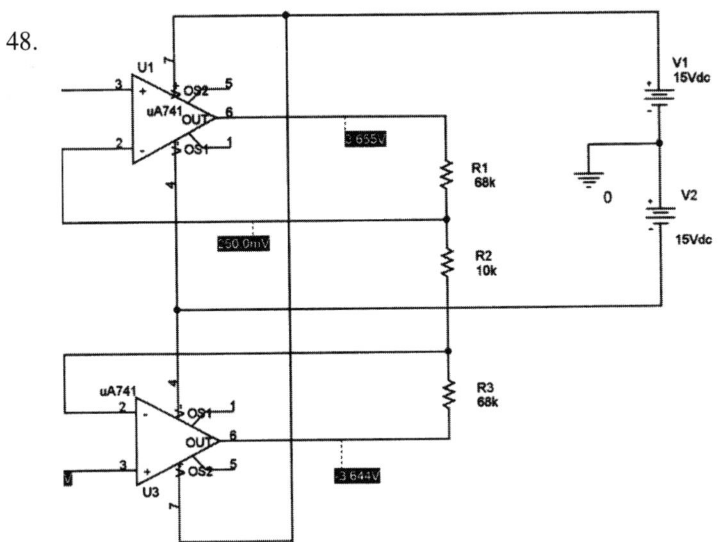

$V_{out} = 3.655\text{ V} - (-3.644\text{ V}) = 7.30\text{ V}$
(same as theoretical value)

50. 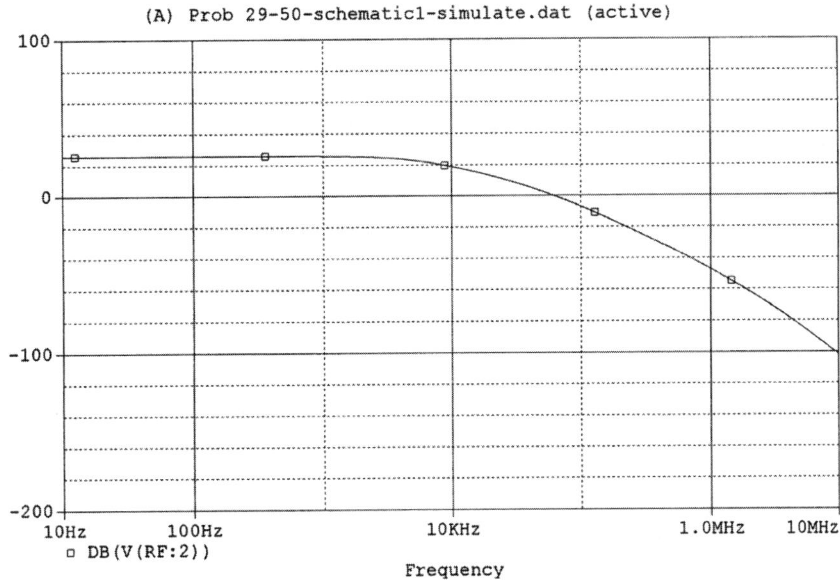

Chapter

30

Oscillators

30.1 Basics of Feedback

2. $$B = \frac{10\ \text{k}\Omega}{10\ \text{k}\Omega + 90\ \text{k}\Omega} = 0.1$$

$$A_{\text{vcl}} = \frac{1000}{1 + (1000)(0.1)} = 9.90$$

30.2 The Relaxation Oscillator

4. a. $$V_{(+)} = \pm\left(\frac{4\ \text{k}\Omega}{4\ \text{k}\Omega + 4\ \text{k}\Omega}\right)15\ \text{V} = \pm 7.5\ \text{V}$$

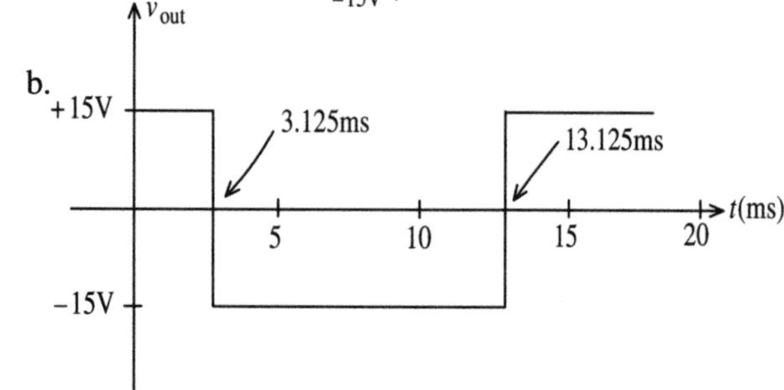

b.

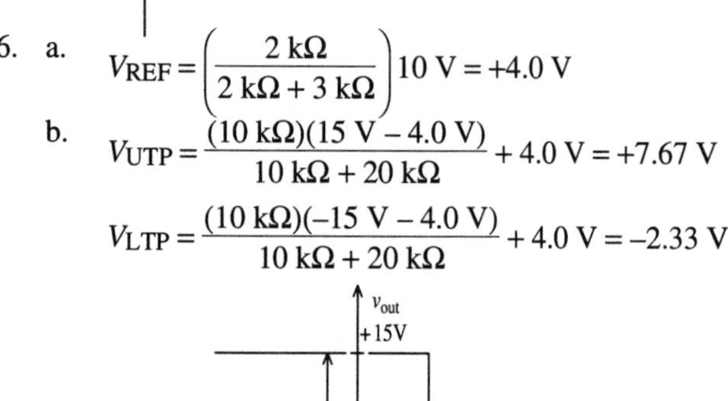

6. a. $$V_{\text{REF}} = \left(\frac{2\ \text{k}\Omega}{2\ \text{k}\Omega + 3\ \text{k}\Omega}\right)10\ \text{V} = +4.0\ \text{V}$$

b. $$V_{\text{UTP}} = \frac{(10\ \text{k}\Omega)(15\ \text{V} - 4.0\ \text{V})}{10\ \text{k}\Omega + 20\ \text{k}\Omega} + 4.0\ \text{V} = +7.67\ \text{V}$$

$$V_{\text{LTP}} = \frac{(10\ \text{k}\Omega)(-15\ \text{V} - 4.0\ \text{V})}{10\ \text{k}\Omega + 20\ \text{k}\Omega} + 4.0\ \text{V} = -2.33\ \text{V}$$

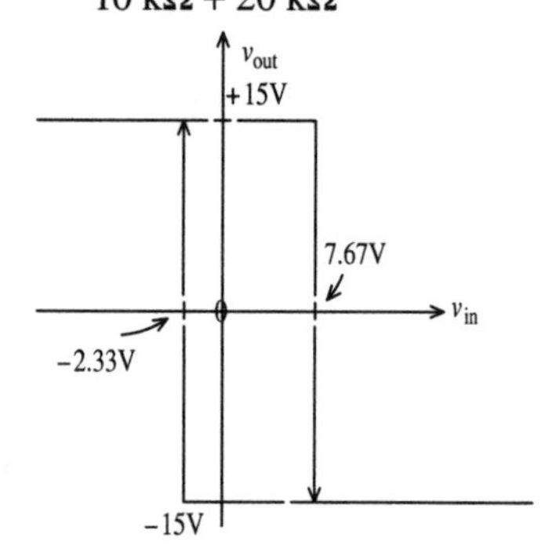

c. $$v_{\text{in}} = 7.67\ \text{V}\ @\ t = \left(\frac{7.67\ \text{V}}{12\ \text{V}}\right)5\ \text{ms} = 3.19\ \text{ms}$$

$$v_{\text{in}} = -2.33\ \text{V}\ @\ t = \left(\frac{-2.33\ \text{V}}{-12\ \text{V}}\right)5\ \text{ms} + 10\ \text{ms} = 10.97\ \text{ms}$$

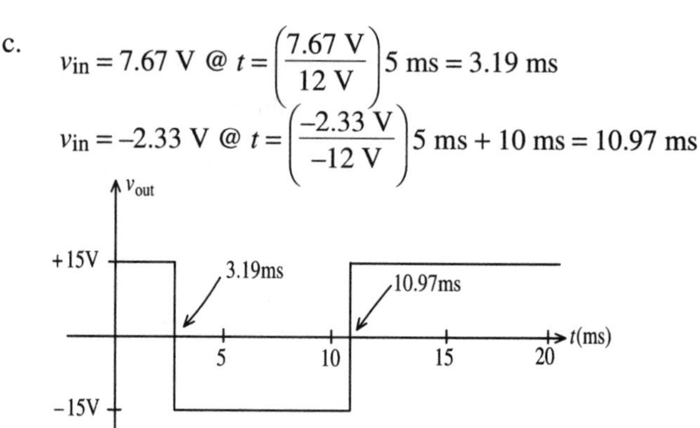

8. a. $$V_{\text{REF}} = \pm\left(\frac{20\ \text{k}\Omega}{20\ \text{k}\Omega + 10\ \text{k}\Omega}\right)12\ \text{V} = \pm 8\ \text{V}$$

$$V_C = 2(8\ \text{V}) = 16\ \text{V}_{\text{p-p}}$$

$$T = 2(20\ \text{k}\Omega)(0.10\ \mu\text{F})\ \ln\left(1 + \frac{2(20\ \text{k}\Omega)}{10\ \text{k}\Omega}\right) = 6.44\ \text{ms}$$

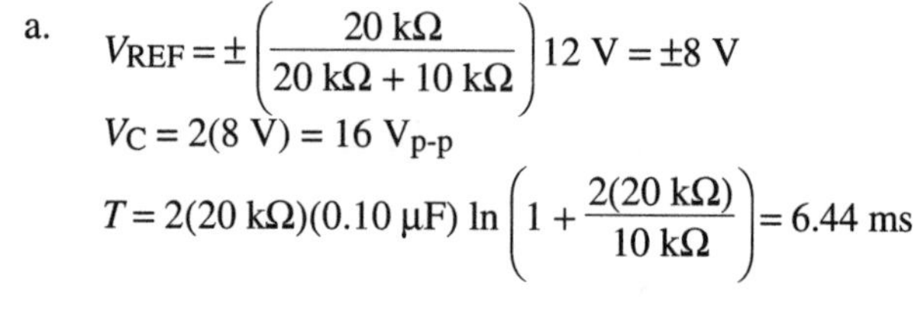

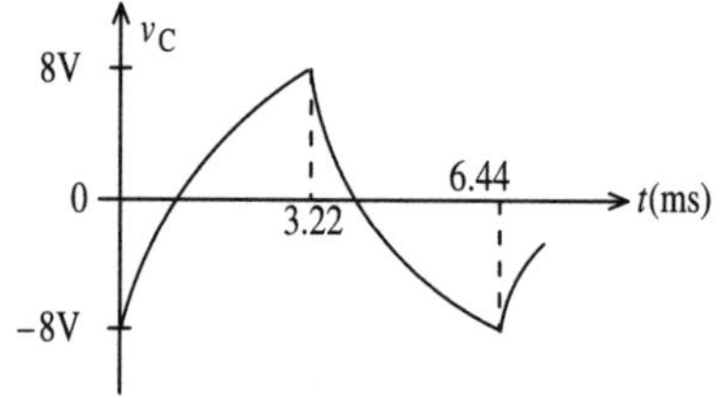

b.

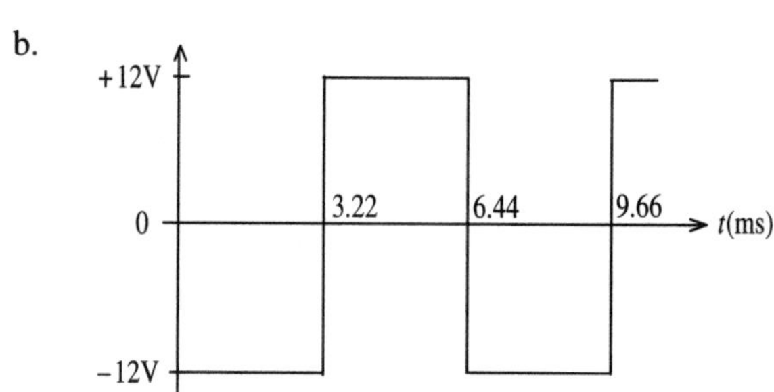

30.3 The Wien Bridge Oscillator

10. $f_o = \dfrac{1}{2\,\pi\,\sqrt{R_1 R_2 C_1 C_2}}$

$C_1 = C_2 = \dfrac{1}{(2\,\pi\,R)(1\text{ kHz})} = 15.92\text{ nF}$

12. $B = \dfrac{2\,R_1}{R_1 + 2\,R_1 + 2\,R_1} = \dfrac{2}{5} = 0.2$

$A = 2.5$

30.4 The Phase-Shift Oscillator

14. a. $f_o = \dfrac{1}{2\,\pi\,\sqrt{6}\,(2.0\text{ k}\Omega)(0.01\ \mu\text{F})} = 3.25\text{ kHz}$

b. $R_{F2} = 29(2.0\text{ k}\Omega) - 47\text{ k}\Omega = 11\text{ k}\Omega$

c. $R_C = R_F = 58\text{ k}\Omega$

d. $\text{BW} = \dfrac{2 \times 10^6}{29} = 68.97\text{ kHz}$

16. $R = \dfrac{1}{2\,\pi\,\sqrt{6}\,(3.0\text{ kHz})(0.047\ \mu\text{F})} = 461\ \Omega$

$R_F = 29(461\ \Omega) = 13.36\text{ k}\Omega$

30.5 LC Oscillators

18. Hartley Oscillator

$f_o = \dfrac{1}{2\,\pi\,\sqrt{(50\ \mu\text{H} + 50\ \mu\text{H})(100\text{ nF})}} = 50.3\text{ kHz}$

30.6 Crystal Oscillators

20.

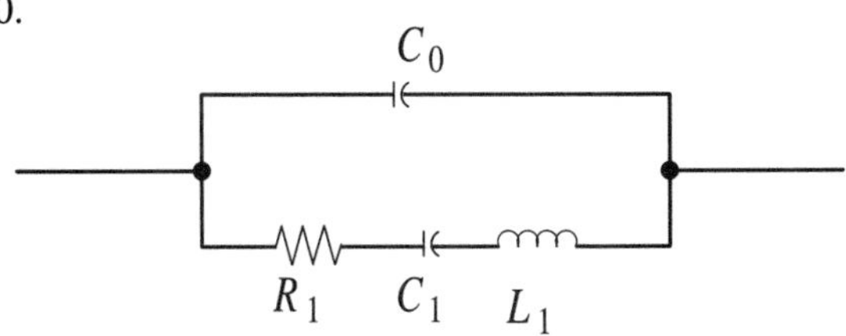

22. For a CMOS oscillator, the components are normally selected to allow oscillation between f_s and f_p.

30.7 The 555 Timer

24. With the capacitor initially uncharged, the output of the bottom comparator of the 555 will be at ~ V_{CC}. The discharge transistor will be OFF. The capacitor charges through R_A and R_B.

The discharge transistor remains OFF until the capacitor voltage reaches 2/3 V_{CC}. At this point, the top comparator of the 555 will be at ~ V_{CC}, causing the discharge transistor to go into saturation.

The capacitor discharges through R_B and the transistor until V_C = 1/3 V_{CC}. At this point, the discharge transistor is cutoff and the process repeats.

26. $R_B = \dfrac{T_1}{C\ln 2} = \dfrac{10\text{ ms}}{(0.47\ \mu\text{F})\ln 2} = 30.7\text{ k}\Omega$

$R_A = \dfrac{T_2}{C\ln 2} - R_B = \dfrac{90\text{ ms}}{(0.47\ \mu\text{F})\ln 2} - 30.7\text{ k}\Omega$

$= 246\text{ k}\Omega$

28. $T_W = 1.10\,R_A C$

$= (1.10)(1.0\text{ M}\Omega)(0.1\ \mu\text{F})$

$= 0.110\text{ s} \quad \equiv 110\text{ ms}$

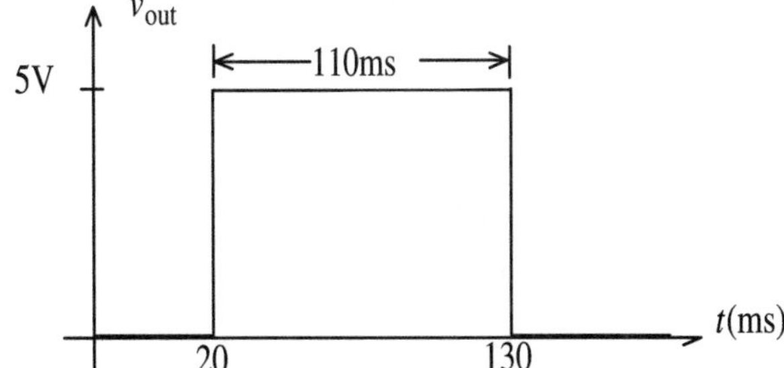

30.8 The Voltage Controlled Oscillator-VCO

30. Wiper at 0%

$$V_C = \left(\frac{33\text{ k}\Omega}{33\text{ k}\Omega + 5\text{ k}\Omega + 0.47\text{ k}\Omega}\right)20\text{ V} = 17.16\text{ V}$$

$$f = \frac{2.4(20\text{ V} - 17.16\text{ V})}{(10\text{ k}\Omega)(\text{lnF})(20\text{ V})} = 34.1\text{ kHz}$$

Wiper at 50%

$$V_C = \left(\frac{33\text{ k}\Omega + 2.5\text{ k}\Omega}{38.47\text{ k}\Omega}\right)20\text{ V} = 18.46\text{ V}$$

$$f = \frac{2.4(20\text{ V} - 18.46\text{ V})}{0.0002} = 18.5\text{ kHz}$$

Wiper at 100%

$$V_C = \left(\frac{33\text{ k}\Omega + 5\text{ k}\Omega}{38.47\text{ k}\Omega}\right)20\text{ V} = 19.76\text{ V}$$

$$f = \frac{2.4(20\text{ V} - 19.76\text{ V})}{0.0002} = 2.93\text{ kHz}$$

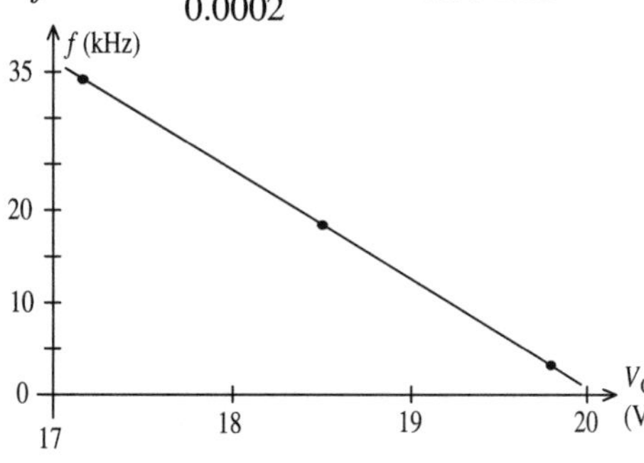

32.

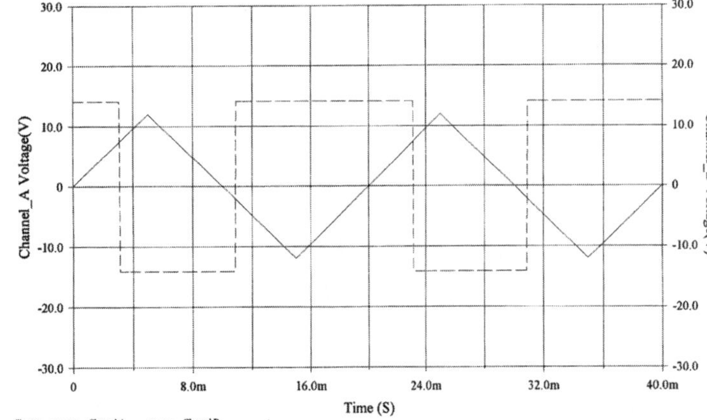

34.

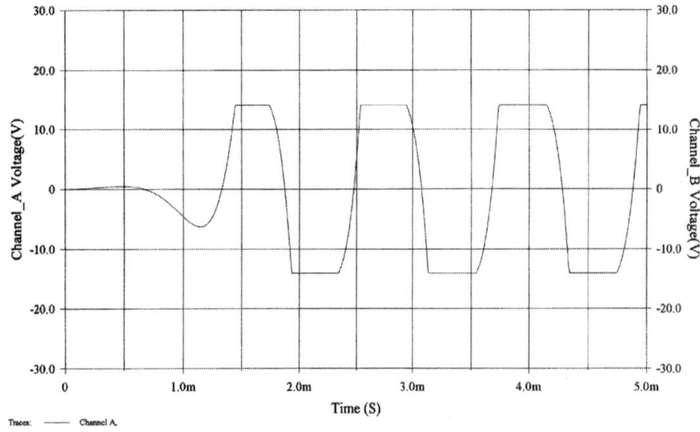

The output waveform can be made more sinusoidal by reducing the size of the feedback resistor R_F.

36.

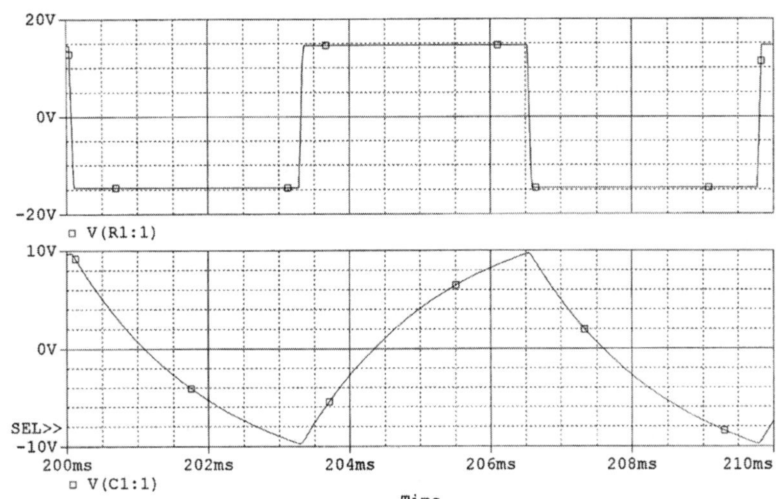

38.

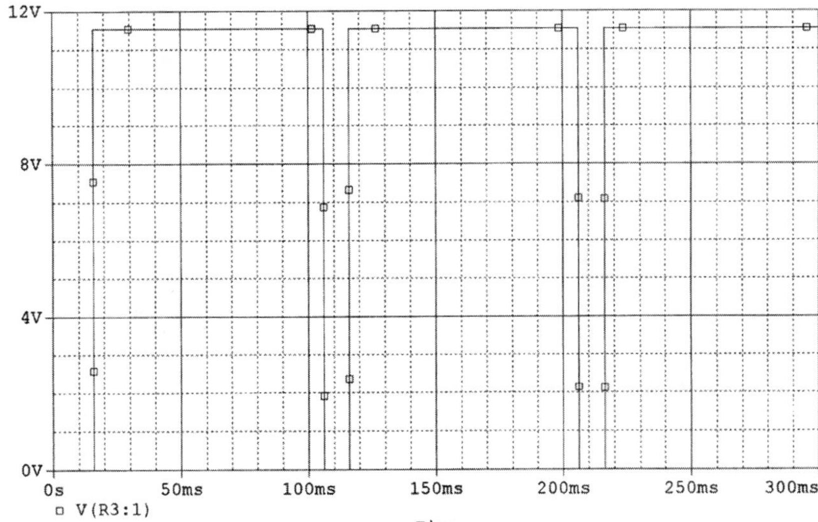

$T_1 = 10$ ms $\quad T_2 = 90$ ms

Chapter

31

Thyristors and Optical Devices

31.2 Triggering Devices

2. a. $V_P = \eta V_{BB} + V_D$

$$\eta = \frac{10\text{ V} - 0.6\text{ V}}{15\text{ V}} = 0.62$$

$$f \approx \frac{1}{(12\text{ k}\Omega)(0.01\ \mu\text{F})\ln\left(\frac{1}{1-0.62}\right)} = 8.61\text{ kHz}$$

b. R_1 provides positive pulses that can be used to trigger SCRs and triacs.

4. Either R_E or C_E (or both) can be changed to result in a frequency of 6.25 kHz.

$$R_E = \frac{1}{(6.25\text{ kHz})(0.01\ \mu\text{F})\ln\left(\frac{1}{1-0.62}\right)} = 16.54\text{ k}\Omega$$

or

$$C_E = \frac{1}{(6.25\text{ kHz})(12\text{ k}\Omega)\ln\left(\frac{1}{1-0.62}\right)} = 13.78\text{ nF}$$

31.3 Silicon-Controlled Rectifiers (SCRs)

6.

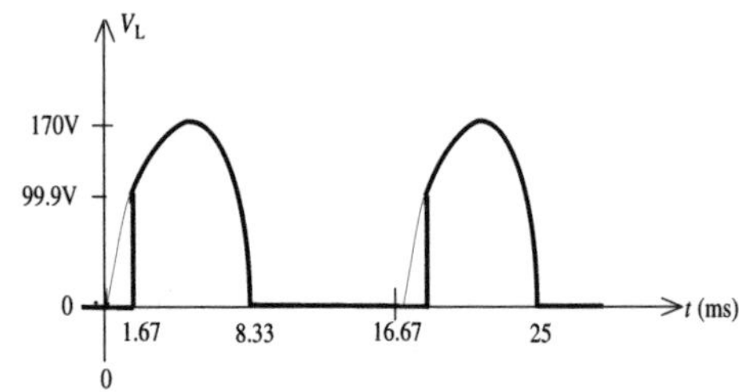

If the triggering circuit delays the firing to 10 ms, then the resultant pulses will be applied to the SCR at a time t = 10 ms – 8.33 ms = 1.67 ms into the next half cycle.

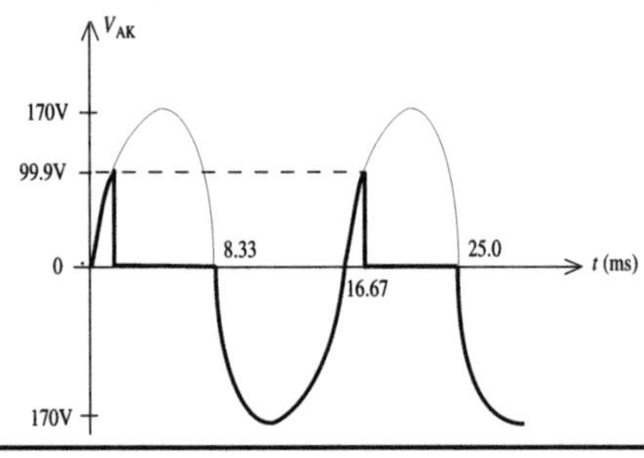

8. Refer to description in Problem 6.

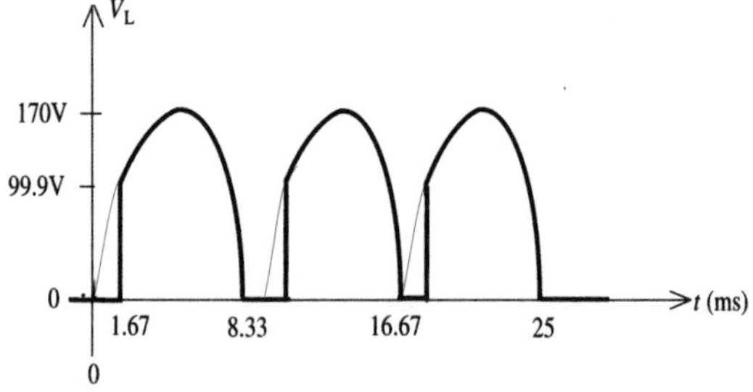

31.4 Triacs

10.

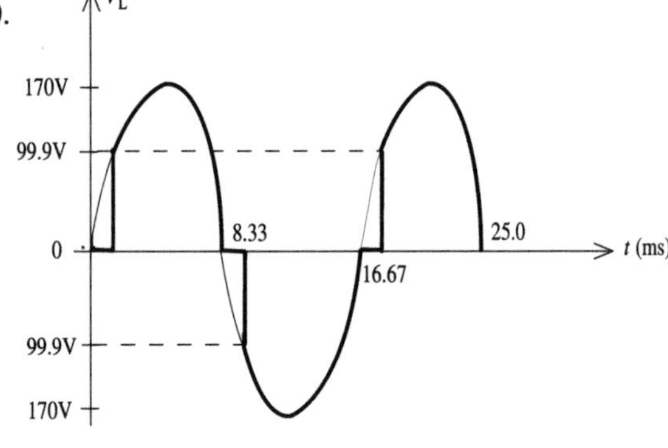

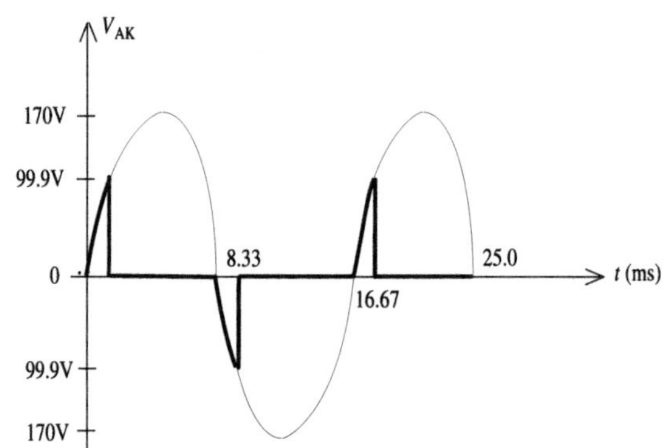

31.5 Power Control Fundamentals

12. $$P_{MAX} = \frac{(120\text{ V})^2}{150\ \Omega} = 96\text{ W}$$

For 135°, $\frac{P_{MAX}}{P} = 0.045$ $P = 4.32\text{ W}$

14. $$P_{MAX} = \frac{(240\text{ V})^2}{20\ \Omega} = 2880\text{ W}$$

For 120°, $\frac{P_{MAX}}{P} = 0.196$ $P = 563\text{ W}$

16. $\frac{P}{P_{MAX}} = 0.4$ For an SCR (1/2 - wave conductor)

$\theta = 60.5°$

18. $\theta_F = 120° \equiv \frac{2\pi}{3}$ $V = (\sqrt{2})240\text{ V} = 339.4\text{ V}$

$$V_{rms} = \sqrt{\left(\frac{1}{\pi}\right)\int_{\frac{2\pi}{3}}^{\pi} (V\sin\theta)^2 d\theta}$$

$$= V\sqrt{\left(\frac{1}{\pi}\right)\left[\frac{\theta}{2} - \frac{1}{4}\sin 2\theta\right|_{\frac{2\pi}{3}}^{\pi}}$$

$$= V\sqrt{\left(\frac{1}{\pi}\right)\left[\left(\frac{\pi}{2} - \frac{1}{4}\sin 2\pi\right) - \left(\frac{\pi}{3} - \frac{1}{4}\sin\frac{4\pi}{3}\right)\right]}$$

$$= (240)(\sqrt{2})\sqrt{\left(\frac{1}{\pi}\right)\left[\frac{\pi}{2} - \left(\frac{\pi}{3} + 0.2165\right)\right]}$$

$+ 106.1\text{ V}$

(Note: $P = \frac{(106.1\text{ V})^2}{20\ \Omega} = 563\text{ W}$—as required.)

31.6 Introduction to Optical Devices

20. $$\lambda = \frac{v}{f} = \frac{3.00 \times 10^8\text{ m/s}}{2.5 \times 10^{14}\text{ Hz}} = 1200\text{ nm} \quad \text{(infrared)}$$

22. $$R = \frac{10\text{ V} - 3.6\text{ V}}{20\text{ mA}} = 320\ \Omega$$

31.8 Optocouplers

24. a. Diode bias current:

$$I_F = \frac{5\text{ V} - 1.5\text{ V}}{0.47\text{ k}\Omega} = 7.45\text{ mA}$$

Diode ac current: (neglecting diode ac resistance)

$$i_d = \frac{1.2\text{ V}_p}{0.47\text{ k}\Omega} = 2.55\text{ mA}_p$$

Transistor operating point:

$I_C = (0.4)(7.45\text{ mA}) = 2.98\text{ mA}$

$V_{CE} = 20\text{ V} - (2.98\text{ mA})(1.2\text{ k}\Omega) = 16.42\text{ V}$

b. $i_c = (0.4)(2.55\text{ mA}) = 1.02\text{ mA}_p$

$v_{out} = (1.02\text{ mA}_P)(1.2\text{ k}\Omega) = 1.22\text{ V}_p$

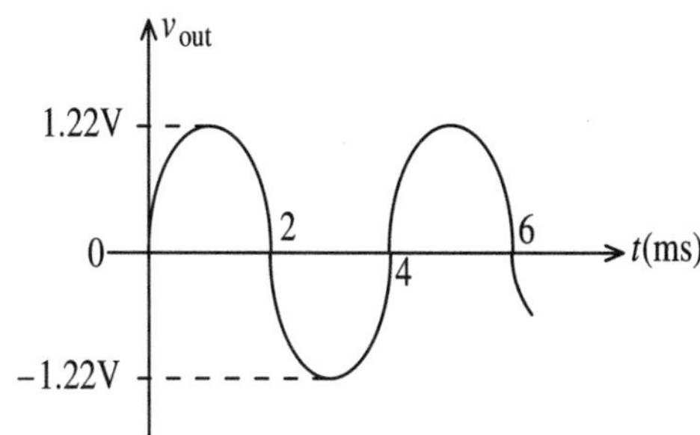

31.9 Semiconductor LASERs

26. Laser light is much more intense than light from LEDs.
Laser light is coherent (in phase).
Laser light is monochromatic (single wavelength.)

LAB MANUAL ANSWERS

Name ______________________________

Date ______________________________

Class ______________________________

Voltage and Current Measurement and Ohm's Law

OBJECTIVES

After completing this lab, you will be able to
- measure voltage, current and resistance in a dc circuit,
- confirm Ohm's law by direct measurement.

EQUIPMENT REQUIRED

☐ Two DMMs
☐ Variable dc power supply

COMPONENTS

☐ Resistors: One 1-kΩ resistor, 1/4-W, 5% tolerance or better
Two 2-kΩ resistors, 1/4-W, 5% tolerance or better

PRELIMINARY

Before you start, review the section on measuring voltage, current and resistance in *A Guide to Lab Equipment and Laboratory Measurements* at the front of this manual.

EQUIPMENT USED

Instrument	Manufacturer/Model No.	Serial No.
DMM #1		
DMM #2		
Power supply		

Table 1-1

TEXT REFERENCE

Section 4.1 OHM'S LAW
Section 4.7 Nonlinear and Dynamic Resistance

DISCUSSION

The most fundamental relationship of circuit theory is Ohm's law. Ohm's law states that in a purely resistive circuit, current is directly proportional to voltage and inversely proportional to resistance. In equation form

$$I = \frac{V}{R} \text{ (Ohm's law)} \tag{1-1}$$

where V is in volts, R is in ohms, I is in amps and reference conventions for voltage and current are as shown as in Figure 1-1. This relationship (which holds for every resistance in a circuit) is an experimental result and we will thus investigate it experimentally. First, you need to learn how to measure voltage and current.

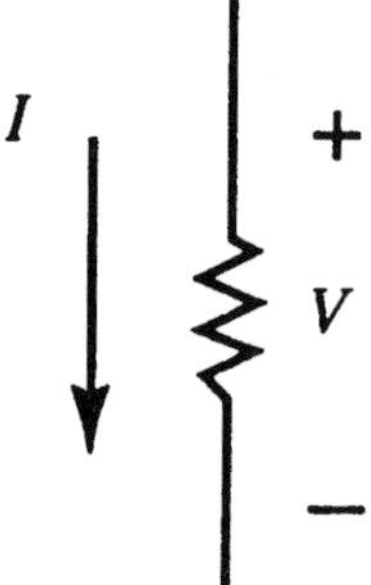

Figure 1-1 Conventions for Ohm's law.

> **Safety Check List**
> Be sure to observe all safety precautions listed in *A Guide to Lab Equipment and Laboratory Measurements* in the front part

DC Voltage Measurement

The basic voltage measuring scheme is shown in Figure 1-2. Be sure to adhere to the lead-color convention depicted and the safety checklist shown.

Current Measurement

The basic test circuit is depicted in Figure 1-3. When connected as shown, the DMM will yield a positive reading, whereas, if the test leads are reversed (so that current enters the COM terminal), the DMM will yield a negative reading.

MEASUREMENTS

Note:
Results shown are ideal. Your results will likely differ but should be close.

PART A: Fixed Resistance, Variable Voltage

1. Measure the value of each resistor and record in Table 1-2. (Mark each 2-kΩ resistor with masking tape so that you can keep track of them.)
2. With power off, select R_2 and assemble the circuit as in Figure 1-4. Be sure to connect the meters so that they indicate positive or up scale values.

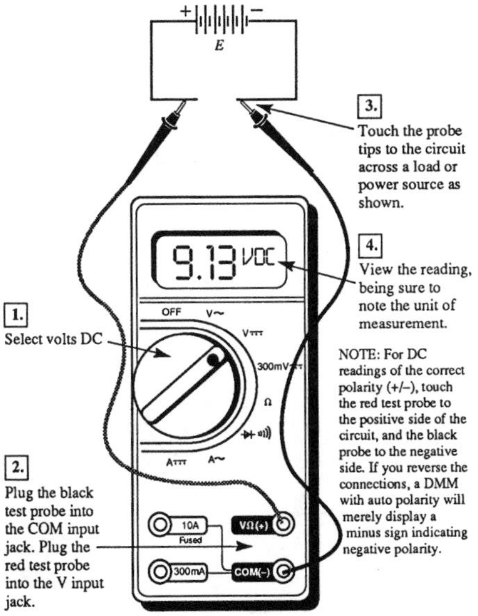

	Nominal	Measured
R_1	1-kΩ	1000
R_2	2-kΩ	2000
R_3	2-kΩ	2000

Table 1-2

> **Safety Checklist**
> - Always turn power off before making changes to your circuit.
> - Select the function (and range if necessary) before connecting the meter. If you do not have autoranging and you don't know the approximate voltage, begin with the highest range and work your way down.
> - Keep your fingers behind the finger guards on the probes when making measurements. (Although this is not essential here because of the low voltages used, it is a good idea to develop safe work habits from the outset.)

E
1. Select volts DC
2. Plug the black test probe into the COM input jack. Plug the red test probe into the V input jack.
3. Touch the probe tips to the circuit across a load or power source as shown.
4. View the reading, being sure to note the unit of measurement.
NOTE: For DC readings of the correct polarity (+/–), touch the red test probe to the positive side of the circuit, and the black probe to the negative side. If you reverse the connections, a DMM with auto polarity will merely display a minus sign indicating negative polarity.
9.13 VDC
OFF
300mV
10A
Fused
300mA
VΩ(+)
COM(–)

Figure 1-2 Making a dc voltage measurement with a DMM. Steps 1 and 2 may be reversed. (Adapted from the ABCs of DMMs. Courtesy of John Fluke Mfg. Co., Inc. Used with permission.)

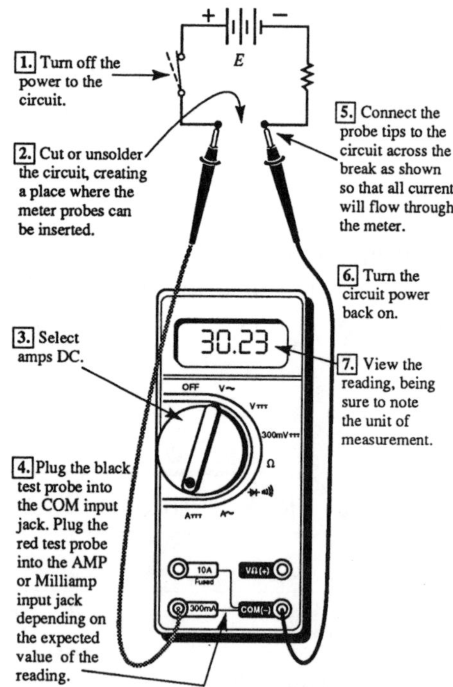
E
1. Turn off the power to the circuit.
2. Cut or unsolder the circuit, creating a place where the meter probes can be inserted.
3. Select amps DC.
4. Plug the black test probe into the COM input jack. Plug the red test probe into the AMP or Milliamp input jack depending on the expected value of the reading.
5. Connect the probe tips to the circuit across the break as shown so that all current will flow through the meter.
6. Turn the circuit power back on.
7. View the reading, being sure to note the unit of measurement.
30.23

(a) Pictorial. Although a hand-held DMM is illustrated a bench-top DMM or a VOM may be used instead.

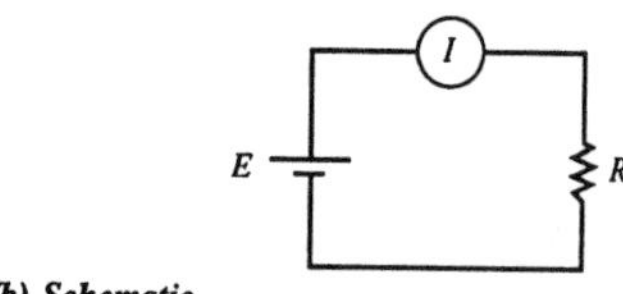
I
E
R

(b) Schematic

Meter Terminal Designations

While the DMM shown has separate terminals for current and voltage, not all meters follow this practice. Some meters for example use a combined input designated VΩA, which means that the current input terminal is the same as the voltage input terminal. In this case, when you set the selector switch to A (or amps), the meter functions as an ammeter, whereas when you set it to V, it functions as a voltmeter. As always, connect the black lead to the COM terminal and the red lead to the other terminal.

Figure 1-3 DC current measurement. (Part (a) adapted from The ABCs of DMMs. Courtesy of John Fluke Mfg. Co. Inc. Used with permission.)

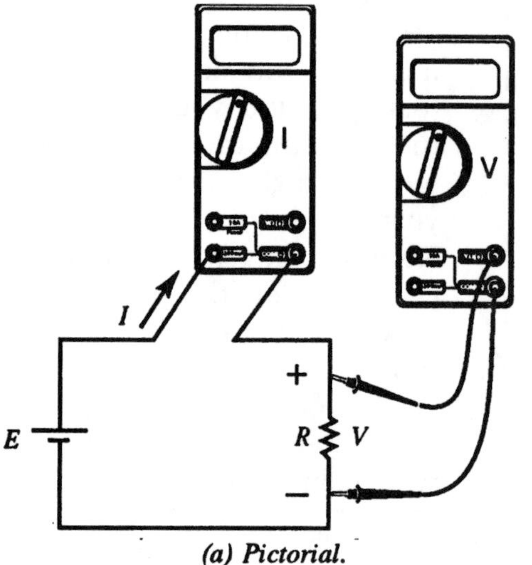
I
V
I
E
+
R
V
−

(a) Pictorial.

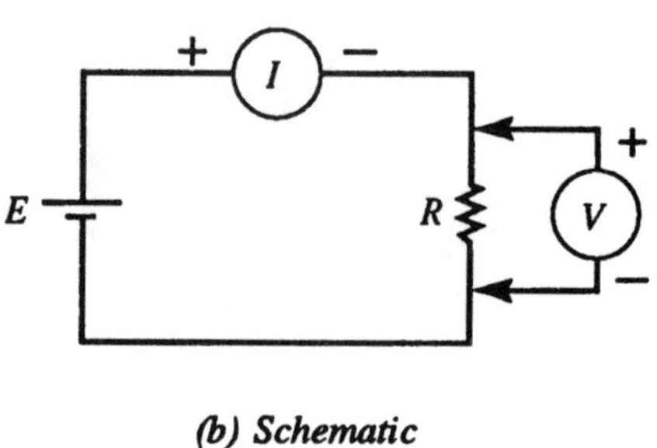
+
I
−
E
R
V
+
−

(b) Schematic

Figure 1-4 Connections for studying Ohm's Law.

a. Set the voltage to $V = 8$ V and measure the current.

$I =$ 4.00 mA (Record this result also in Table 1-3.)

b. Set the voltage to $V = 16$ V and measure the current.

$I =$ 8.00 mA

c. Set the voltage to $V = 4$ V and measure the current.

$I =$ 2.00 mA

d. Based on these observations, for a fixed resistance, how does current vary with voltage (within the limitations of accuracy of your meters and components)?

Current is proportional to applied voltage

PART B: Fixed Voltage, Variable Resistance

3. a. Turn off the power supply. Using both 2-kΩ resistors, connect the circuit as in Figure 1-5. (This doubles the circuit resistance to 4 kΩ.) Set $V = 8$ volts and measure the current.

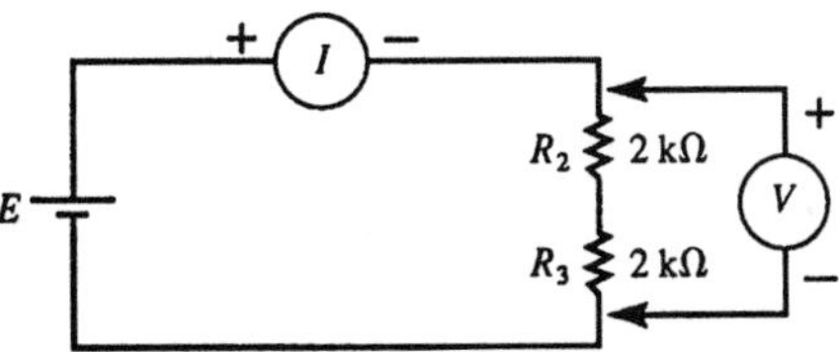

Figure 1-5 Doubling the circuit resistance. Here, $R_T = 4$ kΩ.

$I =$ 2.00 mA. (Record also in Table 1-3.)

b. Turn off the power supply. Using the 1 kΩ resistor, reconnect the circuit as in Figure 1-4. Set $V = 8$ volts and measure the current. $I =$ 8.00 mA. (Record also in Table 1-3.)

c. Consider Table 1-3. Within the accuracy of the results obtained, for a fixed voltage, how does current vary with resistance?

Current is inversely proportional to resistance

	$V = 8$ V	
Test	R	I (mA)
2(a)	2 kΩ	4.00
3(a)	4 kΩ	2.00
3(b)	1 kΩ	8.00

Table 1-3

4. For Tests 2 and 3, compute current using Ohm's law and tabulate in Table 1-4. (Use the measured values of resistance for each case.) If there are differences between calculated and measured current, what is the likely cause? With a good DMM, the differences should be insignificant

			Current I (mA)	
Test	V	R	Calculated	Measured
2(a)	8 V	2000	4.00	Should be very
2(b)	16 V	2000	8.00	close to the
2(c)	4 V	2000	2.00	calculated values
3(a)	8 V	4000	2.00	
3(b)	8 V	1000	8.00	

Table 1-4

PART C: Ohm's Law Graph

5. Using the circuit of Figure 1-4 and the 1-kΩ resistor, vary V from 0 volt to 10 volts in 2 volt increments. Tabulate your results in Table 1-5 and plot the results on the graph of Figure 1-6. Replace R with a 2-kΩ resistor and repeat.
6. Resistance can be calculated at any point on the Ohm's law graph. For the nominal 1-kΩ resistor, at $V = 5$ volts, determine current from Figure 1-6 and compute R using Equation 1-1. How well does it agree with the value of R used in Test 5? Repeat for the nominal 2-kΩ resistor.

*R*1: From graph, $I = 5$ mA ∴ $R_1 = 5$ V/5 mA = 1 kΩ

*R*2: From graph, $I = 2.5$ mA ∴ $R_2 = 5$ V/2.5 mA = 2 kΩ

Agreement is excellent

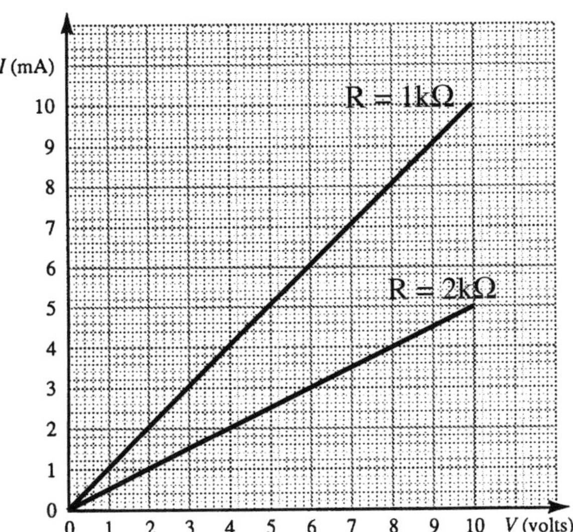

	Current I (mA)	
V	1-kΩ	2-kΩ
0 V	0	0
2 V	2.00	1.00
4 V	4.00	2.00
6 V	6.00	3.00
8 V	8.00	4.00
10 V	10.00	5.00

Figure 1-6 Ohm's law Graph.

7. Resistance may be determined from a *V-I* plot as described in Sec. 4.7 of the text. Select an arbitrary value for ΔV, then from the graph for the 1-kΩ resistor of Fig. 1-6 determine the resulting ΔI. Using these values, compute resistance. Show all work, including a sketch with ΔV and ΔI clearly marked.

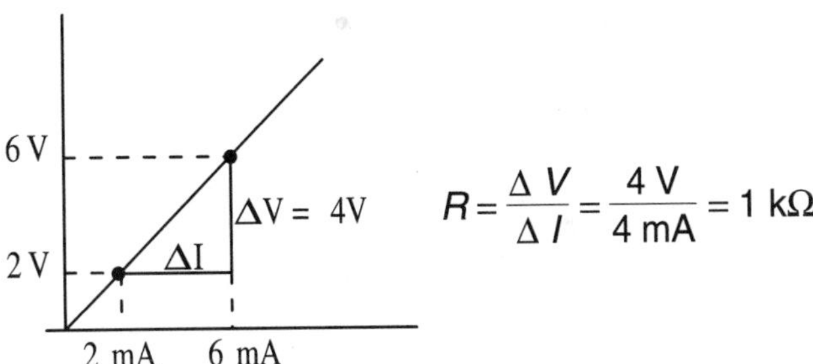

COMPUTER ANALYSIS

8. Using either MultiSIM or PSpice as applicable set up the circuit of Fig. 1-4. Repeat PART A and PART B of the lab and compare to your measured results.

MultiSIM users: See Figure 4-28 of the textbook.

PSpice users: See Figure 4-29 or 4-30 of the textbook.

PROBLEMS

9. A 12-V source is applied to a resistor with color code orange, black, brown. What is the current in mA?

From its color code, $R = 300\ \Omega$. Thus, $I = \dfrac{12\text{ V}}{300\ \Omega} = 40\text{ mA}$

10. Make a sketch to show how to connect voltmeters to measure the voltage across R_2 and R_3 of Fig. 1-5.

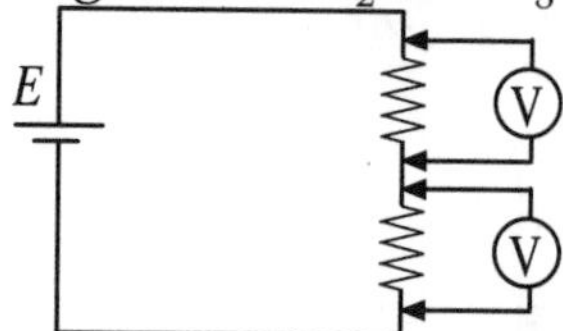

11. For Figure 1-4, $I = 10$ mA. If E is increased by a factor of 16 and R is halved, what is the new value of current?

$$I_{old} = \frac{E}{R} = 10\text{ mA}$$

$$I_{new} = \frac{(16\ E)}{\frac{R}{2}} = 32\left(\frac{E}{R}\right) = 32(10\text{ mA}) = 320\text{ mA}$$

FOR FURTHER INVESTIGATION AND DISCUSSION

Write a short discussion paper on the impact of meter errors on measured values. As the basis for your discussion, consider a 4-digit DMM with an error specification of ±(0.5% of reading + 1 digit) on its dc voltage ranges and ±(1.5% of reading + 2 digits) on its dc current ranges. Consider Figure 1-4. Suppose the meters read 24.00 V and 12.00 mA respectively. Compute the nominal value for resistance (assuming no meter errors) as well as the minimum and maximum resistance values assuming maximum meter errors. Based on this, what can you conclude about accepting results (derived from measurements) at face value?

Voltage and Current Measurement Errors:

Consider measured voltage. If the meter were 100% accurate, the voltage would be 24.00 V exactly. However, the meter can be in error by ±(0.5% + 1 least significant digit). Since 0.5% of 24.00 V is 0.12 V, (0.5% of 24.00 V + 1 least significant digit) is 0.13 V. Thus, $V = 24.00 \pm 0.13$ V. This means that the actual value of the voltage lies somewhere between 23.87 V and 24.13 V. Similarly, the possible error for the current is ±0.20 mA, and the current can thus be anywhere between 11.80 mA and 12.20 mA.

Calculated Resistance

If there were no meter errors, the resistance would be 24.00 V/12.00 mA = 2 kΩ. Call this the nominal resistance. Thus, $R_{nom} = 2$ kΩ. However, based on the measured values,resistance can be as large as $R_{max} = 24.13$ V/11.80 mA = 2.04 kΩ, or as small as $R_{min} = 23.87$ V/12.20 mA = 1.96 kΩ. Thus, $R = 2\text{ k}\Omega \pm .04\text{ k}\Omega$, or expressed in percent, $R = 2\text{ k}\Omega \pm 2\%$. From this we conclude that the worst-case error in the calculated result is greater than the maximum error of either instrument alone. (It can be shown that for small errors, the worst-case error is slightly larger than the sum of the percentage errors of the two meters. We got exactly the sum here because of round-off errors in our calculations.) Thus, you cannot accept results derived from measured values at face value—you must always assume that they contain some error.

NAME ______________________

DATE ______________________

CLASS ______________________

LAB 2

Series dc Circuits

OBJECTIVES

After completing this lab, you will be able to

- assemble a series circuit consisting of a voltage source and several resistors,
- use a DMM to measure voltage and current in a series circuit,
- compare measured values to theoretical calculations and verify Kirchhoff's voltage law,
- measure the effects of connecting several voltage sources in series,
- connect a circuit to ground using the ground terminal of a voltage source and use a DMM to measure voltages between several points and ground,
- measure the internal resistance of several voltage sources.

EQUIPMENT REQUIRED

☐ Digital multimeter (DMM)
☐ dc power supply (2)
Note: Record this equipment in Table 2-1.

COMPONENTS

☐ Resistors: 47-Ω, 100-Ω, 270-Ω, 330-Ω, 470-Ω (1/4-W)
47-Ω, 100-Ω, 270-Ω (2-W)
☐ Batteries: 1.5-V D-cell, 9-V (MN 1604 or equivalent)

EQUIPMENT USED

Instrument	Manufacturer/Model No.	Serial No.
DMM		
dc Supply		
dc Supply		

Table 2-1

TEXT REFERENCE

Section 5.1	SERIES CIRCUITS
Section 5.2	KIRCHHOFF'S VOLTAGE LAW
Section 5.3	RESISTORS IN SERIES
Section 5.4	VOLTAGE SOURCES IN SERIES
Section 5.5	INTERCHANGING SERIES COMPONENTS
Section 5.6	VOLTAGE DIVIDER RULE
Section 5.7	CIRCUIT GROUND
Section 5.10	INTERNAL RESISTANCE OF VOLTAGE SOURCES

DISCUSSION

Two elements are said to be in *series* if they are connected at a single point and if there are no other current-carrying connections at this point. Each element in a series circuit has the same current as, illustrated in Figure 2-1.

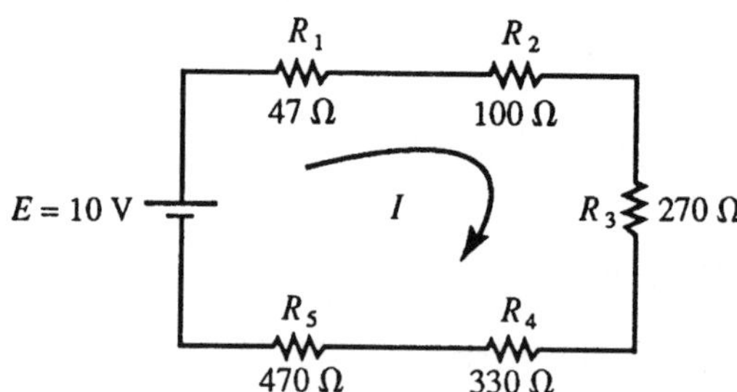

Figure 2-1 Series circuit

The equivalent resistance of n resistors in series, is determined as the summation

$$R_T = R_1 + R_2 + \ldots + R_n \tag{2-1}$$

When these resistors are connected in series with a voltage source, the current in the circuit is given as

$$I = \frac{E}{R_T} \tag{2-2}$$

The voltage drop across any resisistor in a series circuit is determined by using the voltage divider rule, namely

$$V_x = \frac{R_x}{R_T}E \tag{2-3}$$

CALCULATIONS

1. Refer to the the circuit of Figure 2-1. Calculate R_T, I, and the voltage across each resistor. Enter the results in Table 2-2. Show the correct units for each entry.

Resistor	Voltage
$R_1 = 47\ \Omega$	0.386 V
$R_2 = 100\ \Omega$	0.822 V
$R_3 = 270\ \Omega$	2.22 V
$R_4 = 330\ \Omega$	2.71 V
$R_5 = 470\ \Omega$	3.86 V
R_T	1217 Ω
I	8.22 mA

Table 2-2

MEASUREMENTS

2. Connect the resistors as shown in the network of Figure 2-2. Use the DMM (ohmmeter) to measure the resistance across the open terminals. Enter the result below. Compare your measurement to the theoretical calculation recorded in Table 2-2. You should observe only a small discrepancy (no greater than the percent tolerance of the resistors.)

R_T	1217 Ω

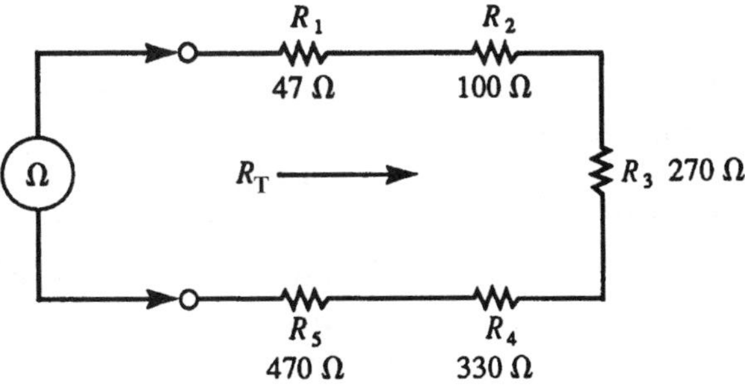

Figure 2-2 Series resistance

3. Connect the voltage source into the circuit as shown in Figure 2-3. With a DMM (voltmeter) connected across the voltage source, adjust the voltage for exactly 10 V.

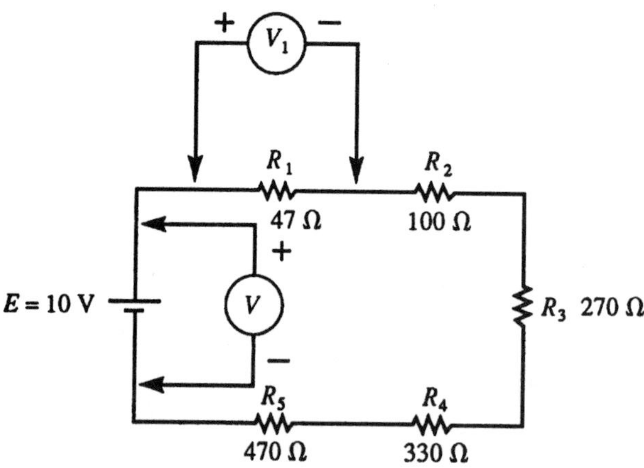

Figure 2-3 Measuring voltage in a series circuit

4. Disconnect the voltmeter from the voltage source and sucessively place it across each of the resistors. Measure the voltage across each resistor in the circuit and record your results in Table 2-3.

	Voltage
V_1	0.386 V
V_2	0.822 V
V_3	2.22 V
V_4	2.71 V
V_5	3.86 V

Table 2-3

5. Turn off the voltage source and switch the DMM from the voltage range to the current range. Disconnect the circuit and insert the ammeter in series with the circuit as shown in Figure 2-4.

> **Points to Note:** The ammeter must be placed in series with the circuit, allowing the circuit current to pass through the meter. It must never be connected across an element, since this will result in a *short circuit* and may damage the meter or the circuit.

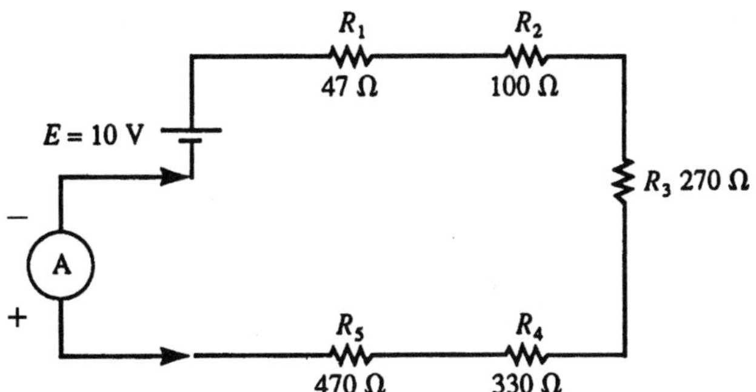

Figure 2-4 Current measurement

Turn the voltage source back on and record the circuit current in the space provided here. If all resistors have a 5% tolerance, you should measure a current that is within 5% of the calculated value of Table 2-2.

I	8.22 mA

6. Obtain a second voltage source or use the second supply of a dual power supply. Modify the series circuit by placing the second source in a *series-aiding connection* with the first voltage source as illustrated in Figure 2-5. Adjust the second supply for 5 V. (The first supply is still 10 V.) Notice that in the series-aiding connection, the positive terminal of the second source is connected to the negative terminal of the first source. Measure and record the voltage drop across each resistor.

	Voltage
V_1	0.579 V
V_2	1.23 V
V_3	3.33 V
V_4	4.07 V
V_5	5.79 V

Table 2-4

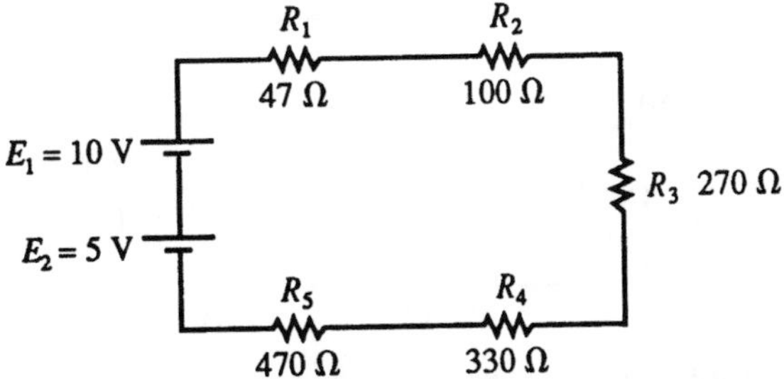

Figure 2-5 Voltage sources in a series-aiding connection

7. Measure the current in the circuit using the method described in Step 5. Enter the result here.

I	12.3 mA

8. Turn both voltage sources off and reverse the terminals of the 5-V supply as shown in Figure 2-6. Turn both supplies on and adjust the voltages if necessary. The voltage sources are now in a *series-opposing connection*. Examine the circuit of Figure 2-6 and determine the correct direction of current. Measure and record the voltage drop across each resistor.

	Voltage
V_1	0.193 V
V_2	0.411 V
V_3	1.11 V
V_4	1.36 V
V_5	1.93 V

Table 2-5

9. Measure the current in the circuit using the method described in Step 5. Enter the result here.

I	4.11 mA

Ground

Electrical and electronic circuits are often connected to *ground*, meaning that this part of the circuit is at the same potential as the ground connection on a three-terminal plug. Since all grounds are connected in a building's electrical panel (as well as the water pipes), special precautions may need to be followed when using instru-

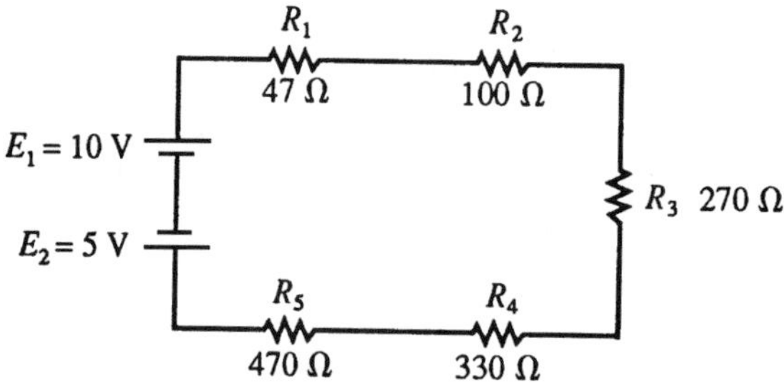

Figure 2-6 Voltage sources in a series-opposing connection

ments that are also grounded. Most dc voltage sources have a separate ground terminal at the front of the instrument, which permit us to connect a circuit to ground.

10. Refer to Figure 2-7(a). Connect the common terminals between the voltage sources to the ground terminal by using either a jumper wire or the grounding strip provided with the voltage source(s). Figure 2-7(b) indicates an alternate way of representing the voltage sources as *point sources*. Point sources simply indicate the potential at a point with respect to the reference (or in this case, ground). The ground symbol may or may not be shown. Connect the common (–) terminal of the DMM (voltmeter) to the ground point. All further voltage measurements are taken with respect to this point. Connect the voltage (+) terminal of the voltmeter to measure E_1, E_2, V_a, V_b, V_c, V_d. Record your results in Table 2-6.

	Voltage
E_1	10 V
E_2	5 V
V_a	9.81 V
V_b	9.40 V
V_c	8.29 V
V_d	6.93 V

Table 2-6

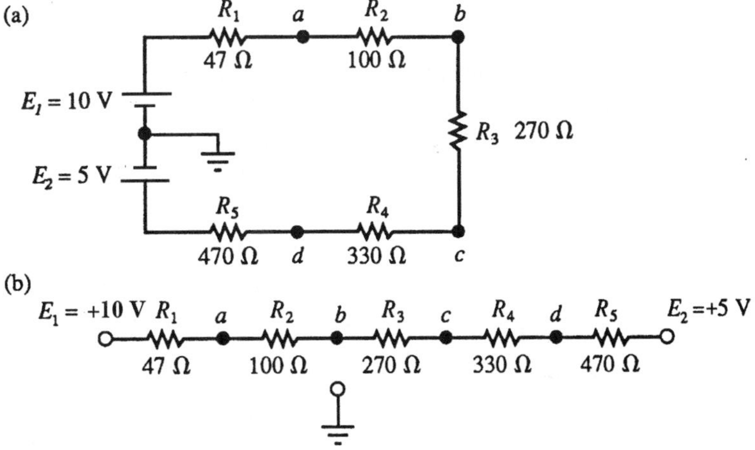

Figure 2-7 Ground connections and point sources

Internal Resistance of Voltage Sources

All voltage sources have some internal resistance, which tends to reduce the voltage between the terminals of the source when the source is under load. The internal resistance of the voltage sources used up to now have very small internal resistance (typically less than 1 Ω). Other sources such as nickel-cadmium and alkaline batteries have relatively large internal resistance. This means that as a circuit requires more current, the voltage across the terminals of the battery will decrease. The magnitude of the internal resistance determines the maximum amount of usable current that a voltage source can provide to a circuit.

11. Use a DMM to measure the voltage across the terminals of a 1.5-V D-cell alkaline battery and a 9-V alkaline battery. Enter the results here.

E(1.5-V cell)	1.60 V
E(9-V cell)	9.33 V

12. Using each of the resistors from the previous part of the lab, construct the circuit shown in Figure 4-8. Measure and record the voltage across the terminals of the batteries for each of the resistors in Table 2-7.

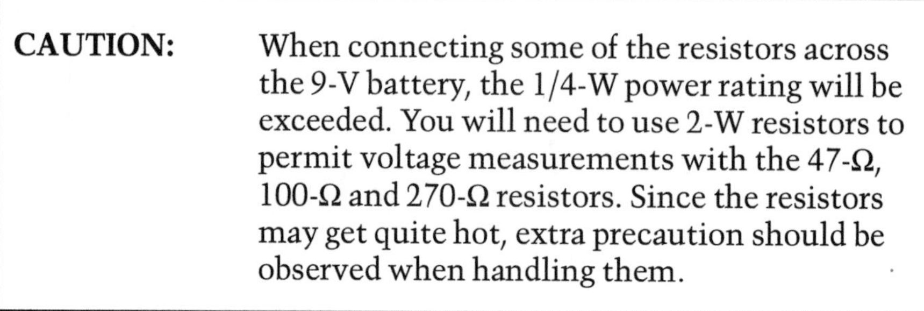
CAUTION: When connecting some of the resistors across the 9-V battery, the 1/4-W power rating will be exceeded. You will need to use 2-W resistors to permit voltage measurements with the 47-Ω, 100-Ω and 270-Ω resistors. Since the resistors may get quite hot, extra precaution should be observed when handling them.

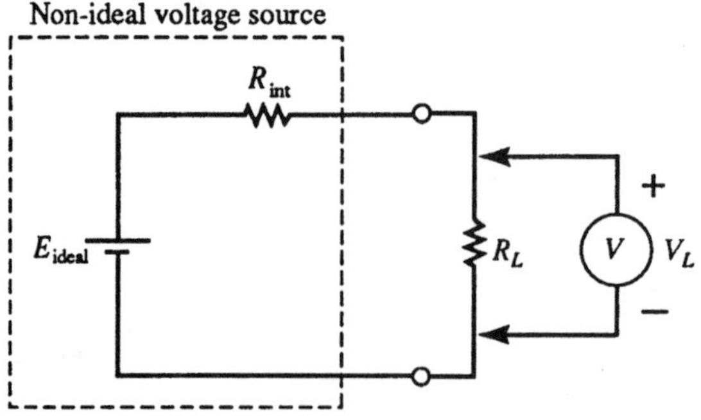

Figure 2-8 Measuring internal resistance of a voltage source

	V_L (1.5-V cell)	V_L (9-V cell)
$R_L = 470\ \Omega$	1.572 V	9.25 V
$R_L = 330\ \Omega$	1.562 V	9.21 V
$R_L = 270\ \Omega$	1.548 V	9.20 V
$R_L = 100\ \Omega$	1.544 V	9.05 V
$R_L = 47\ \Omega$	1.540 V	8.79 V

Table 2-7

CONCLUSIONS

13. Compare the measured resistance of Step 2 to the theoretical resistance recorded in Table 2-2. Determine the percentage variation as shown.

R_T (theoretical) = 1217 Ω R_T (measured) = 1217 Ω

$$\text{percent variation} = \frac{\text{Measurement–Theoretical}}{\text{Theoretical}} \times 100\% \quad (2\text{-}4)$$

percent variation = ____________

variation should be less than 5%.

14. Compare the measured voltage drops of Table 2-3 to the theoretical values recorded in Table 2-2. Indicate which values (if any) have a variation more than the resistor tolerance. Offer an explanation.

Variation should be less than 5% of the theoretical calculation.

15. Examine the measured current of Step 5 and compare it to the theoretical value recorded in Table 2-2. Determine the percentage variation.

percent variation = less than 5%

16. Determine the summation of the voltage drops recorded in Table 2-4. Compare this value to the summation of voltage rises. Is Kirchhoff's voltage law satisfied?

ΣV = 15.0 V ΣE = 15.0 V

Kirchhoff's voltage law is satisfied.

17. Calculate the theoretical current for the circuit of Figure 2-5. Compare this value to the measure value and determine the percent variation.

$I_{theoretical}$ = 12.3 mA percent variation = <5%

18. Determine the summation of the voltage drops recorded in Table 2-5. Compare this value to the summation of voltage rises. Is Kirchhoff's voltage law satisfied?

ΣV = 5.00 V ΣE = 5.00 V

Kirchhoff's voltage law is satisfied.

19. Calculate the theoretical current for the circuit of Figure 4-6. Compare this value to the measure value and determine the percent variation.

$I_{theoretical}$ = 4.11mA percent variation = <5%

20. Calculate the voltages V_{ab}, V_{bc}, and V_{cd} from your measurements in Table 2-6. Compare your calculations to the corresponding measurements recorded in Table 4-5. Notice the direct correlation.

$V_{ab} = V_a - V_b$ = 0.41 V V_2 = 0.411 V

V_{bc} = 1.11 V V_3 = 1.11 V

V_{cd} = 1.36 V V_4 = 1.36 V

21. For each load resistor, evaluate the internal resistance of the 1.5-V battery by applying Ohm's law as shown below. Enter your results in Table 2-8. Use these results to determine the average value of internal resistance.

$$I = \frac{V_L}{R_L} \quad (2\text{-}5)$$

$$R_{int} = \frac{E_{ideal} - V_L}{I} = \left(\frac{E_{ideal} - V_L}{V_L}\right) R_L \quad (2\text{-}6)$$

R_L	R_{int}
470 Ω	8.37 Ω
330 Ω	8.02 Ω
270 Ω	9.07 Ω
100 Ω	3.63 Ω
47 Ω	1.83 Ω
Average value of R_{int}	6.18 Ω

Table 2-8

22. For each load resistor, use equations (2-5) and (2-6) to evaluate the internal resistance of the 9-V battery. Enter your results in Table 2-9. Use these results to determine the average value of internal resistance.

R_L	R_{int}
470 Ω	4.06 Ω
330 Ω	4.30 Ω
270 Ω	3.82 Ω
100 Ω	3.09 Ω
47 Ω	2.88 Ω
Average value of R_{int}	3.63 Ω

Table 2-9

FOR FURTHER INVESTIGATION AND DISCUSSION

Use MultiSIM or PSpice to simulate the circuit of Figure 2-3. Determine the voltage drop across each resistor inthe circuit and compare your results to those of Table 2-3. (Note: In order simulate the circuit, you will need to select a suitable reference point.)

The simulation results are similar to actual measured results.
(See schematic on following page.)

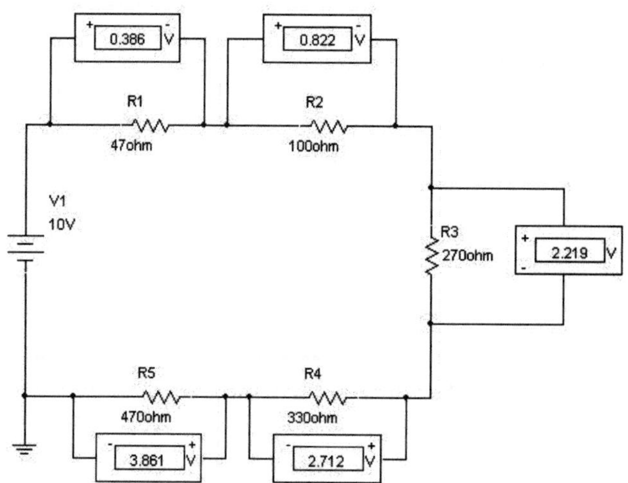

The results are consistent with the measurements.

NAME ______________________

DATE ______________________

CLASS ______________________

LAB 3

Parallel dc Circuits

OBJECTIVES

After completing this lab, you will be able to

- assemble a parallel circuit consisting of a voltage source and several resistors,
- measure voltage and current in a parallel circuit,
- compare measured values to theoretical calculations and verify Kirchhoff's current law.
-

EQUIPMENT REQUIRED

☐ Digital multimeter (DMM)
☐ dc power supply
Note: Record this equipment in Table 3-1.

COMPONENTS

☐ Resistors: 470-Ω, 680-Ω, 1-kΩ, 2.2-kΩ, 4.7-kΩ (1/4-W, 5%)

EQUIPMENT USED

Instrument	Manufacturer/Model No.	Serial No.
DMM		
dc Supply		

Table 3-1

REFERENCE

Section 6.1 PARALLEL CIRCUITS
Section 6.2 KIRCHHOFF'S CURRENT LAW
Section 6.3 RESISTORS IN PARALLEL
Section 6.5 CURRENT DIVIDER RULE
Section 6.6 ANALYSIS OF PARALLEL CIRCUITS

DISCUSSION

Two elements are said to be in a *parallel* connection if they have exactly two nodes in common. Each element in a parallel circuit, as shown in Figure 3-1, has the same voltage across it.

The equivalent conductance of n resistors in parallel, is determined as the summation of conductance

$$G_T = G_1 + G_2 + \ldots + G_n \qquad (3\text{-}1)$$

where the conductance G, of each resistor is found as the reciprocal of resistance

$$G_x = \frac{1}{R_x} \qquad (3\text{-}2)$$

The total resistance of n resistors in parallel is then found as

$$R_T = \frac{1}{G_T} \qquad (3\text{-}3)$$

When a parallel network of resistors is connected in parallel with a voltage source, the current through the voltage source is determined as

$$I = \frac{E}{R_T} \qquad (3\text{-}4)$$

The current through any resisistor in a parallel circuit is calculated using Ohm's law or the current divider rule, namely

$$I_x = \frac{E}{R_x} = \frac{R_T}{R_x}I \qquad (3\text{-}5)$$

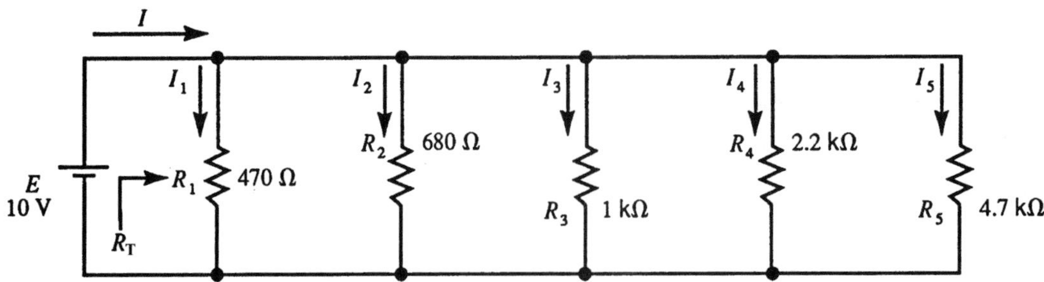

Figure 3-1 Parallel circuit

CALCULATIONS

1. Refer to the the circuit of Figure 3-1. Calculate R_T, I, I_1, I_2, I_3, I_4, and I_5. Enter the results in Table 3-2. Show the correct units for each entry.

I_1	21.3 mA
I_2	14.7 mA
I_3	10.0 mA
I_4	4.55 mA
I_5	2.13 mA

R_T	189.9 Ω
I	52.7 mA

Table 3-2

MEASUREMENTS

2. Connect the resistors as shown in the network of Figure 3-2. Use the DMM (ohmmeter) to measure the resistance across the open terminals. Enter the result here. Compare your measurement to the theoretical calculation in Table 3-2. You should observe only a small discrepancy.

R_T	189.9 Ω

3. Connect the voltage source to the circuit as shown in Figure 3-3. With a DMM (voltmeter) connected across the voltage source, adjust the voltage for exactly 10 V.

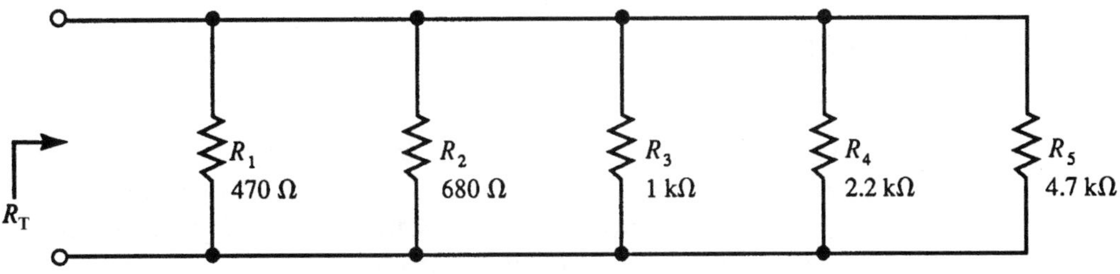

Figure 3-2 Parallel resistance

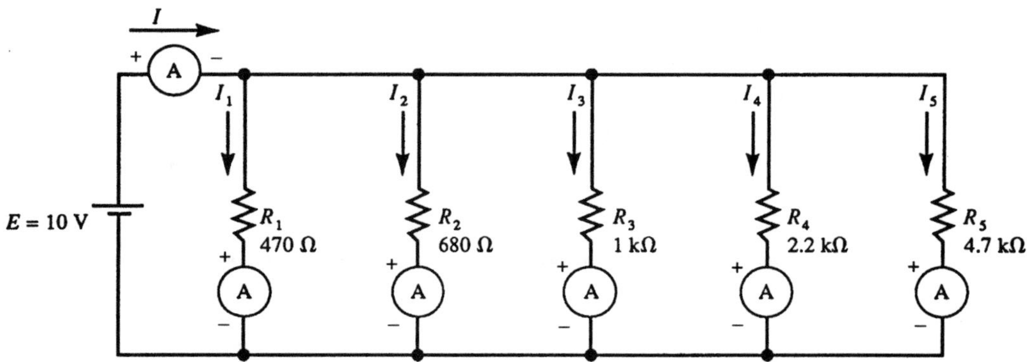

Figure 3-3 Measuring current in a parallel circuit

4. Disconnect the voltmeter from the voltage source. Turn the power supply off, without disturbing the voltage setting on the power supply. Set the DMM to measure current. Sucessively disconnect each branch of the circuit and insert the ammeter into the branch as illustrated in Figure 3-3. Measure the current through the voltage source and through each resistor in the circuit. **Ensure that each branch is reconnected after the ammeter is removed**. Record your results in Table 3-3.

	Current
I	52.7 mA
I_1	21.3 mA
I_2	14.7 mA
I_3	10.0 mA
I_4	4.55 mA
I_5	2.13 mA

Table 3-3

KIRCHHOFF'S CURRENT LAW

Kirchhoff's voltage and current laws provide an important foundation for the analysis of circuits. Kirchhoff's current law states:

The summation of currents entering a node is equal to the summation of currents leaving the node.

We now examine how Kirchhoff's current law can be verified in a laboratory.

5. Relocate the ammeter as shown in Figure 3-4 and measure the currents I_6, I_7, and I_8. Record your results in Table 3-4.

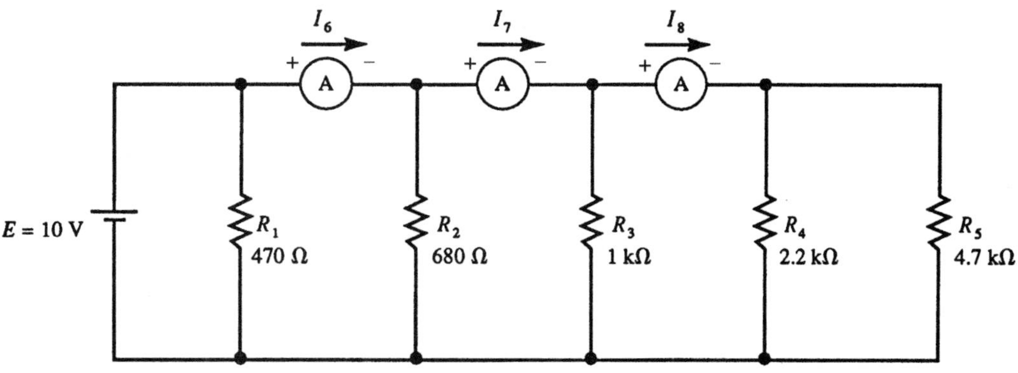

Figure 3-4 Verifying Kirchhoff's Current Law

	Current
I_6	31.4 mA
I_7	16.7 mA
I_8	6.67 mA

Table 3-4

CONCLUSIONS

6. Compare the measured resistance of Step 2 to the theoretical resistance recorded in Table 3-2. Determine the percentage variation as shown.

R_T (theoretical) = 189.9 Ω R_T (measured) = 190 Ω

$$\text{percent variation} = \frac{\text{Measurement–Theoretical}}{\text{Theoretical}} \times 100\% \quad (3\text{-}6)$$

This value will generally be small.

percent variation = ____________

7. Compare the measured currents of Step 4 to the theoretical values recorded in Table 3-2. Indicate which values (if any) have a variation more than the resistor tolerance. Offer an explanation.

All values should be within ± 5% of theoretical values.

____

8. Refer to the data of Table 3-3 and Table 3-4.
   a. Compare current I to the the summation $I_1 + I_2 + I_3 + I_4 + I_5$.

      $I =$ 52.7 mA $\quad I_1 + I_2 + I_3 + I_4 + I_5 =$ 52.7 mA

   b. Compare current I_6 to the the summation $I_2 + I_3 + I_4 + I_5$.

      $I_6 =$ 31.4 mA $\quad I_2 + I_3 + I_4 + I_5 =$ 31.4 mA

   c. Compare current I_7 to the the summation $I_3 + I_4 + I_5$.

      $I_7 =$ 16.7 mA $\quad I_3 + I_4 + I_5 =$ 16.7 mA

   d. Compare current I_8 to the the summation $I_4 + I_5$.

      $I_8 =$ 6.67 mA $\quad I_4 + I_5 =$ 6.68 mA

   e. Do the above calculations and measurements verify Kirchhoff's current law? Explain your answer.

      Kirchhoff's current law will be satisfied.

FOR FURTHER INVESTIGATION AND DISCUSSION

Use MultiSIM or PSpice to simulate the circuit of Figure 3-1. Determine the current through each resistor in the circuit. Compare your results to those of Table 3-2.

The simulation results are similar to actual measured results.

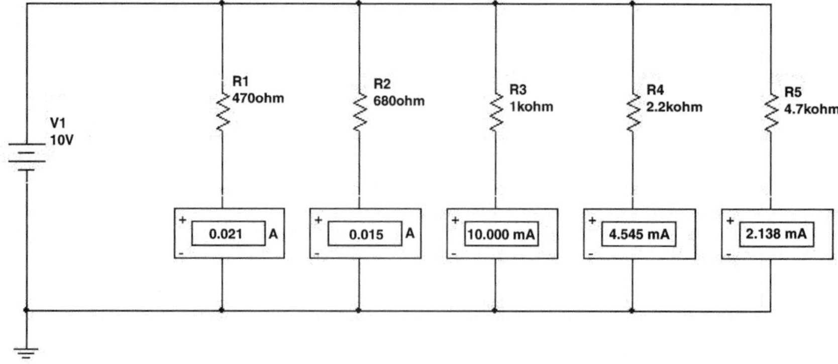

NAME ______________________

DATE ______________________

CLASS ______________________

LAB
4

Series-Parallel dc Circuits

OBJECTIVES

After completing this lab, you will be able to

- assemble a series-parallel circuit consisting of a voltage source and several resistors,
- measure voltage and current in a series-parallel circuit,
- compare measured values to theoretical calculations and verify Kirchhoff's current and voltage laws,
- assemble a zener diode regulator circuit and measure voltages and currents to verify that Kirchhoff's voltage and current laws apply,
- calculate power and verify the law of conservation of energy.

EQUIPMENT REQUIRED

☐ Digital multimeter (DMM)
☐ dc power supply
Note: Record this equipment in Table 4-1.

COMPONENTS

☐ Resistors: 330-Ω, 470-Ω, 680-Ω, 1-kΩ, 2.2-kΩ, 4.7-kΩ (1/4-W, 5%)
☐ Zener diode: 1N4734A (1-W, 5.6-V5%)

EQUIPMENT USED

Instrument	Manufacturer Mo	Serial No.
DMM		
dc Supply		

Table 4-1

TEXT REFERENCE

Section 7.1 THE SERIES-PARALLEL NETWORK
Section 7.2 ANALYSIS OF SERIES-PARALLEL CIRCUITS
Section 7.3 APPLICATIONS OF SERIES-PARALLEL CIRCUITS

DISCUSSION

Regardless of the complexity of a circuit, the basic laws of circuit analysis always apply. While Ohm's law and Kirchhoff's voltage and current laws are used to analyze simple series and parallel circuits, these same laws may be applied to analyze even the most complicated circuit. The following rules apply to all circuits.

The same current occurs through all series elements.

The same voltage appears across all parallel elements.

CALCULATIONS

1. Refer to the the circuit of Figure 4-1. Calculate the total resistance, R_T, seen by the voltage source. Calculate the current, I. Solve for all resistor currents, voltages, and powers. Enter the results in Table 4-2. Show the correct units for all entries.

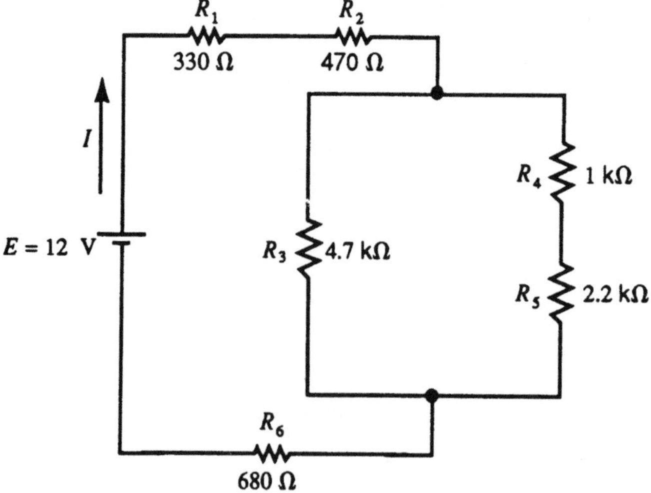

Figure 4-1 Series-parallel circuit

	Current	Voltage	Power
R_1	3.55 mA	1.17 V	4.15 mW
R_2	3.55 mA	1.67 V	5.93 mW
R_3	1.44 mA	6.75 V	9.72 mW
R_4	2.11 mA	2.11 V	4.45 mW
R_5	2.11 mA	4.64 V	9.79 mW
R_6	3.55 mA	2.41 V	8.56 mW

R_T	3380 Ω
I	3.55 mA

Table 4-2 Series-parallel resistance

MEASUREMENTS

2. Connect the resistors as shown in the network of Figure 4-2. Use the DMM (ohmmeter) to measure the resistance across the open terminals. Enter the result here. Compare your measurement to the theoretical calculation in Table 4-2. You should observe only a small discrepancy.

R_T	3380 Ω

3. Connect the voltage source to the circuit as shown in Figure 4-1. With a DMM (voltmeter) connected across the voltage source, adjust the voltage for exactly 12 V.

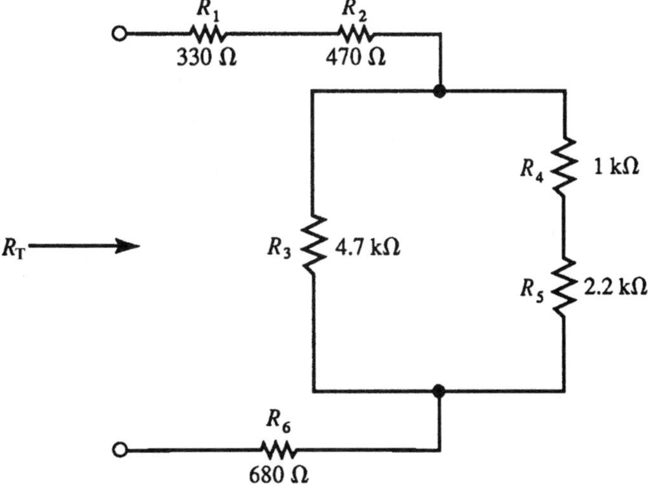

Figure 4-2 Series-parallel resistance

4. Disconnect the voltmeter from the voltage source. Measure the voltage across each resistor in the circuit and record the results in Table 4-3.
5. Set the DMM to measure the currents as illustrated in Figure 4-3. **Ensure that each branch is reconnected after the ammeter is removed.** Record your measurements in Table 4-3.

	Current	Voltage
R_1	3.55 mA	1.17 V
R_2	3.55 mA	1.67 V
R_3	1.44 mA	6.75 V
R_4	2.11 mA	2.11 V
R_5	2.11 mA	4.64 V
R_6	3.55 mA	2.41 V

I	3.55 mA

Table 4-3

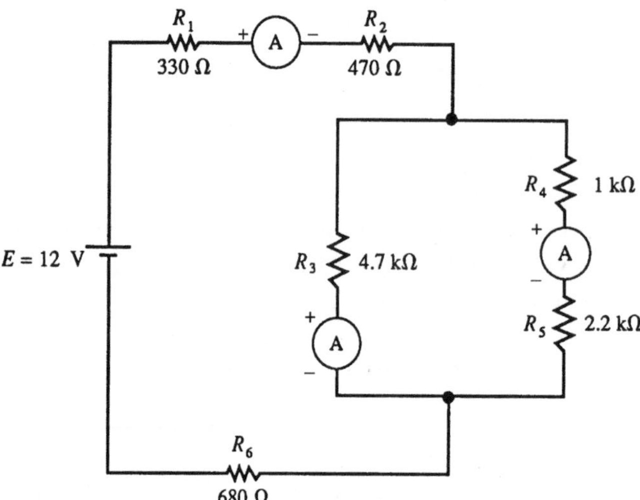

Figure 4-3 Measuring current in a series-parallel circuit

Zener Diode Circuit

In this part of the lab, we apply the principles of circuit analysis to examine the operation of a more complicated circuit. Here we use a *zener diode,* which is a two-terminal semiconductor device normally used as a *voltage regulator* to maintain a constant voltage between two terminals. When the zener diode is placed across a component which has a voltage greater than the *break-over* (zener) voltage of the diode, current through the zener diode forces the voltage across the component to decrease. While most other diodes permit current in only the forward direction (in the direction of the arrow in the diode symbol), the zener diode can conduct in either direction. When used as a voltage regulator, the zener diode is operated in the reverse-biased conditon. This means that when the zener diode is in its *breakover region*, current is against the arrow of the diode symbol.

6. Assemble the circuit shown in Figure 4-4, temporarily omitting the zener diode. Adjust the voltage source for 12 V.
7. Measure the voltages across R_1 and R_2 and record the values here.

V_1	3.92 V
V_2	8.08 V

8. Insert the zener diode into the circuit. Use the DMM (voltmeter) to measure voltages, V_1 and V_2 in the circuit of Figure 4-4. Convert the DMM to measure current and correctly measure currents I_1, I_2, and I_Z. Make sure that you turn off the voltage supply before disconnecting the circuit to insert the ammeter. In the circuit of Figure 4-4, show where you placed the ammeters to measure the currents. Record all measurements in Table 4-4.

Current		Voltage	
$I_1 =$	19.4 mA	$V_1 =$	6.40 V
$I_2 =$	8.23 mA	$V_2 =$	5.60 V
$I_Z =$	11.2 mA		

Table 4-4

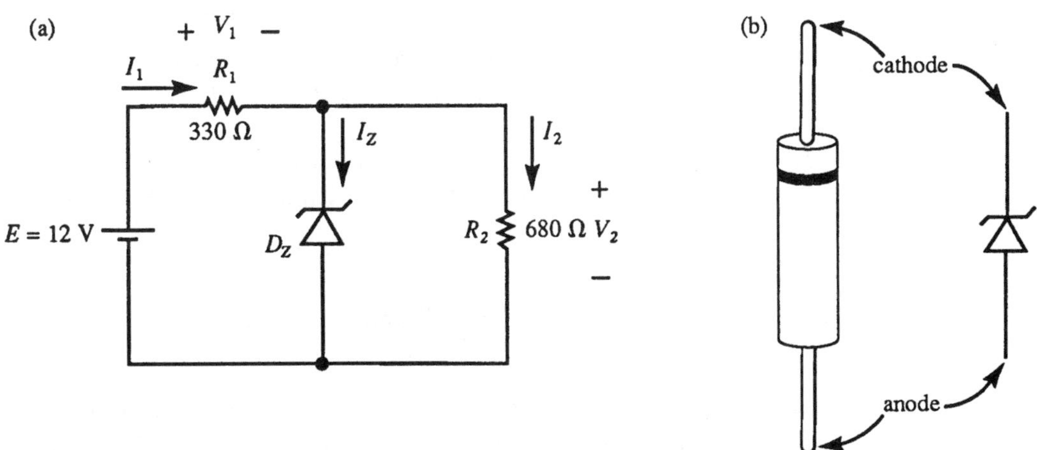

Figure 4-4 Zener diode voltage regulator circuit

CONCLUSIONS

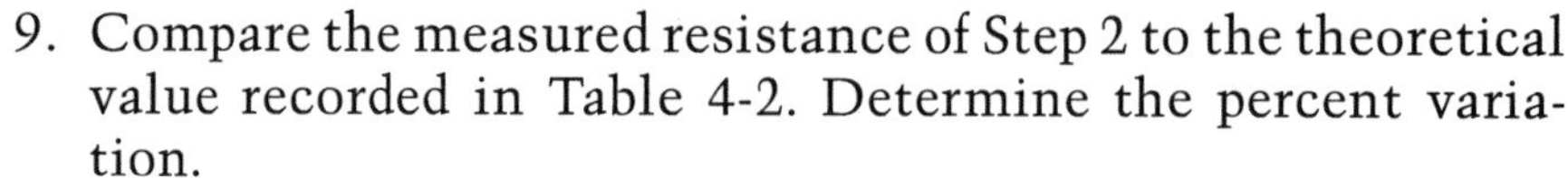

9. Compare the measured resistance of Step 2 to the theoretical value recorded in Table 4-2. Determine the percent variation.

R_T (theoretical) = 3380 Ω R_T (measured) = 3380 Ω

Variation should be small.

percent variation = ____________

10. Compare the measured voltage drops in Table 4-3 to the theoretical values recorded in Table 4-2. Indicate which values (if any) have a variation more than the resistor tolerance. Offer an explanation.

All variations should be less than the resistor tolerances.

11. Compare the measured currents in Table 4-3 to the theoretical values recorded in Table 4-2. Indicate which values (if any) have a variation more than the resistor tolerance. Offer an explanation.

All variations should be less than the resistor tolerances.

12. Refer to the data of Table 4-3.

a. Compare current I to the the summation $I_3 + I_4$

I = 3.55 mA $I_3 + I_4$ = 3.55 mA

b. Do the above calculations and measurements satisfy Kirchhoff's current law? Explain your answer.

13. a. Use the data of Table 4-3 to calculate the power, P_T delivered to the circuit by the voltage source. Enter the result here.

P_T	(12V)(3.55mA) = 42.6 mW

b. Use the voltages and currents of Table 4-3 to determine the power dissipated by each resistor in the circuit. Enter your results in Table 4-5.

	Power
R_1	(3.55 mA)(1.17 V) = 4.15 mW
R_2	(3.55 mA)(1.67 V) = 5.93 mW
R_3	(1.44 mA)(6.75 V) = 9.72 mW
R_4	(2.11 mA)(2.11 V) = 4.64 mW
R_5	(2.11 mA)(4.64 V) = 9.79 mW
R_6	(3.55 mA)(2.41 V) = 8.56 mW

Table 4-5

c. Compare the total power dissipated by the resistors to the total power delivered by the voltage source. Is energy conserved?

The powers are the same.

Energy is conserved.

14. Refer to the circuit of Figure 4-4. Compare the voltage, V_2, with the zener diode removed from the circuit, to the voltage when the diode is in the circuit. How do they compare? Explain briefly why this occurred.

The voltage was larger without the diode in the circuit.

The diode is a regulator.

15. Refer to the data of Table 4-4.

a. Compare current I_1 to the the summation $I_2 + I_Z$.

$$I_1 = I_2 + I_Z$$
$$= 8.23 \text{ mA} + 11.2 \text{ mA}$$
$$= 19.4 \text{ mA} \quad \text{(as required)}$$

I_1 = 19.4 mA $\qquad$ $I_2 + I_Z$ = 19.4 mA

b. Do the calculations and measurements in part a) satisfy Kirchhoff's current law? Explain your answer.

Kirchhoff's current law is satisfied since $\Sigma I_{in} = \Sigma I_{out}$

at the node.

16. a. Use the data in Table 4-4 to calculate the total power, P_T delivered to the circuit by the voltage source. Enter the result here.

P_T	(19.4mA)(12V) = 233 mW

b. Use the voltages and currents of Table 4-4 to determine the power dissipated by the zener diode and by each resistor in the circuit. Enter your results in Table 4-6.

	Power
R_1	(19.4mA)(6.40V) = 124 mW
R_2	(8.23mA)(5.60V) = 46 mW
D_Z	(11.2mA)(5.60V) = 62.7 mW

Table 4-6

c. Compare the total power dissipated by the resistors to the total power delivered by the voltage source. Is energy conserved?

P_T = 233mW = 124mW + 46mW + 63mW

Energy is conserved.

PROBLEMS

17. Refer to the circuit of Figure 4-4. Assume that the zener diode has a break-over voltage of 4.3 V.
    a. Calculate the voltages V_1 and V_2
    b. Determine the currents I_1, I_2 and I_Z
    c. Solve for the powers dissipated by R_1, R_2, and D_Z.
    d. Show that the total power dissipated is equal to the power delivered by the voltage source.

Answers:

a) $V_1 = 7.7$, $V_2 = 4.3$ V
b) $I_1 = 23.33$ mA , $I_2 = 6.32$ mA, $I_Z = 17.01$ mA
c) $P_1 = 180$ mW, $P_2 = 27.2$ mW, $P_Z = 73.1$ mW
d) $P_1 + P_2 + P_Z = 280$ mW $= E \cdot I_1$

NAME ______________________

DATE ______________________

CLASS ______________________

LAB 5

Potentiometers and Rheostats

OBJECTIVES

After completing this lab, you will be able to

- demonstrate the use a variable resistor as a potentiometer to control the voltage applied to a load,
- demonstrate the use a variable resistor as a rheostat to control the current applied to a load,
- measure how the value of a load's resistance affects the voltage across a potentiometer.

EQUIPMENT REQUIRED

☐ Digital multimeter (DMM)
☐ dc power supply
Note: Record this equipment in Table 5-1.

COMPONENTS

☐ Resistors: 5.6-kΩ, 3.3-kΩ, 330-kΩ (1/4-W, 5%)
10-kΩ variable resistor

EQUIPMENT USED

Instrument	Manufacturer/Model No.	Serial No.
DMM		
dc Supply		

Table 5-1

TEXT REFERENCE

Section 3.5 TYPES OF RESISTORS
Section 7.4 POTENTIOMETERS

DISCUSSION

Variable resistors are used extensively in electrical and electronic circuits to control the voltage and current in circuits. When a variable resistor is used to control the voltage (as in the volume control of an amplifier) it is called a *potentiometer*. If the same resistor is used to control the amount of current through a circuit (such as in a light dimmer) it is called a *rheostat*.

Refer to the series circuit of Figure 5-1. The current through this circuit is constant regardless of the location of the wiper arm (terminal *b*) of the variable resistor. If the wiper arm is moved so that it is at the bottom of the resistor, the resistance between terminals *b* and *c* is zero. This results in the voltage, V_L being zero volts. If, however, the wiper arm is moved so that it is at the top of the resistor, the resistance between terminals *b* and *c* will be at a maximum, resulting in a maximum voltage, V_L, appearing between the terminals.

CALCULATIONS

1. Determine the range of the output voltage, V_L for the circuit of Figure 5-1. Calculate the range of output voltage if a 330-kΩ resistor is connected across the output terminals of the circuit. Recalculate the range of output voltage if a 3.3-kΩ resistor is connected across the output terminals of the circuit. Record your results in Table 5-2.

	V_L (min)	V_L (max)
$R_L = \infty$ (open)	0	9.62 V
$R_L = 330$ kΩ	0	9.51 V
$R_L = 3.3$ kΩ	0	4.61 V

Table 5-2

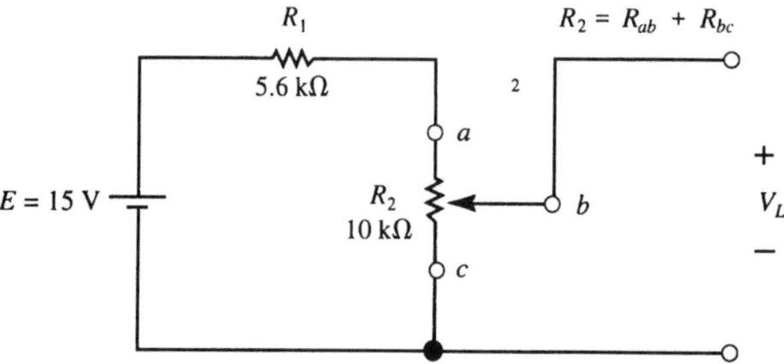

Figure 5-1 Variable resistor used as a potentiometer

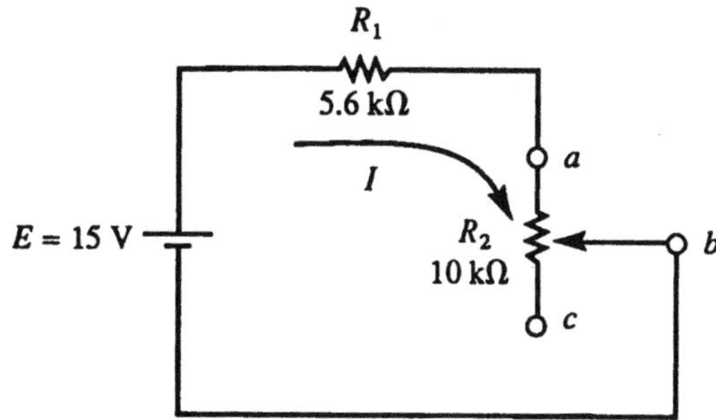

Figure 5-2 Variable resistor used as a rheostat

2. The 10-kΩ resistor in the circuit of Figure 5-1 is easily converted from a potentiometer into a rheostat. Figure 5-2 shows how the variable resistor is used as a rheostat. When the wiper arm is moved so that it is at the top of the resistor, the resistance of the rheostat will be at its minimum value. This means that maximum current will occur in the circuit. If the wiper is moved to the bottom of the resistor, the resistance of the rheostat will be at its maximum value, resulting in the least amount of current.

   Calculate the range of current for the circuit of Figure 5-2.

I(min)	I(max)
0.962 mA	2.68 mA

MEASUREMENTS

3. Assemble the circuit shown in Figure 5-1. Adjust the voltage source for 15 V. With a voltmeter connected between terminals b and c of the potentiometer, use a small screwdriver to adjust the central wiper fully clockwise (CW). Measure and record the output voltage. Now adjust the central wiper fully counterclockwise (CCW). Again measure and record the output voltage.

V_L(CW)	V_L(CCW)
9.62 V	0 V

4. Adjust the potentiometer to obtain an output voltage of 3.0 V. Disconnect the potentiometer from the circuit, being careful not to readjust the potentiometer setting. Measure and record the resistance between terminals b and c of the potentiometer.

R_{bc}	3.12 kΩ

5. Connect a 330-kΩ load resistor between the output terminals. Adjust the voltage source for 15 V. With a voltmeter connected between terminals *b* and *c* of the potentiometer, use a small screwdriver to adjust the central wiper fully clockwise (CW). Measure and record the output voltage. Now adjust the central wiper fully counterclockwise (CCW). Again measure and record the output voltage.

V_L(CW)	V_L(CCW)
9.51 V	0 V

6. Adjust the potentiometer to obtain an output voltage of 3.0 V. Disconnect the potentiometer from the circuit, being careful not to readjust the potentiometer setting. Measure and record the resistance between terminals *b* and *c* of the potentiometer.

R_{bc}	3.14 kΩ

7. Connect a 3.3-kΩ load resistor between the output terminals. Adjust the voltage source for 15 V. With a voltmeter connected between terminals *b* and *c* of the potentiometer, use a small screwdriver to adjust the central wiper fully clockwise (CW). Measure and record the output voltage. Now adjust the central wiper fully counterclockwise (CCW). Again measure and record the output voltage.

V_L(CW)	V_L(CCW
4.61 V	0 V

8. Adjust the potentiometer to obtain an output voltage of 3.0 V. Disconnect the potentiometer from the circuit, being careful not to readjust the potentiometer setting. Measure and record the resistance between terminals *b* and *c* of the potentiometer.

R_{bc}	6.74 kΩ

9. Construct the circuit of Figure 5-2. Place a DMM ammeter into the circuit to measure the current. Use a small screwdriver to adjust the central wiper fully clockwise (CW). Measure and record the circuit current. Now adjust the central wiper fully counterclockwise (CCW). Again measure and record the current.

I(CW)	*I*(CCW)
2.68 mA	0.962 mA

10. Adjust the rheostat so that the measured current is exactly equal to $I_{max}/2$. Remove the rheostat from the circuit, being careful not to readjust the potentiometer setting. Measure and record the resistance between terminals a and b of the potentiometer. The resistance should be exactly equal to R_1.

R_{ab}	5.59 kΩ

CONCLUSIONS

11. Compare the measurements of Step 3 to the theoretical maximum and minimum values of voltage recorded in Table 5-2 for $R_L = \infty$ (open).

The values should be very close.

12. Compare the measurements of Step 5 to the theoretical maximum and minimum values of voltage recorded in Table 5-2 for $R_L = 330\ \text{k}\Omega$.

The values should be very close.

13. Use the measured resistance, R_{bc} of Step 6 to determine the theoretical voltage which would appear across the load, $R_L = 330\ \text{k}\Omega$ in the equivalent circuit of Figure 5-3.

$$V_L = \left(\frac{3.14\text{k}\Omega\ //\ 330\text{k}\Omega}{3.14\text{k}\Omega\ //\ 330\text{k}\Omega + 6.86\text{k}\Omega + 5.6\text{k}\Omega}\right)15\ \text{V}$$

V_L	3.0 V

Compare the above value to the measured load voltage, V_L in Step 6.

They are the same.

14. Compare the measurements of Step 7 to the theoretical maximum and minimum values of voltage recorded in Table 5-2 for $R_L = 3.3\ k\Omega$.

    The values should be very close.

15. Use the measured resistance, R_{bc} of Step 8 to determine the theoretical voltage which would appear across the load, $R_L = 3.3\ k\Omega$ in the equivalent circuit of Figure 5-3.

$$\left(\frac{6.74k\Omega\ //\ 3.3k\Omega}{6.74k\Omega\ //\ 3.3k\Omega + 3.26k\Omega + 5.6k\Omega}\right) 15\ V$$

V_L	300 V

Compare the above value to the measured load voltage, V_L in Step 8.

The values are the same.

16. Compare the measurements of Step 9 to the theoretical maximum and minimum values of current recorded in Step 2.

    They are the same.

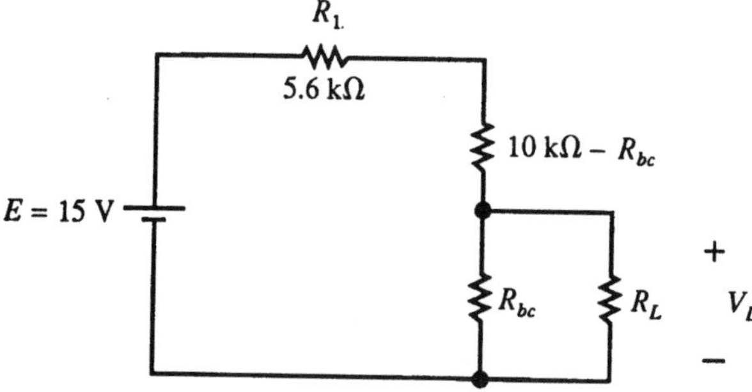

Figure 5-3

NAME ______________________

DATE ______________________

CLASS ______________________

LAB 6

Superposition Theorem

OBJECTIVES

After completing this lab, you will be able to

- calculate currents and voltages in a dc circuit using the superposition theorem,
- measure voltage and current in a multi-source circuit,
- measure the effects of sucessively removing each voltage source from a circuit,
- calculate loop currents and node voltages using mesh analysis and nodal analysis,
- verify the superposition theorem as it applies to dc circuits and show that the results are consistent with results determined using mesh analysis and nodal analysis,

EQUIPMENT REQUIRED

☐ Digital multimeter (DMM)
☐ dc power supply (2)
Note: Record this equipment in Table 6-1.

COMPONENTS

☐ Resistors: 680-Ω, 1-kΩ, 3.3-kΩ (1/4-W, 5%)

EQUIPMENT USED

Instrument	Manufacturer/Model No.	Serial No.
DMM		
dc Supply		
dc Supply		

Table 6-1

TEXT REFERENCE

Section 8.2 SOURCE CONVERSIONS
Section 8.5 MESH ANALYSIS
Section 8.6 NODAL ANALYSIS
Section 9.1 SUPERPOSITION THEOREM

DISCUSSION

Mesh analysis allows us to find the loop currents for a circuit having any number of voltage or current sources. If a circuit contains current sources, these must first be converted to voltage sources.

Nodal analysis is the twin of mesh analysis in that it allows us to calculate nodal voltages of a circuit (with respect to a reference node). If a circuit contains voltage sources, it is necessary to first convert these to current sources.

Analyzing a circuit using mesh or nodal analysis usually requires solving several linear equations. The superposition theorem allows us to simplify the analysis of a multi-source circuit by considering only one source at a time.

The superposition theorem states:

The voltage across (or the current through) a resistor may be determined by finding the sum of the effects due to each independent source in the circuit.

In order to determine the effects due to one source, it is necessary to remove all other sources from the circuit. This is accomplished by replacing voltage sources with short circuits and by replacing current sources with open circuits.

CALCULATIONS

1. Use superposition to calculate currents I_1, I_2, and I_3 in the circuit of Figure 6-1. Record the results.

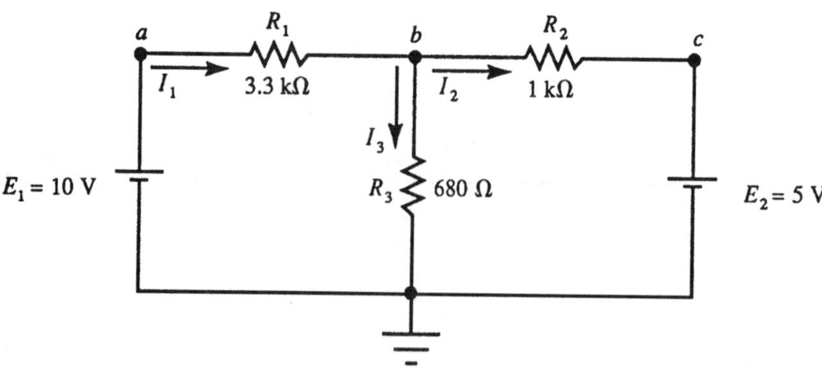

Figure 6-1

$$I_{1(1)} = \frac{10V}{3.3k\Omega + 0.68k\Omega \,//\, 1k\Omega} = \frac{10V}{3.705k\Omega} = 2.70 \text{ mA}$$

$$I_{2(1)} = \left(\frac{0.68k\Omega}{1k\Omega + 0.68k\Omega}\right)2.70mA = 1.09 \text{ mA}$$

$$I_{3(1)} = \left(\frac{1k\Omega}{1k\Omega + 0.68k\Omega}\right)2.70mA = 1.61 \text{ mA}$$

$$I_{2(2)} = -\frac{5V}{1k\Omega + 0.68k\Omega \,//\, 33k\Omega} = -\frac{5V}{1.564k\Omega} = -3.20 \text{ mA}$$

$$I_{1(2)} = -\left(\frac{0.68k\Omega}{3.3k\Omega + 0.68k\Omega}\right)3.20mA = -0.55 \text{ mA}$$

$$I_{3(2)} = 3.20mA - 0.55mA = 2.65 \text{ mA}$$

I_1	2.15 mA
I_2	–2.10 mA
I_3	4.25 mA

2. Use superposition to calculate the currents I_1, I_2, and I_3 in the circuit of Figure 6-2. Record the results below.

$I_{1(1)} = 2.70$ mA $\qquad I_{1(2)} = 0.55$ mA

$I_{2(1)} = 1.09$ mA $\qquad I_{2(2)} = 3.20$ mA

$I_{3(1)} = 1.61$ mA $\qquad I_{3(3)} = -2.65$ mA

$$I_1 = 2.70mA + 0.55mA = 3.25 \text{ mA}$$

$$I_2 = 1.09mA + 3.20mA = 4.29 \text{ mA}$$

$$I_3 = 1.61mA - 2.65mA = -1.04 \text{ mA}$$

I_1	3.25 mA
I_2	4.29 mA
I_3	–1.04 mA

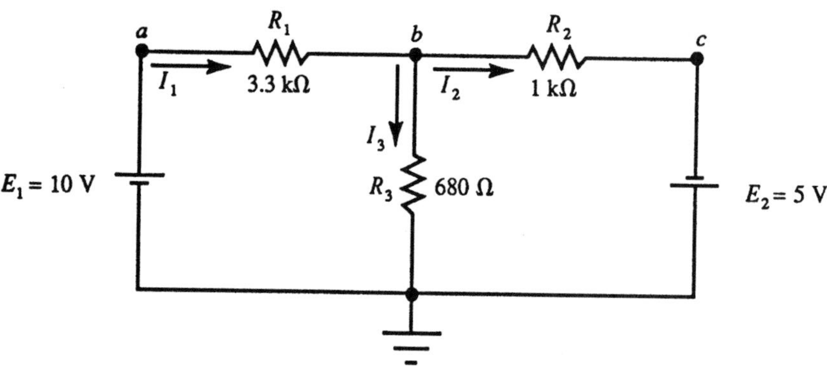

Figure 6-2

MEASUREMENTS

3. Assemble the circuit of Figure 6-1. Measure the voltages V_{ab}, V_b, and V_{bc}. Record your results in Table 6-2, showing the correct polarity for each measurement. Use these measurements and the resistor color codes to calculate the currents I_1, I_2, and I_3 for the circuit. Show the correct polarity for each current. (Use a negative sign to indicate that current is opposite to the indicated direction.)

V_{ab}	7.10 V
V_b	2.89 V
V_{bc}	–2.10 V
I_1	2.15 mA
I_2	–2.10 mA
I_3	4.26 mA

Table 6-2

4. Assemble the circuit of Figure 6-2. Measure the voltages V_{ab}, V_b, and V_{bc}. Record your results in Table 6-3, showing the correct polarity for each measurement. Use these measurements and the resistor color codes to calculate the currents I_1, I_2, and I_3 for the circuit. Show the correct polarity for each current.

V_{ab}	10.71 V
V_b	–0.71 V
V_{bc}	4.29 V
I_1	3.25 mA
I_2	4.29 mA
I_3	–1.04 mA

Table 6-3

5. Remove the voltage source E_2 from the circuit of Figure 6-1 and replace it with a short circuit. Measure the voltages V_{ab}, V_b, and V_{bc} and calculate the currents I_1, I_2, and I_3 due to the voltage source E_1. Record these results in Table 6-4.

$V_{ab(1)}$	8.91 V
$V_{b(1)}$	1.09 V
$V_{bc(1)}$	1.09 V
$I_{1(1)}$	2.70 mA
$I_{2(1)}$	1.09 mA
$I_{3(1)}$	1.61 mA

Table 6-4

6. Remove voltage source E_1 from the circuit of Figure 6-1 and replace it with a short circuit. Measure voltages V_{ab}, V_b, and V_{bc} and use the results to calculate currents I_1, I_2, and I_3 due to the voltage source E_2. Record the results in Table 6-5.

$V_{ab(2)}$	–1.80 V
$V_{b(2)}$	1.80 V
$V_{bc(2)}$	–3.20 V
$I_{1(2)}$	–0.55 mA
$I_{2(2)}$	–3.20 mA
$I_{3(2)}$	2.65 mA

Table 6-5

7. Reverse the polarity of voltage source E_2 as shown in the circuit of Figure 6-2. (Voltage source E_1 is still substituted by a short circuit.) Measure voltages V_{ab}, V_b, and V_{bc} and use the results to calculate currents I_1, I_2, and I_3 due to the voltage source E_2. Record the results in Table 6-6.

$V_{ab(3)}$	1.80 V
$V_{b(3)}$	–1.80 V
$V_{bc(3)}$	3.20 V
$I_{1(3)}$	0.55 mA
$I_{2(3)}$	3.20 mA
$I_{3(3)}$	–2.65 mA

Table 6-6

CONCLUSIONS

8. Compare the measured currents of Table 6-2 to the theoretical currents calculated in Step 1. Determine the percent deviation for each of the currents.

I_1(theoretical) = 2.15 mA percent variation = ~ 0%

I_2(theoretical) = –2.10 mA percent variation = ~ 0%

I_3(theoretical) = 4.26 mA percent variation = ~ 0%

9. Compare the measured currents recorded in Table 6-3 to the theoretical currents calculated in Step 2. Determine the percent deviation for each of the currents.

I_1(theoretical) = 3.25 mA percent variation = ~ 0%

I_2(theoretical) = 4.29 mA percent variation = ~ 0%

I_3(theoretical) = –1.04 mA percent variation = ~ 0%

10. Combine the results of Table 6-4 and Table 6-5.

$V_{ab} = V_{ab(1)} + V_{ab(2)} =$ 7.10 V

$V_b = V_{b(1)} + V_{b(2)} =$ 2.89 V

$V_{bc} = V_{bc(1)} + V_{bc(2)} =$ –2.10 V

$I_1 = I_{1(1)} + I_{1(2)} =$ 2.15 mA

$I_2 = I_{2(1)} + I_{2(2)} =$ –2.10 mA

$I_3 = I_{3(1)} + I_{3(2)} =$ 4.26 mA

Compare the previous results to the measurements recorded in Table 6-2. According to superposition, the results should be the same.

The results should be almost the same.

11. Combine the results of Table 6-4 and Table 6-6.

$V_{ab} = V_{ab(1)} + V_{ab(3)} =$ 10.71 V

$V_b = V_{b(1)} + V_{b(3)} =$ –0.71 V

$V_{bc} = V_{bc(1)} + V_{bc(3)} =$ 4.29 V

$I_1 = I_{1(1)} + I_{1(3)} =$ 3.25 mA

$I_2 = I_{2(1)} + I_{2(3)} =$ 4.29 mA

$I_3 = I_{3(1)} + I_{3(3)} =$ –1.04 mA

Compare the above results to the measurements recorded in Table 6-3. According to superposition, the results should be the same.

Only small variations should appear.

PROBLEMS

12. Apply mesh analysis to calculate the loop currents in the circuit of Figure 6-1. Use the loop currents to determine currents I_1, I_2, and I_3.

Loop A: $(3.98\text{k}\Omega)\, I_A - (0.68\text{k}\Omega)\, I_B = 10\text{V}$

Loop B: $-(0.68\text{k}\Omega)\, I_A + (1.68\text{k}\Omega)\, I_B = -5\text{V}$

$I_A = 2.15\text{mA}$

$I_B = -2.10\text{mA}$

$$I_3 = I_A - I_B = 2.15\text{mA} - (-2.10\text{mA})$$
$$= 4.25\text{ mA}$$

$I_{loop\ 1} =$ 2.15 mA

$I_{loop\ 2} =$ −2.10 mA

I_1	2.15 mA
I_2	−2.10 mA
I_3	4.25 mA

13. Apply mesh anaysis to calculate the loop currents in the circuit of Figure 6-2. Use the loop currents to determine currents I_1, I_2, and I_3.

Loop A: $(3.98\text{k}\Omega)\ I_A - (0.68\text{k}\Omega)\ I_B = 10\text{ V}$

Loop B: $-(0.68\text{k}\Omega)\ I_A + (1.686\text{k}\Omega)\ I_B = 5\text{ V}$

$I_A = 3.25\text{ mA}$

$I_B = 4.29\text{ mA}$

$$I_3 = I_A - I_B = 3.25\text{ mA} - 4.29\text{ mA}$$
$$= -1.04\text{ mA}$$

$I_{loop\ 1} =$ 3.25 mA

$I_{loop\ 2} =$ 4.29 mA

I_1	3.25 mA
I_2	4.29 mA
I_3	−1.04 mA

14. Use nodal analysis to calculate the node voltage V_b in the circuit of Figure 6-1. Your result should be very close to the measured value recorded in Table 6-2.

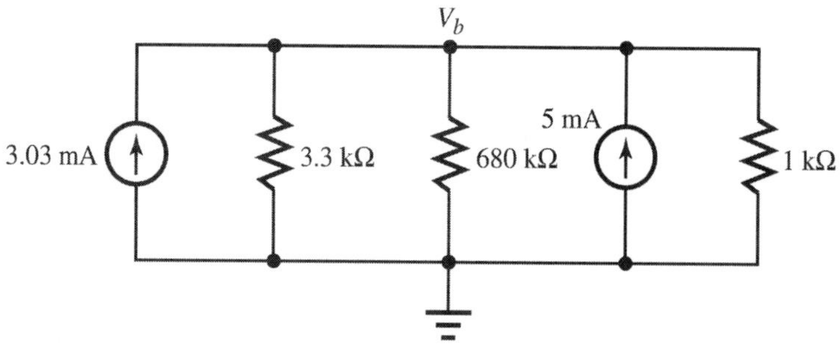

$$\left(\frac{1}{3.3\text{k}\Omega}+\frac{1}{0.68\text{k}\Omega}+\frac{1}{1\text{k}\Omega}\right)V_b = 3.03\text{mA} + 5\text{mA}$$

$$V_b = \frac{8.03\text{mA}}{2.774\text{mS}} = 2.90\text{ V}$$

$V_b =$ 2.90 V

15. Use nodal analysis to calculate the node voltage V_b in the circuit of Figure 6-2. Your result should be very close to the measured value recorded in Table 6-3.

$$\left(\frac{1}{3.3\text{k}\Omega}+\frac{1}{0.68\text{k}\Omega}+\frac{1}{1\text{k}\Omega}\right)V_b = 3.03\text{mA} - 5\text{mA}$$

$$V_b = \frac{-1.97\text{mA}}{2.774\text{mS}} = -0.71\text{ V}$$

$V_b =$ −0.71 V

NAME ______________________________

DATE ______________________________

CLASS ______________________________

LAB 7

Thévenin's and Norton's Theorems (dc)

OBJECTIVES

After completing this lab, you will be able to

- determine the Thévenin and Norton equivalent of a complex circuit,
- analyze a circuit using the Thévenin or Norton equivalent circuit,
- determine the value of load resistance needed to ensure maximum power transfer to the load,
- measure the Thévenin (or Norton) resistance of a circuit using an ohmmeter,
- measure the Thévenin voltage of a circuit using a voltmeter,
- measure the Norton current of a circuit using an ammeter.
- describe how maximum power is transferred to a load when the load resistance is equal to the Thévenin resistance ($R_L = R_{Th}$).

EQUIPMENT REQUIRED

- ☐ Digital multimeter (DMM)
- ☐ dc power supply

  Note: Record this equipment in Table 7-1.

COMPONENT:

☐ Resistors: 3.3-kΩ, 4.7-kΩ, 5.6-kΩ (1/4-W, 5% tolerance)
10-kΩ variable resistor

EQUIPMENT USED

Instrument	Manufacturer/Model No	Serial No.
DMM		
dc Supply		

Table 7-1

TEXT REFERENCE

Section 9-2 THÉVENIN'S THEOREM
Section 9.3 NORTON'S THEOREM
Section 9.4 MAXIMUM POWER TRANSFER THEOREM

DISCUSSION

Thévenin's theorem:

Any linear bilateral network may be reduced to a simplified two-terminal network consisting of a single voltage source, E_{Th}, in series with a single resistor, R_{Th}. Once the original network is simplified, any load connected to the output terminals will behave exactly as if the load were connected in series with E_{Th} and R_{Th}.

Norton's theorem:

Any linear bilateral network may be reduced to a simplified two-terminal network consisting of a single current source, I_N, in parallel with a single resistor, R_N. A Thévenin equivalent circuit is easily converted into a Norton equivalent by performing a source conversion as follows:

$$R_N = R_{Th} \tag{7-1}$$

$$I_N = \frac{E_{Th}}{R_{Th}} \tag{7-2}$$

When a load is connected across the output terminals, the circuit will behave exactly as if the load were connected in parallel with I_N and R_N.

Maximum power transfer theorem:

Maximum power will be delivered to the load resistance when the load resistance is equal to the Thévenin (or Norton) resistance.

CALCULATIONS

1. Determine the Thévenin equivalent of the circuit of Figure 7-1. Sketch the equivalent circuit in the space provided below.

   $R_{Th} = 3.3\text{k}\Omega + 0.68\text{k}\Omega \,//\, 4.7\text{k}\Omega = 3.89\text{k}\Omega$

   $$E_{Th} = \left(\frac{0.68}{4.7 + 0.68}\right) 15\text{V} = 1.90\text{ V}$$

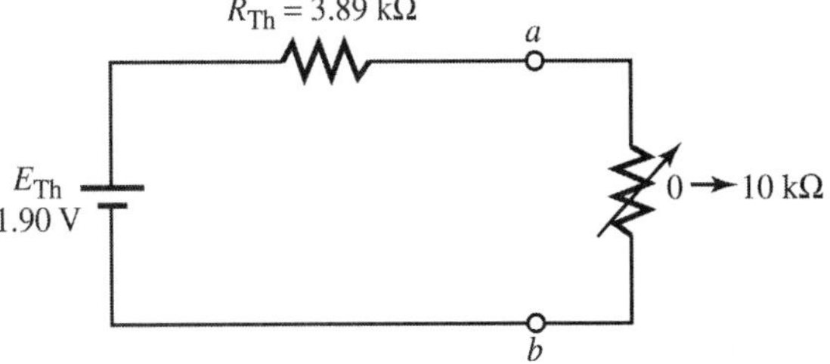

2. Determine the Norton equivalent of the circuit of Figure 7-1. Sketch the equivalent circuit in the space provided below.

   $$I_N = \frac{1.90\text{V}}{3.89\text{k}\Omega} = 0.487\text{ mA}$$

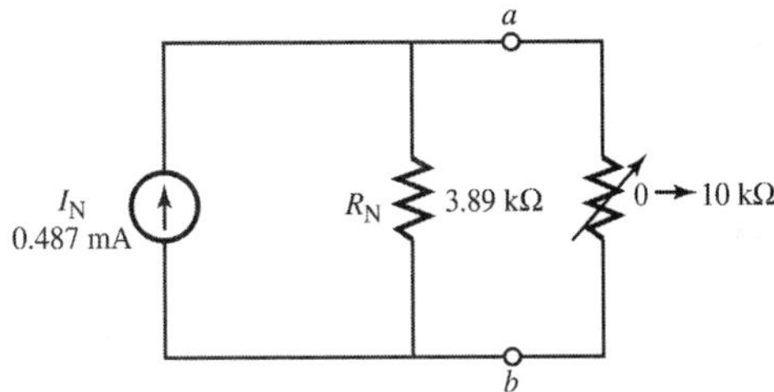

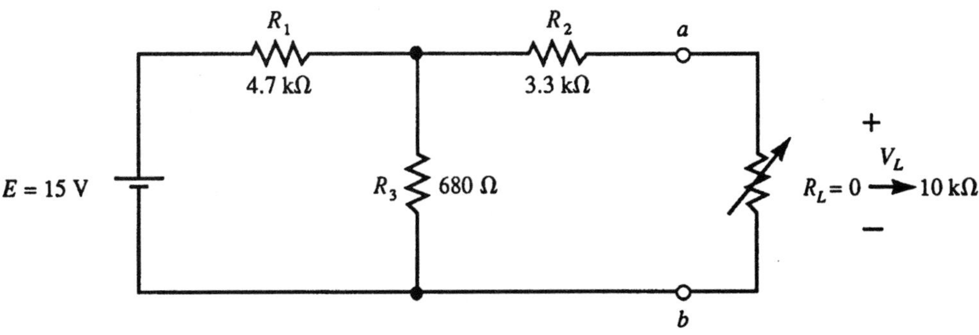

Figure 7-1

3. Calculate the minimum and the maximum voltage V_L which will appear across the load as R_L is varied between 0 and 10 kΩ. Enter the results below.

$V_{L(min)}$	0 V
$V_{L(max)}$	1.36 V

4. Calculate the minimum and the maximum load current I_L which will occur through the load as R_L is varied between 0 and 10 kΩ. Enter the results below.

$I_{L(min)}$	0.136 mA
$I_{L(max)}$	0.487 mA

5. Determine the value of load resistance for which maximum power will be transferred to the load.

R_L	3.89 kΩ

MEASUREMENTS

6. Assemble the circuit of Figure 7-1, temporarily omitting the load resistor R_L. Insert the DMM voltmeter across terminals *a* and *b* and measure the open-circuit voltage.This is the Thévenin voltage E_{Th}. Record the measurement here.

E_{TH}	1.90 V

7. Insert the DMM ammeter between terminals *a* and *b*. Ensure that the ammeter is adjusted to measure the expected Norton current. Because the ammeter is effectively a short circuit, you are measuring the short-circuit current between terminals *a* and *b*. Record the measurement here.

I_N	0.487 mA

8. Remove the voltage source from the circuit and replace it with a short circuit. Place the DMM ohmmeter across terminals *a* and

b and measure the resistance between these terminals.This is the Thévenin resistance R_{Th}. Record the result here.

R_{Th}	3.89 kΩ

9. Reconnect the voltage source into the circuit. Connect the variable 10-kΩ resistor as a rheostat and insert it as the load resistance R_L. Adjust the variable resistor between its minimum and maximum values. Measure and record the maximum and minimum output voltage V_L.

$V_{L\ (min)}$	0 V
$V_{L\ (max)}$	1.36 V

10. Place the DMM ammeter in series with the load resistor R_L. Adjust the variable resistor between its minimum and maximum values. Measure and record the minimum and maximum load current I_L.

$I_{L\ (min)}$	0.136 mA
$I_{L\ (max)}$	0.487 mA

11. Connect the DMM voltmeter across the load resistor. Adjust R_L until the output voltage is exactly half of the Thévenin voltage measured in Step 6. When $V_L = E_{Th}/2$, the load resistor is receiving the maximum amount of power from the circuit. Carefully remove R_L from the circuit, ensuring that the rheostat is not accidently readjusted. Use the DMM ohmmeter to measure the value of R_L. Record the measurement here.

R_L	3.89 kΩ

CONCLUSIONS

12. Compare the measured value of Thévenin voltage E_{Th} in Step 6 to the calculated value of Step 1. Determine the percent variation.

$E_{Th(theoretical)}$ = 1.90 V percent variation = ~ 0%

13. Compare the measured value of Thévenin (or Norton) resistance R_{Th} in Step 8 to the calculated value of Step 1. Determine the percent variation.

$R_{Th(theoretical)}$ = 3.89 kΩ percent variation = ~ 0%

14. Compare the measured value of Norton current I_N in Step 7 to the calculated value of Step 2. Determine the percent variation.

$I_{N(theoretical)}$ = 0.487 mA percent variation = ~ 0%

15. An alternate method of determining the Thévenin (Norton) resistance is by applying Ohm's law to the Thévenin voltage and Norton current. Calculate the value of Thévenin resistance using the measured values of Thévenin voltage and Norton current.

$$R_{Th} = R_N = \frac{E_{Th}}{I_N} \tag{7-3}$$

R_{Th}	3.89 kΩ

Compare this value to the actual measured value of Thévenin resistance of Step 8.

The value should be very close.

16. Compare the measured minimum and maximum voltage V_L to the calculated voltages determined in Step 3. Explain why there is a slight variation.

The ammeter will have a small loading effect.

17. Compare the measured minimum and maximum load current I_L to the calculated currents determined in Step 4.

The values should be very close.

18. When delivering maximum power to the load, how did the actual value of load resistance R_L compare the theoretical value calculated in Step 5.

R_L = 3.89 kΩ is close to the measured Thévenin resistance.

NAME ______________________

DATE ______________________

CLASS ______________________

LAB 8

Capacitors

OBJECTIVES

After completing this lab, you will be able to

- measure capacitance,
- verify capacitor relationships for series and parallel connections,
- verify that a capacitor behaves as an open circuit for steady state dc.

EQUIPMENT REQUIRED

- ☐ DMM
- ☐ Capacitance meter
- ☐ Variable dc power supply

COMPONENTS

- ☐ Capacitors: One each of 1 μF, 0.47 μF and 0.33 μF, non-electrolytic, 35 WVDC or greater
- ☐ Resistors: One each of 2.7-kΩ, 3.9-kΩ, and 10-kΩ, 1/4 W

EQUIPMENT USED

Instrument	Manufacturer/Model No.	Serial No.
DMM		
Capacitance meter†		
Power supply		

†Such as a DMM with capacitance measuring capability, an LCR meter (e.g., the BK Precision 878), a digital capacitance bridge, or an impedance bridge.

Table 8-1

TEXT REFERENCE

Section 10.1 CAPACITANCE
Section 10.7 CAPACITORS IN PARALLEL AND SERIES

DISCUSSION

Practical Note
The farad is a very large quantity; practical capacitors generally range in value from a few picofarads to a few hundred microfarads.

A *capacitor* is a charge storage device and its electrical property is called *capacitance*. The more charge that a capacitor can store for a given voltage, the larger its capacitance. Capacitance, charge and voltage are related by the equation

$$C = \frac{Q}{V} \tag{8-1}$$

where C is capacitance in *farads*, Q is charge stored (in coulombs) and V is the capacitor terminal voltage (in volts). Because of its ability to store charge, a capacitor holds its voltage. That is, if you charge a capacitor, then disconnect the source, a voltage will remain on the capacitor for a considerable length of time. Dangerous voltages can be present on charged capacitors. For this reason, you should discharge capacitors before working with them.

For capacitors in parallel, the total capacitance is the sum of the individual capacitances. That is,

$$C_T = C_1 + C_2 + \ldots + C_N \tag{8-2}$$

For capacitors in series, the total capacitance may be found from

$$\frac{1}{C_T} = \frac{1}{C_1} + \frac{1}{C_2} + \ldots + \frac{1}{C_N} \tag{8-3}$$

Steady State Capacitor Currents and Voltages

Since capacitors consist of conducting plates separated by an insulator, there is no conductive path from terminal to terminal. Thus, when a capacitor is placed across a dc source, its steady state current is zero. This means that a capacitor in steady state looks like an open circuit to dc.

When connected in parallel, the voltage across all capacitors is the same. However, when connected in series, voltage divides in inverse proportion to the size of the capacitances: that is, the smaller the capacitance, the larger the voltage. For capacitors in series as in Figure 8-3(a), the steady dc voltages on capacitors are related by

$$V_x = \left(\frac{C_T}{C_x}\right)E, \quad V_1 = \left(\frac{C_2}{C_1}\right)V_2, \quad V_1 = \left(\frac{C_3}{C_1}\right)V_3 \qquad (8\text{-}4)$$

and so on. (This is the voltage divider rule for capacitance.)

Measuring Capacitance

Measuring capacitance with a modern capacitor tester is straightforward. The general procedure is

1. Short the capacitor's leads to discharge the capacitor. Remove the short.
2. Set the function selector of the tester to the appropriate capacitance range (if not autoranging), then connect the capacitor. Observe polarity markings on polarized capacitors if applicable. (This is not necessary on some testers.)
3. Read the capacitance value directly from the numeric readout.

With such testers, it takes only a few seconds to measure capacitance.

MEASUREMENTS

1. Carefully measure each capacitor and resistor and record their values in Tables 8-2 and 8-3.

Note: These are ideal values. Real components will have some tolerance. Therefore, your values will be somewhat different

	Nominal	Measured
C_1	1 μF	1.00 μF
C_2	0.47 μF	0.470 μF
C_3	0.33 μF	0.330 μF

Table 8-2

	Nominal	Measured
R_1	2.7 kΩ	2.70 kΩ
R_2	3.9 kΩ	3.90 kΩ
R_3	10 kΩ	10.0 kΩ

Table 8-3

2. a. Assemble the circuit of Figure 8-1(a), measure capacitance C_T and record in Table 8-4. Repeat for circuits (b), (c) and (d).
   b. Verify the values measured in (a) by analyzing each circuit using the measured capacitor values from Table 8-2. Record calculated values in Table 8-4. How do they compare to the measured results?

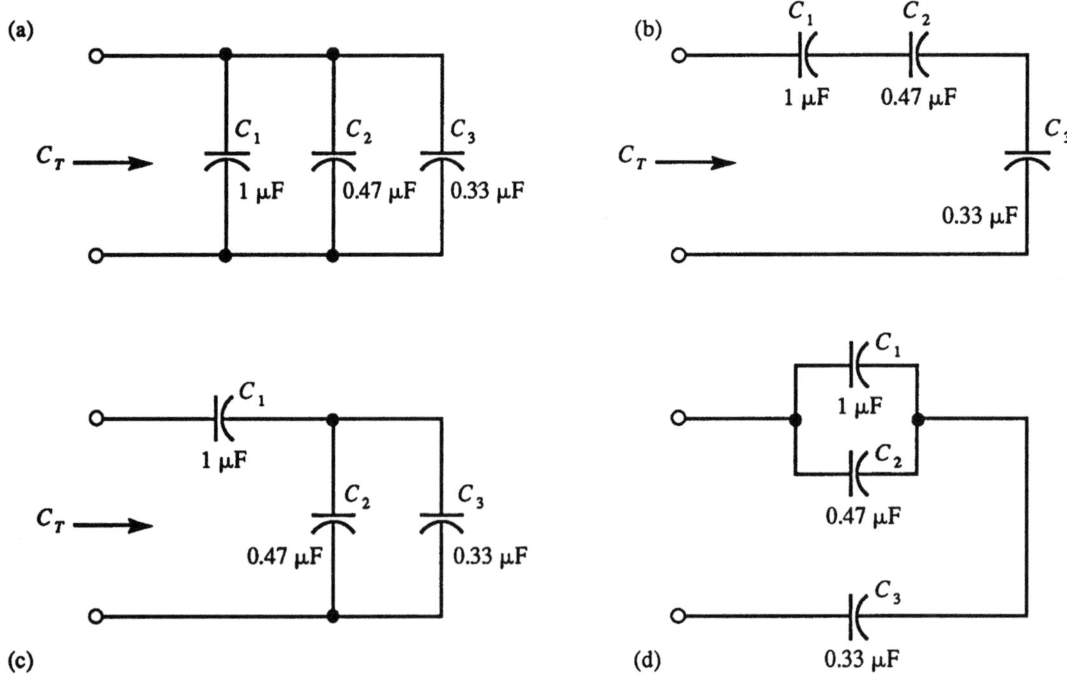

Figure 8-1 Circuits for Test 2

Circuit	Total Capitance C_T (μF) Measured	Calculated	% of Difference
Figure 8-1(a)	Should be close to calculated —depends on tolerances of components	1.80	
Figure 8-1(b)		0.162	
Figure 8-1(c)		0.444	
Figure 8-1(d)		0.270	

Table 8-4

3. a. Assemble the circuit of Figure 8-2. Set E = 18.0 V, measure V_1, V_2, and V_3 and record in Table 8-5.

	Measured	Computed
V_1	Should be close to	2.93
V_2	calculated — depends on	4.23
V_3	tolerances of components.	10.8

Table 8-5

See next page for calculations

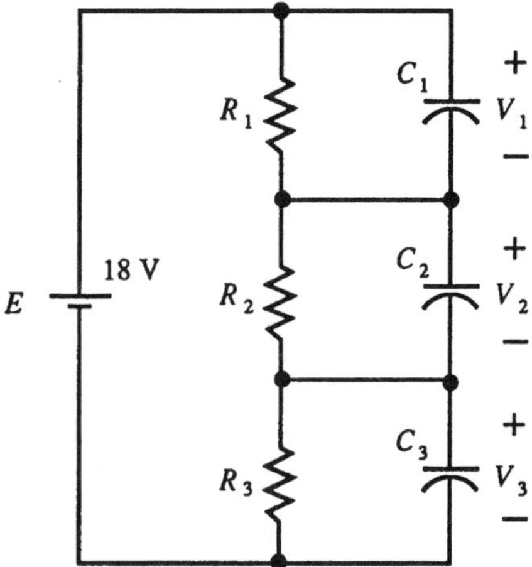

Figure 8-2 Circuit for Test 3

b. Verify the results of Table 8-5 by analyzing the circuit of Figure 8-2 and calculating voltages. Why do Equations 8-4 not apply here? Why do the capacitors not load the circuit?

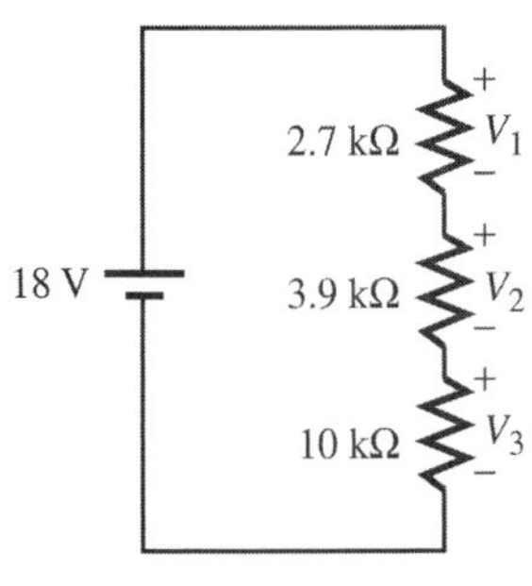

Since the capacitors look like open circuits to steady state dc, they have no effect here, and thus, Equations 8-4 do not apply. Instead, since this is a simple resistive circuit, use the voltage divider rule for resistors.Thus,

$$V_1 = \left(\frac{R_1}{R_T}\right)E = \left(\frac{2.7\text{k}\Omega}{16.6\text{k}\Omega}\right)(18\text{V}) = 2.93\text{ V}$$

Similarly, $V_2 = 4.23$ V and $V_3 = 10.8$ V

PROBLEMS

4. For the circuit of Figure 8-3(a), compute the voltage across each capacitor and record in Table 8-6. Repeat for Figure 8-3(b).

Solution Notes:
1. Apply Eqs. 8-4.
2. For Fig. 8-3(b), C_2 and C_3 are in parallel. Redraw using the equivalent capacitance, then apply Eqs. 8-4.

	Figure 8-3(a)	Figure 8-3(b)
V_1	2.92 V	8.0 V
V_2	6.22 V	10.0 V
V_3	8.86 V	10.0 V

Table 8-6

5. For the circuit of Figure 8-4, compute the voltage across the capacitor.

See solution on the following pages.

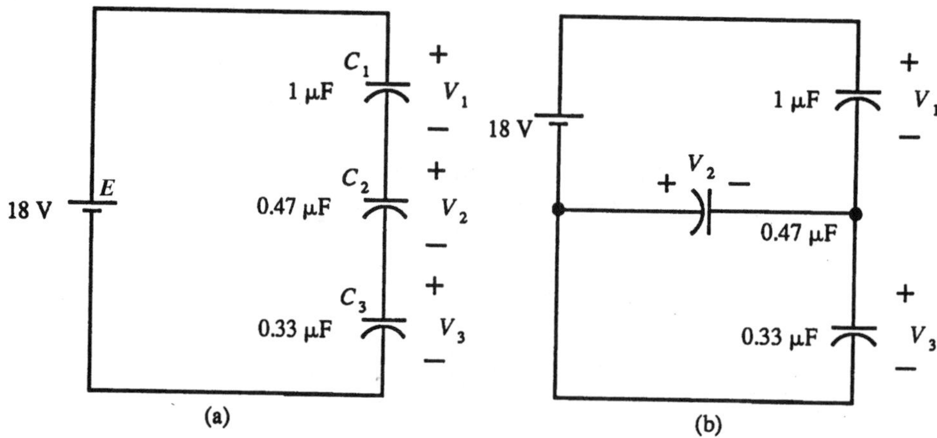

Figure 8-3 Circuits for Part 4

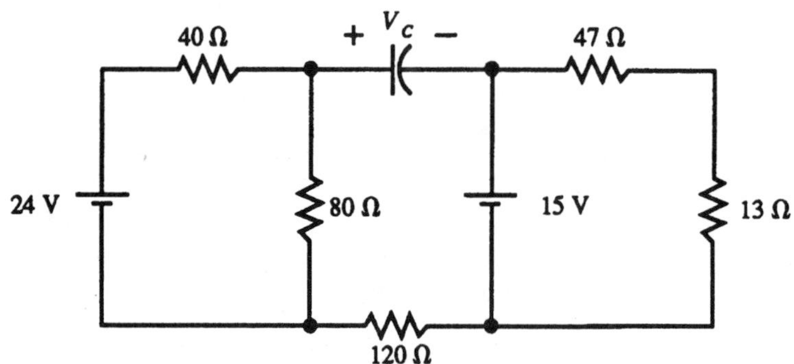

Figure 8-4 Circuit for Part 5

FOR FURTHER INVESTIGATION AND DISCUSSION

See next page for solutions

Capacitors can have quite loose tolerances—that is, the actual capacitance of a capacitor may differ by as much as ±10% to ±20% from its nominal value (i.e., its body marking) depending on the type of capacitor used. Consider two capacitors, $C_1 = 1$ μF ±10% and $C_2 = 0.47$ μF ±20%. Write a short discussion paper on the impact of tolerances. As the basis for your discussion, (a) place the capacitors in parallel and compute the nominal capacitance C_T and the minimum and maximum value that C_T will have if both capacitors are at their worst-case tolerance limits. (b) Repeat if the capacitors are in series. (c) With this as background, show how tolerance errors can impact total capacitance of a more complex circuit. For this last part, consider Figure 8-1(c). Assume that C_3 has a tolerance of ±10%.

Problem 5

Solution: For steady state dc, the capacitor looks like an open circuit. Thus,

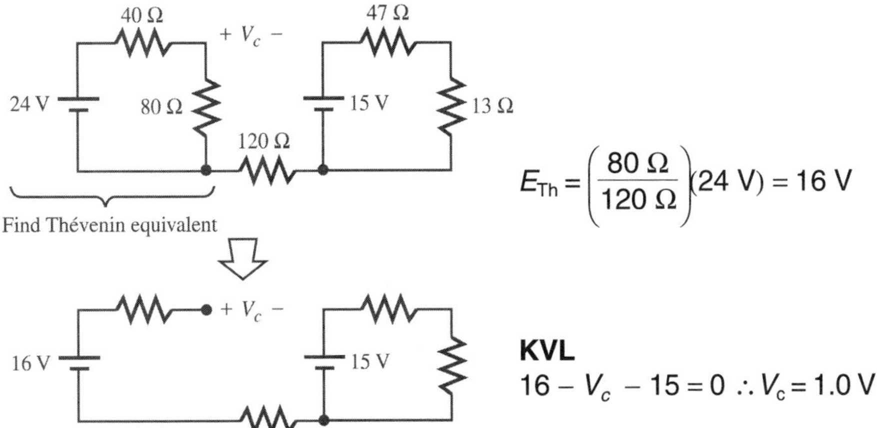

$$E_{Th} = \left(\frac{80\ \Omega}{120\ \Omega}\right)(24\ V) = 16\ V$$

KVL

$$16 - V_c - 15 = 0 \therefore V_c = 1.0\ V$$

For Further Investigation and Discussion

Given: $C_1 = 1\ \mu F \pm 10\% = 1\ \mu F \pm\ 0.1\ \mu F$. Thus, C_1 has a nominal value of 1 μF, but its actual value can lie anywhere between 0.9 μF and 1.1 μF. Similarly, C_2 has a nominal value of 0.47 μF with an actual value that can lie anywhere between 0.376 μF and 0.564 μF.

(a) Parallel Case: $C_T = C_1 + C_2$. Thus the nominal parallel value is $C_{T(nom)} = 1.47\ \mu F$. If both C_1 and C_2 are at their minimum extremes, however, $C_{T(min)} = 0.9\ \mu F + 0.367\ \mu F = 1.28\ \mu F$, while if both are at their maximums, $C_{T(max)} = 1.66\ \mu F$. Thus, the worst-case error here (relative to the nominal value) is about 13%.

(b) Series Case: Using Equation 8-3, you find that $C_{T(nom)} = 0.320\ \mu F$. If both C_1 and C_2 are at their minimum extremes, $C_{T(min)} = 0.265\ \mu F$, whereas if both are at their maximum extremes, $C_{T(max)} = 0.373\ \mu F$. Thus, the worst-case error here (relative to the nominal value) is about 17%.

(c) Figure 8-1(c) (summary only): $C_{T(nom)} = 0.444\ \mu F$. $C_{T(min)} = 0.385\ \mu F$; $C_{T(max)} = 0.503\ \mu F$. Error (relative to the nominal value) is about 13%.

NAME ______________________

DATE ______________________

CLASS ______________________

LAB 9

Capacitor Charging and Discharging

OBJECTIVES

After completing this lab, you will be able to

- measure capacitor charge and discharge times,
- confirm the voltage/current direction convention for capacitors,
- confirm the Thévenin method of analysis for capacitive charging and discharging,

EQUIPMENT REQUIRED

- ☐ DMM, VOM
- ☐ Variable dc power supply
- ☐ Function generator (optional)
- ☐ Oscilloscope (optional)

COMPONENTS

- ☐ Capacitors: 470-µF (electrolytic), 0.01-µF (non-electrolytic)
- ☐ Resistors: 10-kΩ, 20-kΩ, 39-kΩ, 47-kΩ, 1/4-W
- ☐ Switch: Single pole, double throw
- ☐ Stopwatch

Note to the Instructor

Part D of this lab may be run as an instructor demo if your students have not yet had instruction on the oscilloscope.

EQUIPMENT USED

Instrument	Manufacturer/Model No.	Serial No.
DMM		
Power supply		
Function generator (optional)		
Oscilloscope (optional)		

Table 9-1

TEXT REFERENCE

Section 10.8 CAPACITOR CURRENT AND VOLTAGE
Section 11.1 INTRODUCTION
Section 11.2 CAPACITOR CHARGING EQUATIONS
Section 11.4 CAPACITOR DISCHARGING EQUATIONS
Section 11.5 MORE COMPLEX CIRCUITS
Section 11.8 TRANSIENT ANALYSIS USING COMPUTERS

DISCUSSION

Capacitor charging and discharging may be studied using the circuit of Figure 9-1. When the switch is in position 1, the capacitor charges at a rate determined by its capacitance and the resistance through which it charges; when the switch is in position 2, it discharges at a rate determined by its capacitance and the resistance through which it discharges. This phenomenon of charging and discharging is important as it affects the operation of many circuits.

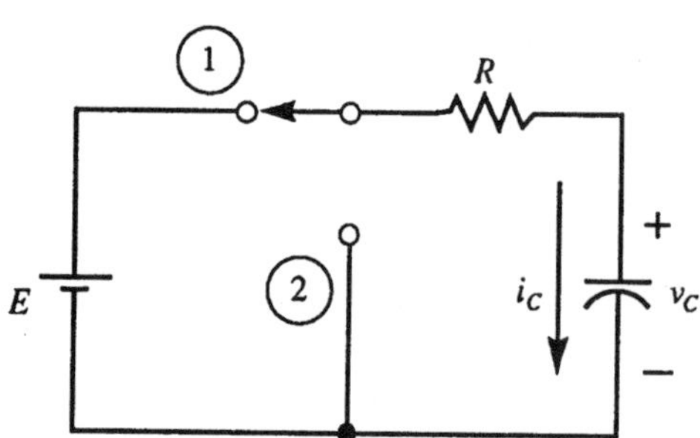

Caution
In this lab, you use electrolytic capacitors. Electrolytics are polarized and must be used with their + lead connected to the positive side of the circuit and their – lead to the negative side. An incorrectly connected electrolytic may explode.

Figure 9-1 Circuit for studying capacitor charging and discharging

Voltage and Current During Charging

Consider Figure 9-2. At the instant the switch is moved to the charge position, current jumps from zero to E/R (since the capacitor looks like a short circuit at this instant). As the capacitor voltage approaches full source voltage, current approaches zero (since the capacitor looks like an open circuit to dc). During charging, voltage and current are given by

$$i_C = \frac{E}{R}e^{-t/RC} \tag{9-1}$$

$$v_C = E(1 - e^{-t/RC}) \tag{9-2}$$

The product RC is referred to as the *time constant* and is given the symbol τ. Thus,

$$\tau = RC \tag{9-3}$$

In one time constant, the capacitor voltage climbs to 63.2% of its final value while the current drops to 36.8% of its initial value. For all practical purposes, charging is complete in five time constants.

Voltage and Current During Discharging

The discharge curves are shown in Figure 9-3. When the switch is moved to position 2, the capacitor looks momentarily like a voltage

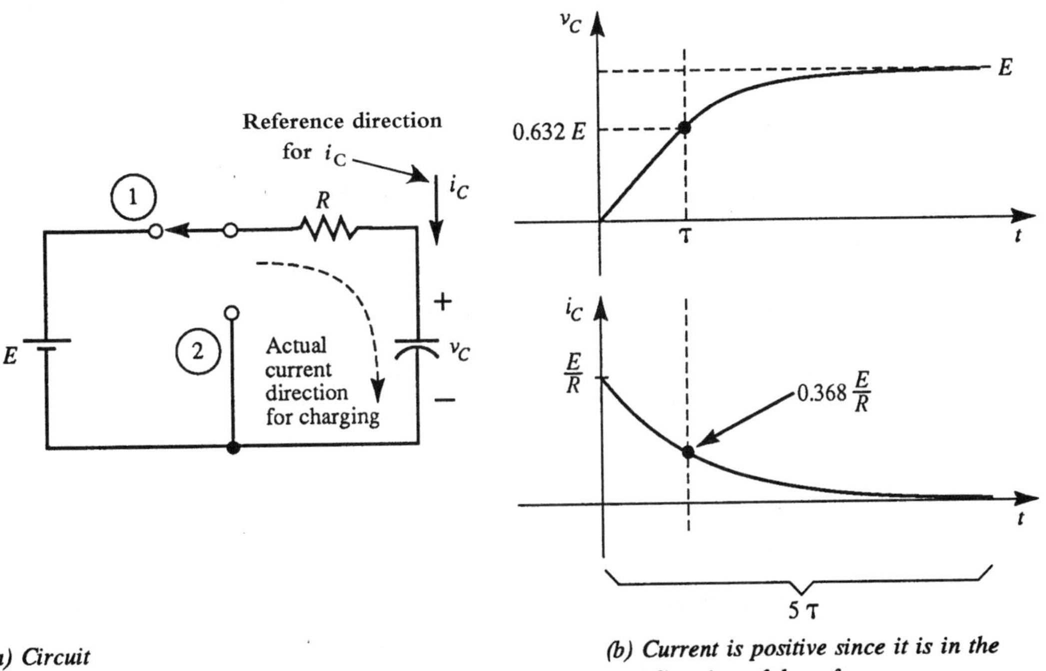

(a) Circuit

(b) Current is positive since it is in the direction of the reference arrow

Figure 9-2 Capacitor voltage and current during charging. Capacitor is initially uncharged

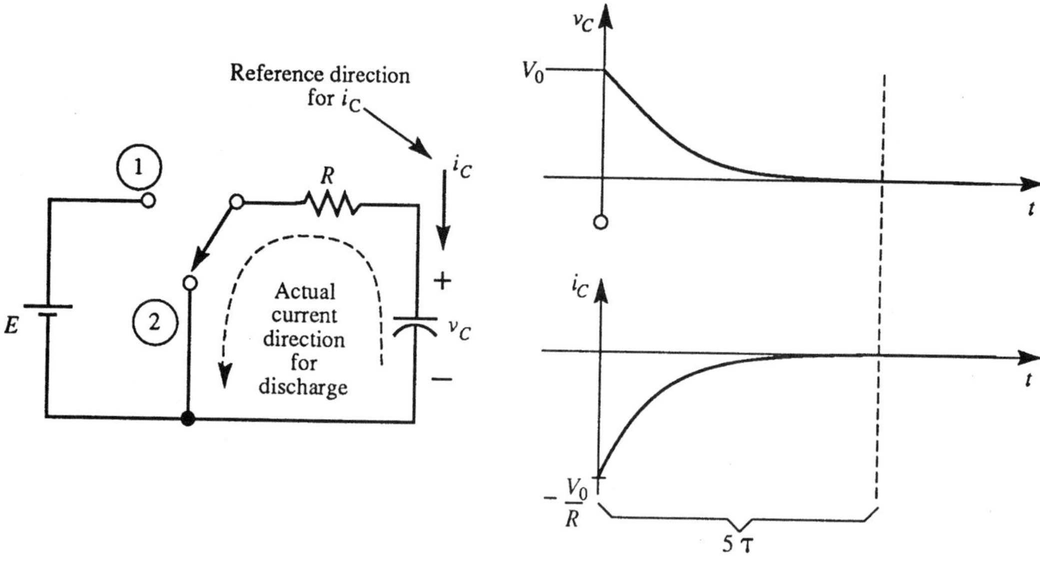

(a) Circuit

(b) Current is negative since it is opposite in direction to the reference arrow.

Figure 9-3 Capacitor voltage and current during discharging

source with value V_o where V_o is the voltage on the capacitor at the instant the switch is moved. (If the capacitor is fully charged, $V_0 = E$.) Current jumps from zero to $-V_0/R$, then decays to zero. (It is negative since it is opposite in direction to the reference as indicated in Figure 9-3a.) Voltage decays from V_o to zero. Equations are

$$i_C = -\frac{V_o}{R}e^{-t/RC} \quad \text{or} \quad i_c = -\frac{E}{R}e^{-t/RC} \tag{9-4}$$

$$v_C = V_o e^{-t/RC} \quad \text{or} \quad v_c = Ee^{-t/RC} \tag{9-5}$$

Discharging takes five time constants. Although for this particular circuit charge and discharge resistances are the same, in general they are different. For this latter case, charge and discharge time constants will be different.

A Final Note

To properly observe capacitor charging and discharging, you need an oscilloscope. Since you may not have studied the oscilloscope at this time, we will examine the basic ideas in other ways. However, at the end of the lab, we have included an instructor demonstration (Part D) using an oscilloscope. Here, you will be able to observe capacitor charging and discharging directly on the screen.

MEASUREMENTS

Practical Notes

1. Use a VOM here with a sensitivity of at least 20 000 ohms per volt to minimize circuit loading.
2. Electrolytic capacitors are polarized devices that require a dc voltage to set up and maintain their oxide film. In this test, the capacitor's voltage varies as it charges and discharges and thus, its oxide film thickness may change throughout the test, resulting in a change in the effective capacitance of the capacitor. As a consequence, the results that you get may differ somewhat from what you calculate (even if you measure the capacitor's value first).

PART A: Charge and Discharge Times

For Part A, use a VOM to observe capacitor voltage and a stopwatch to time charging and discharging. For the large capacitance value required here, you need an electrolytic capacitor. Unfortunately, you will find that your results agree only moderately well with theory—see boxed Note 2. However, the results clearly verify the theory.

1. Assemble the circuit of Figure 9-1 with $R = 10\ \text{k}\Omega$, $C = 470\ \mu\text{F}$ and source voltage about 25 V. Place the switch in the charge position and wait for the capacitor to fully charge. Carefully adjust E until $V = 25$ V across the capacitor.

   a. Compute the time constant for the circuit.

   $\tau_{\text{computed}} = RC =$ $RC = (10\text{k}\Omega)\,(470\mu\text{F}) = 4.7\text{s}$.

   b. Return the switch to the discharge position. Wait for the capacitor to fully discharge, then move the switch to the charge position and using the stopwatch, time how long it takes for the capacitor voltage to reach 15.8 V (i.e., 63.2% of its final voltage). This is the measured time constant.

   $\tau_{\text{measured}} =$ ____________ (charging).

   c. Hold the switch in the charge position until the capacitor voltage stabilizes at 25 volts. Now move the switch to the discharge position and time how long it takes for the voltage to drop to 9.2 V (i.e., to 36.8% of its initial value).

   $\tau_{\text{measured}} =$ ____________ (discharging).

As noted, will likely be a bit higher than the RC product. In my test, I measured about 5 seconds.

2. Change R to 20 kΩ and repeat Test 1.

   a. $\tau_{\text{computed}} =$ 9.4 s

   b. $\tau_{\text{measured}} =$ ____________ (charging)

   c. $\tau_{\text{measured}} =$ ____________ (discharging)

I measured a little over 11 seconds.

3. Describe how the results of Tests 1 and 2 confirm the theory.

   When the time constant was doubled, the measured charge and discharge times doubled as predicted.

PART B: Current Direction

To conform to the standard voltage/current convention, the + sign for voltage v_C must be at the tail of the current direction arrow i_C as indicated in Figure 9-1. This is obviously correct for charging as indicated in Figure 9-2. During discharge, the polarity of the voltage does not change. Thus, for discharging, the current direction arrow must also remain in the clockwise direction, even though we know that actual current is in the opposite direction as indicated in Figure 9-3. The interpretation is that for charging, current is in the same direction as the reference and hence, is positive, while for discharging, it is opposite to the reference and hence, is negative.

4. Add a DMM with autopolarity as in Figure 9-4. Connect the current input jack A to the positive side of the circuit as indicated. (Since the meter measures current *into* terminal A, this connection will yield a positive value when current is in the reference direction and a negative value when opposite to the reference.) We now verify charge and discharge directions experimentally.
   a. Move the switch to charge and note the sign of the multimeter reading. (Don't try to read its value—we are only interested in its sign.) Sign ___+___. Thus, the actual direction of current is ___the same as the reference arrow.___.
   b. Move the switch to discharge and again note the sign. Sign ___–___. Thus, the actual direction of current is ___opposite to the reference arrow.___.

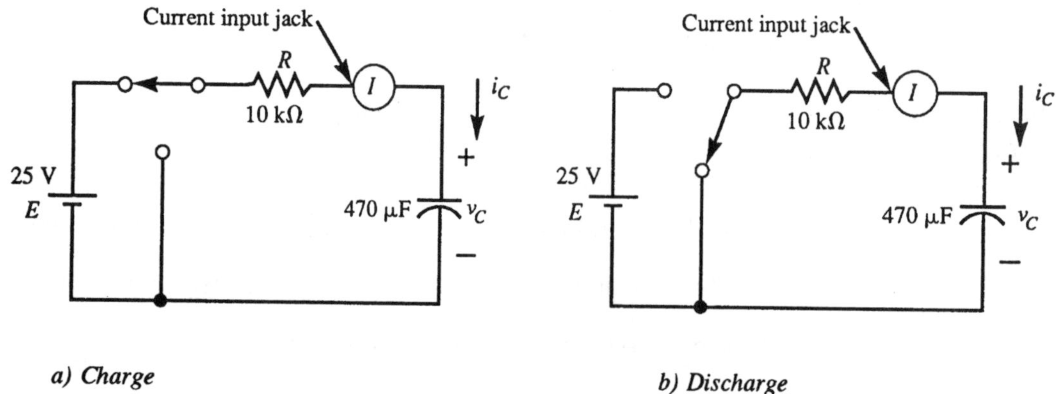

Figure 9-4 Verifying the current direction convention

PART C: More Complex Circuits

For analysis, complex circuits can be reduced to their Thévenin equivalent. In this test, you will verify the Thévenin equivalent method.

5. a. Using Thévenin's theorem, determine the charge and discharge equivalent circuits for the circuit of Figure 9-5(a). Sketch in (b) and (c) respectively.

   b. From the Thévenin equivalents, compute the charge and discharge time constants.

   τ_{charge} = 10.0 s. $\tau_{discharge}$ = 16.5 s.

For the computations of c. and d., I used the universal curves of Figure 11-15 of the text.

   c. For charging, compute capacitor voltage at $t = \tau_{charge}$.

   V_C = 8.66 V.

   $V_C(\tau) = (0.632)(13.7\text{V}) = 8.66$ V

   d. Assume the switch has been in the charge position long enough for the capacitor to fully charge. Now move the switch to discharge and compute the voltage after one discharge time constant. V_C = 5.04V.

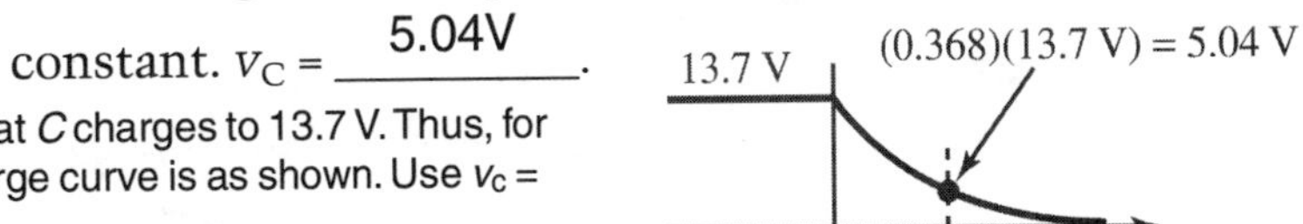

Solution: From Fig. 9-5(b), note that C charges to 13.7 V. Thus, for Fig. 9-5(c), V_0 = 13.7 V. The discharge curve is as shown. Use $v_C = V_0 e^{-t/\tau}$ or Fig. 11-15 of the text.

   e. Assemble the circuit of Figure 9-5(a). Move the switch to charge and with the stopwatch, measure how long it takes for the voltage to reach the value determined in Test 5(c).

Should be reasonably close to value shown

   $\tau_{charge(measured)}$ = 10 s.

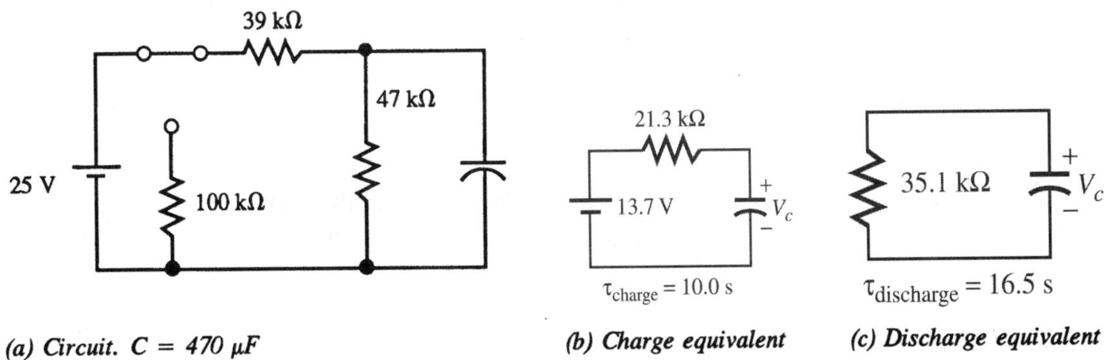

(a) Circuit. C = 470 μF *(b) Charge equivalent* *(c) Discharge equivalent*

Figure 9-5 Thévenin analysis

f. Allow the capacitor to fully charge, then move the switch to discharge and with the stopwatch, measure the time that it takes for the voltage to reach the value determined in Test 5(d).

Should be reasonably close to the value shown → $\tau_{\text{discharge(measured)}} =$ 16.5 s.

Discuss results. In particular, how well do the Thévenin equivalents represent the charging/discharging behavior of the capacitor in the real circuit?

You should find that the measured results are close enough to confirm the Thévenin analysis.

Preliminary Note
Part D is set up as an instructor demonstration. However, if you have already learned how to use the oscilloscope, you may perform this part yourself.

PART D: Charging/Discharging Waveforms

The circuit is shown in Figure 9-6. A function generator simulates switching by applying a signal that cycles between voltage E and ground. A high rate of switching and a small time constant are used to give a waveform that can be viewed on the oscilloscope. Since a non-electrolytic capacitor is used, agreement between theory and practice will be much better than in previous tests.

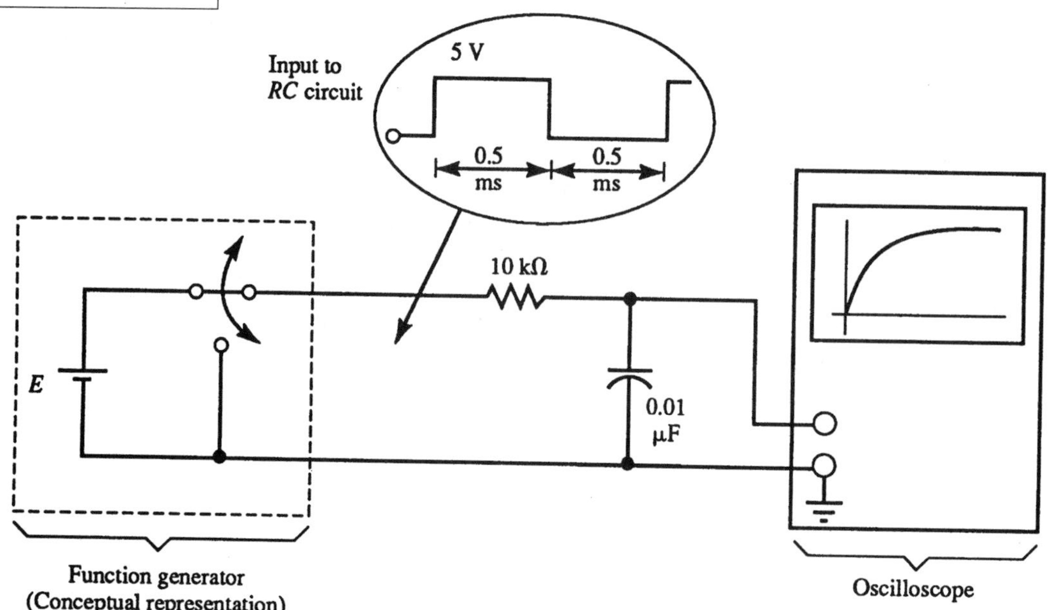

Figure 9-6 Test set-up for Part D

a. Charging Waveform

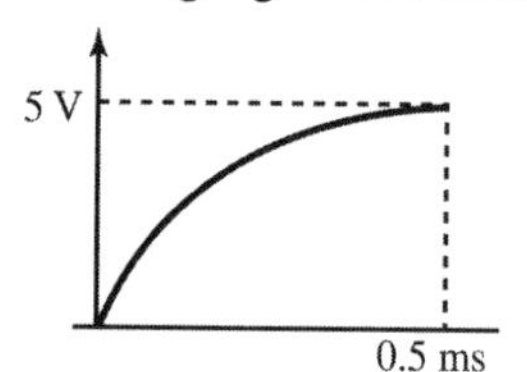

Figure 9-7 Waveform for Test 6

6. a. Measure R and C, then assemble the circuit of Figure 9-6. Using the function generator, apply an input with 0.5 ms high and low times (i.e., $f = 1$ kHz) and adjust the input to 5 V as indicated in Figure 9-6. Set the oscilloscope to display only the charging voltage. Sketch as Figure 9-7.

b. Calculate the time constant using the measured R and C.

$\tau =$ (10 kΩ) (0.01 μF) =100 μs

c. From the scope screen, measure capacitor voltages at $t = \tau, 2\tau, 3\tau, 4\tau$, and 5τ and tabulate.

d. Using circuit analysis techniques, compute voltages at these points. How well do they agree?

e. Display the discharge portion of the waveform and measure capacitor voltages at $t = \tau, 2\tau, 3\tau, 4\tau$, and 5τ and tabulate.

f. Repeat Part d) for the discharge values.

Note
The internal resistance of the function generator is so small relative to the 10 kΩ circuit resistance that we have neglected it.

c. Values should be close to those computed in d.

d. From the universal curve shown in Figure 11-15(a) of the text,
At $t = \tau$ (i.e., 100 μs),
You get $v_C = (0.632)(5V) = 3.16$ V
While at $t = 2\tau$ (i.e., 200 μs),
You get $v_C = (0.865)(5V) = 4.32$ V, etc.
Agreement should be excellent

e. Discharging waveform

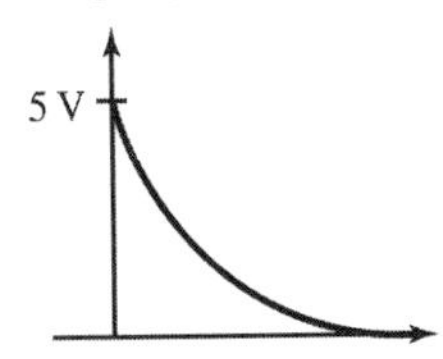

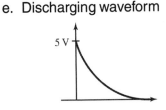

f. From Fig. 11-15(b)
At $t = \tau$ (i.e., 100 μs),
You get $v_C = (0.368)(5V) = 1.84$ V, etc.
Agreement should be excellent.

COMPUTER ANALYSIS

> **PSpice Users**
> Set V1, V2, PW, and PER, TR, TF and TD to 0V, 5V, 0.5ms, 1ms, 1ns, 1ns and 0 respectively. This creates the desired waveform.

7. Using either MultiSIM or PSpice, set up the RC circuit of Figure 9-6 with a pulse source that supplies 5 V for 0.5 ms and 0 V for the next 0.5 ms as indicated in Figure 9-6. (See Section 11.8 and Figure 11-44 or 11-49(c) of the text for reference. Don't forget to use a ground on the bottom end of the source symbol.) Set the capacitor initial voltage to zero and run a transient analysis. Using the cursor, determine voltages at $t = \tau, 2\tau, 3\tau, 4\tau$ and 5τ for both the charge and discharge case. Compare the results to those obtained from the oscilloscope, Test 6.

Please see solution on following pages.

PROBLEMS

8. Assume the circuit of Figure 9-1 has a time constant of 100 μs. If R is doubled and C is tripled, calculate the new time constant.
9. For Figure 9-1, replace the wire between switch position 2 and

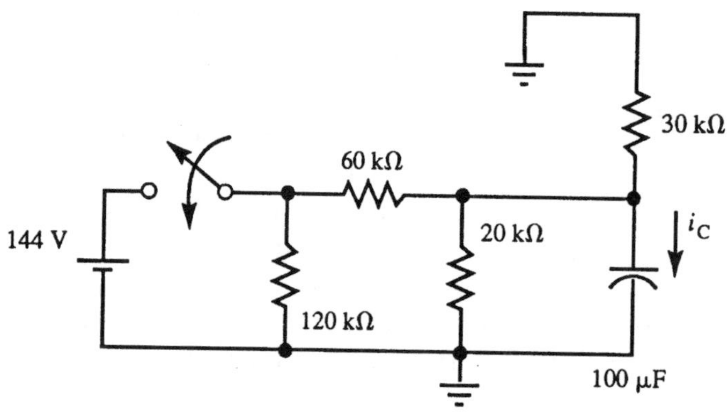

Figure 9-7 Waveform for Test 6.

See next page for solutions

common with a resistor R_2. If $R_2 = 4\ R$ and the capacitor takes 25 ms to reach full charge, how long will it take to discharge?

10. For Figure 9-8, the switch is closed at $t = 0$ s and opened 5 s later. The capacitor is initially uncharged.
    a. Determine the capacitor current i_C at $t = 2$ s.
    b. Determine the capacitor current i_C at $t = 7$ s.

FOR FURTHER INVESTIGATION AND DISCUSSION

Tolerances on resistors and capacitors affect the time constant of circuits and thus affect circuits that rely on RC charging and discharging for their operation. To investigate, assume the resistor of Fig. 9-6 has a tolerance of ±5% and the capacitor ±10%. Write a short discussion paper on the impact of these tolerances on rise and fall waveforms. In your discussion, determine the minimum and maximum values that τ may have, then plot the waveforms for these two cases as well as for the nominal case on the same graph. Using PSpice or MultiSIM, verify these waveforms. Discuss the ramifications of what you have learned.

SOLUTIONS

Problem 7

The time constant for both the charge and discharge case is $\tau = RC = 100\ \mu s$. To measure values on the charging portion of the curve, simply set your cursor to the desired time point—e.g., to determine voltage at one time constant, set the cursor at $t = 100\ \mu s$. For the discharge portion of the curve, however, you must think in terms of shifted time as discussed on page 379 of the text. Since discharge starts at $t = 500\ \mu s$ on the global time scale, one time constant into discharge occurs at $t = 600\ \mu s$. Thus, set your cursor successively at $t = 600\ \mu s$, $700\ \mu s$, etc. to get the desired readings. Results should agree very well with measured values.

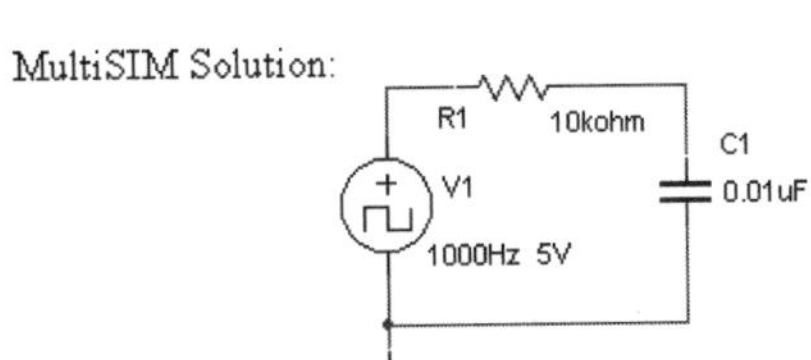

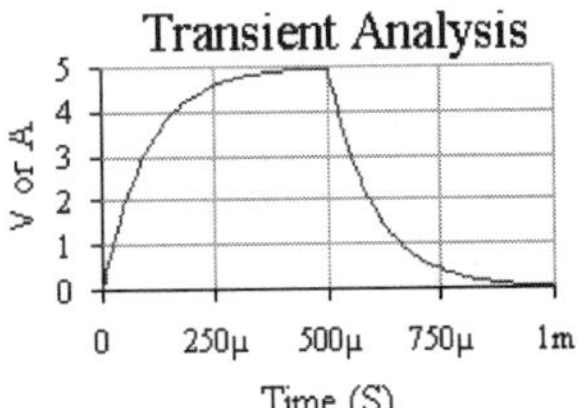

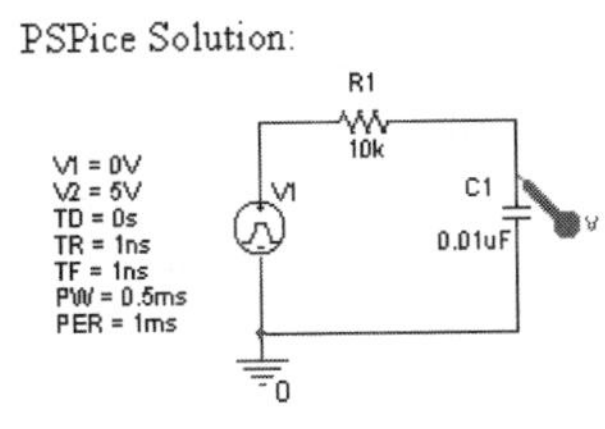

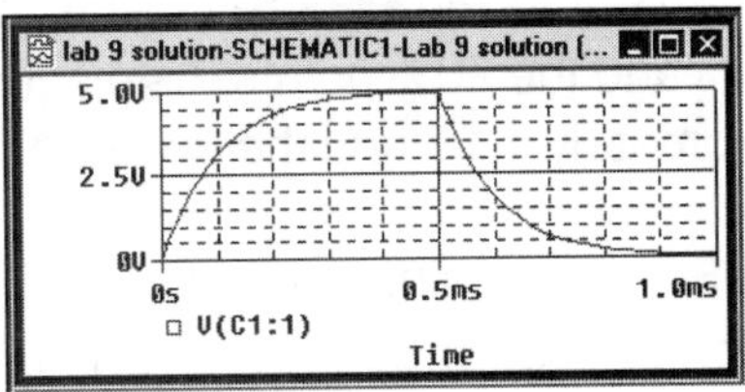

Problem 8

$\tau = RC$ ∴ Doubling R doubles τ

Tripling C triples τ

Thus

$\tau_{new} = (2)(3)\ \tau_{old} = 6\tau_{old} = 600\mu s$

Problem 9

$5\tau_1 = 25ms \therefore \tau_1 = 5\ ms$ where $\tau_1 = RC$

$\tau_2 = (R+R_2)\ C = (R+4R)C$

$\tau_2 = 5RC = 5(5ms) = 25ms$

$5\tau_2 = 125ms$ ←Discharge time

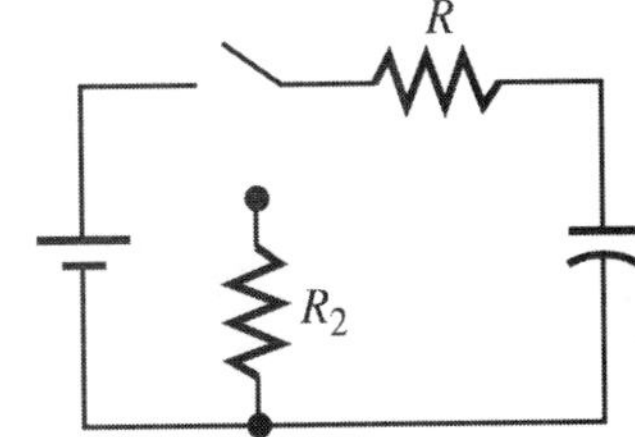

Problem 10: Here is the current waveform.

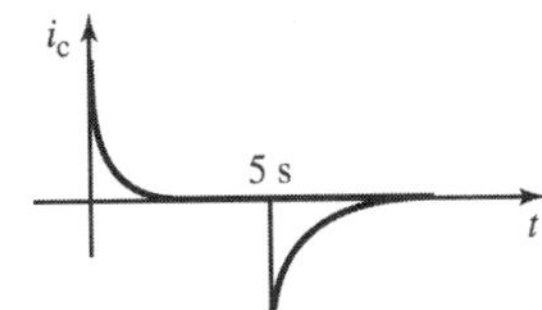

a) **Charging Circuit**

$\tau_1 = (10k\Omega)(100\mu F)$

$= 1s$

$i_c = \frac{E}{R} e^{-t/\tau_1} = 2.4e^{-t}\ mA$

$= 0.325mA$ at $t = 2s$

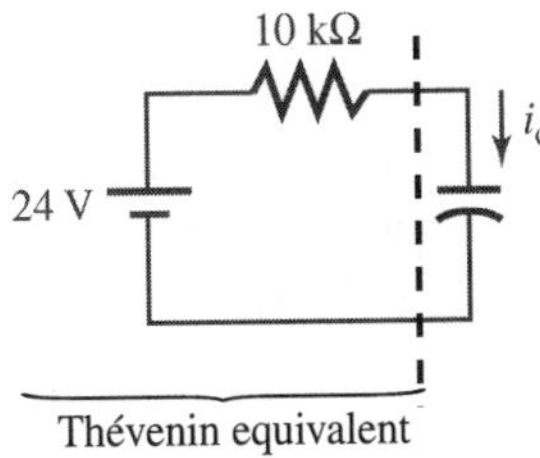

b) **Discharging Circuit**

$V_o = 24\text{V}$

$\tau_2 = 1.125\text{s}$

$$i_c = \frac{-V_o}{R} e^{-t/\tau_2}$$

$$= \frac{-24}{11.25\text{k}\Omega} e^{-t/\tau_2}$$

$$= -2.13e^{-t/1.12}$$

At $t = 2\text{s}$,

$i_c = -0.36\text{mA}$

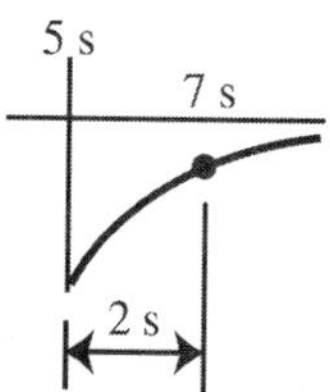

Note that 7s is 2s into discharge.

For Further Investigation and Discussion

The time constant is given by $\tau = RC$. Here, $R = 10\ \text{k}\Omega \pm 5\ \% = 10\ \text{k}\Omega\ \pm 500\ \Omega$ and $C = 0.01\ \mu\text{F}$ $\pm 10\% = 0.01\ \mu\text{F}\ \pm 0.001\ \mu\text{F}$. The nominal time constant is thus $\tau_{(nom)} = (10\ \text{k}\Omega)(0.01\ \mu\text{F}) = 100\ \mu\text{s}$. Taking into account tolerances however, the time constant could be as small as $\tau_{(min)} = (9.5\ \text{k}\Omega)(0.009\ \mu\text{F}) = 85.5\ \mu\text{s}$ or as large as $\tau_{(max)} = (10.5\ \text{k}\Omega)(0.011\ \mu\text{F}) = 115.5\ \mu\text{s}$. Rise time is the time between the 10% and the 90% points. As discussed in Example 11-16 of the text, the 10% point occurs at approximately 0.1 τ and the 90 % point at about 2.3 τ.

Nominal Case: For the nominal case, $t_{rise} \approx (2.3)(100\ \mu\text{s}) - (0.1)(100\ \mu\text{s}) = 220\ \mu\text{s}$.
Minimum Case: $t_{rise} \approx (2.3)(85.5\ \mu\text{s}) - (0.1)(85.5\ \mu\text{s}) = 188\ \mu\text{s}$.
Maximum Case: $t_{rise} \approx (2.3)(115.5\ \mu\text{s}) - (0.1)115.5\ \mu\text{s}) = 254\ \mu\text{s}$.

In both cases, the error (relative to the nominal case) is about 15%. Capacitor charging voltages for the three cases are tabulated below along with a computer generated plot of the waveforms. (The discharge case is not shown, but the analysis is similar.)

	v_C		
t	$\tau_{(min)}$	$\tau_{(nom)}$	$\tau_{(max)}$
0	0	0	0
100 µs	3.45	3.16	2.90
200 µs	4.52	4.32	4.12
300 µs	4.85	4.75	4.63
400 µs	4.95	4.91	4.84
500 µs	4.99	4.97	4.93

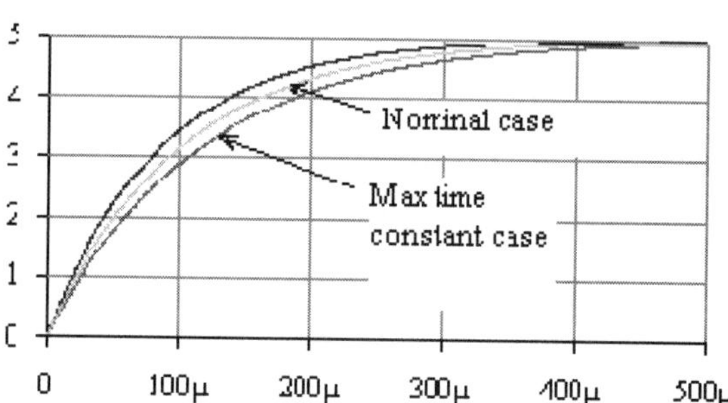

Significance

Tolerances on resistors and capacitors affect timing in *RC* circuits. The maximum percent error is approximately equal to the sum of the maximum percent error in the *R* and *C* components. When you design a timing circuit, be sure to check whether your timing limits have been exceeded. If so, you may have to specify tighter tolerance components for the critical timing part of your circuit—e.g. choose a 1% resistor instead of a 5% one.

NAME ______________________

DATE ______________________

CLASS ______________________

LAB 10

Inductors in dc Circuits

OBJECTIVES

After completing this lab, you will be able to

- determine steady state dc voltages and currents in an *RL* circuit,
- measure the inductive "kick" voltage in an *RL* circuit,
- measure the time constant of an *RL* circuit.

EQUIPMENT REQUIRED

- ☐ DMM
- ☐ Variable dc power supply
- ☐ Function generator
- ☐ Oscilloscope

COMPONENTS

☐ Resistors: 10-Ω, 82-Ω (two), 1-kΩ (1/4-W),
47-Ω, 220-Ω (1/2-W)
120-Ω (two, each 2-W)

☐ Inductors: One, 2.4-mH, powdered iron core, Hammond Part #1534 or equivalent; one approximately 1.5-H, iron core.

Note to the Instructor

Parts C and D of this lab may be run as an instructor demo if your students have not yet had instruction on the oscilloscope.

EQUIPMENT USED

Instrument	Manufacturer/Model No.	Serial No.
DMM		
Power supply		
Function generator		
Oscilloscope		

Table 10-1

TEXT REFERENCE

Section 13.2 INDUCED VOLTAGE AND INDUCTION
Section 13.7 INDUCTANCE AND STEADY STATE DC
Section 14.1 INTRODUCTION
Section 14.2 CURRENT BUILD UP TRANSIENTS
Section 14.4 DE-ENERGIZING TRANSIENTS

DISCUSSION

Induced voltage is determined by Faraday's law. For a coil with a non-magnetic core, induced voltage is directly proportional to the rate of change of current and is given by

$$v_L = L\frac{di}{dt} \tag{10-1}$$

where L is the inductance of the coil and di/dt is the rate of change of the current in the coil. The induced voltage opposes the change in current.

For inductances in series, total inductance is the sum of individual inductances. Thus,

$$L_T = L_1 + L_2 + \ldots + L_N \tag{10-2}$$

For inductances in parallel, total inductance may be found from

$$\frac{1}{L_T} = \frac{1}{L_1} + \frac{1}{L_2} + \ldots + \frac{1}{L_N} \tag{10-3}$$

Since real inductors have coil resistance, Equation 10-3 can only be used in practice if coil resistance is negligible.

Steady State and Transient Response

Steady State dc: As Equation (10-1) shows, voltage results only when current changes. Thus if current is constant (as in steady state dc), the voltage across an inductance is zero. Consequently, *to steady state dc, an inductance looks like a short circuit.*

Current Build up Transients: Simple current build up transients in *RL* circuits may be studied using the circuit of Figure 10-1(a). When the switch is closed, current in the inductor is given by

$$i_L = \frac{E}{R_1}(1 - e^{-R_1 t/L}) \qquad (10\text{-}4)$$

which has a final steady state value of E/R_1 amps as shown in (b). Voltage is given by

$$v_L = Ee^{-R_1 t/L} \qquad (10\text{-}5)$$

As Figures 10-1(b) and (c) show, at the instant the switch is closed, current is zero and full source voltage appears across the inductance. This means that *an inductor, with initial current of zero amps, looks like an open circuit.*

Current Decay Transients: Consider Figure 10-2(a). Assume that the current in the inductor at the instant the switch is opened is I_0. Since current cannot change instantaneously, *a current carrying inductance looks momentarily like a current source of I_0 at the instant of switch operation.* Current then decays to zero according to

$$i_L = I_0 e^{-Rt/L} \qquad (10\text{-}6)$$

where $R = R_1 + R_2$ for the circuit of Figure 10-2. Other voltages and currents can be obtained from these relationships using basic circuit principles. For example, the voltage v_2 across resistor R_2 is $-R_2\, i_L$. Thus, it has the same shape as i_L but is negative as indicated in (c). (Multiplying $-R_2$ times Equation 10-6 yields $v_2 = -I_0\, R_2\, e^{-Rt/L}$ as indicated in Figure 10-2c.) Note that V_0 (which is equal to $-I_0\, R_2$), can be many times larger than the source voltage.

The time constant of an *RL* circuit is given by

$$\tau = L/R \qquad (10\text{-}7)$$

where *R* is the resistance through which the inductor current builds or decays; for Figure 10-2, $\tau = L/R_1$ during current build up and $\tau = L/(R_1 + R_2)$ during current decay. Steady state is reached in 5τ where the appropriate τ (charge or discharge) must be used.

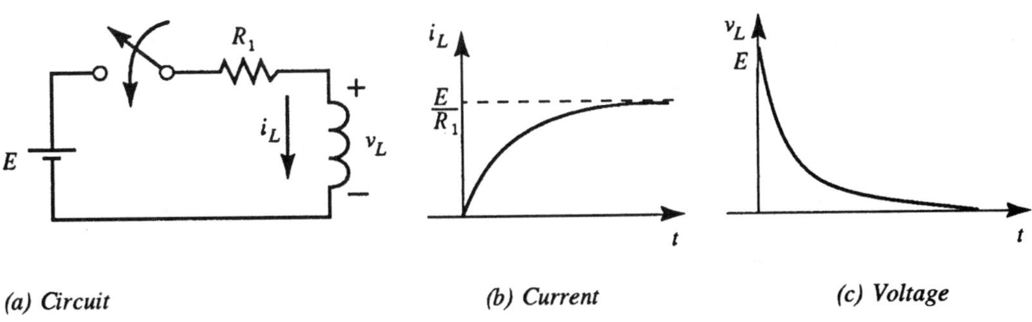

(a) Circuit *(b) Current* *(c) Voltage*

Figure 10-1 Current build up transients

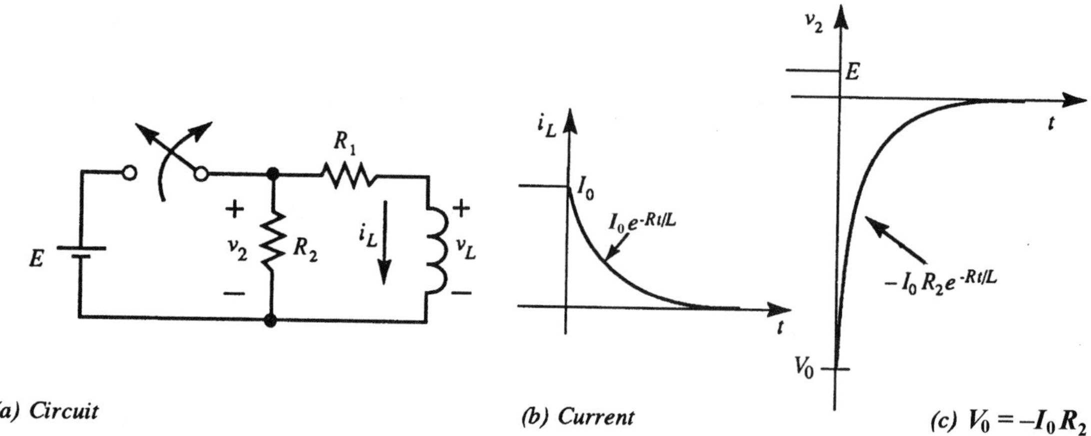

Figure 10-2 Current decay transients. $R = R_1 + R_2$ for (a) and (b).

MEASUREMENTS

PART A: Steady State Voltages and Currents

1. Measure the resistance of each 120 Ω resistor and the resistance of the 2.4-mH inductor and record in Table 10-2.
2. a. Assemble the RL portion of the circuit of Figure 10-3. With the source disconnected, measure input resistance R_{in}.

   $R_{in(measured)}$ = 130.9 Ω

   b. Using circuit analysis techniques, compute R_{in}. $R_{in(computed)}$ = 120 || 12+ 120 = 130.9 Ω. Compare to the measured value.

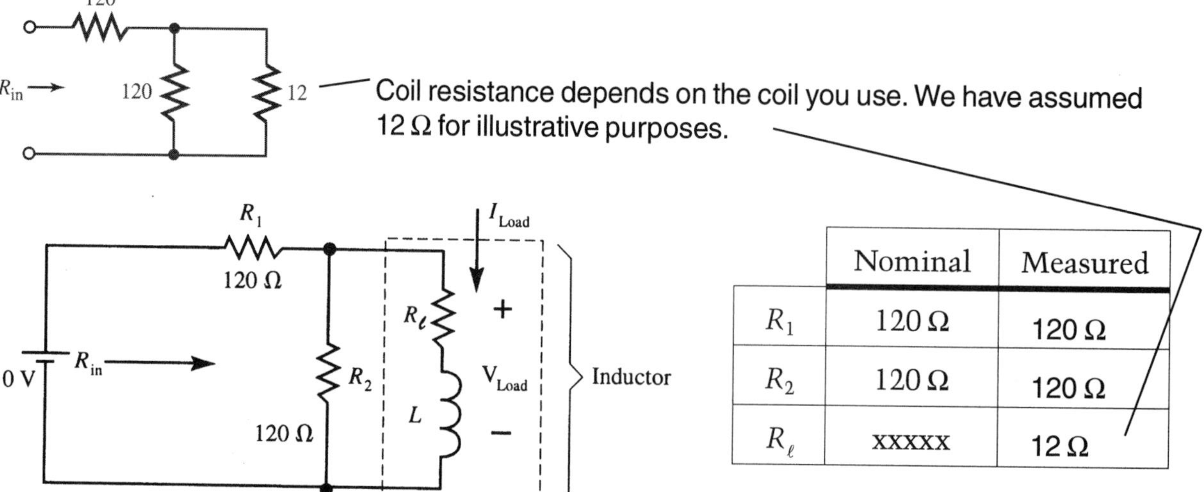

Figure 10-3 Circuit for Test 1

	Nominal	Measured
R_1	120 Ω	120 Ω
R_2	120 Ω	120 Ω
R_ℓ	XXXXX	12 Ω

Table 10-2

c. Connect the source and measure voltage V_{Load} and I_{Load}.

$V_{Load(measured)} =$ 0.833 V $\qquad I_{Load(measured)} =$ 69.4 mA

d. Using circuit analysis techniques, solve for V_{Load} and I_{Load}. Compare to the measured values.

The inductor looks like a short to steady state dc. Thus,

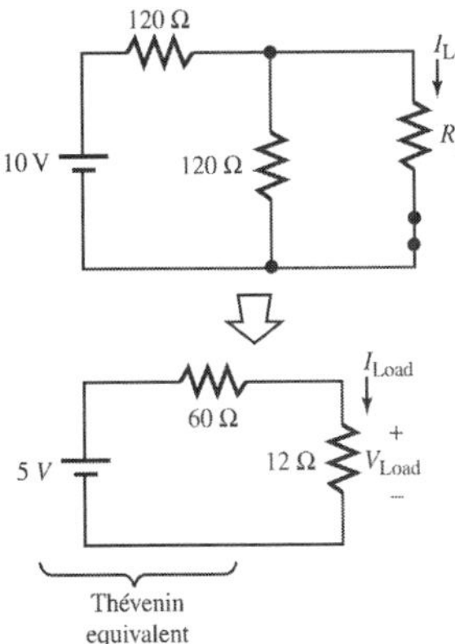

Determine the Thévenin equivalent as indicated. From it,

$$I_{Load} = \frac{5V}{72\Omega} = 69.4 \text{ mA}$$

$$V_{Load} = \left(\frac{12\Omega}{72\Omega}\right)(5V) = 0.833 \text{ V}$$

PART B: More Complex Steady State Circuits

For more complex circuits, use Thévenin's theorem to reduce portions of the circuit as necessary.

3. a. Measure each resistor for the circuit of Figure 10-4 and record in Table 10-3. Use the same inductor as in Figure 10-3.
   b. Determine the Thévenin equivalent of the circuit to the left of the inductor using circuit analysis techniques using the measured resistance values from Table 10-3.

   The circuit can be reduced to $R_{Th} = 115.5\ \Omega$ and $E_{Th} = 5.66$ V. Thus,

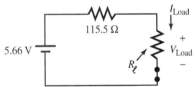

   115.5 Ω
   I_{Load}
   +
   5.66 V
   V_{Load}
   R_ℓ
   −

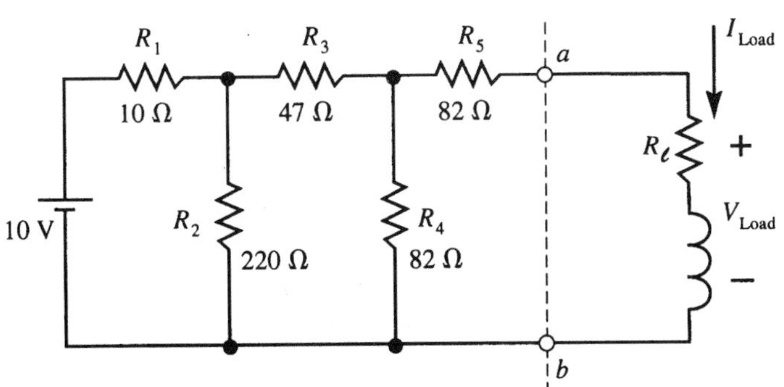

Figure 10-4 Circuit for Test 3. Use resistor values measured in Table 10-3.

	Nominal	Measured
R_1	10 Ω	I used same
R_2	220 Ω	as nominal
R_3	47 Ω	values here
R_4	82 Ω	for illustration
R_5	82 Ω	

Table 10-3

c. Disconnect the inductor and measure the open circuit voltage across a-b. (This is E_{Th}.) $E_{\text{Th(measured)}}$ = 5.66 V.

d. Disconnect the source and replace it with a short circuit. Measure the resistance looking back into the circuit. (This is R_{Th}.)

$R_{\text{Th(measured)}}$ = 115.5 Ω

e. Compare the measured and computed values for E_{Th} and R_{Th}.

Should be close.

f. Remove the short, reconnect the source and inductor and measure I_{Load} and V_{Load}.

I_{Load} = 44.4 mA V_{Load} = 0.533 V

g. Using the Thévenin equivalent determined in (b), compute I_{Load} and V_{Load}. Compare to the measured values of (f).

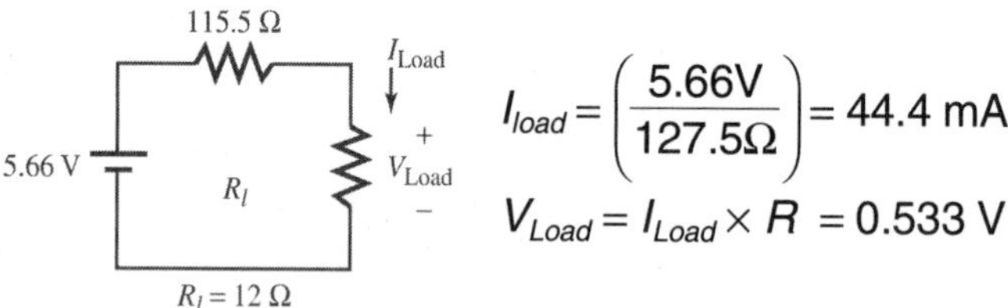

PART C: Inductive "Kick" Voltage

> **Preliminary Note**
> Part C requires the use of an oscilloscope. If you have not yet covered the oscilloscope, this may be run as an instructor demonstration.

In this part of the lab, you will look at the *inductive kick* that results when current in an inductor is interrupted. Use the iron core inductor. (The inductor and resistor values used here are not critical. However, to see the results easily on the scope, you need a time constant of at least a few milliseconds. First determine appropriate resistor values.)

4. a. Measure the dc resistance of the inductor. R_ℓ = See next page.
Consider Figure 10-5(a). Define $R_1' = R_1 + R_\ell$. Select a value for R_1 such that current E/R_1' is easily handled by your power supply. Now select an R_2 that is about five or six times larger than R_1' and such that the discharge time constant $L/(R_1+R_2+R_\ell)$ is a few milliseconds or more. (If you know L, you can compute τ; if you have no way of measuring L, experiment until you get a waveform you can see.)
b. Assemble the circuit with these values and connect the scope probe across resistor R_2 to view the inductive kick voltage v_2.

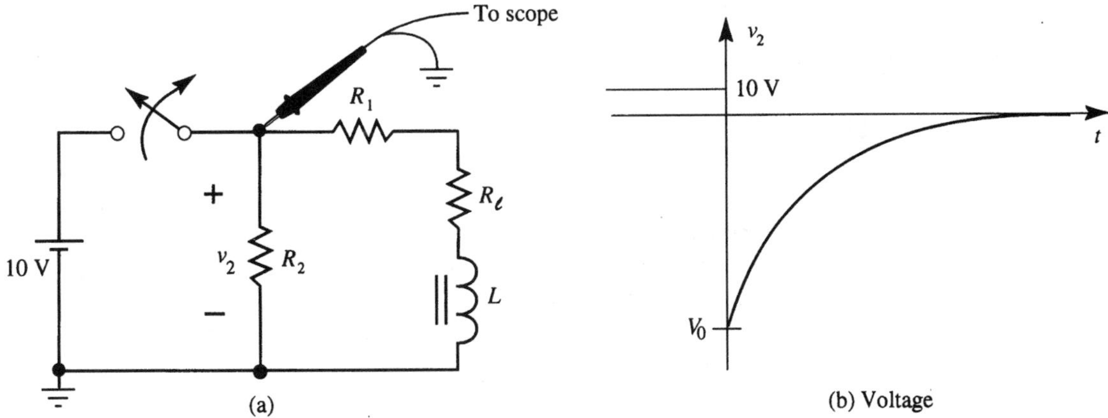

Figure 10-5 Circuit for Test 4

The analysis here is for illustrative purposes only, as it depends on the inductor used. (My inductor had $R_\ell = 213\ \Omega$ and $L = 1.42$ H)

(The waveform will look like that shown in Figure 10-5(b). Voltage V_0 depends on the ratio of R_2 to R_1'. If $R_2 = 5\ R_1'$ and E = 10 V, then $V_0 = -50$ volts.) The waveform is a single shot event that is generated only when you open the switch. Set the scope triggering appropriately—e.g., *Norm* or *Single Sweep*, negative slope. With careful adjustment of triggering and the time base and with repeated operation of the switch, you should be able to observe the voltage spike of (b).

c. From the trace, measure the value of V_0. V_0 = <u>−47 V</u>

d. Using the methods of Section 14.4 of the textbook, compute V_0 and compare to the measured value of (c). How do they compare?

Original Steady State

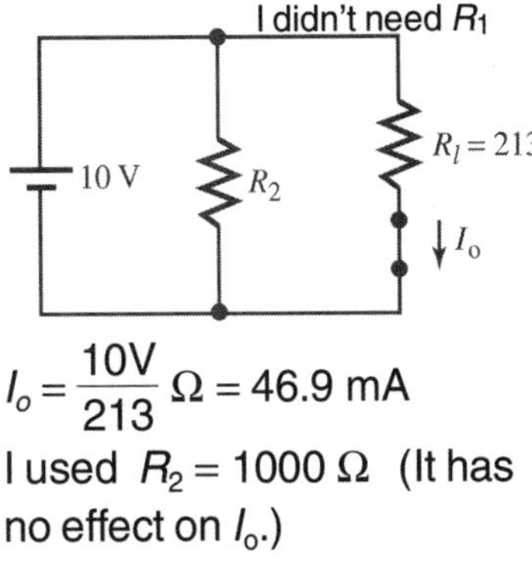

$I_o = \frac{10V}{213}\ \Omega = 46.9$ mA

I used $R_2 = 1000\ \Omega$ (It has no effect on I_o.)

Circuit as it looks at $t = 0^+$

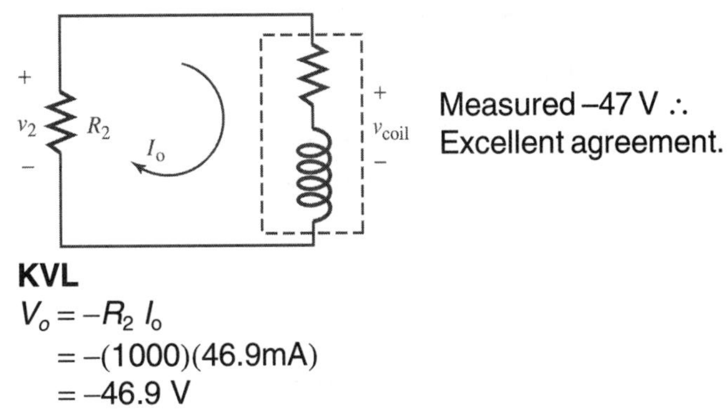

Measured −47 V ∴ Excellent agreement.

KVL

$V_o = -R_2\ I_o$

$= -(1000)(46.9\text{mA})$

$= -46.9$ V

PART D: Measuring the Time Constant

This part may be run as a demo if necessary.

5. a. Measure the resistance of the 1-kΩ resistor and the inductance of the 2.4-mH inductor. (Call the 1-kΩ resistor R_S.) If you do not

have any way to measure inductance, use the nominal value marked on the inductor. Use R_ℓ from Table 10-2.

Coil resistance depends on your coil. I have used $R_\ell = 12\ \Omega$ for purposes of illustration.

R_ℓ = 12.0 Ω L = 2.40 mH R_S = 1000 Ω

b. Assemble the circuit of Figure 10-6. The time constant for the circuit is $\tau = L/R_T$ where R_T is the sum of R_S, R_ℓ and the output resistance R_{out} of your function generator. (This may be determined from the front panel of the generator. A typical output resistance of a function generator is 50 Ω.) Thus, $\tau = \frac{L}{R_T} = \frac{2.4\text{ mH}}{1062\ \Omega} = 2.26\ \mu s$.

c. Set the function generator to the square wave mode at 40 kHz. (This provides ample time for current to build up and decay fully.) Adjust the signal generator and scope so that the amplitude of the v_S waveform is 5 grid lines (i.e., 5V). The waveform should look like that shown in Figure 10-6.

d. Adjust the time base and triggering to get only the build up waveform on the screen. Sketch this waveform as Figure 10-7.

e. Measure the time that it takes for the waveform to reach 63.2% of its final value. This is the measured time constant.

3.16

2.26 μs

$\tau_{measured}$ = 2.26 μs

Compare this value to the value computed in (b).

f. Change triggering to get the decay waveform on the screen. Measure the time constant here and compare to that of (d).

$\tau_{measured}$ = 2.26 μs (Same)

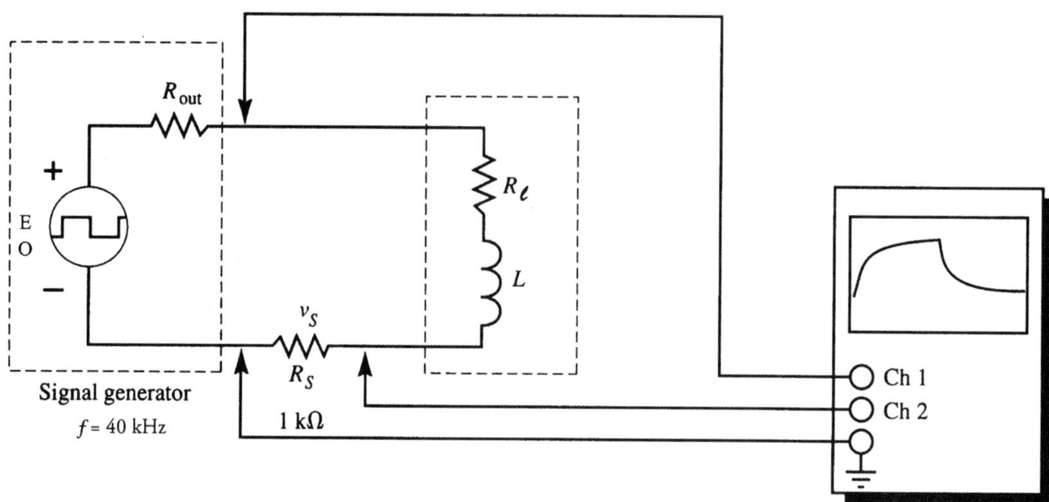

Figure 10-6 Current waveform for Test 5. The scope is triggered on Ch1 and the display is on Ch2. $R_T = R_{out} + R_l + R_S$.

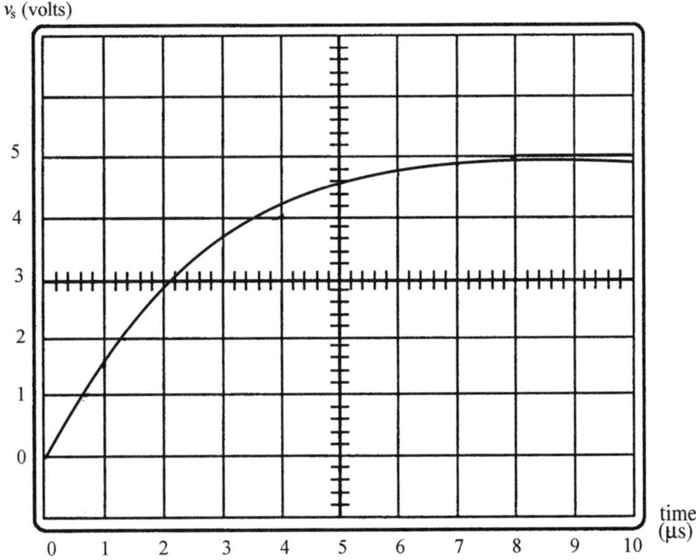

Figure 10-7 Waveform for Test 5

COMPUTER ANALYSIS

6. Using either MultiSIM or PSpice, set up the circuit of Figure 10-6. To create a waveform equivalent to that used in Test 5, use a 40 kHz square wave with equal high and low times. If you are using PSpice, use pulse source VPULSE, whereas, if you are using MultiSIM, use the clock. (For reference, see Section 11.8 of the text.) To determine the amplitude for this pulse, note that in Test 5(c), the peak voltage across R_S is 5 V. This means that the peak current must be 5 mA. Use this to compute E. For example, if $R_{out} = 50\ \Omega$, coil resistance is 12 Ω and $R_S = 1\ \text{k}\Omega$, then you need a pulse amplitude of $E = (5\ \text{mA})(50\ \Omega + 12\ \Omega + 1\ \text{k}\Omega) = 5.31$ V.

   a. Run a transient analysis with the initial inductor current set to zero. If you are using PSpice, you can plot the current directly

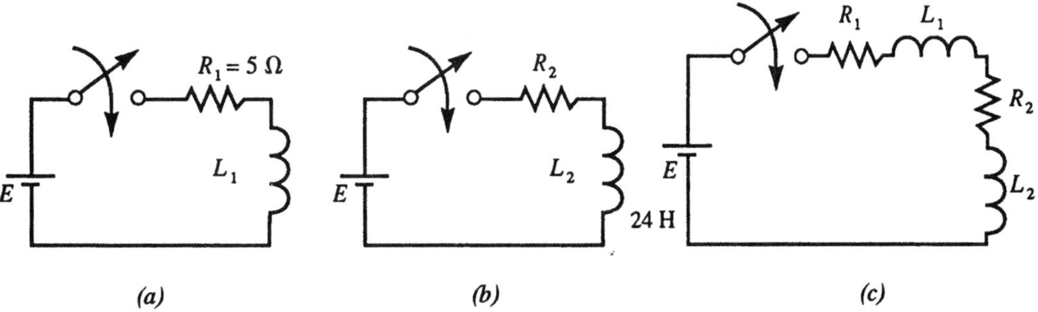

Figure 10-8

using a current marker. If you are using MultiSIM, plot the voltage across the sense resistor R_S, then determine current using Ohm's law.

b. With the cursor, measure the time that it takes for current to rise to 63.2% of its final value. (This is τ.) Compare to the result of Test 5(e). Now measure the time constant on the decay portion and compare to Test 5(f).

PROBLEMS

Solutions for Problems and *For Further Investigation and Discussion* begin on next page

7. For the circuit of Figure 10-2, if $E = 10$ V, $R_1 = 200\ \Omega$, $R_2 = 1200\ \Omega$ and $L = 5$ H,
   a. What voltage appears across the switch at the instant the switch is opened?
   b. How long will the transient last?
8. For the circuit of Figure 10-2, if $R_1 = 200\ \Omega$, $R_2 = 100\ \Omega$ and $L = 5$ H,
   a. What voltage appears across R_2 at the instant the switch is opened?
   b. How long will the transient last?
9. The circuit of Figure 10-8(a) takes 4 s to reach steady state, while that of (b) takes 12 s. The circuits of (a) and (b) are combined as in (c). How long will it take for the circuit of (c) to reach steady state?

FOR FURTHER INVESTIGATION AND DISCUSSION

Remember
Do not perform a full analytic transient analysis to determine the required information

When you disturb an *RL* or an *RC* circuit you trigger a transient, creating voltages and currents that may greatly exceed the circuit's normal steady state values. Many times, however, it is only necessary to determine the general nature of the resulting waveforms and find values at key points—i.e., you do not need a full transient solution. To help develop this idea, consider Figure 10-4. First, replace the 10 V source with a 250-mA dc current source, then install a switch in the leg containing R_4. Assume the coil resistance is negligible. Initially the circuit is in steady state with the switch closed. You then open the switch. Prepare a written analysis of what happens using the following for guidelines.

a. Sketch the shape of the inductor current waveform from some time before the switch is operated to final steady state circuit operation. Using a series of diagrams, calculate the initial steady state current, the final steady state current and the duration of the transient, and mark these on your diagram.
b. Sketch the coil voltage waveform.
c. (Optional) Calculate the peak value of the voltage spike and mark it on your diagram.

Solutions for Problems 6, 7, 8, and 9

6. The PSpice and MultiSIM solutions are shown below. Be sure to set the magnitude of the pulse to 5.31 V as stated in the problem definition to yield a 5 V wave form as indicated. Measurements with the cursor yield 3.16 V at $t = \tau = 2.26\ \mu s$. This should agree well with your measurements. Using the cursor, you can also verify current at 1 time constant into decay. It should be $5e^{-1} = 1.84\text{mA}$.

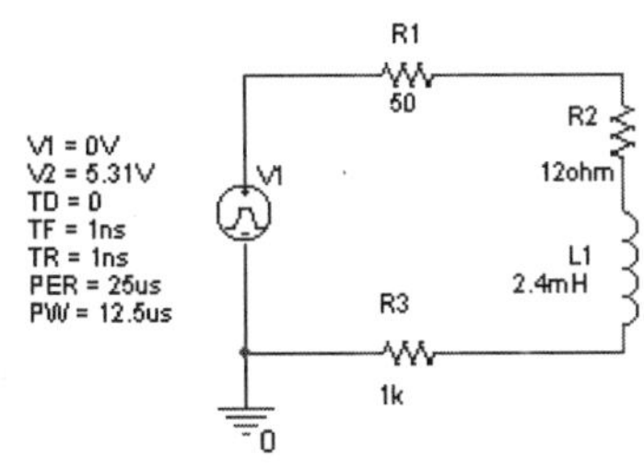

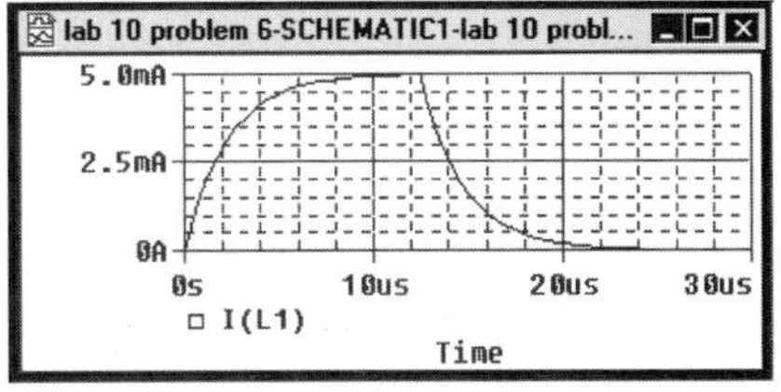

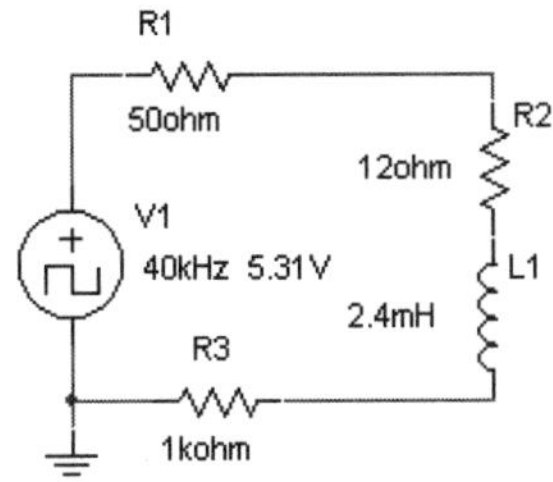

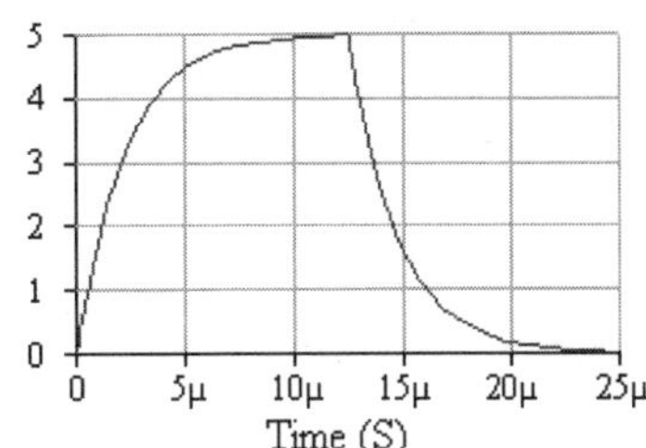

7. (a)

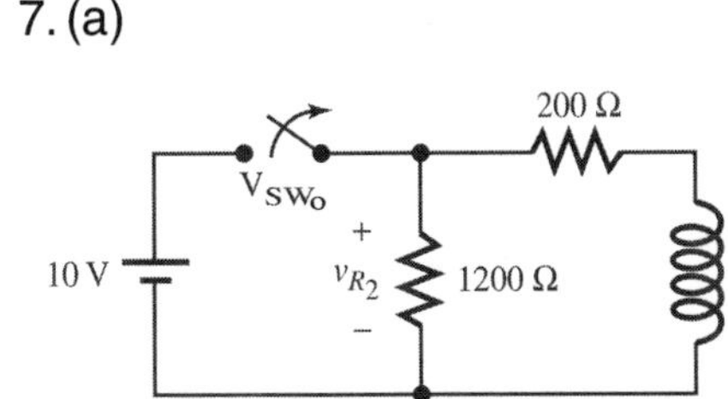

$$I_o = \frac{10\text{V}}{200\Omega} = 50\text{ mA (assuming steady state)}$$

$$\upsilon_{R2} = -R_2 I_o = -1200\Omega(50\text{ mA}) = -60\text{ V at t} = 0^+$$

KVL around the first loop yields: $10\text{ V} - V_{SW_0} - (-60\text{ V}) = 0$. Thus, $V_{SW_0} = 70\text{ V}$.

(b) $\tau = \dfrac{5\text{H}}{1400\Omega} = 3.57\text{ ms}$. Thus the transient lasts $5\tau = 17.9$ ms.

8. (a) Similar to first part of 7a. Thus, at $t = 0^+$, $v_{R2} = -I_o R_2 = -(50\text{ mA})(100\ \Omega) = -5\text{ V}$.
(b) $\tau = 5\text{ H}/300\ \Omega = 16.7$ ms. Thus the transient lasts $5\tau = 83.3$ ms.

9. **Circuit a** Transient lasts $5\tau_1 = 4\text{s}\ \therefore\ \tau_1 = 0.8\text{s}$.

$$\tau_1 = \frac{L_1}{R_1} = \frac{L_1}{5\Omega}\ \therefore\ L_1 = 4\text{ H}$$

Circuit b $5\tau_2 = 12\text{s}.\ \therefore\ \tau_2 = 2.4\text{ s}$

$$\tau_2 = \frac{L_2}{R_2}\ \therefore\ R_2 = \frac{L_2}{\tau_2} = \frac{24\text{H}}{2.4\text{s}} = 10\ \Omega$$

Circuit c

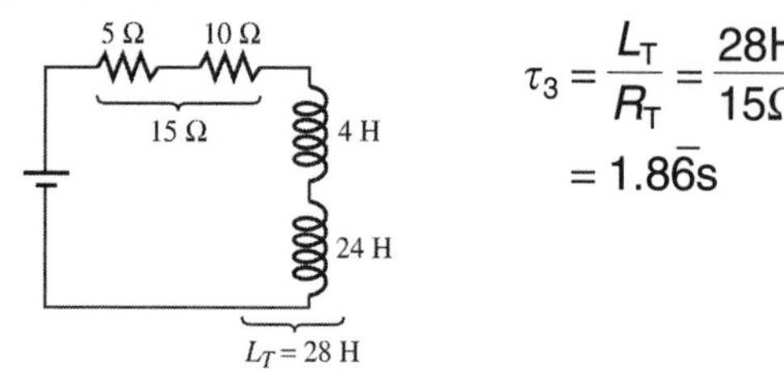

$$\tau_3 = \frac{L_T}{R_T} = \frac{28\text{H}}{15\Omega} = 1.8\bar{6}\text{s}$$

Transient lasts $5\tau_3 = 9.3\bar{3}\text{s}$

Solutions for Further Investigation and Discussion

Substituting a current source for the voltage source yields the circuit of (a). Using Thévenin's theorem, this can be reduced to the circuit of (b).

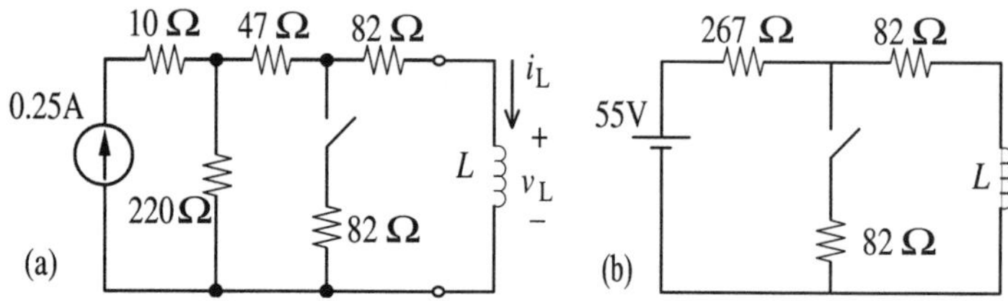

With the switch closed and the circuit in steady state, you get (c). Solving for inductor current yields I_{ss1} = 89.3 mA. If you then open the switch and wait for the new steady state, you get the circuit of (d). Here, I_{ss2} = 158 mA. A sketch of inductor current is shown in (e). As indicated, inductor current rises exponentially from 89.3 mA to158 mA over a time interval of 5τ = where τ = 2.4 mH/349 Ω = 6.88 s. Thus, the transient lasts 34.4 μs.

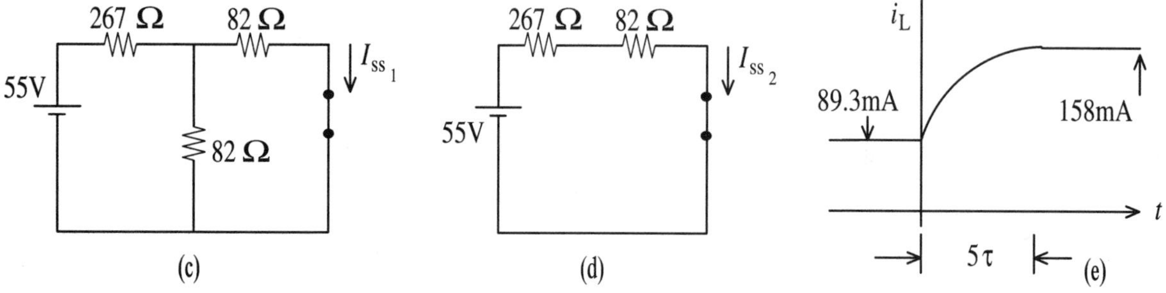

With the switch closed and the circuit in steady state, the voltage across the inductor is zero. Similarly, when the circuit reaches steady state with the switch open, the inductor voltage will again be zero. From our previous experience with transients, we know that a voltage spike will occur at the instant the switch is opened. To determine whether the spike is positive or negative, recall that $v_L = L\, di/dt$. Since current is increasing, *di/dt* is positive—thus, v_L will be positive. The resulting voltage is indicated in (f).

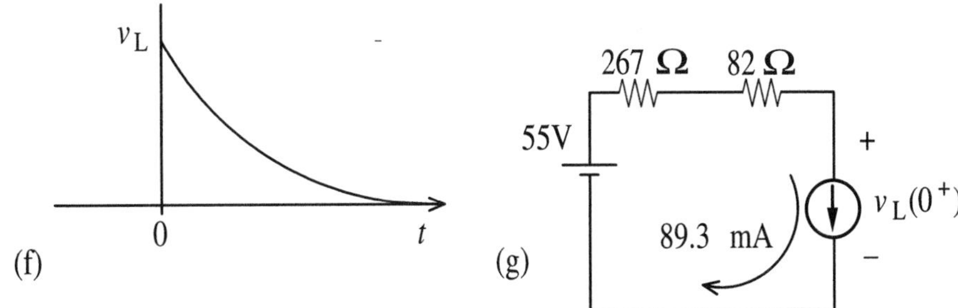

To determine the magnitude of the spike, draw the circuit as it looks at $t = 0^+$. As shown in (g), the inductor looks like a current source of 89.3 mA. Applying KVL yields 55 V – (89.3 mA)(349 Ω) – $v_L = 0$. Thus, $v_L = 23.8$ V at $t = 0^+$.

From the above, you can see that a great deal of information can be obtained without performing a formal transient analysis.

NAME ____________________

DATE ____________________

CLASS ____________________

LAB 11

The Oscilloscope (Part 1) Familiarization and Basic Measurements

OBJECTIVES

After completing this lab, you will be able to

- describe the operation and use of an oscilloscope,
- connect an oscilloscope to a circuit under test and select basic control settings,
- measure dc voltage,
- use an oscilloscope to observe time varying waveforms.

EQUIPMENT REQUIRED

- ☐ Oscilloscope
- ☐ Variable dc power supply
- ☐ Function generator
- ☐ DMM

Preliminary Note

Basic features of the oscilloscope are covered in *A Guide to Lab Equipment and Laboratory Measurements* at the beginning of this manual. You may wish to review this material before doing the lab.

EQUIPMENT USED

Instrument	Manufacturer/Model No.	Serial No.
DMM		
Power supply		
Function generator		
Oscilloscope		

Table 11-1

DISCUSSION

The oscilloscope is the key test and measurement instrument used for studying time varying waveforms. Its main feature is that it displays waveforms on a screen; with an oscilloscope, you can view and study waveforms, measure ac and dc voltages, frequency, period, phase displacement and so on. However, the oscilloscope is a fairly complex instrument and we therefore learn about it in stages. In this lab, we concentrate on operational procedures, front panel controls and a few basic measurements; in Labs 12 and 13, we look at more advanced measurement techniques. Later labs add more detail.

Connecting to the Circuit Under Test

The oscilloscope is connected to the circuit under test by means of a probe (or set of probes) as illustrated in Figure 11-1. The probe includes a measurement tip and a ground clip and connects to the oscilloscope via a flexible, shielded cable which is grounded at the oscilloscope. This ground serves as the reference point with respect to which all signals are measured. The shield helps guard against electrical noise pick up.

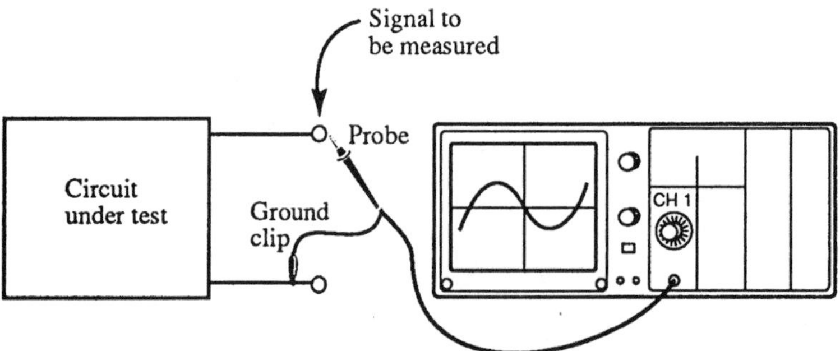

Figure 11-1 The basic oscilloscope measurement circuit

Probes may be "× 1" or "× 10". A "× 10" probe contains a 10:1 voltage divider which attenuates the signal by a factor of 10; thus, when you use a "× 10" probe, you have to multiply the scope readings by a factor of 10 to get the correct input (unless your scope automatically changes scales for you as some models do).

Front Panel Controls

Front panel controls permit you to control the operation of the oscilloscope. They may be grouped functionally as in Table 11-2.

Main Oscilloscope Controls According to Function			
Display	**Vertical**	**Horizontal**	**Triggering**
Intensity	Coupling (ac-gnd-dc)	Sec/Div	Coupling
Focus	Volts/Div	X-position	Source
Beam Finder	Y-position		Level
	Channel Select		Slope
			Mode

Table 11-2

A few of these are summarized below. Others will be introduced in later labs.

Coupling (ac-gnd-dc): Permits selection of coupling. When set to *dc*, the entire signal (ac plus any dc present) is displayed; when set to *ac*, dc signals are blocked by a capacitor and only ac is displayed; when set to *gnd*, the input is grounded. This permits establishing a *0-V base-line* (reference) on the screen.

VOLTS/DIV: This is the scope's vertical sensitivity control. It is a calibrated control that establishes how many volts each major vertical scale division represents. For example, when set for 10-V/DIV, each grid line represents 10 volts. Each channel has its own independent VOLTS/DIV control. A fine adjust control is also provided, but it is not calibrated. Each scale division is usually 1 cm.

Y-Position: This is the vertical position control. Each channel has its own control. It moves the trace up or down for easier observation. It is not calibrated.

Channel Select: Permits displaying Ch1, Ch2, both, or their sum or difference.

SEC/DIV: This is a calibrated control that selects how many seconds each major horizontal division represents. (It is calibrated in s, ms, and μs.) One control handles all channels. (A non-calibrated fine adjust is also provided.)

X-Position: Positions the trace horizontally. One control handles all channels.

Trigger Source: Selects the trigger source, e.g., Ch1, Ch2, an external trigger, or the ac line.

Trigger Level: Permits you to adjust the point on the trigger source waveform where you want triggering to start.

Trigger Slope: Selects whether the scope is to trigger on the positive or negative slope of the trigger source waveform.

Trigger Mode: Modes include *auto, normal* and *single sweep*. In the auto mode, the sweep always occurs, even with no trigger present; in the normal mode, a trigger must be present; in the single sweep mode, a trigger is required but only one sweep results. (Other modes may be provided but we will not consider them here.)

MEASUREMENTS

PART A: General Familiarization

If you have trouble getting a trace on the screen, check the intensity control; if it is set too low, the trace may be very faint or not visible. ***(Caution: Never leave a bright spot on the screen.)*** If adjusting the intensity does not locate the trace, proceed as follows: select Ch1, set triggering to auto, set SEC/DIV to mid range, press and hold the *beam finder* control, then adjust the vertical control to locate the trace.

Tests 1 to 3 are performed with no input applied to the oscilloscope.

1. Rotate the *focus* and *intensity* controls and note their effect. Adjust until you get a sharply focused trace at a comfortable viewing level.
2. Adjust the *vertical position* control and note its effect. Center the trace vertically on the center.
3. Adjust the *horizontal position* control and note its effect. Center the trace horizontally on the screen.
4. Connect a probe to Ch1 and set the channel selector to Ch1. Touch the probe tip to the *calibration test point* on the front panel. (Do not connect the ground clip.) Adjust the *VOLTS/DIV* control, the *SEC/DIV* control and the *trigger controls* until you get the calibration waveform on the screen. (It should be a square wave.)

PART B: Measuring dc Voltage with the Oscilloscope

5. a. Set the channel selector to Ch1 and use a ×1 probe. (Ensure the *VOLTS/DIV* switch for Ch1 is on *CAL*.) Set the trigger to *auto*. Move the *ac-gnd-dc* switch to *gnd* and center the trace. Return the coupling switch to *dc*. Voltage can be

Caution

The ground points on oscilloscopes, power supplies, and other equipment are generally tied to the electrical power system

(continues next page)

determined from the screen using the relationship V = *(deflection)* × *(VOLTS/DIV setting)*.

b. Connect the probe as in Figure 11-2 and set *VOLTS/DIV* to 1 V. With the voltmeter, set the power supply to 2 V and note the deflection on the screen. From this deflection, compute the measured voltage. (It should equal the applied voltage.) Record in Table 11-3.

c. Now change *VOLTS/DIV* to 2 V, set E = 4 V and note the position of the trace. Enter data in Table 11-3 and compute V. Repeat for E = 15 V at 5 *VOLTS/DIV*.

d. Replace the probe with an ×10 probe. Using the oscilloscope, set the supply successively to 10 V, 15 V and 22.5 V. Record data, including the *VOLTS/DIV* settings that you choose. Compare to the meter reading.

ground through the U-ground pin on the electrical power outlet (plug-in). Since this connection ties all ground points together, you must be careful when connecting ground clips, as it is easy to inadvertently short out a component or even accidentally ground an output. While these grounds are required for safety reasons, they make poor signal paths. Therefore, be sure to use the ground clip supplied with the scope probe when making measurements.

Probe	Input Voltage	VOLTS/DIV Setting	Deflection (divisions)	Voltage from Oscilloscope
×1	2 V	1-V	2	2 V
×1	4 V	2-V	2	4 V
×1	15 V	5-V	3	15 V
×10	10 V	0.2	5	10 V
×10	15 V	0.2	7.5	15 V
×10	22.5 V	0.5	4.5	22.5 V

Table 11-3

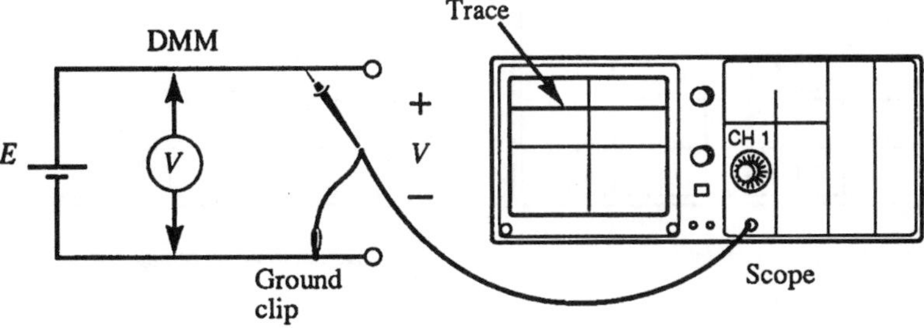

Figure 11-2 Circuit for Test 5

6. Move the input coupling switch to *ac*. Set the supply to the voltages of Table 11-3. What happens? Why?

   All read 0 since the AC input blocks the DC component

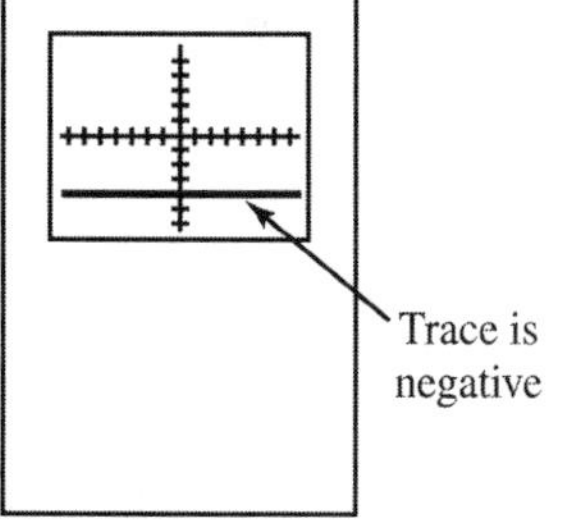

7. Return coupling to *dc*. Now set the trigger to *normal*. Note that the trace disappears. (This is because there is no trigger point in dc to start the sweep.) Return the trigger to *auto*.
8. Make sure your power supply output is floating. Reverse the probe connections to the power supply. Adjust the power supply voltage up and down. Note the deflection on the screen. Describe what happened.

   As the input voltage increases, trace moves further in the negative direction.

PART C Observing Waveforms

Replace the power supply with a function generator. Be sure to connect the ground of the scope to the ground of the generator. Set input coupling to *gnd* and center the trace. Change coupling to *ac*.

9. a. Set the function generator to a 2-kHz sine wave. On the oscilloscope, set the *VOLTS/DIV* switch to 1 V, the trigger to positive slope, and the time base to 0.1 ms/div. Adjust the output voltage of the generator until you get a nicely sized sine wave on the screen, then trim the frequency and adjust the horizontal position and trigger level controls to get one cycle of the waveform to fit between 5 horizontal grid lines. Sketch the waveform as Figure 11-3(a).
   b. Change the trigger slope to negative and repeat (a). Sketch the waveform as Figure 11-3(b).

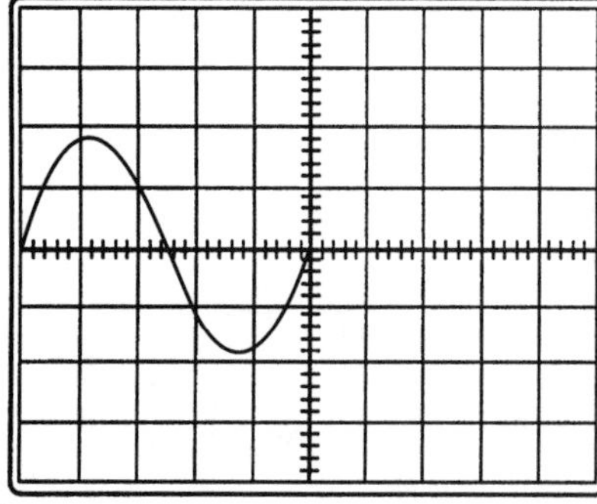

(a) Trigger slope set to positive

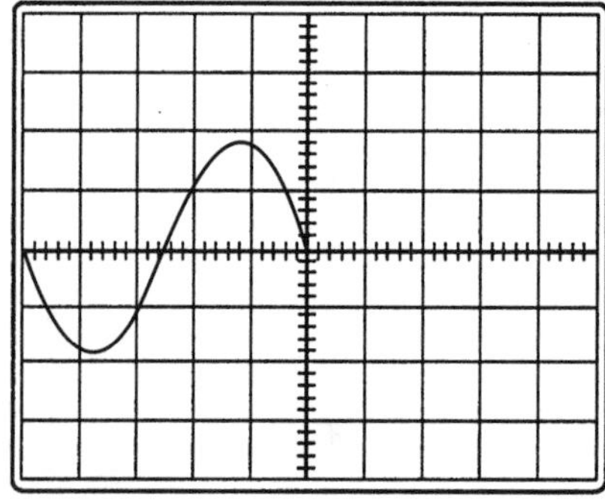

(b) Trigger slope set to negative

Figure 11-3 One cycle of a sine wave

c. Return the trigger slope to positive, then set input coupling to *dc*. (Make sure the dc offset on your function generator is set to zero.) What happens to the waveforms? (Compare to those of Figure 11-2.)

Same as Figure 11–3(a)

d. Return the coupling to *ac*. Set $f = 500$ Hz and change the time base to get 4 cycles on the screen (actually a bit more than four). Sketch here. Be sure to note the time base setting.

Period T = 2 ms

10. Repeat Steps 9(a) and (b) for a square wave and for a triangular wave. Sketch waveforms as Figures 11-4 and 11-5.

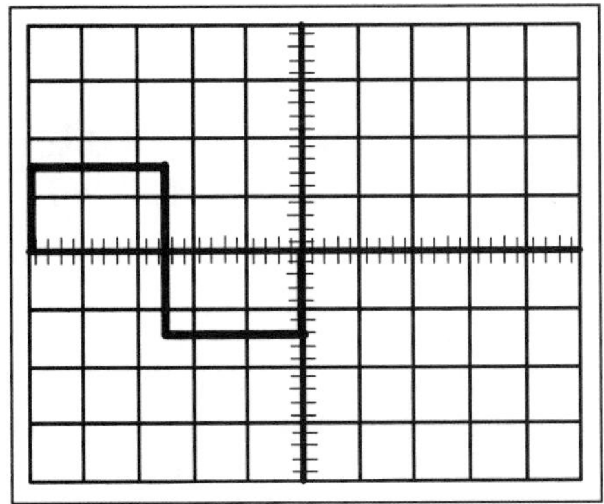

(a) Trigger slope set to positive

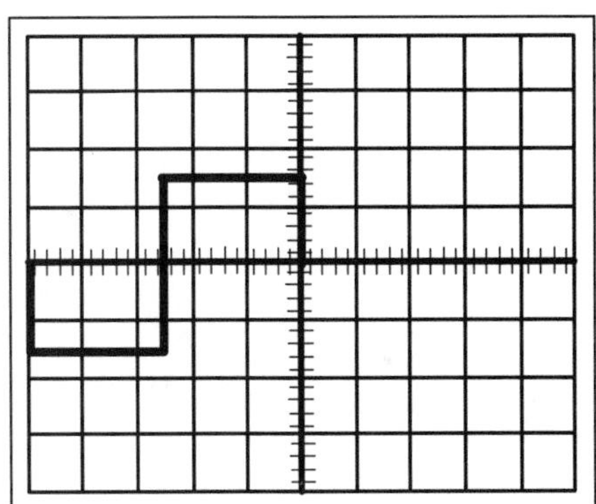

(b) Trigger slope set to negative

Figure 11-4 One cycle of a square wave

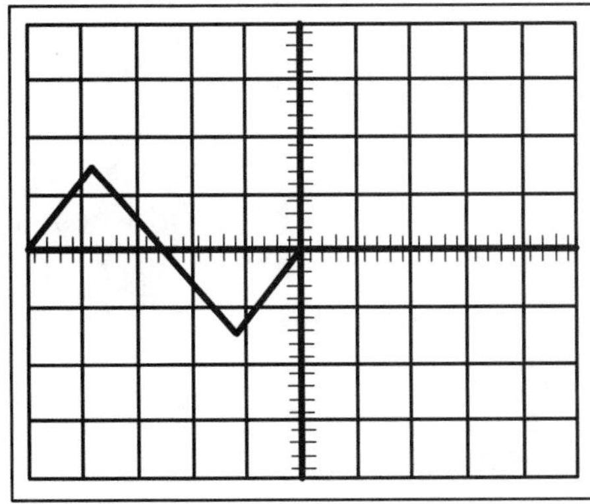

(a) Trigger slope set to positive

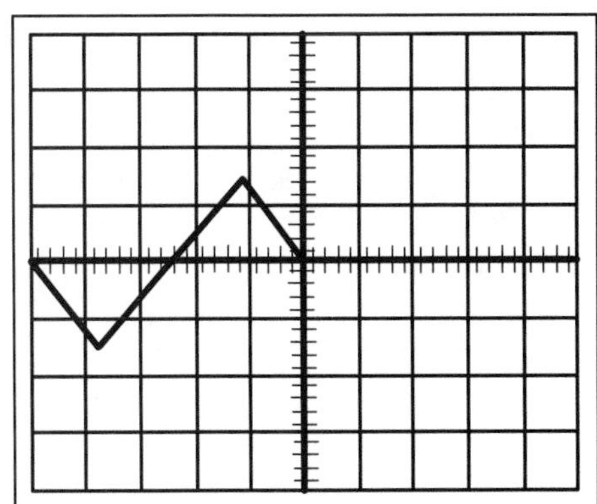

(b) Trigger slope set to negative

Figure 11-5 One cycle of a triangular wave

11. Apply a 20 kHz sine wave and with the time base on *CAL*, display a few cycles on the screen. Now take the time base control off *calibrate* and vary it. Discuss what happens ______

    You get more cycles on the screen but their time axis is no longer calibrated.

PROBLEMS

12. A waveform is faint. What control should be adjusted?

    Intensity

13. A waveform is fuzzy. What control should be adjusted?

    Focus

14. With a ×1 probe and *VOLTS/DIV* (vertical sensitivity) set at 5 V/div, a dc voltage moves the trace up 3.4 grid lines. What is the input voltage? 17 V

15. With a ×1 probe and the vertical sensitivity set at 10 V/div, a dc voltage moves the trace down by 1.2 grid lines. What is the input voltage? −12 V

Solution Problem 16
V = 10 (5 V/div × 2.5 div)
= 125 volts
However, if your scope automically changes scale, it would be direct reading and
V = 12.5 volts

16. With a ×10 probe and the vertical sensitivity control set at 5 V/div, a dc voltage moves the trace up 2.5 grid lines. What is the input voltage? (There are two possible answers, depending on your oscilloscope—see earlier note. Answer in terms of the scope you used in this lab.)
17. Using a ×1 probe and with the vertical sensitivity set to 2 V/div, a dc voltage moves the trace up by 2 and a half grid lines. The *VOLTS/DIV* fine adjust is used to bring the trace up to 3 grid lines high. What is the value of the input voltage? Why?

    2 V/div x 2.5 div = 5 V

    The second reading is meaningless since the volts scale is no longer calibrated.

NAME ______________________

DATE ______________________

CLASS ______________________

Basic ac Measurements: Period, Frequency, and Voltage (The Oscilloscope—Part 2)

OBJECTIVES

After completing this lab, you will be able to use an oscilloscope to

- measure period and frequency of an ac waveform,
- measure amplitude and peak-to-peak voltage,
- measure instantaneous voltage,
- determine the equation for a sinusoidal voltage from the oscilloscope readings.

EQUIPMENT REQUIRED

☐ Oscilloscope
☐ Signal or function generator

EQUIPMENT USED

Instrument	Manufacturer/Model No.	Serial No.
Oscilloscope		
Signal or function generator		

Table 12-1

TEXT REFERENCES

Section 15.4 FREQUENCY, PERIOD, AMPLITUDE, AND PEAK VALUE
Section 15.5 ANGULAR AND GRAPHIC RELATIONSHIPS FOR SINE WAVES
Section 15.6 VOLTAGES AND CURRENTS AS FUNCTIONS OF TIME

> **Note**
> Higher end oscilloscopes can do some of the tasks described here automatically, for example, they can determine the frequency (and other waveform parameters) and display them digitally on the screen. However, we will limit our discussion to the basic functions that are common to all oscilloscopes.

Measuring Period and Frequency: The period of a waveform is the length of one cycle. Since the horizontal scale of an oscilloscope is calibrated in seconds, you can measure the period T directly on the screen, then determine frequency from the relationship $f = 1/T$. For example, if the time base is set to 20 μs per division and one cycle is 4 divisions, then $T = 4(20\ \mu s) = 80\ \mu s$ and $f = 1/80\ \mu s = 12.5$ kHz.

Measuring Voltage: An oscilloscope displays the instantaneous value of its input voltage. Thus, an oscilloscope may be used to measure peak voltage, peak-to-peak voltage, and indeed, the voltage at any point on a waveform. This voltage is measured in the same manner as dc voltage—you determine the deflection of the trace at that point, then multiply by the vertical sensitivity setting.

Equations for Sinusoidal Voltage from Oscilloscope Readings: Mathematically, the voltage at any point on a sine wave can be found from the equation

$$v = V_m \sin \alpha \qquad (12\text{-}1)$$

where α is the angular position on the cycle as indicated in Figure 12-1. If you know V_m, you can determine the voltage at any position by direct substitution into Equation 12-1. (Since one cycle represents 360°, one half cycle represents 180°, one quarter cycle represents 90°, and so on. The angular position at any other point can be determined by direct proportion.)

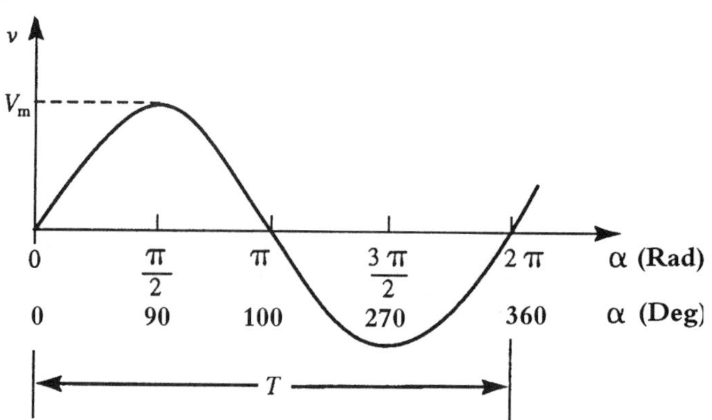

Figure 12-1 A sinusoidal waveform

Practical Note
The frequency scale of many signal generators is not very accurate and you may have to trim the frequency to get the desired period on the oscilloscope.

Voltage as a Function of Time: Equation 12-1 may be rewritten as a function of time as

$$v(t) = V_m \sin\omega t \tag{12-2}$$

where $\omega = 2\pi f = 2\pi/T$ and t is time measured in seconds. By measuring V_m and T on the screen, you can use Equation 12-2 to establish the analytic expression for any measured sinusoidal voltage.

Control Settings: Always select *VOLTS/DIV* and *SEC/DIV* settings to yield best results. For example, if you set the amplitude and time scales to spread a waveform over the screen, you can get more accurate measurements than if you compress the waveform into a small space. (Most settings here and in future labs will be left for you to select.) In addition, make sure that you have established an appropriate zero volt base line for each channel and that the *VOLTS/DIV* and *SEC/DIV* switches are set to their *CAL* (calibrate) positions.

MEASUREMENTS

PART A: Measuring Period and Frequency

1. a. Connect the oscilloscope to the signal generator. Set the oscilloscope time base to 0.1 ms/div, coupling to *ac*, and the trigger slope to *positive*. Adjust the signal generator to obtain a sine wave that is 5 divisions in length. Thus, T = 0.5 ms and f = 2 kHz. Compare f to the frequency set on the generator dial.

   Should be close.

   b. Repeat for a time base setting of 20 μs per division and two cycles in 8 divisions. T = 80 μs and f = 12.5 kHz. Compare to the frequency set on the signal generator dial.

   Should be close.

PART B: Amplitude and Peak-to-Peak for a Sine Wave

2. For best results, set peak-to-peak amplitude rather than zero to peak. Use the vertical control to position the waveform between grid lines. For this test, set the vertical sensitivity to 0.5 V/div and choose a frequency of 1 kHz.

a. Adjust the signal generator to yield a display of 8 grid lines peak-to-peak, centered vertically. What is peak-to-peak voltage? $V_{\text{peak-to-peak}}$ = ___4 V___.

b. What is V_m? V_m = ___2 V___.

c. Sketch the waveform below with V_m and peak-to-peak voltages carefully labeled.

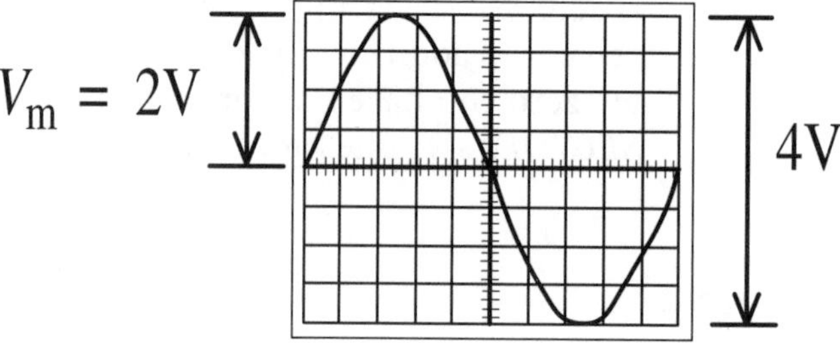

PART C: Instantaneous Value of a Sine Wave

3. a. Set the vertical sensitivity control to 1 V/div, the time base to 0.1 ms/div and obtain a waveform on the screen with a cycle length of exactly 8 divisions. Adjust the signal generator for a peak-to-peak display of 8 grid lines. Sketch the waveform as Figure 12-2. Label the vertical and horizontal axes in volts and ms.

   b. From the screen, measure the voltage at 0.1 ms intervals and record in Table 12-2.

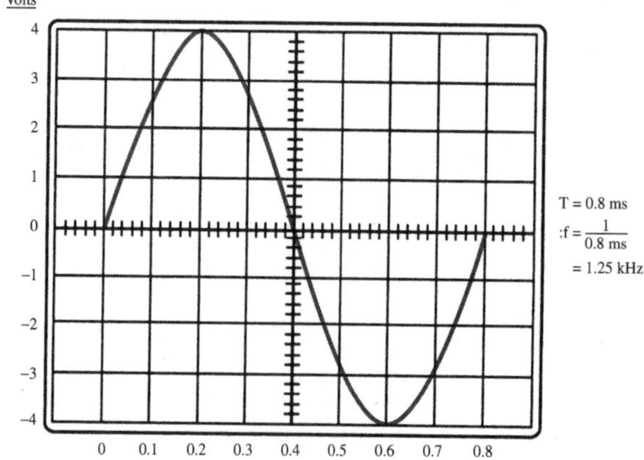

Figure 12-2 Measured waveform for Test 3

c. How many degrees does each 0.1 ms division represent?

45° .

Record the value of α for each value of t shown in Table 12-2.

d. Using Equation 12-1, verify each entry in the table. (Show a few sample calculations.)

$t = 0.1s \Rightarrow \alpha = 45^\circ \therefore v = V_m \sin\alpha = 4 \sin 45^\circ = 2.83$ V

$t = 0.7s \Rightarrow \alpha = 315^\circ \therefore v = 4 \sin 315^\circ = -2.83$ V

		Voltage	
t (ms)	α (deg)	Measured	Computed
0	0	Should be	0
0.1	45	nearly the	2.83
0.2	90	same as the	4
0.3	135	computed	2.83
0.4	180	values	0
0.5	225		–2.83
0.6	270		–4
0.7	315		–2.83
0.8	360		0

Table 12-2

PART D: The Equation for Sinusoidal Voltage

4. a. For the waveform of Figure 12-2, determine ω.

$\omega = 2\pi f = 7854$ rads/s

b. Using the measured values of ω and V_m, write the equation for the voltage in the form of Equation 12-2.

$v(t) = 4 \sin 7845\, t$ V

c. Using this equation, compute v at $t = 50\ \mu s$ and $t = 150\ \mu s$. Show details below.

At $t = 50\ \mu s$, $\upsilon = 4 \sin 7845\ \text{rad/s} \times 50 \times 10^{-6} s = 4 \sin 0.3927$ rad

$= 4 \sin 22.5^\circ$

$= 1.53V$

Similarly at $t = 150\ \mu s$, $v = 3.70$ V

PROBLEMS

5. With the time base set to $0.5\ \mu s/DIV$, four cycles of a waveform occupies 10 divisions. What is the period and the frequency of the waveform?

   Period 1.25 μs Frequency 800 kHz

6. With the *VOLTS/DIV* set to 2 and a ×1 probe, a waveform has an amplitude of 2 1/2 grid lines. The *VOLTS/DIV* fine adjust is used to bring the amplitude up to 3 grid lines high. What is the amplitude of the input voltage?

   Amplitude 5 V

7(c)
$\upsilon = 100 \sin 377 \times 20$ ms
$= 100 \sin 7.54$ rad
$= 100 \sin 432°$
$= 95.1$ V

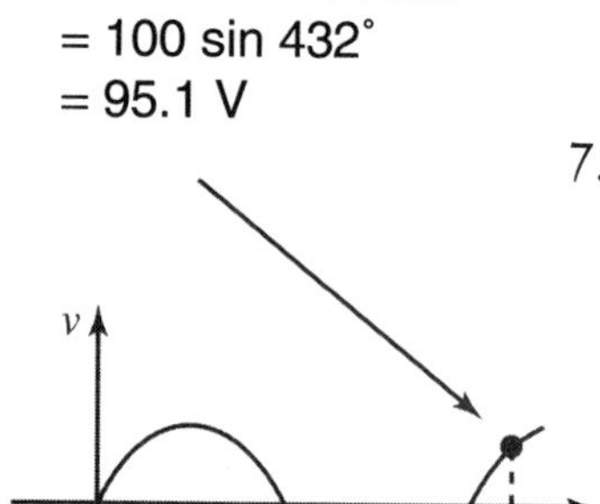

7. Given $v(t) = 100 \sin 377t$
   a. What is the value of V_m? $V_m =$ 100 V
   b. What are the frequency and period?

      $f =$ 60 $T =$ $16.\bar{6}$ ms
   c. Compute the voltage at $t = 20$ ms. Sketch the waveform and show where $t = 20$ ms occurs on the waveform.

8. Determine the equation $v(t)$ for the voltage depicted in Figure 12-3.

Solution: $v = -V_m \sin \omega t$

From the graph, $V_m = 7$ V and $T = 0.4\ \mu s$

Thus, $\omega = \frac{2\pi}{T} = 15.71 \times 10^6$ rad/s

Thus: $v = -7 \sin 15.71 \times 10^6\ t$ V

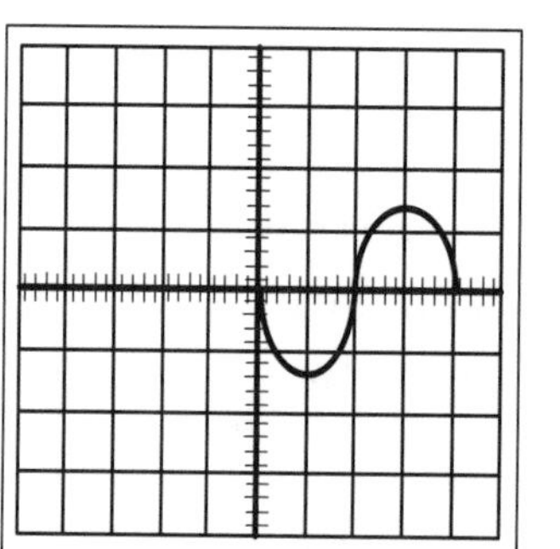

Vertical = 5 V/div

Time base = 0.1 μs/div

Figure 12-3 Assume the waveform starts at time $t = 0$s

NAME ______________________

DATE ______________________

CLASS ______________________

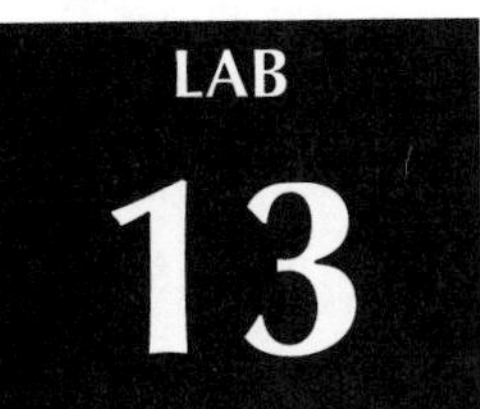

AC Voltage and Current (The Oscilloscope-Part 3, Additional Measurement Techniques)

OBJECTIVES

After completing this lab, you will be able to use an oscilloscope to

- measure rms values for sinusoidal voltage,
- measure superimposed ac and dc voltages,
- measure ac current using a sensing resistor,
- display two waveforms simultaneously on a dual channel oscilloscope,
- measure phase displacement with a dual channel oscilloscope,
- measure voltage using differential measurement techniques.

EQUIPMENT REQUIRED

- ☐ Dual channel oscilloscope
- ☐ Signal or function generator
- ☐ DMM and VOM

COMPONENTS

- ☐ Resistors: 82-Ω, 100-Ω, 150-Ω, 1-kΩ, 2-kΩ, 3.3-kΩ, 5.6-kΩ, 6.8-kΩ, 10-kΩ (all 1/4-W)
- ☐ Capacitor: 0.01-μF
- ☐ Battery: 1.5-V

EQUIPMENT USED

Instrument	Manufacturer/Model	Serial No.
DMM		
VOM		
Dual Channel oscilloscope		
Signal of function generator		

Table 13-1

TEXT REFERENCE

Section 15.6 VOLTAGES AND CURRENTS AS FUNCTIONS OF TIME
Section 15.9 EFFECTIVE VALUES

DISCUSSION

Measuring the rms Voltage of a Sine Wave. An oscilloscope may be used to determine the rms value of a sinusoidal voltage since, for a sine wave, $V_{rms} = 0.707\ V_m$ and V_m can be measured directly on the screen. One of the reasons you might do this is convenience—if you have a signal already displayed on the screen, there is no need to connect a voltmeter. However, a more fundamental reason has to do with frequency—most meters have very limited frequency ranges. For example, many DMMs can measure to only a few kHz (although some can measure to much higher frequencies), while analog VOMs typically can measure up to about 100 kHz. (Check your meter's specs.) On the other hand, even inexpensive oscilloscopes can measure to the tens of MHz, while top of the line units can measure to hundreds of MHz, or even to the GHz range.

Measuring Current. Oscilloscopes can also be used to measure current, although not directly. There are however, two indirect ways to measure current. The first is to insert a known resistor (sometimes called a *sensing resistor*) into the circuit, measure the voltage across it using an oscilloscope, then use Ohm's law to compute current. (This method is inexpensive and widely used. The other method uses a *current probe*, but few introductory courses have access to equipment of this type so we won't consider it.)

The current sensing resistor approach is based on Ohm's law. For a purely resistive circuit, $v = Ri$. Thus, if voltage is sinusoidal, current will be sinusoidal also and vice versa—that is, v and i are in phase. Therefore, if voltage v is

$$v = V_m \sin \omega t$$

then
$$i = I_m \sin \omega t$$

Current can thus be determined by measuring V_m and computing I_m from $I_m = V_m/R$. If the rms value of current is needed, it may be determined from the equation $I_{rms} = 0.707\, I_m$.

Dual-Channel Measurements. With a dual channel oscilloscope, you can display two waveforms simultaneously. This permits you to determine phase relationships between signals, compare wave shapes, and so on.

Differential Voltage Measurements. Sometimes you need to measure the voltage across a component where the normal technique of placing the probe tip at one end and the ground clip at the other end shorts out part of the circuit. For problems such as this, *differential measurement* can be used. In PART E of this lab, you learn how make such measurements.

MEASUREMENTS

PART A: RMS Values and the Frequency Response of ac Meters

We begin with a look at the frequency response of various instruments. Here, we compare the ability of the oscilloscope, DMM, and VOM to measure voltage at different frequencies.

1. a. Assemble the circuit of Figure 13-1. Adjust the signal generator to a 100 Hz sine wave with 12 V peak-to-peak (i.e., $V_m = 6$ V. Thus, $V_{rms} = 0.707 \times 6 = 4.24$ V. This is recorded in Table 13-2 as *Actual rms*.) Now measure and record the rms voltage using the DMM and the VOM.
   b. Repeat step (a) at the other frequencies indicated in Table 13-2.

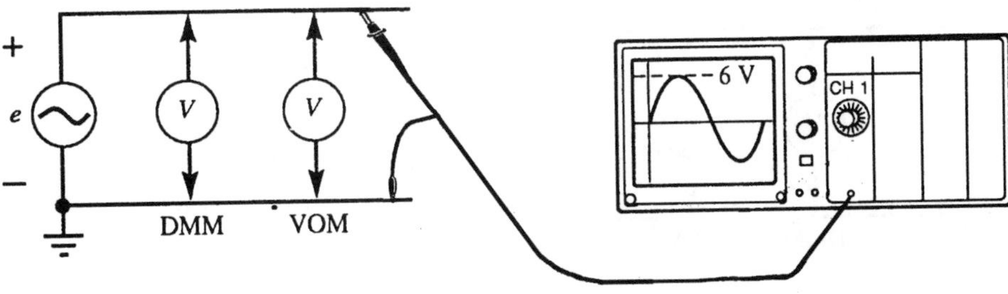

Figure 13-1 Circuit for Test 1

Note: These are actual readings. However, yours may differ, depending on the meters that you used. Still, the concept (i.e., the frequency limitations of meters) should be clear.

Frequency	Scope Reading	Acutal rms	DMM reading	VOM reading
100 Hz	6 V	4.24 V	4.24	4.2
1000 Hz	6 V	4.24 V	4.24	4.2
10000 Hz	6 V	4.24 V	3.87	4.2
100 kHz	6 V	4.24 V	0.001	4.1
1 MHz	6 V	4.24 V	0.001	2.5

Table 13-2

c. What conclusion do you draw from the data of Table 13-2?

The frequency response of the DMM is very limited. The VOM does better, but also degrades at high frequency.

PART B: Superimposed ac and dc

2. Add the 1.5-V battery to the circuit as in Figure 13-2(a). Set the signal generator to a 100-Hz sine wave. Select *ac* coupling (to temporarily block the dc component while you set the ac component) and adjust the output of the generator to $V_m = 2$ V (i.e., 4 $V_{p\text{-}p}$). Return coupling to *dc*.
   a. You now have superimposed ac and dc voltages. Sketch as Figure 13-2(b).
   b. Compute the true rms value for this waveform from $V = \sqrt{V_{dc}^2 + V_{ac}^2}$ where V_{dc} is the dc component of the waveform and V_{ac} is the rms value of its ac component.

   $V =$ 2.06 V.

Solution: $V_{ac} = \dfrac{V_m}{\sqrt{2}} = \dfrac{2\text{ V}}{\sqrt{2}} = 1.41\text{ V}$

$V = \sqrt{(1.5\text{ V})^2 + (1.41\text{ V})^2} = 2.06\text{ V}$

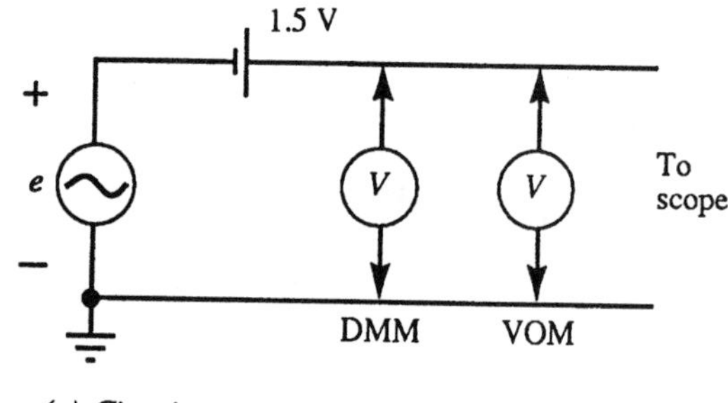

(a) Circuit

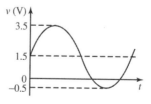

(b) Waveform

Figure 13-2 Circuit for Test 2

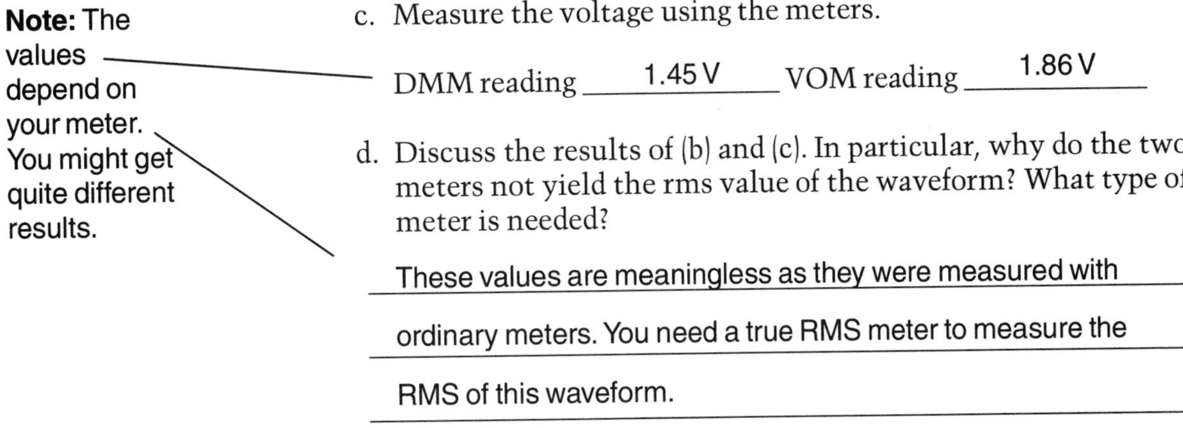

Note: The values depend on your meter. You might get quite different results.

c. Measure the voltage using the meters.

DMM reading 1.45 V VOM reading 1.86 V

d. Discuss the results of (b) and (c). In particular, why do the two meters not yield the rms value of the waveform? What type of meter is needed?

These values are meaningless as they were measured with ordinary meters. You need a true RMS meter to measure the RMS of this waveform.

PART C: Dual Channel Measurements

We now learn how to display two waveforms simultaneously.

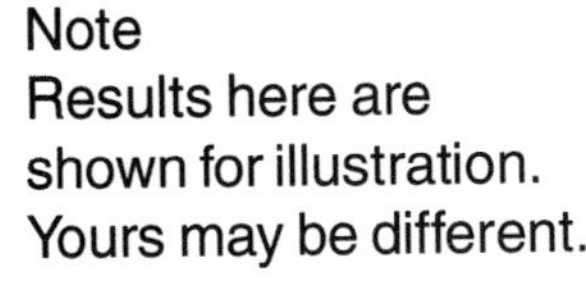

Note
Results here are shown for illustration. Yours may be different.

3. Assemble the circuit of Figure 13-3. Set the channel select switch to *alt* and trigger mode to *auto*. (*Alt* lets you display both Ch1 and Ch2 simultaneously.)
   a. Establish the 0-V baseline for Ch1 by moving its *ac-gnd-dc* switch to *gnd* and adjust its vertical position control until the trace is centered. Repeat for Ch2. (The traces should now be superimposed.) Return both Ch1 and Ch2 to the *ac* position and set triggering to Ch1, positive slope. Set *SEC/DIV* to 50 μs/div.
   b. Set the signal generator to a 2.5-kHz sine wave with $V_m = 3$ V (i.e., 6 V p-p). (You should now have two sine waves on the screen.) Select an appropriate setting for Ch2 and trim the vertical position controls if necessary to ensure that both waveforms are centered about the horizontal axis.
   c. Set the time base to 20 μs/div, and using the time base variable control if necessary, spread one half cycle of the reference waveform (Ch1) over the entire screen. (This results in each

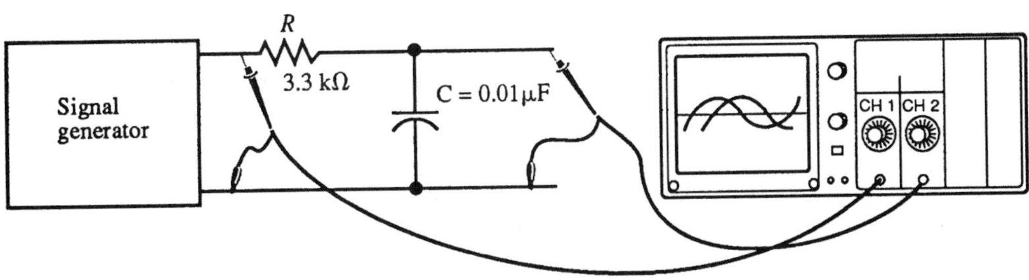

Figure 13-3 Circuit for Test 3. Use $R = 3.3$-kΩ and $C = 0.01$ μF.

major scale division representing 18°.) Now measure the displacement between the waveforms at their zero-crossover points and convert this displacement to degrees.

Displacement = 1.5 div × 18°/div = 27°.
Since v_C lags, θ = −27°

d. As you will learn later, the theoretical displacement is $\theta = \tan^{-1}(1/\omega RC) - 90°$. Compute θ and compare to the result of (c).

$$\theta = \tan^{-1}\left(\frac{1}{\omega RC}\right) - 90° = \tan^{-1}(1.929) - 90°$$
$$= 62.6° - 90° = -27.4° \quad \text{(good agreement)}$$

e. Measure the magnitudes of each waveform. Taking the voltage of Ch1 as reference, sketch the waveforms in this space.

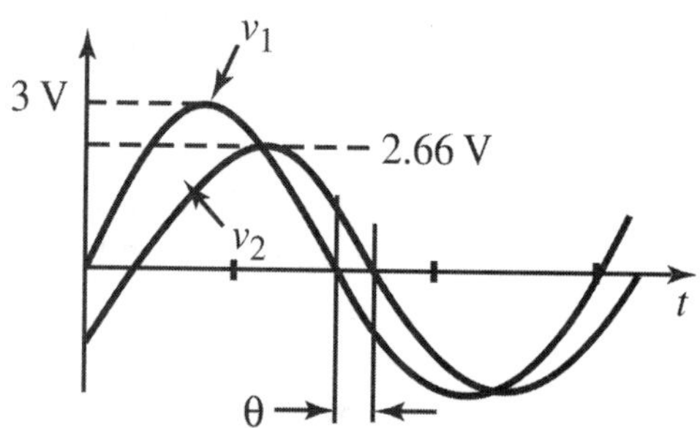

$\omega = 2\pi f$
$= 5000\pi$ rad/s

f. Write the equations for the two voltages, using the values measured above.

$v_1(t) = V_{m1} \sin \omega t = 3 \sin 5000\,\pi\, t$

$v_2(t) = V_{m2} \sin(\omega t - \theta) = 2.66 \sin(5000\,\pi\, t - 27.4°)$

g. Set f = 10 kHz and again measure displacement. Using the equation of Test 3(d), compute displacement and compare it to the measured value.

From scope: 3.6 div ⇒ −64.8°

From $\theta = \tan^{-1}\left(\frac{1}{\omega RC}\right) - 90° = -64.3°$

h. Repeat Test (g) at a frequency of 18 kHz.

From scope: −75.6°

From equation: −75°

PART D: Current Measurement with an Oscilloscope

Consider Figure 13-4(a). The load current I_L is given by $I_L = E/R_L$ where E and I_L are the rms values of the source voltage and load current respectively. To measure this current using an oscilloscope, you can add a sensing resistor R_S as in Figure 13-4(b), then measure the voltage across it, convert to rms, then compute current as $I_L' = V_S/R_S$. (As long as R_S is small compared to R_L, the accuracy will be good.)

4. a. Accurately measure the 100-Ω sensing resistor and R_L. Set up the circuit of Figure 13-4(b). (Note the placement of the sensing resistor. With the resistor placed as shown, you can connect both ground clips of the oscilloscope directly to the ground of the signal generator without fear of ground problems.) Use a 100-Hz sinusoidal source. Using Ch1, set E_m to 3 V (i.e., 6 V p-p).

   b. Measure the voltage across the sensing resistor using Ch2, then convert to rms.

   V_S = 30.7 mV (rms)

   c. Using Ohm's law, determine the rms value of the measured load current

   $I_L' = V_S/R_S$ = 0.307 (mA rms)

   Verify this current by comparing it to that measured by the meter. Same

   d. The load current that you are trying to measure is $I_L = E/R_L$, where E is the rms value of the source voltage. Using the mea-

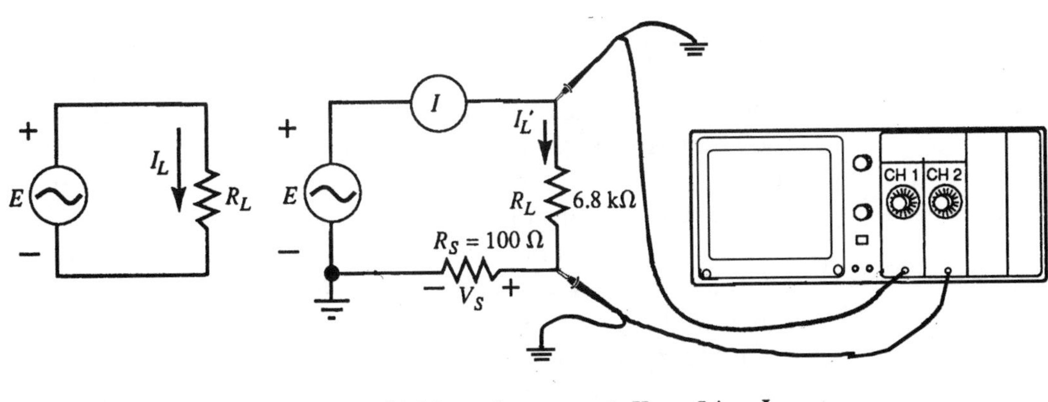

(a) Circuit

(b) Measuring current. Here, $I_L' \approx I_L$.

Figure 13-4 Circuit for Test 4. Use R_S = 100 Ω.

sured value of R_L, compute I_L using this formula and compare to the current determined by the sensing resistor approach in (c).

Note:
$E_m = 3V$
$\therefore E = \frac{3V}{\sqrt{2}}$
$= 2.12V(RMS)$

$I_L = \frac{2.12}{6.8\ k\Omega} = 0.312mA$

The error is 0.005 mA (about 1.6%)

5. Replace R_L of Figure 13-4 with the network of Figure 13-5 and repeat steps 4(b) to 4(d).

V_S = 39.1 mV (rms voltage across R_S); $I_L' = V_S/R_S$ = 0.391 mA

I_L = 0.391 mA (the meter reading);

I_L = 0.391 mA (Determined by circuit analysis)

How do the results compare? 1.76% error

$R_L^1 \rightarrow$

$R_L^1 = 5328\ \Omega$

$I_L = \frac{2.12V}{5328\Omega} = 0.398mA$

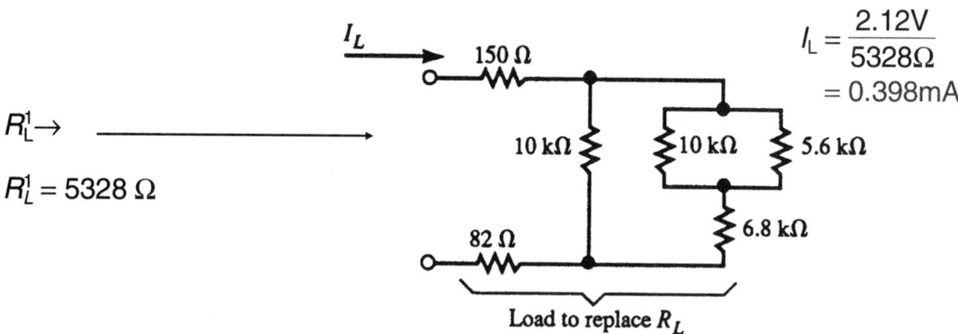

Figure 13-5 Circuit for Test 5. Replace R_L with this network.

PART E: Differential Measurements

Consider Figure 13-6. Suppose you want to measure the voltage across resistor R_1 using an oscilloscope. As a first thought, you might try the connection shown. With this connection, however, the ground lead shorts out out R_2. Alternatively, you might try reversing the probe tip and ground clip connections. However, this shorts the source output to ground. Thus, neither approach is usable. (Of course, you might consider isolating the scope or the source from ground, but this is not desirable either, as you lose the earth safety ground.) A better approach is to use differential measurement as illustrated in Figure 13-7.

In Figure 13-7, Ch1 measures the voltage from point *a* to ground while Ch2 measures the voltage from point *b* to ground. The oscilloscope has a mode (its *differential mode*) that permits you to display Ch1 minus Ch2. This yields a display of v_{ab}, the voltage between points *a* and *b*.

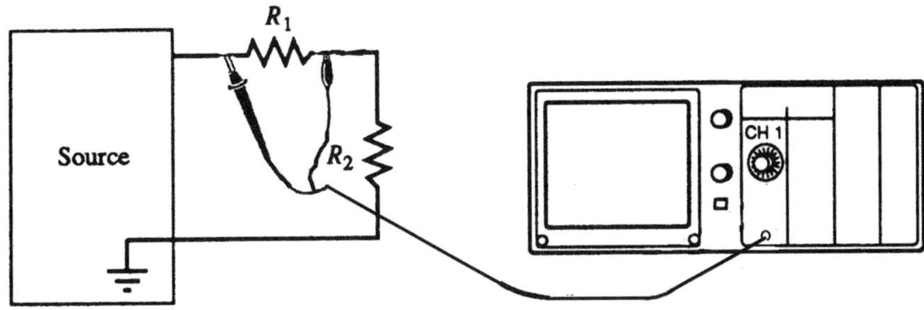

Figure 13-6 An incorrect way to view the voltage across R1

6. a. Assemble the circuit of Figure 13-7. Set the signal generator to a 1 kHz sine wave.
   b. Set *VOLTS/DIV* to the same value for both channels and ensure that they are in the *CAL* position. Center the traces as in Step 3(a). Return the *ac-gnd-dc* switch to *ac* for both channels.
   c. Select Ch1 and set the input voltage to 3 V (i.e., 6 V p-p).
   d. Select the *difference mode* for your oscilloscope. (Details differ for different scopes. For example, some scopes require that you invert Ch2 and add it to Ch1. Check your scope's manual for details or ask your instructor.)
   e. You should now have a display of v_{ab} on your screen. Since $R_1 = 2/3\ R_T$, v_{ab} should be 2/3 of the source voltage. Verify that it is.
7. We will now look at what happens if you had tried to use the circuit of Figure 13-6 to measure the voltage across R_1.
   a. Consider again the circuit of Figure 13-7. Disconnect Probe 2 (i.e., Ch2) and set the channel select back to Ch1. You should see 3 V (i.e., 6 V p-p) on the screen since Ch1 is still measuring full source voltage.
   b. Move the ground clip of Probe 1 to point *b* and note the scope display.

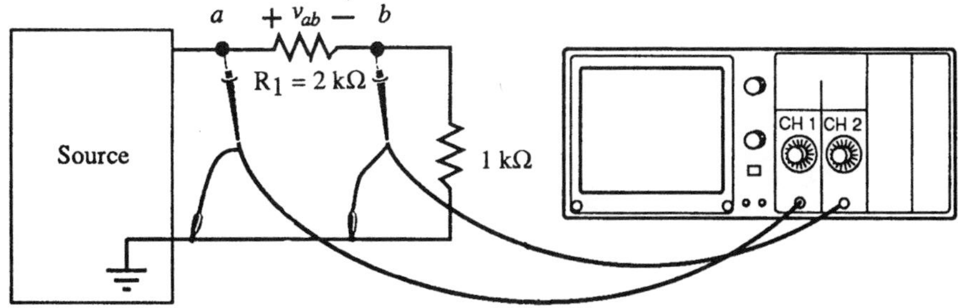

Figure 13-7 The correct way to view the voltage using differential measurement

c. In Test 7(b), your probe is connected from a to b; thus, you are measuring v_{ab}. However, it is different than v_{ab} you measured in Test 6(e). Briefly discuss what you are now seeing.

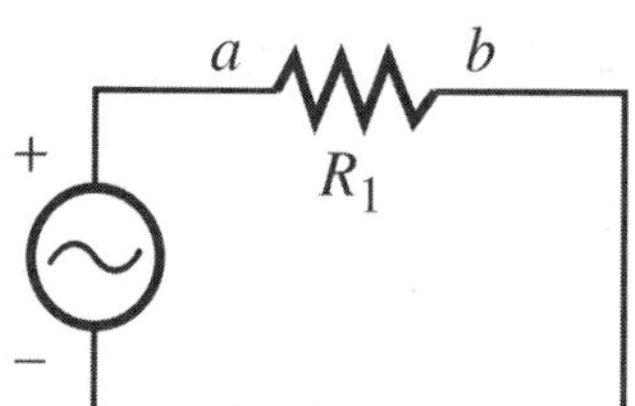

In test 7(b), you shorted out the 1 kΩ resistor. Thus, the full source voltage appears across R_1 as indicated in the diagram. Clearly this is not the v_{ab} of the original circuit, Figure 13-7.

PROBLEMS

8. Given: $v_1(t) = 100 \sin \omega t$ and $v_2(t) = 80 \sin(\omega t + 30°)$ displayed on a scope screen with v_1 as reference. If $f = 100$ Hz, sketch the oscilloscope trace in the space below as Figure 13-8(a).
9. Repeat Question 8 (as Figure 13-8(b)) if v_2 is the reference waveform.

Waveform for 8

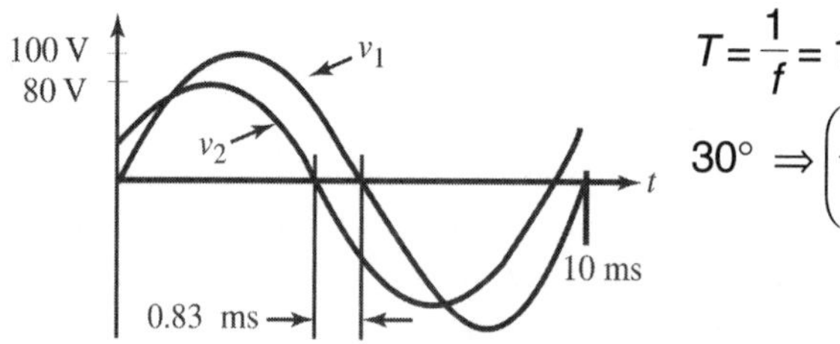

$$T = \frac{1}{f} = 10\text{ms} \Rightarrow 360°$$

$$30° \Rightarrow \left(\frac{30°}{360°}\right) \times 10 \text{ ms} = 0.8\overline{3} \text{ ms}$$

Waveform for 9

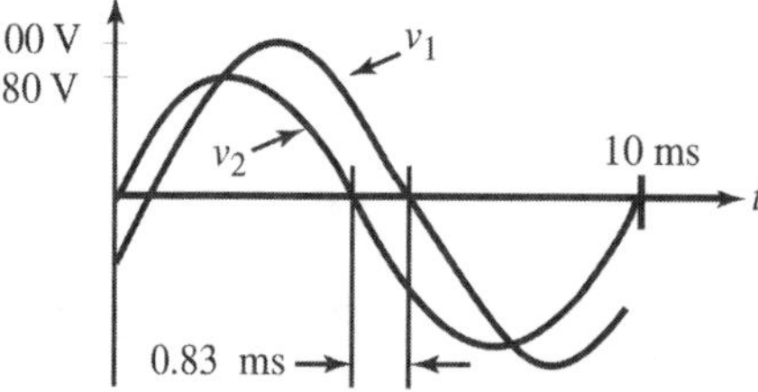

Figure 13-8 (a) Waveform for Question 8 (b) Waveform for Question 9

NAME ______________________

DATE ______________________

CLASS ______________________

LAB 14

Capacitive Reactance

OBJECTIVES

After completing this lab, you will be able to

- measure phase difference between voltage and current in a capacitance,
- measure capacitive reactance and verify theoretically,
- determine the effect of frequency on capacitive reactance.

EQUIPMENT REQUIRED

☐ Dual channel oscilloscope
☐ Signal or function generator
☐ DMM (two)

COMPONENTS

☐ Resistors: 10-Ω, 220-Ω, 1/4-W
☐ Capacitors: 1.0-μF (two), non-electrolytic

EQUIPMENT USED

Instrument	Manufacturer/Model No.	Serial No.
DMM #1		
DMM #2		
Dual channel oscilloscope		
Signal or function generator		

Table 14-1

TEXT REFERENCE

Section 16.6 CAPACITANCE AND SINUSOIDAL AC

DISCUSSION

Capacitance and Sinusoidal ac: When an ideal capacitance is connected to a sinusoidal voltage source, current leads by 90° as illustrated in Figure 14-1. Thus, if

$$v_C = V_m \sin \omega t \tag{14-1}$$

then

$$i_C = I_m \sin(\omega t + 90°) \tag{14-2}$$

where

$$I_m = V_m / X_C \tag{14-3}$$

The quantity X_C is termed *capacitive reactance* and is given by the formula

$$X_C = 1/\omega C \ \Omega \tag{14-4}$$

where $\omega = 2\pi f$ rad/s.

Practical Note
V_C and I_C are the values that you read on meters, while V_m and I_m are the values that you read on the oscilloscope

Effective (rms) Voltage and Current Relationships: In practice, we usually use effective values rather than peak values. Their ratios are the same, however. Thus reactance can also be expressed as

$$X_C = V_C / I_C \ \Omega \tag{14-5}$$

where V_C and I_C are the rms values of v_C and i_C respectively.

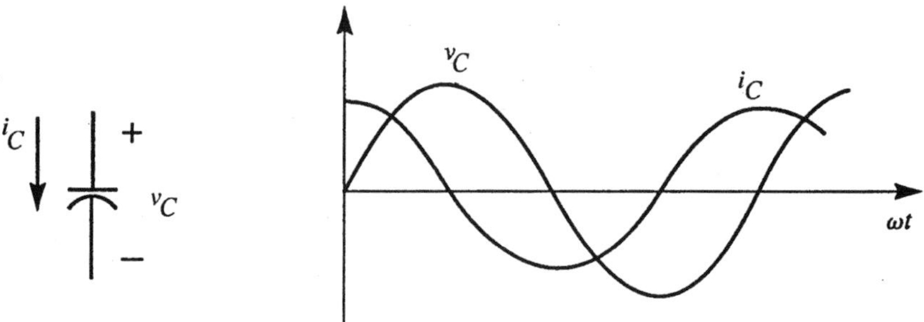

Figure 14-1 Voltage and current for capacitance

MEASUREMENTS

PART A: Phase Relationships for Capacitance

Consider Figure 14-2. Voltage v_S across R_S is in phase with capacitor current i_C. Provided circuit resistance is small compared to X_C, source voltage is approximately equal to the v_C. Thus, the phase dif-

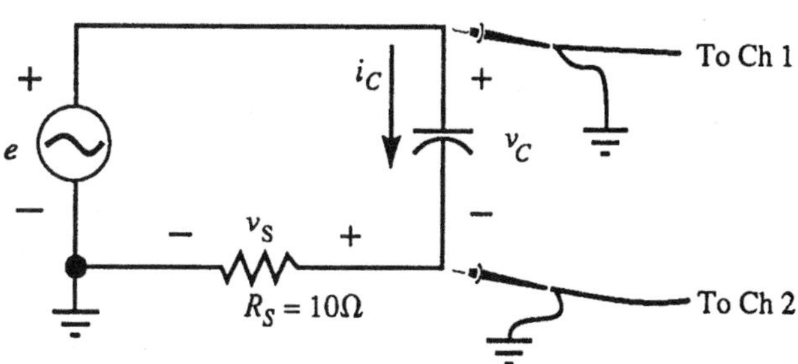

Figure 14-2 Circuit resistance is very small. Therefore, $v_C \approx e$.

ference between Ch1 and Ch2 is approximately equal to the angle between v_C and i_C. It should be close to 90°. Current should lead.

1. a. Assemble the circuit using R_S = 10 Ω and C = 1.0 μF. Set the oscilloscope for dual channel operation.
   b. Set the signal generator to a 500 Hz sine wave. Sketch the waveforms below, appropriately labeled as v_C and i_C. Determine the phase shift between v_C and i_C and indicate on the diagram. How close is it to the theoretical value of 90 degrees?

θ should be about 90°

Note: The technique used here is valid only if $X_c >> R_S$. As you increase f, the inequality becomes poorer and θ no longer is close to 90°

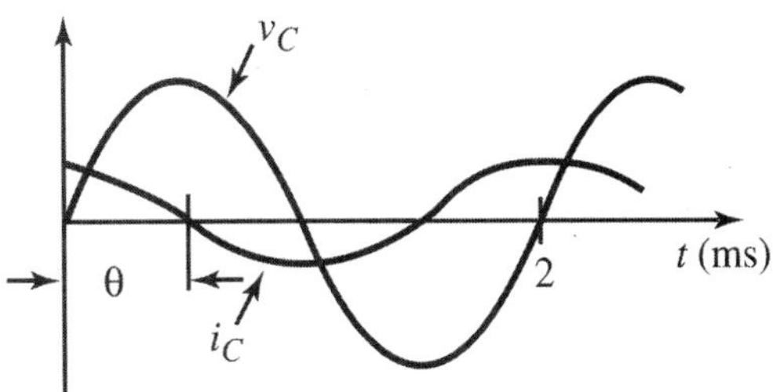

   c. Vary the frequency a few hundred Hz up and down and observe the phase shift. Is there any appreciable change? Based on this observation, state in your own words the relationship between voltage across and current through capacitance.

For small excursions, very little change in θ.

Current leads voltage by 90°. However, see note.

PART B: Magnitude Relationships for Capacitance

2. a. Replace R_S of Figure 14-2 with an accurately measured 220-Ω resistor.

R_S = 220 Ω

Errata Part 2(b): The voltage to be set on the signal generator should have been V_{pp} = 6 V. If you used V_m = 6 V, your measured voltage and current values will be about double those shown. However, X_C and C are correct.

Practical Notes

1. For this lab, you need a DMM with a frequency response up to 1-kHz. (Most DMMs can handle this range.)
2. Since reactance depends on frequency, accurate frequency settings are essential. However, the frequency dial on many signal generators is not accurately calibrated and you may require the oscilloscope to set the frequency. (If you have a generator with a digital readout, the scope should not be necessary.)

b. Set the signal generator to 500 Hz at V_m = 6 V. With a meter (or an oscilloscope if necessary), carefully measure the voltage V_C and the voltage V_S. Calculate current I_C using Ohm's law and the measured value of V_S. Record as rms values.

V_C = 1.75 V V_S = 1.21 V I_C = 5.50 mA

c. Calculate the reactance of the capacitor using the measured V_C and I_C.

$X_{C(\text{measured})} = V_C/I_C = \frac{1.75\text{V}}{5.50\text{ mA}} = 318\ \Omega$

NOTE: Voltages were measured with a DMM. Thus, values shown are RMS.

d. If possible, measure C using a bridge. (Otherwise, use the nominal value.) Compute X_C using Equation 14-4. Compare to the measured value of 2(c).

C = 1.0 μF $X_{C(\text{computed})} = \frac{1}{\omega C} = 318\ \Omega$

3. a. Add the second capacitor in series and determine the equivalent reactance of the series combination using the same procedure that you used in Test 2(b) and (c).

V_C = 2.00 V_S = 0.693

I_C = 3.15 mA $X_{eq(\text{measured})} = \frac{2.00\text{V}}{3.15\text{ mA}} = 635\ \Omega$

b. If possible, measure the second capacitor and compute C_{eq} for the series combination. C_{eq} = 0.5 μ F. Use Equation 14-4 to determine $X_{eq(\text{computed})}$. $X_{eq(\text{computed})}$ = 637Ω. Compare to the measured value of 3(a).

Measured: 635Ω — Computed: 637Ω
Excellent

4. a. Connect both capacitors in parallel and measure total reactance X_T using the same procedure that you used in Test 2(b) and (c).

V_C = 1.24V V_S = 1.72V

I_C = 7.82mA $X_{T(\text{measured})} = \frac{1.24\text{V}}{7.82\text{ mA}} = 159\ \Omega$

b. Compute C_T for the parallel combination. C_T = 2 μF.

Now use Equation 14-4 to determine $X_{T(computed)}$. $X_{T(computed)}$ =

159 Ω. Compare to the measured value of 4(a). Same

PART C: Variation of Reactance with Frequency

5. a. Replace the parallel combination with a single 1.0-μF capacitor and measure V_C and V_S and compute reactance (using the procedure of Test 2) at each of the frequencies listed in Table 14-2. Record as $X_{C(measured)}$.
   b. Using Equation 14-4, compute reactance at each of the frequencies and record as $X_{C(computed)}$.

f (Hz)	V_C	V_S	I_C	$X_{C(measured)}$	$X_{C(computed)}$
100					1.59k Ω
200					796
300	Enter your				531
400	measured				398
500	values here				318
600					265
700					227
800					199
900					177
1000					159

Table 14-2

Should be nearly the same

   c. Using the graph sheet of Figure 14-3, plot measured and computed reactances versus frequency. Label each plot.
   d. Analyze the results. That is, comment on how well the measured values agree with the computed values.

With a good DMM and careful measurements, results should be very close.

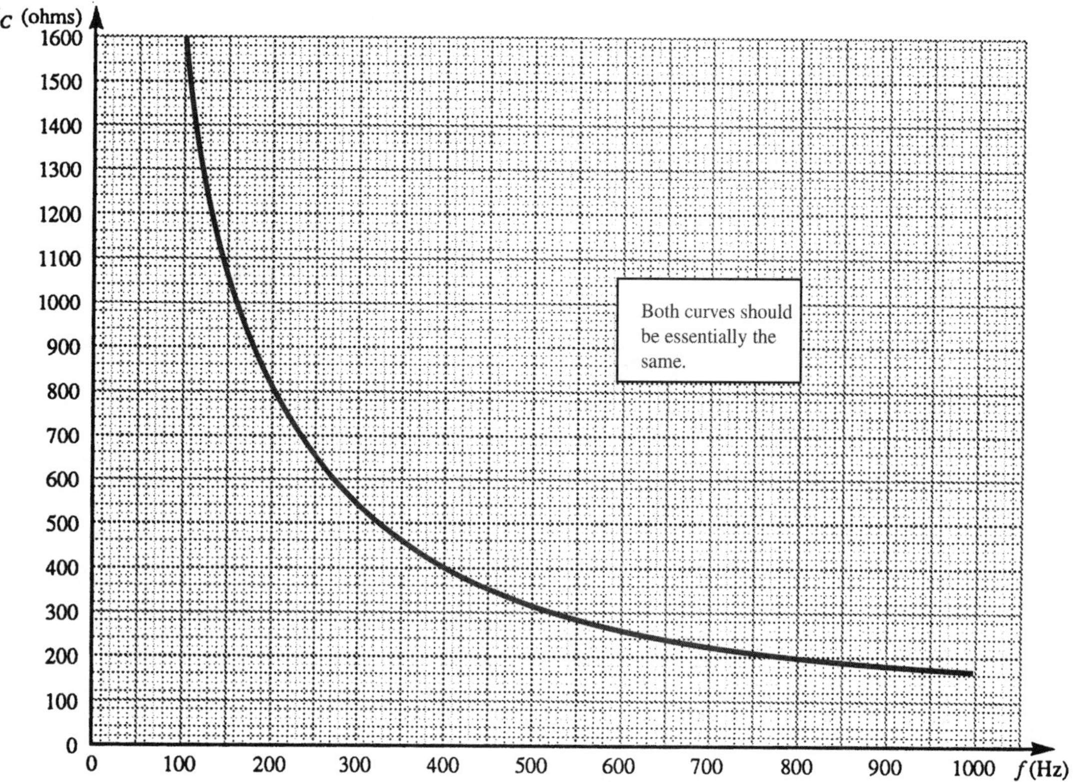

Figure 14-3 Plot of capacitive reactance versus frequency

COMPUTER ANALYSIS

> **Plotting X_C with MultiSIM**
> Note that $X_C = V_c/I_C$. If you set $I_C = 1$ A, $X_C = V_C$. Thus, a plot of V_C is also a plot of X_C—i.e., you can read the reactance in ohms directly from the graph.

6. Using either MultiSIM or PSpice, plot the reactance of a 1 μF capacitor from f = 100 Hz to 1 kHz. Hint: Plotting reactance using PSpice is straightforward—see Example 16-18 in the text. However, the current version of MultiSIM has no provision for plotting anything except voltage. Thus, another approach is needed. A simple method is to use a 1-amp *ac* current source to drive the capacitor, then plot its resulting voltage—see box. Build the circuit on the screen, then use *Options/Preferences* to determine circuit nodes. Now select *AC Analysis*, type in the desired parameters then click *Simulate*. (Choose linear scales for both x and y to match the diagrams in the book.)

Solution is shown on the following page.

PROBLEMS

7. Consider an ideal capacitor. If you double the capacitance and triple the frequency, what happens to the current if the applied sinusoidal voltage remains the same?

Solution is shown on the following page.

SOLUTIONS

Problem 6

MultiSIM Solution: See below. (For this plot, I selected Linear for both the horizontal and vertical scales to correspond to Figure 14-3.) Use AC Sweep and set the Start and End frequencies to 100 Hz and 1000 Hz respectively. Choose enough points to get a good plot (500 should be adequate), then simulate. Using your cursor, you can measure values at different frequencies. Results should agree with the computed values shown in Table 14-2 and plotted as Figure 14-3.

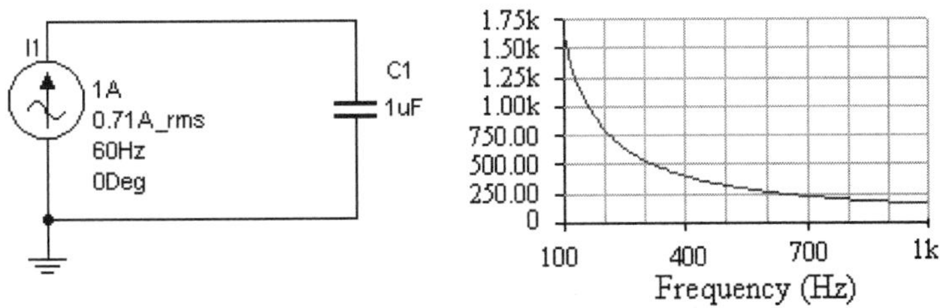

Note
MultiSIM plots the result of an AC frequency analysis in two parts: gain versus frequency and phase versus frequency. In this labe, we want only the gain plot, so I deleted the phase plot. Note also that since MultiSIM plots gain, it doesn't matter what value you specify for the current source—e.g., if you specify a current source of 10 A, it will still give exactly the same results as shown.

Problem 7

7. $X_C = \frac{1}{2\pi fC}$; if you double the capacitance, X_C decreases by a factor of ½, while if you triple the frequency, X_C decreases by a factor of ⅓. Thus, $X_{C_{new}} = \frac{1}{2} \times \frac{1}{3} \times X_{C_{old}} = \frac{1}{6} \times X_{C_{old}}$. Current will therefore be 6 times larger.

NAME ______________________

DATE ______________________

CLASS ______________________

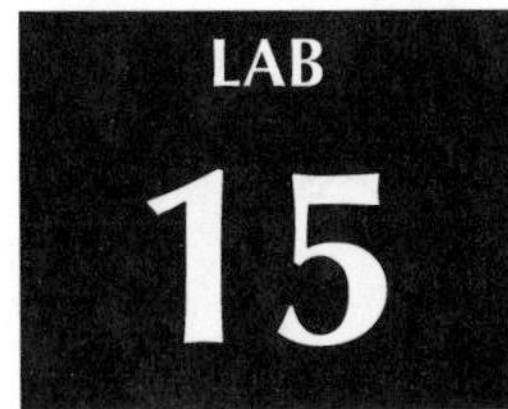

Inductive Reactance

OBJECTIVES

After completing this lab, you will be able to

- measure phase difference between voltage and current in an inductance,
- measure inductive reactance and verify theoretically,
- determine the effect of frequency on inductive reactance.

EQUIPMENT REQUIRED

- ☐ Dual channel oscilloscope
- ☐ Signal or function generator
- ☐ DMM (two)

COMPONENTS

☐ Resistors: 10-Ω, 100-Ω, 1/4-W

☐ Inductors: 2.4-mH, two required. (Hammond Part #1534 or equal. This inductor has a very small resistance which is necessary to approximate an ideal inductor.)

EQUIPMENT USED

Instrument	Manufacturer/Model No.	Serial No.
DMM		
DMM		
Dual channel oscilloscope		
Signal or function generator		

Table 15-1

TEXT REFERENCE

Section 16.5 INDUCTANCE AND SINUSOIDAL AC

DISCUSSION

Inductance and Sinusoidal ac. When an ideal inductance is connected to a sinusoidal voltage source, current lags voltage by 90° as illustrated in Figure 15-1. Thus, if

$$v_L = V_m \sin \omega t \tag{15-1}$$

then

$$i_L = I_m \sin(\omega t - 90°) \tag{15-2}$$

where

$$I_m = V_m / X_L \tag{15-3}$$

The quantity X_L is termed *inductive reactance* and is given by the formula

$$X_L = \omega L \ \Omega \tag{15-4}$$

where $\omega = 2\pi f$ rad/s. Inductive reactance represents the opposition that the inductance presents to current and is directly proportional to the product of inductance and frequency. Thus, the higher the frequency, the greater the opposition.

Effective (rms) Voltage and Current Relationships. In practice, we usually use effective values rather than peak values. Their ratios are the same however. Thus reactance can also be expressed as

$$X_L = V_L / I_L \ \Omega \tag{15-5}$$

where V_L and I_L are the rms values of v_L and i_L respectively. (Note that V_L and I_L are the values that you read on meters, while V_m and I_m are the values that you read on the oscilloscope.)

Practical Inductors. In reality, inductors have resistance as well as inductance—see Figure 15-2(a). However, if X_L is large compared to

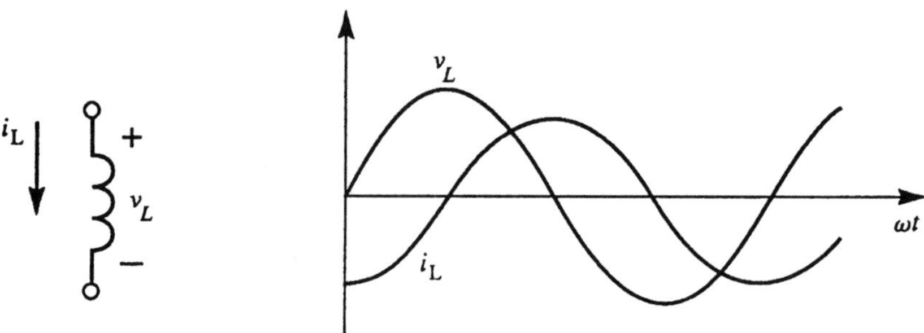

Figure 15-1 Voltage and current for an inductance

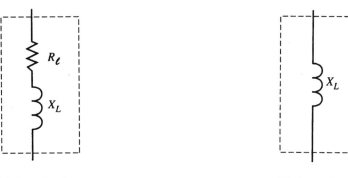

(a) A real inductor *(b) Approximation when R_ℓ has negligible effect.*

Figure 15-2 The ideal inductor approximation

R_ℓ, we can neglect resistance and use the ideal model of (b). This means the simple formulas above apply. (In this lab, we will use an inductance where this approximation is very good at higher frequencies. However, at lower frequencies, the error in the approximation starts to show up. You will have a chance to see how good the approximation is at these lower frequencies.)

MEASUREMENTS

PART A: Phase Relationships for Inductance

Consider Figure 15-3. Voltage v_S across R_S is in phase with inductor current i_L. Provided circuit resistance is small compared to X_L, source voltage is approximately equal to the v_L. Thus, the phase difference between Ch1 and Ch2 is approximately equal to the angle between v_L and i_L. It should be close to 90°.

1. a. Measure coil resistance and inductance and the resistance of the sensing resistor then assemble the circuit of Figure 15-3.

$L =$ 2.40 mH $R_\ell =$ 12.0 Ω $R_S =$ 10.0 Ω

Values depend on your coil. I have used these for illustrative purposes

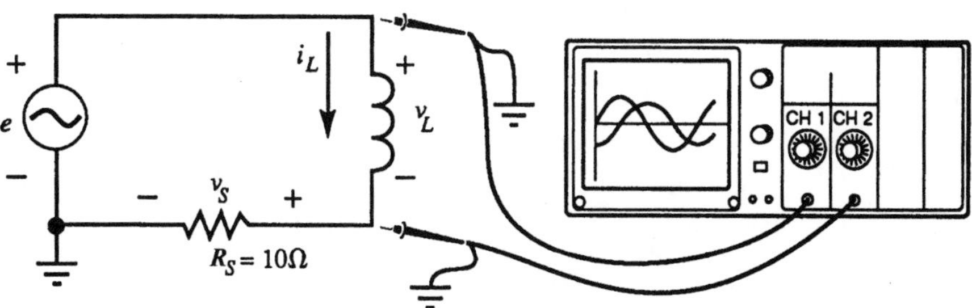

Figure 15-3 Circuit resistance is very small. Therefore, $v_L \approx e$

b. Use a 40 kHz sine wave. Sketch the waveforms below. Label Ch1 as v_L and Ch2 as i_L. Using the procedure of Lab 13, determine the phase shift and indicate it on the diagram. How close is it to the theoretical value of 90°? Vary the frequency a few kHz and observe the shift. Is there any change? Based on this observation, state in your own words the phase relationship between voltage and current for an inductance.

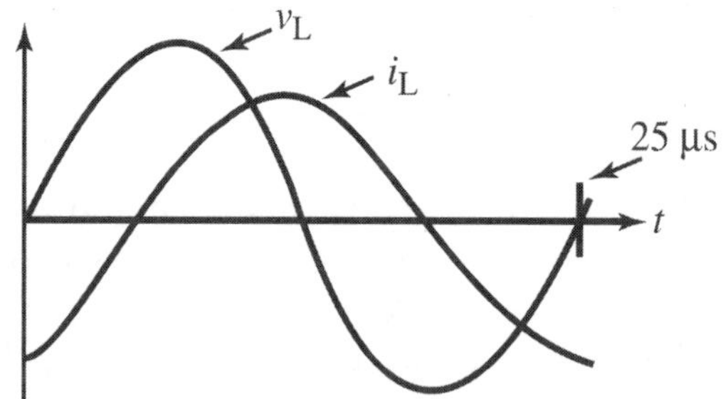

Shift does not change as *f* is varied. Current lags voltage by 90° always.

c. The inductor will behave approximately as an ideal inductor provided $X_L >> R$ where $R = R_l + R_g$. Check the approximation at 40 kHz. Use the measured R_t and L determined in Test 1(a).

$X_L = \omega L = 2\pi f L = 2\pi(40\text{ kHz})(2.40\text{ mH})$

$X_L = 603\ \Omega$

$R = 22\ \Omega$

$\therefore X_L >> R$ and the approximation is good.

Practical Notes

1. For this lab, you need to measure voltages with frequencies up to 10 kHz, so ensure that your DMMs can handle this range. If they cannot, use VOMs (as most VOMs can), or if you do not have suitable meters, make measurements with the oscilloscope.
2. For this lab, you need to be able to set frequency quite accurately. However, the frequency dial on many signal generators is not accurately calibrated. If you have such a generator, use your oscilloscope to set frequency.

PART B: Magnitude Relationships for Inductance

2. a. Replace resistor R_S of Figure 15-3 with an accurately measured 100-Ω resistor.

$R_S =$ 100.0 Ω

The results here depend on the inductor used and your values may be different from these.

b. Set the signal generator to a 10-kHz sine wave, 6 V peak to peak. Measure voltage V_L across the inductor and voltage V_S across R_S. Calculate current I_L using Ohm's law and the measured value of V_S.

$V_L =$ 1.73 $\quad V_S =$ 1.15 $\quad I_L =$ 11.5 mA

These are actual measurements taken with a DMM whose frequency range was over 20 kHz.

c. Calculate the reactance of the inductor using the measured V_L and I_L.

$X_{L(measured)} = V_L/I_L =$ 1.73V/11.5 mA = 150Ω

d. If possible, measure L using a bridge or RLC meter. (Otherwise, use the nominal value.) Compute X_L using Equation 15-4. Compare to the measured value of Test 2(c).

$L =$ 2.40 mH $X_{L(computed)} =$ (2π)(10kHz) (2.40 mH) = 150.8 Ω

Excellent agreement (≈ 0.5% error)

3. a. Add the second inductor in series and determine total reactance using the same procedure that you used in Test 2(b) and (c).

$V_L =$ 1.97 V $V_S =$ 0.66 V

$I_L =$ 6.6 mA $X_{T(measured)} =$ 299 Ω

b. If possible, measure L for the second inductor and compute L_T for the series combination. $L_T =$ 4.8 mH. Now use Equation 15-4 to determine $X_{T(computed)}$. $X_{T(computed)} =$ 301.6 Ω. Compare to the measured value of 3(a).

Calculated: 301.6 Ω — Measured 299 Ω
Excellent agreement. (About 0.9% error)

4. a. Connect both inductors in parallel and determine their equivalent reactance using the procedure that you used in Test 2(b) and (c).

V_L = 1.25 V V_S = 1.66 V

I_L = 16.6 mA $X_{eq(measured)}$ = 75.3 Ω

b. Compute L_{eq} for the parallel combination. L_{eq} = 1.20 mH.

Now use Equation 15-4 to determine $X_{eq(computed)}$. $X_{eq(computed)}$ = 75.4 Ω. Compare to the measured value of 4(a).

Measured: 75.3 Ω — Computed: 75.4 Ω
Excellent agreement

PART C: Variation of Reactance with Frequency

5. a. Using one of the 2.4-mH inductors, measure V_L and V_S and compute reactance (using the procedure of Test 2) at each of the frequencies listed in Table 15-2. Record as $X_{L(measured)}$.
   b. Using Equation 15-4, compute reactance at each frequency and record as $X_{L(computed)}$.
   c. Using the graph sheet of Figure 15-4, plot measured and computed reactances versus frequency. Label each plot.
   d. The plots should pass through X_L = 0 Ω at f = 0 Hz. Do they? (Extrapolate both plots to find out.)
   e. Analyze the results. That is, comment on how well the measured values agree with the computed values. Is the agreement poorer as the frequency gets lower? If so, why?

d. The computed curve does. The measured doesn't because of the coil resistance.
e. The agreement is excellent at high frequency where $X_L >> R_\ell$. As frequency gets smaller, X_L decreases and the agreement becomes poorer.

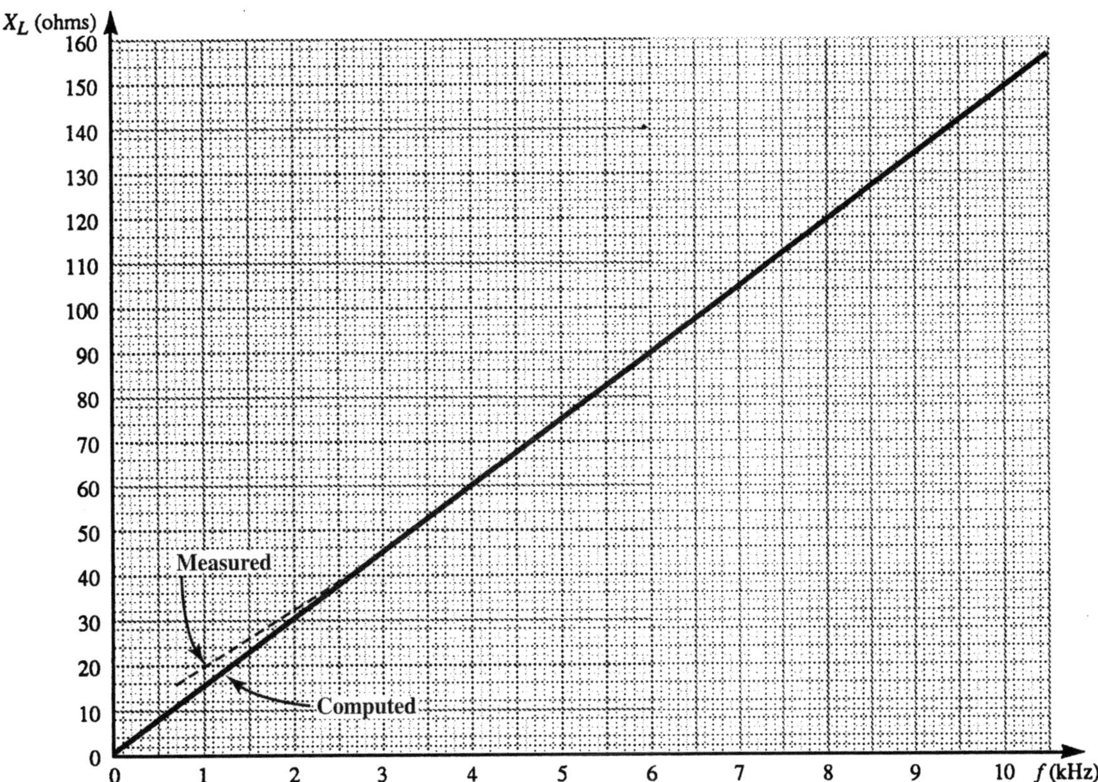

Figure 15-4 Plot of inductive reactance versus frequency

f(kHz)	V_L	V_S	I_L	$X_{L(measured)}$	$X_{L(computed)}$
1				19.4	14.9
2				32.5	29.8
3				45.8	44.7
4	I didn't tabulate as your results will be different.			59.8	59.6
5				75.3	74.5
6				89.8	89.3
7				102	104
8				117	119
9				135	134
10				149	149

↑

Table 15-2 These are my actual measured results. Yours should also be close to the theoretical value column.

PROBLEMS

6. Considering ideal inductors, if you double inductance and triple frequency, what happens to current if the applied sinusoidal voltage remains the same?

$$X_1 = 2\pi f_1 L_1$$
$$X_2 = 2\pi f_2 L_2$$
$$= 2\pi(3f_1)\ (2L_1)$$
$$= 2\pi(3)(2)f_1 L_1.$$
$$= 6(2\pi f_1 L_1) = 6X_{L_1}$$

Reactance increases by a factor of 6 $\therefore I_2 = \frac{1}{6} I_1$

FOR FURTHER INVESTIGATION AND DISCUSSION

Analysis Notes

1. Normally frequency plots are made with a log scale for frequency. However, we want to investigate the linearity of impedance versus frequency—thus, use a linear scale for both the horizontal and vertical axes of your plot.
2. MultiSIM users, see note on page 112.

How well do ideal inductors model real inductors? Investigate this question by comparing the impedance characteristic of an ideal inductor to the more realistic model depicted in Section 13.6, Figure 13-21(a) of the text. Assume a 2.4 mH inductor with resistance of 25 Ω and stray capacitance of 0.5 nF. To aid your discussion, do the following.

a. Using MultiSIM or PSpice, compute and plot the magnitude of the impedance (i.e., the reactance) of the ideal inductor from $f = 1$ Hz to 10 kHz.
b. Repeat using the model of Figure 13-21(a). Run 2 sets of plots, one from $f = 1$ Hz to $f = 10$ kHz, and the other from $f = 1$ Hz to $f = 4$ kHz (to better see the low frequency effects).

Write a short report discussing your findings.

For Further Investigation and Discussion

The reactance (magnitude of the impedance) of an ideal inductor is directly proportional to frequency—i.e., it is a straight line as indicated in Figure 16-28 of the text. (This means that an ideal inductor has an impedance of zero at $f = 0$ Hz.) However, a real inductor also has winding resistance and stray capacitance; thus, it will behave as an ideal inductor only over the frequency range where its resistance and capacitance are negligible—i.e., only over its mid-frequency range. To illustrate, consider the practical coil model of Figure 13-21 in the text. At dc, the coil's inductive component looks like a short circuit while its capacitive component looks like an open circuit. Thus, at dc, the coil looks like a resistor with an impedance equal to the coil's resistance. Now increase frequency. As frequency is increased, coil reactance increases and ultimately becomes large enough to swamp the resistive component. Since the stray capacitance is small, it will initially have a negligible effect. Over the frequency range where the coil resistance swamps the coil resistance but the stray capacitance has a negligible effect, the coil looks purely inductive. However, as frequency is increased, capacitive reactance decreases and ultimately becomes low enough to be felt. Because this reactance is in parallel with the inductance, the impedance of the coil starts to decrease. If the frequency is run high enough, the stray capacitance effect will come to dominate and the coil will look capacitive and its impedance will decrease as frequency increases. (The frequency at which the impedance reaches its maximum is known as *parallel resonant frequency*. However, we will leave the topic of parallel resonance to a later lab.)

The MultiSIM and PSpice traces below confirm the above analysis. As indicated, at low frequency, the impedance approaches 25 Ω (the resistance of the coil). Although not shown (you need to run the analysis to a higher frequency), the graphs also curve at the high frequency end, and if the frequency is run high enough, impedance will decrease. (Try this.) Conclusion: A practical coil behaves like an ideal inductor only over its mid-frequency range.

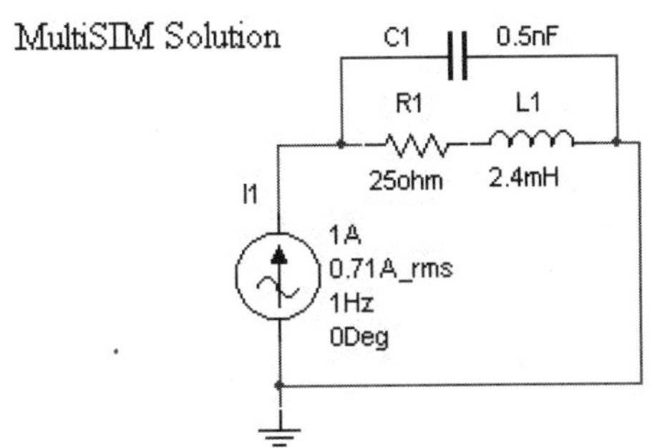

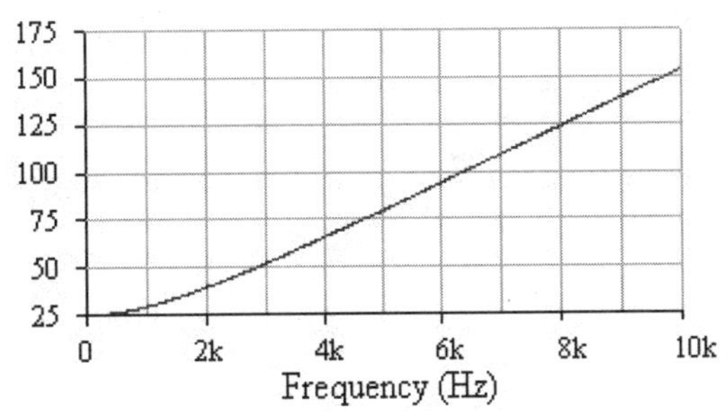

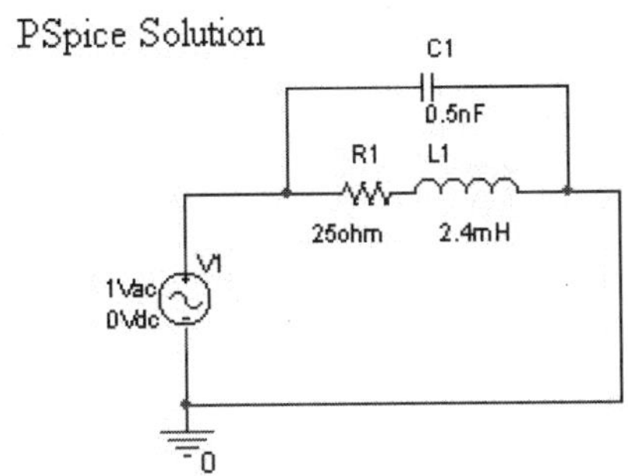

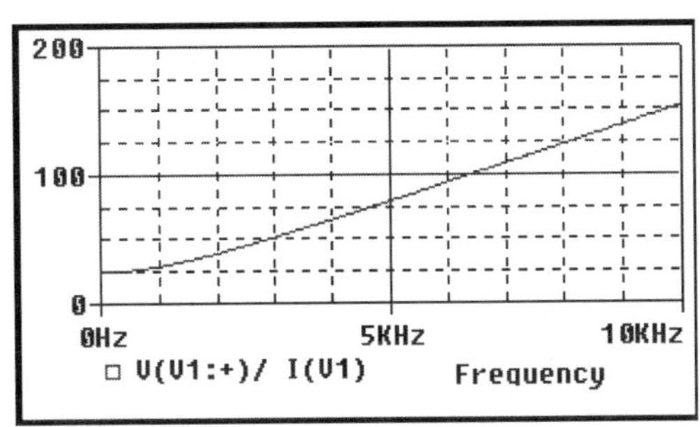

NAME ______________________

DATE ______________________

CLASS ______________________

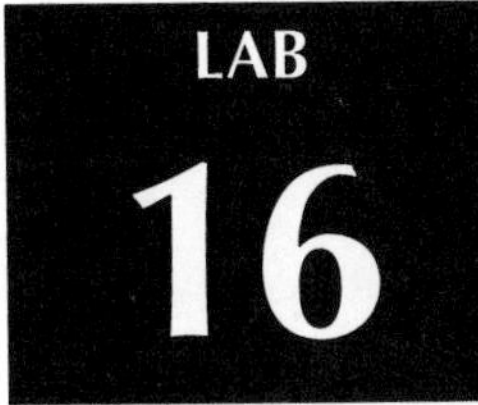

Power in ac Circuits

OBJECTIVES

After completing this lab, you will be able to

- measure power in a single phase circuit,
- verify power relationships,
- verify power factor relationships,
- determine the effect of adding power factor correction.

EQUIPMENT REQUIRED

- ☐ Single-phase wattmeter
- ☐ ac ammeter
- ☐ DMM

COMPONENTS

☐ Resistor:	100-Ω, rated 200-W
☐ Capacitor:	30-μF, non-electrolytic, rated for operation at 120-VAC (1 required)
☐ Inductor:	Approximately 0.2-H, rated to handle 2 amps

Safety Note

In this lab, you will be working with 120 VAC. This voltage is dangerous and you must be aware of and observe safety precautions. Familiarize yourself with your laboratory's safety features. **Ensure that power is off when you are assembling, changing, or otherwise working on your circuit.**

EQUIPMENT USED

Instrument	Manufacturer/Model No.	Serial No.
Single-phase wattmeter		
ac Ammeter		

Table 16-1

TEXT REFERENCE

Section 17.7 THE RELATIONSHIP BETWEEN P, Q AND S
Section 17.8 POWER FACTOR
Section 17.9 AC POWER MEASUREMENT

DISCUSSION

Power in ac Systems. Power to an ac load is given by

$$P = V I \cos \theta \tag{16-1}$$

where V and I are the magnitudes of the rms load voltage and current respectively, and θ is the angle between them. (θ is the angle of the load impedance.) The power factor of the load is

$$F_p = \cos \theta \tag{16-2}$$

Measuring Power in ac Circuits. Power is measured as in Figure 16-1(a) or (b) with the wattmeter connected so that current passes through its current coil CC and load voltage is applied to its voltage sensing circuit. For this lab, either connection will work.

Power Factor Correction. If a load such as that shown in Figure 16-1 has poor power factor (i.e., θ is large), it will draw excessive current relative to the power transferred to it from the source. One way to improve the power flow in the system is to add power factor correction at the load. Since most power system loads are inductive (because they contain inductive elements such as electric motors, lamp ballasts, and so on), this may be done by adding capacitors in parallel across the load. For loads with a poor power factor, this can dramatically reduce source current. It is important to note however that power factor correction does not change the power requirements of the load—it simply supplies the needed reactive power locally, rather than from the source. However, it greatly reduces source current.

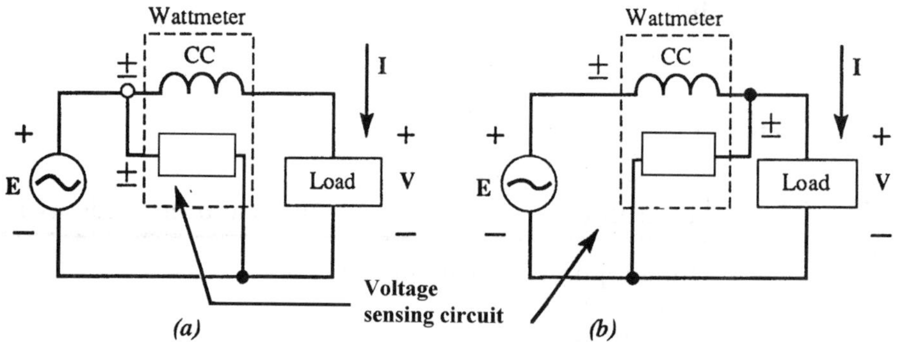

Figure 16-1 Measuring power in an ac circuit. We usually simplify the wattmeter representation as in Figure 16-2.

MEASUREMENTS

If possible, use a variable ac power supply (such as a variable autotransformer) as the source see box.

> **General Safety Notes**
>
> 1. With power off, assemble your circuit and double check it.
>
> 2. Have your instructor check the circuit before you energize it. If you are using a Powerstat or other variable ac source, gradually increase voltage from zero, watching the meters for signs of trouble.
>
> 3. Turn power off before changing your circuit for the next test.
>
> Check with your instructor for specific safety instructions.

PART A: Power in a Purely Resistive Circuit

1. Measure the 100-Ω resistor. $R =$ 100 . Connect the circuit as in Figure 16-2. (The ammeter may be a standard ac ammeter or the ac current range of a DMM. For the load resistance used here, a 2-A range is adequate. Select a wattmeter to match—e.g., a wattmeter with a 300-W scale.) Carefully measure load voltage, current and power and record in Table 16-2.
2. Using the values of V and R measured in Test 1, compute current, then determine power to the load using each of the formulas $P = VI$, $P = I^2R$ and $P = V^2/R$. Compare to the value measured with the wattmeter.

$I = \dfrac{120\text{V}}{100\Omega} = 1.2\text{ A}$

$P = VI = (120\text{V})(1.2\text{A}) = 144\text{ W}$

$P = I^2R = (1.2\text{A})^2\,(100\Omega) = 144\text{ W}$

$P = \dfrac{V^2}{R} = \dfrac{(120\text{V})^2}{100\Omega} = 144\text{ W}$

Should be about the same as measured.

PART B: Power to a Reactive Load

3. a. De-energize the circuit and add 30 μF of capacitance in parallel with the load as in Figure 16-3. Measure load voltage, current, and power and record in Table 16-3.

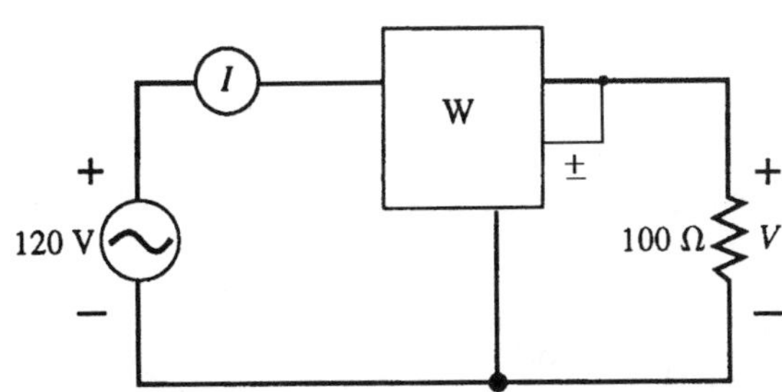

Figure 16-2 Purely resistive load. (The ± voltage connection may be internal to the wattmeter.)

Measured Values	
V	120 V
I	1.2 A
P	144 W

Table 16-2

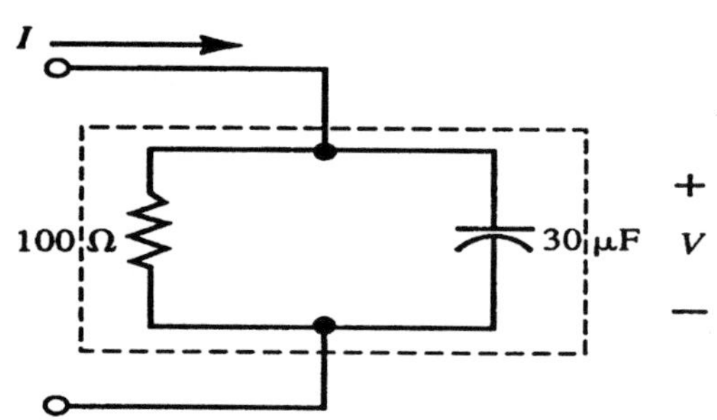

Figure 16-3 Leading power factor load

	Measured Values
V	120 V
I	1.81 A
P	144 W

Table 16-3

b. Calculate real power using the measured voltage and resistance and compare to the measured value.

$$P = \frac{(120\ \text{V})^2}{100\ \Omega} = 144\ \text{W}$$

$$V^2/X_C = \frac{(120\text{V})^2}{88.42} = 163\text{VAR}$$

c. Calculate reactive power Q

$$X_C = \frac{1}{(2\pi)(60\ \text{Hz})(30\ \mu\text{F})} = 88.42\Omega$$

$$Q = V^2/X_C = \frac{(120\text{V})^2}{88.42} = 163\text{VAR}$$

d. Draw the power triangle using the values computed in Tests 3(b) and 3(c). Using the apparent power S from this triangle, compute current. Calculate the percent difference between this and the value measured in Test 3(a). What is the likely source of difference?

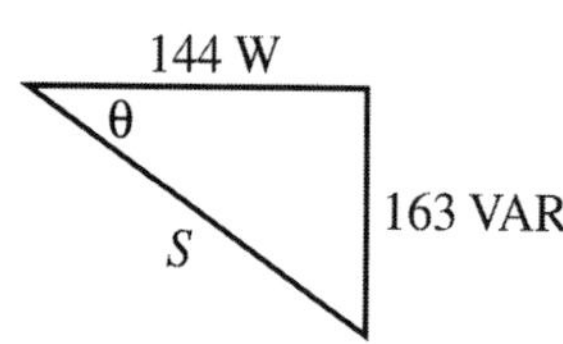

From the triangle, $S = 217$ VA

$$\therefore I = \frac{217\ \text{VA}}{120\ \text{V}} = 1.81\ \text{A}$$

e. Determine the power factor from the data of Table 16-3 and Equation 16-1.

$$\cos\theta = \frac{P}{VI} = \frac{144\text{W}}{(120\text{V})(1.81\text{A})} = 0.663$$

f. Determine the power factor from the power triangle of 3(d).

$$\cos\theta = \frac{P}{S} = \frac{144\text{ W}}{217\text{ VA}} = 0.664$$

g. Determine the load impedance **Z** from Figure 16-3, then calculate power factor using Equation 16-2.

$Z = 100\Omega \parallel (-j88.42) = 66.24\angle -48.5^\circ\ \Omega$

$F_p = \cos 48.5^\circ = 0.663$

h. Compare the values of power factor determined in Steps (e), (f), and (g)—i.e., comment on any differences and why they might have occurred.

They should be essentially the same.

These are the values I get. Yours may be quite different.

Measured Values	
V	120 V
I	1.59 A
P	15.2 W

Table 16-4

Note: Depending on the coil you use, your results may be considerably different.

PART C: Power Factor Correction

4. a. Replace the load with the 0.2-H coil, Figure 16-4(a). (Measure its resistance and inductance first.) Measure load voltage, current and power and record in Table 16-4.
   b. Add the 30 μF as in Figure 16-4(b) and observe the decrease in current. Using the techniques of Chapter 17, solve for source current and compare.

Measured current = 0.27 A

Measured coil parameters: $L = 0.2$ H; resistance = 6 Ω

$X_L = \omega L = (2\pi \times 60)(0.2) = 75.4\ \Omega$

$X_C = \frac{1}{\omega C} = 88.4\ \Omega$

$Z_p = 467\ \Omega\angle 60.8^\circ$

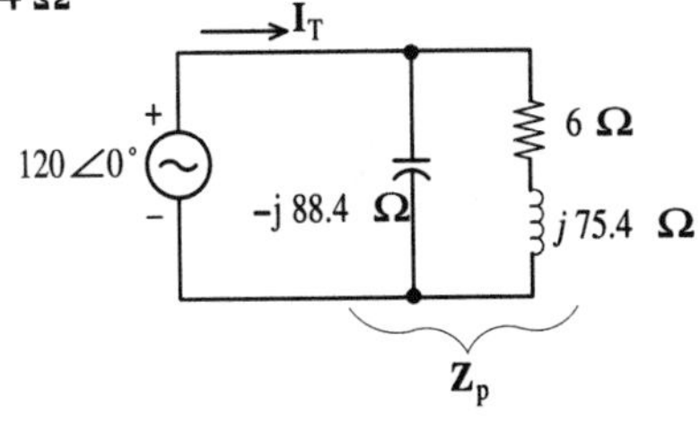

$$I_T = \frac{120\text{ V}}{467\Omega} = 0.26\text{ A}$$

The measured and computed currents agree quite well. Note the dramatic decrease in current from 1.59 A to 0.27 A achieved by power factor correction.

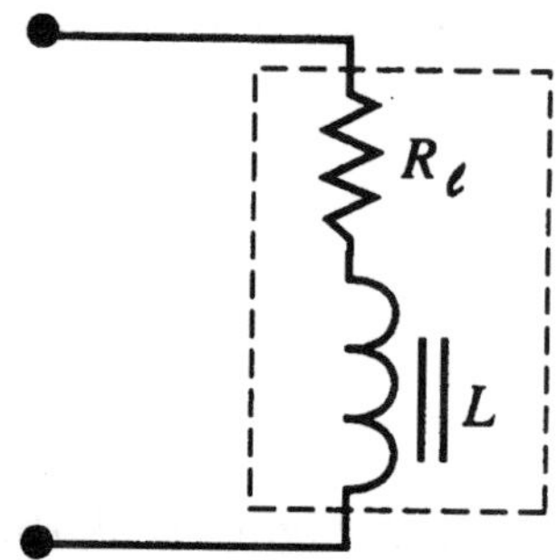

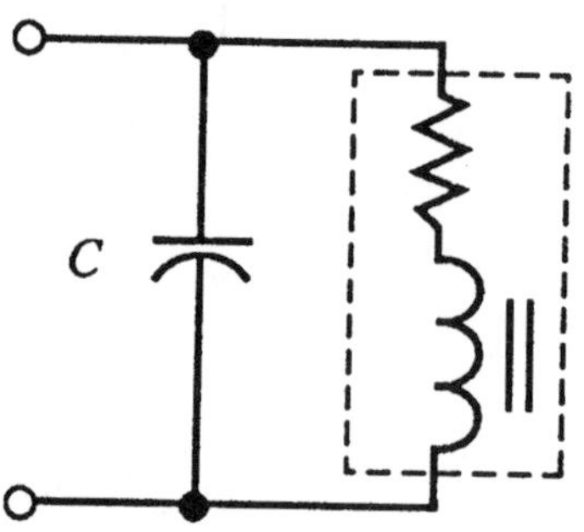

Figure 16-4 (a) Lagging power factor load (b) Power factor correction

COMPUTER ANALYSIS

Consider Figure 17-22 of the text. Using your calculator, convert the plant load to an equivalent resistance and inductance in series. Omitting the capacitor, set up the resulting circuit using either MultiSIM or PSpice.

a. Insert an ammeter (IPRINT if you are using PSPice) and configure for *ac* operation. Set the source frequency to 60Hz and determine the magnitude of the line current.
b. Add the capacitor across the load and again determine the magnitude of the line current.
c. Change the capacitor to the value that yields unity power factor (*see Practice Problem 4*) and again measure current.

How do the results compare to those in the text?

Answer to Computer Analysis on next page.

PROBLEMS

6. A motor delivers 50 hp to a load. The efficiency of the motor is 87% and its power factor is 69%. The source voltage is 277 V, 60 Hz.
   a. Determine the power input to the motor.
   b. Draw the power triangle for the motor.
   c. Determine the source current.
   d. Determine how much capacitance is required to correct the power factor to unity.
   e. What is the source current when the capacitance of (c) is added?
   f. If 50% more capacitance than computed in (c) is added, determine the source current.

Answers to Problems on next page

Computer Analysis

From Example 17-8 of the text, $\mathbf{S}_{plant} = 146$ kW + $j132$ kVAR and $I_{plant} = 328$ A. We want the equivalent $R + jX_L$ of the plant. Noting that $\mathbf{S}_{plant} = P_{plant} + jQ_{plant}$, we see that 146 kW + $j132$ kVAR = (328 A)$^2(R + jX_L)$. Solving yields $R = 1.36\ \Omega$ and $X_L = 1.23\ \Omega$. From this, we obtain $L = 3.25$ mH. The diagrams below show the MultiSIM solution. As you can see, the currents agree with the values computed in Example 17-8. Furthermore, when the capacitor is changed to 973 μF, current drops to 243 A as determined in Practice Problem 4.

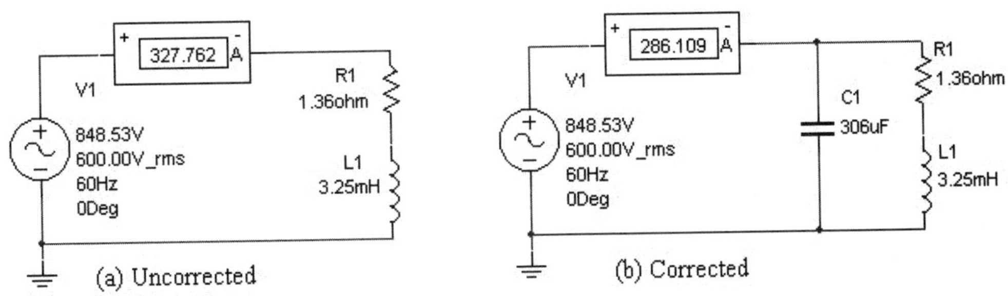

The PSpice solution (see below) is similar to the MultiSIM solution. Use source VAC and configure IPRINT as detailed on page 563 of the text. Answers are found by opening the Output File and scrolling to near the end of the file. To solve for the uncorrected power factor case, delete the capacitor. All answers agree with the solutions in the text.

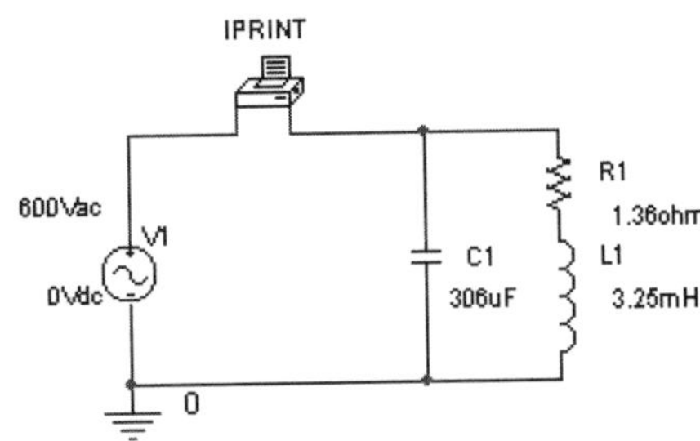

Problem

a) $P_{in} = \frac{P_{out}}{\eta} = \frac{(50\text{ hp})(746)}{0.87} = P_m$

$\therefore\ P_m = 42.87\text{kW}$

b)

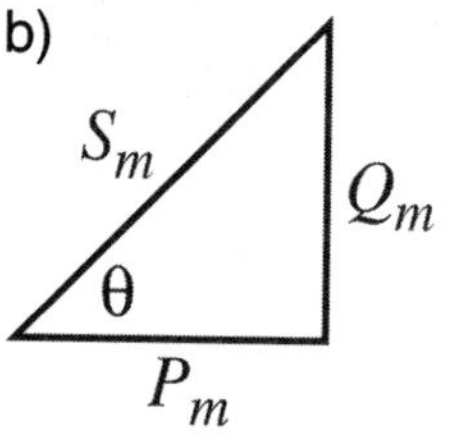

S_m Q_m θ P_m

$\theta = \cos^{-1}(0.69)$
$= 46.4°$
$\therefore S_m = 62.14\text{kVA}$

c) $I = \frac{S_m}{V} = \frac{62.14\text{ kVA}}{277\text{ V}} = 224\text{ A}$

d) Need $Q_c = Q_m = 44.97\text{kVAR} = \frac{V^2}{X_c}$

$\therefore\ X_c = 1.706\Omega\ \therefore\ C = 1555\ \mu\text{F}$

e) $I = \frac{42.87\text{kVA}}{277\text{V}} = 155\text{ A}$

f)

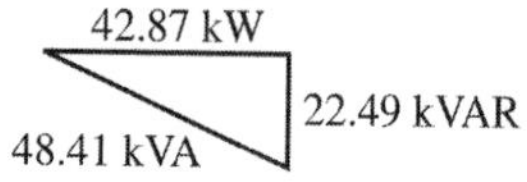

42.87 kW
22.49 kVAR
48.41 kVA

$I = \frac{48.41\text{kVA}}{277\text{V}}$
$= 175\text{ A}$

Note that the current has gone back up from (e) since we added too much capacitance.

NAME ______________________

DATE ______________________

CLASS ______________________

LAB 17

Series ac Circuits

OBJECTIVES

After completing this lab, you will be able to

- calculate current and voltages for a simple series ac circuit,
- measure voltage magnitude and phase angle in a simple series ac circuit,
- verify Kirchhoff's voltage law using measured results,
- measure the internal impedance of a sinusoidal voltage source.

EQUIPMENT REQUIRED

☐ Dual-trace oscilloscope
☐ Signal generator (sinusoidal function generator)
Note: Record this equipment in Table 17-1.

COMPONENTS

☐ Resistors: 680-Ω (1/4-W carbon, 5% tolerance)
☐ Capacitors: 0.22-μF (10% tolerance)

EQUIPMENT USED

Instrument	Manufacturer/Model No.	Serial No.
Oscilloscope		
Signal Generator		

Table 17-1

TEXT REFERENCE

Section 18.1 OHM'S LAW FOR ac CIRCUITS
Section 18.2 AC SERIES CIRCUITS
Section 18.3 KIRCHHOFF'S VOLTAGE LAW & THE VOLTAGE DIVIDER RULE

DISCUSSION

Series ac circuits behave in a manner similar to the operation of dc circuits. Ohm's law, Kirchhoff's current and voltage laws and the various circuit analysis rules apply for ac circuits as well as for dc circuits. The principle differences in these rules and laws apply to ac circuits are outlined as follows:

- All impedances are complex numbers and may be expressed either in rectangular form or polar form (e.g. $\mathbf{Z} = 10\ \Omega + j20\ \Omega = 22.36\ \Omega\angle 63.43^\circ$). The real component of the impedance vector represents the resistance while the imaginary component corresponds to the reactance. The imaginary component of the impedance will be positive if the reactance is inductive and negative if the reactance is capacitive.
- *Time-domain values* such as $v_C = 2 \sin(\omega t + 30^\circ)$ are converted into *phasor domain* ($\mathbf{V}_C = 1.414\ \mathrm{V}\angle 30^\circ$) to permit arithmetic operations using complex numbers.
- Although time domain values are always expressed using peak values, phasor voltages and currents are always expressed with magnitudes in rms (root-mean-square).
- Power calculations are performed using rms values and must consider the *power factor* of the circuit or component.

CALCULATIONS

1. Refer to the circuit of Figure 17-1. Determine the reactance of the capacitor at a frequency of $f = 2$ kHz. Express the circuit impedance $\mathbf{Z}_T$ in both the rectangular form and the polar form.

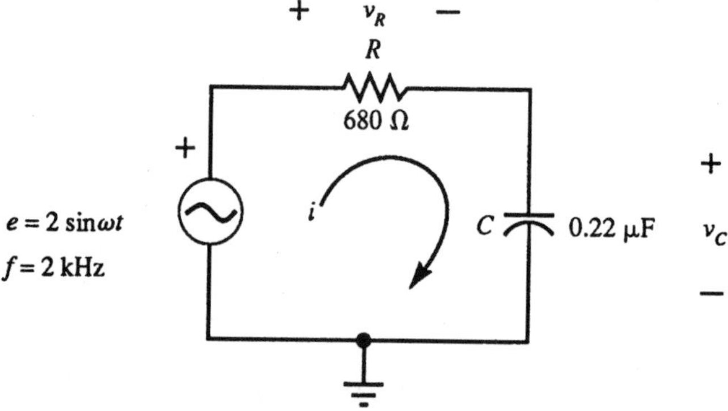

Figure 17-1 Series ac circuit

X_C	361.7 Ω
Z_T	680 Ω – j 361.7 Ω
	770 Ω ∠–28.01°

2. Convert the time domain form of the voltage source of the circuit of Figure 17-1 into its equivalent phasor domain form. Calculate the phasor current **I** and solve for the phasor voltages $\mathbf{V}_R$ and $\mathbf{V}_C$. Enter your results in Table 17-2.

E	1.414 V ∠0°
I	1.84 mA ∠28.01°
$\mathbf{V}_R$	1.25 V ∠28.01°
$\mathbf{V}_C$	0.664 V ∠–61.99°

Table 17-2

3. Use complex algebra together with the phasor forms of the voltages (**E**, $\mathbf{V}_R$ and $\mathbf{V}_C$) to verify that Kirchhoff's voltage law applies.

$$\sum \mathbf{V} = 0 = \mathbf{E} - \mathbf{V}_R - \mathbf{V}_C \qquad (17\text{-}1)$$

4. Convert the phasor forms of **I**, $\mathbf{V}_R$, and $\mathbf{V}_C$ into their equivalent time domain values. Enter the results in Table 17-3.

i	$2.60 \times 10^{-3}\sin(4000\pi t + 28^\circ)$
V_R	$1.77\sin(4000\pi t + 28^\circ)$
V_C	$0.939 \sin (4000\pi t - 62^\circ)$

Table 17-3

MEASUREMENTS

5. Assemble the circuit of Figure 17-1.
6. Refer to the pictorial diagram of Figure 17-2. Connect Ch1 of the oscilloscope to the output of the signal generator. Set the oscilloscope to have an automatic sweep and use Ch1 as the trigger source. Adjust the output of the generator to provide a sinusoidal voltage with an amplitude of 2.0 V ($4.0\ V_{p\text{-}p}$) and a frequency of $f = 2$ kHz ($T = 500\ \mu s$).
7. Use Ch2 of the oscilloscope to observe the signal across the capacitor $\mathbf{V}_C$. (You should still have the output of the signal generator displayed on Ch1.) Notice that the voltage across the capacitor is lagging the generator voltage. Adjust the time/division to provide at least one full cycle on the oscilloscope. Accurately sketch and label both the generator voltage e and the capacitor voltage v_C in the space provided on Graph 17-1. In the space below, record the volts/division setting for each channel and the time/division of the oscilloscope.

Ch1: 0.5 V/Div.

Ch2: 0.5 V/Div.

Time: 50 μs/Div.

8. Use the following expression to calculate the phase angle between capacitor voltage and the generator voltage. (The phase angle is negative since v_C lags e.)

$$\theta = \frac{\Delta t}{T} \times 360^\circ \qquad (17\text{-}2)$$

θ_1	-61.2°

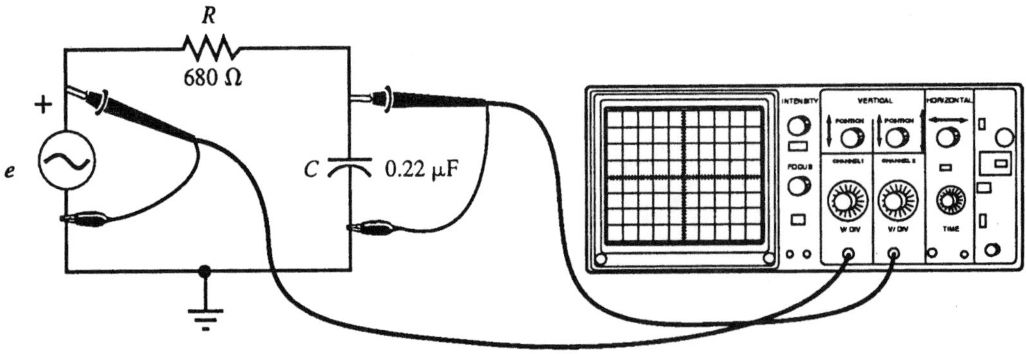

Figure 17-2 Equipment connection for voltage measurement

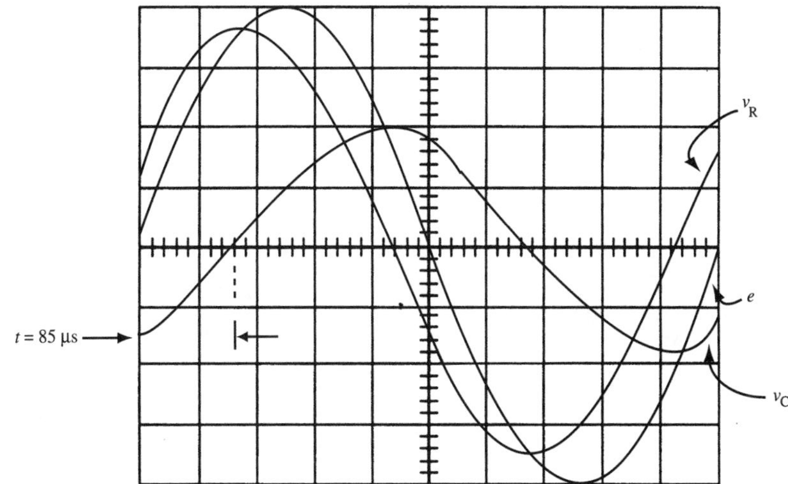

Graph 17-1

9. It is not possible to measure the voltage across the resistor directly since the internal ground connection in the probe of the oscilloscope will result in a short circuit across the capacitor. To overcome this problem, switch the oscilloscope to show the *difference mode* (Ch1 – Ch2), making certain that both Ch1 and Ch2 of the oscilloscope are on the same VOLTS/DIV setting. You should observe a single display, corresponding to the resistor voltage v_R. Since you are using the Ch1 signal as the trigger source, the observed waveform provides the phase shift between the signal generator and the resistor voltage. **Be careful not to adjust the horizontal position. If you accidently move the display, you will need to readjust the display to obtain the waveforms of Step** 7. You should observe that the resistor voltage is leading the generator voltage. Sketch and label the observed resistor voltage v_R as part of Graph 17-1.
10. Calculate the phase shift between the resistor voltage and the generator voltage. Since the resistor voltage is leading the generator voltage, the phase angle is positive.

θ_2	+28.8°

Internal Impedance of Voltage Sources

All signal generators have some internal impedance which tends to reduce the voltage between the terminals of the signal generator when the generator is under load. Most low-frequency signal generators have a nominal internal impedance of 600 Ω. Other signal generators may have impedance values of 50 Ω, 75 Ω or 300 Ω, depending on the application. Figure 17-3 shows a simple representation of the output of a signal generator.

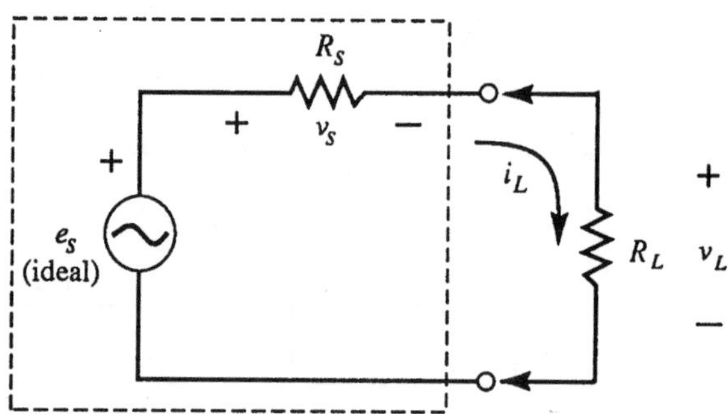

Figure 17-3 Internal impedance of a signal generator

11. Connect the oscilloscope between the output terminals of the signal generator. Adjust the generator to provide a sinusoidal output having an amplitude of 1 V (appearing as 2 $V_{\text{p-p}}$) and a frequency of 1 kHz. Since the signal generator is not loaded, this voltage represents the signal of the ideal voltage source $E_S = 2\ V_{\text{p-p}}$.
12. Connect a 680-Ω load resistor between the output terminals of the signal generator. Reconnect the oscilloscope between the output terminals of the signal generator. You should see that the voltage at the output has now decreased significantly. This represents the loaded output voltage. Measure and record the loaded peak-to-peak output voltage V_L.

V_L	1.06 $V_{\text{p-p}}$

CONCLUSIONS

13. Refer to Graph 17-1. Calculate the amplitude V_R of the resistor voltage and the amplitude V_C of the capacitor voltage. From Steps 8 and 10, evaluate the phase angle (with respect to the generator voltage e) for each of these voltages. Express each voltage in its time domain form [e.g. $v_c = V_c \sin(\omega t + \theta_1)$]. Convert the amplitudes into rms quantities and express each voltage in its phasor form. Enter all results in Table 17-4.

Resistor		Capacitor	
V_R	θ	V_C	ρ
1.75V	28.8°	0.95V	–61.2°
$v_R = 1.75 \sin(4000\pi t + 28.8°)$		$v_C = 0.95 \sin(4000\pi t - 61.2°)$	
$\mathbf{V}_R = 1.24\text{ V} \angle 28.8°$		$\mathbf{V}_C = 0.67\text{ V} \angle -61.2°$	

Table 17-4

14. Compare the measured sinusoidal capacitor voltage v_C of Table 17-4 to the theoretical value of Table 17-2.

The values are quite close. (Variation is due to resolution of the oscilloscope.)

15. Compare the measured sinusoidal resistor voltage v_R of Table 17-4 to the theoretical value of Table 17-2.

The values are very close.

16. Calculate the actual signal generator resistance using Ohm's law and the measurement of Step 12.

R_S	603 Ω

$$R_s = \left(\frac{2\text{ V}_{p\text{-}p} - 1.06\text{ V}_{p\text{-}p}}{1.06\text{ V}_{p\text{-}p}}\right) 680\Omega = 603\ \Omega$$

FOR FURTHER INVESTIGATION AND DISCUSSION

Use MultiSIM or PSpice to simulate the circuit of Figure 17-1. Measure the amplitude and phase angles of $\mathbf{V}_R$ and $\mathbf{V}_C$. Compare these values to the actual observations. Explain any discrepancies

See next page for solutions to *Further Investigation and Discussion*

Further Investigation and Discussion

Resistor voltage:

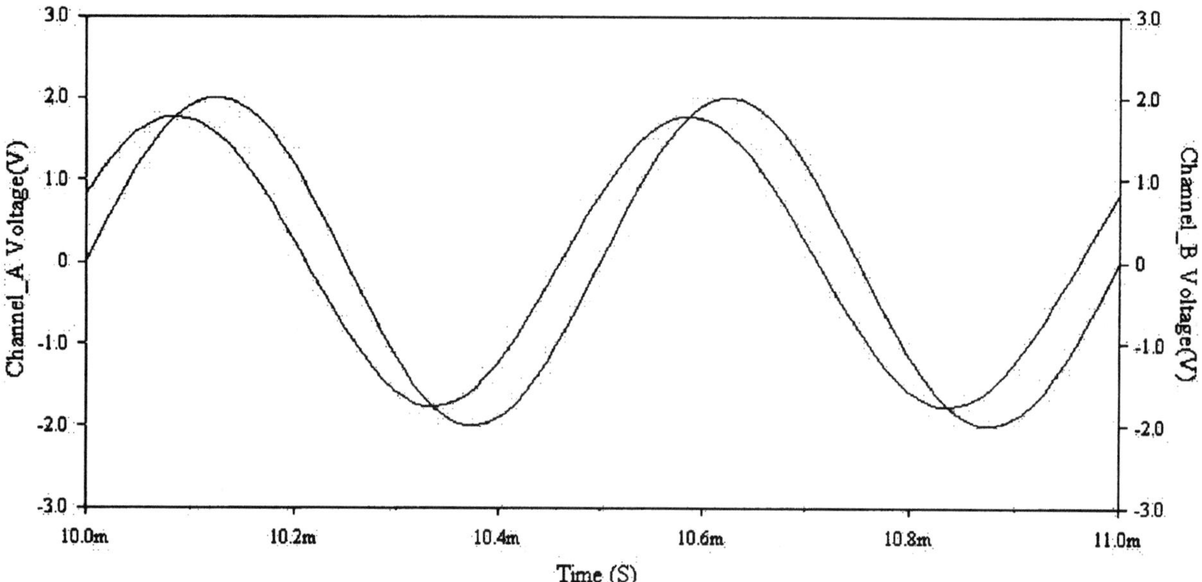

Capacitor voltage:

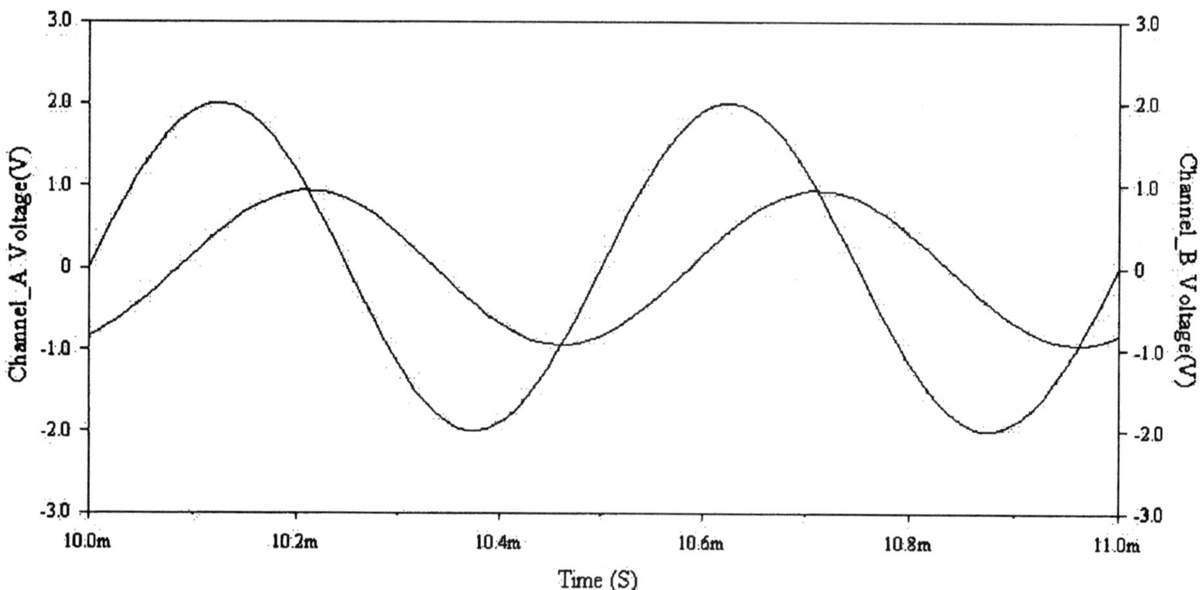

The simulation results are similar to actual measured results.

NAME ____________________

DATE ____________________

CLASS ____________________

LAB 18

Parallel ac Circuits

OBJECTIVES

After completing this lab, you will be able to

- measure voltages in a parallel circuit using an oscilloscope,
- use an oscilloscope to indirectly measure current magnitude and phase angles in a simple parallel ac circuit,
- compare measured values to theoretical calculations and verify Kirchhoff's current law,
- determine the power dissipated by a parallel ac circuit.

EQUIPMENT REQUIRED

☐ Dual-trace oscilloscope
☐ Signal generator (sinusoidal function generator)

Note: Record this equipment in Table 18-1.

COMPONENTS

☐ Resistors:	10-Ω (3), 470-Ω (1/4-W carbon, 5% tolerance)
☐ Capacitors:	3300-pF (10% tolerance)
☐ Inductors:	1-mH (iron core, 5% tolerance—Hammond 1534A or equivalent)

EQUIPMENT USED

Instrument	Manufacturer/Model No.	Serial No.
Oscilloscope		
Signal generator		

Table 18-1

TEXT REFERENCE

Section 18.4 AC PARALLEL CIRCUITS
Section 18-5 KIRCHHOFF'S CURRENT LAW & THE CURRENT DIVIDER RULE

DISCUSSION

The equivalent impedance of a parallel circuit is determined by finding the sum of the admittances of all branches. The important point to remember when calculating total admittance is that all admittances are expressed as complex values. This means that we must use complex algebra to find the solution, which is also a complex number.

Refer to the circuit of Figure 18-1. The equivalent admittance of the circuit is determined as

$$\mathbf{Y}_T = \frac{1}{R} + j\frac{1}{X_C} - j\frac{1}{X_L} \tag{18-1}$$

This gives an equivalent circuit impedance of

$$\mathbf{Z}_T = \frac{1}{\mathbf{Y}_T} = \frac{1}{\frac{1}{R} + j\frac{1}{X_C} - j\frac{1}{X_L}} \tag{18-2}$$

In order to further analyze the circuit, it is necessary to convert the ac voltage source into its equivalent phasor form. The circuit current **I** is then easily determined by applying Ohm's law. The current through each component in the circuit is similarly found by applying Ohm's law to each branch or by applying the current divider rule as follows:

$$\mathbf{I}_x = \frac{\mathbf{E}}{\mathbf{Z}_x} = \frac{\mathbf{Z}_T}{\mathbf{Z}_x}\mathbf{I} \tag{18-3}$$

Regardless of the method used to determine currents, Kirchhoff's current law must apply at any node in the circuit. Therefore,

$$\sum \mathbf{I} = 0 \tag{18-4}$$

where each current is in its phasor form.

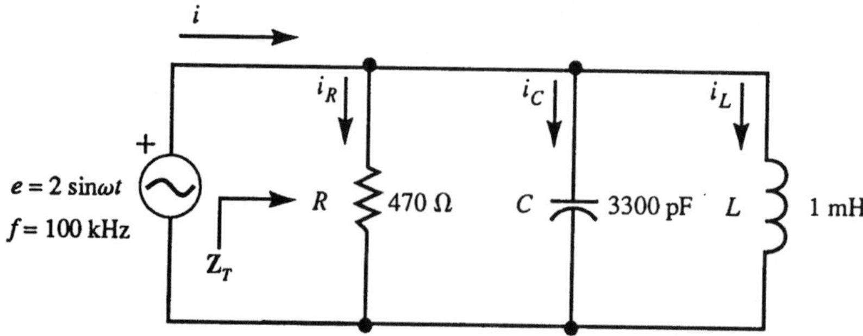

Figure 18-1 Parallel ac circuit

CALCULATIONS

1. Refer to the circuit of Figure 18-1. Determine the reactances of the capacitor and the inductor at a frequency of $f = 100$ kHz. Calculate the circuit impedance $\mathbf{Z}_T$ and express the result in both rectangular and polar form. Enter the data in Table 18-2.

X_C	482.29 Ω
X_L	628.32 Ω
$\mathbf{Z}_T$	458.4Ω ∠–12.76°
	447Ω – $_j$101Ω

Table 18-2

2. Convert the time domain form of the voltage source of the circuit of Figure 18-1 into its equivalent phasor domain form. Calculate the phasor current **I** and solve for the phasor currents $\mathbf{I}_R$, $\mathbf{I}_C$, and $\mathbf{I}_L$. Enter your results in Table 18-3.

E	1.414V ∠0°
I	3.08mA ∠12.76°
$\mathbf{I}_R$	3.01mA ∠0°
$\mathbf{I}_C$	2.93mA ∠90°
$\mathbf{I}_L$	2.25mA ∠–90°

Table 18-3

3. Use complex algebra together with the phasor currents $\mathbf{I}_R$, $\mathbf{I}_C$, and $\mathbf{I}_L$ to verify that Kirchhoff's current law applies at node *a*.

$$\mathbf{I} = \mathbf{I}_R + \mathbf{I}_C + \mathbf{I}_L \tag{18-5}$$

4. Convert the phasor currents **I**, $\mathbf{I}_R$, $\mathbf{I}_C$, and $\mathbf{I}_L$ into their equivalent time domain forms. Enter the results in Table 18-4.

i	$4.36 \times 10^{-3}\sin(\omega t + 12.76°)$
i_R	$4.26 \times 10^{-3}\sin(\omega t)$
i_C	$4.14 \times 10^{-3}\sin(\omega t + 90°)$
i_L	$3.18 \times 10^{-3}\sin(\omega t - 90°)$

$\omega = 200\text{k}\pi$ rad/s

Table 18-4

Current cannot be measured directly with an oscilloscope. However, by strategically placing small series *sensing resistors* into a circuit and then measuring voltage across these resistors, current through each branch is found by applying Ohm's law.

MEASUREMENTS

5. Assemble the circuit of Figure 18-2. Notice that three 10-Ω *sensing resistors* have been added into the circuit to help in determining branch currents. Since these resistors are small in comparison to the impedance in the branch, they will not significantly load the circuit and their effects may be ignored.
6. Connect Ch1 of the oscilloscope to the output of the signal generator at point *a*. Set the oscilloscope to have an automatic sweep and use Ch1 as the *trigger source*. Adjust the output of the generator to provide a sinusoidal voltage with an amplitude of 2.0 V ($4.0\ V_{p\text{-}p}$) and a frequency of $f = 100$ kHz ($T = 10\ \mu s$).
7. Use Ch2 of the oscilloscope to observe the voltage at point *b*. This is the voltage across sensing resistor R_1. Measure the observed peak-to-peak voltage V_1. Measure the phase angle θ_1 of the voltage V_1 with respect to the generator voltage. Record your results in Table 18-5.

   Since the observed waveform is across the 10-Ω resistor, the amplitude of the current *i* is now easily calculated from the peak-to-peak voltage as

$$I = \frac{V_1/2}{10\ \Omega} \tag{18-6}$$

   Write the time-domain expression for *i* using your measurements and calculations. Enter your results in Table 18-5.

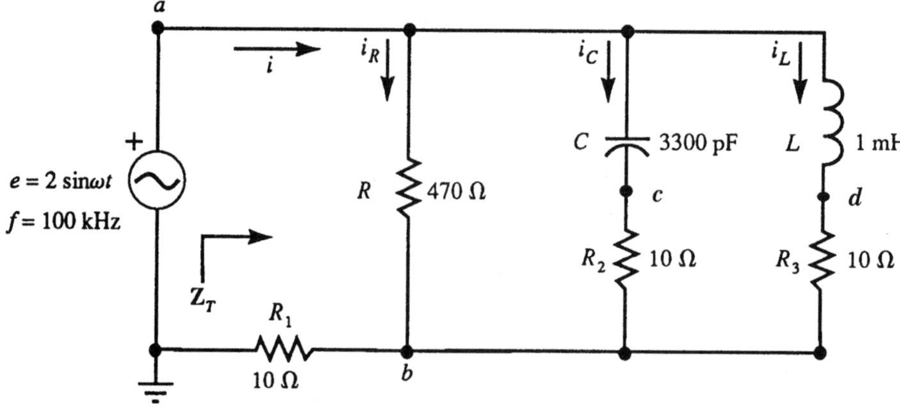

Figure 18-2 Using sensing resistors for current measurement

V_1	0.087	$V_{p\text{-}p}$
θ_1	14.4°	
i	$4.35 \times 10^{-3} \sin(\omega t + 14.4°)$	

Table 18-5

8. Since we no longer need R_1 in the circuit, it may be removed and replaced with a short circuit. Measure the peak-to-peak voltage V_R and calculate current i_R using Ohm's law. Use your measurements and calculations to record the time-domain expression for i_R in Table 18-6.

V_R	4.00	$V_{p\text{-}p}$
θ	0°	
i_R	$4.26 \times 10^{-3} \sin(\omega t)$	

Table 18-6

9. Ensure that Ch1 of the oscilloscope is connected to point a (generator voltage) and that the sensing resistor, R_1 is removed from the circuit.

   Connect Ch2 of the oscilloscope to point c to measure the voltage across the sensing resistor R_2. Record the peak-to-peak voltage V_2. Measure and record the phase angle between the generator voltage and the sensing voltage V_2. You should observe that the voltage V_2 (and hence, the current) is leading the generator voltage. Use your measurements and Ohm's law to determine the sinusoidal expression for i_c. Record the result in Table 18-7.

V_1	0.083	$V_{p\text{-}p}$
θ_2	90°	
i_C	$4.15 \times 10^{-3} \sin(\omega t + 90°)$	

Table 18-7

10. With Ch1 of the oscilloscope connected to point a, connect Ch2 of the oscilloscope to point c. Measure and record the peak-to-peak voltage across the sensing resistor R_3. Measure and record the phase angle between the generator voltage and the sensing voltage V_2. You should observe that the voltage V_3 (and hence, the current) is lagging the generator voltage. Use your measurements and Ohm's law to determine the sinusoidal expression for i_L. Record the result in Table 18-8.

V_3	0.064	$V_{p\text{-}p}$
θ_3	–90°	
i_L	$3.2 \times 10^{-3} \sin(\omega t - 90°)$	

Table 18-8

CONCLUSIONS

11. Compare the measured currents i, i_R, i_C, and i_L of Table 18-5 through Table 18-8 to the theoretical values of Table 18-4.

    The measured values correspond very closely to the theoretical values.

12. Convert each of the measured currents i, i_R, i_C, and i_L into its phasor form. Enter the results in Table 18-9.

$\mathbf{I}$	3.08 mA ∠ 14.4°
$\mathbf{I}_R$	3.01 mA ∠0°
$\mathbf{I}_C$	2.93 mA ∠90°
$\mathbf{I}_L$	2.26 mA ∠–90°

Table 18-9

13. Use complex algebra to show that the data of Table 18-9 verifies Kirchhoff's current law.

$$3.01\text{ mA} \angle 0° + 2.93\text{ mA} \angle 90° + 2.26\text{ mA} \angle -90° \stackrel{?}{=} 3.08\text{ mA} \angle 14.4°$$

$$3.08\text{ mA} \angle 12.5° \cong 3.08\text{ mA} \angle 14.4°$$

14. Use the measured currents $\mathbf{I}$, $\mathbf{I}_R$, $\mathbf{I}_C$, and $\mathbf{I}_L$ to calcultate the total power dissipated by the circuit in Figure 18-2. (You should observe that the sensing resistors dissipate very little power.)

P_T	4.49 mW

NAME ______________________

DATE ______________________

CLASS ______________________

LAB 19

Series-Parallel ac Circuits

OBJECTIVES

After completing this lab, you will be able to

- analyze a series-parallel circuit to determine the current through and voltage across each element in a series-parallel circuit,
- measure voltage across each element in a series-parallel circuit using an oscilloscope and use the measurements to determine the current through each element of a series-parallel circuit,
- calculate the power dissipated by each element in a circuit,
- use measurements to verify that the actual powers dissipated correspond to theory.

EQUIPMENT REQUIRED

☐ Dual trace oscilloscope
☐ Signal generator (sinusoidal function generator)

Note: Record this equipment in Table 19-1.

COMPONENTS

☐ Resistors: 10-Ω (2), 470-Ω (1/4-W carbon, 5% tolerance)
☐ Capacitors: 3300-pF (10% tolerance)
☐ Inductors: 1-mH (iron core, 5% tolerance)

EQUIPMENT USED

Instrument	Manufacturer/Model No.	Serial No.
Oscilloscope		
Signal generator		

Table 19-1

TEXT REFERENCE

Section 18-6 SERIES-PARALLEL CIRCUITS

DISCUSSION

The equivalent impedance of a series-parallel ac circuit is determined in a manner which is similar to that used in finding the equivalent resistance of a series-parallel circuit, with the exception that vector algebra is used in determining the total impedance at a given frequency. It is necessary to decide which elements or branches are in series and which are in parallel. The resultant impedance is the combination of the various connections. Once we have the total impedance, it is a simple matter to calculate the total current. By applying appropriate circuit theory, the current, voltage, and power of the various components of the circuit may then be found.

Refer to the circuit of Figure 19-1. Notice that resistor R and inductor L are in parallel. This parallel connection is then seen to be in series with capacitor C. The total impedance of the circuit is therefore determined as

$$\mathbf{Z}_T = -jX_C + R \parallel jX_L \qquad (19\text{-}1)$$

The power provided to the circuit by the voltage source is calculated as

$$P_T = EI\cos\theta = \frac{E^2}{Z_T}\cos\theta \qquad (19\text{-}2)$$

In the above expression, E and I are the rms values of the sinusoidal voltage e and current i. Z_T is the magnitude of the circuit impedance and is the angle between the current phasor $\mathbf{I} = \mathbf{I}_C$ and the

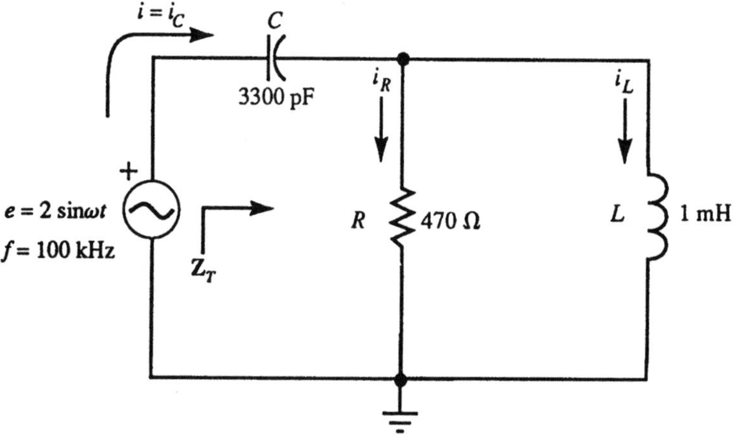

Figure 19-1 Series-parallel circuit

voltage phasor **E**. (This is the same angle as the angle in the impedance vector $\mathbf{Z}_T$.)

On further examination of Figure 19-1, we see that only the resistor can dissipate power. (Inductors and capacitors do not dissipate power.) This means that the total power in the circuit must also be the same as the power dissipated by the resistor, namely

$$P_R = \frac{V_R^2}{R} = I_R^2 R \tag{19-3}$$

where V_R and I_R are rms quantities.

CALCULATIONS

1. Refer to the circuit of Figure 19-1. Determine the reactances of the capacitor and the inductor at a frequency of f = 100 kHz. Calculate the circuit impedance $\mathbf{Z}_T$. Enter all values here.

X_C	482 Ω
X_L	628 Ω
$\mathbf{Z}_T$	396Ω ∠–40.44°

2. Convert the time-domain form of the voltage source into its equivalent phasor-domain form. Calculate the phasor current through each element of the circuit. Enter your results in Table 19-2.

E	1.414V ∠0
$\mathbf{I}_R$	2.86mA ∠77.24°
$\mathbf{I}_C$	3.57mA ∠40.44°
$\mathbf{I}_L$	2.14mA ∠–12.76°

Table 19-2

3. Calculate and record the total power provided to the circuit by the voltage source.

P_T	3.84 mW

4. Use complex algebra to show that currents $\mathbf{I}_R$, $\mathbf{I}_C$, and $\mathbf{I}_L$ satisfy Kirchhoff's current law

$$\sum \mathbf{I} = 0 \qquad (19\text{-}4)$$

$$2.86\text{mA} \angle 77.24^\circ + 2.14\text{mA} \angle -12.76^\circ = 3.57\text{mA} \angle 40.44^\circ$$

MEASUREMENTS

5. Assemble the circuit of Figure 19-2. Notice that two 10-Ω *sensing resistors* have been added to the circuit to help in determining branch currents. Since these resistors are small in comparison to the impedance in the branch, they will not significantly load the circuit.
6. Connect Ch1 of the oscilloscope to the output of the signal generator at point *a*. Set the oscilloscope to an automatic sweep and use Ch1 as the *trigger source*. Adjust the output of the generator to provide a sinusoidal voltage with an amplitude of 2.0 V (4.0 $V_{p\text{-}p}$) at a frequency of $f = 100$ kHz ($T = 10$ μs).
7. Use Ch2 of the oscilloscope to observe the voltage at point *c*. This is the voltage across sensing resistor R_1. Measure the peak-to-peak voltage V_1. Determine the phase angle θ_1 of voltage v_1 with respect to the generator voltage *e*. Write the time-domain expression for *i* using your measurements and calculations. Record your results in Table 19-3.

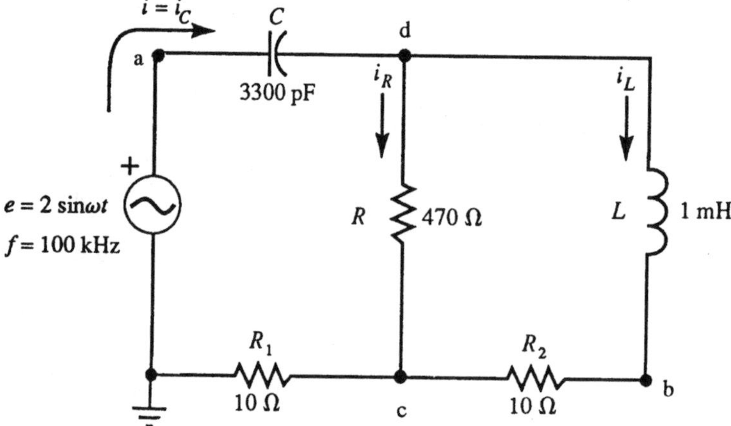

Figure 19-2 Using sensing resistors for current measurement

V_1	0.10	$V_{p\text{-}p}$
θ_1	39.6°	
$i = i_c$	$5 \times 10^{-3} \sin(\omega t + 39.6°)$	

$\omega = 200k\pi$ rad/s

Table 19-3

8. Remove resistor R_1 from the circuit and replace it with a short circuit. Move Ch2 of the oscilloscope to observe the voltage at point *d* (the voltage across resistor *R*). Measure the peak-to-peak voltage V_R and determine phase angle θ_R of voltage v_R with respect to the generator voltage *e*. Record your results in Table 19-4. Determine the amplitude i_R and enter the time-domain expression for i_R in Table 19-4.

V_R	3.80	$V_{p\text{-}p}$
θ_R	75.6°	
i_R	$4.04 \times 10^{-3} \sin(\omega t + 75.6°)$	

Table 19-4

9. With Ch1 of the oscilloscope connected to point *a*, connect Ch2 of the oscilloscope to point *b*. Measure and record the peak-to-peak voltage across the sensing resistor R_2. Measure and record the phase angle between the generator voltage and the sensing voltage V_2. Use your measurements and Ohm's law to determine the sinusoidal expression for i_L. Record the result in Table 19-5.

V_2	0.06	$V_{p\text{-}p}$
θ_2	−10.8°	
i_L	$3.00 \times 10^{-3} \sin(\omega t - 10.8°)$	

Table 19-5

CONCLUSIONS

10. Convert the measured currents i_R, i_C, and i_L of Table 19-3 through Table 19-5 into their phasor forms. Enter your results in Table 19-6 and compare them with the theoretical values of Table 19-2.

$\mathbf{I} = \mathbf{I}_C$	3.54mA $\angle 39.6^\circ$
$\mathbf{I}_R$	2.86mA $\angle 75.6^\circ$
$\mathbf{I}_L$	2.12mA $\angle -10.8^\circ$

Table 19-6

Measured values are close to theoretical values. (Variation due to 'scope resolution)

11. Use complex algebra to verify that the data of Table 19-6 satisfy Kirchhoff's current law.

$$2.86\text{mA} \angle 75.6^\circ + 2.12\text{mA} \angle -10.8^\circ \stackrel{?}{=} 3.54\text{ mA} \angle 39.6^\circ$$

$$3.67\text{ mA} \angle 40.3^\circ \cong 3.54\text{ mA} \angle 39.6^\circ$$

12. Use the phasors **E** and **I** to calculate the total power delivered to the circuit by the voltage source. Enter your calculation in the space provided.

P_T	5.05 mW

13. Now use the rms values of V_R and I_R to determine the power dissipated by the resistor. Enter the result in the space below. How does this value compare with the total power delivered to the circuit by the voltage source? Offer an explanation for any variation.

P_R	3.84 mW

The variation (3.84 mW vs. 5.05 mW) is due to the sensing resistors.

PROBLEMS

See next page for answers to *Problems*

14. Refer to the circuit of Figure 19-1. If the frequency of the signal generator is increased to 200 kHz, determine the following:
    a. Total impedance $\mathbf{Z}_T$,
    b. Currents $\mathbf{I}$, $\mathbf{I}_R$, and $\mathbf{I}_L$,
    c. Power P_R dissipated by the resistor,
    d. Power P_T deliverd by the voltage source.
15. Repeat Problem 14 if the frequency of the generator is decreased to 50 kHz.

14. a) $X_C = 241.14\ \Omega$ $X_L = 1256.64\ \Omega$

$$\mathbf{Z}_T = -j241.14\Omega + (j1256.64\Omega\ //\ 470\Omega)$$
$$= 421.4\ \Omega\ \angle -11.90^\circ$$

b) $$\mathbf{I}_T = \frac{1.414V\ \angle 0^\circ}{421.4\Omega\ \angle -11.90^\circ} = 3.36mA\ \angle 11.90^\circ = \mathbf{I}_C$$

$$\mathbf{I}_R = 3.14\ mA\ \angle 32.41^\circ$$
$$\mathbf{I}_L = 1.18\ mA\ \angle -57.59^\circ$$

c) $P_R = (3.14mA)^2\ (470\Omega) = 4.63mW$

d) $P_T = (1.414V)\ (3.36mA)\ \cos(11.90^\circ) = 4.65mW$

15. a) $X_C = 964.6\Omega$ $X_L = 314.2\Omega$

$$\mathbf{Z}_T = 761.4\ \Omega\ \angle -79.01^\circ$$

b) $\mathbf{I}_T = 1.86mA\ \angle 79.01^\circ = \mathbf{I}_C$

$$\mathbf{I}_R = 1.03mA\ \angle 135.25^\circ$$
$$\mathbf{I}_L = 1.54mA\ \angle 45.25^\circ$$

c) $P_R = 499\ \mu W$

d) $P_T = 501\ \mu W$

NAME ______________________

DATE ______________________

CLASS ______________________

LAB 20

Thévenin's and Norton's Theorems (ac)

OBJECTIVES

After completing this lab, you will be able to

- calculate the Thévenin and Norton equivalents of an ac circuit,
- measure the Thévenin (open circuit) voltage and the Norton (short circuit) current of an ac circuit,
- calculate the Thévenin impedance of a circuit using the measured values of Thévenin voltage and Norton current,
- measure the load impedance which results in a maximum transfer of power to the load.

EQUIPMENT REQUIRED

☐ Dual trace oscilloscope
☐ Signal generator (sinusoidal function generator)
☐ DMM
Note: Record this equipment in Table 20-1.

COMPONENTS

☐ Resistors:	10-Ω, 1.5-kΩ (1/4-W carbon, 5% tolerance)
	5-kΩ variable resistor
☐ Capacitors:	2200-pF (10% tolerance)
☐ Inductors:	2.4-mH (iron core, 5% tolerance)

EQUIPMENT USED

Instrument	Manufacturer/Model No.	Serial No.
Oscilloscope		
Signal generator		
DMM		

Table 20-1

TEXT REFERENCE

Section 20-3 THÉVENIN'S THEOREM—INDEPENDENT SOURCES
Section 20-4 NORTON'S THEOREM—INDEPENDENT SOURCES
Section 20-6 MAXIMUM POWER TRANSFER THEOREM

DISCUSSION

Thévenin's theorem allows us to convert any two-terminal linear bilateral circuit into an equivalent circuit consisting of a voltage source $\mathbf{E}_{\mathrm{Th}}$ in series with an impedance $\mathbf{Z}_{\mathrm{Th}}$ as illustrated in Figure 24-1(a). When a load is connected across the two terminals of the circuit, the current through (or voltage across) the load is easily calculated by analyzing the equivalent circuit. The Thévenin voltage of an equivalent circuit is determined by removing the load from the circuit and measuring the open circuit voltage.

Norton's theorem is the duality of Thévenin's theorem in that it converts any two-terminal linear bilateral circuit into an equivalent circuit consisting of a current source $\mathbf{I}_{\mathrm{N}}$ in parallel with an impedance $\mathbf{Z}_{\mathrm{N}}$ as shown in Figure 20-1(b). The Norton current of an equivalent circuit is determined by replacing the load with a short circuit and measuring the current through the load.

Unlike dc circuits, the Thévenin (and Norton) impedance of an ac circuit cannot be measured directly. Rather, the impedance is determined indirectly by using the equalence between the Thévenin and Norton circuits. Since the circuits are equivalent, the following relationship must apply:

$$\mathbf{Z}_{\mathrm{Th}} = \mathbf{Z}_{\mathrm{N}} = \frac{\mathbf{E}_{\mathrm{Th}}}{\mathbf{I}_{\mathrm{N}}} \qquad (20\text{-}1)$$

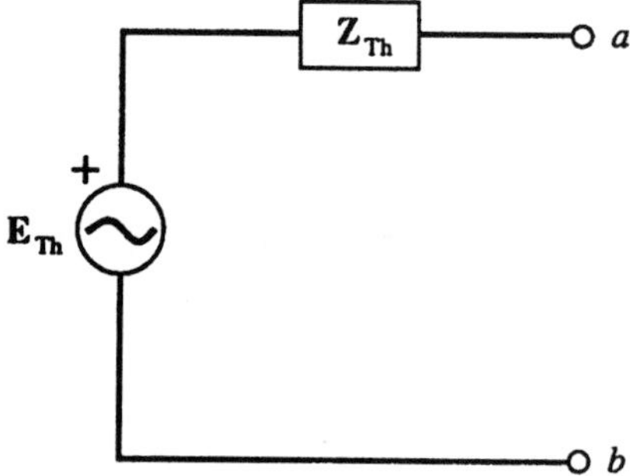

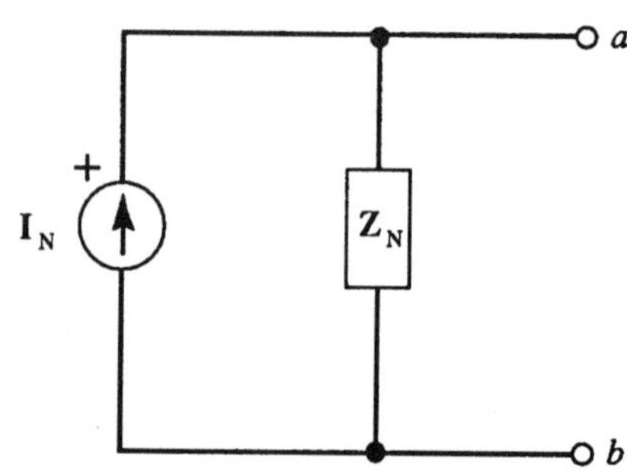

Figure 20-1 (a) Thévenin equivalent circuit (b) Norton equivalent circuit

CALCULATIONS

1. Refer to the circuit of Figure 20-2. Determine the reactances of the capacitor and the inductor at a frequency of $f = 100$ kHz. Enter the results here.

$$X_C = \frac{1}{2\pi fC} = 723.4\Omega$$

$$X_L = 2\pi f\,L = 1507.96\Omega$$

X_C	723 Ω
X_L	1508 Ω

2. Convert the time-domain form of the voltage source in Figure 20-2 into its equivalent phasor-domain form and enter the result here.

E	1.414V ∠0°

3. Determine the Thévenin equivalent circuit to the left of terminals a and b in the circuit of Figure 20-2. Sketch the equivalent circuit in this space.

$$\mathbf{Z}_{Th} = j1508\Omega \;//\; (1500\Omega - j723.4\Omega) = 1484\Omega \angle 36.64^\circ$$

$$\mathbf{E}_{Th} = \left(\frac{j1508}{1500 - j723 - j1508}\right) 1.414\text{V} \angle 0^\circ = 1.26\text{V} \angle 62.38^\circ$$

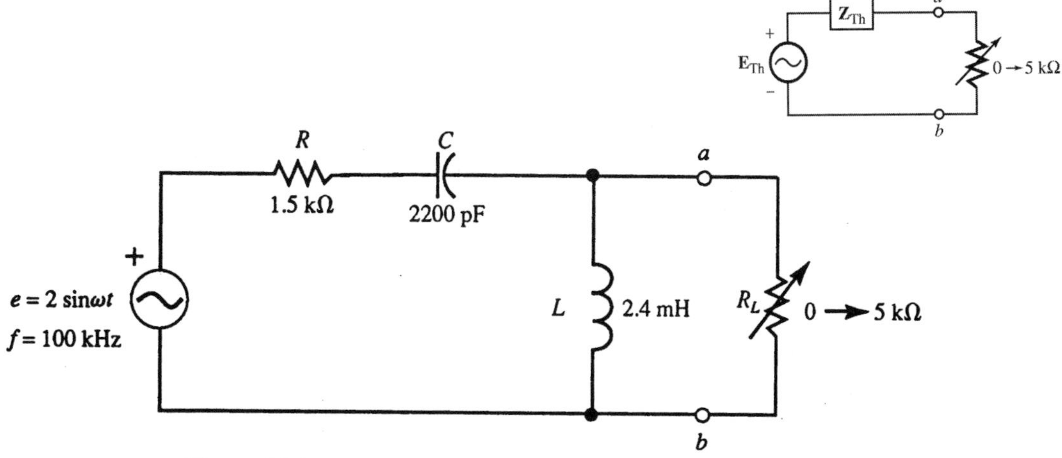

Figure 20-2

4. Determine the Norton equivalent circuit to the left of terminals *a* and *b* in the circuit of Figure 20-2. Sketch the equivalent circuit in this space.

$I_N = 0.85\text{ mA} \angle 25.74°$

$Z_N = Z_{TH}$

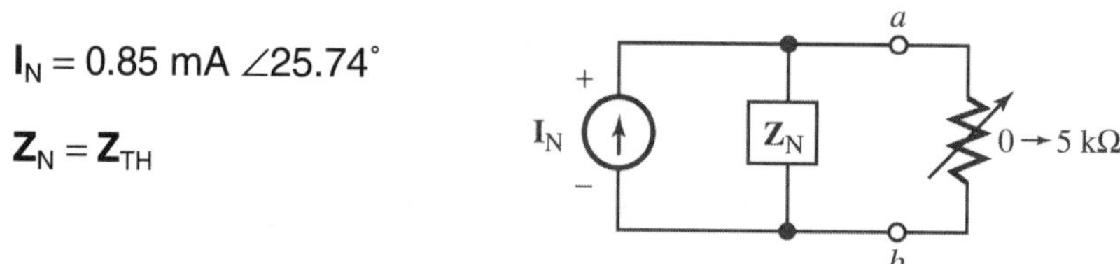

5. *Absolute maximum power* will be delivered to the load impedance when the load is the complex conjugate of the Thévenin (or Norton) impedance. For what value of load impedance $\mathbf{Z}_L$ will the circuit of Figure 20-2 transfer maximum power to the load? Solve for the absolute maximum load power.

$\mathbf{Z}_L$	1190Ω – j886Ω
P_{max}	333 μW

6. The load in the circuit of Figure 20-2 does not have any reactance. In this case, absolute maximum power cannot be transferred to the load. *Relative maximum power* will be transferred to the load impedance when the value of load resistance is equal to the following:

$$R = \sqrt{R_{Th}^2 + X_{Th}^2} \tag{20-2}$$

For what value of load resistance R_L will the circuit of Figure 20-2 transfer maximum power to the load? Solve for the relative maximum load power and enter the results in the space provided.

R_L	1484 Ω
P_{max}	297 μW

MEASUREMENTS

7. Assemble the circuit of Figure 20-2, temporarily omitting the load resistor R_L. Connect Ch1 of the oscilloscope to the output of the signal generator and adjust the generator to provide an output of 2.0 V_p (4.0 V_{p-p}) at $f = 100$ kHz.
8. While using Ch1 as the trigger source of the oscilloscope, connect Ch2 between terminals a and b of the circuit. Measure and record the peak-to-peak value of the open circuit voltage amplitude E_{Th} and the phase shift . (The phase shift is measured with respect to the generator voltage observed on Ch1.)

E_{Th}	3.56	V_{p-p}
P_{max}	61.2°	

9. Place a 10-Ω *sensing resistor* between terminals a and b. The sensing resistor has a very low impedance with respect to the other components in the circuit and so has a minimal loading effect. Readjust the generator voltage to ensure that the output is 2.0 V_p. Measure the peak-to-peak voltage across the sensing resistor and determine the peak-to-peak value of the "short circuit" current I_N and the phase shift θ.

V_{ab}	0.024	V_{p-p}
I_N	2.40	mA_{p-p}
θ	25.2°	

10. Use the DMM to adjust the 5-kΩ variable resistor for a resistance of 500 Ω. Remove the sensing resistor and insert the variable resistor between terminals a and b of the circuit. Adjust the supply voltage for 2.0 V_{p-p} and measure the amplitude of the output voltage, V_L. Enter your measurement in Table 20-2.
11. Remove R_L from the circuit and incrementally increase the resistance by 500 Ω. Repeat Step 10. Keep increasing the load resistance until $R_L = 5$ kΩ. Enter all data in Table 20-2.

R_L	V_L
500 Ω	0.93 V_{p-p}
1000 Ω	1.51
1500 Ω	1.89
2000 Ω	2.15
2500 Ω	2.35
3000 Ω	2.50
3500 Ω	2.61
4000 Ω	2.71
4500 Ω	2.78
5000 Ω	2.85 V_{p-p}

Table 20-2

CONCLUSIONS

12. Convert the measured voltage and phase angle for the Thévenin voltage of Step 8 into its correct phasor form. Record your result in the space provided below. How does this value compare to the theoretical value determined in Step 3?

$\mathbf{E}_{\text{Th}}$	1.26 V $\angle 61.2^\circ$

The value compares quite well. (Resolution of the oscilloscope.)

13. Convert the measured current and phase angle for the Norton current of Step 9 into its correct phasor form. Enter the result below. How does this value compare to the theoretical value determined in Step 4?

$\mathbf{I}_{\text{N}}$	0.849mA $\angle 25.2^\circ$

The value is quite close.

14. Use the phasors of Steps 12 and 13 to calculate the Thévenin

(and Norton) impedance. How does this value compare to the theoretical value determined in Steps 3 and 4?

$\mathbf{Z}_{Th} = \mathbf{Z}_N$	1.48 kΩ ∠36°

The value is very close.

15. Use the data of Table 20-2 to calculate the power delivered to the load for each of the resistor values. (Remember that you will need to convert each voltage measurement into its equivalent rms value in order to calculate the power.) Enter the results in Table 20-3.

R_L	P_L
500 Ω	218 μW
1000 Ω	284
1500 Ω	296
2000 Ω	290
2500 Ω	275
3000 Ω	260
3500 Ω	244
4000 Ω	229
4500 Ω	215
5000 Ω	203

Table 20-3

16. Use the data of Table 20-2 to sketch a graph of power (in microwatts) versus load resistance (in ohms). Connect the points with the best smooth continuous curve. (A correctly drawn curve will not be drawn from point to point.)
17. Use the curve of Graph 20-1 to determine the approximate value of load resistance R_L for which the load receives maximum power from the circuit. Enter the result here. How does this value compare to the value determined in Step 6?

R_L	1500 Ω

The result is very close.

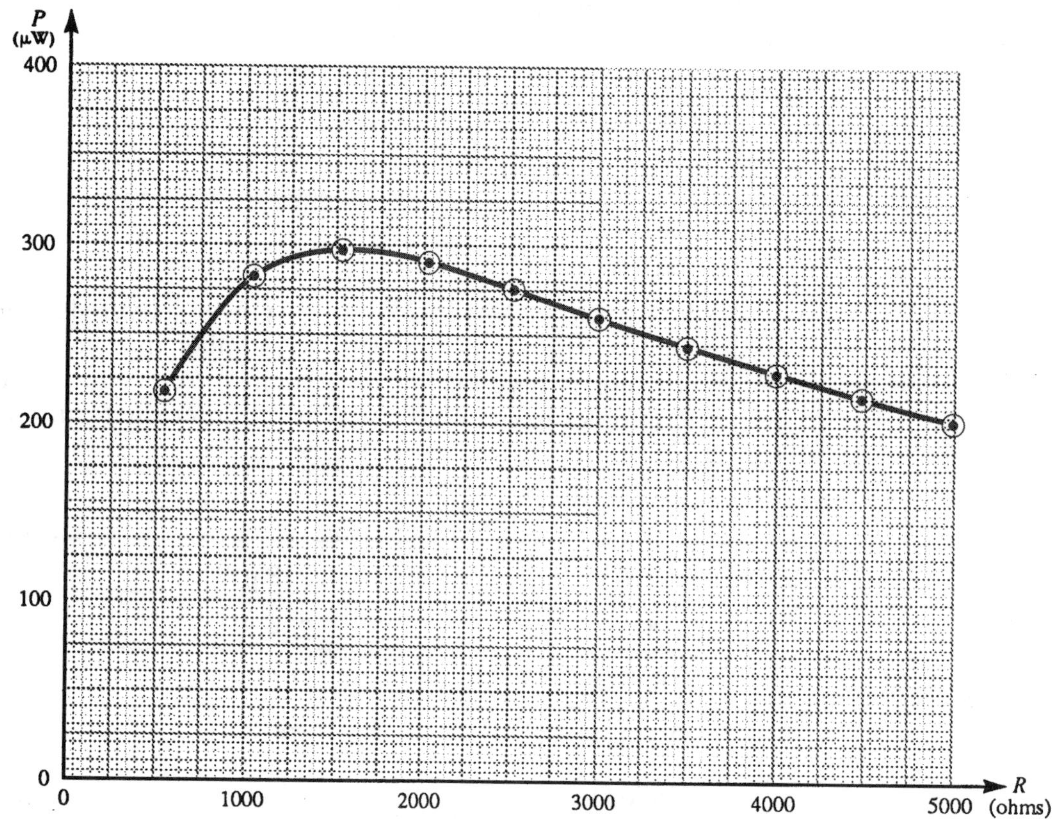

Graph 20-1

PROBLEMS

See next page for answers to *Problems*

18. If the circuit of Figure 20-2 ($f = 100$ kHz) is to provide absolute maximum power to the load, what value of capacitance (in μ or inductance (in mH) must be added in series with the load resistance?
19. Determine the Norton equivalent of the circuit to the left of points a and b in the circuit of Figure 20-2. Assume that the circuit operates at $f = 200$ kHz.
20. Refer to the circuit of Figure 20-2.
    a. Determine the Thévenin equivalent of the circuit to the left of points a and b, assuming that the circuit operates at a frequency of $f = 50$ kHz.
    b. Solve for the load impedance which will result in a maximum transfer of power to the load.
    c. Calculate the maximum power which can be transferred to the load.

18. $X_C = 886\ \Omega \quad C = \dfrac{1}{2\pi f X_C} = 1800\ \text{pF}$

19. $X_C = \dfrac{1}{2\pi\ (200\ \text{kHz})(2200\ \text{pF})} = 361.7\ \Omega$

$X_L = 2\pi\ (200\ \text{kHz})(2.4\ \text{mH}) = 3015.9\ \Omega$

$\mathbf{Z}_N = \text{j}3015.9\ \Omega\ //\ (1500\ \Omega - \text{j}361.7\ \Omega)$

$= 526\ \Omega\ \angle 15.92^\circ$

$\mathbf{I}_N = \dfrac{1.414\ \text{V}\ \angle 0^\circ}{1500\ \Omega - \text{j}361.7\ \Omega} = 0.917\ \text{mA}\ \angle 13.56^\circ$

20. a) $X_C = 1446.9\ \Omega \qquad X_L = 754.0\ \Omega$

$\mathbf{Z}_{TH} = 951.0\ \Omega\ \angle 70.83^\circ = 312.2\ \Omega + \text{j}898.3\ \Omega$

$\mathbf{E}_{TH} = 0.645\ \text{V}\ \angle 114.79^\circ$

b) For maximum power: $\mathbf{Z}_L = 951.0\ \Omega\ \angle{-70.83^\circ}$

c) At maximum power:

$\mathbf{I}_L = \dfrac{0.645\ \text{V}\ \angle 114.79^\circ}{951.0\ \Omega\ \angle 70.83^\circ + 951.0\ \Omega\ \angle{-70.83^\circ}}$

$= 1.03\ \text{mA}\ \angle 114.79^\circ$

$P_{max} = (1.03\ \text{mA})^2\ (312.3\ \Omega)$

$= 333\ \mu\text{W}$

NAME ______________________

DATE ______________________

CLASS ______________________

LAB 21

Series Resonance

OBJECTIVES

After completing this lab, you will be able to

- calculate the resonant frequency of a series resonant circuit,
- solve for the maximum output voltage of a resonant circuit using the *quality factor* Q of the circuit,
- measure the bandwidth of a series resonant circuit,
- measure the impedance at frequencies above and below the resonant frequency and observe that it is purely resistive only at resonance,
- sketch the circuit current as a function of frequency and explain why the response has a bell-shaped curve when plotted on a semi-logarithmic graph.

EQUIPMENT REQUIRED

- ☐ Dual trace oscilloscope
- ☐ Signal generator (sinusoidal function generator)
- ☐ DMM

Note: Record this equipment in Table 21-1.

COMPONENTS

- ☐ Resistors: 15-Ω (1/4-W carbon, 5% tolerance)
- ☐ Capacitors: 0.33-μF (10% tolerance)
- ☐ Inductors: 2.4-mH (iron core, 5% tolerance)

EQUIPMENT USED

Instrument	Manufacturer/Model No.	Serial No.
Oscilloscope		
Signal generator		
DMM		

Table 21-1

TEXT REFERENCE

DISCUSSION

Resonant circuits are used throughout electronics as a means of passing a range of frequencies, while rejecting all other frequencies. These circuits have important applications in communications where they are used in circuits such as receivers to tune into a particular station or channel. Figure 21-1 represents a typical series resonant circuit.

At the resonant frequency, the reactance of the inductor is exactly equal to the reactance of the capacitor. Since they are equal with opposite phase, the reactances cancel and the total impedance of the circuit is purely resistive at resonance. The resonant frequency (in hertz) of a series circuit is given as

$$f_S = \frac{1}{2\pi\sqrt{LC}} \tag{21-1}$$

At the resonant frequency, the current (and power) in the circuit is maximum, resulting in a maximum output voltage appearing across the inductor. Since the reactance of the inductor can be many times greater than the resistance of the circuit, the output voltage may be many times greater than the applied signal. This characteristic is one of the advantages of using a resonant circuit since the out-

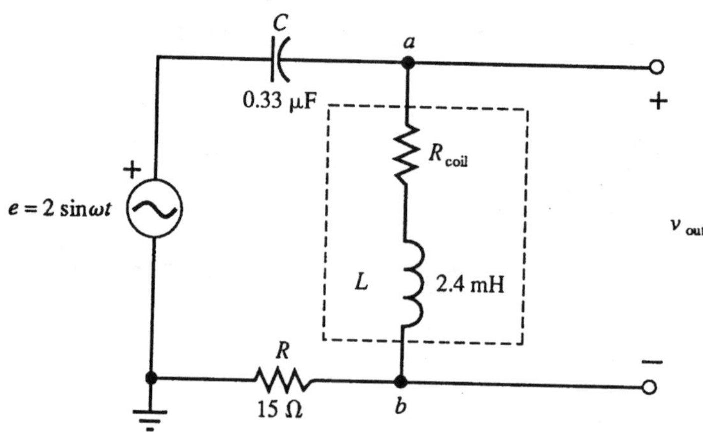

Figure 21-1 Series resonant circuit

put voltage is amplified without the need for *active components* such as transistors.

The *quality factor* Q of a resonant circuit is defined as the ratio of reactive power to the real power at the resonant frequency. It can be shown that the quality factor for the circuit of Figure 21-1 is determined as

$$Q = \frac{X_L}{R} = \frac{\omega L}{R_S + R_{coil}} \qquad (21\text{-}2)$$

The Q of a circuit is used to determine the range of frequencies which will be passed by a given resonant circuit. If the circuit has a high Q (greater than 10), it will pass a narrow range of frequencies and the circuit is said to have a *high selectivity*. Conversely, if the Q of the circuit is small, the circuit will pass a broader range of frequencies and the circuit is said to have a *low selectivity*. The *bandwidth (BW)* of a resonant circuit is defined as the difference between the the half-power frequencies, namely the frequencies at which the circuit dissipates half the power that would be dissipated at resonance. The bandwidth (in hertz) of a resonant circuit is determined as

$$BW = \frac{f_S}{Q} \qquad (21\text{-}3)$$

The half-power frequencies occur on either side of the resonant frequency. If the quality factor of the circuit is large (Q 10) then the half-power frequencies are given approximately as

$$f_1 \cong f_S - \frac{BW}{2} \qquad (21\text{-}4)$$

and

$$f_2 \cong f_S + \frac{BW}{2} \qquad (21\text{-}5)$$

CALCULATIONS

1. Determine the resonant frequency for the circuit of Figure 21-1.

f_S	5655 Hz

2. Prior to starting the lab, obtain an inductor from your lab instructor. Use the DMM ohmmeter to measure the dc resistance of the inductor. Enter the result below.

R_{coil}	12.3 Ω

3. Using the measured resistance of the inductor, calculate the phasor form of current **I** at resonance. Enter the result in the space provided below.

I	51.8mA $\angle 0^\circ$

4. Determine the phasor form of output voltage $\mathbf{V}_{out}$ appearing across the inductor. Enter the result below. You will need to consider the effect of R_{coil}.

$\mathbf{V}_{out}$	4.46V $\angle 81.79^\circ$

5. Calculate the quality factor Q, bandwidth BW, and approximate half-power frequenies f_1 and f_2 for the circuit. Record the results in the space provided.

Q	3.12
BW	1810 Hz
f_1	4750 Hz
f_2	6560 Hz

MEASUREMENTS

6. Assemble the circuit shown in Figure 21-1. Connect Ch1 of the oscilloscope to the output of the signal generator and adjust the generator to provide an amplitude of 2.0 V_p (4.0 $V_{p\text{-}p}$) at a frequency of f = 1 kHz.
7. Connect Ch2 of the oscilloscope across the resistor R and measure the amplitude of V_R. (In order to simplify this measurement, it is generally easier to measure the peak-to-peak voltage and then divide by two.) Use the measured voltage to calculate the amplitude of the current I. Enter the results in Table 21-2.
8. Increase the frequency of the signal generator to the frequencies indicated in Table 21-2. Due to loading effects, the amplitude of the generator will tend to drift. Ensure that the output of the signal generator is kept constant at 2.0 V_p. Measure the amplitude of V_R for each frequency and calculate the corresponding amplitude of current I. Enter the values in Table 21-2.

f	V_R	I
1 kHz	0.0641 V_p	4.27 mA_p
2 kHz	0.141 V_p	9.42 mA_p
3 kHz	0.253 V_p	16.9 mA_p
4 kHz	0.454 V_p	30.3 mA_p
4.5 kHz	0.626 V_p	41.7 mA_p
5 kHz	0.871 V_p	58.1 mA_p
5.5 kHz	1.08 V_p	72.2 mA_p
6 kHz	1.03 V_p	68.8 mA_p
6.5 kHz	0.829 V_p	55.2 mA_p
7 kHz	0.656 V_p	43.7 mA_p
8 kHz	0.453 V_p	30.2 mA_p
9 kHz	0.347 V_p	23.1 mA_p
10 kHz	0.283 V_p	18.8 mA_p

Table 21-2

9. For which frequency f in Table 21-2 is the circuit current a maximum? Adjust the generator to provide an output of 2.0 V_p at this frequency. While observing the oscilloscope, adjust the the generator frequency until the resistor voltage V_R is at the maximum value. Record the resonant frequency f_s and the corresponding resistor voltage V_R in Table 21-3. Calculate the current at resonance.
10. Decrease the frequency until the output voltage V_R is reduced to 0.707 of the maximum value found in Step 9. Record the lower half-power frequency f_1 and the corresponding resistor voltage V_R in Table 21-3. (Ensure that the output of the signal generator is at 2.0 V_p.)

    Increase the frequency above the resonant frequency until the output voltage V_R is again reduced to 0.707 of the maximum value found in Step 9. Record the upper half-power frequency f_2 and the corresponding resistor voltage V_R in Table 21-3. (Ensure that the output of the signal generator is at 2.0 V_p.)

    Calculate the current for each frequency.

f	V_R	I
f_1 = 4820 Hz	0.780 V_p	52.0 mA_p
f_S = 5650 Hz	1.100 V_p	73.3 mA_p
f_2 = 6630 Hz	0.780 V_p	52.0 mA_p

Table 21-3

11. Set the signal generator to the resonant frequency determined in Step 9 and adjust the amplitude for 2.0 V_p. With Ch1 of the oscilloscope at the output of the signal generator, use Ch2 to measure the voltage across resistor R. Calculate the phasor form of current **I** at resonance. (You should observe that v_R and e are in phase.) Record your results here.

V_R	1.100 V_p
θ	0°
I	51.8 mA ∠0°

12. Adjust the signal generator for a frequency $f = f_1$ and a voltage of 2.0 V_p. Measure the magnitude and phase angle of the voltage V_R. Calculate the phasor form of current **I** at this frequency.

V_R	0.780 V_p
θ_1	45°
$\mathbf{I}_1$	36.8mA ∠45°

13. Adjust the signal generator for a frequency $f = f_2$ and a voltage of 2.0 V_p. Measure the magnitude and phase angle of the voltage V_R. Calculate the phasor form of the current **I** at this frequency.

V_R	0.780 V_p
θ_2	– 45°
$\mathbf{I}_2$	36.8mA ∠–45°

14. Set the signal generator to the resonant frequency determined in Step 9 and adjust the amplitude for 2.0 V_p. Place Ch1 of the oscilloscope at terminal *a* of the circuit and Ch2 at terminal *b*. Use the difference mode of the oscilloscope to measure the amplitude of the output voltage. You should observe that the amplitude of this voltage is larger than the amplitude at the output of the signal generator. Record the amplitude of output voltage V_{out} in the space provided.

V_{out}	6.31 V_p

CONCLUSIONS

15. Plot the data of Tables 21-2 and 21-3 on the semi-logaritmic scale of Graph 21-1. Connect the points with the best smooth continuous curve.

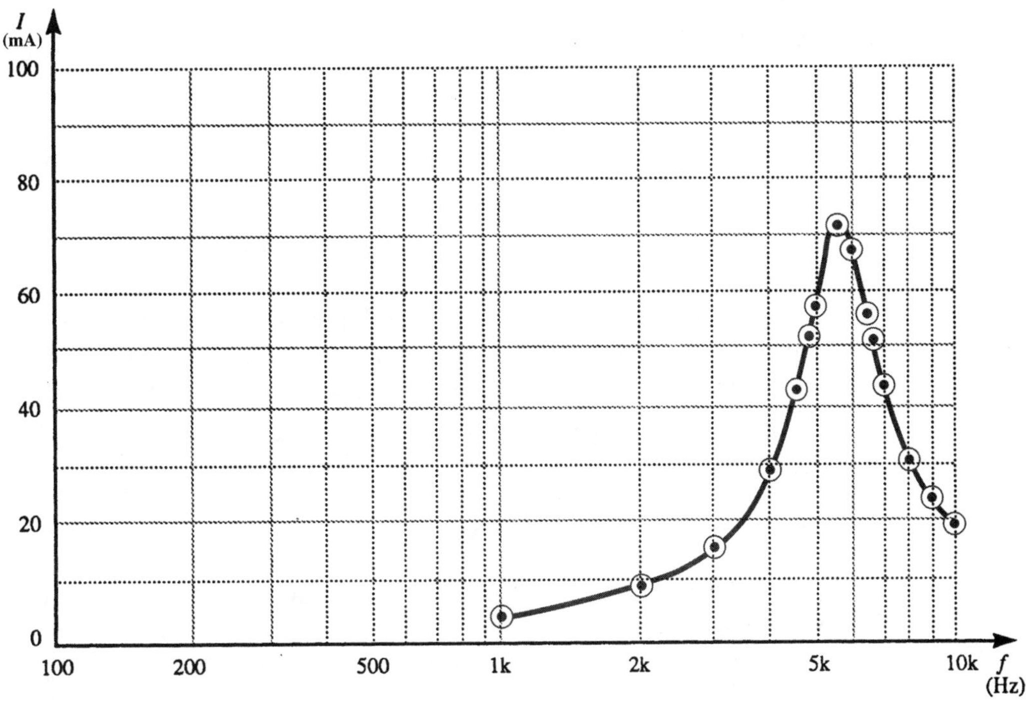

Graph 21-1

16. Compare the measured resonant frequency f_S found in Step 9 to the theoretical frequency determined in Step 1.

The measured resonant frequency of 5650 Hz is very

close to the theoretical resonant freq. (5655 Hz.)

17. Compare the measured half-power frequencies from Step 10 to the theoretical values determined in Step 5.

The measured ½-power frequencies (4820 Hz, 6630 Hz) are close to the calculated values (4750 Hz, 6560 Hz.)

18. Use the measured half-power frequencies to calculate the bandwidth of the circuit. Enter the results below.

$$BW = f_2 - f_1 \tag{21-6}$$

BW	1810 Hz

19. Calculate the Q of the circuit and enter the result in the space provided.

$$Q = \frac{f_S}{\text{BW}} \tag{21-7}$$

Q	3.12

20. Use the data of Step 11 to compare the phase angle of the current with respect to the signal generator at resonance. Based on this result, is the circuit resistive, inductive, or capacitive when $f = f_S$?

Phase angle is 0°. Therefore, the circuit is resistive.

21. Use the data of Step 12 to compare the phase angle of the current with respect to the signal generator when $f = f_1$. Based on this result, is the circuit resistive, inductive, or capacitive when $f < f_S$?

Phase angle is 45°. Therefore, the circuit is capacitive.

22. Use the data of Step 13 to compare the phase angle of the current with respect to the signal generator when $f = f_2$. Based on this result, is the circuit resistive, inductive, or capacitive when $f > f_S$?

Phase angle is – 45°. Therefore, the circuit is inductive.

23. In Step 14, you should have observed that the output voltage of the circuit at resonance is larger than the applied signal generator voltage. Calculate and record the ratio of the amplitudes V_{out}/E. Since the output voltage is taken across the inductor, you should observe that this ratio is very close to the expected Q of the circuit. Compare this result with that obtained in Step 19.

$Q = V_{out}/E$	6.31 V_p/2.0 V_p = 3.16

The above result is very close to Q = 3.12 found in step 19.

FOR FURTHER INVESTIGATION AND DISCUSSION

24. If the resistance of the inductor R_{coil} was higher than the measured value, what would happen to f_S, Q, BW, and the output voltage v_{out} at resonance?

f_S: Stay the same.

Q: Decrease.

BW: Decrease.

v_{out} at resonance: Decrease.

See next page for solutions 25 and 26.

25. Use MultiSIM or PSpice to simulate the circuit of Figure 21-1. Use a coil resistance of $R_{coil} = 5\ \Omega$. Find the resonant frequency, bandwidth, and the quality factor of the circuit.
26. Repeat Step 25 by letting $R_{coil} = 10\ \Omega$.

2

.

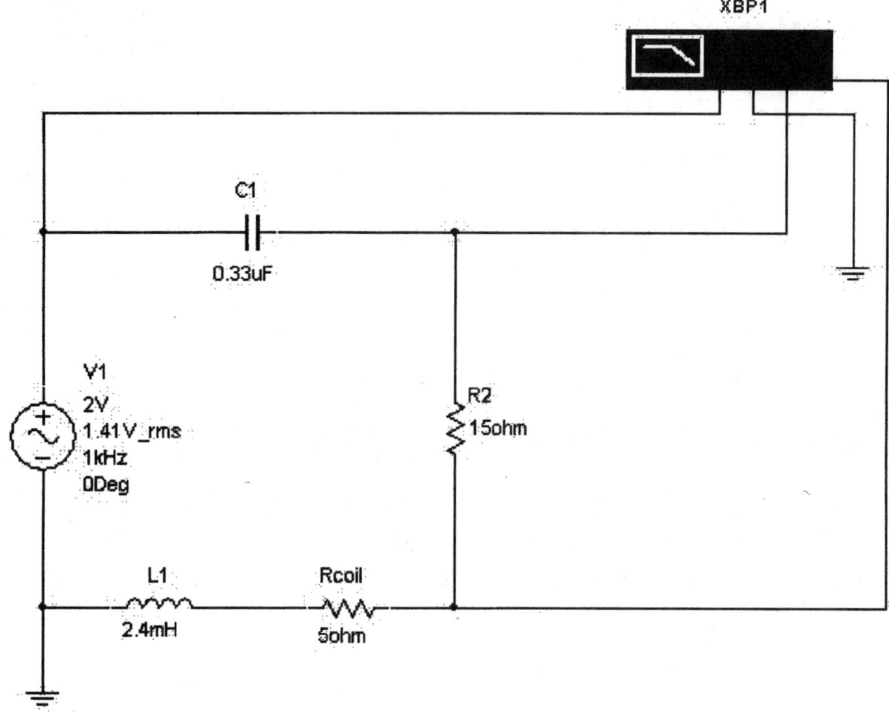

f_0 = 5.65 kHz BW = 1.322 kHz Q = 4.27

26. f_0 = 5.65 kHz BW = 1.659 kHz Q = 3.41

NAME ______________________

DATE ______________________

CLASS ______________________

LAB 22

Parallel Resonance

OBJECTIVES

After completing this lab, you will be able to

- calculate the resonant frequency of a parallel resonant circuit,
- solve for the maximum output voltage of a parallel resonant circuit,
- measure the bandwidth of a parallel resonant circuit,
- measure the impedance at frequencies above and below the resonant frequency and observe that it is purely resistive at resonance,
- sketch the output voltage as a function of frequency and explain why the response has a bell-shaped curve when plotted on a semi-logarithmic graph.

EQUIPMENT REQUIRED

- ☐ Dual trace oscilloscope
- ☐ Signal generator (sinusoidal function generator)
- ☐ DMM

*Note:*Record this equipment in Table 22-1.

COMPONENTS

- ☐ Resistors: 1-kΩ, 1.5-kΩ (1/4-W carbon, 5% tolerance)
- ☐ Capacitors: 0.33-μF (10% tolerance)
- ☐ Inductors: 2.4-mH (iron core, 5% tolerance)

EQUIPMENT USED

Instrument	Manufacturer/Model No.	Serial No.
Oscilloscope		
Signal generator		
DMM		

Table 22-1

TEXT REFERENCE:

Section 21-2 QUALITY FACTOR, Q
Section 21-6 PARALLEL RESONANCE

DISCUSSION

Although series resonant networks are used occasionally in electrical and electronic circuits, parallel resonant networks are the most common type used. Figure 22-1 illustrates a simple parallel resonant network, often called an *LC tank circuit*.

The impedance of the tank circuit is relatively low at all frequencies except at the frequency of resonance. At the resonant frequency, the reactance of the capacitor is exactly equal to the reactance of the inductor. The resulting parallel impedance approaches that of an open circuit. Since the inductor will always have some series resistance due to the coil of wire, the actual impedance of the tank circuit will not be infinitely large. In practice, the impedance of the tank circuit will generally have an impedance between 10 kΩ and 100 kΩ. When the tank circuit is connected across a constant current source (usually a transistor), the voltage across the tank circuit will be relatively high at the resonant frequency and very low at all other frequencies.

The resonant frequency of a tank circuit is found to be

$$f_P = \frac{1}{2\pi\sqrt{LC}}\sqrt{1 - \frac{R_{\text{coil}}^2 C}{L}} \qquad (22\text{-}1)$$

If R_{coil}^2 is at least ten times smaller than the ratio L/C, then the parallel resonant frequency may be approximated as

$$f_P = \frac{1}{2\pi\sqrt{LC}} \qquad (22\text{-}2)$$

The input impedance of a tank circuit at resonance will always be purely resistive, and may be determined by using the *quality factor* Q of the coil as follows:

$$R_P = (Q_{\text{coil}}^2 + 1)R_{\text{coil}} \qquad (22\text{-}3)$$

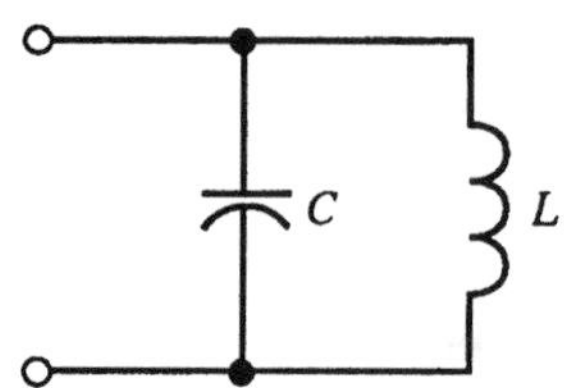

Figure 22-1 Ideal LC tank circuit

If a resistance R_1 is placed in parallel with the tank, the Q of the circuit will be reduced since this resistor absorbs some of the energy from the circuit. Also, if the voltage source has a series resistance R_s, then the Q of the circuit is reduced still further. For the network shown, the quality factor is determined as

$$Q = \frac{R_{eq}}{X_C} \quad \text{where } R_{eq} = R_1 || R_P || R_S \tag{22-4}$$

Notice that the Q of the circuit is determined by placing R_s in parallel with the other resistors. The reason for this becomes apparent if the volage source and its series resistance are converted into an equivalent current source and parallel resistance.

As in the series resonant circuit, the quality factor may be used to determine the bandwidth of the circuit as

$$BW = \frac{f_P}{Q} \tag{22-5}$$

CALCULATIONS

1. Calculate and record the resonant frequency for the circuit of Figure 22-2.

f_P	5655 Hz

2. Prior to starting the lab, obtain an inductor from your lab instructor. Use the DMM ohmmeter to measure the dc resistance of the inductor. Enter the result below.

R_{coil}	12.3 Ω

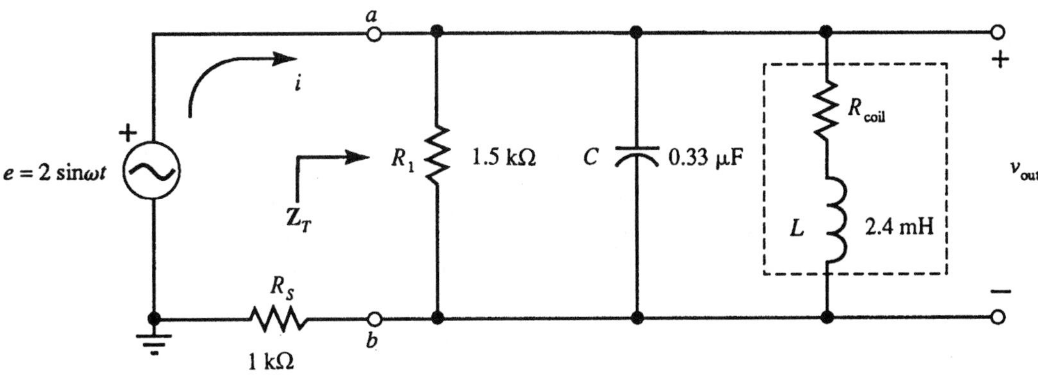

Figure 22-2 Parallel resonant circuit

3. Calculate the equivalent impedance R_P of the LC tank at resonance. Use this value to determine the total impedance $\mathbf{Z}_T$ of the circuit at resonance. (The impedance will be resistive.) Calculate the phasor form of current $\mathbf{I}$ at resonance and determine the output voltage phasor $\mathbf{V}_{out}$. Enter your results below.

$X_C = 85.28\Omega \quad Q_{coil} = 6.93$

$R_P = (Q^2 + 1)(12.3\Omega) = 603.57\ \Omega$

R_P	603.6 Ω
$\mathbf{Z}_T$	430.4Ω ∠0°
$\mathbf{I}$	0.989mA ∠0°
$\mathbf{V}_{out}$	0.426V ∠0°

4. Calculate and record the quality factor Q, bandwidth BW, and half-power frequencies f_1 and f_2 for the circuit.

$$Q \cong \frac{430.4\ \Omega}{85.28\ \Omega} = 5.05$$

Q	5.05
BW	1120 Hz
f_1	5090 Hz
f_2	6210 Hz

MEASUREMENTS

5. Assemble the circuit shown in Figure 22-2. Connect Ch1 of the oscilloscope to the output of the signal generator and adjust the output to have an amplitude of 2.0 V_p (4.0 $V_{p\text{-}p}$) at a frequency of $f = 1$ kHz.
6. Use Ch1 as the trigger source and connect Ch2 of the oscilloscope across the resistor R_S. Set the oscilloscope on the difference mode to display the amplitude of the sinusoidal output voltage. Measure the amplitude of voltage V_{out} and record the results in Table 22-2.
7. Increase the frequency of the signal generator to the frequencies indicated in Table 22-2. Adjust the amplitude of the signal generator to maintain an amplitude of 2.0 V_p for each frequency. Measure and record the amplitude of the output voltage for each frequency.

f	V_{out}
1 kHz	39 mV_p
2 kHz	72 mV_p
3 kHz	124 mV_p
4 kHz	220 mV_p
4.5 kHz	306 mV_p
5 kHz	439 mV_p
5.5 kHz	580 mV_p
6 kHz	569 mV_p
6.5 kHz	443 mV_p
7 kHz	341.0 mV_p
8 kHz	229 mV_p
9 kHz	173 mV_p
10 kHz	140 mV_p

Table 22-2

8. For which frequency f in Table 22-2 is the output voltage a maximum? Adjust the generator to provide an output of 2.0 V_p at this frequency. While observing the oscilloscope, adjust the the generator frequency until voltage V_{out} is at the maximum value. Record the resonant frequency f_P and the corresponding output voltage V_{out} in Table 22-3.

9. Decrease the frequency until the output voltage V_{out} is reduced to 0.707 of the maximum value found in Step 8. Record the lower half-power frequency f_1 and the corresponding output voltage V_{out} in Table 22-3. (Ensure that the output of the signal generator is at 2.0 V_p.)

   Increase the frequency above the resonant frequency until the output voltage V_{out} is again reduced to 0.707 of the maximum value found in Step 8. Record the upper half-power frequency f_2 and the corresponding resistor voltage V_{out} in Table 22-3. (Ensure that the output of the signal generator is at 2.0 V_p.)

	f	V_{out}
$f_1 =$	4950 Hz	425 mV_p
$f_P =$	5710 Hz	602 mV_p
$f_2 =$	6580 Hz	425 mV_p

Table 22-3

10. Set the signal generator to the resonant frequency determined in Step 9 and adjust the amplitude for 2.0 V_p. Measure the magnitude and phase angle (with respect to the signal generator) of the voltage across R_S. Calculate the phasor form of current **I** at resonance. (You should observe that v_S and e are in phase.) Record your results.

V_S	1.40 V_p
θ	3.0°
I	1.00 mA ∠0°

11. Adjust the signal generator for a frequency $f = f_1$ and a voltage of 2.0 V_p. Measure the magnitude and phase angle of the voltage V_S. Calculate the phasor form of current **I** at this frequency. Record these values.

V_R	1.67 V_p
θ	–9.0°
I	1.18 mA ∠– 9.0°

12. Adjust the signal generator for a frequency $f = f_2$ and a voltage of 2.0 V_p. Measure the magnitude and phase angle of the voltage V_S. Calculate the phasor form of the current **I** at this frequency. Record the values.

V_S	1.77 V_p
θ	+11.0°
I	1.25 mA ∠–11.0°

CONCLUSIONS

13. Plot the data of Tables 22-2 and 22-3 on the semi-logarithmic scale of Graph 22-1. Connect the points with the best smooth continuous curve.

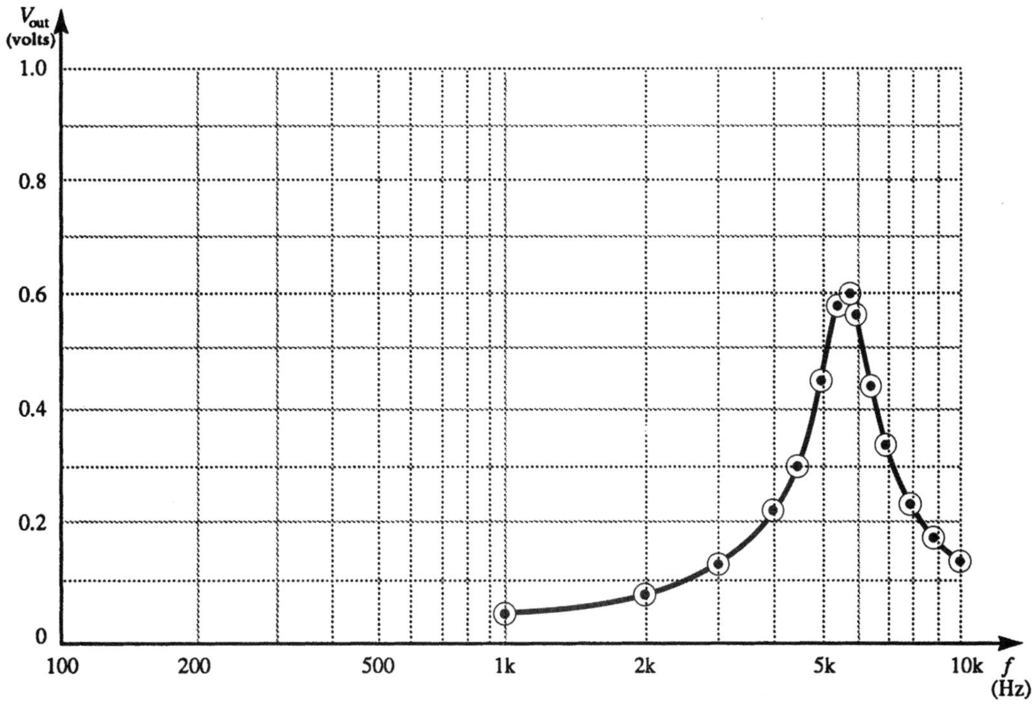

Graph 22-1

14. Compare the measured resonant frequency f_P as found in Step 8 to the theoretical frequency determined in Step 1.

    The measured resonance (5710 Hz) is close to the theoretical (5655 Hz.)

15. Compare the measured half-power frequencies of Step 9 to the theoretical values determined in Step 3.

    The ½ - power frequencies (5710 Hz, 6580 Hz) are close to the theoretical.

16. Calculate and record the bandwidth.

$$BW = f_2 - f_1 \tag{22-6}$$

BW	870 Hz

17. Calculate and record the quality factor Q of the circuit.

$$Q = \frac{f_S}{BW} \qquad (22\text{-}7)$$

Q	6.65

Compare this value of Q to that calculated in Step 3.

The actual Q is a bit higher than the theoretical.

18. Use the data of Step 10 to compare the phase angle of the current with respect to the signal generator at resonance. Based on this result, is the circuit resistive, inductive, or capacitive when $f = f_P$?

Phase angle is 0°. The circuit is resistive.

19. Use the data of Step 11 to compare the phase angle of the current with respect to the signal generator when $f = f_1$. Based on this result, is the circuit resistive, inductive, or capacitive when $f < f_P$?

Phase angle is –9.0°. Circuit is inductive since current lags voltage.

20. Use the data of Step 12 to compare the phase angle of the current with respect to the signal generator when $f = f_2$. Based on this result, is the circuit resistive, inductive, or capacitive when $f > f_P$?

Phase angle is +11.0°. Circuit is capacitive since current leads voltage.

FOR FURTHER INVESTIGATION AND DISCUSSION

21. If the resistance of the inductor R_{coil} was higher than the measured value, what would happen to R_P, Q, and BW at resonance?

R_P:

Decreases.

Q:

Decreases.

BW:

Decreases.

NAME ____________________

DATE ____________________

CLASS ____________________

LAB 23

RC and *RL* Low-Pass Filter Circuits

OBJECTIVES

After completing this lab, you will be able to

- develop the transfer function for a low-pass filter circuit,
- determine the cutoff frequency of a low-pass filter circuit,
- sketch the Bode plot of the transfer fuction for a low-pass filter,
- compare the measured voltage gain response of a low pass filter to the theoretical asymptotic response predicted by a Bode plot,
- explain why the voltage gain of a low-pass filter drops at a rate of 20 dB for each decade increase in frequency.

EQUIPMENT REQUIRED

- ☐ Dual trace oscilloscope
- ☐ Signal generator (sinusoidal function generator)
- ☐ DMM

Note: Record this equipment in Table 23-1.

COMPONENTS

- ☐ Resistors: 75-Ω, 330-Ω (1/4-W carbon, 5% tolerance)
- ☐ Capacitors: 0.47-μF (10% tolerance)
- ☐ Inductors: 2.4-mH (iron core, 5% tolerance)

EQUIPMENT USED

Instrument	Manufacturer/Model No.	Serial No.
Oscilloscope		
Signal generator		

Table 23-1

TEXT REFERENCE

Section 22.3 SIMPLE *RC* AND *RL* TRANSFER FUNCTIONS
Section 22.4 THE LOW-PASS FILTER CIRCUIT

DISCUSSION

Filter circuits are used extensively in electrical and electronic circuits to remove unwanted signals while permitting desired signals to pass from one stage to another. Although there are many types of filter circuits, most filters are *low-pass, high-pass, band-pass,* or *band-reject* filters. As the name implies, *low-pass* filters permit low frequencies to pass from one stage to another. Figure 23-1 shows both *RC* and *RL* low-pass filters.

The frequency at which the low-pass filter begins to attenuate (decrease the amplitude of) a signal is called the *cutoff frequency* or *break frequency* f_C. Specifically, the cutoff frequency is that frequency at which the amplitude of the output voltage is 0.707 of the amplitude of low frequency signals. Since this frequency corresponds to half power, the cutoff frequency is also called the *half-power* or *3-dB down frequency*. (Recall that when the output power is half of the input power, the attenuation of the stage is 3 dB.)

Cutoff frequencies are generally calculated as ω_C in radians per second, since the algebra tends to be fairly straightforward. However, when working with measurements it is easiest to use frequencies expressed as f_C in hertz. The cutoff frequencies for an *RC* low-pass filter are given as follows:

$$\omega_C = \frac{1}{\tau} = \frac{1}{RC} \tag{23-1}$$

and

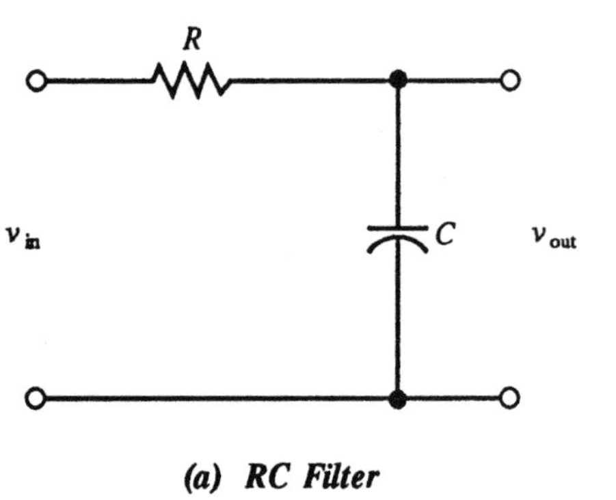

(a) RC Filter

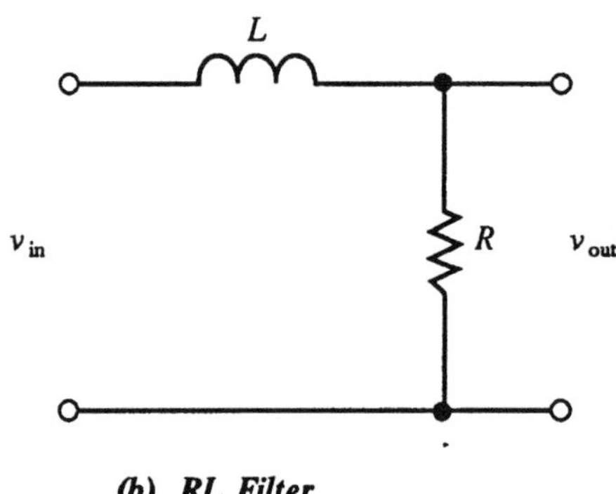

(b) RL Filter

Figure 23-1 Low-pass filters

$$f_C = \frac{\omega_C}{2\pi} = \frac{1}{2\pi RC} \tag{23-2}$$

For an RL low-pass filter, the cutoff frequencies are

$$\omega_C = \frac{1}{\tau} = \frac{R}{L} \tag{23-3}$$

and

$$f_C = \frac{\omega_C}{2\pi} = \frac{R}{2\pi L} \tag{23-4}$$

The frequency response of a filter circuit is generally shown on two semi-logarithmic graphs where the abscissa (horizontal axis) for each graph gives the frequency on a logarithmic scale. The ordinate (vertical axis) of one graph shows the voltage gain in decibels, while the ordinate of the other graph shows the phase shift of the output voltage with respect to the applied input voltage. The voltage gain and phase shift for any frequency are determined by finding the *transfer function TF* of the given filter. The transfer function is defined as the ratio of the output voltage phasor to the input voltage phasor.

$$\mathbf{TF} = \frac{\mathbf{V}_{\text{out}}}{\mathbf{V}_{\text{in}}} \tag{23-5}$$

CALCULATIONS

The *RC* Low-Pass Filter

1. Write the transfer function $\mathbf{TF} = \mathbf{V}_{\text{out}}/\mathbf{E}$ for the RC low-pass filter of Figure 23-2.

$$\text{TF} = \frac{\frac{1}{SC}}{R + \frac{1}{SC}} = \frac{1}{1 + sRC} \equiv \frac{1}{1 + j\omega RC}$$

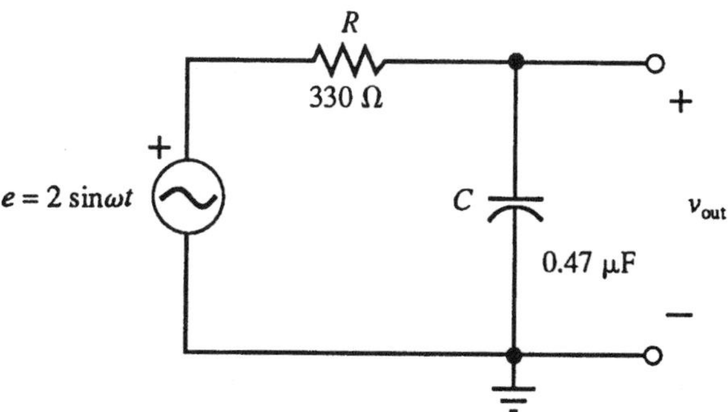

Figure 23-2 *RC* low-pass filter

2. Determine the cutoff frequencies (in radians per second and in hertz) of the circuit in Figure 23-2. Record the values below.

ω_C	6447	rad/s
f_C	1026	Hz

3. Sketch the straight-line approximations of the frequency responses (A_v in dB versus frequency and θ versus frequency) for the *RC* low-pass filter on Graph 23-1.

The *RL* Low-Pass Filter

4. Write the transfer function **TF** = $\mathbf{V}_{out}/\mathbf{E}$ for the *RL* low-pass filter of Figure 23-3.

$$\text{TF} = \frac{R}{sL + R} = \frac{1}{1 + s^{L}\!/_{R}} \equiv \frac{1}{1 + j\omega^{L}\!/_{R}}$$

5. Determine the cutoff frequencies (in radians per second and in hertz) of the circuit in Figure 23-3. Record the values below.

ω_C	31,250	rad/s
f_C	4974	Hz

6. Sketch the straight-line approximations of the frequency responses (A_v in dB versus frequency and θ versus frequency) for the *RL* low-pass filter on Graph 23-2.

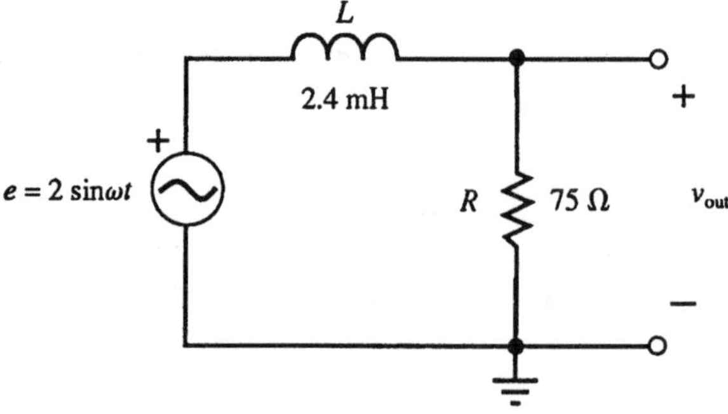

Figure 23-3 *RL* low-pass filter

MEASUREMENTS

The *RC* Low-Pass Filter

7. Assemble the circuit shown in Figure 23-2. Connect Ch1 of the oscilloscope to the output of the signal generator and adjust the output to have an amplitude of 2.0 V_p (4.0 $V_{p\text{-}p}$) at a frequency of f = 100 Hz.
8. Use Ch1 as the trigger source and connect Ch2 of the oscilloscope across the capacitor *C*. Measure the amplitude and phase angle (with respect to *e*) of the sinusoidal output voltage v_{out}. Enter the results in Table 23-2.
9. Increase the frequency of the signal generator to the frequencies indicated in Table 23-2. If necessary, adjust the amplitude of the signal generator to ensure that the output is maintained at 2.0 V_p (4.0 $V_{p\text{-}p}$). Measure the amplitude and phase shift of v_{out} (with respect to *e*) for each frequency.

f	V_{out}	
	Amplitude	Phase shift
100 Hz	2.0 V	–5.6°
200 Hz	1.96 V	–11.0°
400 Hz	1.86 V	–21.4°
800 Hz	1.57 V	–38.1°
1 kHz	1.43 V	–44.3°
2 kHz	0.911 V	–62.9°
4 kHz	0.500 V	–75.7°
8 kHz	0.253 V	–82.7°
10 kHz	0.204 V	–84.1°

Table 23-2

10. Determine the cutoff frequency by adjusting the frequency of the generator until the output voltage has an amplitude of V_{out} = (0.707)(2.0 V_p) = 1.41 V_p. Record the measured cutoff frequency below.

f_C	1.03 kHz

The *RL* Low-Pass Filter

11. Construct the circuit shown in Figure 23-3. Connect Ch1 of the oscilloscope to the output of the signal generator and adjust the output to have an amplitude of 2.0 V_p (4.0 $V_{p\text{-}p}$) at a frequency of $f = 100$ Hz.
12. Use Ch1 as the trigger source and connect Ch2 of the oscilloscope across the resistor R. Measure the amplitude and phase angle (with respect to e) of the sinusoidal output voltage v_{out}. Enter the results in Table 23-3.
13. Increase the frequency of the signal generator to the frequencies indicated in Table 23-3. If necessary, adjust the amplitude of the signal generator to ensure that the output is maintained at 2.0 V_p (4.0 $V_{p\text{-}p}$). Measure the amplitude and phase shift of v_{out} (with respect to e) for each frequency.

f	V_{out}	
	Amplitude	Phase shift
100 Hz	1.96 V	–11.4°
200 Hz	1.86 V	–21.9°
400 Hz	1.56 V	–38.8°
800 Hz	1.06 V	–58.1°
1 kHz	0.89 V	–63.6°
2 kHz	0.48 V	–76.0°
4 kHz	0.25 V	–82.9°
8 kHz	0.12 V	–86.4°
10 kHz	0.10 V	–87.2°

Table 23-3

14. Determine the cutoff frequency by adjusting the frequency of the generator until the output voltage has an amplitude of $V_{out} = (0.707)(2.0\ V_p) = 1.41\ V_p$. Record the measured cutoff frequency here.

f_C	4.97 kHz

CONCLUSIONS

The *RC* Low-Pass Filter

15. Use your measurements recorded in Table 23-2 to calculate the magnitude of the gain as a ratio of the amplitudes V_{out}/V_{in}. Calculate the voltage gain in decibels as

$$[A_v]_{dB} = 20 \log \frac{V_{out}}{V_{in}} \tag{23-6}$$

Record the calculated voltage gain and measured phase shift for each frequency in Table 23-4.

f	$A_v = V_{out}/V_{in}$	$[A_v]_{dB}$	θ
100 Hz	1.0	0 dB	–5.6°
200 Hz	0.98	–0.2 dB	–11.0°
400 Hz	0.93	–0.6 dB	–21.4°
800 Hz	0.785	–2.1 dB	–38.1°
1 kHz	0.715	–2.9 dB	–44.3°
2 kHz	0.451	–6.9 dB	–62.9°
4 kHz	0.250	–12.0 dB	–75.7°
8 kHz	0.127	–17.9 dB	–82.7°
10 kHz	0.102	–19.8 dB	–84.1°

Table 23-4

16. Plot the data of Table 23-4 on the semi-logarithmic scales of Graph 23-1 (page 181 [p. 517 of this I.G.]). Connect the points with the best smooth continuous curve. You should find that the actual response is closely predicted by the straight-line approximations of the Bode plot.
17. Compare the measured cutoff frequency f_C of Step 10 to the theoretical value predicted by the transfer function in Step 2.

    The actual cutoff frequency of 11.03 kHz is very close to the predicted.

The *RL* Low-Pass Filter

18. Use your measurements recorded in Table 23-3 to calculate the magnitude of the gain as a ratio of the amplitudes V_{out}/V_{in}. Determine the voltage gain in decibels. Record the calculated voltage gain and measured phase shift for each frequency in Table 23-5.

f	$A_v = V_{out}/V_{in}$	$[A_v]_{dB}$	θ
100 Hz	0.98	–0.2 dB	–11.4°
200 Hz	0.93	–0.6 dB	–21.9°
400 Hz	1.78	–2.2 dB	–38.8°
800 Hz	0.53	–5.5 dB	–58.1°
1 kHz	0.45	–6.9 db	–63.6°
2 kHz	0.24	–12.4 dB	–76.0°
4 kHz	0.13	–17.7 dB	–82.9°
8 kHz	0.06	–24.4 db	–86.4°
10 kHz	0.05	–26.0 dB	–87.2°

Table 23-5

19. Plot the data of Table 23-5 on the semi-logarithmic scales of Graph 23-2 (page182 [p. 518 of this I.G.]). Connect the points with the best smooth continuous curve. You should find that the actual response is closely predicted by the straight-line approximations of the Bode plot.
20. Compare the measured cutoff frequency f_C of Step 14 to the theoretical value predicted by the transfer function in Step 5.

    The measured frequency is very close to the theoretical frequency.

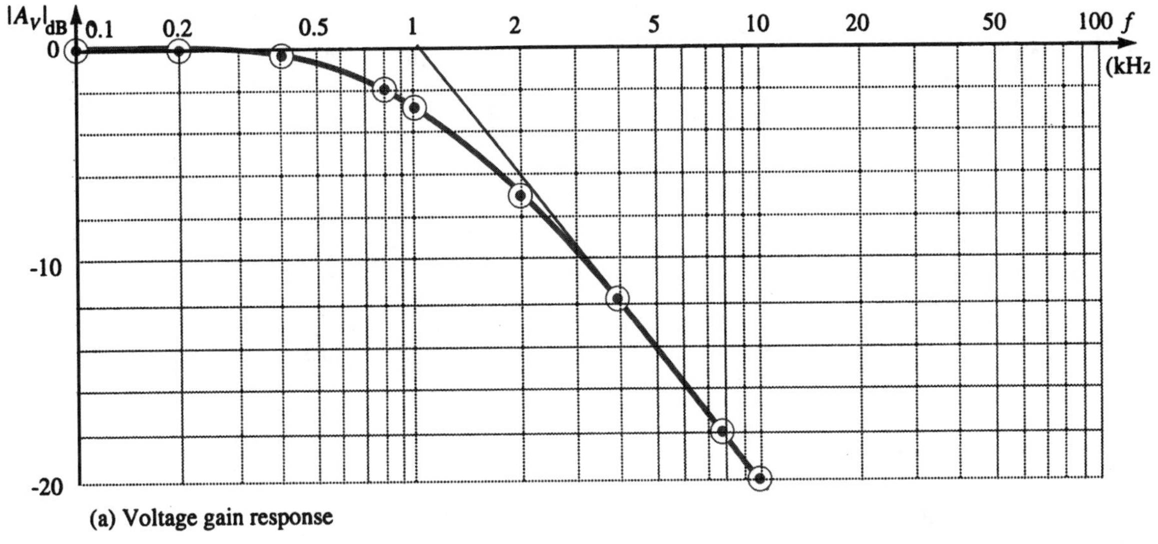

(a) Voltage gain response

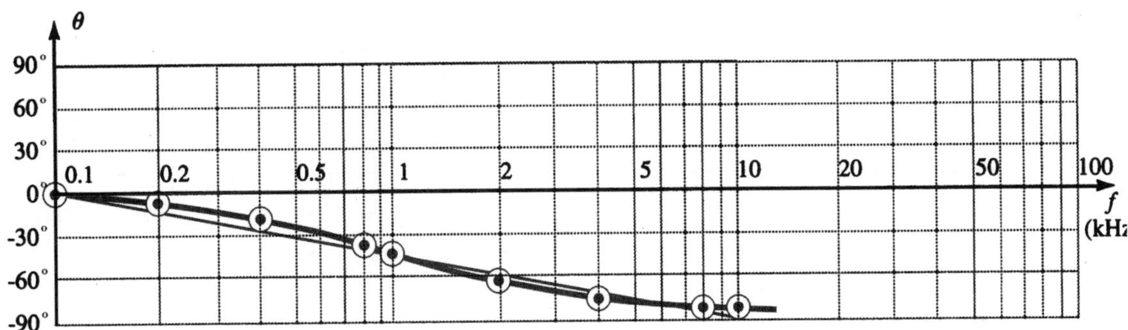

Graph 23-1 Frequency response of an *RC* low-pass filter

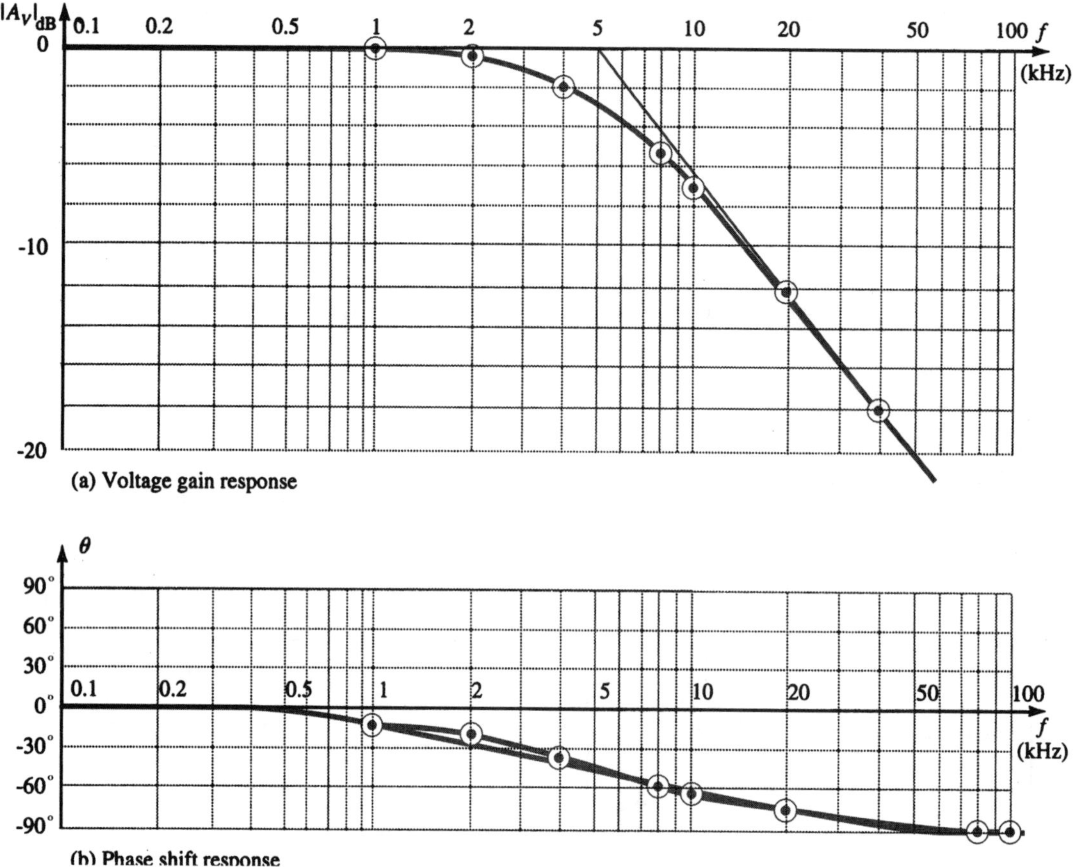

Graph 23-2 Frequency response of an *RL* low-pass filter

FOR FURTHER INVESTIGATION AND DISCUSSION

See next page for answers to *For Further Investigation and Discussion*

21. Use MultiSIM or PSpice to simulate the circuit of Figure 23-2. Obtain the frequency response curves for this circuit and compare the results to the actual measurements.
22. Repeat Step 21 for the circuit of Figure 23-3.

For Further Investigation and Discussion

21.

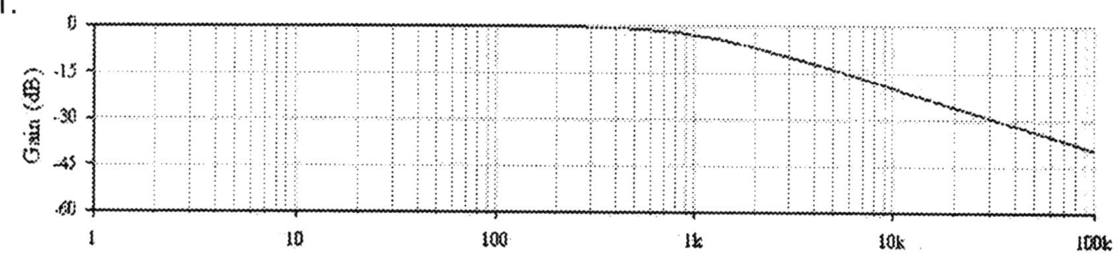

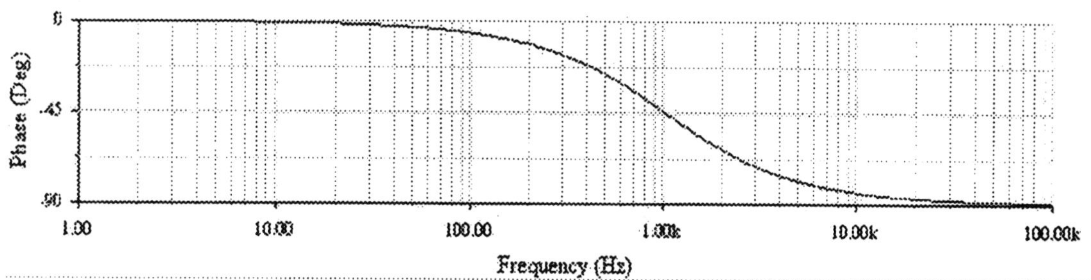

22.

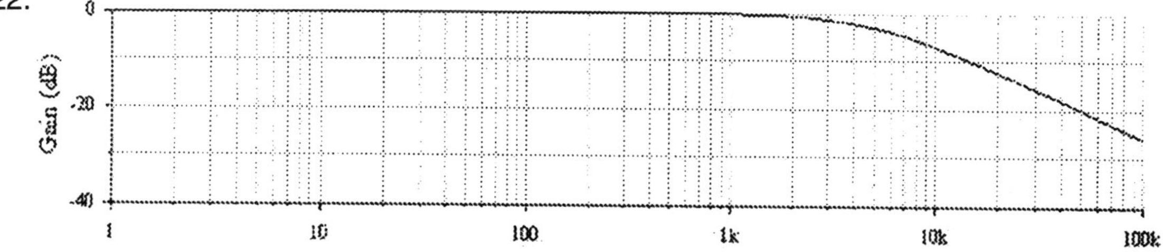

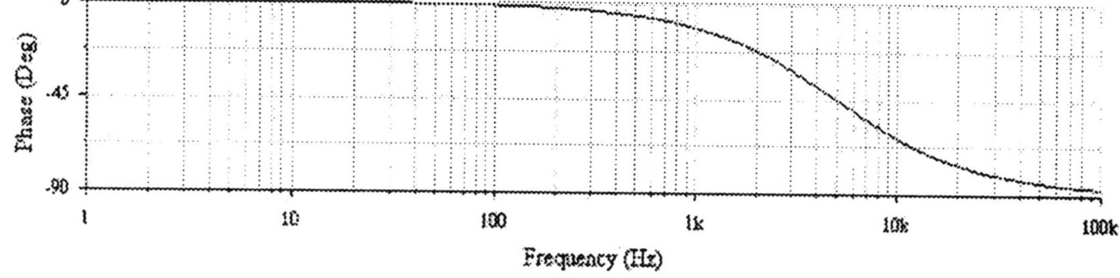

NAME ______________________

DATE ______________________

CLASS ______________________

LAB 24

RC and *RL* High-Pass Filter Circuits

OBJECTIVES

After completing this lab, you will be able to

- develop the transfer function for a high-pass filter circuit,
- determine the cutoff frequency of a high-pass filter circuit,
- sketch the Bode plot of the transfer fuction for a high-pass filter,
- compare the measured voltage gain response of a high-pass filter to the theoretical asymptotic response predicted by a Bode plot,
- explain why the voltage gain of a high-pass filter increases at a rate of 20 dB/decade below the cutoff frequency.

EQUIPMENT REQUIRED

☐ Dual trace oscilloscope
☐ Signal generator (sinusoidal function generator)
☐ DMM
Note: Record this equipment in Table 24-1.

COMPONENTS

☐ Resistors: 75-Ω, 330-Ω (1/4-W carbon, 5% tolerance)
☐ Capacitors: 0.47-μF (10% tolerance)
☐ Inductors: 2.4-mH (iron core, 5% tolerance)

EQUIPMENT USED

Instrument	Manufacturer/Model No.	Serial No.
Oscilloscope		
Signal generator		

Table 24-1

TEXT REFERENCE

Section 22.5 THE HIGH-PASS FILTER CIRCUIT

DISCUSSION

As the name implies, the *high-pass filter* permits high frequencies to pass from the input through to the output of the filter. Due to the abundance of electric motors and fluorescent lights, *60-Hz noise* is the most prevalent unwanted signal around us. Although many applications exist, one of the most common uses for the high-pass filter is to prevent 60-Hz noise from entering a sensitive electrical or electronic system. Figure 24-1 shows both *RC* and *RL* high-pass filters.

As in the low-pass filter circuit, the *cutoff frequency* f_C is that frequency at which the amplitude of the output voltage is 0.707 of the maximum amplitude. However, in the case of high-pass filters, the maximum amplitude occurs for high frequencies rather than for low frequencies. Since this frequency corresponds to half power, the cutoff frequency is also called the *half-power* or *3-dB down frequency*.

The cutoff frequencies for an *RC* high-pass filter are identical to the values for the low-pass *RC* filter and are given as follows:

$$\omega_C = \frac{1}{\tau} = \frac{1}{RC} \qquad (24\text{-}1)$$

and

$$f_C = \frac{\omega_C}{2\pi} = \frac{1}{2\pi RC} \qquad (24\text{-}2)$$

Similarly, for an *RL* high-pass filter, the cutoff frequencies are

$$\omega_C = \frac{1}{\tau} = \frac{R}{L} \qquad (24\text{-}3)$$

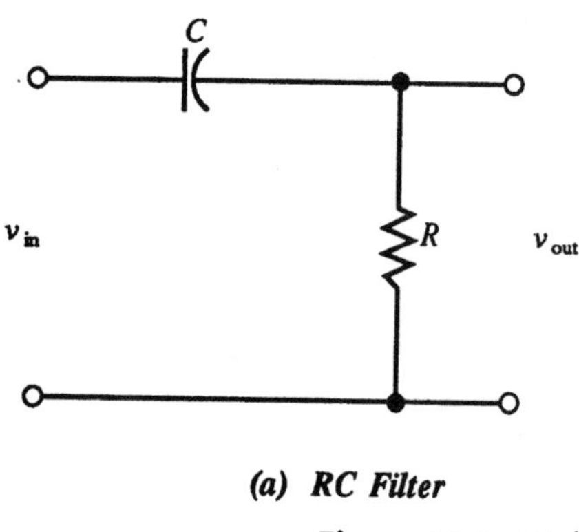

(a) RC Filter

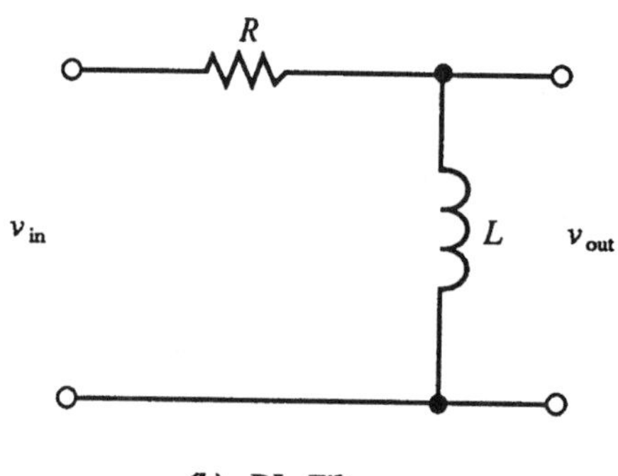

(b) RL Filter

Figure 24-1 High-pass filters

and

$$f_C = \frac{\omega_C}{2\pi} = \frac{R}{2\pi L} \tag{24-4}$$

As in the low-pass filter, the frequency response of a high-pass filter circuit is generally shown on two semi-logarithmic graphs where the abscissa (horizontal axis) for each graph gives the frequency on a logarithmic scale. The ordinate (vertical axis) of one graph shows the voltage gain in decibels, while the ordinate of the other graph shows the phase shift of the output voltage with respect to the applied input voltage. The voltage gain and phase shift for any frequency are determined by finding the *transfer function TF* of the given filter. Recall that the transfer function is defined as the ratio of the output voltage phasor to the input voltage phasor.

$$\text{TF} = \frac{\boldsymbol{V}_{\text{out}}}{\boldsymbol{V}_{\text{in}}} \tag{24-5}$$

CALCULATIONS

The *RC* High-Pass Filter

1. Write the transfer function $\mathbf{TF} = \mathbf{V}_{\text{out}}/\mathbf{E}$ for the *RC* high-pass filter of Figure 24-2.

$$\text{TF} = \frac{R}{\frac{1}{SC} + R} = \frac{sRC}{1 + sRC} \equiv \frac{j\omega RC}{1 + j\omega RC}$$

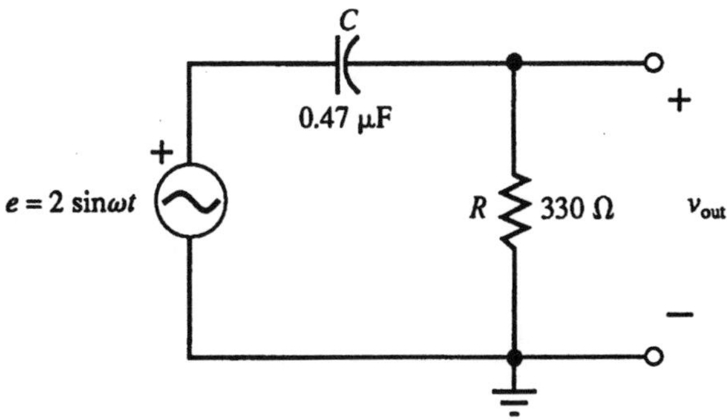

Figure 24-2 *RC* high-pass filter

2. Determine the cutoff frequencies (in radians per second and in hertz) of the circuit in Figure 24-2. Record the values below.

ω_C	6447	rad/s
f_C	1026	Hz

3. Sketch the straight-line approximations of the frequency responses (A_v in dB versus frequency and θ versus frequency) for the *RC* high-pass filter on Graph 24-1 (page 190).

The *RL* High-Pass Filter

4. Write the transfer function **TF** = $\mathbf{V}_{out}/\mathbf{E}$ for the *RL* high-pass filter of Figure 24-3.

$$\text{TF} = \frac{sL}{R + sL} = \frac{s^{L}/_{R}}{1 + s^{L}/_{R}} \equiv \frac{j\omega^{L}/_{R}}{1 + j\omega^{L}/_{R}}$$

5. Determine the cutoff frequencies (in radians per second and in hertz) of the circuit in Figure 24-3. Record the values below.

ω_C	31250	rad/s
f_C	4974	Hz

6. Sketch the straight-line approximations of the frequency responses (A_v in dB versus frequency and θ versus frequency) for the *RL* high-pass filter on Graph 24-2 (page 191).

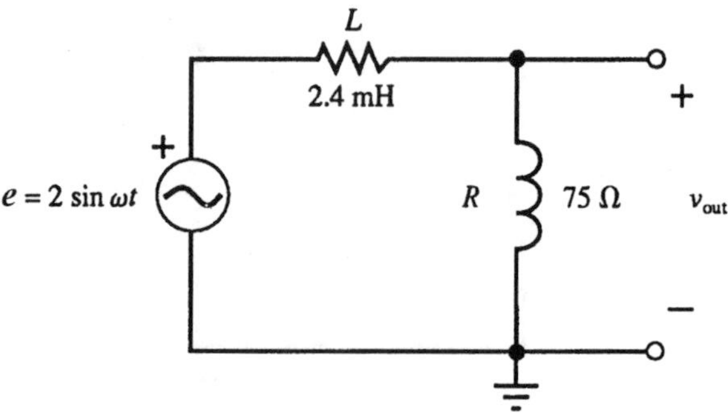

Figure 24-3 *RL* high-pass filter

MEASUREMENTS

The *RC* High-Pass Filter

7. Assemble the circuit shown in Figure 24-2. Connect Ch1 of the oscilloscope to the output of the signal generator and adjust the output to have an amplitude of 2.0 V_p (4.0 $V_{p\text{-}p}$) at a frequency of $f = 100$ Hz.
8. Use Ch1 as the trigger source and connect Ch2 of the oscilloscope across the resistor R. Measure the amplitude and phase angle (with respect to e) of the sinusoidal output voltage v_{out}. Enter the results in Table 24-2.
9. Increase the frequency of the signal generator to the frequencies indicated in Table 24-2. If necessary, adjust the amplitude of the signal generator to ensure that the output is maintained at 2.0 V_p (4.0 $V_{p\text{-}p}$). Measure the amplitude and phase shift of v_{out} (with respect to e) for each frequency.

f	V_{out}	
	Amplitude	Phase shift
100 Hz	0.194 V	+84.4°
200 Hz	0.382 V	+79.0°
400 Hz	0.727 V	+68.7°
800 Hz	1.23 V	+52.1°
1 kHz	1.40 V	+45.7°
2 kHz	1.78 V	+27.2°
4 kHz	1.94 V	+14.4°
8 kHz	1.98 V	+7.3°
10 kHz	1.99 V	+5.9°

Table 24-2

10. Determine the cutoff frequency by adjusting the frequency of the generator until the output voltage has an amplitude of $V_{out} = (0.707)(2.0\ V_p) = 1.41\ V_p$. Record the measured cutoff frequency below.

f_C	1030 Hz

The *RL* High-Pass Filter

11. Construct the circuit shown in Figure 24-3. Connect Ch1 of the oscilloscope to the output of the signal generator and adjust the output to have an amplitude of 2.0 V_p (4.0 $V_{p\text{-}p}$) at a frequency of f = 100 Hz.
12. Use Ch1 as the trigger source and connect Ch2 of the oscilloscope across the inductor L. Measure the amplitude and phase angle (with respect to e) of the sinusoidal output voltage v_{out}. Enter the results in Table 24-3.
13. Increase the frequency of the signal generator to the frequencies indicated in Table 24-3. If necessary, adjust the amplitude of the signal generator to ensure that the output is maintained at 2.0 V_p (4.0 $V_{p\text{-}p}$). Measure the amplitude and phase shift of v_{out} (with respect to e) for each frequency.

f	V_{out}	
	Amplitude	Phase shift
100 Hz	0.394 V	+78.6°
200 Hz	0.746 V	+68.1°
400 Hz	1.25 V	+51.2°
800 Hz	1.70 V	+31.9°
1 kHz	1.79 V	+26.4°
2 kHz	1.94 V	+14.0°
4 kHz	1.98 V	+7.1°
8 kHz	2.00 V	+3.6°
10 kHz	2.00 V	+2.8°

Table 24-3

14. Determine the cutoff frequency by adjusting the frequency of the generator until the output voltage has an amplitude of V_{out} = (0.707)(2.0 V_p) = 1.41 V_p. Record the measured cutoff frequency below.

f_C	4960 Hz

CONCLUSIONS

The *RC* High-Pass Filter

15. Use the measurements recorded in Table 24-2 to calculate the magnitude of the gain as a ratio of the amplitudes V_{out}/V_{in}. Calculate the voltage gain in decibels as

$$[A_v]_{dB} = 20 \log \frac{V_{out}}{V_{in}} \tag{24-6}$$

Record the calculated voltage gain and measured phase shift for each frequency in Table 24-4.

f	$A_v = V_{out}/V_{in}$	$[A_v]_{dB}$	θ
100 Hz	0.097	–20.3 dB	+84.4°
200 Hz	0.191	–14.4 dB	+79.0°
400 Hz	0.364	–8.8 dB	+68.7°
800 Hz	0.615	–4.2 dB	+52.1°
1 kHz	0.700	–3.1 dB	+45.7°
2 kHz	0.89	–1.0 dB	+27.2°
4 kHz	0.97	–0.3 dB	+14.4°
8 kHz	0.99	–0.1 dB	+7.3°
10 kHz	1.00	0 dB	+5.9°

Table 24-4

16. Plot the data of Table 24-4 on the semi-logaritmic scales of Graph 24-1 (next page). Connect the points with the best smooth continuous curve. You should find that the actual response is closely approximated by the Bode plot.

17. Compare the measured cutoff frequency f_C of Step 10 to the theoretical value predicted by the transfer function in Step 2.

    The measured cutoff frequency (1030 Hz) is very close to the theoretical (1026 Hz).

The *RL* High-Pass Filter

18. Use the measurements recorded in Table 24-3 to calculate the magnitude of the gain as a ratio of the amplitudes V_{out}/V_{in}. Determine the voltage gain in decibels. Record the calculated voltage gain and measured phase shift for each frequency in Table 24-5.

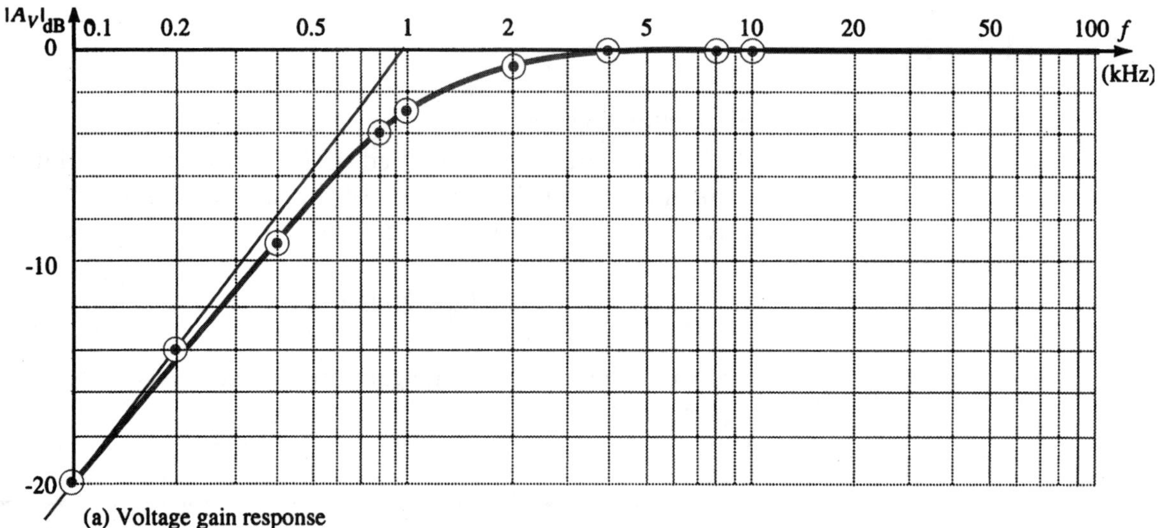

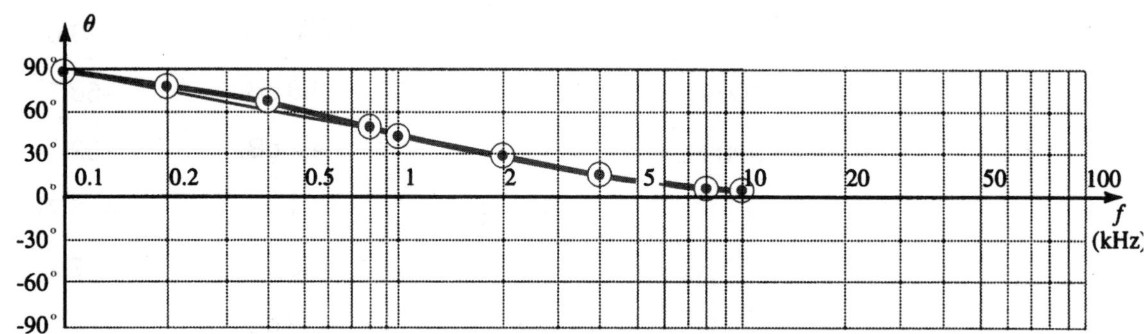

Graph 24-1 Frequency response of an *RC* high-pass filter

f	$A_v = V_{out}/V_{in}$	$[A_v]_{dB}$	θ
100 Hz	0.197	–14.1 dB	+78.6°
200 Hz	0.373	–8.6 dB	+68.1°
400 Hz	0.625	–4.1 dB	+51.2°
800 Hz	0.850	–1.4 dB	+31.9°
1 kHz	0.895	–1.0 dB	+26.4°
2 kHz	0.97	–0.3 dB	+14.0°
4 kHz	0.99	–0.1dB	+7.1°
8 kHz	1.00	0 dB	+3.6°
10 kHz	1.00	0 dB	+2.8°

Table 24-5

19. Plot the data of Table 24-5 on the semi-logarithmic scales of Graph 24-2. Connect the points with the best smooth continuous curve. You should find that the actual response is closely approximated by the Bode plot.
20. Compare the measured cutoff frequency f_C of Step 14 to the theoretical value predicted by the transfer function in Step 5.

The measured cutoff frequency (4960 Hz) is very close to the theoretical (4974 Hz).

FOR FURTHER INVESTIGATION AND DISCUSSION

See next page for answers to *For Further Investigation and Discussion*

21. Use MultiSIM or PSpice to simulate the circuit of Figure 24-2. Obtain the frequency response curves for this circuit and compare the results to the actual measurements.
22. Repeate Step 21 for the circuit of Figure 24-3.

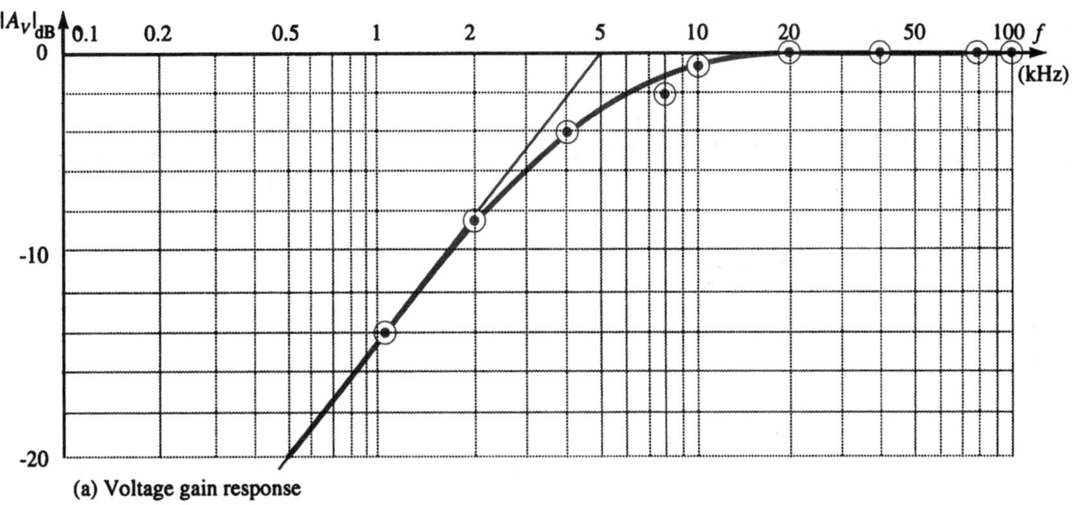

(a) Voltage gain response

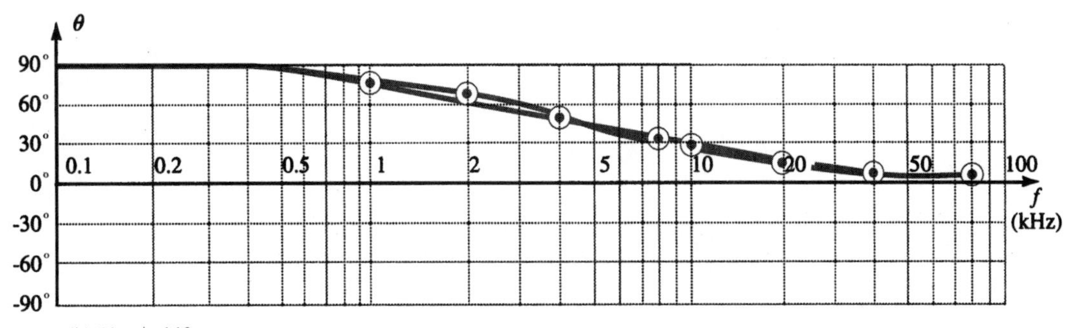

(b) Phase shift response

Graph 24-2 Frequency response of an *RL* high-pass filter

For Further Investigation and Discussion

21.

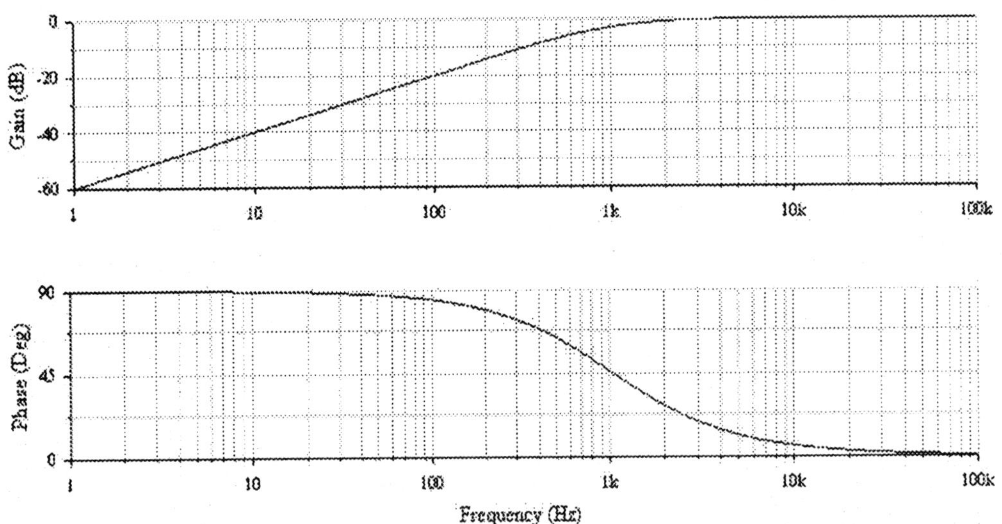

22.

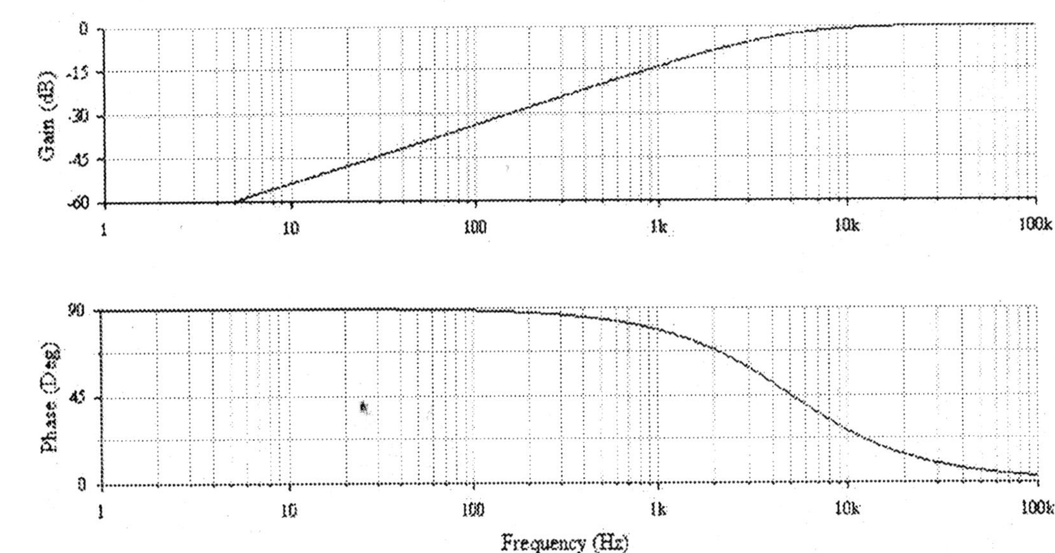

NAME ______________________

DATE ______________________

CLASS ______________________

Bandpass Filter

OBJECTIVES

After completing this lab, you will be able to

- calculate the cutoff frequencies of a bandpass filter by examining the individual low-pass and high-pass stages of a filter,
- derive the transfer function for each stage of a bandpass filter,
- sketch the Bode plot of a bandpass filter from the transfer function of the individual stages,
- explain why the slopes of the voltage gain response is 20 dB/decade on each side of the cutoff frequencies.

EQUIPMENT REQUIRED

☐ Dual trace oscilloscope
☐ Signal generator (sinusoidal function generator)
☐ DMM

Note: Record this equipment in Table 25-1.

COMPONENTS

☐ Resistors: 330-Ω (2) (1/4-W carbon, 5% tolerance)
☐ Capacitors: 0.047-μF, 0.47-μF (10% tolerance)

EQUIPMENT USED

Instrument	Manufacturer/Model No.	Serial No.
Oscilloscope		
Signal generator		

Table 25-1

TEXT REFERENCE

Section 22.6 BANDPASS FILTER

DISCUSSION

Bandpass filters permit a range of frequencies to pass from one stage to another. Many different types of bandpass filters are used throughout electronics. For instance, the typical television receiver uses several stages of filtering to achieve a bandwidth of 6 MHz, while an AM receiver has circuitry which restricts the bandwidth to only 10 kHz. Although bandpass filters can be very elaborate, depending on the application, they can also be constructed simply by combining a low-pass filter and a high-pass filter as shown in Figure 25-1. Since expense and other design difficulties make *RL* filters impractical, *RC* filters are used almost exclusively.

The bandpass filter of Figure 25-1 has two cutoff frequencies as determined by the cutoff frequencies of the individual stages. The frequency below which the high-pass filter attenuates the signal is called the *lower cutoff frequency* f_1. The frequency at which the low-pass filter begins to attenuate is called the *upper cutoff frequency* f_2. As expected, the difference between the two frequencies is the *bandwidth BW*. In order for the circuit to operate predictably, the cutoff frequencies should be separated by at least one *decade* and the first stage must be the high-pass circuit.

The lower cutoff frequency ω_1 in radians per second is found as

$$\omega_1 = \frac{1}{\tau_1} = \frac{1}{R_1 C_1} \tag{25-1}$$

with a corresponding frequency f_1 in hertz,

$$f_1 = \frac{\omega_1}{2\pi} = \frac{1}{2\pi R_1 C_1} \tag{25-2}$$

The upper cutoff frequency ω_2 in radians per second is

$$\omega_2 = \frac{1}{\tau_2} = \frac{1}{R_2 C_2} \tag{25-3}$$

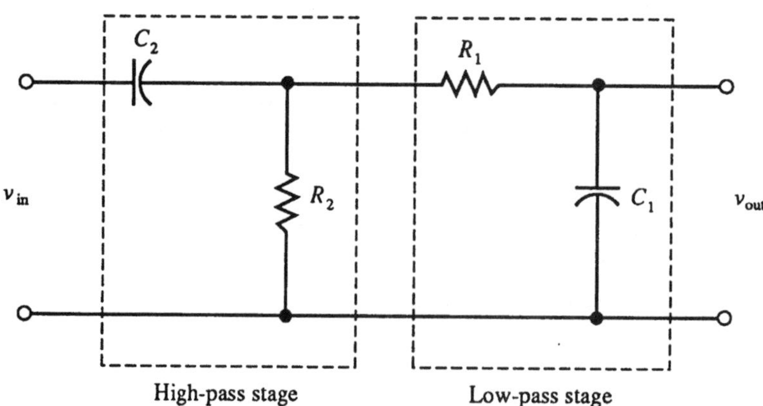

Figure 25-1 Simple bandpass filter

with a corresponding frequency f_2 in hertz,

$$f_2 = \frac{\omega_2}{2\pi} = \frac{1}{2\pi R_2 C_2} \quad (25\text{–}4)$$

The bandwidth of the filter is determined as

$$BW = f_2 - f_1 \quad (25\text{-}5)$$

CALCULATIONS

1. Calculate and record the cutoff frequency (in radians per second and in hertz) for the high-pass stage in the circuit of Figure 25-2.

ω_1	6448	rad/s
f_1	1026	Hz

2. Calculate and record the cutoff frequency (in radians per second and in hertz) for the low-pass stage in the circuit of Figure 25-2.

ω_2	64480	rad/s
f_2	10260	Hz

3. Calculate and record the bandwidth of the filter circuit of Figure 25-2.

BW	9234	Hz

4. From the calculations of Steps 1 and 2 sketch the Bode plots for the bandpass filter of Figure 25-2. Use the semilogarithmic scales of Graph 25-1 (page 198).

Note: Capacitors were shown in the wrong locations (See below.)

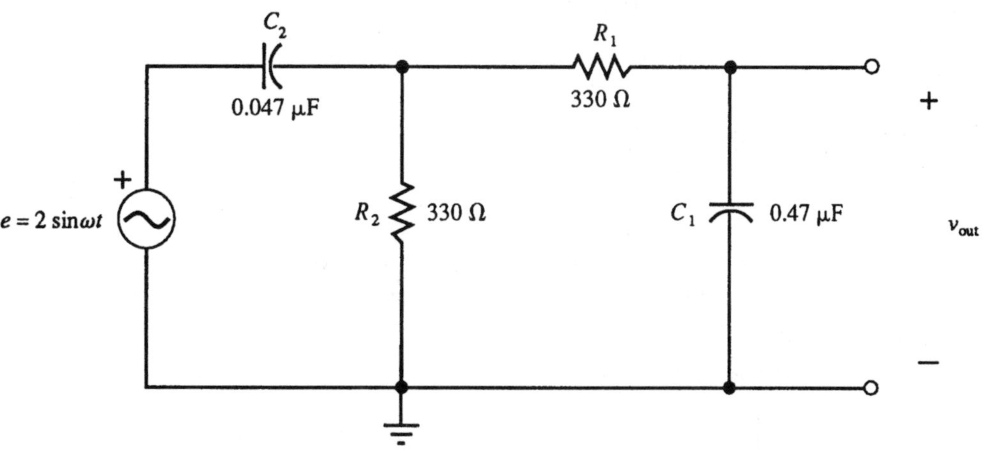

Figure 25-2 Bandpass filter

MEASUREMENTS

5. Assemble the circuit shown in Figure 25-2. Connect Ch1 of the oscilloscope to the output of the signal generator and adjust the output to have an amplitude of 2.0 V_p (4.0 $V_{p\text{-}p}$) at a frequency of $f = 100$ Hz.
6. Use Ch1 as the trigger source and connect Ch2 of the oscilloscope across the output of the circuit. Measure the amplitude and phase angle of the output voltage v_{out} (with respect to e). Enter the results in Table 25-2.
7. Increase the frequency of the signal generator to the frequencies indicated in Table 25-2. Due to loading effects of the circuit, it will be necessary to readjust the amplitude of the signal generator at each frequency to ensure that the output is maintained at 2.0 V_p (4.0 $V_{p\text{-}p}$). Measure and record the amplitude and phase shift of the output voltage v_{out} (with respect to e) for each frequency.

f	v_{out}	
	Amplitude	Phase shift
100 Hz	0.194 V	+83.3°
200 Hz	0.381 V	+76.7°
400 Hz	0.717 V	+64.4°
800 Hz	1.18 V	+45.1°
1 kHz	1.32 V	+37.7°
2 kHz	1.61 V	+14.7°
4 kHz	1.66 V	–6.2°
8 kHz	1.46 V	–28.5°
10 kHz	1.35 V	–36.0°
20 kHz	0.890 V	–57.8°
40 kHz	0.492 V	–72.7°
80 kHz	0.253 V	–81.2°
100 kHz	0.204 V	–83.0°

Table 25-2

8. For which frequency f in Table 25-2 is the output voltage a maximum? Adjust the generator to provide an output of 2.0 V_p (4.0 $V_{p\text{-}p}$) at this frequency. While observing the oscilloscope, ad-

just the the generator frequency until voltage V_{out} is at the maximum value. Measure and record the center frequency f_0 and the corresponding amplitude V_{out}.

f_0 = 3.25 kHz	1.67 V

9. Decrease the frequency until the output voltage V_{out} is reduced to 0.707 of the maximum value found in Step 8. Record the lower half-power frequency f_1 and the corresponding output voltage V_{out}. (Ensure that the output of the signal generator is at 2.0 V_p.)

f_1 = 0.80 kHz	1.18 V

10. Increase the frequency above the center frequency until the output voltage V_{out} is again reduced to 0.707 of the maximum value found in Step 8. Record the upper half-power frequency f_2 and the corresponding resistor voltage V_{out}. (Ensure that the output of the signal generator is at 2.0 V_p.)

f_2 = 13.06 kHz	1.18 V

CONCLUSIONS

11. For each voltage measurement in Table 25-2, determine the voltage gain as both a ratio of amplitudes $A_v = V_{out}/E$ and in decibels as

$$[A_v]_{dB} = 20 \log \frac{V_{out}}{E} \tag{25-6}$$

Record the calculated voltage gain and measured phase shift for each frequency in Table 25-3.

12. Plot the data of Table 25-3 on the semi-logaritmic scale of Graph 25-2. Connect the points with the best smooth continuous curve.
13. Compare the measured cutoff frequencies of Step 9 and 10 to the theoretical frequencies determined in Steps 1 and 2.

The lower cutoff is approx. 200 Hz less and the upper cutoff is approx. 3 kHz high.

14. How do the actual voltage gain and phase shift responses of the output voltage compare to the predicted responses?

The actual data correspond very closely to the theoretical.

f	$A_v = Vout/E$	$[A_v]_{dB}$	θ
100 Hz	0.097	–20.3 dB	+83.3°
200 Hz	0.191	–14.4 dB	+76.7°
400 Hz	0.359	–8.9 dB	+64.4°
800 Hz	0.590	–4.6 dB	+45.1°
1 kHz	0.660	–3.6 dB	+37.7°
2 kHz	0.805	–1.9 dB	+14.7°
4 kHz	0.830	–1.6 dB	–6.2°
8 kHz	0.730	–2.7 dB	–28.5°
10 kHz	0.675	–3.4 dB	–36.0°
20 kHz	0.445	–7.0 dB	–57.8°
40 kHz	0.246	–12.1 dB	–72.7°
80 kHz	0.127	–17.9 dB	–81.2°
100 kHz	0.102	–19.8 dB	–83.0°

Table 25-3

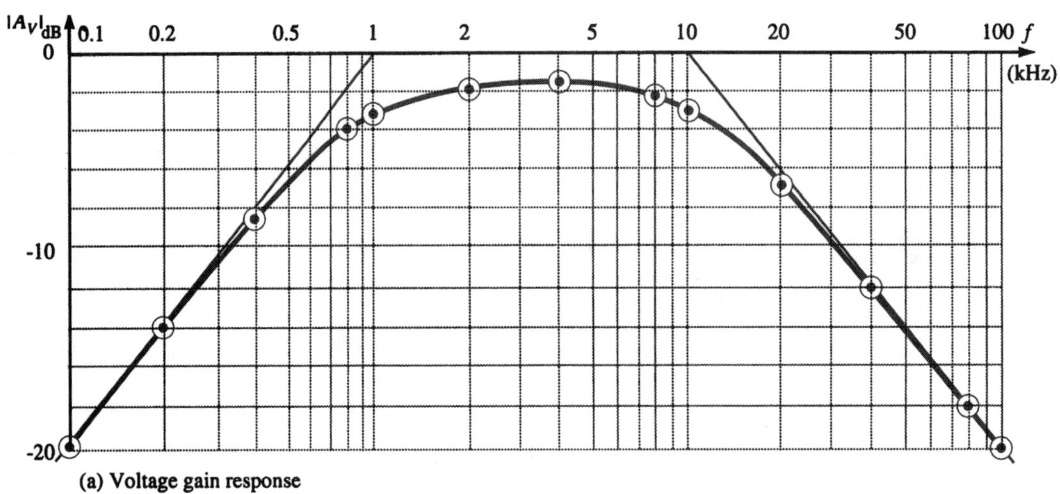

(a) Voltage gain response

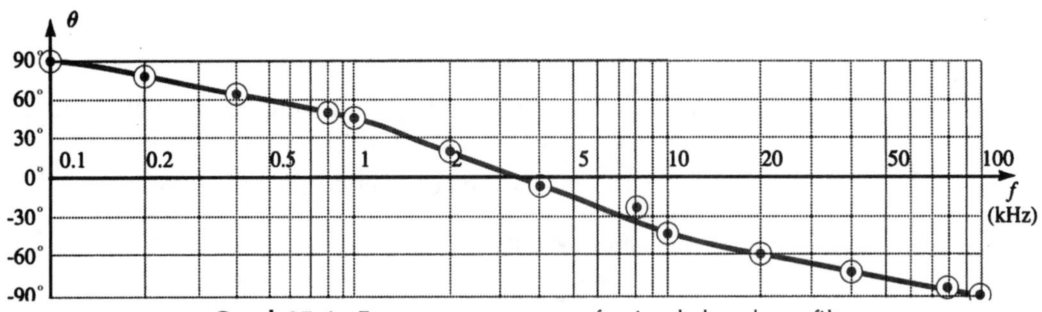

Graph 25-1 Frequency response of a simple bandpass filter

NAME ______________________

DATE ______________________

CLASS ______________________

LAB 26

Voltage, Current, and Power in Balanced Three-Phase Systems

OBJECTIVES

After completing this lab, you will be able to

- verify line and phase voltage relationships for a Y-load,
- verify line and phase current relationships for a Δ-load,
- verify the single-phase equivalent method of analysis.
- measure power in a three-phase system

EQUIPMENT REQUIRED

- ☐ ac ammeters (DMMs with 2-A ranges are adequate)
- ☐ DMMs
- ☐ Single Phase wattmeter (2 required)

POWER SUPPLY

- ☐ Three-phase 120/208 V (60 Hz), preferably variable such as by means of a 3-phase autotransformer

COMPONENTS

- ☐ Resistors: 100-Ω, 200-W (3), 250-Ω, 200-W (3)
- ☐ Capacitors: 10 μF, non-electrolytic, rated for operation at 120 VAC (3 required)

EQUIPMENT USED

Instrument	Manufacturer/Model No.	Serial No.
Single-phase wattmeters		
ac Ammeter or DMM		
DMMs		

Table 26-1

TEXT REFERENCE

Section 24.1 THREE-PHASE VOLTAGE GENERATION
Section 24.3 BASIC THREE-PHASE RELATIONSHIPS
Section 24.5 POWER IN BALANCED SYSTEMS
Section 24.6 MEASURING POWER IN THREE-PHASE CIRCUITS

DISCUSSION

Y-Loads. For a Y-Load, Figure 26-1, line-to-line voltages are $\sqrt{3}$ times line-to-neutral voltages and each line-to-line voltage leads its corresponding line-to-neutral voltage by 30°. Thus,

$$\mathbf{V}_{ab} = \sqrt{3}\ \mathbf{V}_{an}\angle 30^\circ \qquad (26\text{-}1)$$

Current in the neutral of a balanced system (if a neutral line is present), is zero.

Δ-Loads. The magnitude of line current for a balanced Δ-Load, Figure 26-2, is $\sqrt{3}$ times the magnitude of the phase current and each line current lags its corresponding phase current by 30°. Thus,

$$\mathbf{I}_a = \sqrt{3}\ \mathbf{I}_{ab}\angle -30^\circ \qquad (26\text{-}2)$$

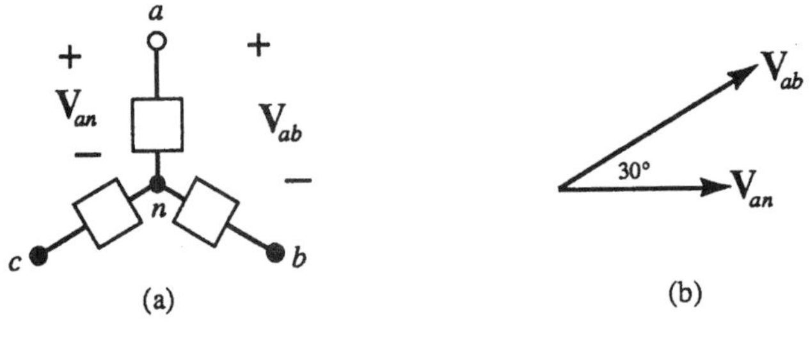

(a) Circuit *(b) Voltage relationships*

Figure 26-1 A balanced Y-load

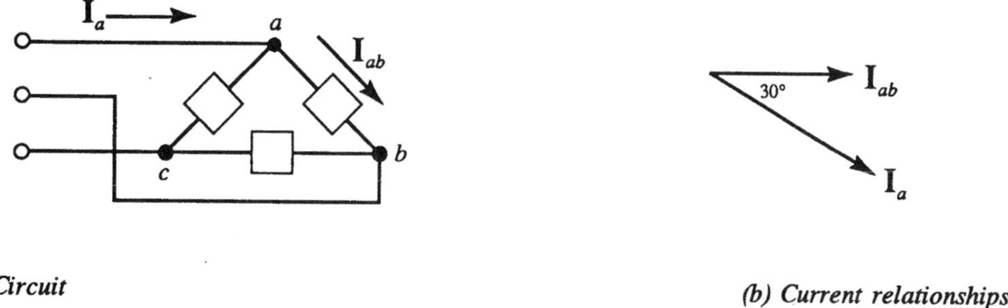

(a) Circuit

(b) Current relationships

Figure 26-2 A balanced Δ-load

> **Safety Note**
> In this lab, you will be working with 120/208 VAC. Such voltages are dangerous and you must be aware of and observe safety precautions. Familiarize yourself with your laboratory's safety practices. **Always ensure that power is off when you are assembling, changing or otherwise working on your circuit.** If possible, use a variable ac power supply (such as a three-phase variable autotransformer) as the source. Start at zero volts and gradually increase the voltage while watching the meters for signs of trouble. In any event, have your instructor check your circuit before you energize it. **USE EXTREME CAUTION IN THIS LAB.**

Equivalent Y and Δ-Loads. For purposes of analysis, a balanced Δ-load may be replaced by an equivalent balanced Y-load with

$$\mathbf{Z}_{\mathrm{Y}} = \mathbf{Z}_{\Delta}/3 \tag{26-3}$$

Single-Phase Equivalent. Since all three phases of a balanced system are identical, any one phase can be taken to represent the behaviour of all. This permits you to reduce a circuit to its *single-phase equivalent*.

Power in Three-Phase Systems. Power in a balanced three-phase system is three times the power to one phase. Power to one phase is given by

$$P_{\phi} = V_{\phi} I_{\phi} \cos \theta_{\phi} \tag{26-4}$$

where V_{ϕ} and I_{ϕ} are the magnitudes of the phase voltage and current and θ_{ϕ}, the angle between them, is the angle of the phase load impedance. This formula applies to both Y and Δ loads. Total power is three times this.

An alternate power formula based on line voltages and currents is

$$P_{\mathrm{T}} = \sqrt{3}\, V_{\mathrm{L}} I_{\mathrm{L}} \cos \theta_{\phi} \tag{26-5}$$

where V_{L} and I_{L} are the magnitudes of the line-to-line voltages and line currents respectively. This formula applies to both Y and Δ loads. Note that the angle in this formula is the angle of the load impedance—it is not the angle between $\mathbf{V}_{\mathrm{L}}$ and $\mathbf{I}_{\mathrm{L}}$.

Measuring Power in Three-Phase Systems. For a 3-wire load, you need only two wattmeters, while for a 4-wire load, you need three wattmeters, Figure 26-3. Note however, the use of individual wattmeters as illustrated here is giving way to the use of integrated, multifunction meters (recall Figure 17-23) that incorporate power/energy measurement for all 3 phases in a single package.

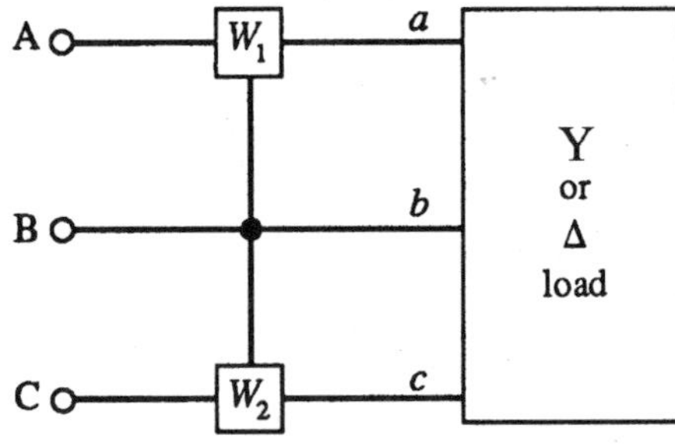

(a) Two-wattmeter method

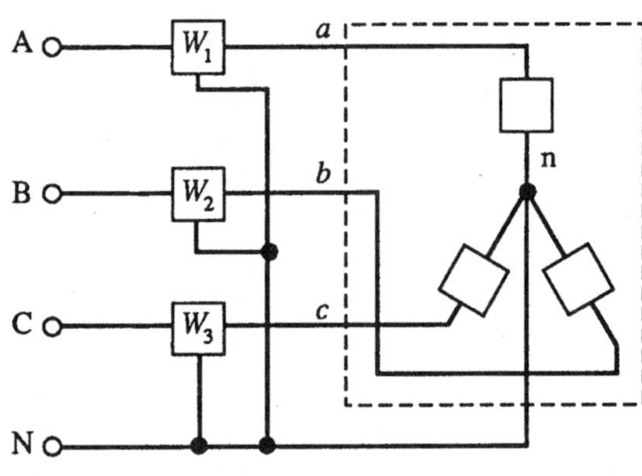

(b) Three-wattmeter method

Figure 26-3 Measuring power in three-phase systems.

MEASUREMENTS

> **General Safety Notes**
>
> 1. With power off, assemble your circuit and have your lab partner double check it.
>
> 2. Have your instructor check the circuit before you energize it. If you are using a Powerstat or other variable ac source, gradually increase voltage from zero, watching the meters for signs of trouble.
>
> 3. Turn power off before changing your circuit for the next test.
>
> Check with your instructor for specific safety instructions.

PART A: Voltages and Currents for a Y-Load

1. With power off, set up the circuit of Figure 26-4. Use DMMs with a current range of 2 A or more to measure current. Observe all saftey precautions—see box.
   a. Set E_{AN} to 120 V (or as close as you can get it) using a DMM, then measure all line-to-neutral and line-to-line voltages at the load. Measure all currents (line and neutral). Record in Table 26.2. Do your measurements confirm the magnitude relationship of Eq. 26-1? $V_{ab} = \sqrt{3}\ V_{an} = \sqrt{3}(120\text{ V}) = 208\text{ V}$ Yes

V_{an}	V_{bn}	V_{cn}	V_{ab}	V_{bc}	V_{ca}	I_a	I_b	I_c	I_n
120V	120V	120V	208V	208V	208V	1.2A	1.2A	1.2A	0A

Table 26-2

   b. Turn power off and remove the neutral conductor from between n and N. Measure the line currents again. Are they the same as in Test 1(a)? Yes
   c. Using the measured source voltage and load resistance, compute the magnitude of the line current and compare to the measured value.

$$I_a = \frac{E_{AN}}{Z_{an}} = \frac{120\text{ V}}{100\ \Omega} = 1.2\text{ A}$$

Should be very close.

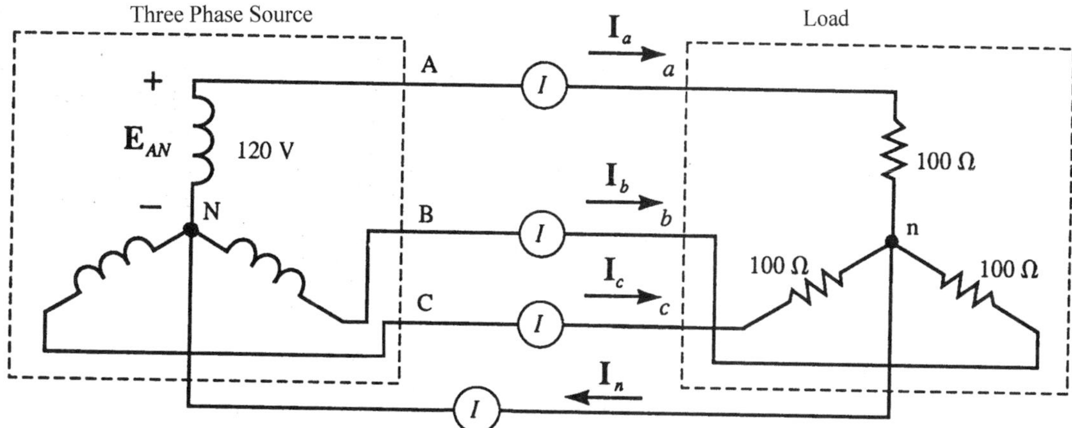

Figure 26-4 Circuit for Test 1. Each resistor is rated 200-W.

PART B: Power to a Y-Load

2. With power off, add wattmeters as in Figure 26-5. Adjust E_{AN} to the same value you used in Part A. (Check currents and note if any have changed. They shouldn't have.)

   W_1 = 216 W W_2 = 216 W

Answers to Part B, questions 3 and 4 are at end of lab.

3. Using circuit analysis, determine P_T. Now sum the wattmeter readings. How well do results agree?
4. Using circuit analysis, determine what W_1 should read. Compare it to the actual reading. Repeat for W_2.

PART C: Power to a Y-Load (Continued)

5. De-energize the circuit and add capacitors as in Figure 26-6. Set the voltage as in Part A. Measure line current and power and record.

   I = 1.28 A W_1 = 263 W W_2 = 169 W

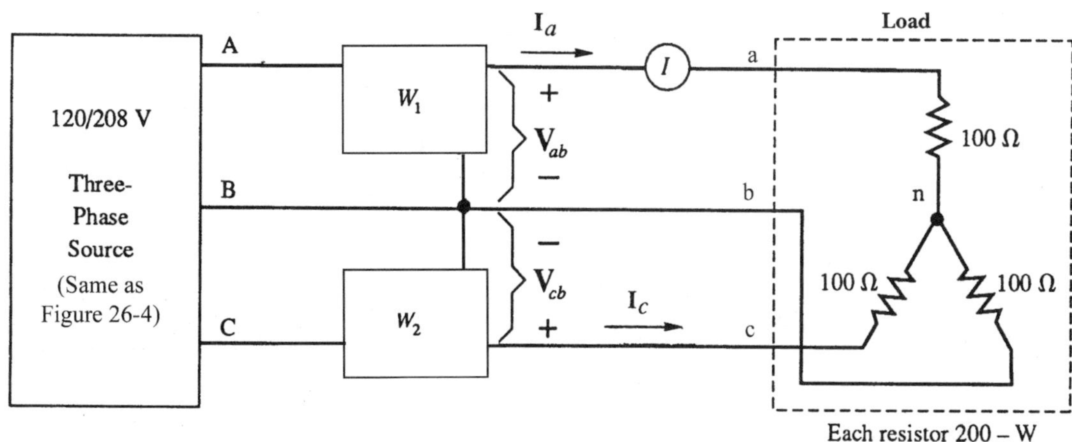

Figure 26-5 Circuit for Test 2 (For details of the 3-phase source, see Figure 26-4

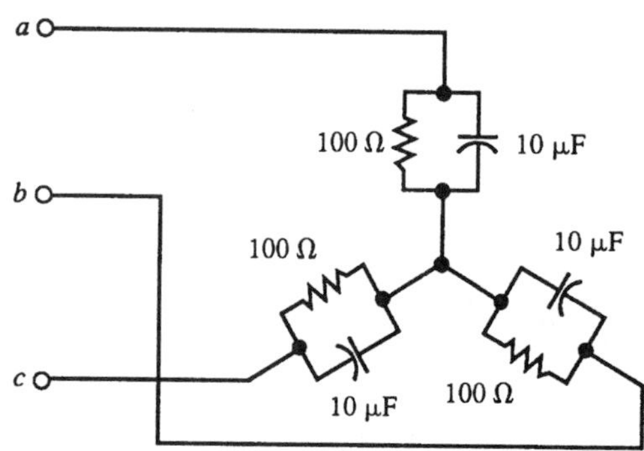

Figure 26-6 Load for Test 5

Answers to Part C, questions 5a and 5b are at end of lab.

a Although the wattmeter readings change, total power should remain unchanged. Why? Verify by using circuit analysis techniques to compute P_T.

b. Using circuit analysis techniques, compute the reading of W_1. Compare to the measured value. Repeat for W_2.

PART D: Currents for a Δ-Load

$I_a = \sqrt{3}\ I_{ab} = \sqrt{3}(0.832)$ $= 1.44$ A ∴ yes

6. Assemble the circuit of Figure 26-7, using 250-Ω resistors. Measure line current I_a and phase current I_{ab}. Do your measurements confirm the magnitude relationship of Eq. 26-2?

$I_a =$ 1.44 A $I_{ab} =$ 0.832 A

Part E: Power to a Δ-Load

7. De-energize the circuit and add wattmeters as in Figure 26-3(a). Set the voltage as in Test A. Measure power and record.

$W_1 =$ 259 W $W_2 =$ 259 W

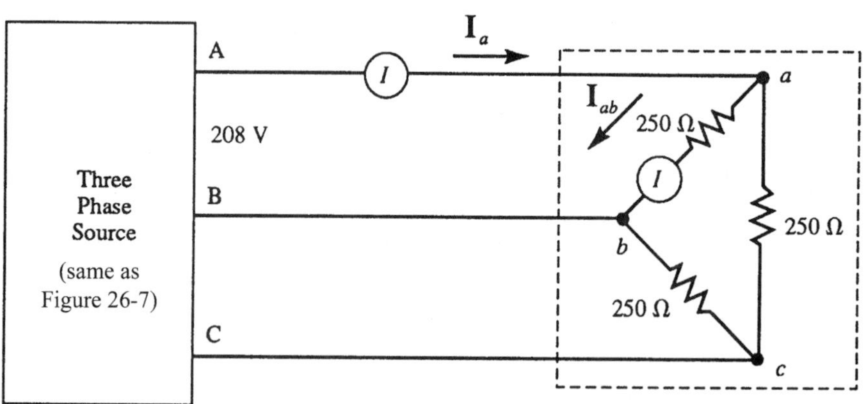

Figure 26-7 Circuit for Test 6. For three phase source, see Figure 26-4.

8. Using circuit analysis techniques, analyze the circuit of Figure 26-7, computing line current, total power and the reading of each wattmeter. Compare your computed results to the measured results. How well do they agree?

PART F: The Single Phase Equivalent

9. Consider the three-phase loads of Figure 26-8(a). (Do not assemble this circuit.) Each resistor of the Y is 250 Ω and each resistor of the Δ is 300 Ω. Source voltage is 120-V, line-to-neutral.
   a. Convert the Δ load to a Y-equivalent then convert the circuit to its single-phase equivalent. Sketch as Figure 26-8(b).
   b. Assemble the single-phase equivalent. Set the source voltage as in Test A and measure line current.

   E_{AN} = 120 V I_A = 1.68 A

   c. Analyze the single-phase equivalent and compare calculated current I_A to that measured in (b).

   $$I_A = \frac{120\text{ V}}{250\Omega} + \frac{120\text{ V}}{100\ \Omega} = 0.48\text{ A} + 1.2\text{ A} = 1.68\text{ A (Same)}$$

PROBLEMS

See pages 544, 545, and 546 for solutions

10. Assume each resistor of the Δ-load of Figure 26-8(a) is replaced with a 10-F capacitor.
    a. Convert the circuit to its single-phase equivalent and sketch.
    b. Calculate the magnitude of the line current I_A.

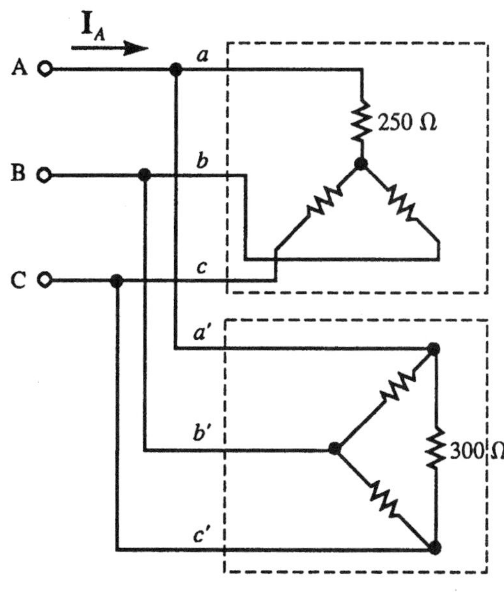

(a) Three-phase circuit

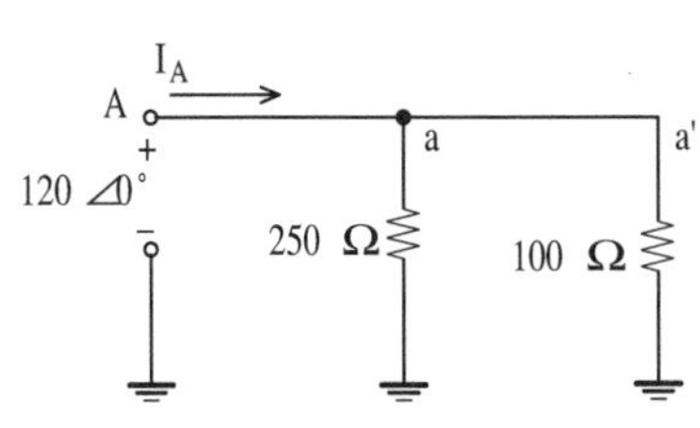

(b) Single phase equivalent

Figure 26-8 Circuit for Test 9

c. Calculate the magnitude of the phase current in the Δ-load.
d. Calculate total power to the combined load.

COMPUTER ANALYSIS

11. Using MultiSIM or PSpice, verify the currents computed in Question 10.

See following pages for solution.

FOR FURTHER INVESTIGATION AND DISCUSSION

> **MultiSIM Users**
> The version of MultiSIM current at the time of writing does not permit you to do this full investigation, as it is only able to plot voltages with respect to ground. Because of this limitation, the only part of this exercise that you can do is Part a, phase voltages.

Using MultiSIM or PSpice, set up the three-phase source of Figure 26-4 and investigate three-phase voltage waveforms. (Since you need time varying waveforms here, use VSIN as your source if you are using PSpice and select Transient Analysis.) Use the following to guide your analysis.

a. Plot waveforms for phase voltages v_{AN}, v_{BN}, and v_{CN}.
b. Repeat for line voltages v_{AB}, v_{BC}, and v_{CA}.
c. Plot v_{AN} and v_{AB} on the same graph; then, using the cursor, measure values and verify the magnitude and phase relationships of Eq. 26-1.

Write a short report confirming how your study verifies the results discussed in the text.

Part B Solution

3. $I_\varphi = \dfrac{120\text{V}}{100\Omega} = 1.2\text{A} \qquad P_\varphi = (120\text{V})(1.2\text{A}) = 144 \text{ W}$

$P_T = 3\,P_\varphi = 3(144) = 432 \text{ W}$

Check $W_1 + W_2 = 432 \text{ W}$

4.

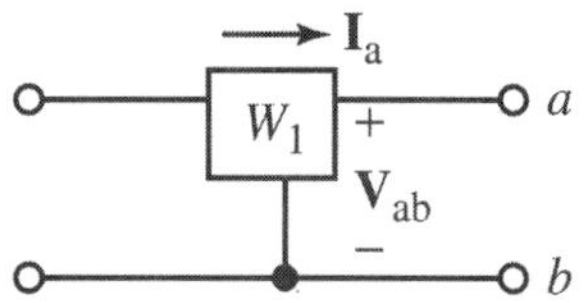

$\mathbf{V}_{an} = 120\ \angle 0^\circ$

$\mathbf{I}_a = 1.2\text{A}\ \angle 0^\circ$

$\mathbf{V}_{ab} = 208\ \angle 30^\circ$

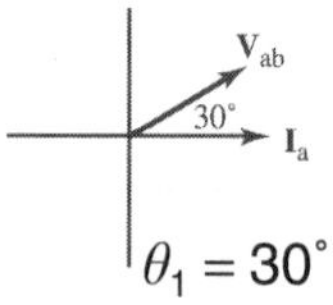

$\theta_1 = 30^\circ$
where
θ_1 = angle between $\mathbf{V}_{ab}$ and $\mathbf{I}_a$

$W_1 = \mathbf{V}_{ab}\,\mathbf{I}_a \cos\theta_1$
$= (208)(1.2)\cos 30^\circ$
$= 216 \text{ W}$ (Same as measured)

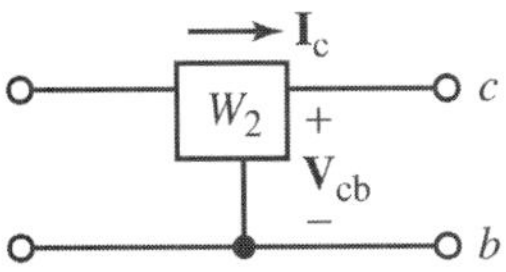

$\mathbf{V}_{bc} = 208\ \angle{-90^\circ}$ $\mathbf{V}_{cb} = -\mathbf{V}_{bc} = 208\ \angle 90^\circ$

$\mathbf{I}_c = \dfrac{\mathbf{V}_{cn}}{\mathbf{Z}_{cn}} = 1.2\text{A}\ \angle{+120^\circ}$

$W_2 = \mathbf{V}_{cb}\,\mathbf{I}_c \cos\theta_2$

$= (208)(1.2)\cos 30^\circ$

$= 216\text{ W}$ (Same as measured)

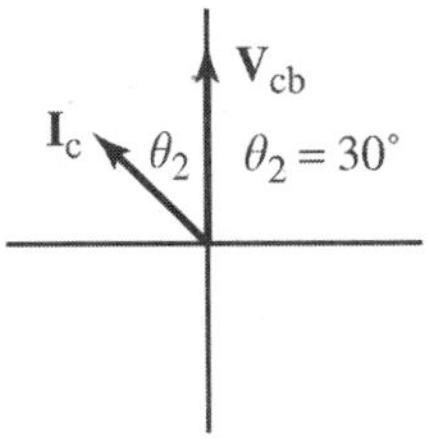

$\theta_2 = 30^\circ$

Part C Solution

5a. $P_\varphi = \dfrac{V_\varphi^2}{R_\varphi} = \dfrac{(120\text{ V})^2}{100\ \Omega} = 144\text{ W}$ which is the same as before.

$P_T = 3P_\varphi = 3(144\text{ W}) = 432\text{ W}$

The capacitors dissipate no power, therefore power does not change. However, they change the power factor of the load, therefore meter readings change. However, their sum is the same as before.

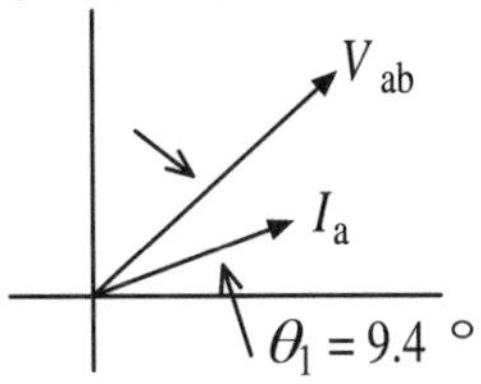

b. $\mathbf{Z}_\varphi = (-j265\ \Omega)||(100\ \Omega) = 93.6\Omega\ \angle{-20.6^\circ}\ \therefore\ \theta_\varphi = -20.6^\circ$

Consider W_1: $\mathbf{V}_{ab} = 208\text{ V}\angle 30^\circ$

$\mathbf{I}_a = 1.2\text{ A}\angle 20.6^\circ\ \therefore\ \theta_1 = 9.4^\circ$

$\theta_1 = 9.4^\circ$

$W_1 = V_{ab}\,I_a\cos\theta_1 = (208\text{V})(1.28\text{A})\cos 9.4^\circ = 263\text{ W}$

Similarly: $W_2 = (208\text{ V})(1.28\text{ A})\cos 50.6^\circ = 169\text{ W}$

Same as measured

Part E Solution

8. $I_{ab} = \dfrac{V_{ab}}{Z_{ab}} = \dfrac{(208\text{ V})}{250\ \Omega} = = 0.832\text{ A}\ \therefore$ $I_a = \sqrt{3}(0.832) = 1.44\text{ A}$ $\therefore \mathbf{I}_a = 1.44\ \angle 0^\circ$

$P_T = 3P_\varphi = 3\left\{\dfrac{(208\text{ V})^2}{250\ \Omega}\right. = 519\text{ W}$

$\left.\begin{matrix}\mathbf{V}_{ab} = 208\text{ V}\angle 30^\circ \\ \mathbf{I}_a = 1.44\ \angle 0^\circ\end{matrix}\right\}$ Thus $W_1 = (208\text{ V})(1.44\text{A})\cos 30^\circ = 259.4\ W$

Similarly, $W_2 = 259.4\text{ W}$ $\therefore\ W_1 + W_2 = 518.8\text{ W}$ Note: $P_T = W_1 + W_2\ \therefore$ agrees

Problems

10. The equivalent capacitance to use in the Y is 30 μF. Thus:

a.

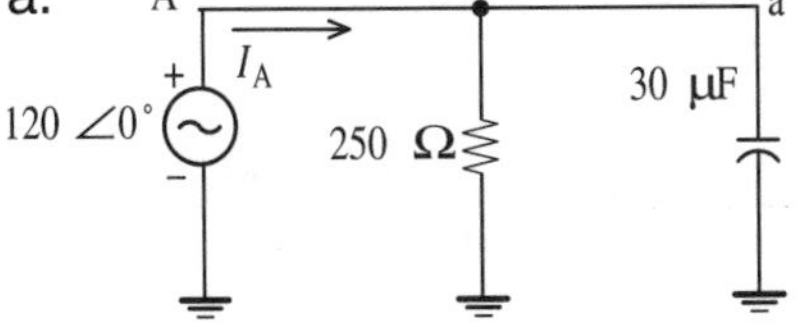

$X_C = \dfrac{1}{\omega C} = 88.4\ \Omega$

b. $I_A = \dfrac{120\angle 0^\circ}{250\ \Omega} + \dfrac{120\angle 0^\circ}{-j88.4\ \Omega}$

$= 1.44\text{ A}\angle 70.5^\circ$ $\therefore \mathbf{I}_a = 1.44\text{ A}$

c. $I_{a'b'} = \frac{V_{a'b'}}{Z_{a'b'}} = \frac{208\text{ V}}{3(88.4\ \Omega)} = 0.784\text{ A}$

d. Power to capacitor is zero.

Thus, $P_T = 3P_y = 3\left\{\frac{(120\text{ V})^2}{250\ \Omega}\right\} = 57.6\text{ W}$

Computer Analysis

11. **MultiSIM:** The schematic is shown below. Remember that MultiSIM does not accept negative angles; use 240° instead of –120° for $\mathbf{E}_{BN}$. (If you are using MultiSIM 2001, you will need to use an angle of 120° for $\mathbf{E}_{BN}$, and 240° for $\mathbf{E}_{CN}$ instead of the angles shown. This is because MultiSIM 2001 doesn't accept angles as expected—recall the notes on pages 525 and 560 of the text. Click the power swith to ON to initiate simulation. Note that answers agree exactly with the currents computed in Problem 10.

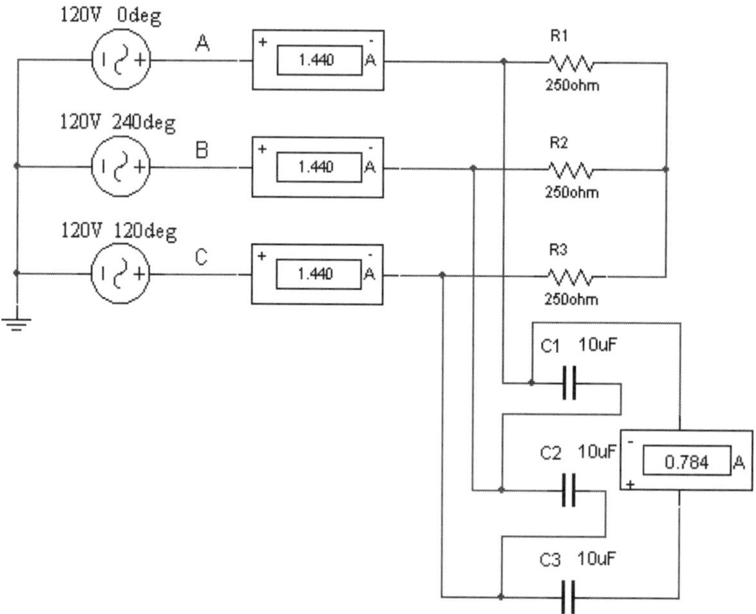

PSpice: The PSpice solution looks like the solution above, except that IPRINT devices are used to measure current. (Be sure to configure them for AC operation.) Use VAC for all sources. (Note that PSpice accepts negative angles, so you can enter –120° for $\mathbf{E}_{BN}$ rather than 240° as indicated above.) Follow the general procedure outlined on page 904 of the text. Results agree with the answers computed in Problem 10.

NAME ______________________

DATE ______________________

CLASS ______________________

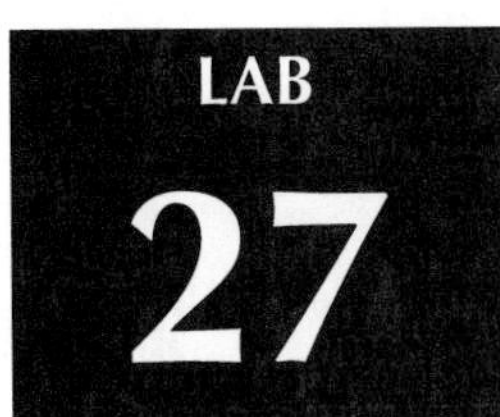

The Iron-Core Transformer

OBJECTIVE

After completing this lab, you will be able to

- verify the turns ratio and phase relationships for a transformer,
- verify the concept of reflected impedance,
- determine the frequency response of an audio transformer,
- measure the regulation of a power transformer.

Safety Note
In parts of this lab, you will be working with 120 VAC. This is a dangerous voltage and you must be aware of and observe safety precautions. Familiarize yourself with your lab's safety practices and use extreme caution at all times. Always ensure that power is off when you are assembling, changing or otherwise wotking on circuits with dangerous voltages.

EQUIPMENT REQUIRED

☐ Oscilloscope
☐ DMM
☐ Signal or function generator

COMPONENTS

☐ Resistors: 10-Ω, 100-Ω (each 1/4 W), 10-Ω, 25-W
☐ Audio transformer (Hammond 145F or equivalent)
☐ 120/12.6-V filament transformer (Hammond 167L12 or equivalent)

EQUIPMENT USED

Instrument	Manufacturer/Model No.	Serial No.
Oscilloscope		
DMM		
Signal or function generator		

Table 27-1

TEXT REFERENCE

Section 23.2 THE IRON-CORE TRANSFORMER: THE IDEAL MODEL
Section 23.3 REFLECTED IMPEDANCE
Section 23.8 VOLTAGE AND FREQUENCY EFFECTS

DISCUSSION

We look first at the ideal transformer. An ideal transformer, Figure 27-1(a), is one that is characterized by its turns ratio

$$a = N_p/N_s \tag{27-1}$$

where N_p and N_s are its primary and secondary turns respectively. Voltage and current ratios are given by

$$\mathbf{V}_p/\mathbf{V}_s = V_p/V_s = a \tag{27-2}$$

$$\mathbf{I}_p/\mathbf{I}_s = I_p/I_s = 1/a \tag{27-3}$$

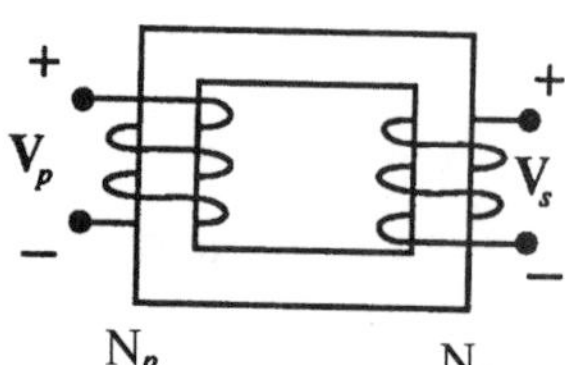

(a) Pictorial

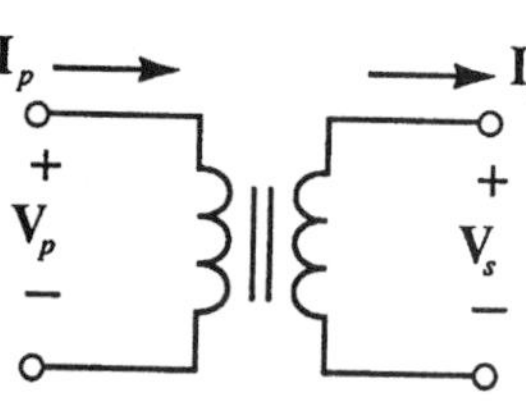

(b) Schematic

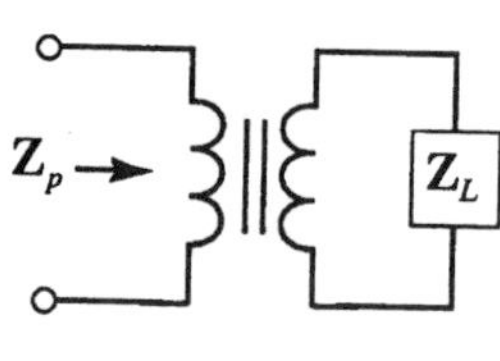

(c) Reflected impedance

Figure 27-1 The ideal transformer

Reflected Impedance. Load impedance $\mathbf{Z}_L$, Figure 27-1(c), is reflected into the primary as

$$\mathbf{Z}_p = a^2\,\mathbf{Z}_L \tag{27-4}$$

All impedances in the secondary (whether part of the load or not) are reflected in this fashion.

Phasing. Depending on the relative direction of windings, the secondary voltage is either in-phase or 180° out-of-phase with respect to the primary—see Practical Note 1.

Real Transformers. Real transformers differ from the ideal in that they have primary and secondary winding resistances, leakage flux, core losses and a few other non-ideal characteristics as described in Sections 23.6 to 23.8 of the text. In this lab, you will observe some of these—you will look in particular at the regulation of a power transformer and the bandwidth limitations of an audio transformer.

Voltage Ratios. The voltage ratio of an iron-core transformer under no-load is the same as it turns ratio. However (because of internal voltage drops), the ratio under load is different—see Note 2.

MEASUREMENTS

PART A: Turns Ratio

1. Consider Figure 27-2. Observing suitable safety precautions, apply full rated voltage to the transformer.

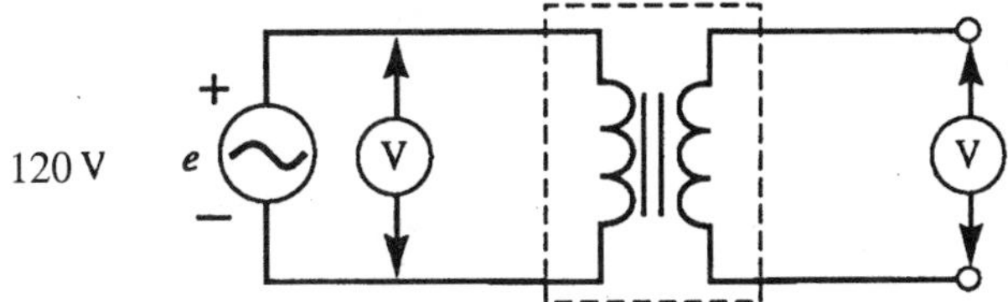

Figure 27-2 Circuit for Test 1. Use a filament transformer (or equivalent) with a 120 V primary and a low voltage (about 20 V or less) secondary.

> **Practical Notes**
> 1. Small transformers usually have color coded leads to identify corresponding (dotted) terminals while power transformers often use letter designations H1, X1, etc.—check the data sheet or nameplate of your transformer for details.
> 2. Some data sheets list the ratio of primary voltage to secondary voltage under load, some under no load and some list both. For example, the Hammond 167L12 suggested for this lab has a no-load specification of 115V/13.8V and a full-load specification of 115V/12.6V.

a. Measure primary and secondary voltages.

Note:
Numbers shown here are for illustrative purposes only.

V_p = 120 V ; V_s = 14.4 V

Determine the turns ratio using Equation 27-2.

$a_{(\text{measured})} = \frac{120\text{ V}}{14.4\text{ V}} = 8.33$

b. Determine the turns ratio from its no-load data sheet and compare it to that of Test 1(a). $a_{(\text{Name-plate})} = \frac{115}{13.8} = 8.33$

PART B: Phase Relationships

2. Using the audio transformer, assemble the circuit of Figure 27-3. Set the source to a 1-kHz sine wave with an amplitude of 8 V (i.e., 16 $V_{p\text{-}p}$). Mark the transformer terminals for reference in determining phase relationships.
   a. Measure the magnitude and phase of v_{cd} relative to the primary voltage and sketch in Figure 27-4. Now reverse the secondary scope leads and sketch v_{dc}. Based on these observations, add the missing dot to the transformer of Figure 27-3. Explain how you determined the position of this dot.

For the waveforms shown in Fig 27-4, v_{cd} is in phase with voltage v_{ab}. Thus, terminal c has the same polarity relative to d as terminal a has relative to b. Thus, a and c are corresponding terminals. Thus, mark c with a dot as shown below.

V_p = 16V V_s = 9V $a = \frac{16}{9} = 1.78$

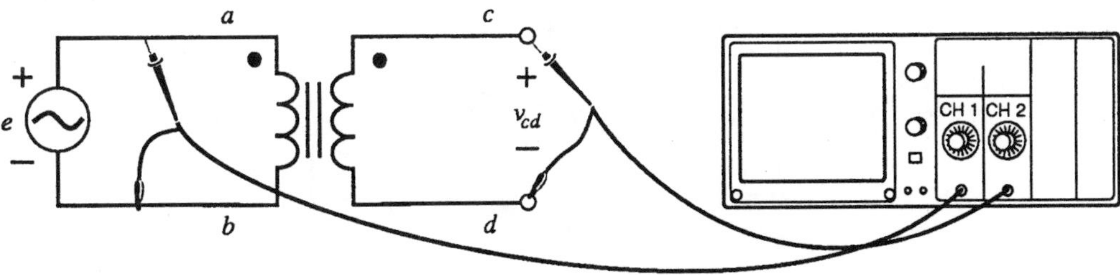

Figure 27-3 Circuit for Test 2 (use the audio transformer)

Note:
Your waveforms may be the same or opposite, depending on how you marked your terminals. If they are opposite, this means the dot in Fig. 27-3 is at terminal d.

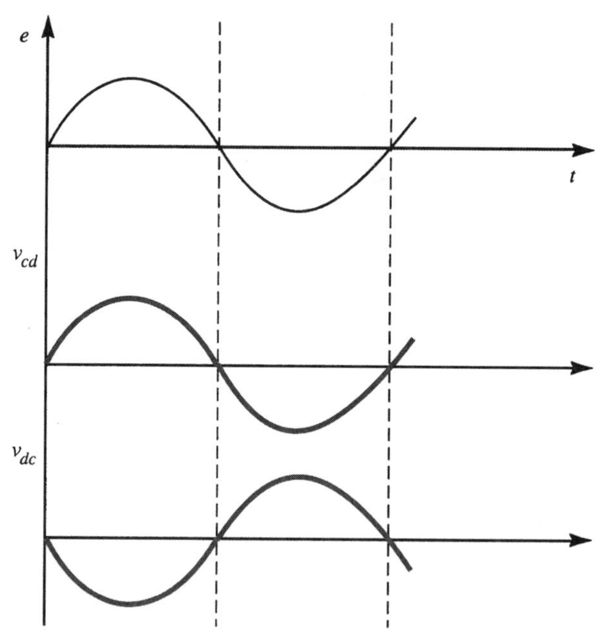

Figure 27-4 Waveforms for Test 2(a)

b. Based on the measurements of Test 2(a), what is the turns ratio for this transformer? a = ________

PART C: Reflected Impedance

3. Measure the 10-Ω sensing resistor and the 100-Ω load resistor, then assemble the circuit of Figure 27-5, using the audio transformer. Connect probes as shown.

R_{sen} = 1.78 R_L = 10

a. Using the differential mode of the oscilloscope, set the input voltage V_p of the transformer to 16 V peak-to-peak, 1-kHz.

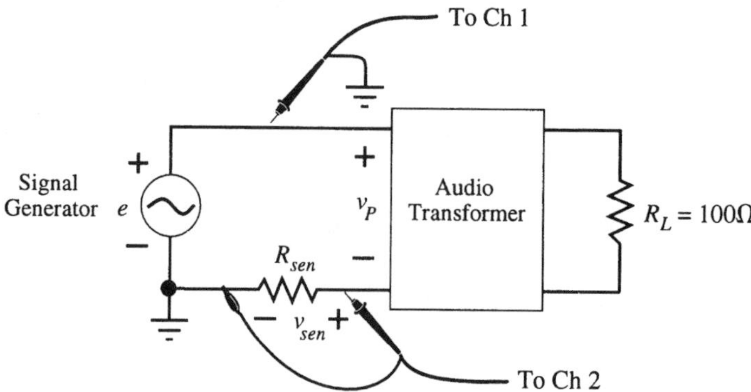

Figure 27-5 Circuit for Test 3

b. Select Ch2 and measure the voltage across the sensing resistor. From this, calculate the primary current.

V_{sen} = ________ I_p = ________

Note:
Interpret these numbers as representative since your transformer will likely be different from mine.

c. Using the results of Test 3(a) and (b), determine the magnitude of the input impedance to the transformer.

$Z_{in(measured)} = \frac{16V}{42mA} = 381\ \Omega$

d. For an ideal transformer, input impedance is $Z_p = a^2 Z_L$. However, real transformers have winding resistance and leakage reactance. Neglecting leakage reactance, we get the circuit of Figure 27-6. The winding resistance can now be reflected into the primary along with the load resistance. Adding to this, the primary winding resistance, we get (approximately) an input impedance Z_{in} of

$$Z_{in} = R_p + a^2(R_s + R_L) \qquad (27\text{-}5)$$

Measurements. Measure primary and secondary winding resistances R_p and R_s using an ohmmeter, then use Equation 27-5 to compute the input impedance for the transformer. Compare to the value determined in (c) i.e., calculate the percent difference. If they differ, what are the likely sources of the difference?

$R_P = 44\ \Omega$

$R_S = 8\ \Omega$

$a = 1.78$

$Z_{in} = 44 + (1.78)^2 (8 + 100) = 386\ \Omega$

$\text{Percent error} = \frac{386-381}{386} \times 100 = 1.6\%$

Sources of error: We neglected leakage reactance and used dc resistance instead of ac resistance

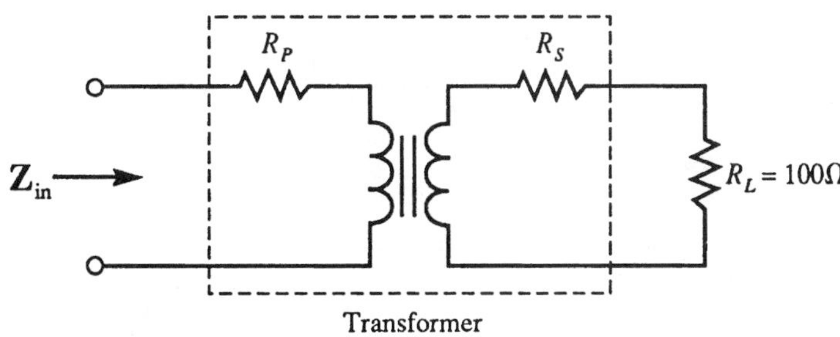

Figure 27-6 Transformer circuit with winding resistance included

Note: Again, interpret these results as representative, as your transformer will likely be different from mine.

For answer to 4c, see Section 23.8 of the text book.

PART D: Frequency Response of a Transformer

4. a. Using the audio transformer, reconnect the circuit of Figure 27-3, but add a 100 Ω load resistor between points *c* and *d*. Maintain the input voltage constant at 6 V (i.e., 12 $V_{p\text{-}p}$) and measure the output voltage and record in Table 27-2.
   b. Compute the ratio of output voltage to input voltage over the range of frequencies tested and plot as Figure 27-7.
   c. From the observed data, what conclusion can you draw about the validity of the ideal model?

f	V_{out}	V_{out}/V_{in}
100 Hz	2.6	0.43
500 Hz	2.7	0.45
1 kHz	2.7	0.45
5 kHz	2.2	0.37
10 kHz	1.8	0.30
15 kHz	1.6	0.27
20 kHz	1.4	0.23

Table 27-2

PART E: Load Voltage Regulation

5. Ideally, a transformer will deliver constant output voltage. In reality, due to internal voltage drops, the output voltage falls as load current increases. In this test, we look at how badly the transformer voltage drops.
   a. Omitting the primary side voltmeter and observing suitable safety precautions, set up the circuit of Figure 27-2 and apply full rated voltage to the transformer.
   b. With a meter, measure the open circuit (no-load) voltage on the 12.6-V winding.

   V_{NL} = 14.2 V

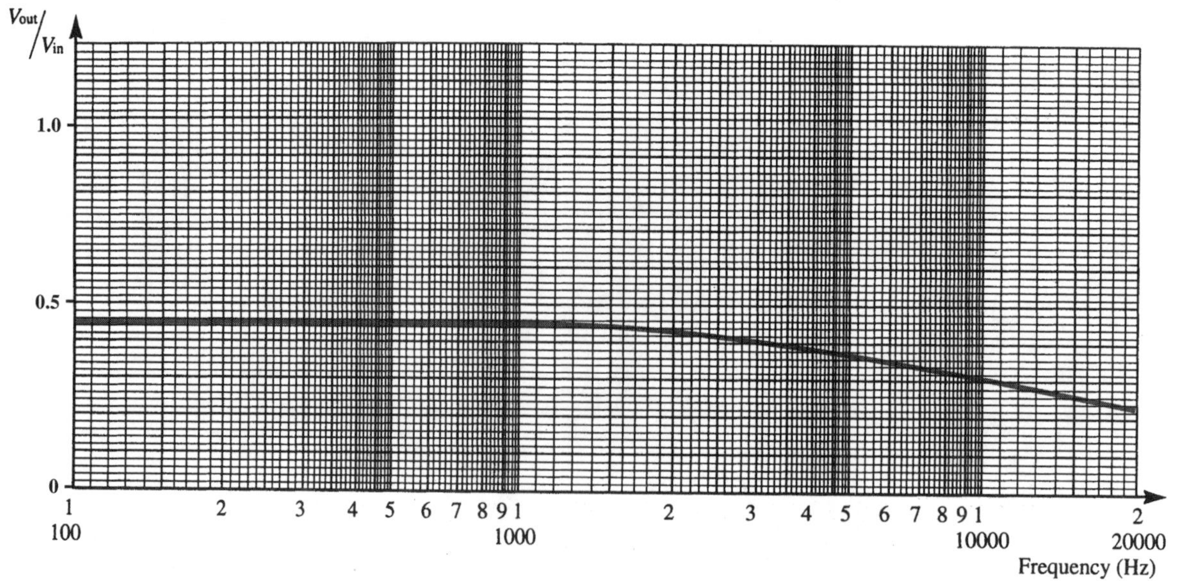

Figure 27-7 Frequency response for an audio transformer

c. Connect a load resistor that will draw full rated current (or nearly full-rated current). (If you use the Hammond 167L12 as recommended, you will need about 6 Ω, capable of dissipating 25 W. Since this is not a standard resistor, use a 10-Ω resistor instead. You will easily observe the regulation.) Measure output voltage under load. V_{FL} = 13.2 V

d. Compute the regulation of the transformer using the formula

$$\text{Regulation} = \left(\frac{V_{NL} - V_{FL}}{V_{FL}}\right) \times 100\%$$

$$\text{Reg} = \left(\frac{14.2 - 13.2}{13.2}\right) \times 100 = 7.6\%$$

PROBLEMS

See page 554 for answers to *Problems*

6. An ideal transformer with a turns ratio of $a = 5$ has a load of $\mathbf{Z}_L = 10\ \Omega\ \angle 30°$. Source voltage is $\mathbf{E} = 120\ \text{V}\ \angle 0°$.
   a. Compute the load voltage and load current as in Example 23-4 of the text.
   b. Using Equation 27-3, compute source current.
   c. Compute the input impedance $\mathbf{Z}_p$.
   d. Using $\mathbf{Z}_p$, compute source current and compare to the result obtained in (b).
7. A certain load requires a voltage that does not exceed 124 V or drop below 117 V. Two transformers are available, each with a no-load voltage of 120 V. Transformer 1 has a rated maximum regulation of ±3% of its no-load voltage and Transformer 2 is rate 120-V ±3 V. Is either transformer suitable for the application? Perform an analysis to find out.

COMPUTER ANALYSIS

Ideal Transformers in MultiSIM and PSpice
MultiSIM: Use the virtual transformer (found in the *Basic* parts bin). Double click its symbol and set parameters as noted in Section 23.12 of the text to make it correspond to the ideal model. Note that MultiSIM requires the use of

8. Using MultiSIM or PSpice and an ideal transformer with turns ratio $a = 5$ and $E = 120$ V, set up and emulate the circuit of Figure 27-3. (Omit the oscilloscope.) (PSpice users: Use source VSIN. Also place a large value resistor (say 100kΩ) across the secondary terminals of the transformer since PSpice does not like floating nodes.) Investigate waveforms, phase relationships and transformation ratios. Specifically, use the cursor to measure voltage magnitudes and in your analysis, use these to verify the turns ratio. Be sure to get printouts for both the in-phase and out-of-phase cases.

See solution on the following pages.

a ground on both sides of the transformer.
PSpice: Use XFRM_LINEAR. (See boxed note in Section 23.12 of the text to refresh your memory on how to set it up to represent an ideal iron-core transformer.)

9. Consider a 10:1 iron-core transformer with R_p = 16 Ω, L_p = 100 mH, R_s = 0.16 Ω, L_s = 1 mH and a load consisting of a 10 μF capacitor in parallel with a 4 Ω resistor. The source is 120 V∠0°.
   a. Using MultiSIM or PSpice, solve for the load voltage. (This is full-load voltage.) Now solve for no-load voltage, then compute regulation.
   b. Solve the above problem manually (with your calculator) and compare results.

See solution on the following pages.

FOR FURTHER INVESTIGATION AND DISCUSSION

Using the equivalent circuit of Figure 23-41 of the text and MultiSIM or PSpice, investigate the frequency response of an audio transformer. Use the following parameter values: R_P = 1 Ω, L_P = 0.125 mH, R_S = 0.04 Ω, L_S = 0.005 mH, R_C = 500 Ω, L_m = 0.1 H, turns ratio a = 5 and a speaker load of 8 Ω, purely resistive. (Omit the stray capacitances). Use a 1 V AC source and run a frequency response curve from 10 Hz to 30 kHz. Submit a printout of your circuit plus the response curve. Write a short analysis of your investigation, describing in your own words the significance of what the curve shows in terms of the transformer's impact on sound quality in an audio system. Other points to cover include 1) over what range does the ideal model apply and why, and 2) what causes the curve to fall off at each end of the frequency spectrum?

Problems

6. a)

$$\mathbf{V}_L = \frac{120\angle 0^\circ}{5} = 24\angle 0^\circ$$

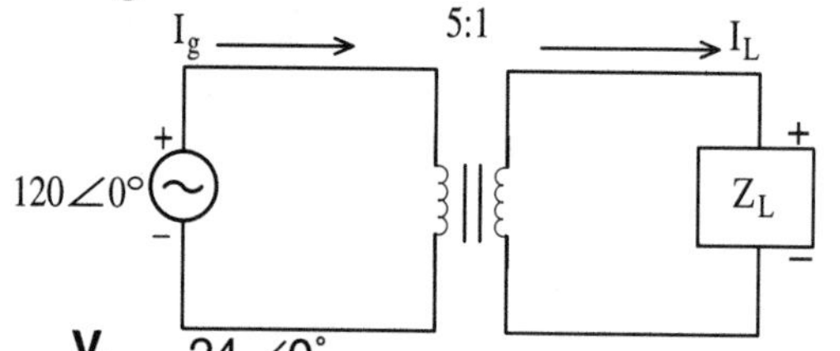

I_g → 5:1 → I_L; 120∠0°; Z_L

$$\mathbf{I}_L = \frac{\mathbf{V}_L}{\mathbf{Z}_L} = \frac{24\angle 0^\circ}{10\angle 30^\circ} = 2.4\text{A}\angle -30^\circ$$

b) $\mathbf{I}_g = \dfrac{\mathbf{I}_L}{a} = 0.48\text{ A}\angle -30^\circ$

c) $\mathbf{Z}_P = a^2\mathbf{Z}_L = (5)^2(10\angle 30^\circ) = 250\Omega\angle 30^\circ$

d) $\mathbf{I}_g = \dfrac{120\text{V}\angle 0^\circ}{250\Omega\angle 30^\circ} = 0.48\text{A}\angle -30^\circ$ (Same)

7. Transformer 1:
V_{out} = 120 V ±(3.5% of 120 V)
= 120 ±4.2 V
∴ could be as low as 115.8 V or as high as 124.2 V
∴ unacceptable

Transformer 2: V_{out} = 120 V ± 3 V
This is within the acceptable limits.
∴ Transformer 2 is suitable.

8. **MultiSIM:** The solution is shown below. Double click the transformer and set the turns ratio as described on page 862 of the text book. (Also set its other parameters as indicated.) Perform a transient analysis and display the source voltage and the output voltage. (The in-phase case is shown below.) To measure the voltage ratio, set the cursor at the peak of the waveform (i.e., at $t = 4.1667$ ms for a 60 Hz voltage), measure both peak voltages, then compute their ratio. You should get 5. To display the out-of-phase solution, move the secondary ground to Point *c* and run the analysis again.

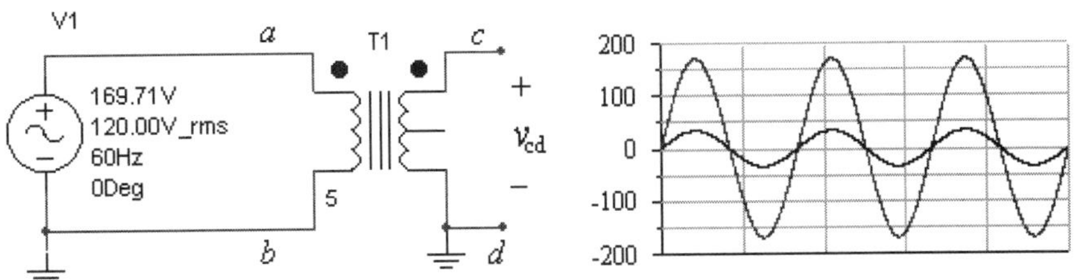

PSpice: The solution is shown below. Double click the transformer and set coupling to 1. Following the procedure of page 862 of the text set the turns ratio to 5.(For example, if you set $L_1 = 25000$ H and $L_2 = 1000$ H, you get $a = 5$.) Run a transient analysis and measure peak voltages with your cursors. As indicated, $a = 170\text{V}/34\text{V} = 5$. To do the out-of-phase case, double click the transformer and set coupling to –5, then run the analysis again.

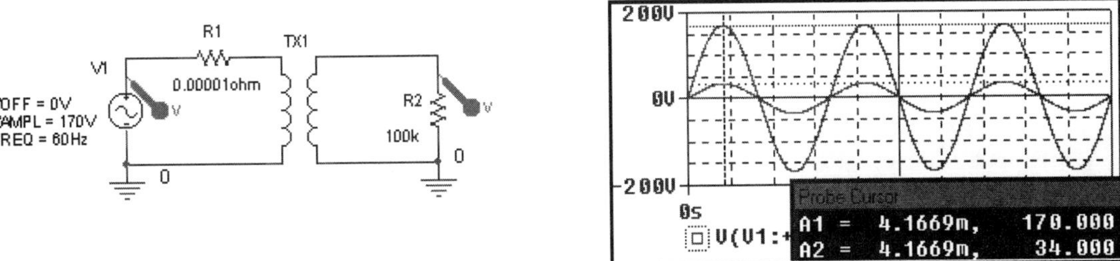

9. **MultiSIM:** The solution is shown below. Double click the transformer and set its parameters as described in Problem 8. Answers agree with the analytic solution shown in Part (b) on the following page.

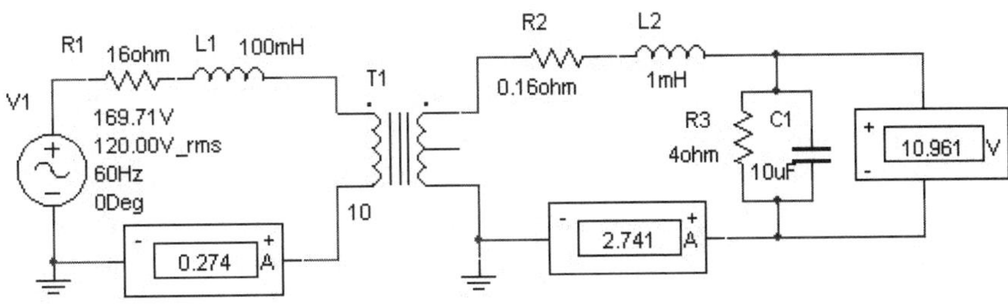

PSpice: The solution is shown below. Use source VAC and AC Sweep for analysis. Set Start and End frequencies to 60Hz and Points to 1. Set the transformer turns ratio to 10 using the procedure described on page 862 of the text. Answers are found in the View Output file. They agree with the analytic solution shown in Part b below.

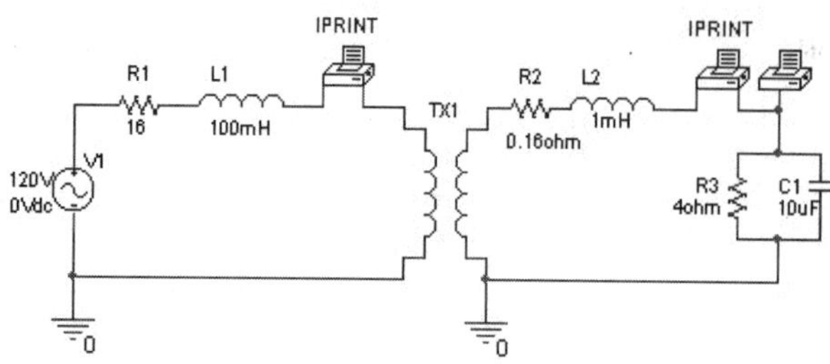

9(b) Analytic Solution:

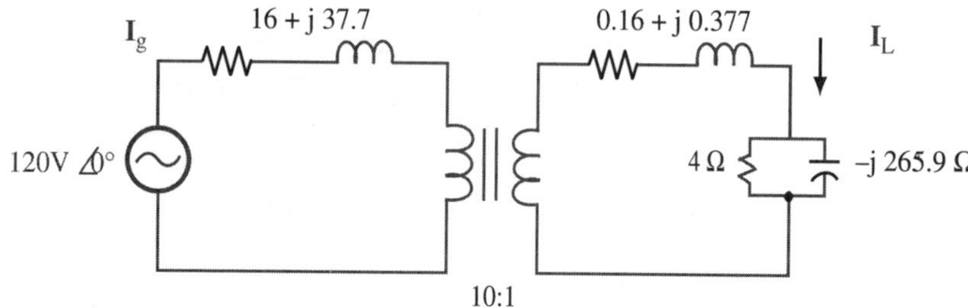

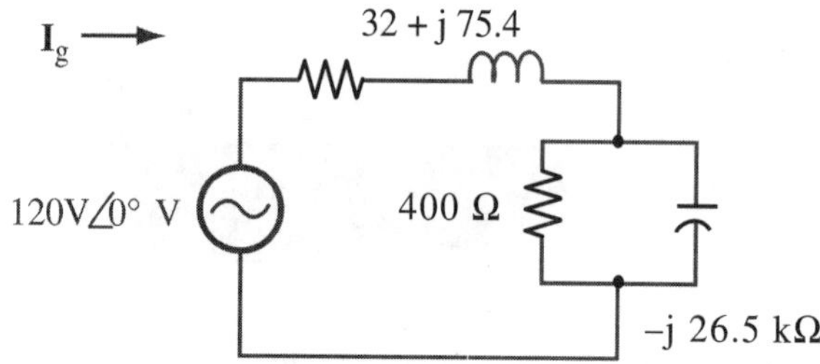

$$\mathbf{I}_g = \frac{120\angle 0^\circ \text{ V}}{32 + j75.4 + 400 \| (-j\,26.5\text{ k})} = 0.274 \text{ A} \angle -9.12^\circ$$

$\mathbf{I}_L = a\,\mathbf{I}_g = 2.74 \text{ A} \angle -9.14^\circ$

$\mathbf{V}_L = \mathbf{I}_L \mathbf{Z}_L = 10.8 \text{ V} \angle -9.99^\circ$

Solution: For Further Investigation and Discussion

The diagrams below show the MultiSIM and PSpice solutions. The basic reasons for the drop-off of the curves at each end are outlined in the text (Section 23.8) and will not be repeated here. The significance on sound quality is that low frequency bass notes are attenuated by the drop off at the low frequency end as are high frequency treble notes by the drop off at the high frequency end. If the low-end drop-off frequency is too high, music loses some of its bass tones, whereas if the high-end drop-off is too low, music loses some of its treble tones. The ideal transformer model represents the flat portion of the curve only.

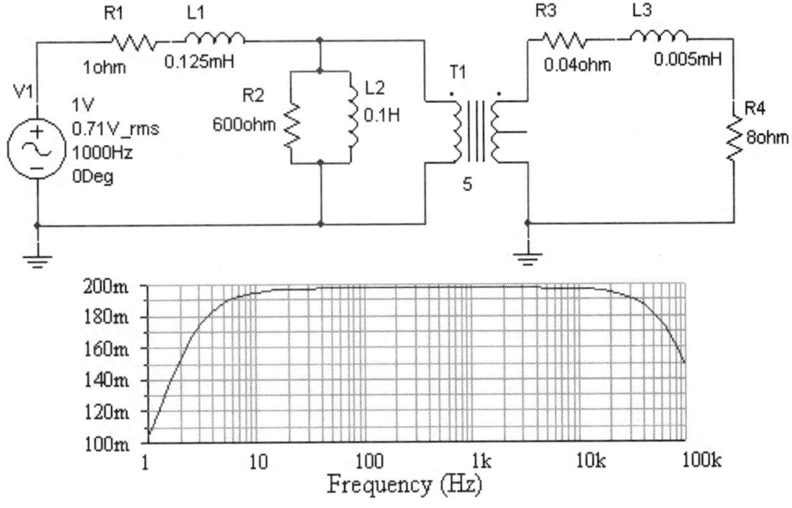

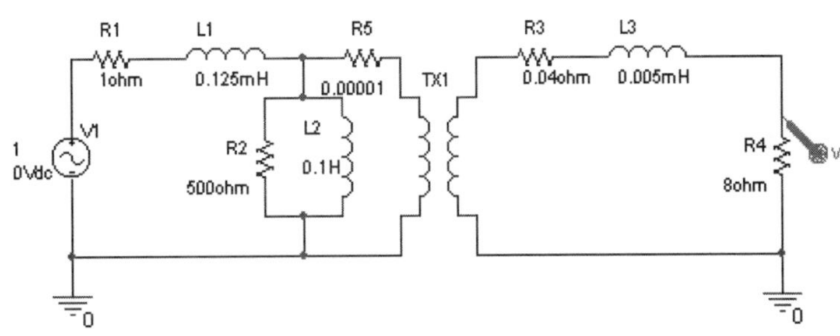

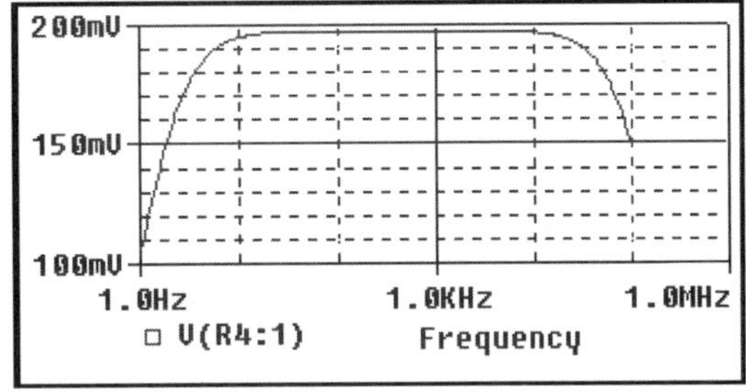

Bonus Investigation: The curves illustrated do not extend down to the half-power points. Broaden the frequency range and determine from the plots the bandwidth between half-power points.

Note

As noted in Lab 14, MultiSIM plots gain versus frequency. Thus, it does not matter what value of voltage you use for input, the result will be as shown.

NAME ______________________

DATE ______________________

CLASS ______________________

LAB 28

Mutual Inductance and Loosely Coupled Circuits

OBJECTIVE

After completing this lab, you will be able to

- determine mutual inductance experimentally,
- measure mutual voltage and verify theoretically,
- compare calculated and measured results for coupled circuits.

EQUIPMENT REQUIRED

- ☐ Oscilloscope, dual channel
- ☐ Signal or function generator
- ☐ Inductance meter or bridge

COMPONENTS

- ☐ 455 kHz IF (*intermediate frequency*) transformer
- ☐ Resistor: 10-Ω, 1/4-W
- ☐ Capacitors: 1-μF, non-electrolytic (two required)

EQUIPMENT USED

Instrument	Manufacturer/Model No.	Serial No.
Oscilloscope		
Signal or function generator		
Inductance meter or bridge		

Table 28-1

TEXT REFERENCE

Section 23.9 LOOSELY COUPLED CIRCUITS
Section 23.10 MAGNETIC COUPLING IN NETWORK ANALYSIS
Section 23.11 COUPLED IMPEDANCE

DISCUSSION

If two coils with mutual coupling are connected in series so that their fluxes add as in Figure 28-1(a), their total inductance is

$$L_{T}+ = L_1 + L_2 + 2M \qquad (28\text{-}1)$$

where L_1 and L_2 are the self-inductances of coils *1* and *2* and M is the mutual coupling between them. If the coils are connected so that their fluxes subtract as in (b), total inductance is

$$L_{T}- = L_1 + L_2 - 2M \qquad (28\text{-}2)$$

The mutual inductance between the coils can be found from the formula

$$M = (L_{T}+ - L_{T}-)/4 \qquad (28\text{-}3)$$

(Since inductances L_1, L_2, L_T+ and L_T- can be measured with a standard inductance meter, you can use Equation 28-3 to determine mutual inductance experimentally.) Self and mutual inductances are related by the formula

$$M = k\sqrt{L_1 L_2} \qquad (28\text{-}4)$$

where k is called the *coefficient of coupling*. For tightly coupled coils, $k = 1$; for loosely coupled coils, k is much less than 1.

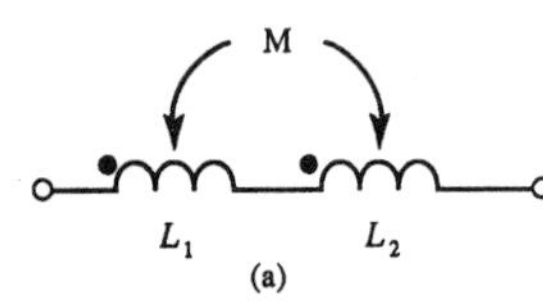

(a) Additive fluxes

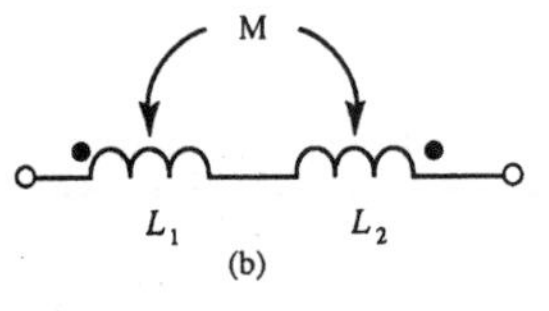

(b) Subtractive fluxes

Figure 28-1 Coupled coils

Equations for Coupled Circuits. If coupled coils are connected as in Figure 28-2(a), their voltages and currents are related by the formulas

$$v_1 = R_1 i_1 + L_1\frac{di_1}{dt} \pm M\frac{di_2}{dt} \qquad (28\text{-}5)$$

$$v_2 = \pm M\frac{di_1}{dt} + R_2 i_2 + L_2\frac{di_2}{dt} \qquad (28\text{-}6)$$

where the sign of M is determined by the dot convention—i.e., if both currents enter (or leave) dotted terminals, then the sign to use with M is positive, while if one current enters a dotted terminal and the other leaves, the sign to use is negative. For sinusoidal excitation as shown in Figure 28-2(b), Equations 28-5 and 28-6 become

$$\mathbf{V}_1 = (R_1 + j\omega L_1)\mathbf{I}_1 \pm j\omega M\mathbf{I}_2 \qquad (28\text{-}7)$$

$$\mathbf{V}_2 = \pm j\omega M\mathbf{I}_1 + (R_2 + j\omega L_2)\mathbf{I}_2 \qquad (28\text{-}8)$$

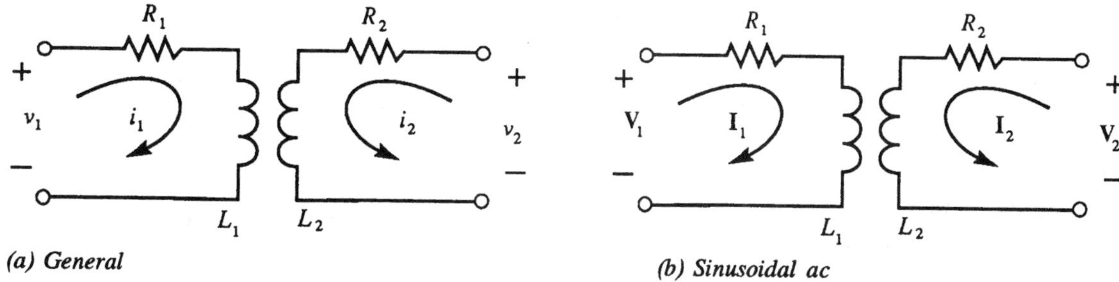

Figure 28-2 Coupled coils

MEASUREMENTS

For this lab, use a 455 kHz IF (*intermediate frequency*) transformer with coils wound on a ferrite core. (Note: Some IF transformers come with small capacitors connected. Make sure you disconnect them.)

Note: All values used in this lab are for illustrative purposes. Depending on the coil you use, your values may be quite different.

PART A: Coil Parameters and Mutual Inductance

1. a. Measure the primary and secondary inductances and resistances using an *LRC* meter or impedance bridge.

L_1 = 3.39 mH R_1 = 44.6 Ω

L_2 = 3.43 mH R_2 = 44.5 Ω

b. Mark the coil ends for identification, then connect the primary and secondary coils in series as in Figure 28-1. Measure the inductance of the series connection, then reverse the connections and measure again.

L_{T+} 7.26 mH L_{T-} = 6.38 mH

Use Equation 28-3 to compute M. M = 0.22 mH

Use Equation 28-4 to compute k. k = 0.0645

Is this transformer loosely coupled or tightly coupled? loosely

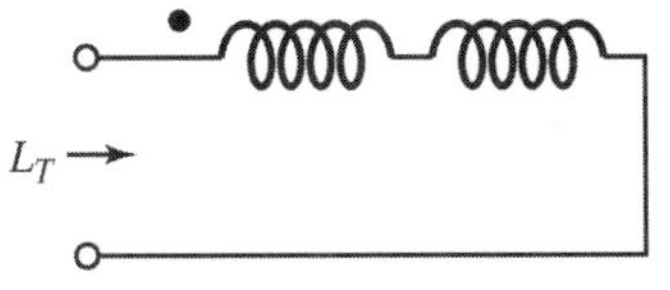

c. Use the results of Test 1(b) to determine the dotted ends for the coils. (Mark the dotted ends as you will need this information later.) Describe how you arrived at this conclusion.

Mark coil 1 as shown. Now measure L_T. If $L_T = L_T^+$,

then mark the left end of coil 2 with a dot also.

PART B: Mutually Induced Voltage

Note
All voltages and currents in PARTs B and C are shown as peak values since measurements are made via a scope.

2. Measure the value of the 10-Ω sensing resistor R_S, then assemble the circuit as in Figure 28-3.

   R_S = 10 Ω

   a. Set the source voltage to 4 V_p (8 $V_{p\text{-}p}$) at f = 1 kHz. Measure $\mathbf{V}_S$, magnitude and angle (using the oscilloscope) and record below. Compute input current $\mathbf{I}_1$, magnitude, and angle. (You can leave the results in peak volts and amps, rather than convert to rms.)

   $\mathbf{V}_S$ = 0.67 V $\angle$–20° $\mathbf{I}_1$ = 67 mA $\angle$–20 (peak)

   b. With Probe 1 still measuring e, move Probe 2 to measure secondary voltage v_2. Measure magnitude and angle.

   $\mathbf{V}_2$ = 94 m V $\angle$72° (peak)

   c. Using the measured values of E, R_1, R_S and L_1, compute current $\mathbf{I}_1$. Thus,

$\omega L_1 = (2\pi)(1000)(3.39\text{mH}) = 21.3\ \Omega$

$$I_1 = \frac{E}{R_1 + R_S + j\omega L_1} = \frac{4\angle 0^\circ\ \text{V}}{54.6 + j21.3} = 68\angle -21^\circ \text{mA}$$

   Compare to the result measured in (a).

   Measured: 67 $\angle$–20° mA
   Computed: 68 $\angle$–21° mA

   Excellent agreement.

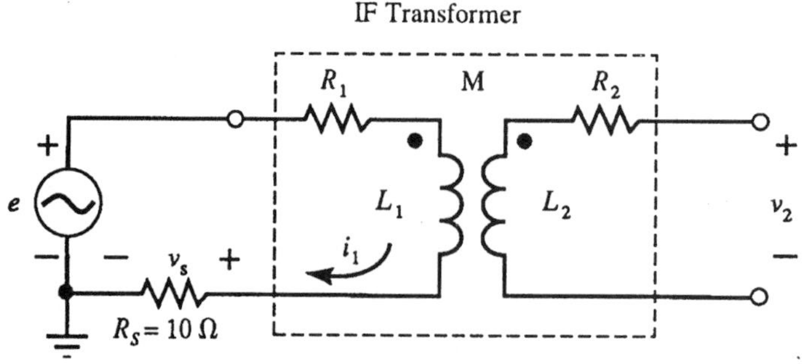

Figure 28-3 Circuit for Test 2. The secondary is open-circuited here.

d. Compute $\mathbf{V}_2$ from the relationship

$$\mathbf{V}_2 = j\omega M\mathbf{I}_1 = (j2\pi \times 1000)\,(0.22\text{mH})\,(68\,\angle{-21}^\circ\text{mA}) = 94\,\angle 69^\circ\text{mV}$$

Compare to the result measured in (b).

Measured: 94 mV $\angle 72^\circ$
Computed: 94 mV $\angle 69^\circ$

Very good agreement.

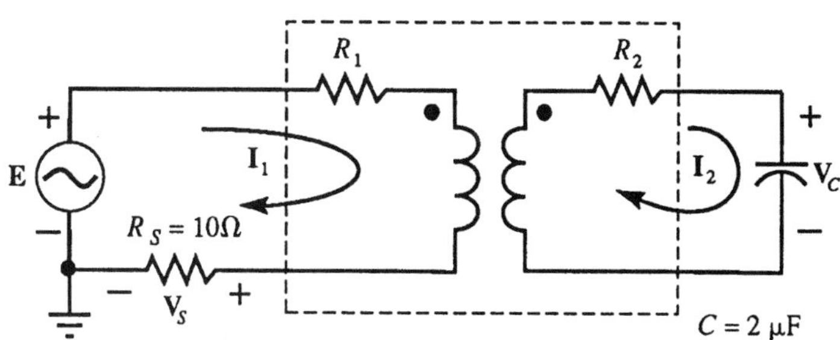

Figure 28-4 Circuit for Test 3

PART C: Coupled Circuit Equations

3. Add 2 μF of capacitance to the secondary circuit as in Figure 28-4.
   a. Set e to 4 V_p (8 $V_{p\text{-}p}$). Carefully measure $\mathbf{V}_S$ and $\mathbf{V}_2$ as before.

      $\mathbf{V}_S =$ 0.67 mV $\angle{-22}^\circ$ $\mathbf{V}_2 =$ 100 mV $\angle 29^\circ$

      Compute current $\mathbf{I}_1 = \mathbf{V}_S/R_1 =$ 67 mA $\angle{-22}^\circ$

See last page of lab for answers to 3b and c and Computer Analysis.

   b. Write mesh equations for this circuit and solve for $\mathbf{I}_1$ and $\mathbf{I}_2$. Using the computed value of $\mathbf{I}_2$, calculate $\mathbf{V}_2$. Compare $\mathbf{I}_1$ and $\mathbf{V}_2$ to the values measured in 3(a). How well do they agree?
   c. Solve for $\mathbf{I}_1$ using the coupled impedance equation

$$\mathbf{Z}_{\text{in}} = \mathbf{Z}_1 + \frac{(\omega M)^2}{\mathbf{Z}_2 + \mathbf{Z}_L}$$

      Compare to the measured value.

COMPUTER ANALYSIS

> **Note re: MultiSIM**
> At the time of writing, MultiSIM has no simple way to handle loosely coupled circuits. Therefore, omit #4 and #5.

Use XFRM_LINEAR for the following.

4. Consider Figure 28-3. Using the parameter values that you measured in Part A, simulate this circuit using PSpice and determine $\mathbf{V}_2$. Compare to the measured value.

5. Simulate the circuit of Figure 28-4 using PSpice. Using the parameter values that you measured in Part A, determine $\mathbf{I}_2$ and $\mathbf{V}_2$. Compare to the measured values.

PROBLEM

See next page for answer to *Problem*

6. Write equations for the circuit of Figure 28-5 and solve for $\mathbf{I}_1$, $\mathbf{I}_2$ and $\mathbf{V}_2$.

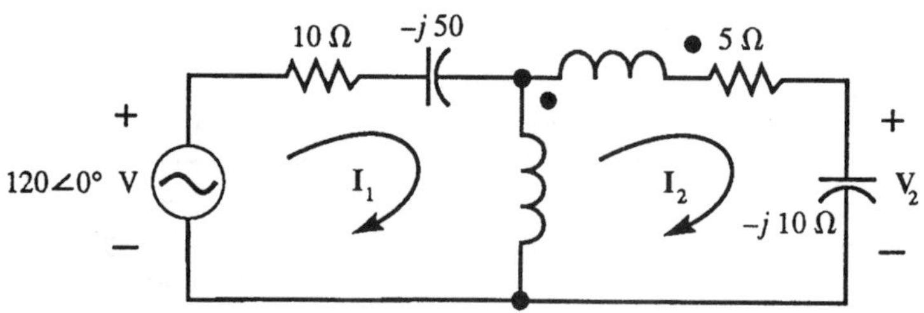

Figure 28-5 $X_{L_1} = 25\ \Omega$ $X_{L_2} = 30\ \Omega$ $X_M = 2\ \Omega$

FOR FURTHER INVESTIGATION AND DISCUSSION

Use PSpice to simulate the circuit of Figure 28-5 at $f = 60$ Hz. Your written report should explain how you used XFRM_LINEAR to model the circuit coupling shown, as well as anything else you had to do to solve this problem.

3. b)

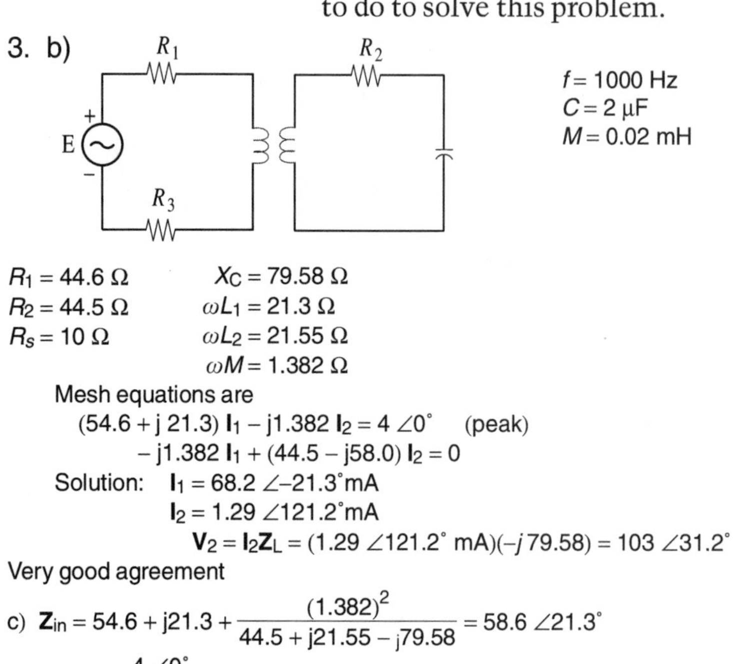

$f = 1000$ Hz
$C = 2\ \mu F$
$M = 0.02$ mH

$R_1 = 44.6\ \Omega$ $X_C = 79.58\ \Omega$
$R_2 = 44.5\ \Omega$ $\omega L_1 = 21.3\ \Omega$
$R_s = 10\ \Omega$ $\omega L_2 = 21.55\ \Omega$
$\omega M = 1.382\ \Omega$

Mesh equations are

$$(54.6 + j\,21.3)\,\mathbf{I}_1 - j1.382\,\mathbf{I}_2 = 4\angle 0^\circ \quad \text{(peak)}$$
$$-j1.382\,\mathbf{I}_1 + (44.5 - j58.0)\,\mathbf{I}_2 = 0$$

Solution: $\mathbf{I}_1 = 68.2\angle{-21.3^\circ}\text{mA}$
$\mathbf{I}_2 = 1.29\angle 121.2^\circ\text{mA}$
$\mathbf{V}_2 = \mathbf{I}_2\mathbf{Z}_L = (1.29\angle 121.2^\circ\ \text{mA})(-j\,79.58) = 103\angle 31.2^\circ\ \text{mV}$

Very good agreement

c) $$\mathbf{Z}_{in} = 54.6 + j21.3 + \frac{(1.382)^2}{44.5 + j21.55 - j79.58} = 58.6\angle 21.3^\circ$$

$$\mathbf{I}_1 = \frac{4\angle 0^\circ}{58.6\angle 21.30^\circ} = 68.2\text{mA}\angle{-21.3^\circ}$$

Measured: $\mathbf{I}_1 = 67\text{mA}\angle{-22^\circ}$

∴ Very good agreement.

Solutions for Problems 4, 5 and 6

4. Create the circuit shown below using XFRM_LINEAR and source VAC. Place a large valued resistor across the output (because PSpice will not work with an open circuit). Run the simulation using AC Sweep and $f = 1000$ Hz. View the output file. You should get $\mathbf{V}_2 = 94.3$ mV $\angle 68.7^\circ$ as computed in Part 2(d).

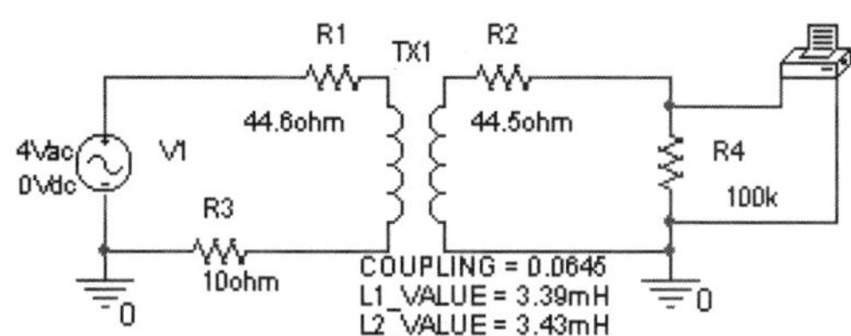

5. Use the same circuit as in Problem 4 except replace the load resistor with a 2 μF capacitor. Answers agree with those that we computed in Part 3.

Problem 6

Loop 1

$\mathbf{E} - (R_1 - jX_{c1})\,\mathbf{I}_1 - j\,\omega L_1(\mathbf{I}_1 - \mathbf{I}_2) + j\,\omega M\,\mathbf{I}_2 = 0$

Gather terms and substitute values yields

$$(10 - j25)\mathbf{I}_1 - j27\mathbf{I}_2 = 120\ \angle 0^\circ \quad .... (1)$$

Loop 2

$j\,\omega L_1(\mathbf{I}_1 - \mathbf{I}_2) - j\,\omega M\,\mathbf{I}_2 - j\,\omega L_2\,\mathbf{I}_2 + j\,\omega M\,(\mathbf{I}_1 - \mathbf{I}_2) - 5\mathbf{I}_2 - (-\,j10\mathbf{I}_2) = 0$

Thus $\quad -\,j27\,\mathbf{I}_1 + (5 + j49)\,\mathbf{I}_2 = 0 \qquad .... (2)$

Solving (1) and (2) yields

$\mathbf{I}_1 = 2.90\ \angle 73.9^\circ$A
$\mathbf{I}_2 = 1.59\ \angle 79.7^\circ$A
$\mathbf{V}_L = \mathbf{I}_L\mathbf{Z}_L = 15.9\ \angle{-10.3^\circ}$ V

For Further Investigation and Discussion

Using standard formulas, compute inductances and capacitances. Thus $L_1 = X_{Lt}/\omega = (25\ \Omega)/(2\pi \times 60\ \text{Hz}) = 66.3$ mH. Similarly, $l_2 = 79.6$ mH, $C_1 = 53.05$ μF and $C_2 = 265.3$ μF. From Equation 28-4, $k = 0.073$. Because the dots are at opposite ends of the coils, enter this as a negative value as shown on the PSpice schematic below. Run the simulation using AC Sweep and $f = 60$ Hz. View the output file. You should get the same answers as computed in Problem 6.

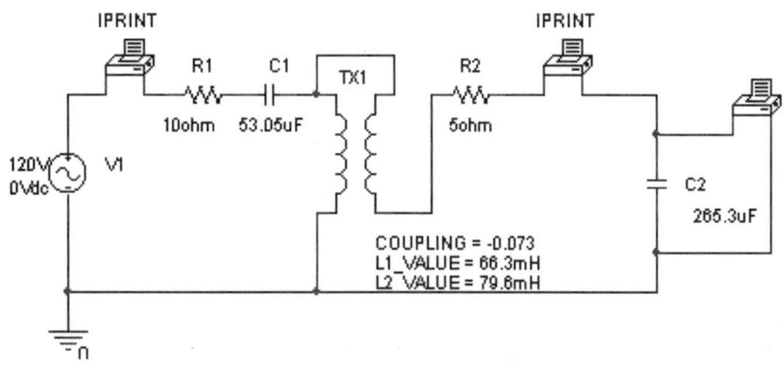

NAME ______________________

DATE ______________________

CLASS ______________________

LAB

29

The Basic Power Supply: Rectification, Filtering, and Regulation

OBJECTIVES

After completing this lab, you will be able to

- Construct half and full wave rectifier circuits,
- Measure and analyze filtered waveforms,
- Measure load regulation,
- Use a 3-terminal regulator to regulate dc supplies,
- Calculate the ripple rejection of a regulated supply.

EQUIPMENT REQUIRED

- ☐ DMM
- ☐ Two-channel oscilloscope

COMPONENTS

- ☐ Class 2 transformer 12 VAC, 500 mA
- ☐ 1N4004 diodes or equivalent (4 required)
- ☐ Resistors (1 each): 560-Ω, 1/2-W; 100-Ω, 1-W; 220-Ω, 1-W; 51-Ω, 10-W
- ☐ 470 μF electolytic capacitor (1 only)
- ☐ 7805 voltage regulator and data sheet

CAUTION

Be sure to turn off the power before you assemble or make changes to your circuit.

TEXT REFERENCE

Circuit Analysis with Devices: Theory and Practice
Section 25.7 HALF AND FULL WAVE RECTIFIER CIRCUITS
Section 25.8 POWER SUPPLY FILTERING

DISCUSSION

Diodes are designed for various purposes—signal diodes for high frequency, low power applications, rectifier diodes for higher current power supply applications, and so on. Because we are dealing with power supplies here, we require rectifier diodes and have chosen the popular 1N4004.

Rectification produces pulsating dc. Such crude dc, however, is unsuitable for most applications and requires smoothing. The simplest approach to smoothing is to place a large value capacitor across the load. This capacitor (known as a filter) helps level out the waveform, but some ripple remains.

In addition to the ripple problem, the output voltage of a power supply falls off as load current is increased. This change from no load voltage (V_{NL}) to full load voltage (V_{FL}) is termed regulation and is defined as

$$\text{Regulation} = \frac{V_{NL} - V_{FL}}{V_{FL}} \times 100\% \qquad (29\text{-}1)$$

In practice, you want a power supply with small ripple and small regulation. A simple way to improve performance is to add an inexpensive 3-terminal regulator to your circuit. This reduces both ripple and regulation. The ability of a regulator to reduce ripple (referred to as *ripple rejection*), is defined as the degree to which the regulator is able to prevent ripple voltage from passing from its input to its output. It is expressed in dB as

$$[\text{ripple rejection}]_{dB} = 20 \log\left(\frac{V_{\text{ripple(in)}}}{V_{\text{ripple(out)}}}\right) \qquad (29\text{-}2)$$

In this lab, we use the 7805, a popular, inexpensive and widely used solid-state, 3-terminal voltage regulator.

MEASUREMENTS

Note:
Values shown are for illustrative purposes. Your values may be different.

PART A: Half-Wave Rectifier Circuit and Filtering

1. Construct the half-wave circuit of Figure 29-1(a).
2. Connect an oscilloscope across the load resistor. Set the scope to its dc mode and sketch load voltage v_L in Figure 29-2(a). Be sure to show key voltage and time measurement data. Carefully measure peak voltage and record.

V_m = 19 V

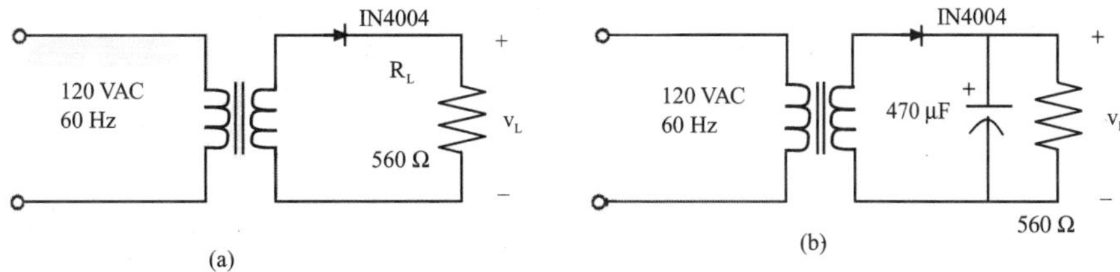

Figure 29-1 Half-wave rectification

> **Caution**
> Turn the power off before inserting the capacitor. Note also that the capacitor is polarized. Be sure you place it in the circuit with the correct polarity.

3. Add a filter capacitor (see Caution) as in Figure 29-1(b). Connect both oscilloscope probes across the resistor to measure load voltage. Set Channel 1 to dc coupling and Channel 2 to ac coupling.
   a. Sketch the dc waveform in Figure 29-2(b), carefully labeling voltage and time axes.

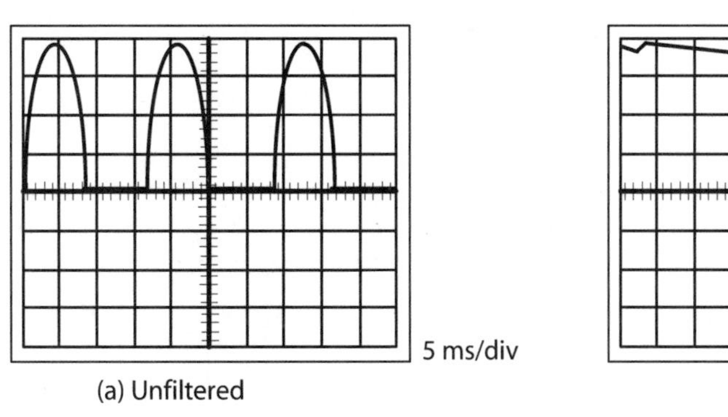

(a) Unfiltered

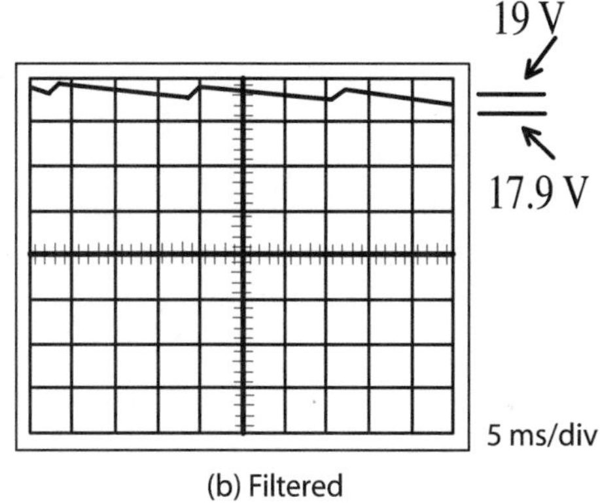

(b) Filtered

Figure 29-2

   b. Expand the vertical scale on Channel 2 and measure peak-to-peak ripple and ripple frequency and sketch the waveform in Figure 29-3 and carefully label.

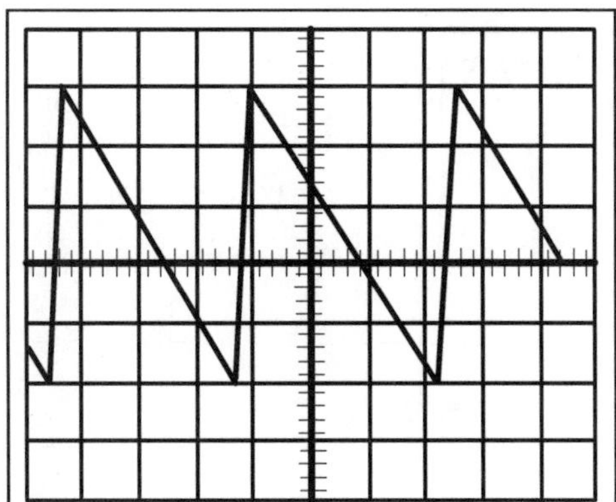

$V_{r_{pp}}$ = 1.1 V

f_{ripple} = 60 Hz

Scale: 0.2 V/div

Values shown are for illustrative purposes.

Figure 29-3 AC ripple

4. Measure dc load voltage and ac load voltage using your DMM.

   $V_{L(dc)}$ = 18.4 V $V_{L(ac)}$ = 0.3 V

PART B: Full-Wave Rectifier Circuit and Filtering

5. Using $R_L = 560\ \Omega$, assemble the full-wave bridge circuit of Figure 29-4, temporarily omitting the capacitor.
   a. Using the oscilloscope (dc coupled), observe and sketch (in Figure 29-5) the load voltage.
   b. Add the capacitor (see Caution) and using dc coupling, sketch the filtered waveform on the same graph. Label voltage magnitudes.
   c. Change to ac coupling and measure the ripple frequency,

   f_{ripple} = 120 Hz

6. Make load measurements as follows and record in Table 29-1:
   a. With an ac-coupled oscilloscope, measure the peak-to-peak ripple voltage and record.

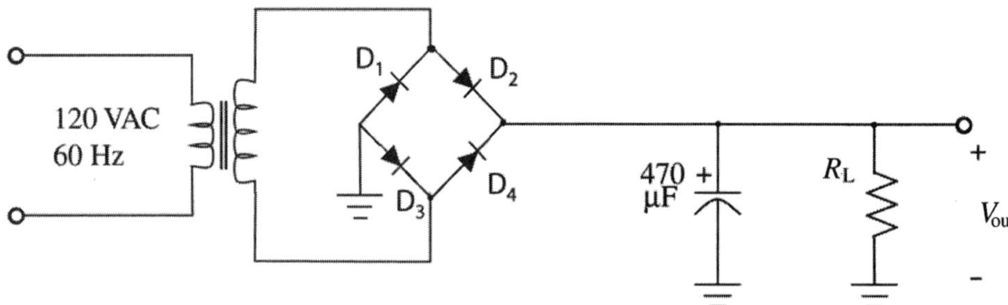

Figure 29-4 Full-wave bridge

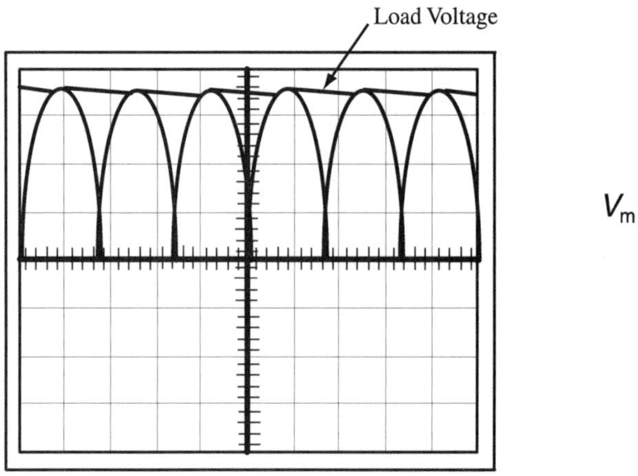

V_m = 18.3 V

Figure 29-5

Measured values are for illustrative purposes. Yours may be different.

b. With a DMM set to dc, measure load voltage $V_{out(dc)}$ and record. Compute load current I_{dc} and record.

7. Repeat Step 6 using a 220-Ω resistor.
8. Repeat Step 6 using the 100-Ω load. **Caution: The resistor may become quite hot.**
9. Repeat Step 6 using the 51-Ω load. **Caution: The resistor will become quite hot.**

Agreement is good for $V_{out(dc)}$, but gets worse as R_L gets smaller because the approximation becomes poorer.

R_L (ohms)	Measured		I_{dc} (mA)	Computed	
	$V_{r_{p-p}}$	$V_{out(dc)}$		$V_{r_{p-p}}$	$V_{out(dc)}$
560	0.50	17.9	32	0.57	18.0
220	1.2	17.6	80	1.42	17.6
100	2.4	17.0	170	2.98	16.8
51	4.2	16.2	318	5.42	15.6

Table 29-1

PART C: 3-Terminal Voltage Regulator Circuit

10. Using the 560 Ω-resistor and a 7805, 5-V regulator, set up the circuit of Figure 29-6.
11. Make measurements as follows and record results in Table 29-2.
    a. Set your DMM to dc and measure load voltage $V_{out(dc)}$. Calculate load current I_{dc}.
    b. Set your oscilloscope to ac coupled and measure the output ripple voltage $V_{r_{p-p}}$.
12. Repeat Step 11 using the 220-Ω resistor.
13. Repeat Step 11 using the 100-Ω resistor.
14. Repeat Step 11 using the 51-Ω resistor.

R_L (ohms)	Measured		I_{dc} (mA)
	$V_{r_{p-p}}$	$V_{out(dc)}$	
560	<1 mV	5.00	8.93
220	≈1 mV	5.00	22.7
100	1.5 mV	5.00	50.0
51	3 mV	4.99	97.8

Table 29-2

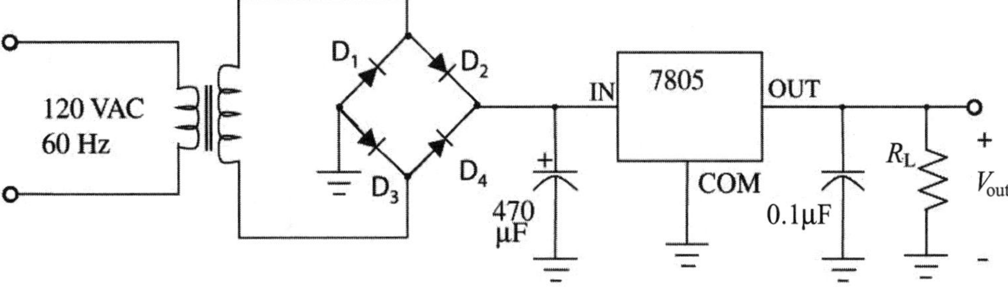

Figure 29-6 Regulated supply

15. With the 51-Ω resistor still connected, use the oscilloscope to measure the peak-to-peak ripple voltage at the input to the regulator.

$V_{ripple(input)}$ = 1.5 V

CALCULATIONS, DISCUSSION AND CONCLUSIONS

Answers to questions 16–21 are on last page of lab.

16. Using the techniques of Chapter 25, Section 25.8 of the text and the value of V_m measured in Step 2, compute peak-to-peak ripple voltage and dc load voltage for the half-wave filtered waveform and compare to your measured results.
17. In Step 3 you measured the ac component of the load voltage (the ripple) using an oscilloscope and in Step 4, you measured it with a DMM set to AC. Based on your results, comment on how useful a DMM is in determining ripple voltage and why.
18. Using the techniques of Chapter 25, Section 25.8 of the text and the value of V_m measured in Step 5, compute peak-to-peak ripple voltage and dc load voltage for the full-wave filtered waveform for each value of load resistance and record in Table 29-1. How do these compare to your measured results?
19. Using the graph of Figure 29-7 and your data from Steps 6 to 9, plot load dc voltage versus load current for the unregulated supply.
20. From the graph of Figure 29-7, compute regulation.
21. Repeat 19 and 20 for the regulated supply, using the graph of Figure 29-8. Compare the percent regulation for the unregulated supply against that for the regulated supply.

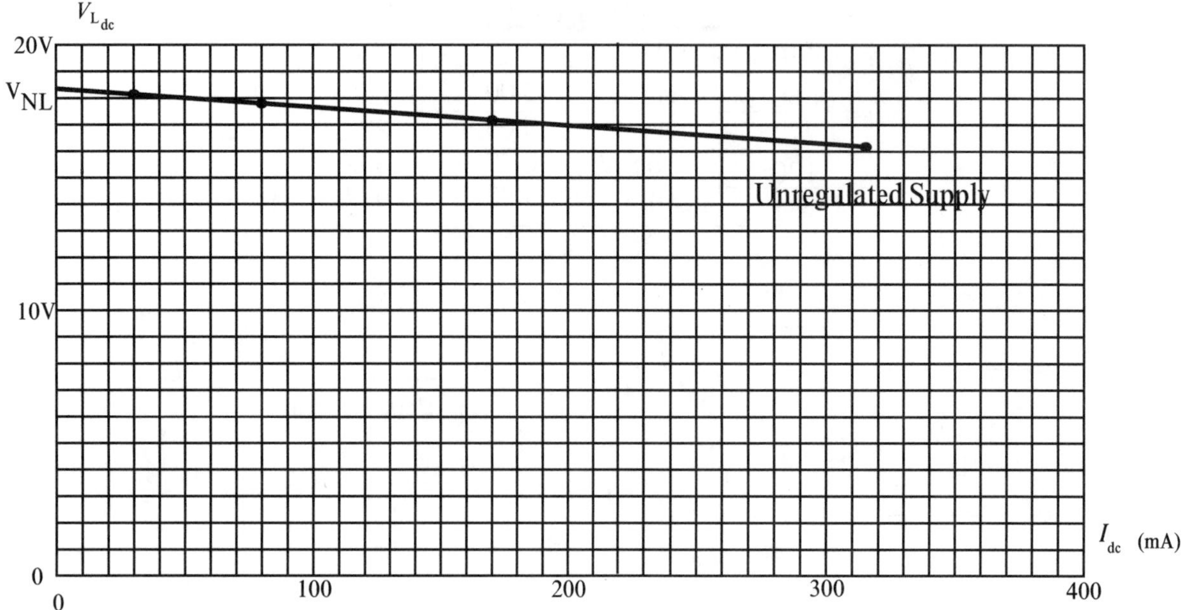

Figure 29-7

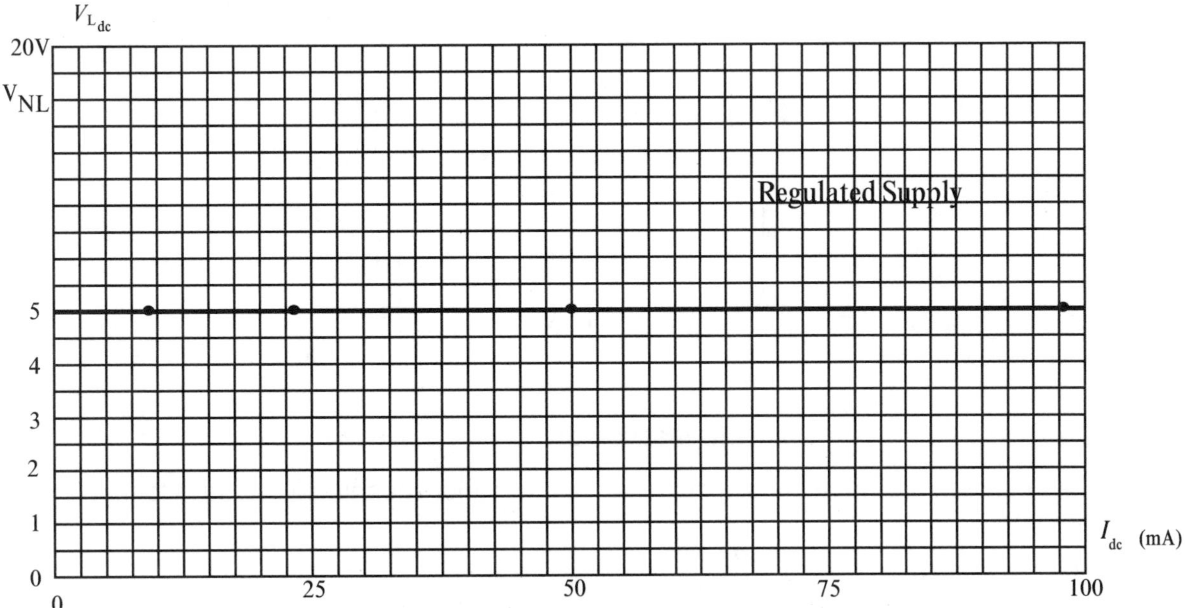

Figure 29-8

Answers to questions 22–24 are on last page of lab.

22. For the regulated supply, compute ripple rejection at a load current of $I_{dc} \approx 100$ mA based on your measured data.

COMPUTER ANALYSIS

23. Using either MultiSIM or PSpice, determine V_{dc} and peak-to-peak ripple for the circuit of Figure 29-4 with $R_L = 51\ \Omega$. Hint: For simplicity, omit the transformer and drive the rectifier combination directly from an AC source whose voltage E_m is two diode drops greater than V_m as measured in Step 5a. How do these results compare to the measured results?
24. To investigate how a filter capacitor affects ripple, run simulations with $C = 100\ \mu F$, $C = 220\ \mu F$, $C = 330\ \mu F$ and $C = 1000\ \mu F$ for the case $R_L = 51\ \Omega$, and plot ripple voltage versus C. Submit your graph with a commentary on your findings.

PROBLEMS

Refer to the manufacturer's data sheet to answer the following.

25. What is the minimum required input voltage for the 7805?

7 V

26. What is the maximum input voltage that can be applied?

25 V

27. What is the maximum output load current?

1.5 A

16. $V_{r_{pp}} = \dfrac{2V_m}{1+\dfrac{2R_LC}{T}} = \dfrac{2(19\text{ V})}{1+\dfrac{2(560\Omega)(470\ \mu\text{F})}{16.\overline{6}\text{ ms}}} = 1.17\text{ V}$

$V_{dc} = V_m - \dfrac{V_{r_{pp}}}{2} = 18.4\text{ V}$ (Same as measured)

17. DMM is calibrated to measure sinusoidal AC. It thus yields meaningless results for ripple measurements.

18. For $R_L = 560\ \Omega$, $V_{r_{pp}} = \dfrac{2(18.3\text{ V})}{1+\dfrac{2(560\ \Omega)(470\ \mu\text{F})}{8.\overline{3}\text{ ms}}} = 0.57\text{ V}$

$V_{dc}\} = V_m - \dfrac{V_{r_{pp}}}{2} = 18.0\text{ V}$ (Measured $V_{dc} = 17.9\text{ V}$ $\therefore$ very close)

20. $\text{Reg} = \left(\dfrac{V_{NL}-V_{FL}}{V_{FL}}\right)\times 100 = \left(\dfrac{18.2-16.2}{16.2}\right)\times 100 = 12.4\%$ This is very poor regulation.

21. $\text{Reg} = \left(\dfrac{5.00-4.99}{4.99}\right)\times 100 = 0.2\%$ This is very good regulation.

22. Ripple rejection $= 20\log\left(\dfrac{1.5\text{ V}}{3\text{ mV}}\right) = 54\text{ dB}$

23. $E_m = V_m + 2\,V_D$. From Figure 29-5, Vm = 18.3 V. Assuming a diode drop of $V_D = 0.7$ V yields $E_m = 19.7$ V. Computer solutions using this value are shown below. (Review Section 25.9 of the text book for operational details if necessary.) MultiSIM yields a ripple of 4.2 V and a dc load voltage of 16.3 V, while PSpice yields 4.1 V and 16.0 V. These compare well with the measured values of 4.2 V and 16.2 V respectively.

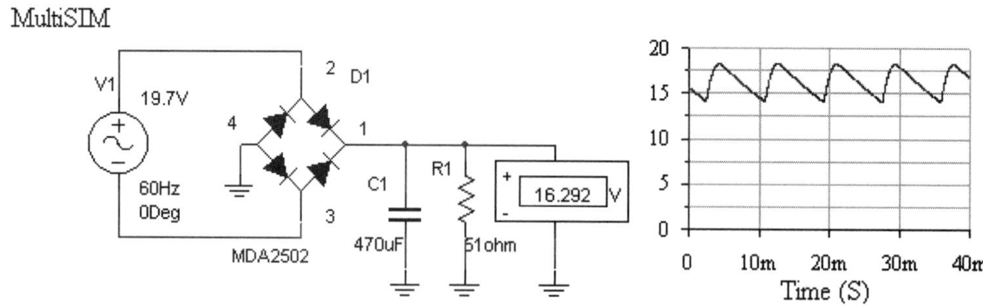

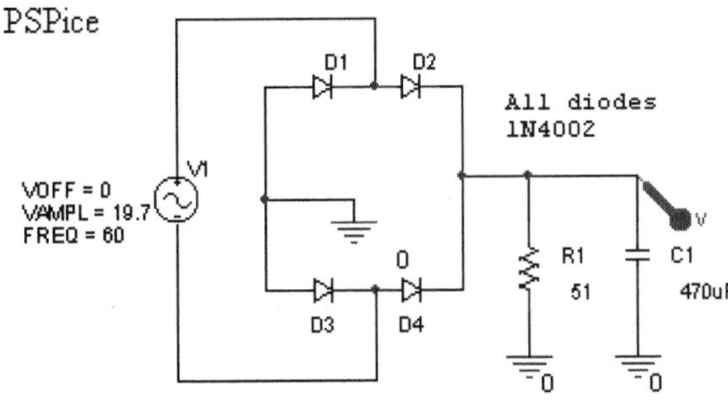

Note: As you saw in Chapter 25 of the ext, V_D is somewhat dependent on load current and 0.7 V is simply its nominal value. At the relatively high current caused by a 51 Ω load resistor, V_D will be somewhat higher. You might want to try running the simulations again at $V_D = 0.8$ V and 0.9 V to investigate what effect this has on the solutions.

24. The results below are based on a MultiSIM simulation. Results for PSpice are similar.

C	Ripple
100 μF	11 V
220 μF	7.2 V
330 μF	5.4 V
470 μF	4.2 V
1000 μF	2.3 V

As *C* is made larger, ripple decreases. Remember however (see Section 25.8 of the text), larger capacitors result in larger diode current spikes. Practical design is a compromise.

NAME ______________________

DATE ______________________

CLASS ______________________

LAB

30

Introduction to Transistor Amplifiers

Objectives

After completing this lab, you will be able to

- calculate the operating point of a transistor,
- use a digital multimeter to measure the operating point of a transistor,
- calculate the theoretical voltage gain, input impedance, and output impedance of a CE amplifier,
- use an oscilloscope to measure the voltage gain, input impedance, and output impedance of a CE amplifier.

Equipment Required

- ☐ Digital multimeter (DMM)
- ☐ dc power supply
- ☐ Signal generator (sinusoidal function generator)
- ☐ Two-channel oscilloscope
- ☐ *Note:* Record this equipment in Table 30-1.

Components

- ☐ Transistors: 2N3904 npn
- ☐ Resistors: 180-Ω, 820-Ω, 1-kΩ(two), 1.5-kΩ, 2.2-kΩ, 10-kΩ, 3.3-kΩ.
- ☐ Capacitors: 10-μF electrolytic (two), 470-μF electrolytic.

EQUIPMENT USED

Instrument	Manufacturer/Model No.	Serial No.
DMM		
dc power supply		
Oscilloscope		
Signal Generator		

Table 30-1

TEXT REFERENCE

Circuit Analysis with Devices: Theory and Practice
Section 26.6 TRANSISTOR BIASING
Section 27.2 BJT SMALL-SIGNAL MODELS
Section 27.4 THE COMMON-EMITTER AMPLIFIER

DISCUSSION

The universal-bias transistor circuit shown in Figure 30-1 is the most commonly used transistor amplifier circuit. When correctly

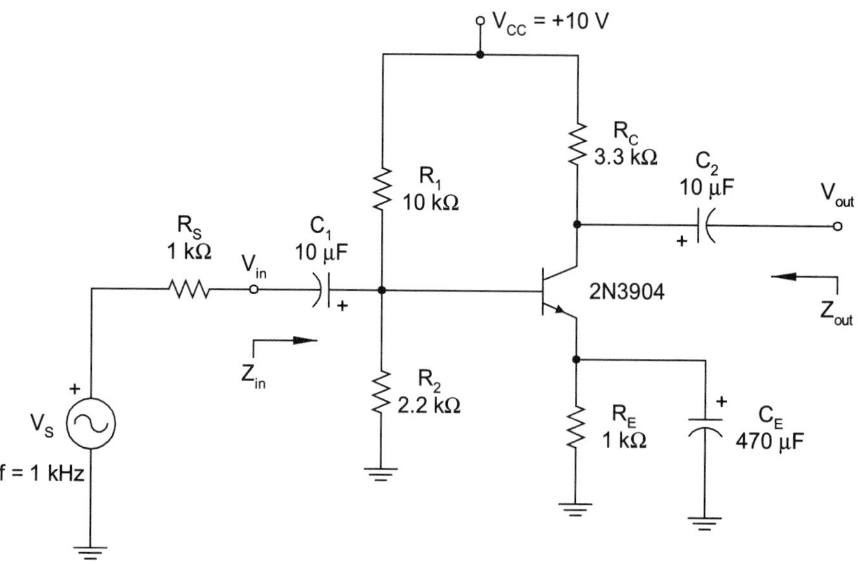

Figure 30-1 Universal bias CE amplifier

designed, the universal-bias amplifier is very stable. This means that the amplifier has highly predictable results even when the transistor beta changes due to variation in the manufacturing process or due to temperature.

In this lab you will measure the operating point (also called the quiescent or Q-point) of a transistor. Once the transistor is biased correctly, you will apply a sinusoidal voltage at the input of the transistor amplifier and observe that the output signal will be amplified by the transistor circuit.

CALCULATIONS

1. Refer to the circuit of Figure 30-1. Calculate I_C and V_{CE} at the operating point. Show your work in the space provided below.

$$V_B = \left(\frac{2.2\ \text{k}\Omega}{12.2\ \text{k}\Omega}\right) 10\ \text{V} = 1.80\ \text{V}$$

$$V_E = 1.80\ \text{V} - 0.7\ \text{V} = 1.10\ \text{V}$$

$$I_E = \frac{1.10\ \text{V}}{1\ \text{k}\Omega} = 1.10\ \text{mA} \approx I_C$$

$$V_{CE} = 10\ \text{V} - (1.10\ \text{mA})(4.3\ \text{k}\Omega) = 5.27\ \text{V}$$

I_{CQ}	1.10	mA
V_{CEQ}	5.27	V

MEASUREMENTS

2. Construct the circuit shown in Figure 30-1. Ensure that you place the electrolytic capacitors correctly.
3. Measure and record the following dc voltages using a dc multimeter (DMM).

V_B	1.80	V
V_E	1.10	V
V_C	6.37	V

4. Use the measurements of Step 3 to calculate the operating point of the transistor. Enter your values in the space provided.

$$I_C = \frac{10\text{ V} - 6.37\text{ V}}{3.3\text{ k}\Omega}$$
$$= 1.10\text{ mA}$$
$$V_{CE} = 6.37\text{ V} - 1.10\text{ V} = 5.27\text{ V}$$

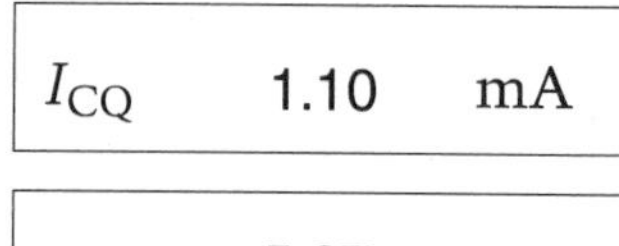

V_{CEQ} 5.27 V

If your measured results are not within 10% of the calculated values of Step 1, call your instructor to determine the source of the problem.

5. With the oscilloscope connected to v_{in}, adjust the signal generator to apply a sinusoidal signal of 20 m$V_{p\text{-}p}$ and 1 kHz to v_{in}.
6. Measure and record the output voltage v_{out}.

v_{out} 2.80 $V_{p\text{-}p}$

7. Calculate the voltage gain of the amplifier and enter the result in the space provided.

A_v −140

8. Without adjusting the signal generator, measure and record the voltage at the output of the signal generator. Use your measurement to calculate the input impedance of the amplifier. Show your calculations in the space provided.

v_{gen} 0.04 $V_{p\text{-}p}$

z_{in} 1185 Ω

9. Without adjusting the signal generator, connect a load resistor of 4.7 kΩ between v_{out} and ground in the circuit of Figure 30-1. Measure the new value of output voltage. (You should find that the voltage has decreased from the value found in Step 6.) Use your measurement to calculate the output impedance of the circuit.

v_{out}	1.64	$V_{p\text{-}p}$

z_{out}	3.3 k	Ω

10. Modify the circuit as illustrated in Figure 30-2.

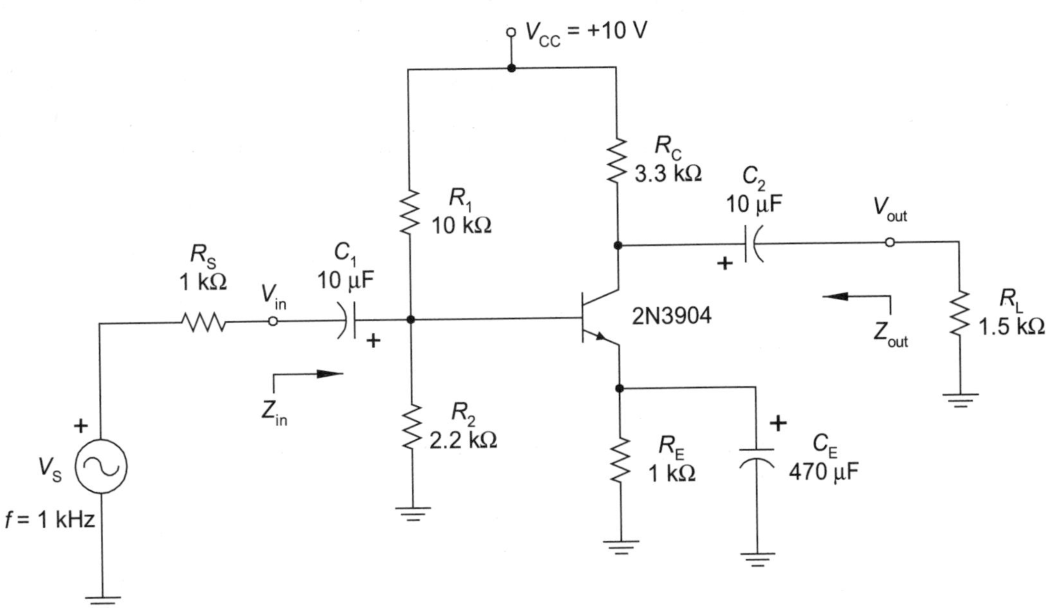

Figure 30-2 Universal bias CE amplifier with load resistor

11. Measure and record the following dc voltages using a dc multimeter (DMM).

V_B	1.80	V

V_E	1.10	V

V_C	6.37	V

If your measured values have changed from those found in Step 3, call your instructor to determine the source of the problem.

12. With the oscilloscope connected to v_{in}, adjust the signal generator to apply a sinusoidal signal of 20 m$V_{p\text{-}p}$ and 1 kHz to v_{in}.
13. Measure and record the output voltage v_{out}.

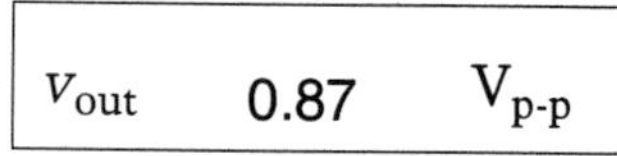

14. Calculate the voltage gain of the amplifier and enter the result in the space provided.

A_v –43.7

15. Without adjusting the signal generator, measure and record the voltage at the output of the signal generator. Use your measurement to calculate the input impedance of the amplifier. Show your calculations in the space provided.

v_{gen} 0.04 $V_{p\text{-}p}$

z_{in} 1185 Ω

16. Did the value of input impedance change from the value found in Step 8. Circle the correct answer.

17. Modify the circuit as illustrated in Figure 30-3.

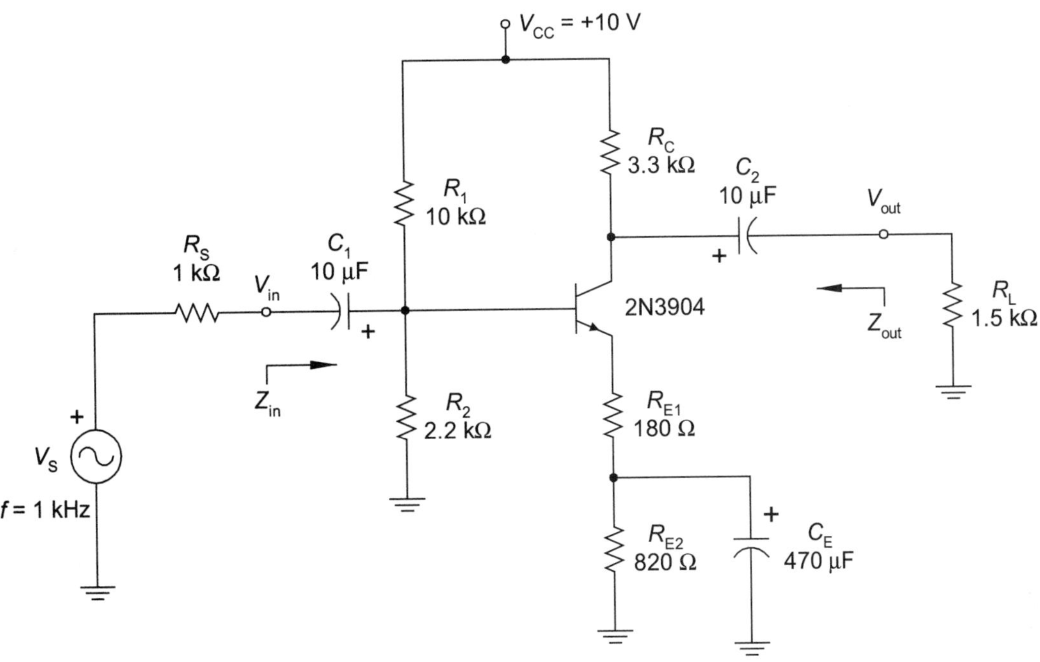

Figure 30-3 Universal bias CE amplifier with partially bypassed emitter resistor

18. Measure and record the following dc voltages using a dc multimeter (DMM).

V_B	1.80	V
V_E	1.10	V
V_C	6.37	V

If your measured values have changed from those found in Step 3, call your instructor to determine the source of the problem.

19. With the oscilloscope connected to v_{in}, adjust the signal generator to apply a sinusoidal signal of 20 m$V_{p\text{-}p}$ and 1 kHz to v_{in}.
20. Measure and record the output voltage v_{out}.

v_{out}	0.10	$V_{p\text{-}p}$

21. Calculate the voltage gain of the amplifier and enter the result in the space provided.

A_v	–5.0

22. Without adjusting the signal generator, measure and record the voltage at the output of the signal generator. Use your measurement to calculate the input impedance of the amplifier. Show your calculations in the space provided.

v_{gen}	31.8 m	$V_{p\text{-}p}$

z_{in}	1700	Ω

23. Did the value of input impedance change from the value found in Step 8. Circle the correct answer.

yes/no (yes circled)

Problem:

Refer to the circuit of Figure 30-3. Assume that $\beta_{ac} = 150$.

a. Sketch the ac equivalent circuit in the space provided below.

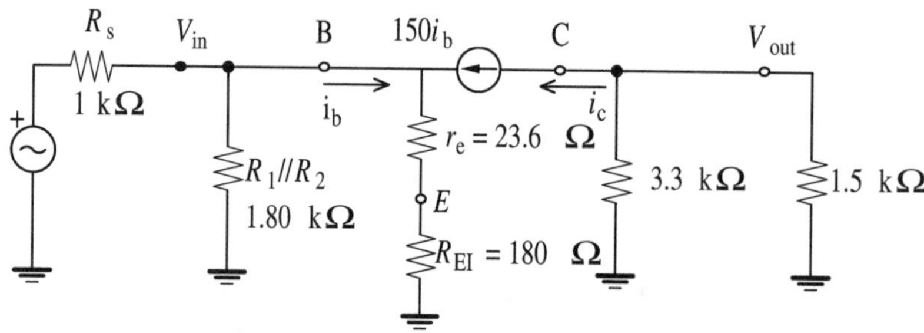

b. Calculate the voltage gain A_v, input impedance z_{in}, and output impedance z_{out}. Show your work in the space provided.

$$A_v = \frac{-150i_b(3.3\ \text{k}\Omega/1.5\ \text{k}\Omega)}{151i_b(23.6\Omega + 180\ \Omega)} = -5.03$$

A_v	–5.03

z_{in}	1.70 k	Ω

$$Z_{in} = \left[\frac{i_e(23.6\ \Omega + 180\ \Omega)}{i_b}\right] // 10\ \text{k}\Omega\ //2.2\ \text{k}\Omega = 1.70\ \text{k}\Omega$$

z_{out}	3.3 k	Ω

NAME ______________________

DATE ______________________

CLASS ______________________

LAB 31

The Differential Amplifier

Objectives

After completing this lab, you will be able to

- measure single-ended voltage gain of a differential amplifier,
- recognize the phase difference between the input and each of the outputs of a differential amplifier,
- measure double-ended voltage gain of a differential amplifier,
- measure the common-mode gain of a differential amplifier,
- calculate the common-mode rejection ratio (CMRR) of a differential amplifier as both a ratio and in dB.

Equipment Required

- ☐ Digital multimeter (DMM)
- ☐ Dual power supply
- ☐ Signal generator (sinusoidal function generator)
- ☐ Two-channel oscilloscope

Note: Record this equipment in Table 31-1.

Components

- ☐ Transistors: 2N3904 npn (three)
- ☐ Resistors: 1-kΩ (three), 2.2-kΩ (two), 2.7-kΩ (two),
- ☐ Diodes: 1N4735A zener diode ($V_Z = 6.2$ V)
- ☐ Capacitors: 10-μF electrolytic (two).

EQUIPMENT USED

Instrument	Manufacturer/Model No.	Serial No.
DMM		
Dual power supply		
Oscilloscope		
Signal Generator		

Table 31-1

TEXT REFERENCE

Circuit Analysis with Devices: Theory and Practice
Section 28.2 THE DIFFERENTIAL AMPLIFIER AND COMMON-MODE SIGNALS

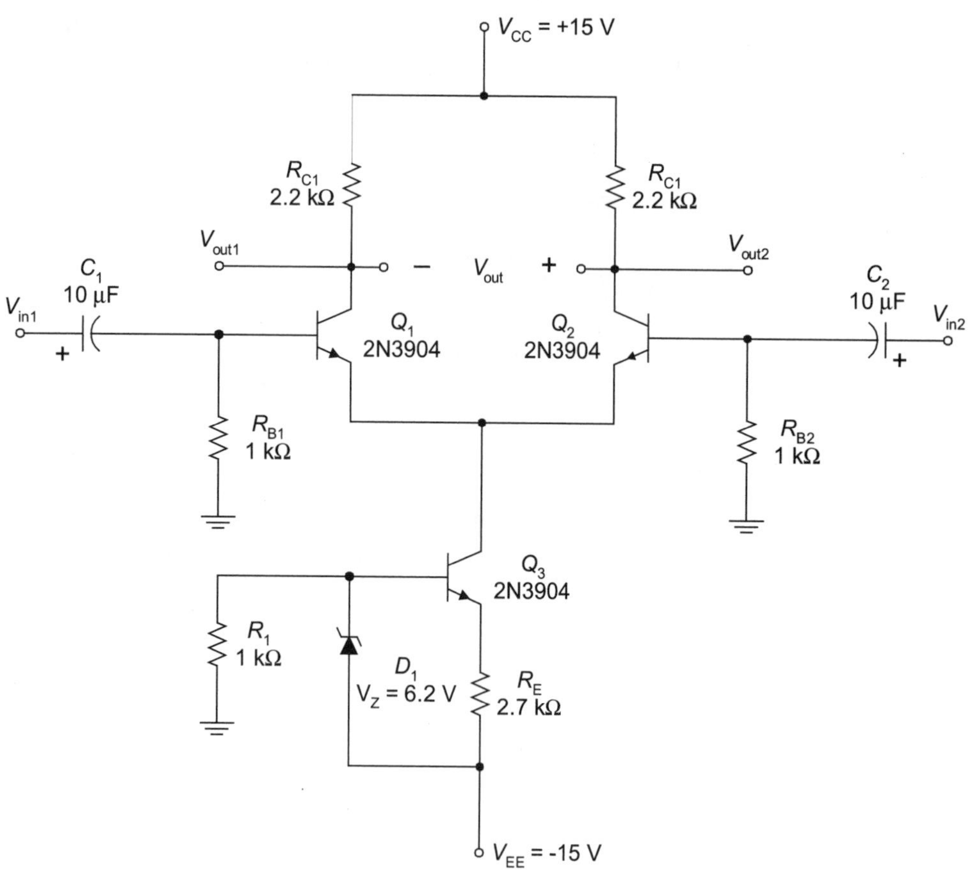

Figure 31-1 Differential amplifier

MEASUREMENTS

1. Build the circuit shown in Figure 31-1.
2. Measure and record the following voltages with a DMM.

V_{B1} 0 V	V_{B2} 0 V	V_{B3} −8.8 V
V_{C1} 12.8 V	V_{C2} 12.8 V	V_{C3} −9.5 V
$V_{E1} = V_{E2} = V_{C3}$ −0.7 V		

Using the measurements of Step 2, calculate the following:

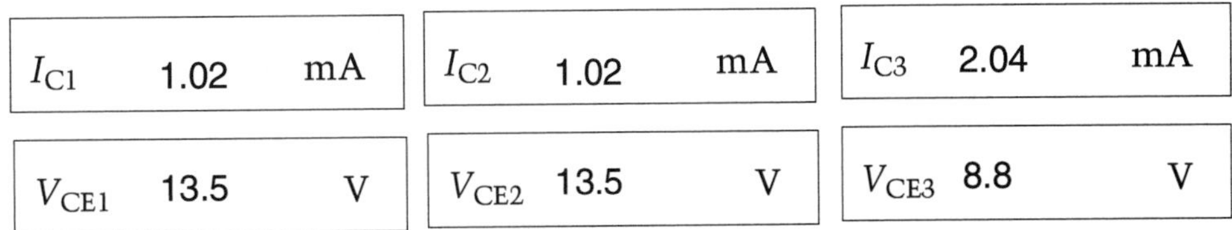

I_{C1} 1.02 mA	I_{C2} 1.02 mA	I_{C3} 2.04 mA
V_{CE1} 13.5 V	V_{CE2} 13.5 V	V_{CE3} 8.8 V

Single-ended differential amplifier

4. Connect v_{in2} to ground. Apply a suitable 1-kHz sinusoidal signal to v_{in1}. Measure v_{in1} on CH1 of the oscilloscope and v_{out1} and v_{out2} on CH2. Record all values.

V_{in1} 10 m $V_{p\text{-}p}$	V_{out2} 430 $V_{p\text{-}p}$	V_{out2} 430 $V_{p\text{-}p}$

5. Are v_{in1} and v_{out1} in phase or out of phase? out of phase
6. Are v_{in1} and v_{out2} in phase or out of phase? in phase
7. Calculate the theoretical single-ended voltage gain of the amplifier.

$$A_{d(S.E.)} = \frac{v_{out}}{v_{in1}} = -\frac{R_C}{2r_e} \qquad (31\text{-}1)$$

$A_{d(S.E.)}$ −43.2

8. Calculate the actual single-ended voltage gain of the amplifier from the measurements of Step 4.

$A_{d(S.E.)}$ −43

Double-ended differential amplifier

9. Without readjusting the signal generator voltage or frequency, connect CH1 of the oscilloscope to v_{out1} and CH2 to v_{out2}. Place the oscilloscope into its CH2 – CH1 mode and measure the differential voltage at the output.

v_{out} 860 m $V_{p\text{-}p}$

10. Calculate the theoretical differential voltage gain of the amplifier.

$$A_{d(D.E.)} = \frac{v_{out}}{v_{in1}} = \frac{R_C}{r_e} \qquad (31\text{-}2)$$

$A_{d(D.E.)}$ 86

11. Calculate the actual differential voltage gain of the amplifier from the measurement of Step 9.

$A_{d(D.E.)}$ 86

12. Leave the two channels of the oscilloscope connected as in Step 11. With one end of the signal generator connected to the signal ground, connect the other terminal to both inputs, v_{in1} and v_{in2}. Increase the output of the generator until you are able to measure a suitable common-mode output voltage, v_{out}. Record your value.

v_{out} 10 m $V_{p\text{-}p}$

13. Return your oscilloscope to normal operation and measure the common-mode input voltage. Record your value.

v_{in} 10.8 $V_{p\text{-}p}$

14. Use the results of Steps 12 and 13 to calculate the common-mode voltage gain.

A_{cm} 3.7×10^{-3}

15. Calculate the common-mode rejection ratio.

$$\text{CMRR} = \frac{A_{d(D.E.)}}{A_{cm}} \qquad (31\text{-}3)$$

CMRR 21,200

16. Calculate the common-mode rejection ratio in decibels.

$$[\text{CMMR}]_{\text{dB}} = 20 \log \text{CMRR} \qquad (31\text{-}4)$$

CMRR	86.5	dB

COMPUTER SIMULATION

17. Use either MultiSIM or PSpice to simulate the circuit of Figure 31-1. Apply a 10 m$V_{\text{p-p}}$ signal to v_{in1} and connect v_{in2} to ground. Observe and record the voltages observed at v_{out1} and v_{out2}.

See schematic on next page

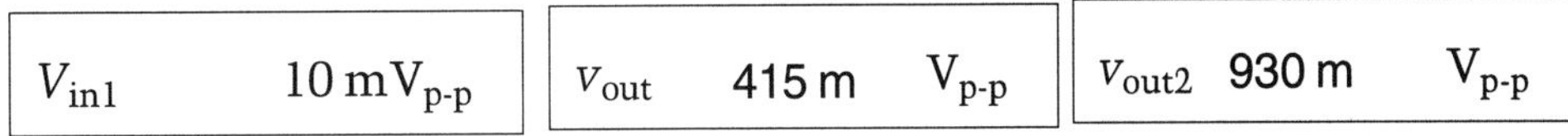

18. Use the measurements of Step 17 to calculate both the single-ended voltage gain and the double-ended voltage gain of the amplifier. Record your calculations in the space provided.

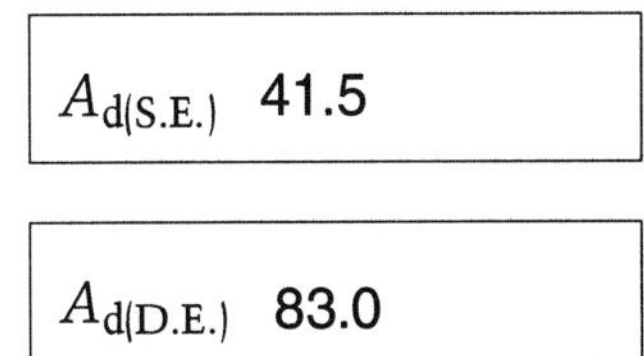

19. Compare the results observed in the computer simulation to the actual measured values. Offer an explanation for any discrepancy.

The results are very close.

17.

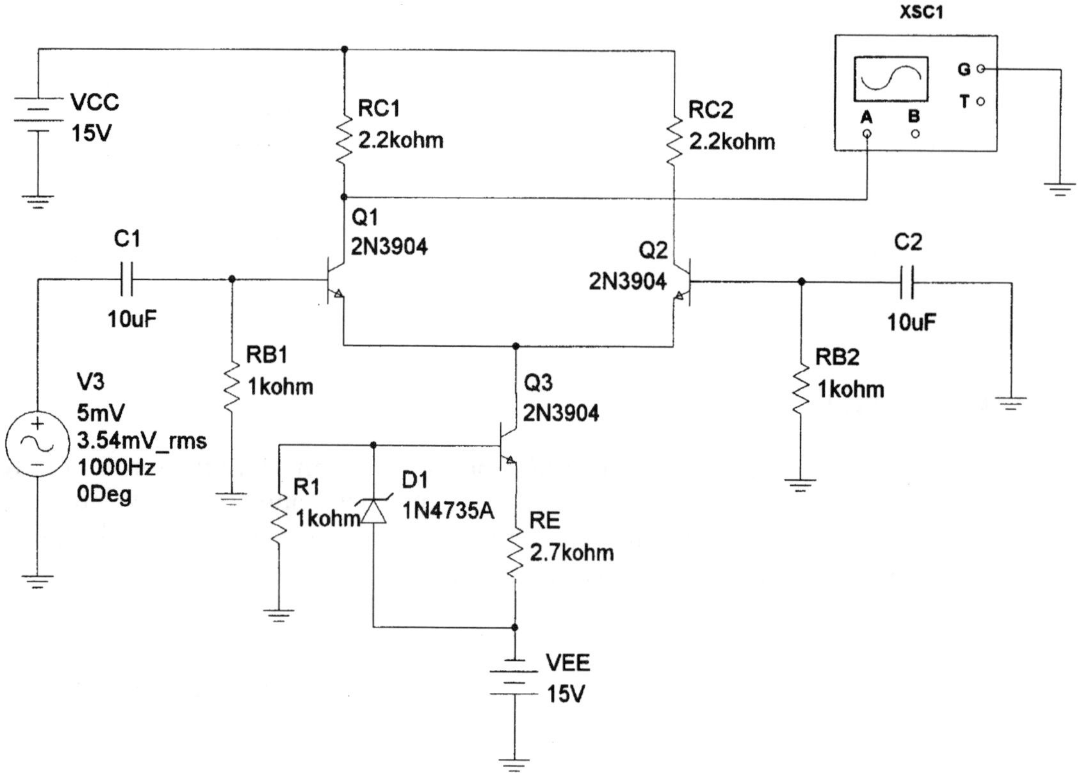
XSC1
G
T
A
B
VCC
15V
RC1
2.2kohm
RC2
2.2kohm
Q1
2N3904
Q2
2N3904
C1
10uF
C2
10uF
RB1
1kohm
RB2
1kohm
V3
5mV
3.54mV_rms
1000Hz
0Deg
Q3
2N3904
R1
1kohm
D1
1N4735A
RE
2.7kohm
VEE
15V

NAME ______________________

DATE ______________________

CLASS ______________________

LAB 32

Introduction to Op-Amps

Objectives

After completing this lab, you will be able to

- calculate voltage gain, input impedance, and output impedance of an inverting operational amplifier (op-amp) circuit at mid frequency,
- measure and plot the voltage gain as a function of frequency for an inverting op-amp circuit,
- measure the upper cutoff frequency of an op-amp and compare the result to that obtained from the manufacturer's specification,
- sketch the frequency response of an inverting op-amp circuit on semi-log graph paper,
- observe and measure the operation of an op-amp adder circuit.

Equipment Required

☐ Digital multimeter (DMM)
☐ Dual Power Supply
☐ Signal generator (sinusoidal function generator)
☐ Two-channel oscilloscope
Note: Record this equipment in Table 32-1.

Components

☐ Op-Amps: 741C op-amp (8-pin package)
☐ Resistors: 150-Ω (two), 1.0-kΩ, 1.2-kΩ, 10-kΩ, 75-kΩ (three).

EQUIPMENT USED

Instrument	Manufacturer/Model No.	Serial No.
DMM		
Dual power supply		
Oscilloscope		
Signal Generator		

Table 32-1

TEXT REFERENCE

Circuit Analysis with Devices: Theory and Practice
Section 28.1 INTRODUCTION TO THE OPERATIONAL AMPLIFIER
Section 28.3 NEGATIVE FEEDBACK
Section 28.4 THE INVERTING AMPLIFIER

CALCULATIONS

1. Given the circuit shown in Figure 32-1, calculate A_v, z_{in}, and z_{out}.

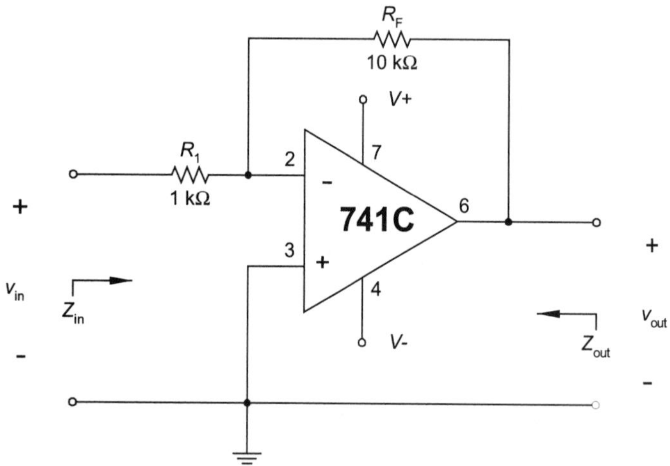

Figure 32-1 Inverting amplifier

A_v −10	z_{in} 1 k Ω	z_{out} 0 Ω

MEASUREMENTS

2. Adjust the dual power supply to provide ±15 V with respect to the common (ground) point. Connect the power to the op-amp as illustrated in Figure 32-1. The pins shown in the illustration are for the 8-pin DIP package. If you use a different package, you will need to obtain the pin numbers from the manufacturer's specification.
3. Adjust the sinusoidal generator to provide an input voltage, $v_{in} = 0.1\ V_{p\text{-}p}$ at a frequency of 1 kHz. Measure the output voltage, v_{out}.

v_{out}	1.0	$V_{p\text{-}p}$

4. Use the measured values of Step 3 to calculate the mid-frequency voltage gain of the op-amp circuit.

A_v	–10.0

5. Measure the input impedance and the output impedance of the amplifier.

z_{in}	1 k		Z_{out}	0	Ω

6. Keeping the amplitude of the signal constant, adjust the frequency of the signal generator and measure the output voltage at each of the indicated frequencies. Use your measurements to calculate voltage gain and gain in decibels at each frequency. Calculate the voltage gain in decibels using the following expression:

$$\left[A_v\right]_{dB} = 20 \log\left|\frac{v_{out}}{v_{in}}\right| \tag{32-1}$$

Enter your data in Table 32-2 and show one set of calculations in the space provided.

7. Adjust the frequency of the generator so that the output voltage is exactly 0.707 of the value measured in Step 2. Measure and record the upper cutoff frequency of the amplifier.

f_H	100 k	Hz

Frequency	v_{out} ($V_{p\text{-}p}$)	A_v	$[A_v]_{dB}$
10 Hz	1.0	–10	+20
20 Hz	1.0	–10	+20
50 Hz	1.0	–10	+20
100 Hz	1.0	–10	+20
200 Hz	1.0	–10	+20
1 kHz	1.0	–10	+20
2 kHz	1.0	–10	+20
5 kHz	1.0	–10	+20
10 kHz	1.0	–10	+20
20 kHz	0.96	–9.6	+19.6
50 kHz	0.88	–8.8\	+18.9
100 kHz	0.71	–7.1	+17.0
200 kHz	0.44	–4.4	+12.9
500 kHz	0.20	–2.0	+6.0
1 MHz	0.10	–1.0	0

Table 32-2 Frequency response measurements

Sample calculations:

$$A_V = -\frac{0.96}{0.10} = -9.6$$

$$[A_V]_{dB} = 20 \log 9.6 = 19.6 \text{ dB}$$

8. Plot the data of Table 32-2 as a semi-logarithmic graph.
9. Refer to the manufacturer's specifications and determine the gain-bandwidth product for the 741C op-amp.

Gain-bandwidth product	1 M	Hz

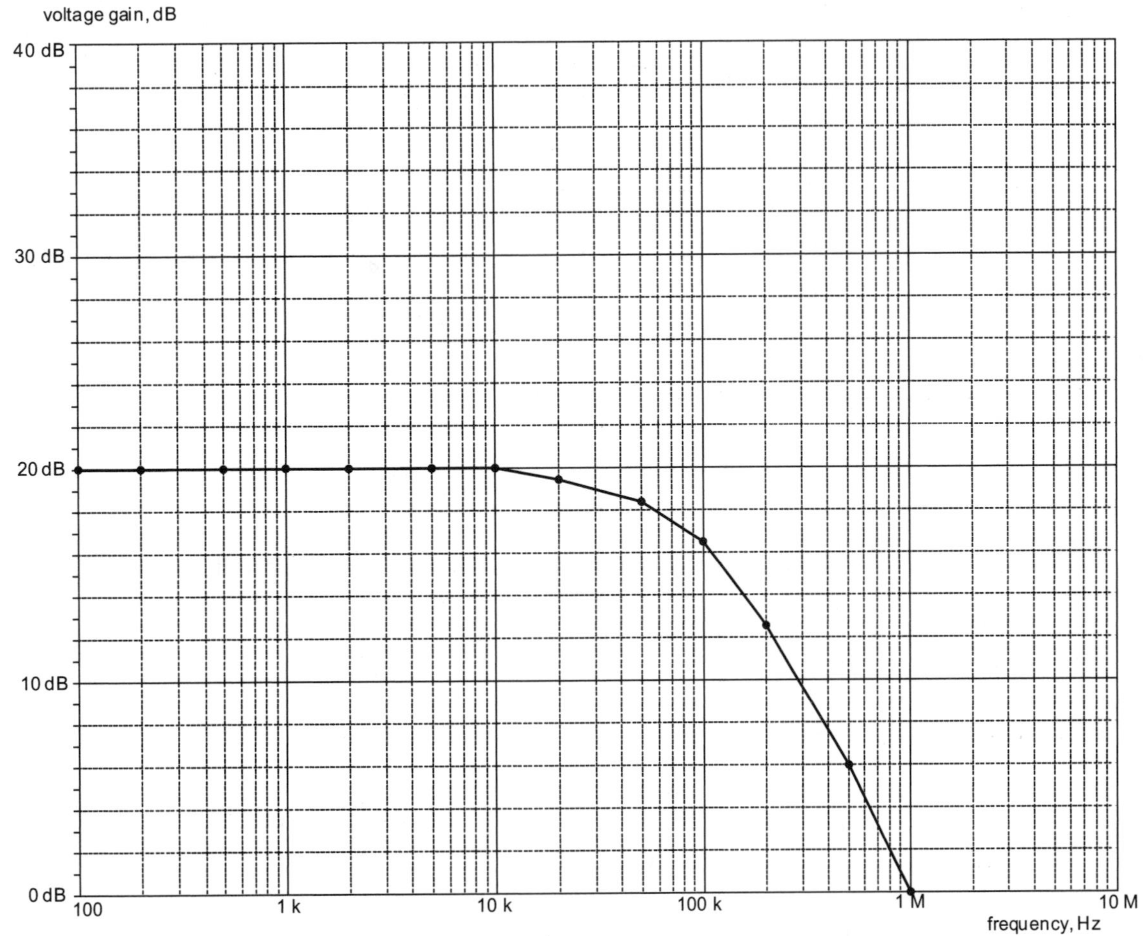

Graph 32-1 Frequency response of an inverting amplifier

10. Use the gain-bandwidth product and the mid-frequency gain of the amplifier to determine the theoretical upper cutoff frequency of the amplifier.

$$f_H = \frac{1\text{ MHz}}{10} = 100\text{ kHz}$$

f_H	100 k	Hz

How well does the actual bandwidth compare to the theoretical bandwidth?

The values are very close.

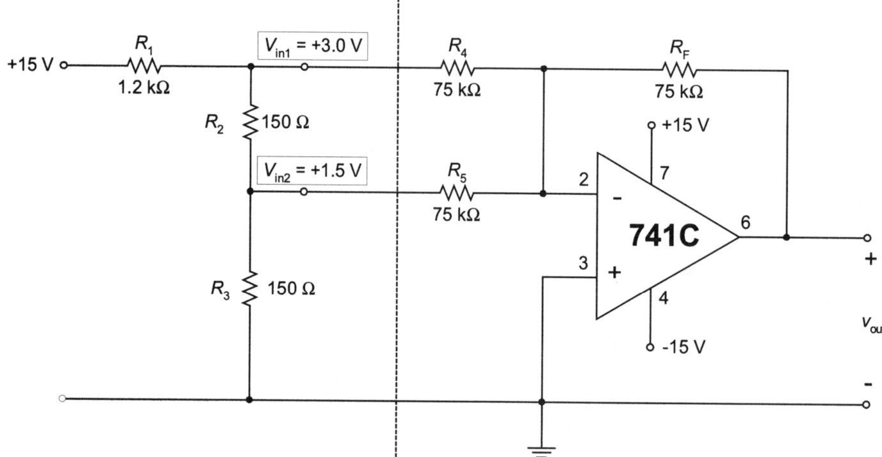

Figure 32-2 Inverting two-input adder

11. Given the circuit shown in Figure 32-2, predict the output voltage, V_{out}.

V_{out}	–4.5	V

12. Use a digital multimeter to measure the output voltage of the circuit of Figure 32-2.

V_{out}	–4.5	V

How well does the actual output voltage compare to the theoretical output?

The values are very close.

FOR FURTHER INVESTIGATION AND DISCUSSION

How does the bandwidth (upper cutoff frequency) of an op-amp circuit amplifier depend on the gain of the amplifier? To aid in your discussion, do the following:

Answers to *For Further Investigation and Discussion* on next two pages.

a. Use MultiSIM or PSpice to simulate the circuit shown in Figure 32-1. Use the Bode plotter (MultiSIM) or the Probe processor (PSpice) to determine the frequency response of the amplifier. Use cursors to determine the upper cutoff frequency of the amplifier.

b. Modify the circuit of Figure 32-1 by letting R_F = 20 kΩ, and repeat Part a.

As the gain increases, the bandwidth decreases

a.

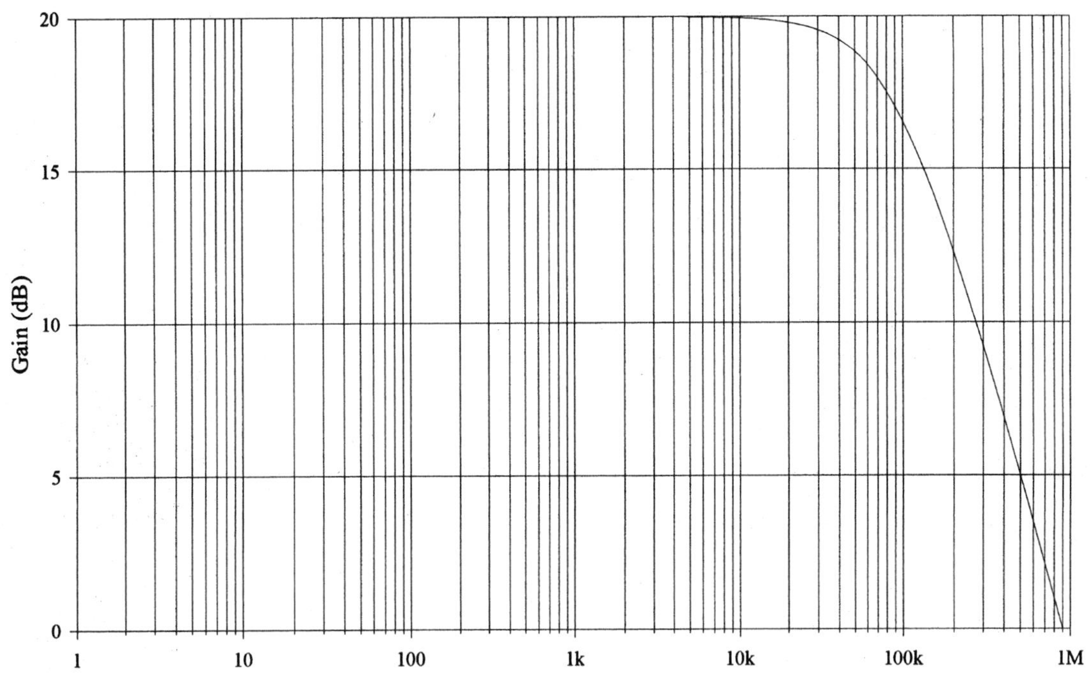

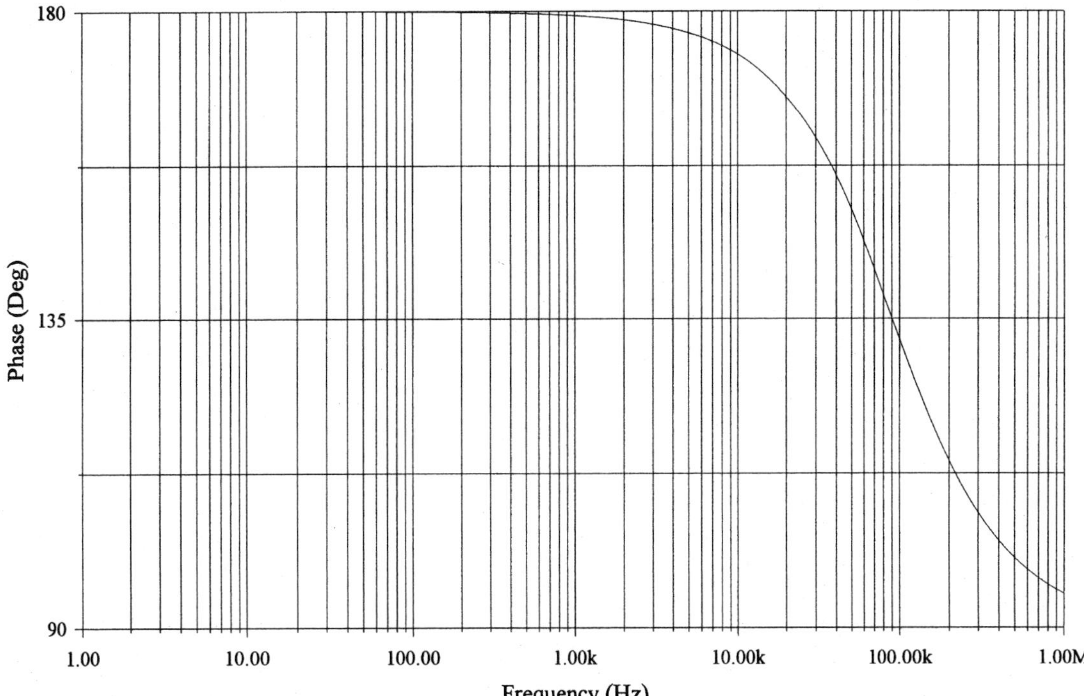

b.

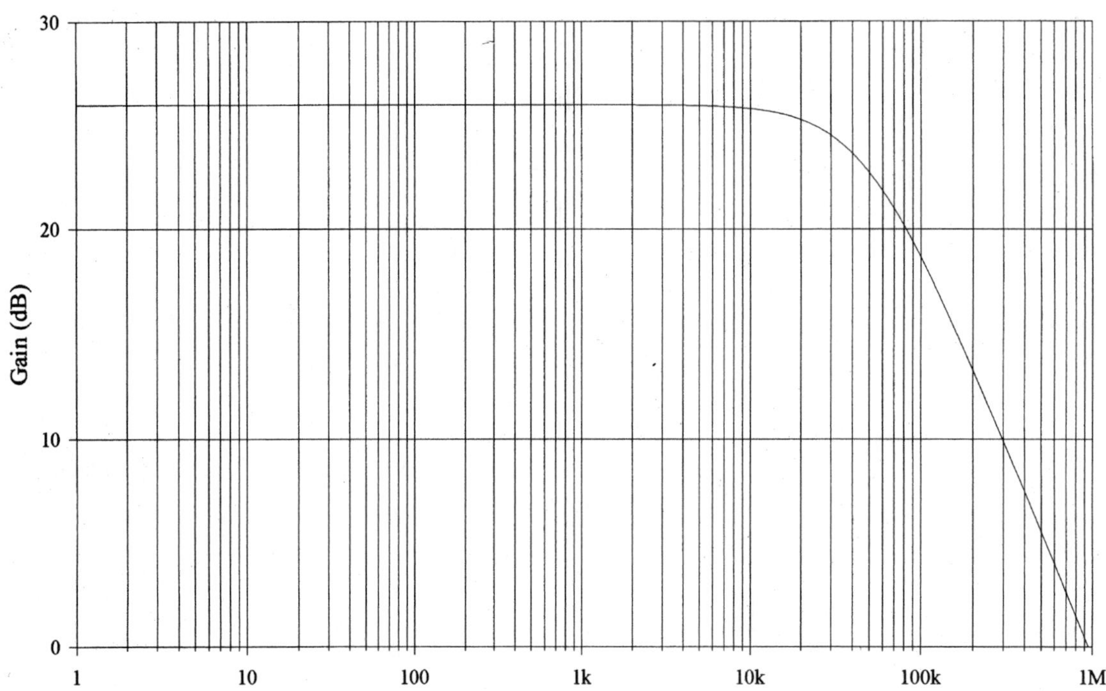
30
20
10
0
Gain (dB)
1
10
100
1k
10k
100k
1M
Traces: —— Bode Result,

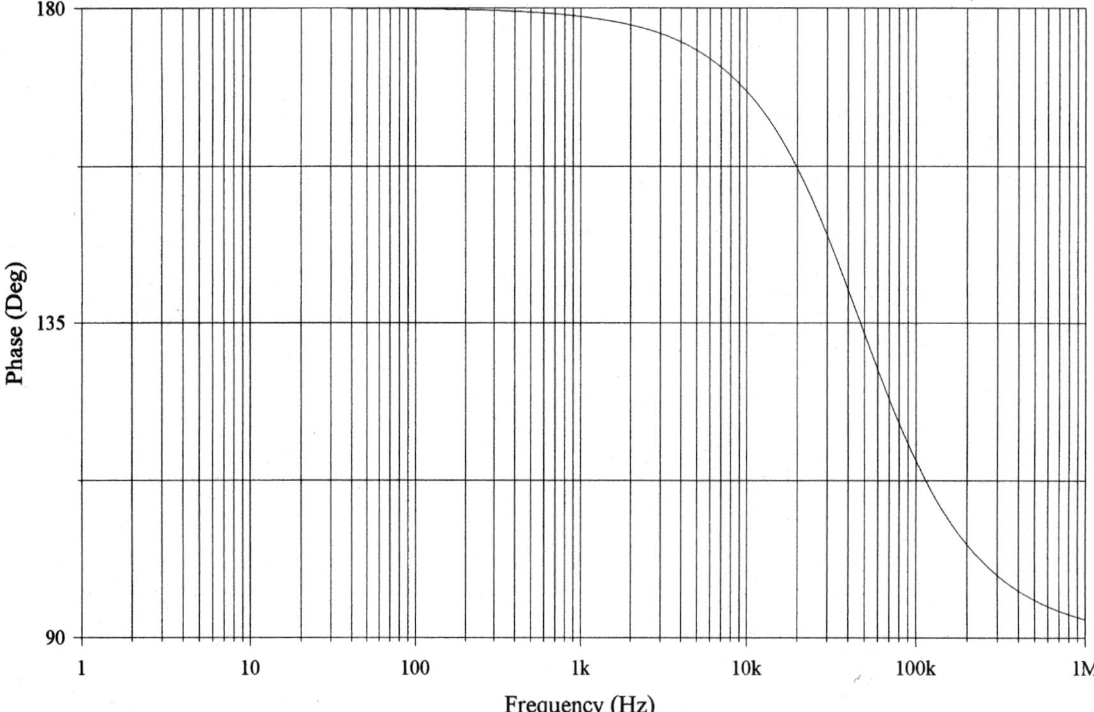
180
135
90
Phase (Deg)
1
10
100
1k
10k
100k
1M
Frequency (Hz)
Traces: —— Bode Result,

NAME ______________________

DATE ______________________

CLASS ______________________

Non-Inverting Op-Amps

Objectives

After completing this lab, you will be able to

- calculate voltage gain of a non-inverting operational amplifier (op-amp) circuit at mid frequency,
- calculate input impedance and output impedance of a non-inverting op-amp circuit,
- measure voltage gain of a non-inverting op-amp circuit,
- measure the upper cutoff frequency of a non-inverting amplifier,
- measure loading effect with and without a buffer circuit.

Equipment Required

☐ Digital multimeter (DMM)
☐ Dual power supply
☐ Signal generator (sinusoidal function generator)
☐ Two-channel oscilloscope

Note: Record this equipment in Table 33-1.

Components

☐ Op-Amps: 741C op-amp (8-pin package)
☐ Resistors: 1.0-kΩ (two), 9.1-kΩ, 10-kΩ, 10-MΩ (two),
☐ 10-kΩ potentiometer.

EQUIPMENT USED

Instrument	Manufacturer/Model No.	Serial No.
DMM		
Dual power supply		
Oscilloscope		
Signal Generator		

Table 33-1

TEXT REFERENCE

Circuit Analysis with Devices: Theory and Practice
Section 28.5 THE NON-INVERTING AMPLIFIER

CALCULATIONS

1. Given the circuit shown in Figure 33-1, calculate A_v, z_{in}, and z_{out}.

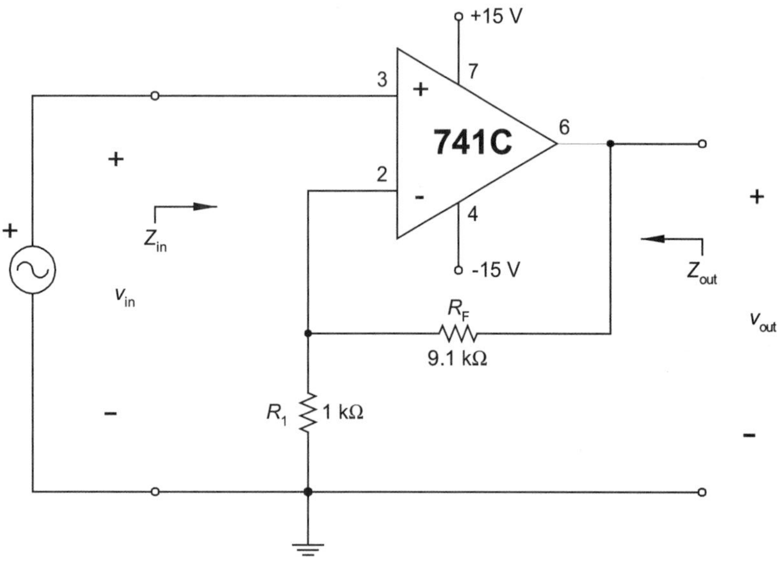

Figure 33-1 Non-inverting amplifier

A_v 10.1	z_{in} ∞ Ω	z_{out} 0 Ω

MEASUREMENTS

2. Adjust the dual power supply to provide ±15 V with respect to the common (ground) point. Connect the power to the op-amp as illustrated in Figure 33-1. The pins shown in the illustration are for the 8-pin DIP package. If you use a different package, you will need to obtain the pin numbers from the manufacturer's specification.
3. Adjust the sinusoidal generator to provide an input voltage, $v_{in} = 0.1\ V_{p\text{-}p}$ at a frequency of 1 kHz. Measure the output voltage, v_{out}.

v_{out1}	1.01	$V_{p\text{-}p}$

4. Use the measured values of Step 3 to calculate the mid-frequency voltage gain of the op-amp circuit.

A_v	10.1

5. Modify the circuit by adding only the 10-MΩ resistor at the input as shown in Figure 33-2. Be careful that you do not readjust the generator voltage. Since an oscilloscope connected at the input of the op-amp will load the circuit you will need to take measurements at the output. Measure and record the output voltage with the 10-MΩ resistor in the circuit.

v_{out2}	1.01	$V_{p\text{-}p}$

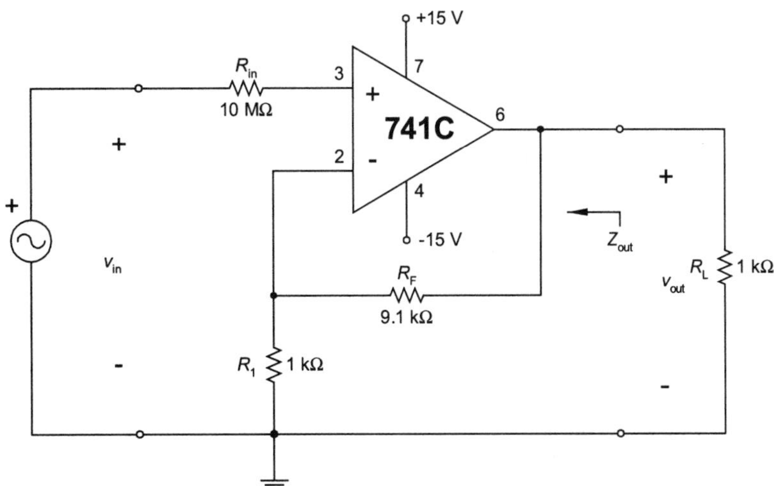

Figure 33-2 Circuit for measuring input and output impedance

6. Use Equation 33-1 to calculate z_{in} using the voltage measurements of Steps 3 and 5.

$$z_{in} = \left(\frac{V_{out(no\ load)}}{V_{(outloaded)} - V_{out(no\ load)}} \right) R_{in} \qquad (33\text{-}1)$$

z_{in}	∞	Ω

7. Modify the circuit by adding a 1-kΩ resistor at the output as shown in Figure 33-2. Measure the resulting output voltage and use this value as well as the value from Step 3 to calculate the output impedance of the amplifier.

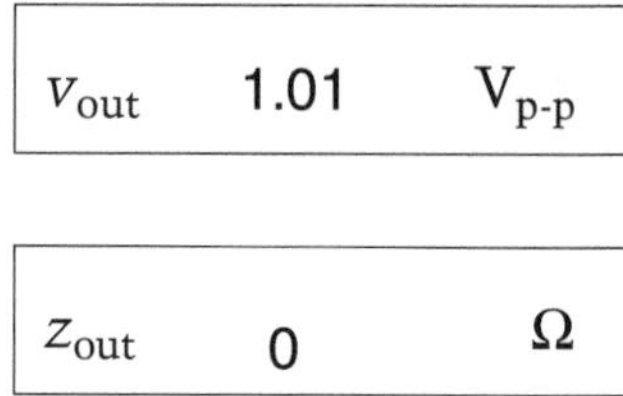

8. Construct the voltage follower circuit shown in Figure 33-3 and adjust the sinusoidal generator to provide an input voltage, V_{in} = 0.1 $V_{p\text{-}p}$ at a frequency of 1 kHz. Measure the output voltage, V_{out}.

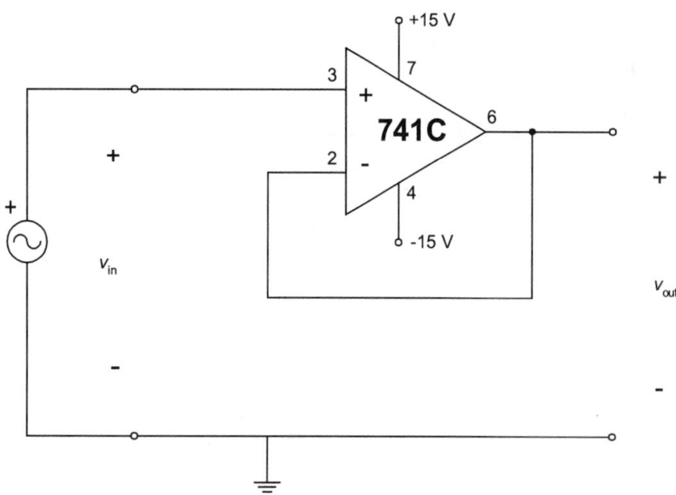

Figure 33-3 Voltage follower circuit

9. Calculate the mid-frequency voltage gain of the op-amp circuit of Figure 33-3.

A_v	1.0

10. Connect a potentiometer to the +15V as shown in the left-hand side of Figure 33-4 (non-loaded) and adjust the center terminal to provide 10 V as measured with a DMM. **Do not readjust the value of the potentiometer again.**

11. Now place a load resistor, $R_L = 10\ \text{k}\Omega$ across the terminals of the potentiometer. Measure and record the resulting output voltage, V_{out}. You should have observed that the voltage went down. Explain why the measurements are different.

V_{out}	8.18	V

The loading effect reduces the effective resistance at V_{REF}

12. Now place a buffer circuit between the potentiometer and the load as shown in Figure 33-5. Once again measure and record the output voltage, V_{out}. You should have observed that the output voltage is now the same as the reference voltage on the potentiometer.

V_{out}	10	V

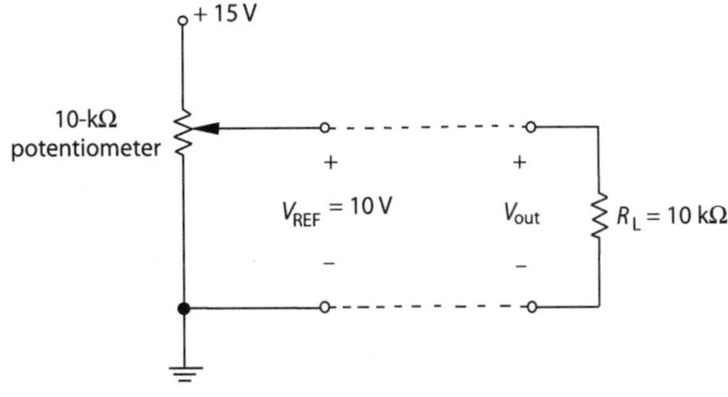

Figure 33-4 Loading effect of a potentiometer

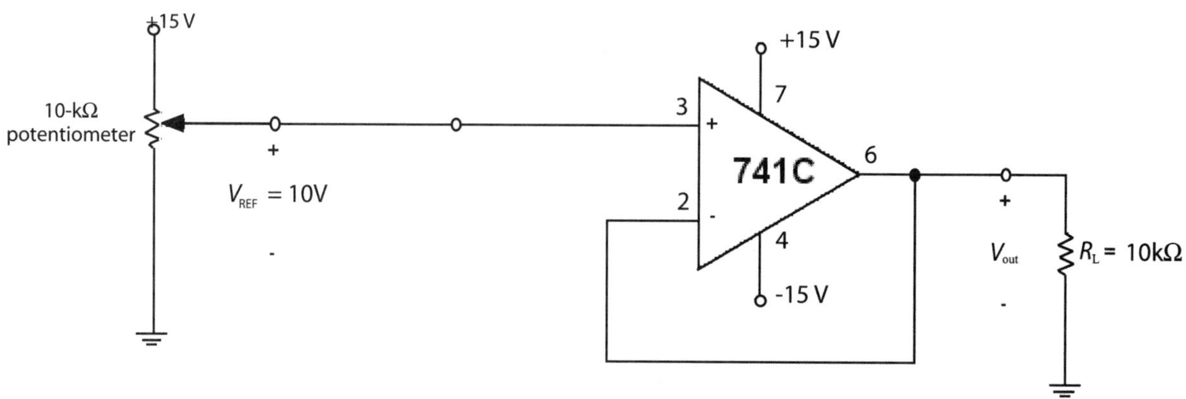

Figure 33-5 Application of a voltage follower

FOR FURTHER INVESTIGATION AND DISCUSSION

13. Use MultiSIM or PSpice to simulate the circuit of Figure 33-1. Determine the voltage gain of this circuit and compare the predicted value to your actual measured value of Step 4.

See schematic at end of lab.

A_V	10.3

Results are very close.

14. Use MultiSIM or PSpice to simulate the circuit of Figure 33-3. Determine the voltage gain of this circuit and compare the predicted value to your actual measured value of Step 9.

A_V	1.00

The results are identical

15. A standard digital multimeter has an input resistance of 10 MΩ when used to measure voltage. For normal applications, the high input resistance of the meter will not load a circuit. This however, is not true the circuit resistance is very large. Explain how a buffer circuit can be used to measure voltage in a circuit having very high resistances. Use a simple schematic to help in your discussion.

See answer at end of lab.

13.

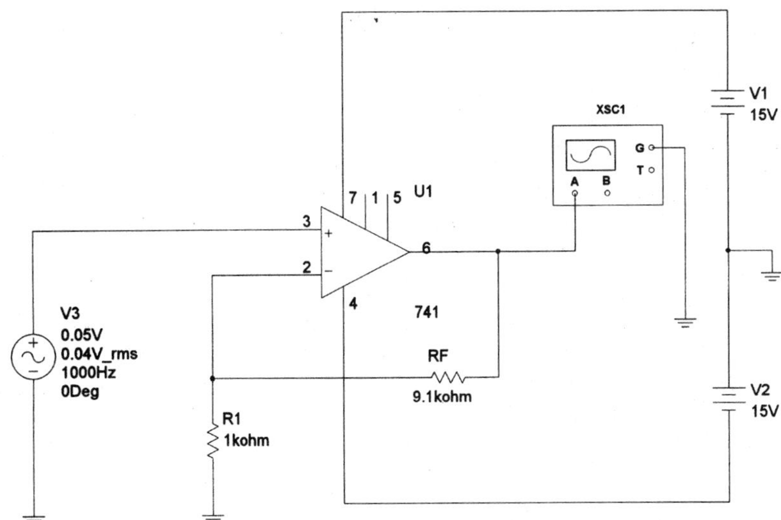

15. Place a buffer circuit (as illustrated) between the circuit under test and the voltmeter. The loading effect will be negligible.

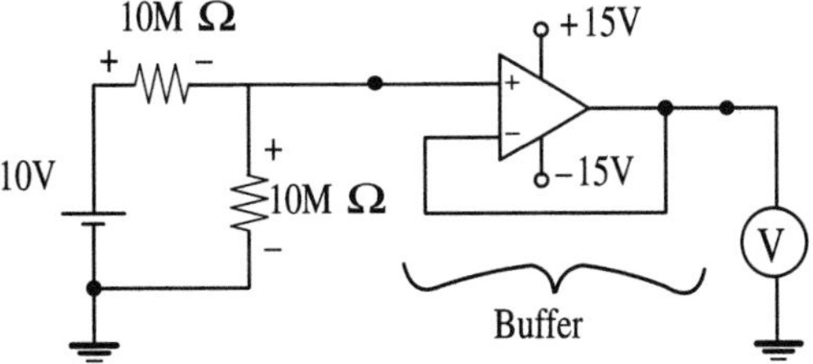

NAME ______________________

DATE ______________________

CLASS ______________________

LAB 34

Op-Amp Applications

Objectives

After completing this lab, you will be able to

- calculate and measure the voltage and voltage gain for a balanced line driver,
- properly use an op-amp to build and connect a differential amplifier (receiver circuit) to a balanced line,
- correctly connect a common-mode signal to a differential amplifier and measure the common-mode voltage gain,
- measure the differential voltage gain of a differential amplifier,
- calculate the common-mode rejection ratio (CMRR) of an amplifier,
- predict and measure the frequency response of an integrator circuit,
- plot the frequency response of an integrator on semi-logarithmic graph paper,
- measure the output of an integrator circuit when a square wave is applied to the input circuit.

Equipment Required

- ☐ Digital multimeter (DMM)
- ☐ Dual power supply
- ☐ Signal generator (sinusoidal function generator)
- ☐ Two-channel oscilloscope

Note: Record this equipment in Table 34-1.

Components

- ☐ Op-Amps: 741C op-amp (two), TL071 op-amp
- ☐ Resistors: 5.1-kΩ (three), 9.1-kΩ, 10-Ω (four), 47-kΩ, 51-kΩ, 100-kΩ, 10-kΩ potentiometer.
- ☐ Capacitors: 0.01-μF

EQUIPMENT USED

Instrument	Manufacturer/Model No.	Serial No.
DMM		
Dual power supply		
Oscilloscope		
Signal Generator		

Table 34-1

TEXT REFERENCE

Circuit Analysis with Devices: Theory and Practice
Section 29.3 INTEGRATORS AND DIFFERENTIATORS
Section 29.4 INSTRUMENTATION AMPLIFIERS

MEASUREMENTS

1. Construct the circuit shown in Figure 34-1.
2. Apply a sinusoidal input signal of v_{in} = 0.1 $V_{p\text{-}p}$. Measure and record on the following page, the waveforms observed at v_{out1}, v_{out2}, and v_{out}. The display of the input voltage is shown as a reference.

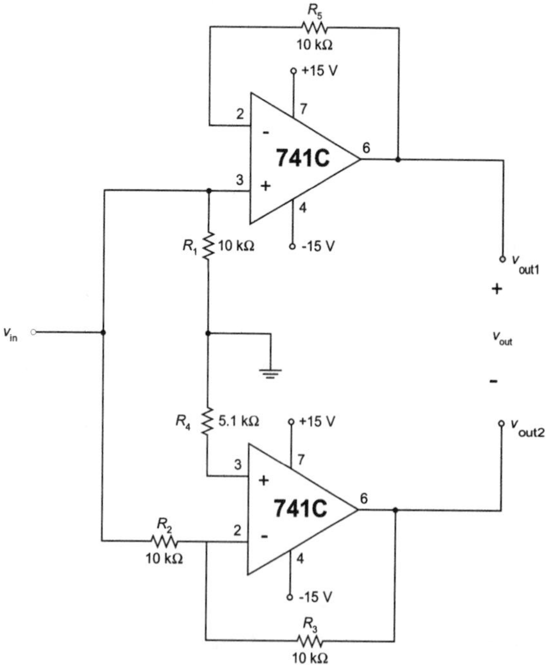

Figure 34-1 Balanced line driver

3. Calculate $A_{v1} = \frac{V_{out1}}{V_{in}}$, $A_{v2} = \frac{V_{out2}}{V_{in}}$, and $A_v = \frac{V_{out}}{V_{in}}$. Record the values adjacent to each display.

V_{out1}	0.1	$V_{p\text{-}p}$
A_{v1}	1.00	

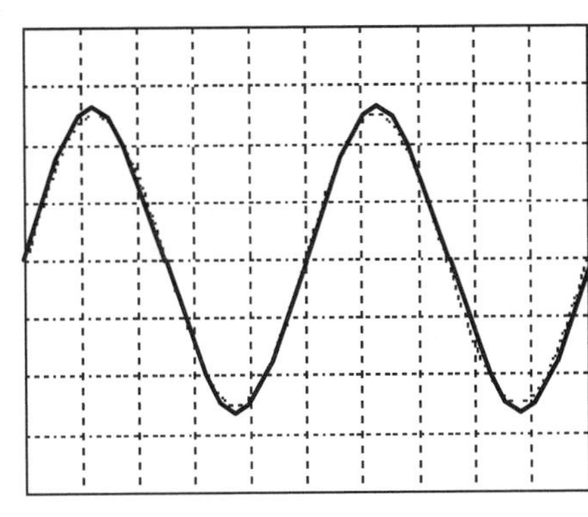

V_{out2}	0.10	$V_{p\text{-}p}$
A_{v2}	−1.00	

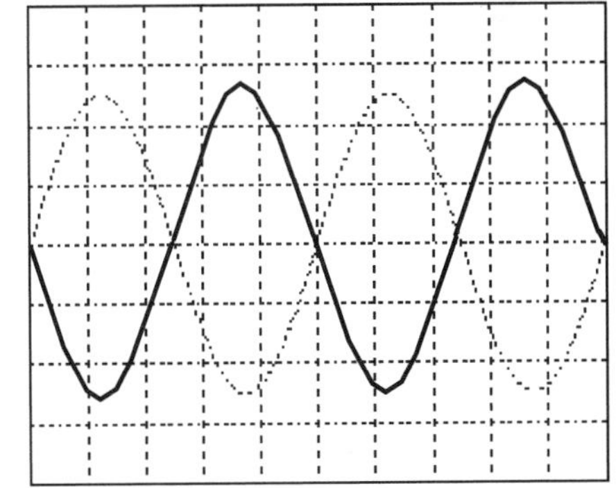

V_{out}	0.20	$V_{p\text{-}p}$
A_v	2.0	

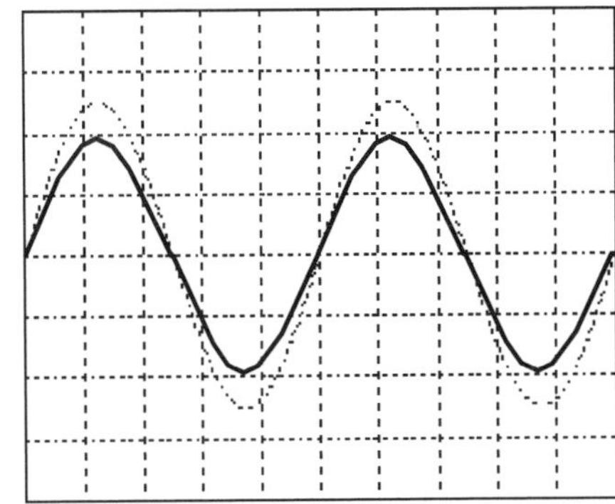

4. Connect a 1-kΩ load across the output terminals. Does the output voltage change? (Circle the correct answer.)

yes/no (no circled)

5. **Do not disassemble the circuit of Figure 34-1.** Construct the circuit shown in Figure 34-2. Use the TL071 op-amp. The pinout for this op-amp is identical to that of the 741C.

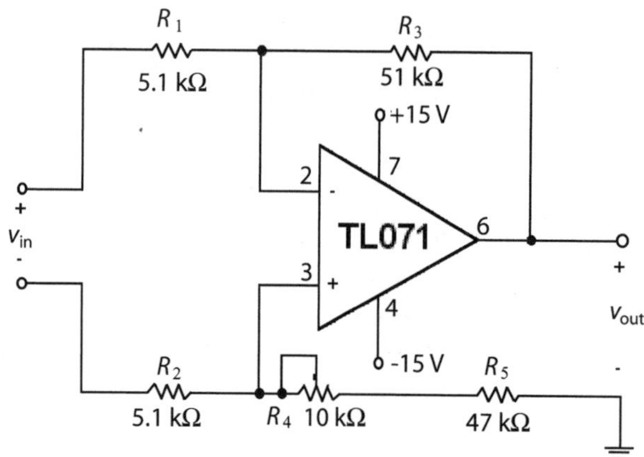

Figure 34-2 Differential amplifier (receiver circuit)

6. Connect a common mode signal of approximately 10 $V_{p\text{-}p}$ to the input of the amplifier. Adjust the 10-kΩ potentiometer to minimize the output voltage. Measure the common-mode output voltage and calculate the common-mode gain of the amplifier.

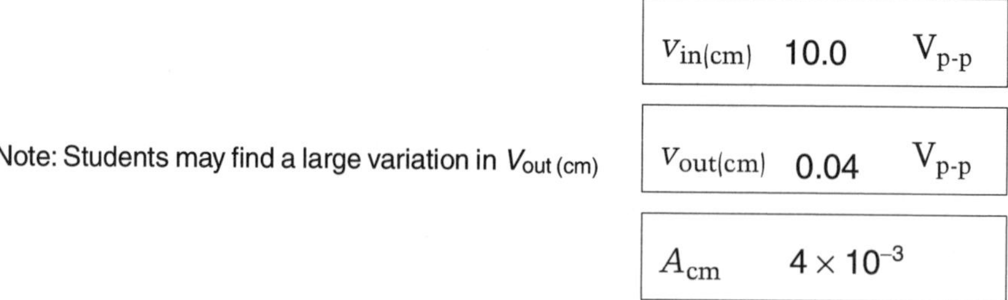

$V_{in(cm)}$ 10.0 $V_{p\text{-}p}$
Note: Students may find a large variation in $V_{out\,(cm)}$
$V_{out(cm)}$ 0.04 $V_{p\text{-}p}$
A_{cm} 4×10^{-3}

7. Connect the input of the receiver circuit (Figure 34-2) to the output of the line driver (Figure 34-1). Measure the overall voltage gain of the resulting circuit.

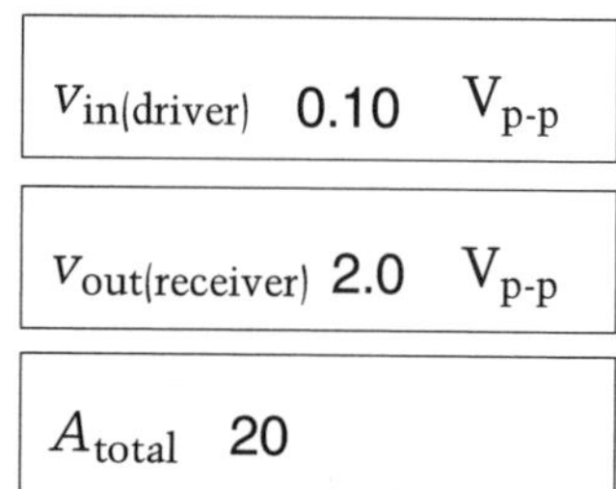

$V_{in(driver)}$ 0.10 $V_{p\text{-}p}$
$V_{out(receiver)}$ 2.0 $V_{p\text{-}p}$
A_{total} 20

8. Calculate the differential voltage, A_d, of the receiver section.

$$A_V = \frac{-51\ \text{k}\Omega}{5.1\ \text{k}\Omega} = -10$$

A_d −10

9. Calculate the common-mode rejection ratio.

$$\text{CMRR} = \left| \frac{A_d}{A_{cm}} \right| \tag{34-1}$$

CMRR	2500

10. Calculate the common-mode rejection ratio in decibels.

$$[\text{CMMR}]_{\text{dB}} = 20 \log \text{CMRR} \tag{34-2}$$

CMRR	68.0	dB

11. Construct the circuit shown in Figure 34-3.
12. Apply a sinusoidal input signal of $v_{in} = 0.1\ V_{p\text{-}p}$. Measure and record the output voltage, v_{out} at the frequencies shown in Table 34-1. Calculate voltage gain.

Frequency	v_{out} ($V_{p\text{-}p}$)	A_v	$[A_v]_{dB}$
10 Hz	1.0	10	20
20 Hz	1.0	10	20
50 Hz	1.0	10	20
100 Hz	0.85	8.5	18.6
200 Hz	0.6	6.0	15.6
1 kHz	0.155	1.6	–3.8
2 kHz	0.080	0.8	–1.9
5 kHz	0.032	0.32	–9.9
10 kHz	0.016	0.16	–16.9
20 kHz	0.008	0.08	–21.9
50 kHz	0.004	0.04	–28.0
100 kHz	0.002	0.02	–34.0

Table 34-1 Frequency response measurements

13. Plot the data of Table 34-1 as a semi-logarithmic graph (Graph 34-1).

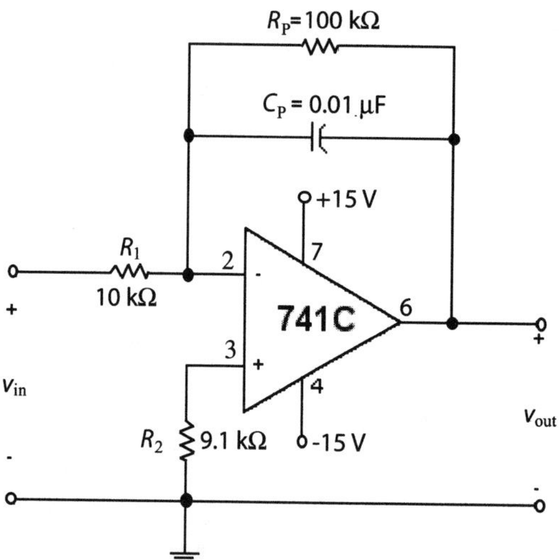

Figure 34-3 Integrator

14. Apply a 10-kHz square wave input having v_{in} = 5.0 $V_{p\text{-}p}$. Measure the output with an ac-coupled oscilloscope and record your observation in the space provided. Indicate the correct peak-to-peak output voltage and phase relationship.

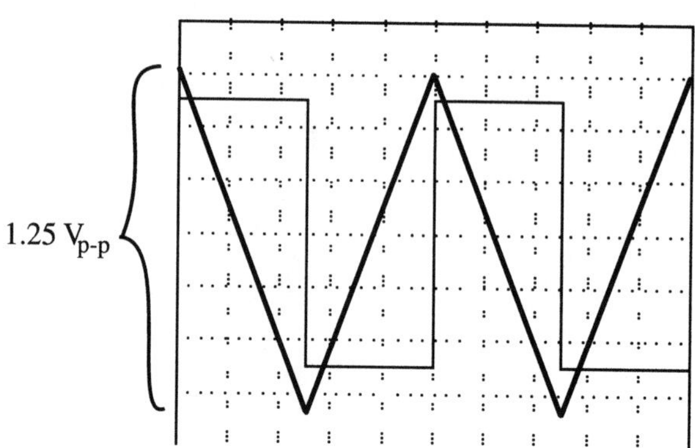

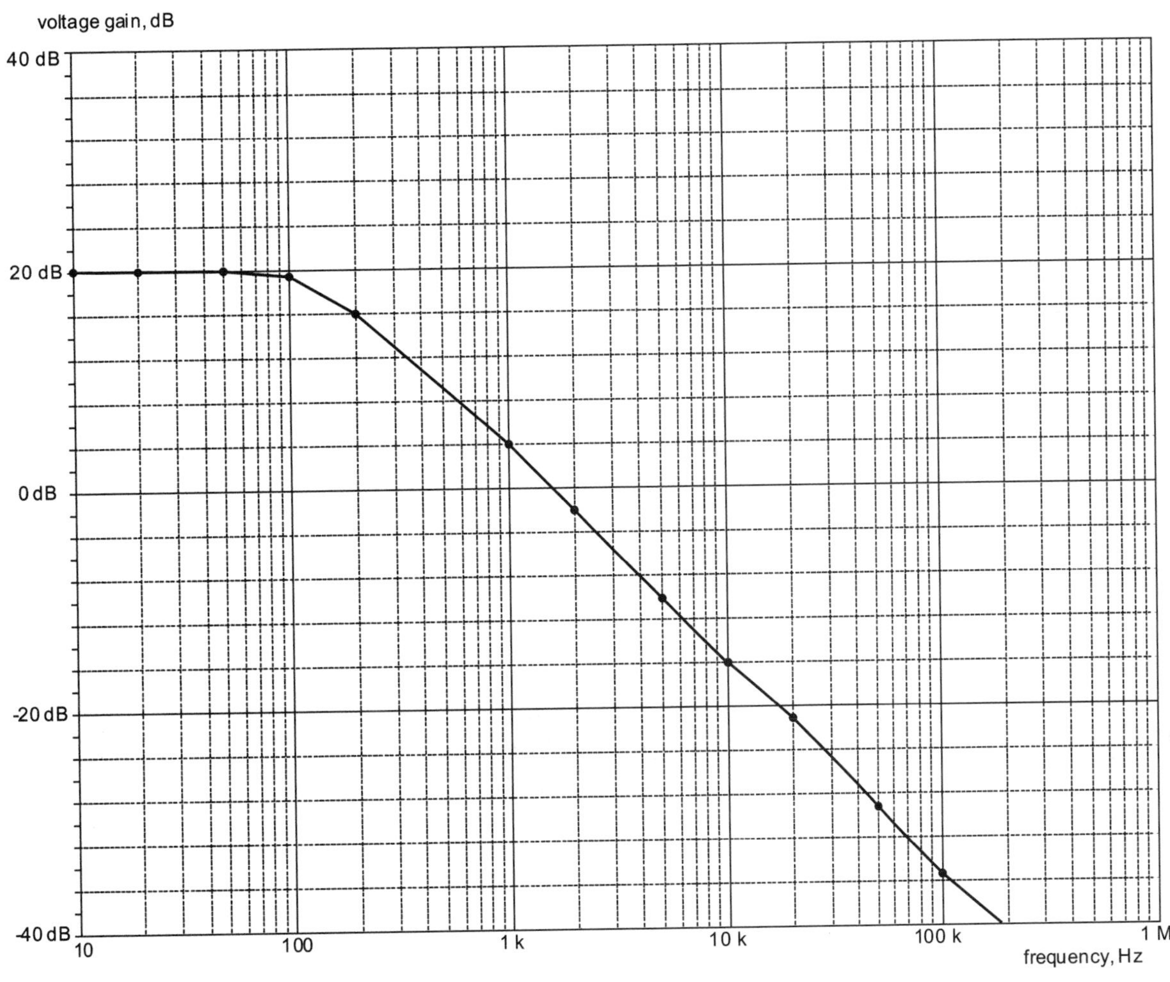

Graph 34-1 Frequency response of an op-amp integrator

FOR FURTHER INVESTIGATION AND DISCUSSION

15. Use calculus to derive the expression for output voltage for the circuit of Figure 34-3. Compare the theoretical calculations to the actual measurements.

$$I_{dc} = \frac{2.5\ \text{V}}{10\ \text{k}\Omega} = 0.25\ \text{mA}$$

$$V_{out} = -V_c = -\frac{1}{C}\int I_{dc}\, dt$$

$$= -\frac{I_{dc}}{C}\, t$$

$$= -\frac{0.25\text{mA})(50\ \mu\text{s})}{0.01\ \mu\text{F}} = -1.25\ V_{p\text{-}p}$$

16. Use MultiSIM or PSpice to simulate the circuit of Figure 34-1. Measure the output voltage of the circuit and compare the predicted results to those obtained in the lab.

V_{out1} = 100 mV_{p-p} and is in phase with the input.
V_{out2} = 100 mV_{p-p} and is out of phase with the input.
These results are consistent with the measurements.

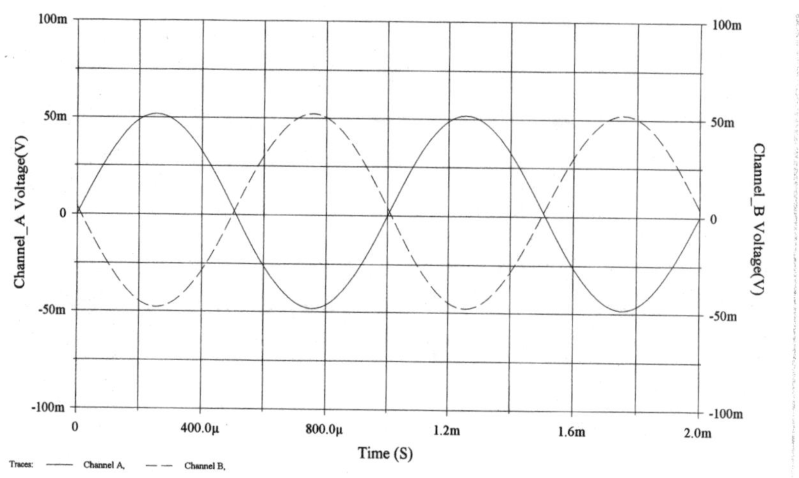

17. Use MultiSIM or PSpice to simulate the circuit of Figure 34-3. Measure the output voltage of the circuit and compare the predicted results to those obtained in the lab.

V_{out} = 1.30 V_{p-p}
This result is consistent with the measured value.

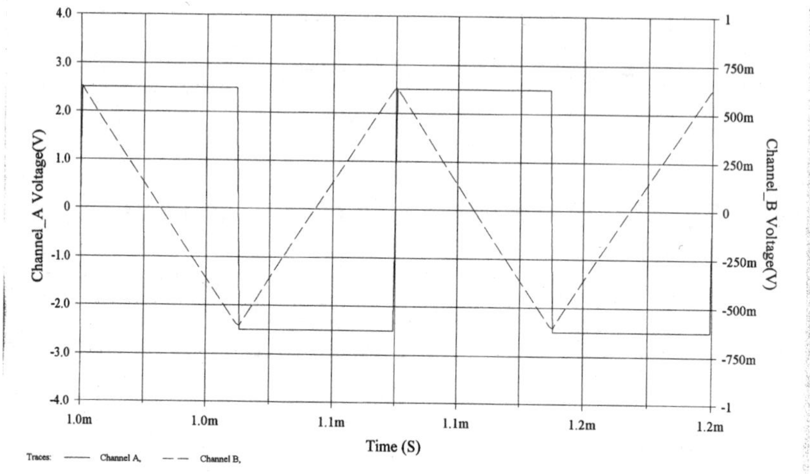

NAME ______________________

DATE ______________________

CLASS ______________________

Op-Amp Characteristics

Objectives

After completing this lab, you will be able to

- use the NULL OFFSET terminals of an op-amp to minimize the output offset voltage,
- determine the slew rate of an op-amp from the manufacturer's specifications,
- given the slew rate, determine the maximum sinusoidal frequency that can be applied to an op-amp for a given amplitude,
- given the slew rate, determine the maximum amplitude of a sinusoidal waveform for a given frequency,
- measure the slew rate of an op-amp using a square-wave input.

Equipment Required

- ☐ Digital multimeter (DMM)
- ☐ Dual power supply
- ☐ Signal generator (sinusoidal function generator)
- ☐ Two-channel oscilloscope

Note: Record this equipment in Table 35-1.

Components

- ☐ Op-Amps: 741C op-amp
- ☐ Resistors: 1-kΩ, 10-kΩ (four), 10-kΩ potentiometer.

EQUIPMENT USED

Instrument	Manufacturer/Model No.	Serial No.
DMM		
Dual power supply		
Oscilloscope		
Signal Generator		

Table 35-1

TEXT REFERENCE

Circuit Analysis with Devices: Theory and Practice
Section 28.6 OP-AMP SPECIFICATIONS

MEASUREMENTS

1. Construct the circuit shown in Figure 35-1.

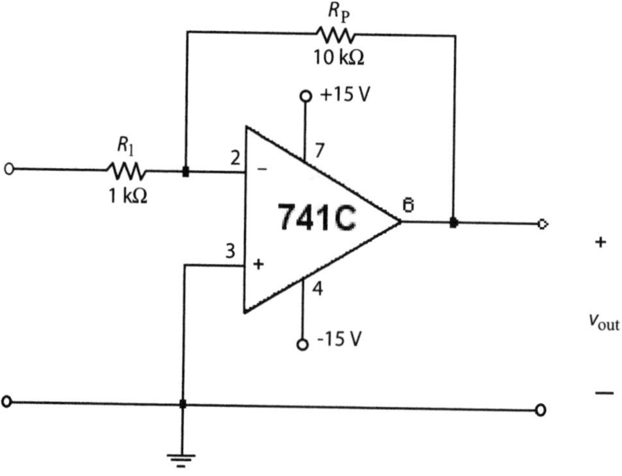

Figure 35-1 Offset measurement circuit

2. With no voltage applied at the input, measure the output voltage with a sensitive DMM. Record the offset voltage.

$V_{out(offset)}$ 1.3 m V

3. Place a 10-kΩ potentiometer between the NULL-OFFSET terminals of the op-amp as shown in Figure 35-2. Adjust the potentiometer so that $V_{out(offset)} = 0$ V.
4. Refer to the manufacturer's specification of the 741 op-amp and determine the slew rate. Use the correct units for this specification and record the value in the space provided below.

Slew rate 0.5 V/μs

5. Apply an input sinusoidal input signal so that the output voltage of the op-amp is $v_{out} = 20\ V_{p\text{-}p}$. Adjust the frequency of the generator until the output becomes distorted (appears triangular). For a 20 $V_{p\text{-}p}$ (10-V amplitude) at approximately what maximum frequency is the output no longer distorted?

f_{max} 8 Hz

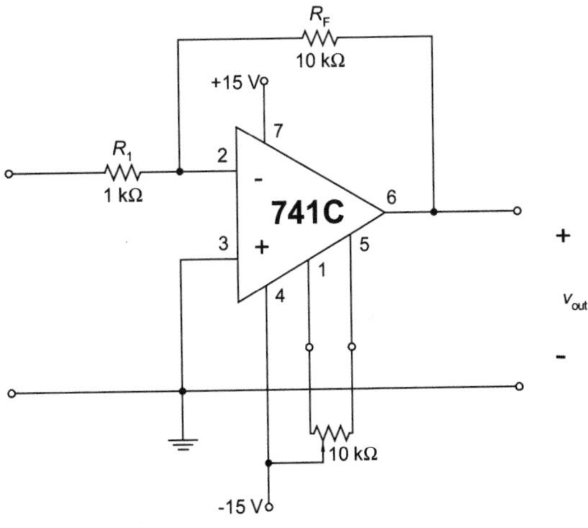

Figure 35-2 NULL-OFFSET adjust

6. Calculate the theoretical maximum frequency from the following expression:

$$2\pi f A \leq \text{slew rate} \tag{35-1}$$

$$f_{max} = \frac{0.5\ \text{V}/\mu\text{s}}{2\pi(10\ \text{V})}$$

$f_{max(theor)}$ 7.96 k Hz

7. Apply an input sinusoidal input signal at a frequency of 20 kHz. While observing the output of the op-amp, adjust the amplitude of the sine wave until the output just begins to distort. What is the maximum peak-to-peak voltage at which the output is not distorted? What is the amplitude?

$$A_{max} = \frac{0.5\ \text{V}/\mu\text{s}}{2\pi(20\ \text{kHz})} = 3.98\ \text{V}$$

$V_{out(max)}$ 7.96 $V_{p\text{-}p}$

$V_{out(max)}$ 3.98 $V_{p\text{-}p}$

8. Use Equation 35-1 to calculate the theoretical maximum amplitude.

$V_{out(max)}$ 3.98 $V_{p\text{-}p}$

9. Adjust the signal generator to provide a 1-kHz square wave with an amplitude of 10 V_p (20 $V_{p\text{-}p}$). Measure and record the slew rate of the waveform that you observe at the output of the op-amp. You may need to use the × 10 magnifier on the oscilloscope to determine the time.

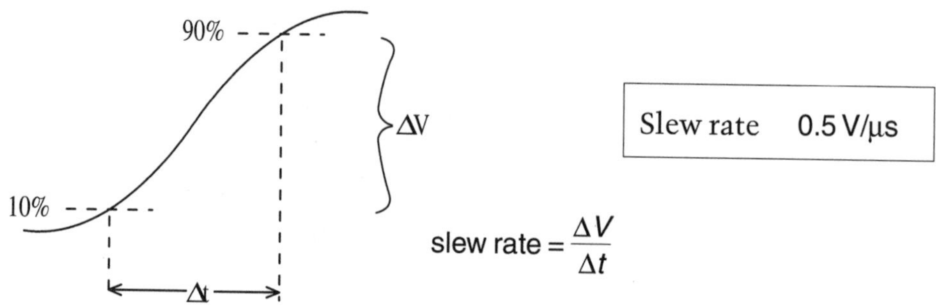

NAME ______________________

DATE ______________________

CLASS ______________________

LAB 36

Schmitt Trigger and Free-running Multivibrator

Objectives

After completing this lab, you will be able to

- construct an op-amp Schmitt trigger circuit,
- observe and measure the voltage waveforms at the input and output of a Schmitt trigger circuit,
- predict the UTP (upper trip point) and LTP (lower trip point) of a Schmitt trigger circuit,
- modify the Schmitt trigger circuit as a free-running multivibrator (square-wave generator).

Equipment Required

- ☐ Digital multimeter (DMM)
- ☐ Dual power supply
- ☐ Signal generator (sinusoidal function generator)
- ☐ Two-channel oscilloscope

Note: Record this equipment in Table 36-1.

Components

- ☐ Op-Amps: 741C op-amp
- ☐ Resistors: 1-kΩ, 5.1-kΩ, 10-kΩ, 12-kΩ
- ☐ Capacitors: 0.47 μF radial lead film.

EQUIPMENT USED

Instrument	Manufacturer/Model No.	Serial No.
DMM		
Dual power supply		
Oscilloscope		
Signal Generator		

Table 36-1

TEXT REFERENCE

Circuit Analysis with Devices: Theory and Practice
Section 30.1 BASICS OF FEEDBACK

MEASUREMENTS

1. Construct the circuit shown in Figure 36-1.

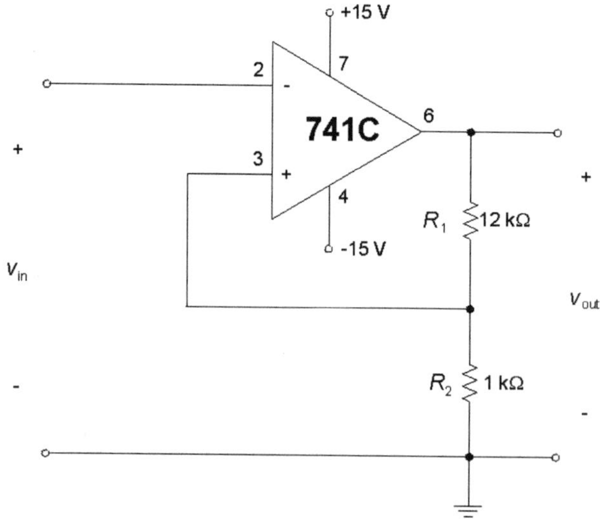

Figure 36-1 Op-amp Schmitt trigger circuit

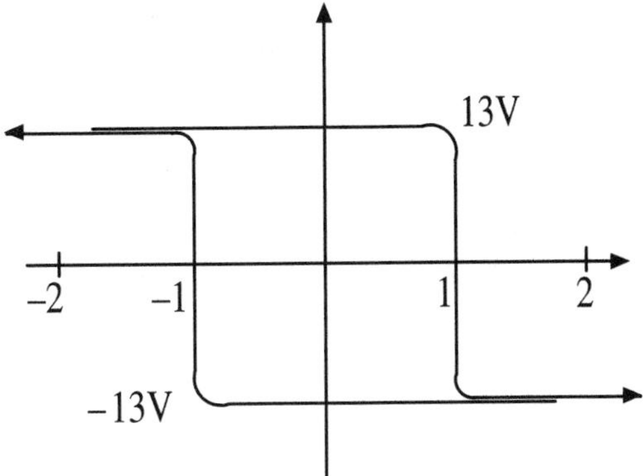

Figure 36-2 Transfer curve for a Schmitt trigger

2. Assuming that V_{SAT} = 13 V, sketch the transfer curve for the circuit (Figure 36-2).
3. Apply a triangular waveform having a frequency f = 100 Hz to the input of the circuit of Figure 36-1. Let v_{in} = 4 $V_{p\text{-}p}$. Simultaneously display both the input and output voltages on the oscilloscope.
4. In the space provided in figure 36-3, sketch the output voltage, showing all voltage and time measurements. Indicate the vertical setting used for Channel 2.

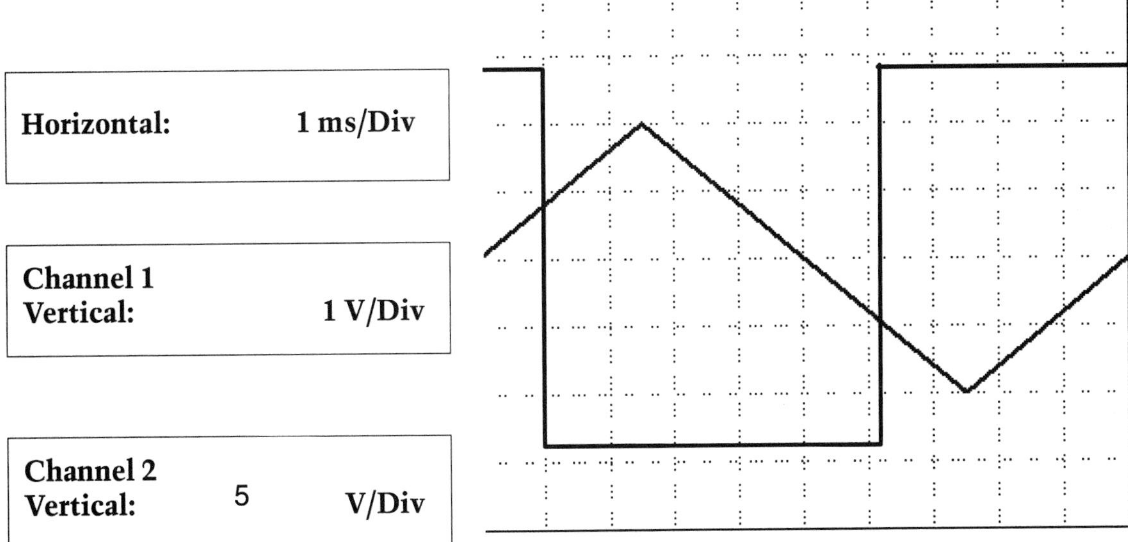

Figure 36-3 Output waveform of a Schmitt trigger circuit

5. Refer to Figure 36-2. For what value of input voltage does the output voltage go from a high voltage to a low voltage? This represents the upper trip point (UTP) of the Schmitt trigger.

UTP	1.0	V

6. Refer to Figure 36-2. For what value of input voltage does the output voltage go from a low voltage to a high voltage? This represents the lower trip point (LTP) of the Schmitt trigger

LTP	−1.0	V

7. Turn off the power to the voltage source and modify the previous circuit as shown in Figure 36-4.
8. Measure and record the voltages observed across the capacitor and the output voltage observed in the circuit of Figure 36-4. Sketch the output observed in the space provided on the following page. Label each display and provide the oscilloscope settings in the space provided.

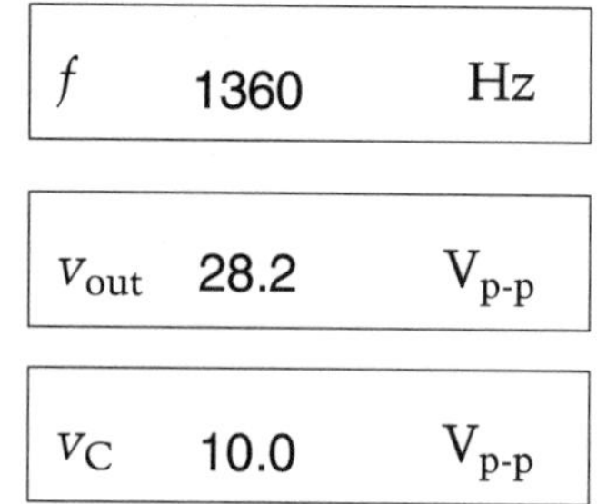

f	1360	Hz
V_{out}	28.2	$V_{p\text{-}p}$
V_C	10.0	$V_{p\text{-}p}$

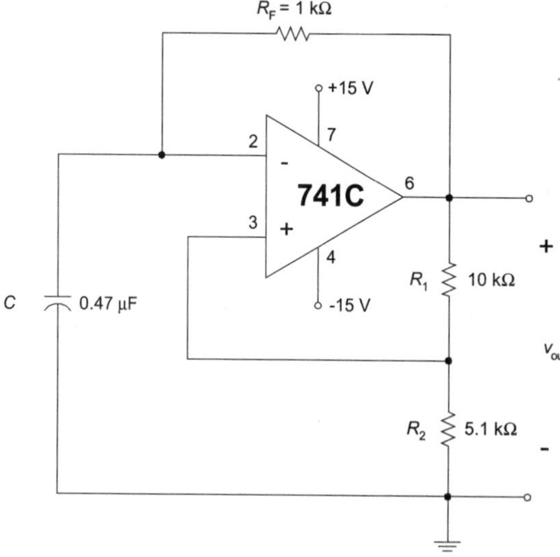

Figure 36-4 Free-running multivibrator circuit

Horizontal:	200 μ	**s/Div**
Channel 1 Vertical:	2	**V/Div**
Channel 2 Vertical:	5	**V/Div**

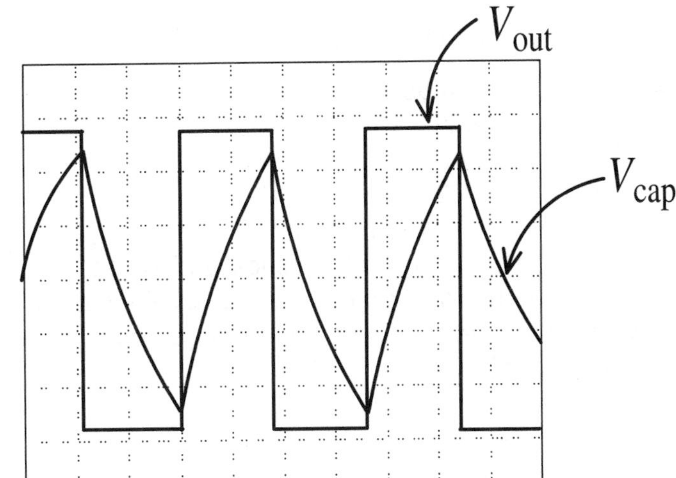

FOR FURTHER INVESTIGATION AND DISCUSSION

9. Assuming that the output voltage of the free-running multivibrator circuit of Figure 36-4 starts at $V_{out} = +V_{SAT} = +13$ V, describe the operation of the circuit during one full period of operation. As part of your discussion, include calculations involving the appropriate charge and discharge times and capacitor voltages. Determine the theoretical period of oscillation and compare this result to the actual measured period.

See next page for answer to 10.

10. Use either MultiSIM or PSpice to obtain the period and frequency of oscillation of the multivibrator circuit. Compare this result to the actual measured value and offer an explanation for any discrepancy.

9. Operation of the circuit:

a. The capacitor charges through R_F and attempts to charge to $V_{SAT} = +13$ V. The charging time constant of the circuit is $\tau = R_F C = 470\ \mu s$.

b. Once the capacitor voltage reaches a reference voltage determined by the voltage divider of R_1 and R_2, $V_{REF} = \left(\dfrac{R_2}{R_1 + R_2}\right)(\pm V_{SAT}) = \pm 4.39$ V, the output of the circuit will go to the "negative rail," $-V_{SAT} = -13$ V.

c. The capacitor will now attempt to charge to the value of $-V_{SAT}$. Once again the charging capacitor will go to only –4.39 V before the output once again switches, this time to the "positive rail," $+V_{SAT} = +13$ V.

d. The process repeats indefinitely.

e. The time needed to go from –4.39 V to +4.39 V represents half a period of oscillation and is determined as follows:

f. $v_c(t) = (13\text{ V} = 4.39\text{ V})(1 - e^{\frac{t}{-\tau}}) - 4.39\text{ V}$

g. $4.39\text{ V} = (13\text{ V} + 4.38\text{ V})(1 - e^{\frac{T}{2(470\mu s)}}) -4.39\text{ V}$

h. $e^{\frac{T}{2(470\mu s)}} = 1 - \dfrac{8.78}{17.39}$

i. $T = -(\ln 0.495)2(470\ \mu s)$

$= 661\ \mu s \qquad (f = 1513\text{ Hz})$

j. The variation between the theoretical and the actual frequency of oscillation is due to the variation between in the saturation voltage. If the saturation voltage is greater than 13 V, the capacitor will require a longer time to charge, resulting in an increased period (and a reduced frequency of oscillation).

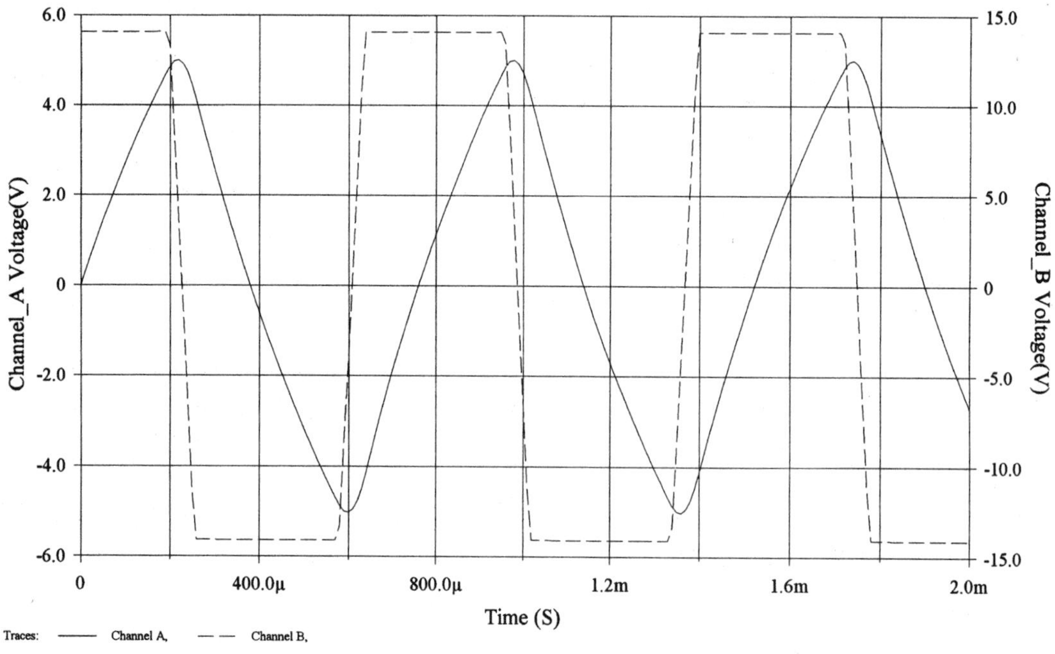

The period (and frequency) of oscillation compares well to the measured values. (Any discrepancy would be the result of variation in the op-amp saturation voltages.)

NAME ______________________

DATE ______________________

CLASS ______________________

LAB 37

Op-Amp Function Generator

Objectives

After completing this lab, you will be able to

- construct an op-amp multivibrator, integrator, and filter to produce a function generator,
- observe and measure the voltage waveforms at the input and output of the various parts of the function generator,
- calculate the predicted results from theoretical values,
- use MultiSIM to observe the predicted results.

Equipment Required

☐ Digital multimeter (DMM)
☐ Dual power supply
☐ Signal generator (sinusoidal function generator)
☐ Two-channel oscilloscope
Note: Record this equipment in Table 37-1.

Components

☐ Op-Amps: 741C op-amp (two)
☐ Resistors: 1-kΩ (three), 10-kΩ, 12-kΩ, 100-kΩ
☐ Capacitors: 0.1-μF, 0.47 μF radial lead film.

EQUIPMENT USED

Instrument	Manufacturer/Model No.	Serial No.
DMM		
Dual power supply		
Oscilloscope		
Signal Generator		

Table 37-1

TEXT REFERENCE

Circuit Analysis with Devices: Theory and Practice
Section 30.1 BASICS OF FEEDBACK
Section 30-2 RELAXATION OSCILLATOR

MEASUREMENTS

1. Construct the circuit shown in Figure 37-1.

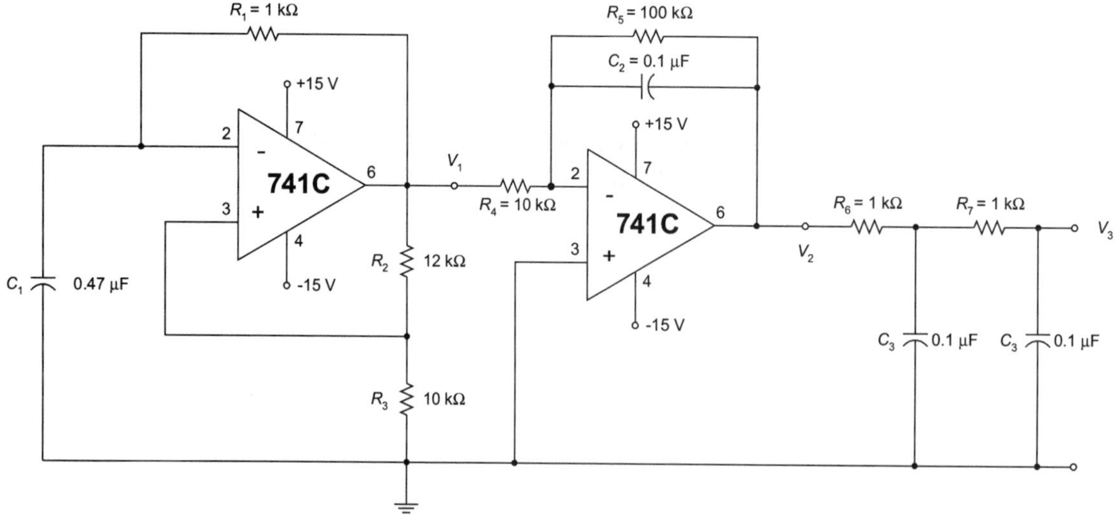

Figure 37-1 Op-amp function generator circuit

2. Sketch the voltage appearing at the points labeled as V_1 and V_2 showing all oscilloscope settings in the space provided below.

Horizontal:	200 μ	s/Div
Channel 1 Vertical:	5	V/Div
Channel 2 Vertical:	1	V/Div

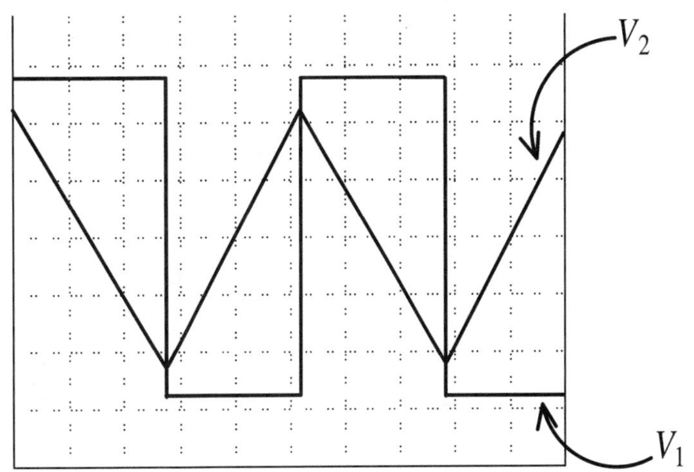

3. Sketch the voltage appearing at the points labeled as V_1 and V_3 showing all oscilloscope settings in the space provided below.

Horizontal:	200 μ	s/Div
Channel 1 Vertical:	5	V/Div
Channel 2 Vertical:	0.5	V/Div

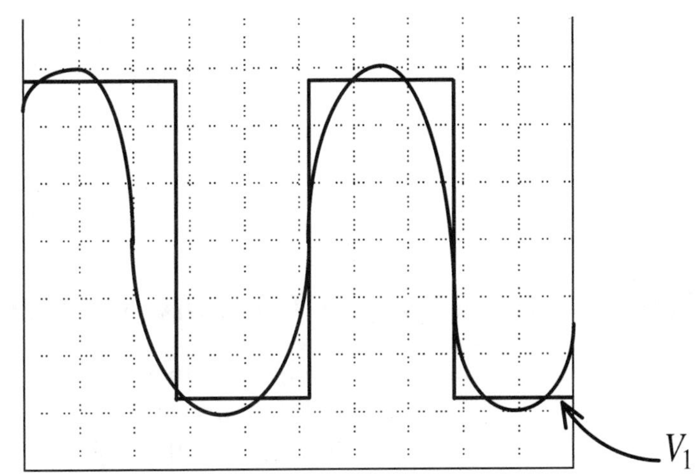

4. Determine the frequency of oscillation from your measurements.

$T = 1.02$ ms

f_{measured} 982 Hz

5. Using the component values provided, calculate the theoretical frequency of oscillation.

$$\tau = R_F C = 470\ \mu s$$
$$V_{REF} = \left(\frac{10\ k\Omega}{22k\Omega}\right) 14\ V = 6.36\ V$$
$$6.36\ V = -6.36\ V + (14\ V + 6.36\ V)(1 - e^{-\frac{T}{2(470\ \mu s)}})$$
$$e^{-\frac{T}{2(470 \mu s)}} = -0.3752$$
$$T = 921.5\ \mu s$$

$f_{\text{theoretical}}$ 1.09 k Hz

6. Determine the cutoff frequency for the filter section.

$$\tau = (1\ k\Omega)(0.1\ \mu F) = 100\ \mu s$$
$$f = \frac{1}{2\pi(100\ \mu s)}$$
$$= 1592\ Hz$$

f_{cutoff} 1.59 k Hz

FOR FURTHER INVESTIGATION AND DISCUSSION

7. Use either MultiSIM or PSpice to simulate the circuit of Figure 37-1. Obtain a printout of the oscilloscope displays (MultiSIM) or the Probe postprocessor (PSpice) and submit these with the lab.

See next page for answers to *Further Investigation and Discussion*

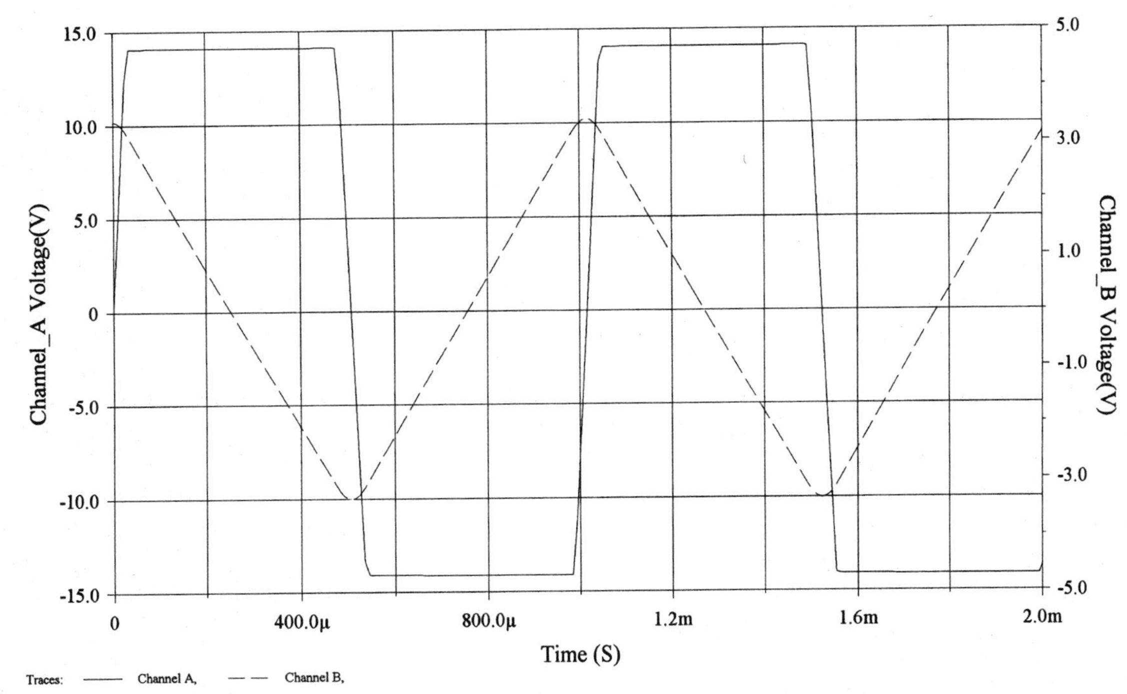

15.0
10.0
5.0
0
-5.0
-10.0
-15.0
Channel_A Voltage(V)
5.0
3.0
1.0
-1.0
-3.0
-5.0
Channel_B Voltage(V)
0
400.0µ
800.0µ
1.2m
1.6m
2.0m
Time (S)
Traces: Channel A, Channel B,

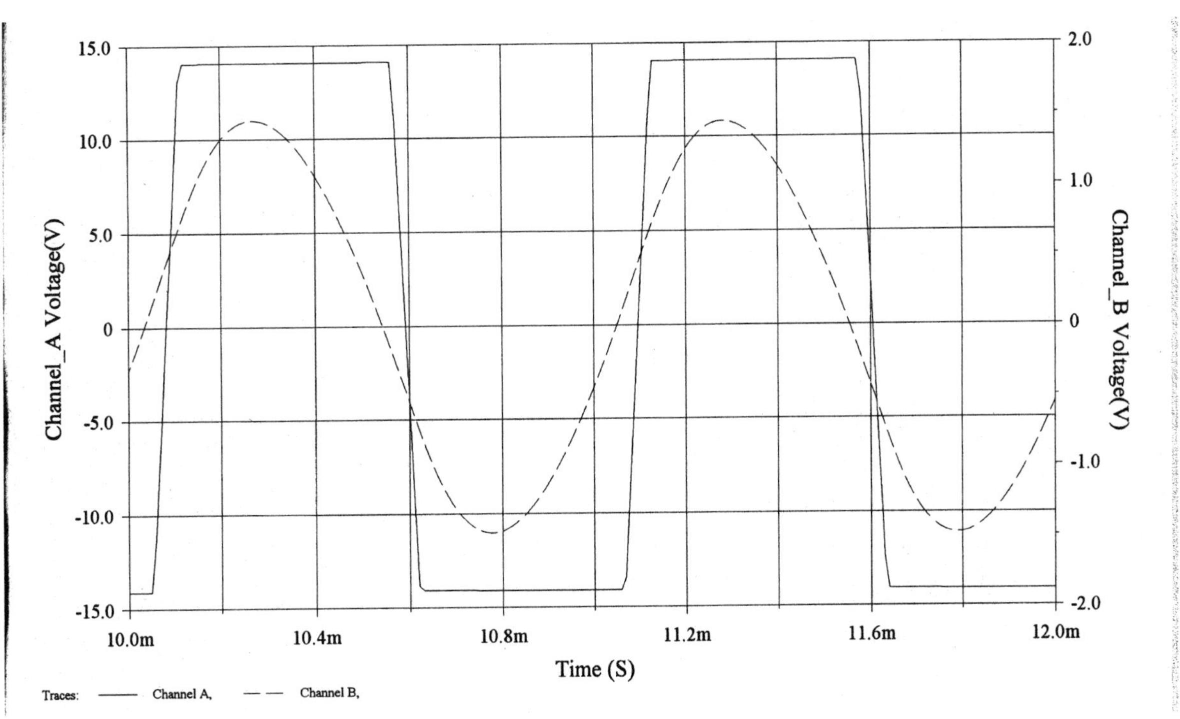

15.0
10.0
5.0
0
-5.0
-10.0
-15.0
Channel_A Voltage(V)
2.0
1.0
0
-1.0
-2.0
Channel_B Voltage(V)
10.0m
10.4m
10.8m
11.2m
11.6m
12.0m
Time (S)
Traces: Channel A, Channel B,

NAME ______________________________

DATE ______________________________

CLASS ______________________________

LAB 38

Phase-shift Oscillator

Objectives

After completing this lab, you will be able to

- construct an op-amp Schmitt trigger circuit,
- construct a phase-shift oscillator,
- explain the general operation of the phase-shift oscillator,
- measure the output frequency of a phase-shift oscillator and compare the results to the theoretical value,
- use zener diodes to improve the operation of a phase-shift oscillator).

Equipment Required

- ☐ Digital multimeter (DMM)
- ☐ Dual power supply
- ☐ Signal generator (sinusoidal function generator)
- ☐ Two-channel oscilloscope

Note: Record this equipment in Table 38-1.

Components

- ☐ Op-Amps: 741C op-amp
- ☐ Resistors: 1-kΩ (three), 22-kΩ, 27-kΩ, 20-kΩ potentiometer
- ☐ Capacitors: 0.022-μF radial lead film (three)
- ☐ Diodes: 1N4733A 5.1-V zener (two).

EQUIPMENT USED

Instrument	Manufacturer/Model No.	Serial No.
DMM		
Dual power supply		
Oscilloscope		
Signal Generator		

Table 38-1

TEXT REFERENCE

Circuit Analysis with Devices: Theory and Practice
Section 30.4 THE PHASE-SHIFT OSCILLATOR

DISCUSSION

1. Figure 38-1 shows the circuit of a typical phase-shift oscillator.

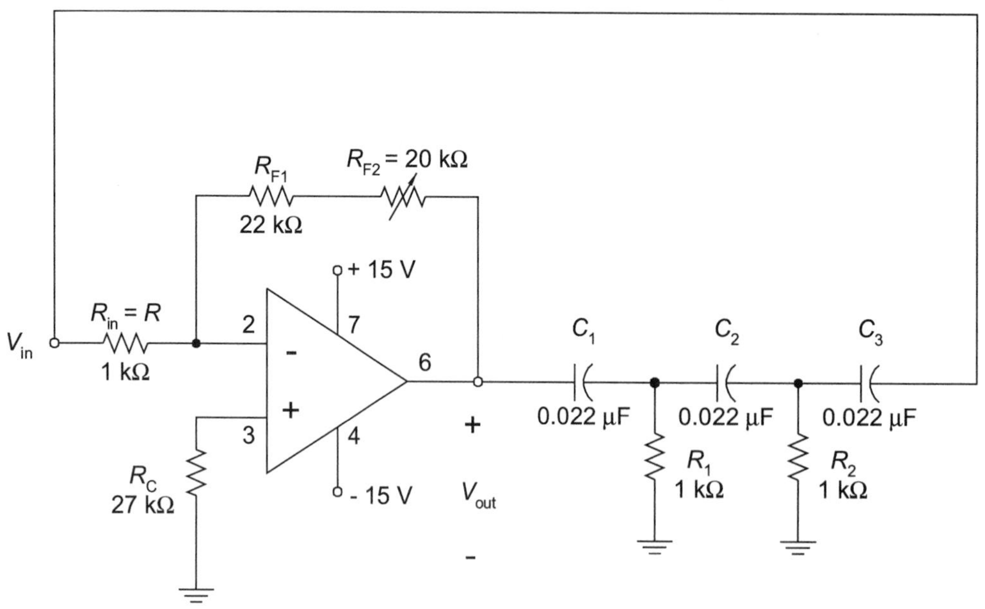

Figure 38-1 The phase-shift oscillator

In the circuit of Figure 38-1, the resistors R_1, R_2, and R_{in}, in combination with capacitors C_1, C_2, and C_3 set up the feedback path. In order for the amplifier to oscillate, the feedback path must provide for 180° of phase shift and the amplifier must have sufficient gain to provide for an overall gain of unity (1) for the circuit.

The resonant frequency of the phase-shift oscillator is determined from the following expression:

$$f = \frac{1}{2\pi\sqrt{6}RC} \tag{38-1}$$

The R-C network has a gain of 1/29 at this frequency, and so the op-amp must provide for the balance of the gain. In other words, the gain of the op-amp must be $A_v = -29$ to result in an overall gain of unity (1).

2. Determine the theoretical resonant frequency of the oscillator.

f	2953	Hz

MEASUREMENTS

3. Connect the circuit and adjust the feedback resistor, R_{F2} for a value of 20 kΩ. This value will provide sufficient gain for the amplifier to begin to oscillate. However, the gain will likely be too large, resulting in distortion. Sketch the resultant waveform in the space provided. Show the oscilloscope settings beside the display.

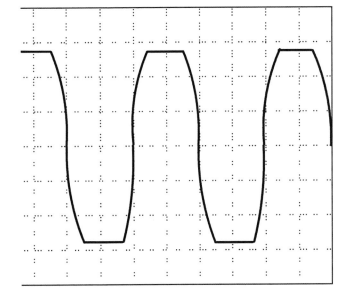

Horizontal:	100 μ	**s/Div**
Channel 1 Vertical:	5	**V/Div**
Channel 2 Vertical:		**V/Div**

4. Adjust the potentiometer to result in minimum distortion. Measure the observed frequency.

f	2830	Hz

5. What happens if you continue to lower the value of the potentiometer resistance?

Oscillations stop.

6. Readjust R_{F2} to provide for the least distortion, while maintaining the oscillation. Turn off the power to the circuit and then turn the power back on. Did oscillations resume?

No. (Note: Sometimes they will!)

7. The operation of the phase-shift oscillator circuit can be improved by introducing a variable feedback path through two zener diodes as shown in Figure 38-2. When the voltage at the output is low, the zener diodes are effectively open circuits, allowing a large amount of gain in the op-amp circuit. As the voltage at the output increases, the zener diodes will maintain a constant voltage across feedback resistance.

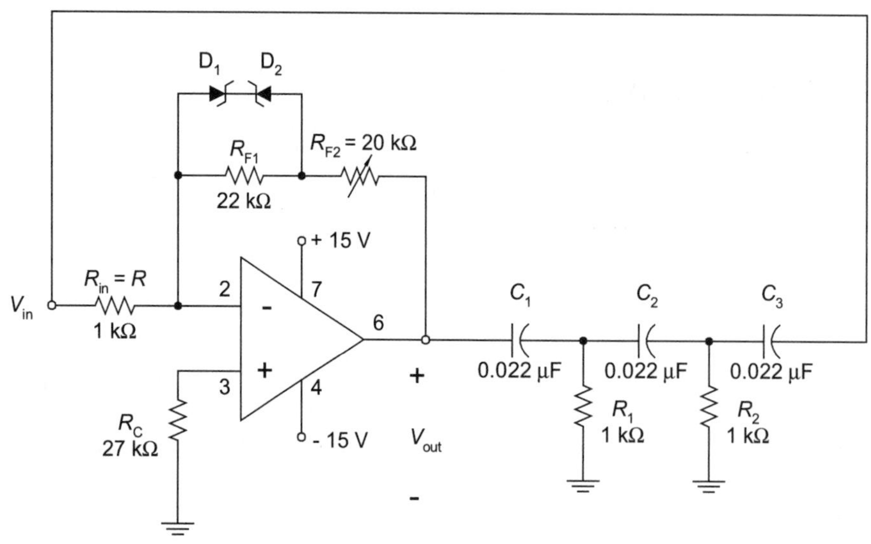

Figure 38-2 Phase-shift oscillator with zener diode distortion control

8. Modify the circuit as illustrated in Figure 38-2. Adjust R_{F2} to provide for the least distortion, while maintaining the oscillation. Turn off the power and then turn it back on. Did oscillations resume?

   Yes.

9. Sketch the resultant waveform and indicate the observed frequency and amplitude. Show the oscilloscope settings beside the display.

Horizontal: 100μ **s/Div**

Channel 1 Vertical: **V/Div**

Channel 2 Vertical: **V/Div**

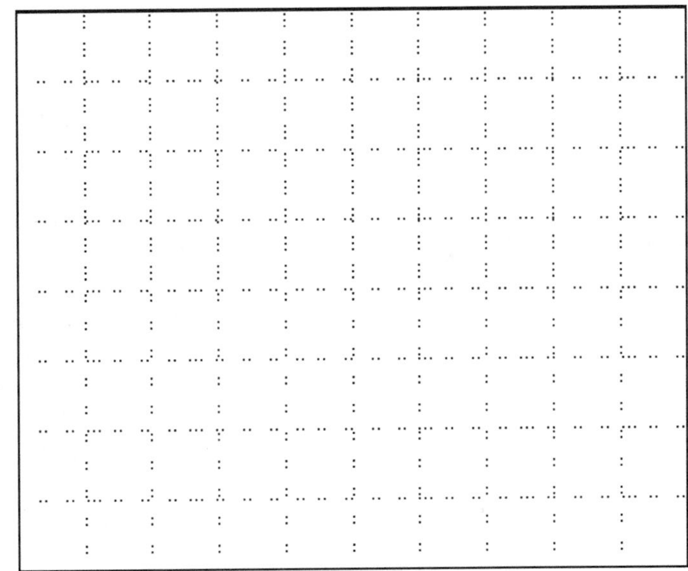

f 2880 Hz

Measured amplitude 16 $V_{p\text{-}p}$

10. The zener diodes control the amplitude of the output voltage. You should observe that the output voltage has amplitude determined as follows

$$V_p = 2V_z \qquad (38\text{-}2)$$

$V_Z = 5.1$ V

$V_{P(Theoretical)} = 10.2$ V

11. Use the above expression to calculate the theoretical amplitude.

Theoretical amplitude 20.4 $V_{p\text{-}p}$

12. Compare your measured amplitude to the predicted value.

The theoretical amplitude is greater than the measured value (by about 20%).

FOR FURTHER INVESTIGATION AND DISCUSSION

Use either MultiSIM or PSpice to simulate the operation of the circuit in Figure 38-1. Compare the observed frequency to the actual measured value and offer an explanation for any discrepancy.

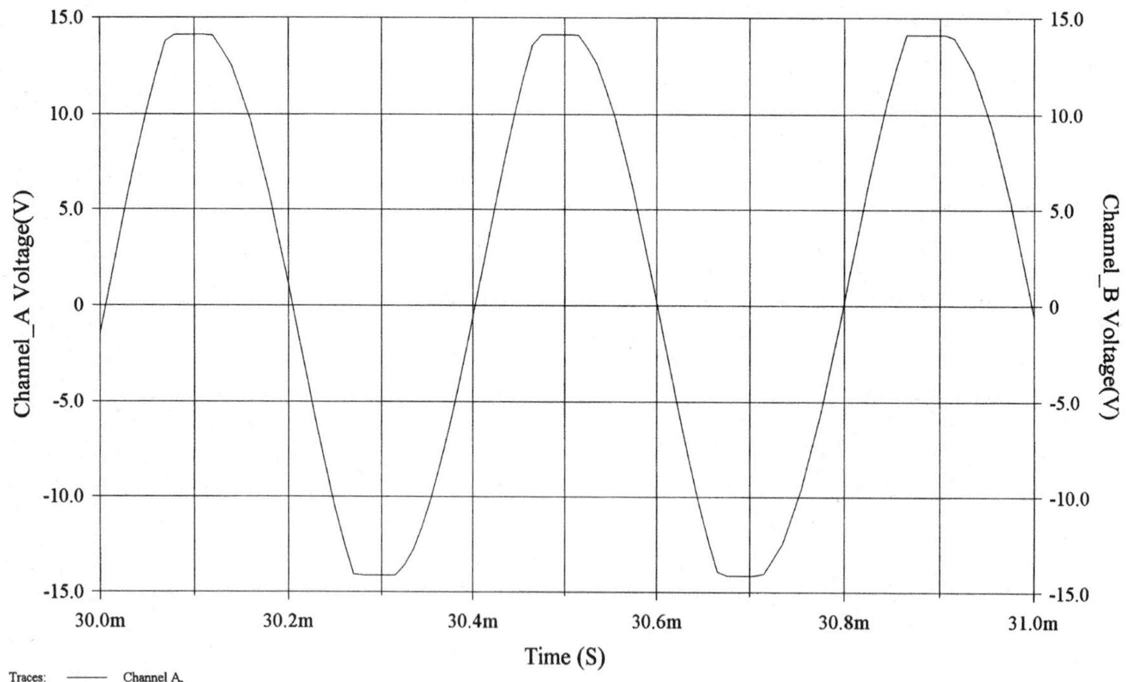

The measured period is $T = 396\mu s$ resulting in $f = 2522$ Hz. The variation is likely due to variation in the value of R_{F2}.

NAME ______________________

DATE ______________________

CLASS ______________________

LAB 39

Applications of a 555 Timer

Objectives

- After completing this lab, you will be able to
- construct a relaxation oscillator using a 555 timer,
- explain the basic operation of a 555 timer,
- calculate the frequency of oscillation of a 555 timer,
- use a 555 timer to control the duration of an alarm.

Equipment Required

- ☐ dc power supply
- ☐ Two-channel oscilloscope

Note: Record this equipment in Table 39-1.

Components

- ☐ ICs: NE555 timer (or equivalent)
- ☐ Resistors: 1.2-kΩ, 7.5-kΩ (two), 51-kΩ 1.0-MΩ
- ☐ Capacitors: 0.01-μF, 0.1-μF radial lead film, 4.7-μF electrolytic
- ☐ Diodes: Light emitting diode
- ☐ Miscellaneous: Momentary SPDT switch (optional)

EQUIPMENT USED

Instrument	Manufacturer/Model No.	Serial No.
dc power supply		
Oscilloscope		

Table 39-1

TEXT REFERENCE

Circuit Analysis with Devices: Theory and Practice
Section 30.7 THE 555 TIMER

DISCUSSION

1. Figure 39-1 shows the internal circuit of a 555 Timer.

   In the circuit shown in Figure 39-1, the 5-kΩ resistors form a voltage divider network. Each resistor will drop a voltage of $V_{CC}/3$. These voltages are then applied to the inputs of two comparators, with the outputs of the comparators applied to an R-S flip-flop circuit.

   If the *control* voltage is less than $V_{CC}/3$, then the output of the bottom comparator will go high, causing the R-S flip-flop to *set* ($\bar{Q} = 0$). The output of the 555 timer will be $+ V_{CC}$. The discharge transistor will be off.

   If the *threshold* voltage goes above $2\ V_{CC}/3$, then the output of the top comparator will go high, causing the R-S flip-flop to *reset* ($\bar{Q} = 1$). The output of the 555 timer will be zero volts. The B-E junction of the discharge transistor will be forward biased.

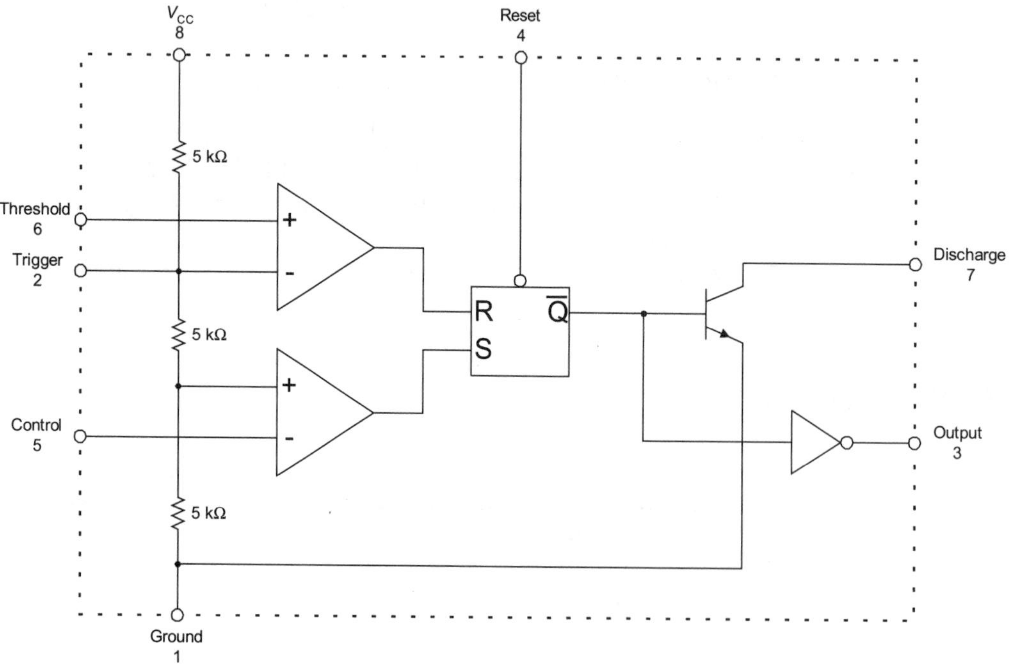

Figure 39-1 The 555 timer

When used as a relaxation oscillator as illustrated in Figure 39-2, the period of oscillation is determined as

$$T = (\ln 2)(R_A + 2R_B)C \quad (39\text{-}1)$$

which results in a frequency of oscillation of

$$f = \frac{1}{(\ln 2)(R_A + 2R_B)C} \approx \frac{1.44}{(R_A + 2R_B)C} \quad (39\text{-}2)$$

CALCULATIONS

2. Determine the theoretical frequency of the circuit shown in Figure 39-2.

$$f = \frac{1.44}{(22.5\ \text{k}\Omega)(0.1\ \mu\text{F})} = 640\ \text{Hz}$$

$f_{\text{theoretical}}$ 640 Hz

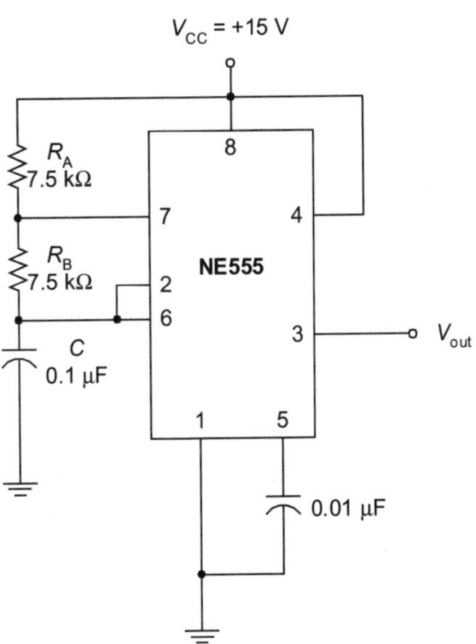

Figure 39-2 Relaxation oscillator

MEASUREMENTS

3. Build the circuit as shown in Figure 39-2.
4. Measure and record the actual frequency of operation.

f_{measured}	640	Hz

5. Record the waveform observed across the capacitor. Sketch the resultant waveform in the space provided. Show the oscilloscope settings beside the display.

Horizontal:	0.5 m	s/Div

Channel 1 Vertical:	5	V/Div

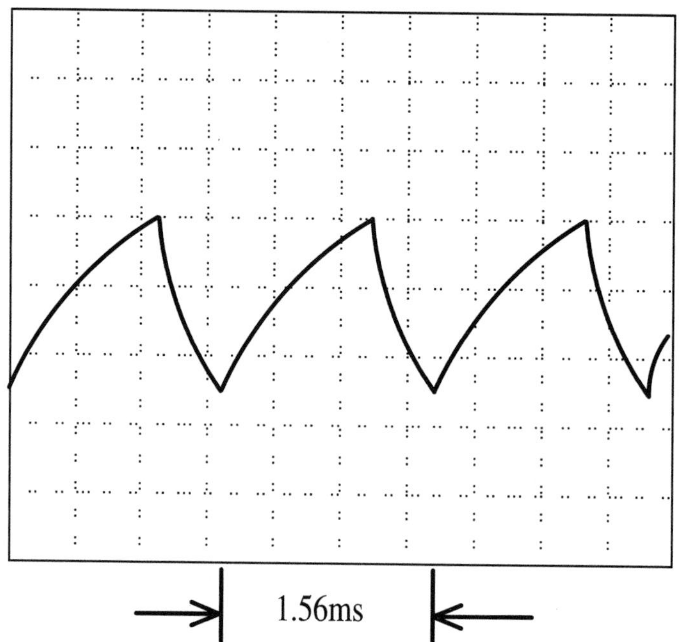

6. Record the waveform observed at the output. Sketch the resultant waveform in the space provided. Show the oscilloscope settings beside the display.

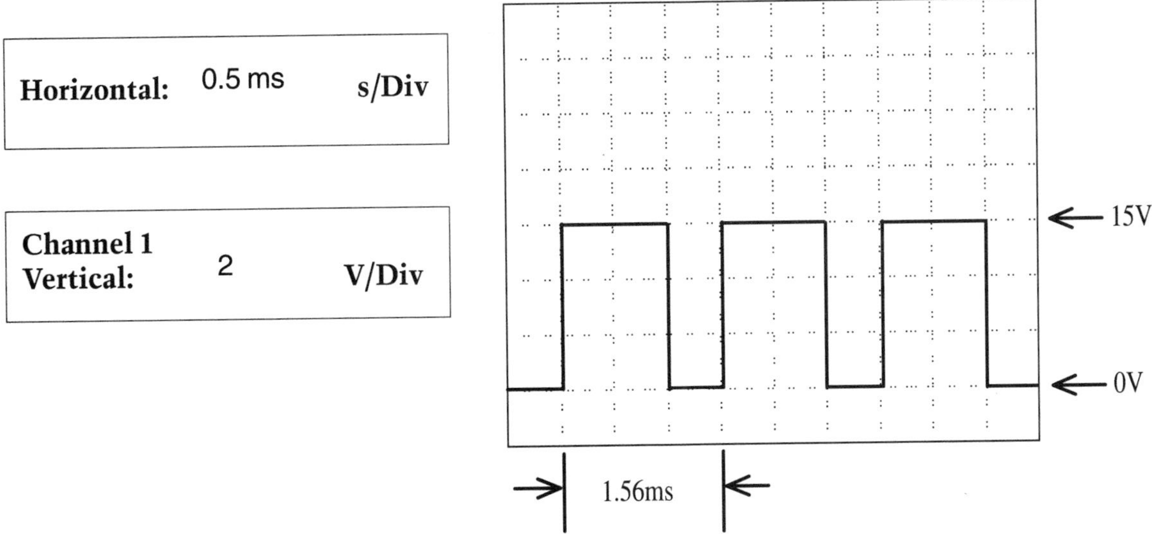

DISCUSSION

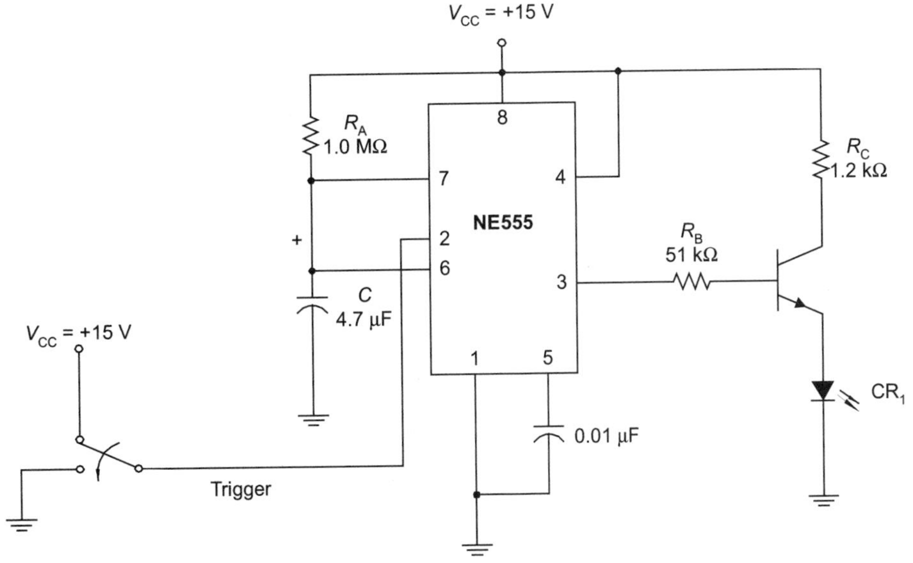

Figure 39-3

7. Besides providing astable operation as a relaxation oscillator, the 555 timer can be used as a monostable circuit, providing a single pulse each time the trigger voltage goes low. The resulting output

pulse will have a minimum duration, regardless of how short the trigger pulse was. This condition is ideally suited for alarm circuits, which will continue to provide an alarm, even if the alarm trigger was reset. The duration of the output pulse is determined by the timing circuit, and can be adjusted to be active from several seconds up to many minutes. The monostable circuit is shown in Figure 39-3.

The duration of the pulse is determined as

$$T_w = (\ln 3)R_A C \approx 1.10 R_A C \tag{39-3}$$

CALCULATIONS

8. Determine the theoretical duration of the pulse that will resulting when the trigger of the 555 timer in Figure 39-3 goes low.

$T_{theoretical}$ 5.17 s

MEASUREMENTS

9. Use a momentary switch or manually remove the trigger from V_{CC} = 15 V and connect this point to ground as illustrated in Figure 39-3. You should observe that the LED representing an alarm will come on. Reconnect the trigger to V_{CC} = 15 V. Use a watch to measure the time that the "alarm" remains on. Record this value in the space provided.

$T_{measured}$ ~5 s

FOR FURTHER INVESTIGATION AND DISCUSSION

See next page for answers to *For Further Investigation and Discussion*

10. Use either MultiSIM or PSpice to simulate the operation of the circuit in Figure 39-2. Compare the observed frequency to the actual measured value and offer an explanation for any discrepancy.
11. Describe the operation of the monostable circuit shown in Figure 39-3. In your discussion, include the expected capacitor voltage and show how the pulse duration is determined by the charging of the capacitor.

10.

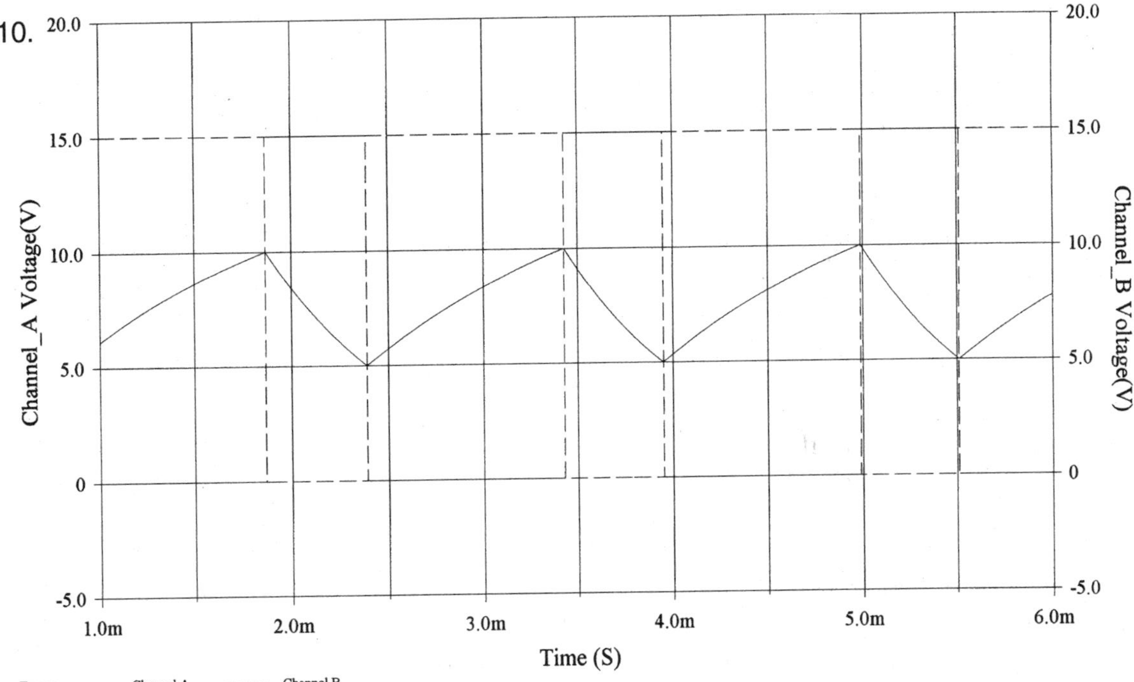

11. Operation of the circuit

a. Since the trigger terminal is normally kept at a high voltage, the comparator in the 555 timer will be normally *reset*. This means that the discharge transistor will normally be saturated, preventing the timing capacitor from charging. The output of the 555 timer will be at zero volts, keeping the external transistor in cutoff. The LED will remain off.

b. When the trigger terminal goes to ground through the external switch (representing an alarm condition), the comparator in the 555 timer will be *set*, meaning that the discharge transistor will be cutoff. The external transistor will now be saturated, resulting in the LED turning on. This condition will continue even though the external switch may be returned to its non-alarm condition.

c. The LED will remain on until the capacitor voltage reaches 2 $V_{CC}/3$. The time to reach this condition is determined by the timing resistor and capacitor and is determined as follows:

$$v_C(t) = \frac{2V_{CC}}{3} = V_{CC}(1 - e^{-\frac{t}{R_A C}})$$

$$T_W = -R_A C \ln(1 - \frac{2}{3})$$

$$= (1\ \text{M}\Omega)(4.7\ \mu\text{F})(1.099)$$

$$= 5.16\ \text{s}$$

d. At this point, the comparator once again resets and the LED goes off.

NAME ______________________

DATE ______________________

CLASS ______________________

LAB 40

Voltage Controlled Oscillator

Objectives

After completing this lab, you will be able to

- explain the basic principles of operation of the LM566 Voltage Controlled Oscillator,
- calculate the frequency of oscillation of a VCO circuit,
- determine the minimum modulating voltage of a VCO circuit,
- measure the output voltages of a VCO circuit,
- sketch the relationship of frequency as a function of the modulating voltage of a VCO,
- apply a sinusoidal input signal at the input of a VCO and observe the frequency modulated output voltage.

Equipment Required

- ☐ dc power supply
- ☐ Digital multimeter
- ☐ Signal generator
- ☐ Two-channel oscilloscope

Note: Record this equipment in Table 40-1.

Components

- ☐ ICs: LM566C voltage controlled oscillator
- ☐ Resistors: 510-Ω, 10-kΩ, 5-kΩ potentiometer, 18-kΩ, 1.0-MΩ
- ☐ Capacitors: 4.7-nF radial lead film, 10-μF electrolytic

EQUIPMENT USED

Instrument	Manufacturer/Model No.	Serial No.
DMM		
Dual power supply		
Oscilloscope		
Signal Generator		

Table 40-1

TEXT REFERENCE

Circuit Analysis with Devices: Theory and Practice
Section 30.8 THE VOLTAGE CONTROLLED OSCILLATOR - VCO

DISCUSSION

1. Figure 40-1 shows the internal circuit of the LM566C voltage controlled oscillator.

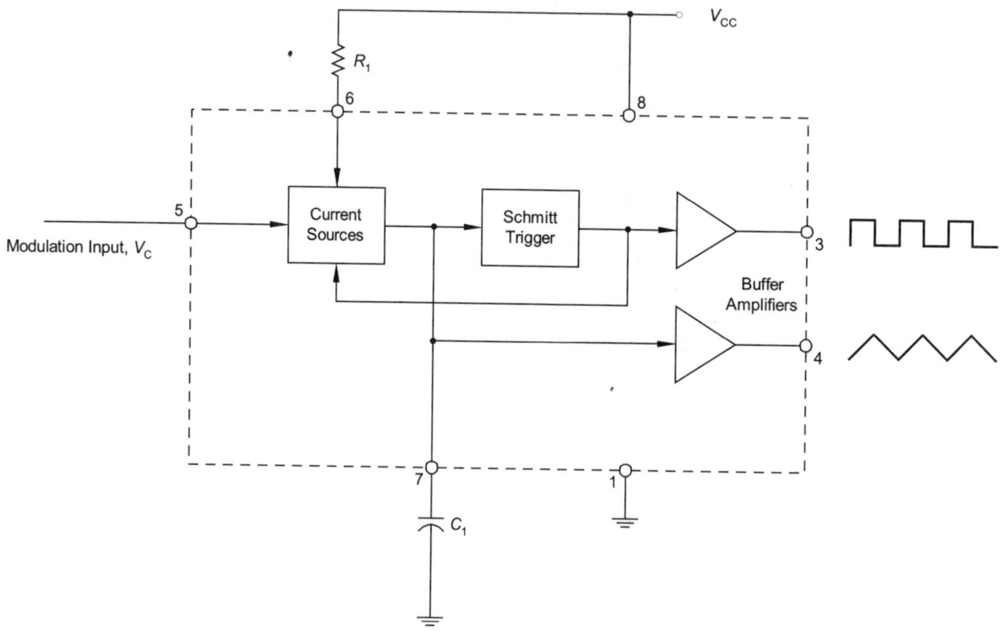

Figure 40-1 The LM566C voltage controlled oscillator

2. The voltage controlled oscillator, VCO, is a device that generates both a square wave and a triangular wave. A timing resistor, R_1, a timing capacitor, C_1, and an externally applied modulating voltage, V_C, determine the frequency of oscillation as follows:

$$f_0 = \frac{2.4}{R_1 C_1}\left(\frac{V_{CC} - V_C}{V_{CC}}\right) \tag{40-1}$$

CALCULATIONS

3. Refer to the manufacturer's specifications to answer the following questions:
   a. What is the maximum operating frequency of the LM566C VCO?

f_{max}	1 M	Hz

   b. If the supply voltage is selected to be V_{CC} = 15 V, what is the minimum voltage that must be applied to the modulation input, V_C?

$V_{C(min)} = V_{CC(0.75)}$

$V_{C(min)}$	11.25	V

4. Refer to the circuit shown in Figure 40-2. What is the minimum voltage that you expect at the modulating input terminal?

$$V_C = \left(\frac{18\ \text{k}\Omega}{23.51\ \text{k}\Omega}\right) 15\ \text{V} = 11.48\ \text{V}$$

$V_{C(min)}$	11.48	V

5. What is the maximum voltage that you expect at the modulating input terminal?

$$V_C = \left(\frac{23\ \text{k}\Omega}{23.51\ \text{k}\Omega}\right) 15\ \text{V} = 14.67\ \text{V}$$

$V_{C(max)}$	14.67	V

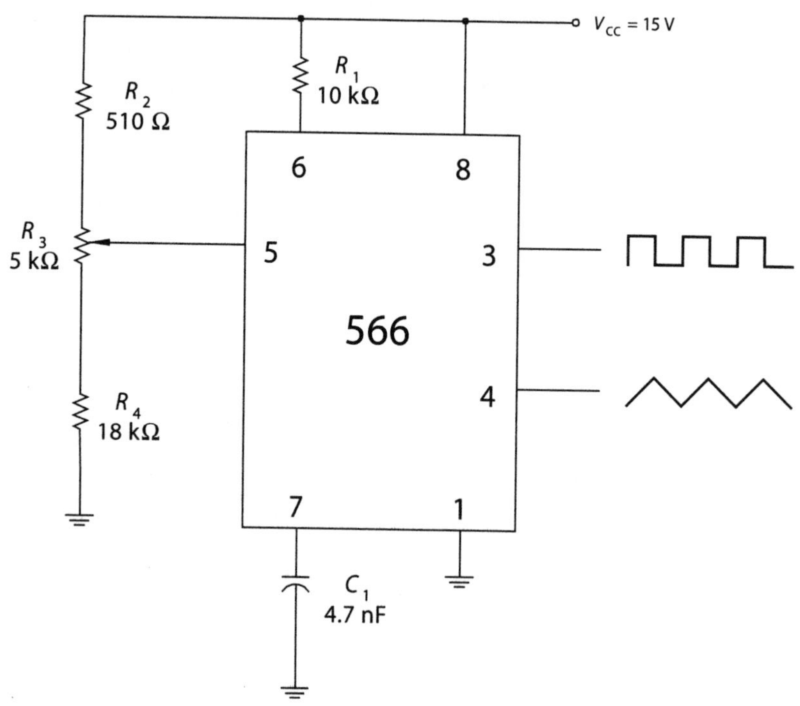

Figure 40-2 Voltage controlled oscillator circuit

6. Using the values from Steps 4 and 5, determine the frequency range of the output signal as the potentiometer is varied from 0 to 5 kΩ.

$$f = \left(\frac{2.4}{47 \times 10_s^{-6}}\right)\left(\frac{15\text{ V} - 14.67\text{ V}}{15\text{ V}}\right) = 1123\text{ Hz}$$

$$f = \left(\frac{2.4}{47 \times 10_s^{-6}}\right)\left(\frac{15\text{ V} - 11.48\text{ V}}{15\text{ V}}\right) = 11983\text{ Hz}$$

f = 1.12 k Hz to 11.98 k Hz

MEASUREMENTS

7. Construct the circuit of Figure 40-2. Adjust the 5-kΩ potentiometer so that V_C is at its minimum value. Record this value.

$V_{C(min)}$	11.48	V

8. Place your oscilloscope into its dc mode. Measure and record the signal appearing at each of the outputs. Show the oscilloscope settings beside the display. Label the reference voltage (0 V) for each waveform.

Square Wave Output:

Channel 1 Vertical:	**V/Div**
Horizontal: 20 μ	**s/Div**
Frequency: 12 kHz	**Hz**
V_{out}	$V_{p\text{-}p}$

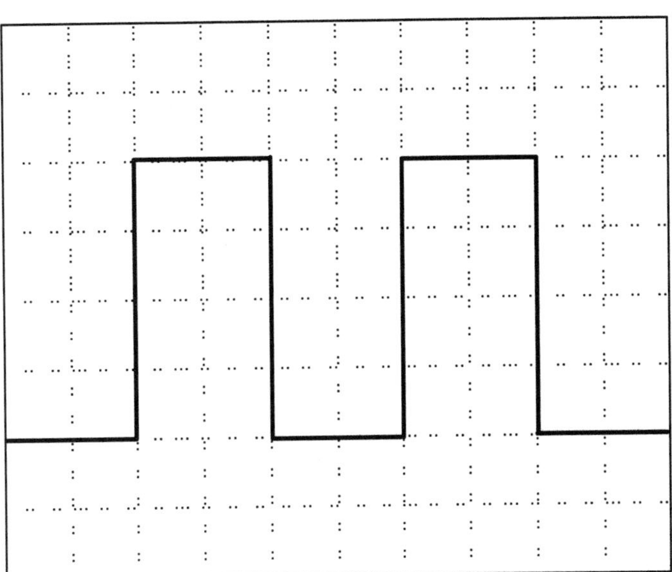

Sawtooth Wave Output:

Channel 1 Vertical:	**V/Div**
Horizontal: 20 μ	**s/Div**
Frequency: 12 kHz	**Hz**
V_{out}	$V_{p\text{-}p}$

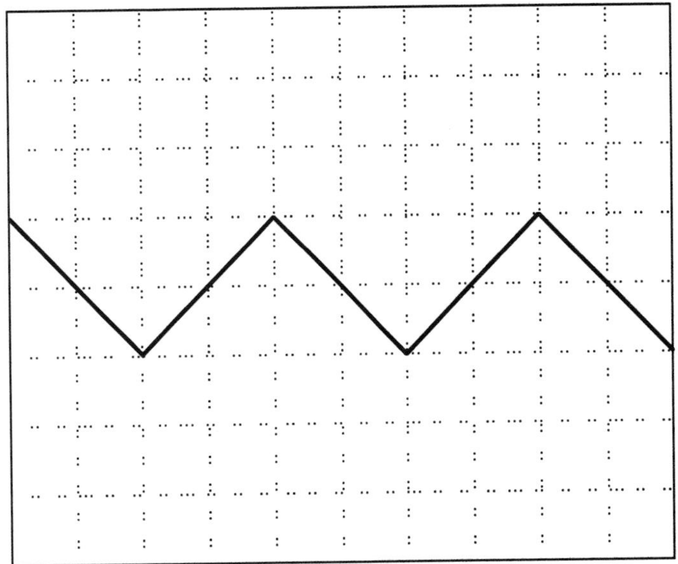

Sawtooth Wave Output:

9. Adjust the 5-kΩ potentiometer so that V_C has the quantities indicated in Table 40-1. Measure and record the corresponding amplitude and frequency of the square wave for each voltage setting.

V_C	f	$V_{out(p\text{-}p)}$
11.5 V	11.9 kHz	
12.0 V	10.2 kHz	
12.5 V	8.5 kHz	
13.0 V	6.8 kHz	
13.5 V	5.1 kHz	
14.0 V	3.4 kHz	
14.5	1.7 kHz	

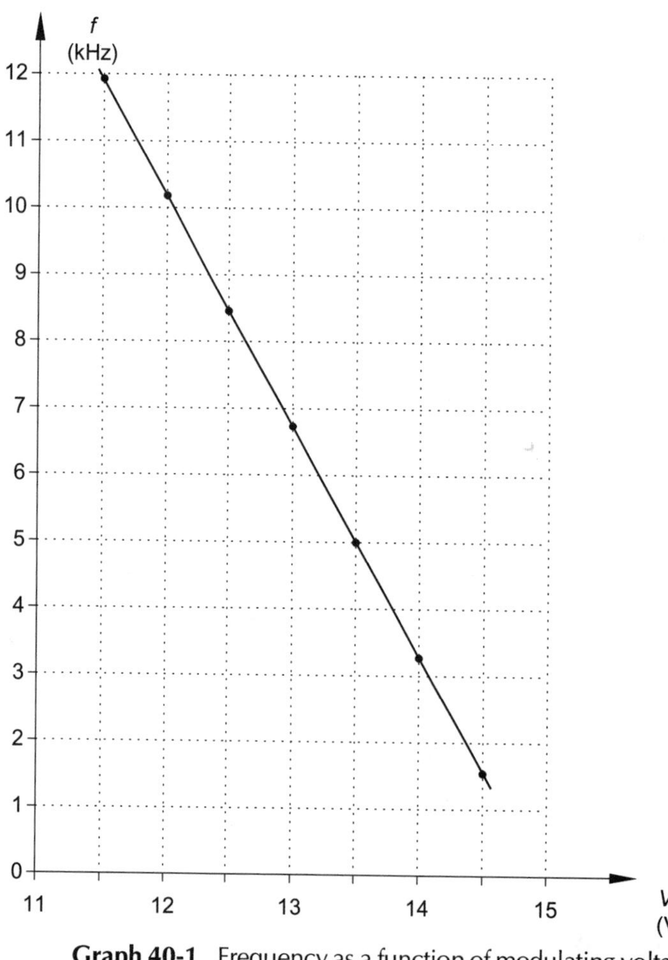

Graph 40-1 Frequency as a function of modulating voltage for an LM566C VCO

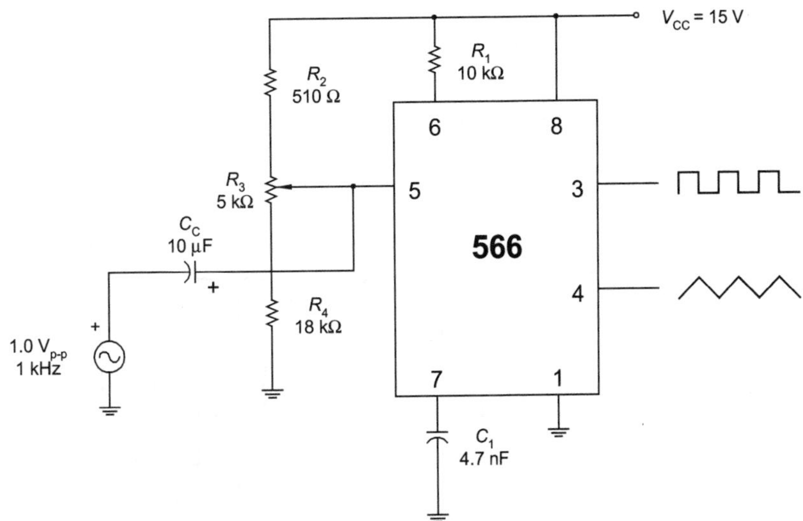

Figure 40-3 Voltage controlled oscillator used as a frequency modulator circuit

Table 40-1 Amplitude and frequency of the square wave as a function of modulating voltage

10. Plot the frequency as a function of modulating voltage in the Graph 40-1. Join the points using the best smooth continuous curve.
11. Modify the VCO circuit as shown in Figure 40-3.
12. Set the signal generator to provide a 1-$V_{p\text{-}p}$ sinusoidal waveform at a frequency of 1 kHz. Connect the sinusoidal voltage to Ch. 1 of your oscilloscope. Use Ch. 2 of your oscilloscope to observe the resulting square wave output signal of the VCO circuit. Sketch the result in the space provided on the following page. In order to observe the FM signal output signal, you will need to adjust your oscilloscope to provide a single trace.

Square Wave Output:

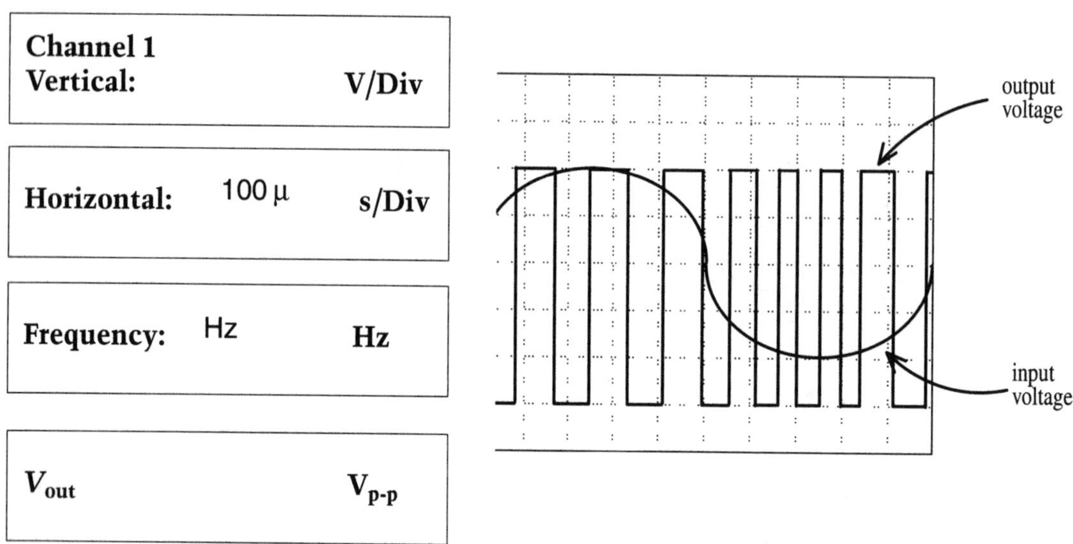

Note: It is best to adjust the bias voltage (using R_3) to a value of about 13 V. This provides an fm signal that varies between 5.1 kHz and 8.5 kHz.

NAME ____________________

DATE ____________________

CLASS ____________________

SCR Triggering Circuit

Objectives

After completing this lab, you will be able to

- build a test circuit to determine the *peak point*, *valley point*, and the *intrinsic standoff ratio* of a unijunction transistor (UJT),
- build a UJT relaxation oscillator and compare the predicted frequency to the actual measured frequency,
- build a test circuit to examine the operation of a silicon controlled rectifier (SCR) and determine the approximate *holding current* of the SCR.

Equipment Required

- ☐ dc power supply
- ☐ Digital multimeter
- ☐ Two-channel oscilloscope

Note: Record this equipment in Table 41-1.

Components

- ☐ Resistors: 47-Ω, 120-Ω, 1-kΩ (two), 20-kΩ potentiometer
- ☐ Capacitors: 0.33-μF radial lead film.
- ☐ Miscellaneous: C106 Silicon Controlled Rectifier, 2N4870 Unijunction Transistor, 24-V transformer (Ensure that the primary side of the transformer is safely connected to 120 VAC.)

EQUIPMENT USED

Instrument	Manufacturer/Model No.	Serial No.
dc power supply		
Signal generator		
Oscilloscope		

Table 41-1

TEXT REFERENCE

Circuit Analysis with Devices: Theory and Practice
Section 31.2 TRIGGER DEVICES
Section 31.3 SILICON CONTROLLED RECTIFIERS - SCRS

MEASUREMENTS

1. Obtain the manufacturer's specification sheet for the 2N4870 (UJT) Unijunction Transistor. Determine the location of the base terminals, B_1 and B_2. Using a DMM ohmmeter, measure and record the interbase resistance, R_{BB}.

R_{BB}	6.0 k	Ω

2. Build the UJT test circuit illustrated in Figure 41-1.

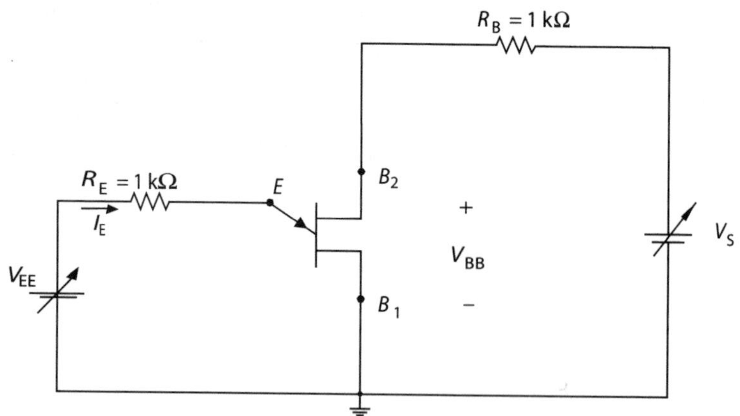

Figure 41-1 UJT test circuit

3. Adjust V_S to provide a voltage of $V_S = 10.0$ V.
4. With a DMM voltmeter connected between the emitter and ground, slowly increase V_{BB} until V_E suddenly drops. The maximum value to which V_E rises is called the *peak point*, and is designated as V_P. Record this value.

V_P	6.6	V

5. Increase V_{EE} and observe that V_E also increases. Reduce V_{EE} and observe that V_E once again increases. You have located the *valley point* of the UJT characteristic curve. For the valley point, measure and record the valley voltage, V_V and the valley current, I_V. Note that you "measure" the current by measuring the voltage across the 1-kΩ emitter resistance and then use Ohm's law to calculate the current.

V_V	1.2	V

I_V	0.005	mA

6. Determine the *intrinsic standoff ratio*, η, by applying the following equation:

$$V_p = \eta v V_{BB} + V_D \quad (41\text{-}1)$$

where V_D is the voltage across a forward-biased silicon diode. Let $V_D = 0.6$ V.

η	0.6

7. Refer to the manufacturer's specifications and provide typical values for and R_{BB}.

η	0.56 → 0.75	
R_{BB}	4 k → 9.1	kΩ

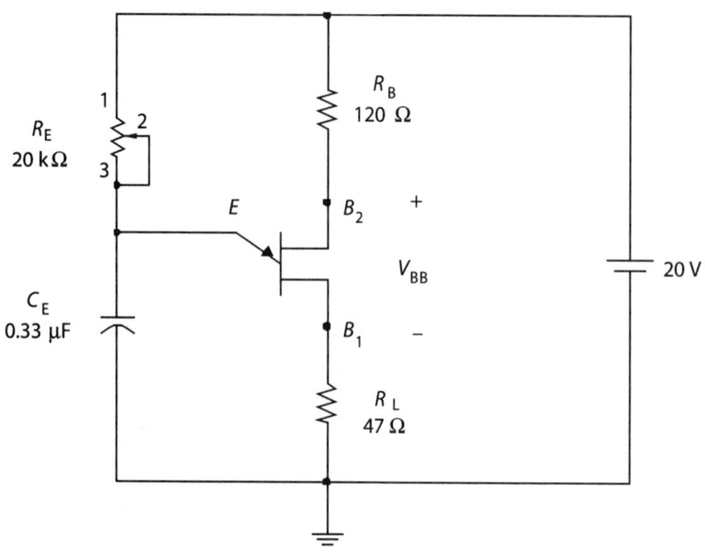

Figure 41-2 UJT relaxation oscillator

8. Construct the UJT relaxation oscillator circuit shown in Figure 41-2. Connect Channel 1 of the oscilloscope between the emitter and ground. Connect Channel 2 between base B_1 and ground.
9. Vary the 20-kΩ potentiometer and observe the effect. Adjust the potentiometer to result in an oscillator frequency of 500 Hz. Sketch the waveforms observed at the emitter and at B_1. Label each measurement and show the oscilloscope settings beside the display.

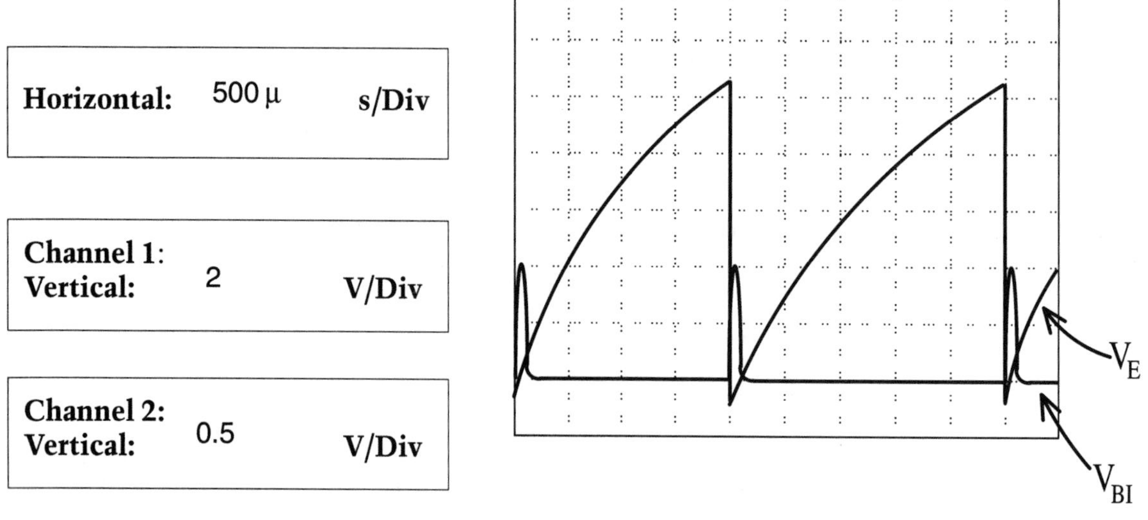

10. Disconnect the supply voltage and carefully remove the potentiometer from the circuit without changing its value. Measure and record the resistance between terminals 1 and 2 of the potentiometer.

R_E	6.60 k	Ω

11. Calculate the theoretical oscillator frequency using the following expression. Compare the theoretical frequency to the actual measured frequency.

$$f \approx \frac{1}{R_E C_E \ln\left(\frac{1}{1-\eta}\right)} \quad (41\text{-}2)$$

f	0.500	Hz

12. Modify the circuit as illustrated in Figure 41-3.

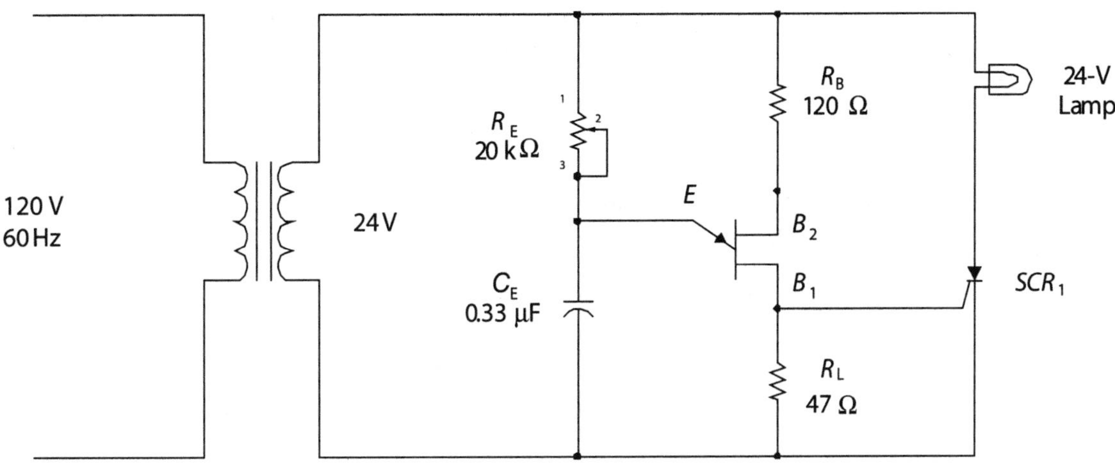

Figure 41-3 UJT phase control of an SCR

13. Adjust the potentiometer to provide a firing angle of 90°. Use the oscilloscope to observe the voltage across the load. Sketch the waveform and show the oscilloscope settings beside the display.

Horizontal:	5 m	s/Div

Channel 1: Vertical:	10	V/Div

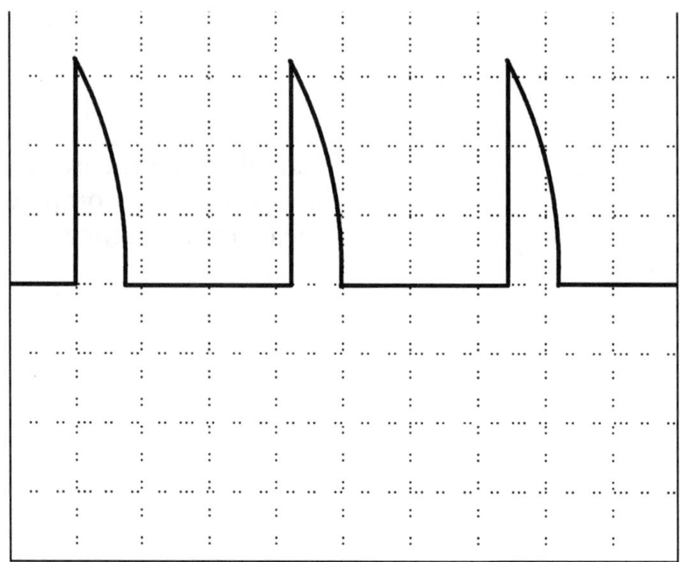

14. Use the oscilloscope to observe the voltage across the SCR. Sketch the waveform and show the oscilloscope settings beside the display.

Horizontal:	5 m	s/Div

Channel 1: Vertical:	10	V/Div

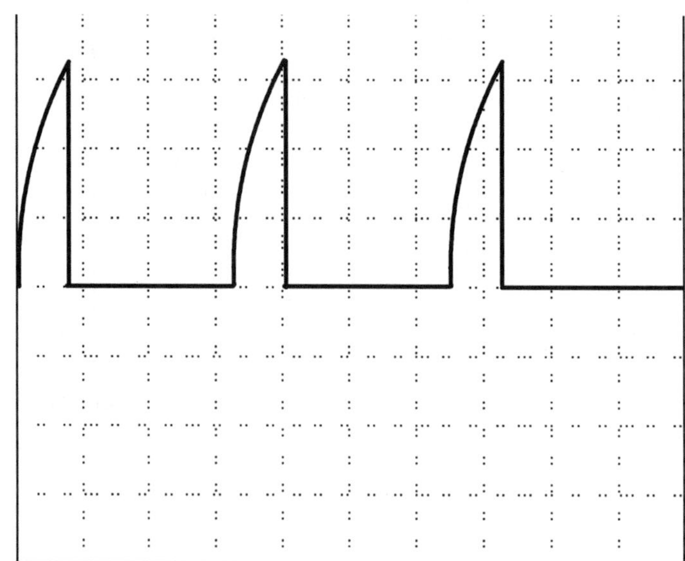